Table of Contents – Quick Check Solutions

Randy Gallaher

Kevin Bodden

Student Solutions Manual

for

Intermediate Algebra

Michael Sullivan, III

Katherine R. Struve

Taken from:

Student Solutions Manual
by Randy Gallaher and Kevin Bodden
for *Intermediate Algebra*
by Michael Sullivan, III and Katherine R. Struve

Custom Publishing

New York   Boston   San Francisco
London   Toronto   Sydney   Tokyo   Singapore   Madrid
Mexico City   Munich   Paris   Cape Town   Hong Kong   Montreal

Taken from:

Student Solutions Manual
by Randy Gallaher and Kevin Bodden
for *Intermediate Algebra*
by Michael Sullivan, III and Katherine R. Struve
Copyright © 2007 by Pearson Education, Inc.
Published by Prentice Hall
Upper Saddle River, New Jersey 07458

This special edition published in cooperation with Pearson Custom Publishing.

Printed in the United States of America

10 9 8 7 6 5 4

2009360971

NM

Pearson
Custom Publishing
is a division of

www.pearsonhighered.com

ISBN 10: 0-558-39484-1
ISBN 13: 978-0-558-39484-4

Table of Contents – Student Solutions Manual

Preface

This Student Solutions Manual (SSM) supplements *Intermediate Algebra* by Michael Sullivan, III and Katherine Struve. We hope it will be a valuable resource as you teach your Intermediate Algebra course. This manual consists of two parts. The first portion provides detailed solutions to the Quick Check exercises that are embedded within each section of the textbook. The second portion contains solutions to the odd-numbered exercises from the Exercise Sets, and to both odd- and even-numbered exercises from the Preparing for Sections, Putting the Concepts Together, Chapter Reviews, Chapter Tests, and Cumulative Reviews. For exercises requiring calculators, screenshots from TI-84 Plus graphing calculators have been used. We have made a concerted effort to make this manual easy to read and follow. For each section, problems have been worked using the same methods as the textbook examples. We have also tried to make this manual as error free as possible. If you have suggestions or corrections, please feel free to email us at the addresses below.

We would like to thank Jenny Crawford and Sarah Street for their attention to detail as they accuracy checked the final manuscript for this manual. We would also like to thank Bill Bodden (Kevin's father) and Zeno Forbes (Randy's father-in-law) for checking the early page proofs as the manual evolved.

We offer special thanks Ann Heath at prentice Hall for all her prompt help, often under hectic circumstances. You organization skills are inspiring!

Most importantly, we would like to thank our wives (Angie Bodden and Karen Gallaher) and our children (Shawn, Payton and Logan Bodden, and Ethan, Ben and Annie Gallaher) for their patience and support. Thanks for putting up with us when work had to come first and for enduring the many late hours of typing.

Randy Gallaher and Kevin Bodden
Department of Mathematics
Lewis & Clark Community College
5800 Godfrey Road
Godfrey, IL 62035
rgallahe@lc.edu   kbodden@lc.edu

Chapter R – Quick Checks

1. We will let D represent the set of all digits that are less than 5.
   set-builder: $D = \{x \mid x \text{ is a digit less than 5}\}$
   roster: $\{0, 1, 2, 3, 4\}$

2. We will let G represent the set of all digits that are greater than or equal to 6.
   set-builder:
   $G = \{x \mid x \text{ is a digit greater than or equal to 6}\}$
   roster: $\{6, 7, 8, 9\}$

3. The statement $B \subseteq A$ is true because all the elements that are in B are also in A.

4. The statement $B = C$ is false because there are elements in B (a and b) that are not in C. There is also an element in C, namely d, that is not in B.

5. The statement $B \subset D$ is false. In order for B to be a proper subset of D, it must be the case that all the elements that are in B are also in D. In addition, there must be elements in D that are not in B. Since $B = D$, this is not the case.

6. The statement $\varnothing \subseteq A$ is true. The empty set is a subset of every set.

7. The statement $5 \in \{0, 1, 2, 3, 4, 5\}$ is true because 5 is an element of the set.

8. The statement Michigan $\notin$ {Illinois, Indiana, Michigan, Wisconsin} is false because Michigan **is** an element of the set.

9. The statement $\frac{8}{3} \in \{x \mid x = \frac{p}{q}$ where p and q are digits, $q \neq 0\}$ is true because $\frac{8}{3}$ is of the form $\frac{p}{q}$ where $p = 8$ and $q = 3$.

10. 10 and $\frac{12}{4} = 3$ are the only counting numbers.

11. 10, $\frac{0}{3} = 0$, and $\frac{12}{4} = 3$ are the whole numbers.

12. -9, 10, $\frac{0}{3} = 0$, and $\frac{12}{4} = 3$ are the integers.

13. $\frac{7}{3}$, -9, 10, $4.\overline{56}$, $\frac{0}{3}$, $-\frac{4}{7}$, and $\frac{12}{4}$ are the rational numbers.

14. $5.7377377737777\ldots$ and π are the irrational numbers. Note that $5.7377377737777\ldots$ is irrational because the decimal portion is non-terminating and non-repeating.

15. All numbers listed except $\sqrt{-4}$ are real numbers. There is no real number whose square is -4.

16. a. To truncate, we remove all digits after the third decimal place. So, 5.694392 truncated to three decimal places is 5.694.

    b. To round to three decimal places, we first examine the digit in the fourth decimal place and then truncate. Since the fourth decimal place contains a 3, we do not change the digit in the third decimal place. Thus, 5.694392 rounded to three decimal places is 5.694.

17. a. To truncate, we remove all digits after the second decimal place. So, -4.9369102 truncated to two decimal places is -4.93.

    b. To round to two decimal places, we first examine the digit in the third decimal place and then truncate. Since the third decimal place contains a 6, we increase the digit in the second decimal place by 1. Thus, -4.9369102 rounded to two decimal places is -4.94.

18. $\left\{-2, 0, \frac{1}{2}, 3, 3.5\right\}$

19. $3 < 6$ because 3 is further to the left on a number line.

20. $-3 < -2$ because -3 is further to the left on a number line.

21. $\frac{2}{3} = 0.\overline{6}$ and $\frac{1}{2} = 0.5$.

$\frac{2}{3} > \frac{1}{2}$ because $\frac{2}{3}$ is further to the right on a number line.

22. $\frac{5}{7} \approx 0.714$.

$\frac{5}{7} > 0.7$ because $\frac{5}{7}$ is further to the right on a number line.

23. $\frac{2}{3} = 0.\overline{6}$ and $\frac{10}{15} = 0.\overline{6}$.

$\frac{2}{3} = \frac{10}{15}$ because the numbers are the same.

R.3 Quick Checks

1. $|6| = 6$ because the distance from 0 to 6 on the real number line is 6 units.

2. $|-10| = 10$ because the distance from 0 to -10 on the real number line is 10 units.

3. $18 + (-6)$
One number is positive, while the other is negative. We determine the absolute value of each number: $|18| = 18$ and $|-6| = 6$. We now subtract the smaller absolute value from the larger and obtain $18 - 6 = 12$. Because the number with the larger absolute value is positive, the sum will be positive. So, $18 + (-6) = 12$.

4. $-21 + 10$
One number is positive, while the other is negative. We determine the absolute value of each number: $|-21| = 21$ and $|10| = 10$. We now subtract the smaller absolute value from the larger and obtain $21 - 10 = 11$. Because the number with the larger absolute value is negative, the sum will be negative. So, $-21 + 10 = -11$.

5. $-5.4 + (-1.2)$
Both numbers are negative, so we first determine their absolute values: $|-5.4| = 5.4$ and $|-1.2| = 1.2$. We now add the absolute values and obtain $5.4 + 1.2 = 6.6$. Because both numbers to be added are negative, the sum is also negative. So, $-5.4 + (-1.2) = -6.6$.

6. $-6.5 + 4.3$
One number is positive, while the other is negative. We determine the absolute value of each number: $|-6.5| = 6.5$ and $|4.3| = 4.3$. We now subtract the smaller absolute value from the larger and obtain $6.5 - 4.3 = 2.2$. Because the number with the larger absolute value is negative, the sum will be negative. So, $-6.5 + 4.3 = -2.2$.

7. $-9 + 9$
One number is positive, while the other is negative. We determine the absolute value of each number: $|-9| = 9$ and $|9| = 9$. Since the absolute values are the same, the difference will be 0. So, $-9 + 9 = 0$.

8. The additive inverse of 5 is -5 because $5 + (-5) = 0$.

9. The additive inverse of $\frac{4}{5}$ is $-\frac{4}{5}$ because $\frac{4}{5} + \left(-\frac{4}{5}\right) = 0$.

10. The additive inverse of -12 is $-(-12) = 12$ because $-12 + 12 = 0$.

11. The additive inverse of $-\frac{5}{3}$ is $-\left(-\frac{5}{3}\right) = \frac{5}{3}$ because $-\frac{5}{3} + \frac{5}{3} = 0$.

12. $6 - 2 = 6 + (-2) = 4$

13. $4 - 13 = 4 + (-13) = -9$

14. $-3 - 8 = -3 + (-8) = -11$

15. $12.5 - 3.4 = 12.5 + (-3.4) = 9.1$

16. $-8.5-(-3.4)=-8.5+3.4=-5.1$

17. $-6.9-9.2=-6.9+(-9.2)=-16.1$

18. $-6\cdot(8)=-(6\cdot8)=-48$

19. $12\cdot(-5)=-(12\cdot5)=-60$

20. $4\cdot14=56$

21. $-7\cdot(-15)=7\cdot15=105$

22. $-1.9\cdot(-2.7)=1.9\cdot2.7=5.13$

23. The multiplicative inverse of 10 is $\dfrac{1}{10}$.

24. The multiplicative inverse of -8 is $-\dfrac{1}{8}$.

25. The multiplicative inverse of $\dfrac{2}{5}$ is $\dfrac{5}{2}$.

26. The multiplicative inverse of $-\dfrac{1}{5}$ is $-\dfrac{5}{1}=-5$.

27. $\dfrac{2\cdot6}{2\cdot5}=\dfrac{\cancel{2}\cdot6}{\cancel{2}\cdot5}=\dfrac{6}{5}$

28. $\dfrac{-5\cdot9}{-2\cdot5}=\dfrac{-(5\cdot9)}{-(2\cdot5)}=\dfrac{5\cdot9}{2\cdot5}=\dfrac{\cancel{5}\cdot9}{2\cdot\cancel{5}}=\dfrac{9}{2}$

29. $\dfrac{25}{15}=\dfrac{5\cdot5}{3\cdot5}=\dfrac{5\cdot\cancel{5}}{3\cdot\cancel{5}}=\dfrac{5}{3}$

30. $\dfrac{-24}{20}=-\dfrac{6\cdot4}{5\cdot4}=-\dfrac{6\cdot\cancel{4}}{5\cdot\cancel{4}}=-\dfrac{6}{5}$

31. $\dfrac{2}{3}\cdot\left(-\dfrac{5}{4}\right)=-\dfrac{2\cdot5}{3\cdot4}$

$=-\dfrac{2\cdot5}{3\cdot2\cdot2}$

$=-\dfrac{\cancel{2}\cdot5}{3\cdot\cancel{2}\cdot2}$

$=-\dfrac{5}{3\cdot2}$

$=-\dfrac{5}{6}$

32. $\dfrac{5}{3}\cdot\dfrac{12}{25}=\dfrac{5\cdot12}{3\cdot25}$

$=\dfrac{5\cdot3\cdot4}{3\cdot5\cdot5}$

$=\dfrac{\cancel{5}\cdot\cancel{3}\cdot4}{\cancel{3}\cdot\cancel{5}\cdot5}$

$=\dfrac{4}{5}$

33. $\dfrac{4}{3}\div\dfrac{8}{3}=\dfrac{4}{3}\cdot\dfrac{3}{8}$

$=\dfrac{4\cdot3}{3\cdot8}$

$=\dfrac{\cancel{4}\cdot\cancel{3}}{\cancel{3}\cdot\cancel{4}\cdot2}$

$=\dfrac{1}{2}$

34. $\dfrac{\tfrac{10}{3}}{\tfrac{5}{12}}=\dfrac{10}{3}\cdot\dfrac{12}{5}$

$=\dfrac{10\cdot12}{3\cdot5}$

$=\dfrac{2\cdot\cancel{5}\cdot\cancel{3}\cdot4}{\cancel{3}\cdot\cancel{5}}$

$=8$

35. $\dfrac{3}{11}+\dfrac{2}{11}=\dfrac{3+2}{11}=\dfrac{5}{11}$

36. $\dfrac{8}{15}-\dfrac{13}{15}=\dfrac{8-13}{15}=\dfrac{-5}{15}=-\dfrac{\cancel{5}}{3\cdot\cancel{5}}=-\dfrac{1}{3}$

37. $\dfrac{3}{7}+\dfrac{8}{7}=\dfrac{3+8}{7}=\dfrac{11}{7}$

38. $\dfrac{8}{5}-\dfrac{3}{5}=\dfrac{8-3}{5}=\dfrac{5}{5}=1$

39. $20=2\cdot2\cdot5$

$15=3\cdot5$

The common factor is 5. The remaining factors are 2, 2, and 3.

$LCD=2\cdot2\cdot3\cdot5=60$

$\dfrac{3}{20}=\dfrac{3}{20}\cdot\dfrac{3}{3}=\dfrac{3\cdot3}{20\cdot3}=\dfrac{9}{60}$

$\dfrac{2}{15}=\dfrac{2}{15}\cdot\dfrac{4}{4}=\dfrac{2\cdot4}{15\cdot4}=\dfrac{8}{60}$

40. $18 = 2 \cdot 3 \cdot 3$

$45 = 3 \cdot 3 \cdot 5$

The common factors are 3 and 3. The remaining factors are 2 and 5.

$LCD = 3 \cdot 3 \cdot 2 \cdot 5 = 90$

$\dfrac{5}{18} = \dfrac{5}{18} \cdot \dfrac{5}{5} = \dfrac{5 \cdot 5}{18 \cdot 5} = \dfrac{25}{90}$

$-\dfrac{1}{45} = -\dfrac{1}{45} \cdot \dfrac{2}{2} = -\dfrac{1 \cdot 2}{45 \cdot 2} = -\dfrac{2}{90}$

41. $LCD = 2 \cdot 2 \cdot 5 \cdot 3 = 60$

$\dfrac{3}{20} + \dfrac{2}{15} = \dfrac{3}{20} \cdot \dfrac{3}{3} + \dfrac{2}{15} \cdot \dfrac{4}{4}$

$= \dfrac{9}{60} + \dfrac{8}{60}$

$= \dfrac{9+8}{60}$

$= \dfrac{17}{60}$

42. $LCD = 2 \cdot 7 \cdot 3 = 42$

$\dfrac{5}{14} - \dfrac{11}{21} = \dfrac{5}{14} + \left(\dfrac{-11}{21}\right)$

$= \dfrac{5}{14} \cdot \dfrac{3}{3} + \left(\dfrac{-11}{21} \cdot \dfrac{2}{2}\right)$

$= \dfrac{15}{42} + \left(\dfrac{-22}{42}\right)$

$= \dfrac{15 + (-22)}{42}$

$= \dfrac{-7}{42} = \dfrac{-1 \cdot 7}{6 \cdot 7}$

$= -\dfrac{1}{6}$

43. $LCD = 5 \cdot 5 \cdot 6 = 150$

$\dfrac{-4}{25} - \dfrac{7}{30} = \dfrac{-4}{25} + \left(\dfrac{-7}{30}\right)$

$= \dfrac{-4}{25} \cdot \dfrac{6}{6} + \left(\dfrac{-7}{30} \cdot \dfrac{5}{5}\right)$

$= \dfrac{-24}{150} + \left(\dfrac{-35}{150}\right)$

$= \dfrac{-24 + (-35)}{150}$

$= -\dfrac{59}{150}$

44. $LCD = 2 \cdot 3 \cdot 3 \cdot 5 = 90$

$-\dfrac{5}{18} - \dfrac{1}{45} = \dfrac{-5}{18} + \left(\dfrac{-1}{45}\right)$

$= \dfrac{-5}{18} \cdot \dfrac{5}{5} + \left(\dfrac{-1}{45} \cdot \dfrac{2}{2}\right)$

$= \dfrac{-25}{90} + \left(\dfrac{-2}{90}\right)$

$= \dfrac{-25 + (-2)}{90}$

$= \dfrac{-27}{90}$

$= -\dfrac{3 \cdot 9}{10 \cdot 9}$

$= -\dfrac{3}{10}$

45. $5(x+3) = 5 \cdot x + 5 \cdot 3$

$= 5x + 15$

46. $-6(x+1) = -6 \cdot x + (-6) \cdot 1$

$= -6x - 6$

47. $-4(z-8) = -4 \cdot z - (-4) \cdot 8$

$= -4z + 32$

48. $\dfrac{1}{3}(6x+9) = \dfrac{1}{3} \cdot 6x + \dfrac{1}{3} \cdot 9$

$= \dfrac{6x}{3} + \dfrac{9}{3}$

$= 2x + 3$

R.4 Quick Checks

1. $4^3 = 4 \cdot 4 \cdot 4 = 64$

2. $(-7)^2 = (-7) \cdot (-7) = 49$

3. $(-10)^3 = (-10) \cdot (-10) \cdot (-10) = -1000$

4. $\left(\dfrac{2}{3}\right)^3 = \dfrac{2}{3} \cdot \dfrac{2}{3} \cdot \dfrac{2}{3} = \dfrac{8}{27}$

5. $-8^2 = -(8 \cdot 8) = -64$

6. $-(-5)^3 = -\left[(-5) \cdot (-5) \cdot (-5)\right] = -(-125) = 125$

7. $5 \cdot 2 + 6 = 10 + 6 = 16$

8. $3 \cdot 2 + 5 \cdot 6 = 6 + 30 = 36$

9. $4 \cdot (5 + 3) = 4 \cdot 8 = 32$

10. $8 \cdot (9 - 3) = 8 \cdot 6 = 48$

11. $(12 - 4) \cdot (18 - 13) = 8 \cdot 5 = 40$

12. $(4 + 9) \cdot (6 - 4) = 13 \cdot 2 = 26$

13. $\dfrac{3 + 7}{4 + 9} = \dfrac{10}{13}$

14. $1 - 4 + 8 \cdot 2 + 5 = 1 - 4 + 16 + 5$
$$= 22 - 4$$
$$= 18$$

15. $25 \cdot \left[2(8 - 3) \right] = 25 \cdot \left[2(5) \right]$
$$= 25 [10]$$
$$= 250$$

16. $\dfrac{3 + 5}{2 \cdot (9 - 4)} = \dfrac{8}{2 \cdot (5)} = \dfrac{8}{10} = \dfrac{4}{5}$

17. $6 + 5 \cdot 2 = 6 + 10 = 16$

18. $(3 + 9) \cdot 4 = 12 \cdot 4 = 48$

19. $\dfrac{3 + 7}{4 + 5} = \dfrac{10}{9}$

20. $\dfrac{7 + 5}{4 + 10} = \dfrac{12}{14} = \dfrac{6}{7}$

21. $4 + \left[(8 - 3) \cdot 2 \right] = 4 + \left[5 \cdot 2 \right]$
$$= 4 + 10$$
$$= 14$$

22. $\left[4 \cdot (6 - 2) - 9 \right] = 4 \cdot 4 - 9$
$$= 16 - 9$$
$$= 7$$

23. $-8 + 2 \cdot 5^2 = -8 + 2 \cdot 25$
$$= -8 + 50$$
$$= 42$$

24. $5 \cdot 3 - 3 \cdot 2^3 = 5 \cdot 3 - 3 \cdot 8$
$$= 15 - 24$$
$$= -9$$

25. $5 \cdot (10 - 8)^2 = 5 \cdot 2^2$
$$= 5 \cdot 4$$
$$= 20$$

26. $3 \cdot (-2)^2 + 6 \cdot 3 - 3 \cdot 4^2 = 3 \cdot 4 + 6 \cdot 3 - 3 \cdot 16$
$$= 12 + 18 - 48$$
$$= 30 - 48$$
$$= -18$$

27. $\dfrac{4 + 6^2}{2 \cdot 3 + 2} = \dfrac{4 + 36}{2 \cdot 3 + 2}$
$$= \dfrac{4 + 36}{6 + 2}$$
$$= \dfrac{40}{8}$$
$$= 5$$

28. $-3 \cdot \left| 7^2 - 2 \cdot (8 - 5)^3 \right| = -3 \cdot \left| 7^2 - 2 \cdot 3^3 \right|$
$$= -3 \cdot |49 - 2 \cdot 27|$$
$$= -3 \cdot |49 - 54|$$
$$= -3 \cdot |-5|$$
$$= -3 \cdot 5$$
$$= -15$$

R.5 Quick Checks

1. The word *sum* indicates addition so we write $3 + 11$.

2. The word *product* indicates multiplication so we write $6 \cdot 7$.

3. The word *quotient* indicates division so we write $\dfrac{y}{4}$.

4. The word *difference* indicates subtraction so we write $3 - z$.

5. *Twice* means to multiply by 2 and *difference* indicates subtraction.
$2(x - 3)$

6. The word *plus* indicates addition and the word *ratio* indicates division.

$$5 + \frac{z}{2}$$

7. $-5x + 3$

$$-5(2) + 3 = -10 + 3 = -7$$

8. $y^2 - 6y + 1$

$$(-4)^2 - 6(-4) + 1 = 16 + 24 + 1 = 40 + 1 = 41$$

9. $\dfrac{w+8}{3w}$

$$\frac{(4)+8}{3(4)} = \frac{12}{12} = 1$$

10. $|4x - 5|$

$$\left|4\left(\frac{1}{2}\right) - 5\right| = |2 - 5| = |-3| = 3$$

11. $118x$

$x = 100:\quad 118(100) = 11,800$ Yen

$x = 1000:\quad 118(1000) = 118,000$ Yen

$x = 10,000:\quad 118(10,000) = 1,180,000$ Yen

12. $\dfrac{5}{9}(x - 32)$

$x = 32:\quad \dfrac{5}{9}(32 - 32) = \dfrac{5}{9}(0) = 0°\text{ C}$

$x = 86:\quad \dfrac{5}{9}(86 - 32) = \dfrac{5}{9}(54) = 30°\text{ C}$

$x = 212:\quad \dfrac{5}{9}(212 - 32) = \dfrac{5}{9}(180) = 100°\text{ C}$

13. $4x - 9x = (4 - 9)x = -5x$

14. $-2x^2 + 13x^2 = (-2 + 13)x^2 = 11x^2$

15. $-5x - 3x + 6 - 3 = (-5 - 3)x + (6 - 3)$
$$= -8x + 3$$

16. $6x - 10x - 4y + 12y = (6 - 10)x + (-4 + 12)y$
$$= -4x + 8y$$

17. $10y - 3 + 5y + 2 = 10y + 5y - 3 + 2$
$$= (10 + 5)y + (-3 + 2)$$
$$= 15y - 1$$

18. $0.5x^2 + 1.3 + 1.8x^2 - 0.4$
$$= 0.5x^2 + 1.8x^2 + 1.3 - 0.4$$
$$= (0.5 + 1.8)x^2 + (1.3 - 0.4)$$
$$= 2.3x^2 + 0.9$$

19. $4z + 6 - 8z - 3 - 2z$
$$= 4z - 8z - 2z + 6 - 3$$
$$= (4 - 8 - 2)z + (6 - 3)$$
$$= -6z + 3$$

20. $3(x - 2) + x = 3 \cdot x - 3 \cdot 2 + x$
$$= 3x - 6 + x$$
$$= 3x + x - 6$$
$$= 4x - 6$$

21. $5(y + 3) - 10y - 4 = 5 \cdot y + 5 \cdot 3 - 10y - 4$
$$= 5y + 15 - 10y - 4$$
$$= 5y - 10y + 15 - 4$$
$$= -5y + 11$$

22. $3(z + 4) - 2(3z + 1)$
$$= 3 \cdot z + 3 \cdot 4 - 2 \cdot 3z - 2 \cdot 1$$
$$= 3z + 12 - 6z - 2$$
$$= 3z - 6z + 12 - 2$$
$$= -3z + 10$$

23. $-4(x - 2) - (2x + 4)$
$$= -4 \cdot x - (-4) \cdot 2 - 2x - 4$$
$$= -4x + 8 - 2x - 4$$
$$= -4x - 2x + 8 - 4$$
$$= -6x + 4$$

24. $\dfrac{1}{2}(6x + 4) - \dfrac{15x + 5}{5} = \dfrac{1}{2} \cdot 6x + \dfrac{1}{2} \cdot 4 - \dfrac{15}{5}x - \dfrac{5}{5}$
$$= 3x + 2 - 3x - 1$$
$$= 3x - 3x + 2 - 1$$
$$= 1$$

25.
$$\frac{5x-1}{3}+\frac{5x+9}{2}=\frac{5}{3}x-\frac{1}{3}+\frac{5}{2}x+\frac{9}{2}$$
$$=\frac{5}{3}x+\frac{5}{2}x-\frac{1}{3}+\frac{9}{2}$$
$$=\frac{10}{6}x+\frac{15}{6}x-\frac{2}{6}+\frac{27}{6}$$
$$=\frac{25}{6}x+\frac{25}{6}$$
$$=\frac{25x+25}{6}\quad\text{or}\quad\frac{25(x+1)}{6}$$

26. We need to determine whether the value of the variable causes division by 0. That is, we need to determine if the value makes $x-4=0$.

   a. When $x=2$, we have that
$x-4=2-4=-2$, so 2 is in the domain of the variable.

   b. When $x=0$, we have that
$x-4=0-4=-4$, so 0 is in the domain of the variable.

   c. When $x=4$, we have that $x-4=4-4=0$, so 4 is **not** in the domain of the variable.

   d. When $x=-3$, we have that
$x-4=-3-4=-7$, so -3 is in the domain of the variable.

27. We need to determine whether the value of the variable causes division by 0. That is, we need to determine if the value makes $x+3=0$.

   a. When $x=2$, we have that $x+3=2+3=5$, so 2 is in the domain of the variable.

   b. When $x=0$, we have that $x+3=0+3=3$, so 0 is in the domain of the variable.

   c. When $x=4$, we have that $x+3=4+3=7$, so 4 is in the domain of the variable.

   d. When $x=-3$, we have that
$x+3=-3+3=0$, so -3 is **not** in the domain of the variable.

28. We need to determine whether the value of the variable causes division by 0. That is, we need to determine if the value makes $x^2+x-6=0$.

   a. When $x=2$, we have that
$x^2+x-6=(2)^2+(2)-6=4+2-6=0$, so 2 is **not** in the domain of the variable.

   b. When $x=0$, we have that
$x^2+x-6=(0)^2+(0)-6=-6$, so 0 is in the domain of the variable.

   c. When $x=4$, we have that
$x^2+x-6=(4)^2+(4)-6=14$, so 4 is in the domain of the variable.

   d. When $x=-3$, we have that
$x^2+x-6=(-3)^2+(-3)-6=9-3-6=0$, so -3 is **not** in the domain of the variable.

QC – 7

Chapter 1 – Quick Checks

1.1 Quick Checks

1. $-5x + 3 = -2$

   Let $x = -2$ in the equation.

   $$-5(-2) + 3 \overset{?}{=} -2$$
   $$10 + 3 \overset{?}{=} -2$$
   $$13 \neq -2$$

   $x = -2$ is not a solution to the equation.

   Let $x = 1$ in the equation.

   $$-5(1) + 3 \overset{?}{=} -2$$
   $$-5 + 3 \overset{?}{=} -2$$
   $$-2 = -2 \checkmark$$

   $x = 1$ is a solution to the equation.

   Let $x = 3$ in the equation.

   $$-5(3) + 3 \overset{?}{=} -2$$
   $$-15 + 3 \overset{?}{=} -2$$
   $$-12 \neq -2$$

   $x = 3$ is not a solution to the equation.

2. $3x + 2 = 2x - 5$

   Let $x = 0$ in the equation.

   $$3(0) + 2 \overset{?}{=} 2(0) - 5$$
   $$0 + 2 \overset{?}{=} 0 - 5$$
   $$2 \neq -5$$

   $x = 0$ is not a solution to the equation.

   Let $x = 6$ in the equation.

   $$3(6) + 2 \overset{?}{=} 2(6) - 5$$
   $$18 + 2 \overset{?}{=} 12 - 5$$
   $$20 \neq 7$$

   $x = 6$ is not a solution to the equation.

   Let $x = -7$ in the equation.

   $$3(-7) + 2 \overset{?}{=} 2(-7) - 5$$
   $$-21 + 2 \overset{?}{=} -14 - 5$$
   $$-19 = -19 \checkmark$$

   $x = -7$ is a solution to the equation.

3. $-3(z + 2) = 4z + 1$

   Let $z = -3$ in the equation.

   $$-3((-3) + 2) \overset{?}{=} 4(-3) + 1$$
   $$-3(-1) \overset{?}{=} -12 + 1$$
   $$3 \neq -11$$

   $z = -3$ is not a solution to the equation.

   Let $z = -1$ in the equation.

   $$-3((-1) + 2) \overset{?}{=} 4(-1) + 1$$
   $$-3(1) \overset{?}{=} -4 + 1$$
   $$-3 = -3 \checkmark$$

   $z = -1$ is a solution to the equation.

   Let $z = 2$ in the equation.

   $$-3((2) + 2) \overset{?}{=} 4(2) + 1$$
   $$-3(4) \overset{?}{=} 8 + 1$$
   $$-12 \neq 9$$

   $z = 2$ is not a solution to the equation.

4. $3x + 8 = 17$
   $$3x + 8 - 8 = 17 - 8$$
   $$3x = 9$$
   $$\frac{3x}{3} = \frac{9}{3}$$
   $$x = 3$$

   Check:

   $$3(3) + 8 \overset{?}{=} 17$$
   $$9 + 8 \overset{?}{=} 17$$
   $$17 = 17 \checkmark$$

   Solution set: $\{3\}$

5. $-4a - 7 = 1$
   $$-4a - 7 + 7 = 1 + 7$$
   $$-4a = 8$$
   $$\frac{-4a}{-4} = \frac{8}{-4}$$
   $$a = -2$$

   Check:

   $$-4(-2) - 7 \overset{?}{=} 1$$
   $$8 - 7 \overset{?}{=} 1$$
   $$1 = 1 \checkmark$$

   Solution set: $\{-2\}$

6.
$$5y + 1 = 2$$
$$5y + 1 - 1 = 2 - 1$$
$$5y = 1$$
$$\frac{5y}{5} = \frac{1}{5}$$
$$y = \frac{1}{5}$$

Check:
$$5\left(\frac{1}{5}\right) + 1 \overset{?}{=} 2$$
$$1 + 1 \overset{?}{=} 2$$
$$2 = 2 \checkmark$$

Solution set: $\left\{\dfrac{1}{5}\right\}$

7.
$$2x + 3 + 5x + 1 = 4x + 10$$
$$7x + 4 = 4x + 10$$
$$7x + 4 - 4x = 4x + 10 - 4x$$
$$3x + 4 = 10$$
$$3x + 4 - 4 = 10 - 4$$
$$3x = 6$$
$$\frac{3x}{3} = \frac{6}{3}$$
$$x = 2$$

Check:
$$2(2) + 3 + 5(2) + 1 \overset{?}{=} 4(2) + 10$$
$$4 + 3 + 10 + 1 \overset{?}{=} 8 + 10$$
$$18 = 18 \checkmark$$

Solution set: $\{2\}$

8.
$$4b + 3 - b - 8 - 5b = 2b - 1 - b - 1$$
$$-2b - 5 = b - 2$$
$$-2b - 5 - b = b - 2 - b$$
$$-3b - 5 = -2$$
$$-3b - 5 + 5 = -2 + 5$$
$$-3b = 3$$
$$\frac{-3b}{-3} = \frac{3}{-3}$$
$$b = -1$$

Check:
$$4(-1) + 3 - (-1) - 8 - 5(-1) \overset{?}{=} 2(-1) - 1 - (-1) - 1$$
$$-4 + 3 + 1 - 8 + 5 \overset{?}{=} -2 - 1 + 1 - 1$$
$$-3 = -3 \checkmark$$

Solution set: $\{-1\}$

9.
$$2w + 8 - 7w + 1 = 3w - 1 + 2w - 5$$
$$-5w + 9 = 5w - 6$$
$$-5w + 9 - 5w = 5w - 6 - 5w$$
$$-10w + 9 = -6$$
$$-10w + 9 - 9 = -6 - 9$$
$$-10w = -15$$
$$\frac{-10w}{-10} = \frac{-15}{-10}$$
$$w = \frac{3}{2}$$

Check:
$$2\left(\frac{3}{2}\right) + 8 - 7\left(\frac{3}{2}\right) + 1 \overset{?}{=} 3\left(\frac{3}{2}\right) - 1 + 2\left(\frac{3}{2}\right) - 5$$
$$3 + 8 - \frac{21}{2} + 1 \overset{?}{=} \frac{9}{2} - 1 + 3 - 5$$
$$\frac{3}{2} = \frac{3}{2} \checkmark$$

Solution set: $\left\{\dfrac{3}{2}\right\}$

10.
$$4(x - 1) = 12$$
$$4x - 4 = 12$$
$$4x - 4 + 4 = 12 + 4$$
$$4x = 16$$
$$\frac{4x}{4} = \frac{16}{4}$$
$$x = 4$$

Check:
$$4(4 - 1) \overset{?}{=} 12$$
$$4(3) \overset{?}{=} 12$$
$$12 = 12 \checkmark$$

Solution set: $\{4\}$

11.
$$-2(x - 4) - 6 = 3(x + 6) + 4$$
$$-2x + 8 - 6 = 3x + 18 + 4$$
$$-2x + 2 = 3x + 22$$
$$-2x + 2 - 3x = 3x + 22 - 3x$$
$$-5x + 2 = 22$$
$$-5x + 2 - 2 = 22 - 2$$
$$-5x = 20$$
$$\frac{-5x}{-5} = \frac{20}{-5}$$
$$x = -4$$

Check:

$$-2(-4-4)-6 \stackrel{?}{=} 3(-4+6)+4$$

$$-2(-8)-6 \stackrel{?}{=} 3(2)+4$$

$$16-6 \stackrel{?}{=} 6+4$$

$$10 = 10 \checkmark$$

Solution set: $\{-4\}$

12. $4(x+3)-8x = 3(x+2)+x$

$$4x+12-8x = 3x+6+x$$

$$-4x+12 = 4x+6$$

$$-4x+12-4x = 4x+6-4x$$

$$-8x+12 = 6$$

$$-8x+12-12 = 6-12$$

$$-8x = -6$$

$$\frac{-8x}{-8} = \frac{-6}{-8}$$

$$x = \frac{3}{4}$$

Check:

$$4\left(\frac{3}{4}+3\right)-8\left(\frac{3}{4}\right) \stackrel{?}{=} 3\left(\frac{3}{4}+2\right)+\frac{3}{4}$$

$$4\left(\frac{15}{4}\right)-6 \stackrel{?}{=} 3\left(\frac{11}{4}\right)+\frac{3}{4}$$

$$15-6 \stackrel{?}{=} \frac{33}{4}+\frac{3}{4}$$

$$9 = 9 \checkmark$$

Solution set: $\left\{\frac{3}{4}\right\}$

13. $5(x-3)+3(x+3) = 2x-3$

$$5x-15+3x+9 = 2x-3$$

$$8x-6 = 2x-3$$

$$8x-6-2x = 2x-3-2x$$

$$6x-6 = -3$$

$$6x-6+6 = -3+6$$

$$6x = 3$$

$$\frac{6x}{6} = \frac{3}{6}$$

$$x = \frac{1}{2}$$

Check:

$$5\left(\frac{1}{2}-3\right)+3\left(\frac{1}{2}+3\right) \stackrel{?}{=} 2\left(\frac{1}{2}\right)-3$$

$$5\left(-\frac{5}{2}\right)+3\left(\frac{7}{2}\right) \stackrel{?}{=} 1-3$$

$$-\frac{25}{2}+\frac{21}{2} \stackrel{?}{=} -2$$

$$-2 = -2 \checkmark$$

Solution set: $\left\{\frac{1}{2}\right\}$

14. $\frac{3y}{2}+\frac{y}{6} = \frac{10}{3}$

$$6\left(\frac{3y}{2}+\frac{y}{6}\right) = 6\left(\frac{10}{3}\right)$$

$$6 \cdot \frac{3y}{2}+6 \cdot \frac{y}{6} = 6 \cdot \frac{10}{3}$$

$$9y+y = 20$$

$$10y = 20$$

$$\frac{10y}{10} = \frac{20}{10}$$

$$y = 2$$

Check:

$$\frac{3(2)}{2}+\frac{2}{6} \stackrel{?}{=} \frac{10}{3}$$

$$3+\frac{1}{3} \stackrel{?}{=} \frac{10}{3}$$

$$\frac{10}{3} = \frac{10}{3} \checkmark$$

Solution set: $\{2\}$

15. $\frac{3x}{4}-\frac{5}{12} = \frac{5x}{6}$

$$12\left(\frac{3x}{4}-\frac{5}{12}\right) = 12\left(\frac{5x}{6}\right)$$

$$12 \cdot \frac{3x}{4}-12 \cdot \frac{5}{12} = 12 \cdot \frac{5x}{6}$$

$$9x-5 = 10x$$

$$9x-5-9x = 10x-9x$$

$$-5 = x$$

Check:

$$\frac{3(-5)}{4}-\frac{5}{12} \stackrel{?}{=} \frac{5(-5)}{6}$$

$$\frac{-15}{4}-\frac{5}{12} \stackrel{?}{=} -\frac{25}{6}$$

$$\frac{-45}{12}-\frac{5}{12} \stackrel{?}{=} -\frac{25}{6}$$

$$-\frac{50}{12} \stackrel{?}{=} -\frac{25}{6}$$

$$-\frac{25}{6} = -\frac{25}{6} \checkmark$$

Solution set: $\{-5\}$

QC – 10

16.

$$\frac{x+2}{6}+2=\frac{5}{3}$$

$$6\left(\frac{x+2}{6}+2\right)=6\left(\frac{5}{3}\right)$$

$$6\cdot\frac{(x+2)}{6}+6\cdot2=6\cdot\frac{5}{3}$$

$$x+2+12=10$$

$$x+14=10$$

$$x+14-14=10-14$$

$$x=-4$$

Check:

$$\frac{-4+2}{6}+2\overset{?}{=}\frac{5}{3}$$

$$\frac{-2}{6}+2\overset{?}{=}\frac{5}{3}$$

$$-\frac{1}{3}+\frac{6}{3}\overset{?}{=}\frac{5}{3}$$

$$\frac{5}{3}=\frac{5}{3}\checkmark$$

Solution set: $\{-4\}$

17.

$$\frac{4x+3}{9}-\frac{2x+1}{2}=\frac{1}{6}$$

$$18\left(\frac{4x+3}{9}-\frac{2x+1}{2}\right)=18\left(\frac{1}{6}\right)$$

$$18\cdot\frac{(4x+3)}{9}-18\cdot\frac{(2x+1)}{2}=18\cdot\frac{1}{6}$$

$$2(4x+3)-9(2x+1)=3$$

$$8x+6-18x-9=3$$

$$-10x-3=3$$

$$-10x-3+3=3+3$$

$$-10x=6$$

$$\frac{-10x}{-10}=\frac{6}{-10}$$

$$x=-\frac{3}{5}$$

Check:

$$\frac{4\left(-\frac{3}{5}\right)+3}{9}-\frac{2\left(-\frac{3}{5}\right)+1}{2}\overset{?}{=}\frac{1}{6}$$

$$\frac{\frac{-12}{5}+\frac{15}{5}}{9}-\frac{\frac{-6}{5}+\frac{5}{5}}{2}\overset{?}{=}\frac{1}{6}$$

$$\frac{\frac{3}{5}}{9}-\frac{\frac{-1}{5}}{2}\overset{?}{=}\frac{1}{6}$$

$$\frac{3}{5}\cdot\frac{1}{9}+\frac{1}{5}\cdot\frac{1}{2}\overset{?}{=}\frac{1}{6}$$

$$\frac{1}{15}+\frac{1}{10}\overset{?}{=}\frac{1}{6}$$

$$\frac{2}{30}+\frac{3}{30}\overset{?}{=}\frac{5}{30}$$

$$\frac{5}{30}=\frac{5}{30}\checkmark$$

Solution set: $\left\{-\frac{3}{5}\right\}$

18. Our first step is to multiply both sides of the equation by 10 to eliminate the decimals.

$$10(0.2t+1.4)=10(0.8)$$

$$2t+14=8$$

$$2t+14-14=8-14$$

$$2t=-6$$

$$\frac{2t}{2}=\frac{-6}{2}$$

$$t=-3$$

Check:

$$0.2(-3)+1.4\overset{?}{=}0.8$$

$$-0.6+1.4\overset{?}{=}0.8$$

$$0.8=0.8\checkmark$$

Solution set: $\{-3\}$

19. Our first step is to multiply both sides of the equation by 100 to eliminate the decimals.

$$100(0.07x - 1.3) = 100(0.05x - 1.1)$$
$$7x - 130 = 5x - 110$$
$$7x - 130 - 5x = 5x - 110 - 5x$$
$$2x - 130 = -110$$
$$2x - 130 + 130 = -110 + 130$$
$$2x = 20$$
$$\frac{2x}{2} = \frac{20}{2}$$
$$x = 10$$

Check:
$$0.07(10) - 1.3 \overset{?}{=} 0.05(10) - 1.1$$
$$0.7 - 1.3 \overset{?}{=} 0.5 - 1.1$$
$$-0.6 = -0.6 \checkmark$$

Solution set: $\{10\}$

20. Our first step is to multiply both sides of the equation by 10 to eliminate the decimals.

$$10\left[0.4(y+3)\right] = 10\left[0.5(y-4)\right]$$
$$4(y+3) = 5(y-4)$$
$$4y + 12 = 5y - 20$$
$$4y + 12 - 5y = 5y - 20 - 5y$$
$$-y + 12 = -20$$
$$-y + 12 - 12 = -20 - 12$$
$$-y = -32$$
$$\frac{-y}{-1} = \frac{-32}{-1}$$
$$y = 32$$

Check:
$$0.4(32+3) \overset{?}{=} 0.5(32-4)$$
$$0.4(35) \overset{?}{=} 0.5(28)$$
$$14 = 14 \checkmark$$

Solution set: $\{32\}$

21.
$$4(x+2) = 4x + 2$$
$$4x + 8 = 4x + 2$$
$$4x + 8 - 4x = 4x + 2 - 4x$$
$$8 = 2$$

The last statement is a contradiction. The equation has no solution.

Solution set: $\{\ \}$ or $\varnothing$

22.
$$3(x-2) = 2x - 6 + x$$
$$3x - 6 = 3x - 6$$
$$3x - 6 - 3x = 3x - 6 - 3x$$
$$-6 = -6$$

The last statement is an identity. All real numbers are solutions.

Solution set: $\mathbb{R}$

23.
$$-4x + 2 + x + 1 = -4(x+2) + 11$$
$$-3x + 3 = -4x - 8 + 11$$
$$-3x + 3 = -4x + 3$$
$$-3x + 3 + 4x = -4x + 3 + 4x$$
$$x + 3 = 3$$
$$x + 3 - 3 = 3 - 3$$
$$x = 0$$

This is a conditional equation.

Solution set: $\{0\}$

24.
$$-3(z+1) + 2(z-3) = z + 6 - 2z - 15$$
$$-3z - 3 + 2z - 6 = -z - 9$$
$$-z - 9 = -z - 9$$
$$-z - 9 + z = -z - 9 + z$$
$$-9 = -9$$

The last statement is an identity. All real numbers are solutions.

Solution set: $\mathbb{R}$

1.2 Quick Checks

1. $3y = 21$

2. $2(3 + x) = 5x$

3. $x - 10 = \dfrac{x}{2}$

4. $y - 3 = 5y$

5. Let x = the first of the consecutive even integers.
Second: $x+2$
Third: $x+4$

$$x+(x+2)+(x+4)=60$$
$$x+x+2+x+4=60$$
$$3x+6=60$$
$$3x+6-6=60-6$$
$$3x=54$$
$$\frac{3x}{3}=\frac{54}{3}$$
$$x=18$$

The three consecutive even integers are 18, 20, and 22.

Check:
$$18+(18+2)+(18+4)=18+20+22=60$$

6. Let x = the first of the consecutive integers.
Second: $x+1$
Third: $x+2$

$$x+(x+1)+(x+2)=78$$
$$x+x+1+x+2=78$$
$$3x+3=78$$
$$3x+3-3=78-3$$
$$3x=75$$
$$\frac{3x}{3}=\frac{75}{3}$$
$$x=25$$

The three consecutive integers are 25, 26, and 27.

Check:
$$25+(25+1)+(25+2)=25+26+27=78$$

7. Let w = Melody's hourly wage.
Overtime rate: $1.5w$

$$40w+6(1.5w)=735$$
$$40w+9w=735$$
$$49w=735$$
$$\frac{49w}{49}=\frac{735}{49}$$
$$w=15$$

Melody makes \$15 per hour.

Check:
$$40(15)+6[1.5(15)]=600+6(22.5)$$
$$=600+135$$
$$=735$$

8. Let w = Jim's regular hourly rate.
Saturday rate: $1.5w$
Sunday rate: $2w$

$$30w+6(1.5w)+4(2w)=564$$
$$30w+9w+8w=564$$
$$47w=564$$
$$\frac{47w}{47}=\frac{564}{47}$$
$$w=12$$

Jim's regular hourly rate is \$12 per hour.

Check:
$$30(12)+6[1.5(12)]+4[2(12)]$$
$$=360+6(18)+4(24)$$
$$=360+108+96$$
$$=564$$

9. Let m = the number of miles.
EZ-Rental cost = Do It Yourself cost

$$35+0.15m=20+0.25m$$
$$0.15m=-15+0.25m$$
$$-0.1m=-15$$
$$\frac{-0.1m}{-0.1}=\frac{-15}{-0.1}$$
$$m=150$$

The rental costs will be the same for 150 miles.

Check:
$$35+0.15(150)=35+22.5=\$57.50$$
$$20+0.25(150)=20+37.5=\$57.50$$

10. Let m = the number of minutes used.
Company A cost = Company B cost

$$12+0.1m=0.15m$$
$$12=0.05m$$
$$\frac{12}{0.05}=\frac{0.05m}{0.05}$$
$$240=m$$

The monthly costs will be the same for 240 minutes.

Check:
$$12+0.1(240)=12+24=36$$
$$0.15(240)=36$$

11. Let x = the desired result.
$$x=0.4(100)=40$$
40% of 100 is 40.

12. Let x = the desired value.
$$8 = 0.05(x)$$
$$\frac{8}{0.05} = \frac{0.05x}{0.05}$$
$$160 = x$$
8 is 5% of 160.

13. Let p = the desired percent (as a decimal).
$$15 = p \cdot 20$$
$$15 = 20p$$
$$\frac{15}{20} = \frac{20p}{20}$$
$$0.75 = p$$
15 is 75% of 20.

14. Let p = the original price.
Discount: $0.3p$
$$p - 0.3p = 21$$
$$0.7p = 21$$
$$\frac{0.7p}{0.7} = \frac{21}{0.7}$$
$$p = 30$$
The original price of the shirt was $30.

15. Let c = Milex's cost for a spark plug.
Mark up: $0.35c$
$$c + 0.35c = 1.62$$
$$1.35c = 1.62$$
$$\frac{1.35c}{1.35} = \frac{1.62}{1.35}$$
$$c = 1.2$$
Milex's cost for each spark plug is $1.20.

16. Note that 1 month is $\frac{1}{12}$ year.
$$I = Prt$$
$$I = (6500)(0.06)\left(\tfrac{1}{12}\right) = 32.5$$
The interest charge on Dave's car loan after 1 month is $32.50.

17. Note that 6 months is $\frac{1}{2}$ year.
$$I = Prt$$
$$I = (1400)(0.015)\left(\tfrac{1}{2}\right) = 10.50$$
The interest paid after 6 months would be $10.50.
The balance is the original amount in the account plus the accrued interest.
$$1400 + 10.50 = 1410.50$$
The account will have a balance of $1410.50.

18. Let x = the amount invested in Aaa-rated bonds.
B-rated bonds: $90,000 - x$
Int. from Aaa-rated + Int. from B-rated = 5400
$$0.05x + 0.09(90,000 - x) = 5400$$
$$0.05x + 8100 - 0.09x = 5400$$
$$8100 - 0.04x = 5400$$
$$-0.04x = -2700$$
$$\frac{-0.04x}{-0.04} = \frac{-2700}{-0.04}$$
$$x = 67,500$$
Sophia should place $67,500 in Aaa-rated bonds and $90,000 - \$67,500 = \$22,500$ in B-rated bonds.

19. Let x = the amount invested in a 5-yr CD.
Corporate bonds: $25,000 - x$
CD interest + bond interest = total interest
$$0.04x + 0.09(25,000 - x) = 0.08(25,000)$$
$$0.04x + 2250 - 0.09x = 2000$$
$$2250 - 0.05x = 2000$$
$$-0.05x = -250$$
$$\frac{-0.05x}{-0.05} = \frac{-250}{-0.05}$$
$$x = 5000$$
Steve should invest $5000 in the CD and $25,000 - \$5000 = \$20,000$ in corporate bonds.

20. Let x = pounds of Tea A.
Tea B pounds: $10 - x$

	Tea A	Tea B	Mix
price per pound	4	2.75	3.50
pounds	x	$10 - x$	10
revenue	$4x$	$2.75(10-x)$	$3.5(10)$

We want the individual revenues to be the same as the revenue from the mix. Therefore, we get
$$4x + 2.75(10 - x) = 3.5(10)$$
$$4x + 27.5 - 2.75x = 35$$
$$1.25x + 27.5 = 35$$
$$1.25x = 7.5$$
$$\frac{1.25x}{1.25} = \frac{7.5}{1.25}$$
$$x = 6$$
You should blend 6 pounds of Tea A and $10 - 6 = 4$ pounds of Tea B.

21. Let x = pounds of cashews.
Cashews: $30 - x$

	cashews	peanuts	Mix
price per pound	6	1.5	3
pounds	x	$30 - x$	30
revenue	$6x$	$1.5(30-x)$	$3(30)$

We want the individual revenues to be the same as the revenue from the mix. Therefore, we get

$$6x + 1.5(30 - x) = 3(30)$$
$$6x + 45 - 1.5x = 90$$
$$4.5x + 45 = 90$$
$$4.5x = 45$$
$$\frac{4.5x}{4.5} = \frac{45}{4.5}$$
$$x = 10$$

You should blend 10 pounds of cashews and $30 - 10 = 20$ pounds of peanuts.

22. We want to know when the distance traveled by both cars will be the same.
Let t = the time of travel by the Cavalier.
Then the time of travel for the BMW will be $t - 2$ since it left two hours later.

Cavalier distance = BMW distance

$$(\text{rate})(\text{time})_{\text{Cavalier}} = (\text{rate})(\text{time})_{\text{BMW}}$$
$$40t = 60(t - 2)$$
$$40t = 60t - 120$$
$$-20t = -120$$
$$t = 6$$

The BMW will catch the Cavalier after the Cavalier has been traveling for 6 hours (4 hours for the BMW). When the BMW catches the Cavalier, both cars will have traveled $40(6) = 240$ miles.

23. We want to know when the distance traveled by both the train and the helicopter will be the same.
Let t = the time of travel by the train.
Then the time of travel for the helicopter will be $t - 4$ since it left four hours later.

train distance = helicopter distance

$$(\text{rate})(\text{time})_{\text{train}} = (\text{rate})(\text{time})_{\text{helicopter}}$$
$$50t = 90(t - 4)$$
$$50t = 90t - 360$$
$$-40t = -360$$
$$t = 9$$

The helicopter will catch the train after the train has been traveling for 9 hours (5 hours for the helicopter). When the helicopter catches the train, both the helicopter and the train will have traveled $50(9) = 450$ miles.

1.3 Quick Checks

1. $A = \pi r^2$

2. $V = \pi r^2 h$

3. $C = 175x + 7000$

4. $s = \dfrac{1}{2}gt^2$

5. a.

$$A = \frac{1}{2}bh$$
$$2 \cdot A = 2 \cdot \frac{1}{2}bh$$
$$2A = bh$$
$$\frac{2A}{b} = \frac{bh}{b}$$
$$\frac{2A}{b} = h \quad \text{or} \quad h = \frac{2A}{b}$$

b. $h = \dfrac{2A}{b} = \dfrac{2(10)}{4} = 5$

A triangle whose area is 10 square inches and whose base is 4 inches has a height of 5 inches.

QC – 15

6. a.
$$P = 2a + 2b$$
$$P - 2a = 2a + 2b - 2a$$
$$P - 2a = 2b$$
$$\frac{P - 2a}{2} = \frac{2b}{2}$$
$$\frac{P - 2a}{2} = b \quad \text{or} \quad b = \frac{P - 2a}{2}$$

b. $b = \dfrac{P - 2a}{2}$

$$b = \frac{60 - 2(20)}{2} = \frac{60 - 40}{2} = \frac{20}{2} = 10$$

A parallelogram whose perimeter is 60 cm and whose adjacent length is 20 cm has a length of 10 cm.

7.
$$I = P \cdot r \cdot t$$
$$\frac{I}{r \cdot t} = \frac{P \cdot r \cdot t}{r \cdot t}$$
$$\frac{I}{rt} = P \quad \text{or} \quad P = \frac{I}{rt}$$

8.
$$Ax + By = C$$
$$Ax + By - Ax = C - Ax$$
$$By = C - Ax$$
$$\frac{By}{B} = \frac{C - Ax}{B}$$
$$y = \frac{C - Ax}{B}$$

9.
$$2xh - 4x = 3h - 3$$
$$2xh - 4x - 3h = 3h - 3 - 3h$$
$$2xh - 4x - 3h = -3$$
$$2xh - 4x - 3h + 4x = -3 + 4x$$
$$2xh - 3h = 4x - 3$$
$$h(2x - 3) = 4x - 3$$
$$\frac{h(2x - 3)}{2x - 3} = \frac{4x - 3}{2x - 3}$$
$$h = \frac{4x - 3}{2x - 3}$$

10.
$$S = na + (n - 1)d$$
$$S = na + nd - d$$
$$S = n(a + d) - d$$
$$S + d = n(a + d) - d + d$$
$$S + d = n(a + d)$$
$$\frac{S + d}{a + d} = \frac{n(a + d)}{a + d}$$
$$\frac{S + d}{a + d} = n \quad \text{or} \quad n = \frac{S + d}{a + d}$$

11. Let $w =$ the width of the pool in feet. Then the length is $l = w + 10$.
$$P = 2l + 2w$$
$$180 = 2(w + 10) + 2w$$
$$180 = 2w + 20 + 2w$$
$$180 = 4w + 20$$
$$160 = 4w$$
$$40 = w$$
The pool is 40 feet wide and $40 + 10 = 50$ feet long.

12. Since the bookcase is rectangular, we can consider the height as the length in our formula. Let $w =$ the width of the bookcase in inches. Then the height is $h = w + 32$.
$$P = 2(\text{length}) + 2(\text{width})$$
$$224 = 2(w + 32) + 2(w)$$
$$224 = 2w + 64 + 2w$$
$$224 = 4w + 64$$
$$160 = 4w$$
$$40 = w$$
The opening of the bookcase has a width of 40 inches and a height of $40 + 32 = 72$ inches.

13.
$$A = 2\pi r^2 + 2\pi rh$$
$$51.8 = 2\pi(1.5)^2 + 2\pi(1.5)h$$
$$51.8 - 2\pi(1.5)^2 = 2\pi(1.5)h$$
$$\frac{51.8 - 2\pi(1.5)^2}{2\pi(1.5)} = h$$

```
(51.8-2π(1.5)²)/
(2π(1.5))
        3.996150701
```

The height of the can is roughly 4.00 inches.

14.
$$A = 2\pi r^2 + 2\pi rh$$
$$72.7 = 2\pi (1.625)^2 + 2\pi (1.625) h$$
$$72.7 - 2\pi (1.625)^2 = 2\pi (1.625) h$$
$$\frac{72.7 - 2\pi (1.625)^2}{2\pi (1.625)} = h$$

```
(72.7-2π(1.625)²
)/(2π(1.625))
        5.4953473
```

The height of the can is about 5.50 inches.

1.4 Quick Checks

1. $-3 \leq x \leq 2$

Interval: $[-3, 2]$

Graph:

2. $3 \leq x < 6$

Interval: $[3, 6)$

Graph:

3. $x \leq 3$

Interval: $(-\infty, 3]$

Graph:

4. $\frac{1}{2} < x < \frac{7}{2}$

Interval: $\left(\frac{1}{2}, \frac{7}{2} \right)$

Graph:

5. $(0, 5]$

Inequality: $0 < x \leq 5$

Graph:

6. $(-6, 0)$

Inequality: $-6 < x < 0$

Graph:

7. $(5, \infty)$

Inequality: $x > 5$

Graph:

8. $\left(-\infty, \frac{8}{3} \right]$

Inequality: $x \leq \frac{8}{3}$

Graph:

9. $\quad x + 3 > 5$
$$x + 3 - 3 > 5 - 3$$
$$x > 2$$

Interval: $(2, \infty)$

Solution set: $\{x \mid x > 2\}$

Graph:

10. $\quad \frac{1}{3} x \leq 2$
$$3 \cdot \frac{1}{3} x \leq 3 \cdot 2$$
$$x \leq 6$$

Interval: $(-\infty, 6]$

Solution set: $\{x \mid x \leq 6\}$

Graph:

QC – 17

11.
$$4x - 3 < 13$$
$$4x - 3 + 3 < 13 + 3$$
$$4x < 16$$
$$\frac{4x}{4} < \frac{16}{4}$$
$$x < 4$$
Interval: $(-\infty, 4)$

Solution set: $\{x \mid x < 4\}$

Graph:

12.
$$3x + 1 > x - 5$$
$$3x + 1 - 1 > x - 5 - 1$$
$$3x > x - 6$$
$$3x - x > x - 6 - x$$
$$2x > -6$$
$$\frac{2x}{2} > \frac{-6}{2}$$
$$x > -3$$
Interval: $(-3, \infty)$

Solution set: $\{x \mid x > -3\}$

Graph:

13.
$$-2x + 1 \le 3x + 11$$
$$-2x + 1 - 1 \le 3x + 11 - 1$$
$$-2x \le 3x + 10$$
$$-2x - 3x \le 3x + 10 - 3x$$
$$-5x \le 10$$
$$\frac{-5x}{-5} \ge \frac{10}{-5}$$
$$x \ge -2$$
Interval: $[-2, \infty)$

Solution set: $\{x \mid x \ge -2\}$

14.
$$-5x + 12 < x - 3$$
$$-5x + 12 - 12 < x - 3 - 12$$
$$-5x < x - 15$$
$$-5x - x < x - 15 - x$$
$$-6x < -15$$
$$\frac{-6x}{-6} > \frac{-15}{-6}$$
$$x > \frac{5}{2}$$
Interval: $\left(\frac{5}{2}, \infty\right)$

Solution set: $\left\{x \mid x > \frac{5}{2}\right\}$

15.
$$4(x - 2) < 3x - 4$$
$$4x - 8 < 3x - 4$$
$$4x - 8 + 8 < 3x - 4 + 8$$
$$4x < 3x + 4$$
$$4x - 3x < 3x + 4 - 3x$$
$$x < 4$$
Interval: $(-\infty, 4)$

Solution set: $\{x \mid x < 4\}$

16.
$$-2(x + 1) \ge 4(x + 3)$$
$$-2x - 2 \ge 4x + 12$$
$$-2x - 2 + 2 \ge 4x + 12 + 2$$
$$-2x \ge 4x + 14$$
$$-2x - 4x \ge 4x + 14 - 4x$$
$$-6x \ge 14$$
$$\frac{-6x}{-6} \le \frac{14}{-6}$$
$$x \le -\frac{7}{3}$$
Interval: $\left(-\infty, -\frac{7}{3}\right]$

Solution set: $\left\{x \mid x \le -\frac{7}{3}\right\}$

17. $7 - 2(x+1) \le 3(x-5)$

$7 - 2x - 2 \le 3x - 15$

$-2x + 5 \le 3x - 15$

$-2x + 5 - 5 \le 3x - 15 - 5$

$-2x \le 3x - 20$

$-2x - 3x \le 3x - 20 - 3x$

$-5x \le -20$

$\dfrac{-5x}{-5} \ge \dfrac{-20}{-5}$

$x \ge 4$

Interval: $[4, \infty)$

Solution set: $\{x \mid x \ge 4\}$

18. $\dfrac{3x+1}{5} \ge 2$

$5 \cdot \dfrac{3x+1}{5} \ge 5 \cdot 2$

$3x + 1 \ge 10$

$3x + 1 - 1 \ge 10 - 1$

$3x \ge 9$

$\dfrac{3x}{3} \ge \dfrac{9}{3}$

$x \ge 3$

Interval: $[3, \infty)$

Solution set: $\{x \mid x \ge 3\}$

19. $\dfrac{2}{5}x + \dfrac{3}{10} < \dfrac{1}{2}$

$10\left(\dfrac{2}{5}x + \dfrac{3}{10}\right) < 10 \cdot \dfrac{1}{2}$

$4x + 3 < 5$

$4x + 3 - 3 < 5 - 3$

$4x < 2$

$\dfrac{4x}{4} < \dfrac{2}{4}$

$x < \dfrac{1}{2}$

Interval: $\left(-\infty, \dfrac{1}{2}\right)$

Solution set: $\left\{x \mid x < \dfrac{1}{2}\right\}$

20. $\dfrac{1}{2}(x+3) > \dfrac{1}{3}(x-4)$

$6 \cdot \dfrac{1}{2}(x+3) > 6 \cdot \dfrac{1}{3}(x-4)$

$3(x+3) > 2(x-4)$

$3x + 9 > 2x - 8$

$3x + 9 - 9 > 2x - 8 - 9$

$3x > 2x - 17$

$3x - 2x > 2x - 17 - 2x$

$x > -17$

Interval: $(-17, \infty)$

Solution set: $\{x \mid x > -17\}$

21. Let b = annual balance in dollars.
The annual cost is the sum of the annual fee and the interest charge. To find the interest charge, we use the simple interest formula $I = P \cdot r \cdot t$ and let $t = 1$ year.

Bank A cost < Bank B cost

$\text{fee}_A + \text{interest}_A < \text{fee}_B + \text{interest}_B$

$25 + 0.099b < 0 + 0.149b$

$25 + 0.099b < 0.149b$

$25 + 0.099b - 0.099b < 0.149b - 0.099b$

$25 < 0.05b$

$\dfrac{25}{0.05} < \dfrac{0.05b}{0.05}$

$500 < b \qquad \text{or} \qquad b > 500$

The card from Bank A will cost less if the annual balance is more than \$500.

22. Let x = the number of candy boxes.

$R > C$

$12x > 8x + 96$

$12x - 8x > 8x + 96 - 8x$

$4x > 96$

$\dfrac{4x}{4} > \dfrac{96}{4}$

$x > 24$

Revenue will exceed costs when more than 24 boxes of candy are sold.

1.5 Quick Checks

1. $A \cap B = \{1,3,5\}$

2. $A \cap C = \{2,4,6\}$

3. $A \cup B = \{1,2,3,4,5,6,7\}$

4. $A \cup C = \{1,2,3,4,5,6,8\}$

5. $B \cap C = \{ \ \}$ or $\varnothing$

6. $B \cup C = \{1,2,3,4,5,6,7,8\}$

7. $A \cap B$ is the set of all real numbers that are greater than 2 and less than 7.

   Solution set: $\{x \mid 2 < x < 7\}$

   Interval: $(2,7)$

8. $A \cup C$ is the set of real numbers that are greater than 2 or less than or equal to -3.

   Solution set: $\{x \mid x \le -3 \text{ or } x > 2\}$

   Interval: $(-\infty,-3] \cup (2,\infty)$

9. $2x+1 \ge 5 \quad$ and $\quad -3x+2 < 5$

   $\qquad 2x \ge 4 \qquad\qquad -3x < 3$

   $\qquad\ x \ge 2 \qquad\qquad\quad x > -1$

   We need $x \ge 2$ and $x > -1$.

   Solution set: $\{x \mid x \ge 2\}$

   Interval: $[2,\infty)$

10. $4x-5 < 7 \quad$ and $\quad 3x-1 > -10$

    $\qquad 4x < 12 \qquad\qquad 3x > -9$

    $\qquad\ x < 3 \qquad\qquad\ x > -3$

    We need $x < 3$ and $x > -3$.

    Solution set: $\{x \mid -3 < x < 3\}$

    Interval: $(-3,3)$

11. $-8x+3 < -5 \quad$ and $\quad \dfrac{2}{3}x+1 < 3$

    $\quad -8x < -8$

    $\qquad\ x > 1 \qquad\qquad\quad \dfrac{2}{3}x < 2$

    $\qquad\qquad\qquad\qquad\qquad\ x < 3$

    We need $x > 1$ and $x < 3$.

    Solution set: $\{x \mid 1 < x < 3\}$

    Interval: $(1,3)$

12. $3x-5 < -8 \quad$ and $\quad 2x+1 > 5$

    $\qquad 3x < -3 \qquad\qquad 2x > 4$

    $\qquad\ x < -1 \qquad\qquad\ x > 2$

    We need $x < -1$ and $x > 2$. Looking at the graphs of the inequalities separately we see that there are no such numbers that satisfy both inequalities. Therefore, the solution set is empty.

    Solution set: $\{ \ \}$ or $\varnothing$

    Interval: none

13. $5x+1 \le 6 \quad$ and $\quad 3x+2 \ge 5$

    $\qquad 5x \le 5 \qquad\qquad 3x \ge 3$

    $\qquad\ x \le 1 \qquad\qquad\ x \ge 1$

    We need $x \le 1$ and $x \ge 1$. Looking at the graphs of the inequalities separately we see that the only number that is both less than or equal to 1 and greater than or equal to 1 is the number 1.

    Solution set: $\{1\}$

    Interval: $[1,1]$

14. $\qquad -2 < 3x+1 < 10$

    $\quad -2-1 < 3x+1-1 < 10-1$

    $\qquad\ -3 < 3x < 9$

    $\qquad\ \dfrac{-3}{3} < \dfrac{3x}{3} < \dfrac{9}{3}$

    $\qquad\ -1 < x < 3$

    Solution set: $\{x \mid -1 < x < 3\}$

    Interval: $(-1,3)$

QC – 20

15.
$$0 < 4x - 5 \le 3$$
$$0 + 5 < 4x - 5 + 5 \le 3 + 5$$
$$5 < 4x \le 8$$
$$\frac{5}{4} < \frac{4x}{4} \le \frac{8}{4}$$
$$\frac{5}{4} < x \le 2$$

Solution set: $\left\{ x \mid \dfrac{5}{4} < x \le 2 \right\}$

Interval: $\left(\dfrac{5}{4}, 2 \right]$

16.
$$3 \le -2x - 1 \le 11$$
$$3 + 1 \le -2x - 1 + 1 \le 11 + 1$$
$$4 \le -2x \le 12$$
$$\frac{4}{-2} \ge \frac{-2x}{-2} \ge \frac{12}{-2}$$
$$-2 \ge x \ge -6 \quad \text{or} \quad -6 \le x \le -2$$

Solution set: $\{ x \mid -6 \le x \le -2 \}$

Interval: $[-6, -2]$

17. $x + 3 < 1 \quad \text{or} \quad x - 2 > 3$
$$\quad x < -2 \qquad\quad x > 5$$
We need $x < -2$ or $x > 5$.

Solution set: $\{ x \mid x < -2 \text{ or } x > 5 \}$

Interval: $(-\infty, -2) \cup (5, \infty)$

18. $3x + 1 \le 7 \quad \text{or} \quad 2x - 3 > 9$
$$\quad 3x \le 6 \qquad\quad 2x > 12$$
$$\quad x \le 2 \qquad\qquad x > 6$$
We need $x \le 2$ or $x > 6$.

Solution set: $\{ x \mid x \le 2 \text{ or } x > 6 \}$

Interval: $(-\infty, 2] \cup (6, \infty)$

19. $2x - 3 \ge 1 \quad \text{or} \quad 6x - 5 \ge 1$
$$\quad 2x \ge 4 \qquad\quad 6x \ge 6$$
$$\quad x \ge 2 \qquad\qquad x \ge 1$$
We need $x \ge 2$ or $x \ge 1$.

Solution set: $\{ x \mid x \ge 1 \}$

Interval: $[1, \infty)$

20. $\dfrac{3}{4}(x+4) < 6 \quad \text{or} \quad \dfrac{3}{2}(x+1) > 15$
$$\quad x + 4 < 8 \qquad\quad x + 1 > 10$$
$$\quad x < 4 \qquad\qquad x > 9$$
We need $x < 4$ or $x > 9$.

Solution set: $\{ x \mid x < 4 \text{ or } x > 9 \}$

Interval: $(-\infty, 4) \cup (9, \infty)$

21. $3x - 2 > -5 \quad \text{or} \quad 2x - 5 \le 1$
$$\quad 3x > -3 \qquad\quad 2x \le 6$$
$$\quad x > -1 \qquad\qquad x \le 3$$
If we look at the graph of the inequalities separately, we see that the union of their solution sets is the set of real numbers.

Solution set: $\{ x \mid -\infty < x < \infty \}$

Interval: $(-\infty, \infty)$

22. $-5x - 2 \le 3 \quad \text{or} \quad 7x - 9 > 5$
$$\quad -5x \le 5 \qquad\quad 7x > 14$$
$$\quad x \ge -1 \qquad\qquad x > 2$$
We need $x \ge -1$ or $x > 2$. Since the solution set of the inequality $x > 2$ is a subset of the solution set for the inequality $x \ge -1$, we only need to consider $x \ge -1$.

Solution set: $\{ x \mid x \ge -1 \}$

Interval: $[-1, \infty)$

QC – 21

23. Let x = taxable income (in dollars). The federal income tax in the 25% bracket is $4090 plus 25% of the amount over $29,700. In general, the income tax for the 25% bracket is given by
$4090 + 0.25(x - 29,700)$
Because the federal income tax is between $4,090 and $14,652.50, we have
$$4090 \le 4090 + 0.25(x - 29,700) \le 14,652.50$$
$$4090 \le 4090 + 0.25x - 7425 \le 14,652.50$$
$$4090 \le 0.25x - 3335 \le 14,652.50$$
$$7425 \le 0.25x \le 17,987.50$$
$$29,700 \le x \le 71,950$$
To be in the 25% tax bracket, an individual would have an income between $29,700 and $71,950.

24. Let x = number of minutes. The long distance plan charges $4.95 per month and $0.07 per minute. In general, the charge is given by $4.95 + 0.07x$. Sophia's charges ranged from $13.00 to $22.80, so we get the inequality
$$13.00 \le 4.95 + 0.07x \le 22.80$$
$$8.05 \le 0.07x \le 17.85$$
$$115 \le x \le 255$$
Over the course of the year, Sophia's monthly minutes were between 115 minutes and 255 minutes.

1.6 Quick Checks

1. $|x| = 7$

   $x = 7$ or $x = -7$ because both numbers are 7 units away from 0 on a real number line.
   Solution set: $\{-7, 7\}$

2. $|z| = 1$

   $z = 1$ or $z = -1$ because both numbers are 1 unit away from 0 on a real number line.
   Solution set: $\{-1, 1\}$

3. $|2x - 3| = 7$

   $2x - 3 = 7$ or $2x - 3 = -7$
   $\quad 2x = 10 \qquad\qquad 2x = -4$
   $\quad\; x = 5 \qquad\qquad\;\; x = -2$

   Check:
   Let $x = 5$:   Let $x = -2$:
   $|2(5) - 3| \overset{?}{=} 7$ $|2(-2) - 3| \overset{?}{=} 7$
   $|10 - 3| \overset{?}{=} 7$ $|-4 - 3| \overset{?}{=} 7$
   $\quad 7 = 7 \checkmark$ $\quad 7 = 7 \checkmark$

   Solution set: $\{-2, 5\}$

4. $|3x - 2| + 3 = 10$

   $|3x - 2| = 7$
   $3x - 2 = 7$ or $3x - 2 = -7$
   $\quad 3x = 9 \qquad\qquad 3x = -5$
   $\quad\; x = 3 \qquad\qquad\;\; x = -\dfrac{5}{3}$

   Check:
   Let $x = 3$:   Let $x = -\dfrac{5}{3}$:
   $|3(3) - 2| + 3 \overset{?}{=} 10$ $\left|3\left(-\dfrac{5}{3}\right) - 2\right| + 3 \overset{?}{=} 10$
   $|9 - 2| + 3 \overset{?}{=} 10$ $|-5 - 2| + 3 \overset{?}{=} 10$
   $\quad 7 + 3 \overset{?}{=} 10$ $\quad 7 + 3 \overset{?}{=} 10$
   $\quad 10 = 10 \checkmark$ $\quad 10 = 10 \checkmark$

   Solution set: $\left\{-\dfrac{5}{3}, 3\right\}$

5. $|-5x+2|-2=5$

$\quad\quad |-5x+2|=7$

$\quad -5x+2=7 \quad$ or $\quad -5x+2=-7$

$\quad\quad -5x=5 \quad\quad\quad\quad -5x=-9$

$\quad\quad\quad x=-1 \quad\quad\quad\quad\quad x=\dfrac{9}{5}$

Check:

Let $x=-1:$ $\quad\quad\quad$ Let $x=\dfrac{9}{5}:$

$|-5(-1)+2|-2\overset{?}{=}5 \quad \left|-5\left(\dfrac{9}{5}\right)+2\right|-2\overset{?}{=}5$

$\quad\quad |5+2|-2\overset{?}{=}5 \quad\quad\quad |-9+2|-2\overset{?}{=}5$

$\quad\quad\quad 7-2\overset{?}{=}5 \quad\quad\quad\quad\quad 7-2\overset{?}{=}5$

$\quad\quad\quad\quad 5=5 \checkmark \quad\quad\quad\quad\quad\quad 5=5 \checkmark$

Solution set: $\left\{-1,\dfrac{9}{5}\right\}$

6. $3|x+2|-4=5$

$\quad\quad 3|x+2|=9$

$\quad\quad\quad |x+2|=3$

$\quad x+2=3 \quad$ or $\quad x+2=-3$

$\quad\quad x=1 \quad\quad\quad\quad x=-5$

Check:

Let $x=1:$ $\quad\quad\quad$ Let $x=-5:$

$3|1+2|-4\overset{?}{=}5 \quad\quad 3|-5+2|-4\overset{?}{=}5$

$\quad 3(3)-4\overset{?}{=}5 \quad\quad\quad 3(3)-4\overset{?}{=}5$

$\quad 9-4\overset{?}{=}5 \quad\quad\quad\quad 9-4\overset{?}{=}5$

$\quad\quad 5=5 \checkmark \quad\quad\quad\quad\quad 5=5 \checkmark$

Solution set: $\{-5,1\}$

7. $|5x+3|=-2$

Since absolute values are never negative, this equation has no solution.

Solution set: $\{\ \}$ or $\varnothing$

8. $|2x+5|+7=3$

$\quad\quad |2x+5|=-4$

Since absolute values are never negative, this equation has no solution.

Solution set: $\{\ \}$ or $\varnothing$

9. $|x+1|+3=3$

$\quad\quad |x+1|=0$

$\quad\quad x+1=0$

$\quad\quad\quad x=-1$

Check:

Let $x=-1$

$|-1+1|+3\overset{?}{=}3$

$\quad\quad 0+3\overset{?}{=}3$

$\quad\quad\quad 3=3 \checkmark$

Solution set: $\{-1\}$

10. $|x-3|=|2x+5|$

$\quad x-3=2x+5 \quad$ or $\quad x-3=-(2x+5)$

$\quad\quad x=2x+8 \quad\quad\quad x-3=-2x-5$

$\quad\quad -x=8 \quad\quad\quad\quad\quad x=-2x-2$

$\quad\quad\quad x=-8 \quad\quad\quad\quad 3x=-2$

$\quad\quad\quad\quad\quad\quad\quad\quad\quad\quad x=-\dfrac{2}{3}$

Check:

Let $x=-8$ $\quad\quad\quad$ Let $x=-\dfrac{2}{3}$

$|-8-3|\overset{?}{=}|2(-8)+5| \quad \left|-\dfrac{2}{3}-3\right|\overset{?}{=}\left|2\left(-\dfrac{2}{3}\right)+5\right|$

$|-11|\overset{?}{=}|-16+5| \quad\quad \left|-\dfrac{11}{3}\right|\overset{?}{=}\left|-\dfrac{4}{3}+5\right|$

$\quad 11=11 \checkmark \quad\quad\quad\quad\quad \dfrac{11}{3}=\dfrac{11}{3} \checkmark$

Solution set: $\left\{-8,-\dfrac{2}{3}\right\}$

QC – 23

11. $|8z+11|=|6z+17|$

$8z+11=6z+17$ or $8z+11=-(6z+17)$

$\qquad 8z=6z+6 \qquad\qquad 8z+11=-6z-17$

$\qquad 2z=6 \qquad\qquad\qquad 8z=-6z-28$

$\qquad z=3 \qquad\qquad\qquad 14z=-28$

$\qquad\qquad\qquad\qquad\qquad\qquad z=-2$

Check:

Let $z=-2$:

$$|8(-2)+11|\overset{?}{=}|6(-2)+17|$$

$$|-16+11|\overset{?}{=}|-12+17|$$

$$5=5 \checkmark$$

Let $z=3$:

$$|8(3)+11|\overset{?}{=}|6(3)+17|$$

$$|24+11|\overset{?}{=}|18+17|$$

$$35=35 \checkmark$$

Solution set: $\{-2,3\}$

12. $|3-2y|=|4y+3|$

$3-2y=4y+3$ or $3-2y=-(4y+3)$

$\quad -2y=4y \qquad\qquad 3-2y=-4y-3$

$\quad -6y=0 \qquad\qquad\quad -2y=-4y-6$

$\quad y=0 \qquad\qquad\qquad\; 2y=-6$

$\qquad\qquad\qquad\qquad\qquad\quad y=-3$

Check:

Let $y=0$: $\qquad\qquad$ Let $y=-3$:

$$|3-2(0)|\overset{?}{=}|4(0)+3| \quad |3-2(-3)|\overset{?}{=}|4(-3)+3|$$

$$|3|\overset{?}{=}|3| \qquad\qquad\qquad |3+6|\overset{?}{=}|-12+3|$$

$$3=3 \checkmark \qquad\qquad\qquad\qquad 3=3 \checkmark$$

Solution set: $\{-3,0\}$

13. $|2x-3|=|5-2x|$

$2x-3=5-2x$ or $2x-3=-(5-2x)$

$\quad 2x=8-2x \qquad\qquad 2x-3=-5+2x$

$\quad 4x=8 \qquad\qquad\qquad\; 2x=-2+2x$

$\quad x=2 \qquad\qquad\qquad\quad 0=-2 \;\text{false}$

The second equation leads to a contradiction.
Therefore, the only solution is $x=2$.

Check:

Let $x=2$:

$$|2(2)-3|\overset{?}{=}|5-2(2)|$$

$$|4-3|\overset{?}{=}|5-4|$$

$$1=1 \checkmark$$

Solution set: $\{2\}$

14. $|x|\le 5$

$-5\le x\le 5$

Solution set: $\{x\,|\,-5\le x\le 5\}$

Interval: $[-5,5]$

15. $|x|<\dfrac{3}{2}$

$-\dfrac{3}{2}<x<\dfrac{3}{2}$

Solution set: $\left\{x\,\middle|\,-\dfrac{3}{2}<x<\dfrac{3}{2}\right\}$

Interval: $\left(-\dfrac{3}{2},\dfrac{3}{2}\right)$

16. $|x+3|<5$

$-5<x+3<5$

$-5-3<x+3-3<5-3$

$-8<x<2$

Solution set: $\{x\,|\,-8<x<2\}$

Interval: $(-8,2)$

17. $|2x-3| \le 7$

$-7 \le 2x-3 \le 7$

$-7+3 \le 2x-3+3 \le 7+3$

$-4 \le 2x \le 10$

$\dfrac{-4}{2} \le \dfrac{2x}{2} \le \dfrac{10}{2}$

$-2 \le x \le 5$

Solution set: $\{x \,|\, -2 \le x \le 5\}$

Interval: $[-2,5]$

18. $|7x+2| < -3$

Since absolute values are never negative, this inequality has no solution.

Solution set: $\{\ \}$ or $\varnothing$

19. $|x|+4 < 6$

$|x| < 2$

$-2 < x < 2$

Solution set: $\{x \,|\, -2 < x < 2\}$; Interval: $(-2,2)$

20. $|x-3|+4 \le 8$

$|x-3| \le 4$

$-4 \le x-3 \le 4$

$-4+3 \le x-3+3 \le 4+3$

$-1 \le x \le 7$

Solution set: $\{x \,|\, -1 \le x \le 7\}$

Interval: $[-1,7]$

21. $3|2x+1| \le 9$

$|2x+1| \le 3$

$-3 \le 2x+1 \le 3$

$-3-1 \le 2x+1-1 \le 3-1$

$-4 \le 2x \le 2$

$\dfrac{-4}{2} \le \dfrac{2x}{2} \le \dfrac{2}{2}$

$-2 \le x \le 1$

Solution set: $\{x \,|\, -2 \le x \le 1\}$

Interval: $[-2,1]$

22. $|-3x+1|-5 < 3$

$|-3x+1| < 8$

$-8 < -3x+1 < 8$

$-8-1 < -3x+1-1 < 8-1$

$-9 < -3x < 7$

$\dfrac{-9}{-3} > \dfrac{-3x}{-3} > \dfrac{7}{-3}$

$3 > x > -\dfrac{7}{3}$ or $-\dfrac{7}{3} < x < 3$

Solution set: $\left\{x \,|\, -\dfrac{7}{3} < x < 3\right\}$

Interval: $\left(-\dfrac{7}{3},3\right)$

23. $|x| \ge 6$

$x \le -6$ or $x \ge 6$

Solution set: $\{x \,|\, x \le -6 \text{ or } x \ge 6\}$

Interval: $(-\infty,-6] \cup [6,\infty)$

24. $|x| > \dfrac{5}{2}$

$x < -\dfrac{5}{2}$ or $x > \dfrac{5}{2}$

Solution set: $\left\{x \,|\, x < -\dfrac{5}{2} \text{ or } x > \dfrac{5}{2}\right\}$

Interval: $\left(-\infty,-\dfrac{5}{2}\right) \cup \left(\dfrac{5}{2},\infty\right)$

25. $|x+3| > 4$

$x+3 < -4$ or $x+3 > 4$

$x < -7 \qquad x > 1$

Solution set: $\{x \,|\, x < -7 \text{ or } x > 1\}$

Interval: $(-\infty,-7) \cup (1,\infty)$

QC – 25

26. $|4x-3| \geq 5$

$4x-3 \leq -5 \quad$ or $\quad 4x-3 \geq 5$

$\quad 4x \leq -2 \qquad\qquad 4x \geq 8$

$\quad x \leq -\dfrac{1}{2} \qquad\qquad x \geq 2$

Solution set: $\left\{ x \mid x \leq -\dfrac{1}{2} \text{ or } x \geq 2 \right\}$

Interval: $\left(-\infty, -\dfrac{1}{2} \right] \cup [2, \infty)$

27. $|-3x+2| > 7$

$-3x+2 < -7 \quad$ or $\quad -3x+2 > 7$

$\quad -3x < -9 \qquad\qquad -3x > 5$

$\quad x > 3 \qquad\qquad\quad x < -\dfrac{5}{3}$

Solution set: $\left\{ x \mid x < -\dfrac{5}{3} \text{ or } x > 3 \right\}$

Interval: $\left(-\infty, -\dfrac{5}{3} \right) \cup (3, \infty)$

28. $|2x+5| - 2 > -2$

$\quad |2x+5| > 0$

$2x+5 < 0 \quad$ or $\quad 2x+5 > 0$

$\quad 2x < -5 \qquad\qquad 2x > -5$

$\quad x < -\dfrac{5}{2} \qquad\qquad x > -\dfrac{5}{2}$

Solution set: $\left\{ x \mid x \neq -\frac{5}{2} \right\}$

Interval: $\left(-\infty, -\frac{5}{2} \right) \cup \left(-\frac{5}{2}, \infty \right)$

29. $|6x-5| \geq 0$

Since absolute values are always nonnegative, all real numbers are solutions to this inequality.

Solution set: $\{ x \mid x \text{ is any real number} \}$

Interval: $(-\infty, \infty)$

30. $|2x+1| > -3$

Since absolute values are always nonnegative, all real numbers are solutions to this inequality.

Solution set: $\{ x \mid x \text{ is any real number} \}$

Interval: $(-\infty, \infty)$

31. $|x-4| \leq \dfrac{1}{32}$

$-\dfrac{1}{32} \leq x-4 \leq \dfrac{1}{32}$

$-\dfrac{1}{32} + 4 \leq x-4+4 \leq \dfrac{1}{32} + 4$

$-\dfrac{1}{32} + \dfrac{128}{32} \leq x \leq \dfrac{1}{32} + \dfrac{128}{32}$

$\dfrac{127}{32} \leq x \leq \dfrac{129}{32}$

The acceptable belt widths are between $\frac{127}{32}$ inches and $\frac{129}{32}$ inches.

32. $|p-9| \leq 1.7$

$-1.7 \leq p-9 \leq 1.7$

$-1.7 + 9 \leq p-9+9 \leq 1.7 + 9$

$7.3 \leq p \leq 10.7$

The percentage of people that have been shot at is between 7.3 percent and 10.7 percent.

Chapter 2 – Quick Checks

2.1 Quick Checks

1. A: quadrant I
   B: quadrant IV
   C: y-axis
   D: quadrant III

2. A: quadrant II
   B: x-axis
   C: quadrant IV
   D: quadrant I

3. **a.** Let $x = 2$ and $y = -3$.

   $$2(2) - 4(-3) \overset{?}{=} 12$$
   $$4 + 12 \overset{?}{=} 12$$
   $$16 = 12 \text{ False}$$

   The point $(2, -3)$ is not on the graph.

   b. Let $x = 2$ and $y = -2$.

   $$2(2) - 4(-2) \overset{?}{=} 12$$
   $$4 + 8 \overset{?}{=} 12$$
   $$12 = 12 \checkmark$$

   The point $(2, -2)$ is on the graph.

c. Let $x = \dfrac{3}{2}$ and $y = -\dfrac{9}{4}$.

$$2\left(\dfrac{3}{2}\right) - 4\left(-\dfrac{9}{4}\right) \overset{?}{=} 12$$
$$3 + 9 \overset{?}{=} 12$$
$$12 = 12 \checkmark$$

The point $\left(\dfrac{3}{2}, -\dfrac{9}{4}\right)$ is on the graph.

4. **a.** Let $x = 1$ and $y = 4$.

   $$(4) \overset{?}{=} (1)^2 + 3$$
   $$4 \overset{?}{=} 1 + 3$$
   $$4 = 4 \checkmark$$

   The point $(1, 4)$ is on the graph.

   b. Let $x = -2$ and $y = -1$.

   $$(-1) \overset{?}{=} (-2)^2 + 3$$
   $$-1 \overset{?}{=} 4 + 3$$
   $$-1 = 7 \text{ False}$$

   The point $(-2, -1)$ is not on the graph.

   c. Let $x = -3$ and $y = 12$.

   $$(12) \overset{?}{=} (-3)^2 + 3$$
   $$12 \overset{?}{=} 9 + 3$$
   $$12 = 12 \checkmark$$

   The point $(-3, 12)$ is on the graph.

5. $y = 3x + 1$

x	$y = 3x + 1$	(x, y)
-2	$y = 3(-2) + 1 = -5$	$(-2, -5)$
-1	$y = 3(-1) + 1 = -2$	$(-1, -2)$
0	$y = 3(0) + 1 = 1$	$(0, 1)$
1	$y = 3(1) + 1 = 4$	$(1, 4)$
2	$y = 3(2) + 1 = 7$	$(2, 7)$

6. $2x + 3y = 8$

$$3y = -2x + 8$$
$$y = -\frac{2}{3}x + \frac{8}{3}$$

x	$y = -\frac{2}{3}x + \frac{8}{3}$	(x, y)
-5	$y = -\frac{2}{3}(-5) + \frac{8}{3} = 6$	$(-5, 6)$
-2	$y = -\frac{2}{3}(-2) + \frac{8}{3} = 4$	$(-2, 4)$
1	$y = -\frac{2}{3}(1) + \frac{8}{3} = 2$	$(1, 2)$
4	$y = -\frac{2}{3}(4) + \frac{8}{3} = 0$	$(4, 0)$
7	$y = -\frac{2}{3}(7) + \frac{8}{3} = -2$	$(7, -2)$

7. $y = x^2 + 3$

x	$y = x^2 + 3$	(x, y)
-2	$y = (-2)^2 + 3 = 7$	$(-2, 7)$
-1	$y = (-1)^2 + 3 = 4$	$(-1, 4)$
0	$y = (0)^2 + 3 = 3$	$(0, 3)$
1	$y = (1)^2 + 3 = 4$	$(1, 4)$
2	$y = (2)^2 + 3 = 7$	$(2, 7)$

8. $x = y^2 + 2$

y	$x = y^2 + 2$	(x, y)
-2	$x = (-2)^2 + 2 = 6$	$(6, -2)$
-1	$x = (-1)^2 + 2 = 3$	$(3, -1)$
0	$x = (0)^2 + 2 = 2$	$(2, 0)$
1	$x = (1)^2 + 2 = 3$	$(3, 1)$
2	$x = (2)^2 + 2 = 6$	$(6, 2)$

9. $x = (y - 1)^2$

y	$x = (y - 1)^2$	(x, y)
-1	$x = (-1 - 1)^2 = 4$	$(4, -1)$
0	$x = (0 - 1)^2 = 1$	$(1, 0)$
1	$x = (1 - 1)^2 = 0$	$(0, 1)$
2	$x = (2 - 1)^2 = 1$	$(1, 2)$
3	$x = (3 - 1)^2 = 4$	$(4, 3)$

QC – 28

10. To find the intercepts, we look for the points where the graph crosses or touches either coordinate axis. From the graph, we see that the intercepts are $(-5,0)$, $(0,-0.9)$, $(1,0)$, and $(6.7,0)$.

    The x-intercepts are the points where the graph crosses or touches the x-axis. From the graph we see that the x-intercepts are -5, 1, and 6.7.

    The y-intercept is the point where the graph crosses the y-axis. From the graph we see that the y-intercept is -0.9.

11. **a.** Locate the value 250 along the x-axis, go up to the graph, and then read the corresponding value on the y-axis. According to the graph, the cost of refining 250 thousand gallons of gasoline per hour is $200 thousand.

    b. Locate the value 400 along the x-axis, go up to the graph, and then read the corresponding value on the y-axis. According to the graph, the cost of refining 400 thousand gallons of gasoline per hour is $350 thousand.

    c. Since the horizontal axis represents the number of gallons per hour than can be refined, the graph ending at 700 thousand gallons per hour represents the capacity of the refinery per hour.

    d. The intercept is $(0,100)$. This represents the fixed costs of operating the refinery. That is, refining 0 gallons per hour costs $100 thousand.

2.2 Quick Checks

1. The first element of the ordered pair comes from the set 'Friend' and the second element is the corresponding element from the set 'Birthday'.
   {(Max, November 8), (Alesia, January 20), (Trent, March 3), (Yolanda, November 8), (Wanda, July 6), (Elvis, January 8)}

2. The first elements of the ordered pairs make up the domain and the second elements make up the range.

3. The domain is the set of all inputs and the range is the set of all outputs. The inputs are the elements in the set 'Friend' and the outputs are the elements in the set 'Birthday'.
   Domain:
   {Max, Alesia, Trent, Yolanda, Wanda, Elvis}
   Range:
   {January 20, March 3, July 6, November 8, January 8}

4. The domain is the set of all inputs and the range is the set of all outputs. The inputs are the first elements in the ordered pairs and the outputs are the second elements in the ordered pairs.
   Domain: Range:
   {1, 5, 8, 10}   {3, 4, 13}

5. First we notice that the ordered pairs on the graph are $(-2,0)$, $(-1,2)$, $(-1,-2)$, $(2,3)$, $(3,0)$, and $(4,-3)$.
   The domain is the set of all x-coordinates and the range is the set of all y-coordinates.
   Domain: Range:
   $\{-2,-1,2,3,4\}$ $\{-3,-2,0,2,3\}$

6. To find the domain, we first determine the x-values for which the graph exists. The graph exists for all x-values between -2 and 4, inclusive. Thus, the domain is $\{x\,|\,-2\le x\le 4\}$, or $[-2,4]$ if we use interval notation.

   To find the range, we first determine the y-values for which the graph exists. The graph exists for all y-values between -2 and 2, inclusive. Thus, the range is $\{y\,|\,-2\le y\le 2\}$, or $[-2,2]$ if we use interval notation.

7. To find the domain, we first determine the x-values for which the graph exists. The graph exists for all x-values on a real number line. Thus, the domain is $\{x \mid x \text{ is any real number}\}$, or $(-\infty, \infty)$ if we use interval notation.

To find the range, we first determine the y-values for which the graph exists. The graph exists for all y-values on a real number line. Thus, the range is $\{y \mid y \text{ is any real number}\}$, or $(-\infty, \infty)$ if we use interval notation.

8. $y = 3x - 8$

x	$y = 3x - 8$	(x, y)
-1	$y = 3(-1) - 8 = -11$	$(-1, -11)$
0	$y = 3(0) - 8 = -8$	$(0, -8)$
1	$y = 3(1) - 8 = -5$	$(1, -5)$
2	$y = 3(2) - 8 = -2$	$(2, -2)$
3	$y = 3(3) - 8 = 1$	$(3, 1)$

Domain: $\{x \mid x \text{ is any real number}\}$ or $(-\infty, \infty)$

Range: $\{y \mid y \text{ is any real number}\}$ or $(-\infty, \infty)$

9. $y = x^2 - 8$

x	$y = x^2 - 8$	(x, y)
-3	$y = (-3)^2 - 8 = 1$	$(-3, 1)$
-2	$y = (-2)^2 - 8 = -4$	$(-2, -4)$
0	$y = (0)^2 - 8 = -8$	$(0, -8)$
2	$y = (2)^2 - 8 = -4$	$(2, -4)$
3	$y = (3)^2 - 8 = 1$	$(3, 1)$

Domain: $\{x \mid x \text{ is any real number}\}$ or $(-\infty, \infty)$

Range: $\{y \mid y \geq -8\}$ or $[-8, \infty)$

10. $x = y^2 + 1$

y	$x = y^2 + 1$	(x, y)
-2	$x = (-2)^2 + 1 = 5$	$(5, -2)$
-1	$x = (-1)^2 + 1 = 2$	$(2, -1)$
0	$x = (0)^2 + 1 = 1$	$(1, 0)$
1	$x = (1)^2 + 1 = 2$	$(2, 1)$
2	$x = (2)^2 + 1 = 5$	$(5, 2)$

Domain: $\{x \mid x \geq 1\}$ or $[1, \infty)$

Range: $\{y \mid y \text{ is any real number}\}$ or $(-\infty, \infty)$

2.3 Quick Checks

1. The relation is a function because each element in the domain (Friend) corresponds to exactly one element in the range (Birthday).
   Domain: {Max, Alesia, Trent, Yolanda, Wanda, Elvis}
   Range: {January 20, March 3, July 6, November 8, January 8}

2. The relation is not a function because there is an element in the domain, 210, that corresponds to more than one element in the domain. If 210 is selected from the domain, a single sugar content cannot be determined.

3. The relation is a function because there are no ordered pairs with the same first coordinate, but different second coordinates.
   Domain: $\{-3, -2, -1, 0, 1\}$

   Range: $\{0, 1, 2, 3\}$

4. The relation is not a function because there are two ordered pairs, $(-3, 2)$ and $(-3, 6)$, with the same first coordinate, but different second coordinates.

QC – 30

5. $y = -2x + 5$

The relation is a function since there is only 1 output than can result for each input.

6. $y = \pm 3x$

The relation is not a function since a single input for x will yield two output values for y. For example, if $x = 1$, then $y = \pm 3$.

7. $y = x^2 + 5x$

The relation is a function since there is only 1 output than can result for each input.

8. $x + y^2 = 9$

The relation is not a function since a single input for x can yield two output values for y. For example, if $x = 0$, then we have
$$0 + y^2 = 9$$
$$y^2 = 9$$
$$y = \pm 3$$

9. The graph is that of a function because every vertical line will cross the graph in at most one point.

10. The graph is not that of a function because a vertical line can cross the graph in more than one point.

11. $f(x) = 3x + 2$
$$f(4) = 3(4) + 2$$
$$= 12 + 2$$
$$= 14$$

12. $g(x) = -2x^2 + x - 3$
$$g(-2) = -2(-2)^2 + (-2) - 3$$
$$= -2(4) - 5$$
$$= -8 - 5$$
$$= -13$$

13. $f(x) = 3x + 2$
$$f(x-2) = 3(x-2) + 2$$
$$= 3x - 6 + 2$$
$$= 3x - 4$$

14. $f(x) - f(2) = [3x + 2] - [3(2) + 2]$
$$= 3x + 2 - 8$$
$$= 3x - 6$$

15. $f(x) = -2x + 9$

x	$y = f(x) = -2x + 9$	(x, y)
-2	$f(-2) = -2(-2) + 9 = 13$	$(-2, 13)$
0	$f(0) = -2(0) + 9 = 9$	$(0, 9)$
2	$f(2) = -2(2) + 9 = 5$	$(2, 5)$
4	$f(4) = -2(4) + 9 = 1$	$(4, 1)$
6	$f(6) = -2(6) + 9 = -3$	$(6, -3)$

16. $f(x) = x^2 + 2$

x	$y = f(x) = x^2 + 2$	(x, y)
-3	$f(-3) = (-3)^2 + 2 = 11$	$(-3, 11)$
-1	$f(-1) = (-1)^2 + 2 = 3$	$(-1, 3)$
0	$f(0) = (0)^2 + 2 = 2$	$(0, 2)$
1	$f(1) = (1)^2 + 2 = 3$	$(1, 3)$
3	$f(3) = (3)^2 + 2 = 11$	$(3, 11)$

17. $f(x) = |x-2|$

x	$y = f(x) = |x-2|$	(x, y)
-2	$f(-2) = |-2-2| = 4$	$(-2, 4)$
0	$f(0) = |0-2| = 2$	$(0, 2)$
2	$f(2) = |2-2| = 0$	$(2, 0)$
4	$f(4) = |4-2| = 2$	$(4, 2)$
6	$f(6) = |6-2| = 4$	$(6, 4)$

18. a. Independent variable: t (number of days)
Dependent variable: A (square miles)

b. $A(t) = 0.25\pi t^2$

$A(30) = 0.25\pi (30)^2 \approx 706.86$ sq. miles

After the tanker has been leaking for 30 days, the circular oil slick will cover about 706.86 square miles.

2.4 Quick Checks

1. $f(x) = 3x^2 + 2$

The function tells us to square a number x, multiply by 3, and then add 2. Since these operations can be performed on any real number, the domain of f is the set of all real numbers. The domain can be written as $\{x \mid x \text{ is any real number}\}$, or $(-\infty, \infty)$ in interval notation.

2. $h(x) = \dfrac{x+1}{x-3}$

The function tells us to divide $x+1$ by $x-3$. Since division by 0 is not defined, the denominator $x-3$ can never be 0. Therefore, x can never equal 3. The domain can be written as $\{x \mid x \neq 3\}$, or $(-\infty, 3) \cup (3, \infty)$ in interval notation.

3. $A(r) = \pi r^2$

Since r represents the radius of the circle, it must take on positive values. Therefore, the domain is $\{r \mid r > 0\}$, or $(0, \infty)$ in interval notation.

4. a. The arrows on the ends of the graph indicate that the graph continues indefinitely. Therefore, the domain is $\{x \mid x \text{ is any real number}\}$, or $(-\infty, \infty)$ in interval notation.
The function reaches a maximum value of 2, but has no minimum value. Therefore, the range is $\{y \mid y \leq 2\}$, or $(-\infty, 2]$ in interval notation.

b. The intercepts are $(-2, 0)$, $(0, 2)$, and $(2, 0)$. The x-intercepts are -2 and 2, and the y-intercept is 2.

5. a. Since $(-3, -15)$ and $(1, -3)$ are on the graph of f, then $f(-3) = -15$ and $f(1) = -3$.

b. To determine the domain, notice that the graph exists for all real numbers. Thus, the domain is $\{x \mid x \text{ is any real number}\}$, or $(-\infty, \infty)$ in interval notation.

c. To determine the range, notice that the function can assume any real number. Thus, the range is $\{y \mid y \text{ is any real number}\}$, or $(-\infty, \infty)$ in interval notation.

d. The intercepts are $(-2, 0)$, $(0, 0)$, and $(2, 0)$. The x-intercepts are -2, 0, and 2. The y-intercept is 0.

e. Since $(3, 15)$ is the only point on the graph where $y = f(x) = 15$, the solution set to $f(x) = 15$ is $\{3\}$.

6. a. When $x = -2$, then

$$f(x) = -3x + 7$$
$$f(-2) = -3(-2) + 7$$
$$= 6 + 7$$
$$= 13$$

Since $f(-2) = 13$, the point $(-2, 13)$ is on the graph. This means the point $(-2, 1)$ is **not** on the graph.

b. If $x = 3$, then

$$f(x) = -3x + 7$$
$$f(3) = -3(3) + 7$$
$$= -9 + 7$$
$$= -2$$

The point $(3, -2)$ is on the graph.

c. If $f(x) = -8$, then

$$f(x) = -8$$
$$-3x + 7 = -8$$
$$-3x = -15$$
$$x = 5$$

If $f(x) = -8$, then $x = 5$. The point $(5, -8)$ is on the graph.

7. Maria's distance from home is a function of time so we put time (in minutes) on the horizontal axis and distance (in blocks) on the vertical axis. Starting at the origin (0, 0), we draw a straight line to the point (5, 5). The ordered pair (5, 5) represents Maria being 5 blocks from home after 5 minutes. From the point (5, 5), we draw a straight line to the point (7, 0) that represents her trip back home. The ordered pair (7, 0) represents Maria being back at home after 7 minutes. Draw a line segment from $(7, 0)$ to

$(8, 0)$ to represent the time it takes Maria to find her keys and lock the door. Next, draw a line segment from $(8, 0)$ to $(13, 8)$ that represents her 8 block run in 5 minutes. Then draw a line segment from $(13, 8)$ to $(14, 11)$ that represents her 3 block run in 1 minute. Now draw a horizontal line from $(14, 11)$ to $(16, 11)$ that represents Maria's resting period. Finally, draw a line segment from $(16, 11)$ to $(26, 0)$ that

represents her walk home.

Chapter 3 – Quick Checks

3.1 Quick Checks

1. $y = 2x - 3$

Let $x = -1,\ 0,\ 1,$ and 2.

$x = -1:\quad y = 2(-1) - 3$
$\qquad\qquad y = -2 - 3$
$\qquad\qquad y = -5$

$x = 0:\quad y = 2(0) - 3$
$\qquad\qquad y = 0 - 3$
$\qquad\qquad y = -3$

$x = 1:\quad y = 2(1) - 3$
$\qquad\qquad y = 2 - 3$
$\qquad\qquad y = -1$

$x = 2:\quad y = 2(2) - 3$
$\qquad\qquad y = 4 - 3$
$\qquad\qquad y = 1$

Thus, the points $(-1, -5)$, $(0, -3)$, $(1, -1)$, and $(2, 1)$ are on the graph.

2. $\dfrac{1}{2}x + y = 2$

Let $x = -2,\ 0,\ 2,$ and 4.

$x = -2:\quad \dfrac{1}{2}(-2) + y = 2$
$\qquad\qquad\quad -1 + y = 2$
$\qquad\qquad\qquad\quad y = 3$

$x = 0:\quad \dfrac{1}{2}(0) + y = 2$
$\qquad\qquad\quad 0 + y = 2$
$\qquad\qquad\qquad y = 2$

$x = 2:\quad \dfrac{1}{2}(2) + y = 2$
$\qquad\qquad\quad 1 + y = 2$
$\qquad\qquad\qquad y = 1$

$x = 4:\quad \dfrac{1}{2}(4) + y = 2$
$\qquad\qquad\quad 2 + y = 2$
$\qquad\qquad\qquad y = 0$

Thus, the points $(-2, 3)$, $(0, 2)$, $(2, 1)$, and $(4, 0)$ are on the graph.

3. $-6x + 3y = 12$

Let $x = -2, -1,\ 0,$ and 1.

$x = -2:\quad -6(-2) + 3y = 12$
$\qquad\qquad\quad 12 + 3y = 12$
$\qquad\qquad\qquad\quad 3y = 0$
$\qquad\qquad\qquad\quad\ y = 0$

$x = -1:\quad -6(-1) + 3y = 12$
$\qquad\qquad\quad 6 + 3y = 12$
$\qquad\qquad\qquad\ 3y = 6$
$\qquad\qquad\qquad\ \ y = 2$

$x = 0:\quad -6(0) + 3y = 12$
$\qquad\qquad\ 0 + 3y = 12$
$\qquad\qquad\qquad 3y = 12$
$\qquad\qquad\qquad\ y = 4$

$x = 1:\quad -6(1) + 3y = 12$
$\qquad\qquad\ -6 + 3y = 12$
$\qquad\qquad\qquad 3y = 18$
$\qquad\qquad\qquad\ y = 6$

Thus, the points $(-2, 0)$, $(-1, 2)$, $(0, 4)$, and $(1, 6)$ are on the graph.

QC – 34

4. $x + y = 4$

To find the y-intercept, let $x = 0$ and solve for y.

$x = 0$: $\quad 0 + y = 4$

$\qquad\qquad\quad y = 4$

The y-intercept is 4, so the point $(0, 4)$ is on the graph. To find the x-intercept, let $y = 0$ and solve for x.

$y = 0$: $\quad x + 0 = 4$

$\qquad\qquad\quad x = 4$

The x-intercept is 4, so the point $(4, 0)$ is on the graph.

5. $4x - 5y = 20$

To find the y-intercept, let $x = 0$ and solve for y.

$x = 0$: $\quad 4(0) - 5y = 20$

$\qquad\qquad\quad\; -5y = 20$

$\qquad\qquad\qquad\quad y = -4$

The y-intercept is -4, so the point $(0, -4)$ is on the graph. To find the x-intercept, let $y = 0$ and solve for x.

$y = 0$: $\quad 4x - 5(0) = 20$

$\qquad\qquad\quad 4x = 20$

$\qquad\qquad\qquad x = 5$

The x-intercept is 5, so the point $(5, 0)$ is on the graph.

6. $3x - 2y = 0$

To find the y-intercept, let $x = 0$ and solve for y.

$x = 0$: $\quad 3(0) - 2y = 0$

$\qquad\qquad\qquad -2y = 0$

$\qquad\qquad\qquad\quad y = 0$

The y-intercept is 0, so the point $(0, 0)$ is on the graph. To find the x-intercept, let $y = 0$ and solve for x.

$y = 0$: $\quad 3x - 2(0) = 0$

$\qquad\qquad\quad 3x = 0$

$\qquad\qquad\qquad x = 0$

The x-intercept is 0, so the point $(0, 0)$ is on the graph. Since the x- and y-intercepts both result in the origin, we must find other points on the graph. Let $x = -2$ and 2, and solve for y.

$x = -2$: $\quad 3(-2) - 2y = 0$

$\qquad\qquad\qquad -6 - 2y = 0$

$\qquad\qquad\qquad\quad -2y = 6$

$\qquad\qquad\qquad\qquad y = -3$

$x = 2$: $\quad 3(2) - 2y = 0$

$\qquad\qquad\quad 6 - 2y = 0$

$\qquad\qquad\quad\; -2y = -6$

$\qquad\qquad\qquad\quad y = 3$

Thus, the points $(-2, -3)$ and $(2, 3)$ are also on the graph.

7. The equation $x = 5$ will be a vertical line with x-intercept 5.

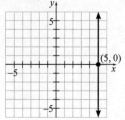

8. The equation $y = -4$ will be a horizontal line with y-intercept -4.

9. **a.** The independent variable is the number of miles driven, x. It does not make sense to drive a negative number of miles, we have that the domain of the function is $\{x \mid x \geq 0\}$ or, using interval notation, $[0, \infty)$.

   b. To determine the y-intercept, we find $C(0) = 0.35(0) + 40 = 40$. The y-intercept is 40, so the point $(0, 40)$ is on the graph.

   c. $C(80) = 0.35(80) + 40 = 28 + 40 = 68$. If the truck is driven 80 miles, the rental cost will be \$68.

   d. We plot the independent variable, *number of miles driven*, on the horizontal axis and the dependent variable, *rental cost*, on the vertical axis. From parts (b) and (c), we have that the points $(0, 40)$ and $(80, 68)$ are on the graph. We find one more point by evaluating the function for $x = 200$:
   $C(200) = 0.35(200) + 40 = 70 + 40 = 110$.

   The point $(200, 110)$ is also on the graph.

   e. We solve $C(x) = 85.50$:
   $$0.35x + 40 = 85.50$$
   $$0.35x = 45.50$$
   $$x = 130$$
   If the rental cost is \$85.50, then the truck was driven 130 miles.

3.2 Quick Checks

1. $m = \dfrac{y_2 - y_1}{x_2 - x_1} = \dfrac{12 - 3}{3 - 0} = \dfrac{9}{3} = 3$

   For every 1 unit of increase in x, y will increase by 3 units.

2. $m = \dfrac{y_2 - y_1}{x_2 - x_1} = \dfrac{-4 - 3}{3 - (-1)} = \dfrac{-7}{4} = -\dfrac{7}{4}$

   For every 4 units of increase in x, y will decrease by 7 units. For every 4 units of decrease in x, y will increase by 7 units.

3. $m = \dfrac{y_2 - y_1}{x_2 - x_1} = \dfrac{2 - 2}{-3 - 3} = \dfrac{0}{-6} = 0$

   The line is horizontal.

4. $m = \dfrac{y_2 - y_1}{x_2 - x_1} = \dfrac{-1 - 4}{-2 - (-2)} = \dfrac{-5}{0} =$ undefined

   The line is vertical.

5. $m_1 = \dfrac{4 - 3}{6 - 1} = \dfrac{1}{5}$; $m_2 = \dfrac{8 - 3}{1 - 1} = \dfrac{5}{0} =$ undefined ;

   $m_3 = \dfrac{7 - 3}{-3 - 1} = \dfrac{4}{-4} = -1$; $m_4 = \dfrac{3 - 3}{-4 - 1} = \dfrac{0}{-5} = 0$

6. **a.**

   (graph: Total Revenue (\$) vs. Number of Bicycles)

   b. Average rate of change $= \dfrac{28{,}000 - 0}{25 - 0}$
   $= \$1120$ per bicycle

   For each bicycle sold, total revenue increased by \$1120 when between 0 and 25 bicycles were sold.

c. Average rate of change $= \dfrac{59,160 - 53,400}{150 - 102}$

$= \$120$ per bicycle

For each bicycle sold, total revenue increased by $120 when between 102 and 150 bicycles were sold.

d. No, the revenue does not grow linearly. The average rate of change (slope) is not constant.

7. a. Start at $(-1, 3)$. Because $m = \dfrac{1}{3}$, move 3 units to the right and 1 unit up to find point $(2, 4)$.

b. Start at $(-1, 3)$. Because $m = -4 = -\dfrac{4}{1}$, move 1 unit to the right and 4 units down to find point $(0, -1)$.

c. Because $m = 0$, the line is horizontal passing through the point $(-1, 3)$.

8. $y - y_1 = m(x - x_1)$

$y - 5 = 2(x - 3)$

To graph the line, start at $(3, 5)$. Because $m = 2 = \dfrac{2}{1}$, move 1 unit to the right and 2 units up to find point $(4, 7)$.

9. $y - y_1 = m(x - x_1)$

$y - 3 = -4(x - (-2))$

$y - 3 = -4(x + 2)$

To graph the line, start at $(-2, 3)$. Because $m = -4 = -\dfrac{4}{1}$, move 1 unit to the right and 4 units down to find point $(-1, -1)$.

10. $y - y_1 = m(x - x_1)$

$y - (-4) = \dfrac{1}{3}(x - 3)$

$y + 4 = \dfrac{1}{3}(x - 3)$

To graph the line, start at $(3, -4)$. Because $m = \dfrac{1}{3}$, move 3 units to the right and 1 unit up to find point $(6, -3)$.

QC – 37

11. Because the line is horizontal, we know that the slope is $m = 0$. Using $(x_1, y_1) = (4, -2)$, we have that

$$y - y_1 = m(x - x_1)$$
$$y - (-2) = 0(x - 4)$$
$$y + 2 = 0$$
$$y = -2$$

To graph the line, we draw a horizontal line that passes through the point

12. $3x - y = 2$

$$-y = -3x + 2$$
$$y = \frac{-3x + 2}{-1}$$
$$y = 3x - 2$$

The slope is 3 and the y-intercept is -2. To graph the line, begin at $(0, -2)$ and move to the right 1 unit and up 3 units to find the point $(1, 1)$.

13. $6x + 2y = 8$

$$2y = -6x + 8$$
$$y = \frac{-6x + 8}{2}$$
$$y = -3x + 4$$

The slope is -3 and the y-intercept is 4. To graph the line, begin at $(0, 4)$ and move to the right 1 unit and down 3 units to find the point $(1, 1)$.

14. $3x - 2y = 7$

$$-2y = -3x + 7$$
$$y = \frac{-3x + 7}{-2}$$
$$y = \frac{3}{2}x - \frac{7}{2}$$

The slope is $\frac{3}{2}$ and the y-intercept is $-\frac{7}{2}$. To graph the line, begin at $\left(0, -\frac{7}{2}\right)$ and move to the right 2 units and up 3 units to find the point $\left(2, -\frac{1}{2}\right)$.

15. $7x + 3y = 0$

$$3y = -7x$$
$$y = -\frac{7}{3}x$$

The slope is $-\frac{7}{3}$ and the y-intercept is 0. To graph the line, begin at $(0, 0)$ and move to the right 3 units and down 7 units to find point $(3, -7)$.

16. $m = \dfrac{y_2 - y_1}{x_2 - x_1} = \dfrac{9-3}{4-1} = \dfrac{6}{3} = 2$

$$y - y_1 = m(x - x_1)$$
$$y - 3 = 2(x - 1)$$
$$y - 3 = 2x - 2$$
$$y = 2x + 1$$

The slope is 2 and the *y*-intercept is 1.

17. $m = \dfrac{y_2 - y_1}{x_2 - x_1} = \dfrac{2-4}{2-(-2)} = \dfrac{-2}{4} = -\dfrac{1}{2}$

$$y - y_1 = m(x - x_1)$$
$$y - 4 = -\dfrac{1}{2}(x - (-2))$$
$$y - 4 = -\dfrac{1}{2}x - 1$$
$$y = -\dfrac{1}{2}x + 3$$

The slope is $-\dfrac{1}{2}$ and the *y*-intercept is 3.

18. $m = \dfrac{y_2 - y_1}{x_2 - x_1} = \dfrac{-4-2}{3-3} = \dfrac{-6}{0} =$ undefined

The slope is undefined, so the line is vertical. The equation of the line is $x = 3$.

19. a. Let *a* represent the age of the mother and *W* represent the weight of the birth weight.

$$m = \dfrac{3370 - 3280}{32 - 22} = 9 \text{ grams per year}$$
$$W - 3280 = 9(a - 22)$$
$$W - 3280 = 9a - 198$$
$$W = 9a + 3082$$

Using function notation, we have $W(a) = 9a + 3082$.

b. $W(30) = 9(30) + 3082 = 3352$

We predict the birth weight would be 3352 grams.

c. The slope indicates that, if the mother's age increases by 1 year, the birth weight will increase by 9 grams.

d. $9a + 3082 = 3310$
$$9a = 228$$
$$a \approx 25.33$$

We expect the mother would be about 25 years old.

3.3 Quick Checks

1. The slope of $L_1 : y = 3x + 1$ is $m_1 = 3$. The slope of $L_2 : y = -3x - 3$ is $m_2 = -3$. Since the two slopes are not equal, the lines are not parallel.

2.

$L_1 : 6x + 3y = 3$	$L_2 : -8x - 4y = 12$
$3y = -6x + 3$	$-4y = 8x + 12$
$y = \dfrac{-6x+3}{3}$	$y = \dfrac{8x+12}{-4}$
$y = -2x + 1$	$y = -2x - 3$

Since the slopes $m_1 = -2$ and $m_2 = -2$ are equal but the *y*-intercepts are different, the two lines are parallel.

3.

$L_1 : -3x + 5y = 10$	$L_2 : 6x + 10y = 10$
$5y = 3x + 10$	$10y = -6x + 10$
$y = \dfrac{3x+10}{5}$	$y = \dfrac{-6x+10}{10}$
$y = \dfrac{3}{5}x + 2$	$y = -\dfrac{3}{5}x + 1$

Since the slopes $m_1 = \dfrac{3}{5}$ and $m_2 = -\dfrac{3}{5}$ are not equal, the two lines are not parallel.

4. The slope of the line we seek is $m = 3$, the same as the slope of $y = 3x + 1$. The equation of the line is

$$y - y_1 = m(x - x_1)$$
$$y - 8 = 3(x - 5)$$
$$y - 8 = 3x - 15$$
$$y = 3x - 7$$

5. The slope of the line we seek is $m = -\dfrac{3}{2}$, the same as the slope of the line

$$3x + 2y = 10$$
$$2y = -3x + 10$$
$$y = \frac{-3x + 10}{2}$$
$$y = -\frac{3}{2}x + 5$$

Thus, the equation of the line we seek is

$$y - y_1 = m(x - x_1)$$
$$y - 4 = -\frac{3}{2}\left(x - (-2)\right)$$
$$y - 4 = -\frac{3}{2}(x + 2)$$
$$y - 4 = -\frac{3}{2}x - 3$$
$$y = -\frac{3}{2}x + 1$$

6. The negative reciprocal of -3 is $\dfrac{-1}{-3} = \dfrac{1}{3}$. Any line whose slope is $\dfrac{1}{3}$ will be perpendicular to a line whose slope is -3.

7. The slope of $L_1 : y = 5x - 3$ is $m_1 = 5$. The slope of $L_2 : y = -\dfrac{1}{5}x - 4$ is $m_2 = -\dfrac{1}{5}$. Since the two slopes are negative reciprocals (i.e., since $5\left(-\dfrac{1}{5}\right) = -1$), the lines are perpendicular.

8.
$$L_1 : 4x - y = 3 \qquad\qquad L_2 : x - 4y = 2$$
$$-y = -4x + 3 \qquad\qquad -4y = -x + 2$$
$$y = \frac{-4x + 3}{-1} \qquad\qquad y = \frac{-x + 2}{-4}$$
$$y = 4x - 3 \qquad\qquad y = \frac{1}{4}x - \frac{1}{2}$$

Since the slopes $m_1 = 4$ and $m_2 = \dfrac{1}{4}$ are not negative reciprocals (i.e., since $4 \cdot \dfrac{1}{4} = 1 \neq -1$), the two lines are not perpendicular.

9. The slope of the line we seek is $m = -\dfrac{1}{2}$, the negative reciprocal of the slope of the line $y = 2x + 1$. Thus, the equation of the line we seek is

$$y - y_1 = m(x - x_1)$$
$$y - 2 = -\frac{1}{2}\left(x - (-4)\right)$$
$$y - 2 = -\frac{1}{2}(x + 4)$$
$$y - 2 = -\frac{1}{2}x - 2$$
$$y = -\frac{1}{2}x$$

10. The slope of the line we seek is $m = -\dfrac{4}{3}$, the negative reciprocal of the slope of the line

$$3x - 4y = 8$$
$$-4y = -3x + 8$$
$$y = \frac{-3x + 8}{-4}$$
$$y = \frac{3}{4}x - 2$$

Thus, the equation of the line we seek is

$$y - y_1 = m(x - x_1)$$
$$y - (-4) = -\frac{4}{3}(x - (-3))$$
$$y + 4 = -\frac{4}{3}x - 4$$
$$y = -\frac{4}{3}x - 8$$

3.4 Quick Checks

1. a. $x = 4,\ y = 1 \quad -2(4) + 3(1) \overset{?}{\geq} 3$

$$-8 + 3 \overset{?}{\geq} 3$$
$$-5 \geq 3 \quad \text{False}$$

So, $(4, 1)$ is not a solution to $-2x + 3y \geq 3$.

b. $x = -1,\ y = 2 \quad -2(-1) + 3(2) \overset{?}{\geq} 3$

$$2 + 6 \overset{?}{\geq} 3$$
$$8 \geq 3 \quad \text{True}$$

So, $(-1, 2)$ is a solution to $-2x + 3y \geq 3$.

c. $x = 2,\ y = 3 \quad -2(2) + 3(3) \overset{?}{\geq} 3$

$$-4 + 9 \overset{?}{\geq} 3$$
$$5 \geq 3 \quad \text{True}$$

So, $(2, 3)$ is a solution to $-2x + 3y \geq 3$.

d. $x = 0,\ y = 1 \quad -2(0) + 3(1) \overset{?}{\geq} 3$

$$0 + 3 \overset{?}{\geq} 3$$
$$3 \geq 3 \quad \text{True}$$

So, $(0, 1)$ is a solution to $-2x + 3y \geq 3$.

2. Replace the inequality symbol with an equal sign to obtain $y = -2x + 3$. Because the inequality is strict, graph $y = -2x + 3$ using a dashed line.

Test Point: $(0, 0)$: $\quad 0 \overset{?}{<} -2(0) + 3$

$$0 \overset{?}{<} 0 + 3$$
$$0 \overset{?}{<} 3 \quad \text{True}$$

Therefore, $(0, 0)$ is a solution to $y < -2x + 3$.

Shade the half-plane that contains $(0, 0)$.

3. Replace the inequality symbol with an equal sign to obtain $6x - 3y = 15$. Because the inequality is non-strict, graph $6x - 3y = 15\ (y = 2x - 5)$ using a solid line.

Test Point: $(0, 0)$: $\quad 6(0) - 3(0) \overset{?}{\leq} 15$

$$0 \leq 15 \quad \text{True}$$

Therefore, $(0, 0)$ is solution to $6x - 3y \leq 15$.

Shade the half-plane that contains $(0, 0)$.

4. Replace the inequality symbol with an equal sign to obtain $2x + y = 0$. Because the inequality is strict, graph $2x + y = 0$ $(y = -2x)$ using a dashed line.

Test Point: $(1, 1)$: $2(1) + 1 \overset{?}{<} 0$

$$2 + 1 \overset{?}{<} 0$$

$$3 \overset{?}{<} 0 \quad \text{False}$$

Therefore, $(1, 1)$ is not a solution to $2x + y < 0$.

Shade the half-plane that does not contain $(1, 1)$.

5. a. Let x = the number of Chicken Breast filets. Let y = the number of Frosties.
$$430x + 330y \le 800$$

b. $x = 1$, $y = 1$: $430(1) + 330(1) \overset{?}{\le} 800$

$$430 + 330 \overset{?}{\le} 800$$

$$760 \le 800 \quad \text{True}$$

Yes, Avery can stay within his allotment of Calories by eating one Chicken Breast filet and one Frosty.

c. $x = 2$, $y = 1$: $430(2) + 330(1) \overset{?}{\le} 800$

$$860 + 330 \overset{?}{\le} 800$$

$$1190 \le 800 \quad \text{False}$$

No, Avery cannot stay within his allotment of Calories by eating two Chicken Breast filets and one Frosty.

3.5 Quick Checks

1. a. From Example 1, the daily fixed costs were $2000 with a variable cost of $80 per bicycle. The tax of $1 per bicycle changes the variable cost to $81 per bicycle. Thus, the cost function is $C(x) = 81x + 2000$.

b. Label the horizontal axis x and the vertical axis C. To graph the function, we plot a few points:
$$C(0) = 81(0) + 2000 = 2000$$
$$C(5) = 81(5) + 2000 = 2405$$
$$C(10) = 81(10) + 2000 = 2810$$
So the points $(0, 2000)$, $(5, 2405)$, and $(10, 2810)$ are on the graph.

c. $C(18) = 81(18) + 2000 = 3458$

So, the cost of manufacturing 18 bicycles in a day is $3458.

d. $C(x) = 4025$
$$81x + 2000 = 4025$$
$$81x = 2025$$
$$x = 25$$
So, 25 bicycles can be manufactured for a cost of $4025.

2. a. We let $C(x)$ represent the monthly cost of operating the car after driving x miles, so $C(x) = mx + b$. The monthly cost before the car is driven is $250, so $C(0) = 250$. The C-intercept of the linear function is 250. Because the maintenance and gas cost is $0.18 per mile, the slope of the linear function is 0.18. The linear function that relates the monthly cost of operating the car as a of mile driven is $C(x) = 0.18x + 250$.

b. The car cannot be driven a negative distance, the number of miles driven, x, must be greater than or equal to zero. In addition, there is no definite maximum number of miles that the car can be driven. Therefore, the implied domain of the function is $\{x \mid x \ge 0\}$, or using interval notation $[0, \infty)$.

c. $C(320) = 0.18(320) + 250 = 307.6$

So, the monthly cost of driving 320 miles is $307.60.

d. Label the horizontal axis x and the vertical axis C. From part (a) we know $C(0) = 250$, and from part (c) we know $C(320) = 307.6$, so $(0, 250)$ and $(320, 307.60)$ are on the graph.

e. $C(x) = 282.40$

$0.18x + 250 = 282.40$

$0.18x = 32.40$

$x = 180$

So, Roberta can drive 180 miles each month for the monthly cost of $282.40.

3. a. Because C varies directly with g, we know that $C = kg$ for some constant k. Because $C = \$22.39$ when $g = 8$ gallons, we obtain

$C = kg$

$22.39 = k \cdot 8$

$k = \dfrac{22.39}{8} = 2.79875$

So, we have that $C = 2.79875g$, or writing this as a linear function, $C(g) = 2.79875g$.

b. $C(5.5) = 2.79875(5.5) = 15.393125$

So, the cost of 5.5 gallons would be approximately $15.39.

c. Label the horizontal axis g and the vertical axis C. From the problem we know the point $(8, 22.39)$ is on the graph, and from part (b), we know the point $(5.5, 15.39)$ is on the graph.

4. a.

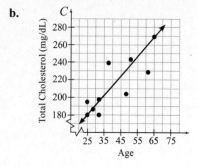

b. From the scatter diagram, we can see that as the age increases, the total cholesterol also increases.

5. Non-linear

6. Linear with a positive slope.

7. a. Answers will vary. We will use the points $(25, 180)$ and $(65, 269)$.

$m = \dfrac{269 - 180}{65 - 25} = \dfrac{89}{40} = 2.225$

$y - 180 = 2.225(x - 25)$

$y - 180 = 2.225x - 55.625$

$y = f(x) = 2.225x + 124.375$

b.

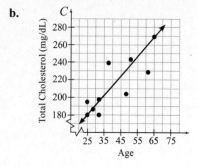

QC – 43

c. $f(39) = 2.225(39) + 124.375 = 211.15$

We predict that the total cholesterol of a 39 year old will be approximately 211 mg/dL.

d.   The slope of the linear function is 2.225. This means that, for males, the total cholesterol increases by 2.225 mg/dL for each one-year increase in age. The *y*-intercept, 124.375, would represent the total cholesterol of a male who is 0 years old. Thus, it does not make sense to interpret this *y*-intercept.

Chapter 4 – Quick Checks

4.1 Quick Checks

1. $\begin{cases} 2x + 3y = 7 & (1) \\ 3x + y = -7 & (2) \end{cases}$

   a. Let $x = 3$ and $y = 1$ in both equations (1) and (2).

   Equation (1): $2(3) + 3(1) \overset{?}{=} 7$

   $$6 + 3 \overset{?}{=} 7$$

   $$9 \neq 7$$

   Equation (2): $3(3) + 1 \overset{?}{=} -7$

   $$9 + 1 \overset{?}{=} -7$$

   $$10 \neq -7$$

   These values do not satisfy either equation. Therefore, the ordered pair $(3, 1)$ is not a solution.

   b. Let $x = -4$ and $y = 5$ in both equations (1) and (2).

   Equation (1): $2(-4) + 3(5) \overset{?}{=} 7$

   $$-8 + 15 \overset{?}{=} 7$$

   $$7 = 7$$

   Equation (2): $3(-4) + 5 \overset{?}{=} -7$

   $$-12 + 5 \overset{?}{=} -7$$

   $$-7 = -7$$

   These values satisfy both equations, so the ordered pair $(-4, 5)$ is a solution.

   c. Let $x = -2$ and $y = -1$ in both equations (1) and (2).

   Equation (1): $2(-2) + 3(-1) \overset{?}{=} 7$

   $$-4 - 3 \overset{?}{=} 7$$

   $$-7 \neq 7$$

   Equation (2): $3(-2) + (-1) \overset{?}{=} -7$

   $$-6 - 1 \overset{?}{=} -7$$

   $$-7 = -7$$

   Although these values satisfy equation (2), they do not satisfy equation (1). Therefore, the ordered pair $(-2, -1)$ is not a solution.

2. $\begin{cases} y = -3x + 10 & (1) \\ y = 2x - 5 & (2) \end{cases}$

   The two equations are in slope-intercept form. Graph each equation and find the point of intersection.

   The solution is the ordered pair $(3, 1)$.

3. $\begin{cases} 2x + y = -1 & (1) \\ -2x + 2y = 10 & (2) \end{cases}$

   Equation (1) in slope-intercept form is $y = -2x - 1$. Equation (2) in slope-intercept form is $y = x + 5$. Graph each equation and find the point of intersection.

   The solution is the ordered pair $(-2, 3)$.

4. $\begin{cases} y = -3x - 5 & (1) \\ 5x + 3y = 1 & (2) \end{cases}$

   Substituting $-3x - 5$ for y in equation (2), we obtain

   $$5x + 3(-3x - 5) = 1$$

   $$5x - 9x - 15 = 1$$

   $$-4x - 15 = 1$$

   $$-4x = 16$$

   $$x = -4$$

   Substituting -4 for x in equation (1), we obtain $y = -3(-4) - 5 = 12 - 5 = 7$.

   The solution is the ordered pair $(-4, 7)$.

5. $\begin{cases} 2x + y = -2 & (1) \\ -3x - 2y = -2 & (2) \end{cases}$

Equation (1) solved for y is $y = -2x - 2$.

Substituting $-2x - 2$ for y in equation (2), we obtain

$$-3x - 2(-2x - 2) = -2$$
$$-3x + 4x + 4 = -2$$
$$x + 4 = -2$$
$$x = -6$$

Substituting -6 for y in equation (1), we obtain

$$2(-6) + y = -2$$
$$-12 + y = -2$$
$$y = 10$$

The solution is the ordered pair $(-6, 10)$.

6. $\begin{cases} -2x + y = 4 & (1) \\ -5x + 3y = 7 & (2) \end{cases}$

Multiply both sides of equation (1) by -3 and add the result to equation (2).

$$6x - 3y = -12$$
$$\underline{-5x + 3y = 7}$$
$$x \qquad = -5$$

Substituting -5 for x in equation (1), we obtain

$$-2(-5) + y = 4$$
$$10 + y = 4$$
$$y = -6$$

The solution is the ordered pair $(-5, -6)$.

7. $\begin{cases} -3x + 2y = 3 & (1) \\ 4x - 3y = -6 & (2) \end{cases}$

Multiply both sides of equation (1) by 4, multiply both sides of equation (2) by 3, and add the results.

$$-12x + 8y = 12$$
$$\underline{12x - 9y = -18}$$
$$-y = -6$$
$$y = 6$$

Substituting 6 for y in equation (1), we obtain

$$-3x + 2(6) = 3$$
$$-3x + 12 = 3$$
$$-3x = -9$$
$$x = 3$$

The solution is the ordered pair $(3, 6)$.

8. $\begin{cases} -3x + y = 2 & (1) \\ 6x - 2y = 1 & (2) \end{cases}$

Multiply both sides of equation (1) by 2 and add the result to equation (2).

$$-6x + 2y = 4$$
$$\underline{6x - 2y = 1}$$
$$0 = 5$$

The equation $0 = 5$ is false, so the system has no solution. The solution set is $\varnothing$ or $\{\ \}$. The system is inconsistent.

The graphs of the equations (shown below) are parallel, which supports the statement that the system has no solution.

9. $\begin{cases} -3x + 2y = 8 & (1) \\ 6x - 4y = -16 & (2) \end{cases}$

Multiply both sides of equation (1) by 2 and add the results.

$$-6x + 4y = 16$$
$$\underline{6x - 4y = -16}$$
$$0 = 0$$

The equation $0 = 0$ is true, so the system is dependent. The solution is

$$\{(x, y) \mid -3x + 2y = 8\}.$$

The graphs of the equations (shown below) coincide, which supports the statement that the system is dependent.

4.2 Quick Checks

1. Let c represent the cost of a cheeseburger and let s represent the cost of a medium shake.
$$\begin{cases} 4c + 2s = 10.10 & (1) \\ 3c + 3s = 10.35 & (2) \end{cases}$$
Multiply both sides of equation (1) by 3, multiply both sides of equation (2) by -2, and add the results.
$$12c + 6s = 30.30$$
$$\underline{-6c - 6s = -20.70}$$
$$6c \quad = 9.60$$
$$c = 1.60$$
Substituting 1.60 for c in equation (1), we obtain
$$4(1.60) + 2s = 10.10$$
$$6.40 + 2s = 10.10$$
$$2s = 3.70$$
$$s = 1.85$$
A cheeseburger costs $1.60. A medium shake costs $1.85.

2. Let x and y represent the length and width of the rectangle, respectively.
$$\begin{cases} 2x + 2y = 360 & (1) \\ x = 2y & (2) \end{cases}$$
Substituting $2y$ for x in equation (1), we obtain
$$2(2y) + 2y = 360$$
$$4y + 2y = 360$$
$$6y = 360$$
$$y = 60$$
Substituting 60 for y in equation (2), we obtain
$$x = 2(60) = 120 .$$
The length is 120 yards, and the width is 60 yards.

3. Because angles 1 and 3 are supplemental, and because angles 1 and 5 must be equal, we obtain the following system
$$\begin{cases} (x + 3y) + (3x + y) = 180 \\ x + 3y = 5x + y \end{cases}$$
Simplify each equation.
$$\begin{cases} 4x + 4y = 180 & (1) \\ -4x + 2y = 0 & (2) \end{cases}$$
Add the two equations.
$$4x + 4y = 180$$
$$\underline{-4x + 2y = 0}$$
$$6y = 180$$
$$y = 30$$

Substituting 30 for y in equation (2), we obtain
$$-4x + 2(30) = 0$$
$$-4x + 60 = 0$$
$$-4x = -60$$
$$x = 15$$
Thus, $x = 15$ and $y = 30$.

4. Let a represent the amount invested in the Aaa-rated bond, and let b represent the amount invested in the B-rated bond. We organize the information in the table below, using the interest formula: Interest = Principal × rate × time .

	Principal $	Rate %	Time Yr	Interest $
Aaa-rated bond	a	0.05	1	$0.05a$
B-rated bond	b	0.10	1	$0.10b$
Total	120,000			7200

Using the columns for Principal and Interest, we obtain the following system.
$$\begin{cases} a + b = 120,000 & (1) \\ 0.05a + 0.10b = 7200 & (2) \end{cases}$$
Solving equation (1) for b, we obtain
$b = 120,000 - a$. Substituting $120,000 - a$ for b in equation (2), we obtain
$$0.05a + 0.10(120,000 - a) = 7200$$
$$0.05a + 12000 - 0.10a = 7200$$
$$-0.05a + 12000 = 7200$$
$$-0.05a = -4800$$
$$a = 96,000$$
Substituting 96,000 for a into equation (1), we obtain $96,000 + b = 120,000$
$$b = 24,000$$
Maria should invest $96,000 in the Aaa-rated bond and $24,000 in the B-rated bond.

5. Let c represent the weight of cashews to be used and let p represent the weight of peanuts to be used. We organize the information in the table below, using the formula

   Price per pound × Number of pounds = Revenue .

	Price per pound	Number of pounds	Revenue
Cashews	7.00	c	$7c$
Peanuts	2.50	p	$2.5p$
Trail mix	4.00	30	$4(30)=120$

   Using the columns for Number of pounds and Revenue, we obtain the following system.

   $$\begin{cases} c+p=30 & (1) \\ 7c+2.5p=120 & (2) \end{cases}$$

   Solving equation (1) for c yields $c=30-p$.

   Substituting $30-p$ for c in equation (2), we obtain

   $$7(30-p)+2.5p=120$$
   $$210-7p+2.5p=120$$
   $$210-4.5p=120$$
   $$-4.5p=-90$$
   $$p=20$$

   Substituting 20 for p in equation (1) yields

   $$c+20=30$$
   $$c=10$$

   The trail mix requires 10 pounds of cashews and 20 pounds of peanuts.

6. Let a represent the airspeed of the plane, and let w represent the impact of wind resistance on the plane. We organize the information in the table below.

	Distance	Rate	Time
Against Wind (West)	1200	$a-w$	4
With Wind (East)	1200	$a+w$	3

   Using the formula Distance = Rate × Time , we obtain the following system.

   $$\begin{cases} 1200=4(a-w) \\ 1200=3(a+w) \end{cases}$$

   Simplify each equation.

   $$\begin{cases} 4a-4w=1200 & (1) \\ 3a+3w=1200 & (2) \end{cases}$$

   Multiply both sides of equation (1) by 3,

multiply both sides of equation (2) by 4, and add the results

$$12a-12w=3600$$
$$12a+12w=4800$$
$$\overline{24a \qquad =8400}$$
$$a=350$$

Substituting 350 for a in equation (2) yields

$$3(350)+3w=1200$$
$$1050+3w=1200$$
$$3w=150$$
$$w=50$$

The airspeed of the plain is 350 miles per hour. The impact of wind resistance on the plane is 50 miles per hour.

7. **a.** If one Austrian Pine tree is sold, revenue will be $230. If two trees are sold, revenue will be $230(2) = \$460$. If x trees are sold, revenue will be $\$230x$. The revenue function is $R(x) = 230x$.

   b. The cost function is $C(x) = ax+b$ where a is the variable cost and b is the fixed cost. With $a=160$ and $b=2100$, the cost function is $C(x)=160x+2100$.

   c.

   d. $R(x)=C(x)$

   $$230x=160x+2100$$
   $$70x=2100$$
   $$x=30$$
   $$R(30)=230(30)=6900$$
   $$C(30)=160(30)+2100=6900$$

   The break-even point is (30, 6900).

   If 30 Austrian Pine trees are sold, the cost and revenue will be even at $6900.

4.3 Quick Checks

1. a. Substitute $x = 3$, $y = 2$, and $z = -2$ into all three equations.

Equation (1): $3 + 2 + (-2) \overset{?}{=} 3$

$$3 = 3$$

Equation (2): $3(3) + 2 - 2(-2) \overset{?}{=} -23$

$$9 + 2 + 4 \overset{?}{=} -23$$

$$15 \neq -23$$

Equation (3): $-2(3) - 3(2) + 2(-2) \overset{?}{=} 17$

$$-6 - 6 - 4 \overset{?}{=} 17$$

$$-16 \neq 17$$

Although these values satisfy equation (1), they do not satisfy equations (2) and (3). Therefore, the ordered triple $(3,\ 2, -2)$ is not a solution of the system.

b. Substitute $x = -4$, $y = 1$, and $z = 6$ into all three equations.

Equation (1): $-4 + 1 + 6 \overset{?}{=} 3$

$$3 = 3$$

Equation (2): $3(-4) + 1 - 2(6) \overset{?}{=} -23$

$$-12 + 1 - 12 \overset{?}{=} -23$$

$$-23 = -23$$

Equation (3): $-2(-4) - 3(1) + 2(6) \overset{?}{=} 17$

$$8 - 3 + 12 \overset{?}{=} 17$$

$$17 = 17$$

Because these values satisfy all three equations, the ordered pair $(-4,\ 1,\ 6)$ is a solution of the system.

2. $\begin{cases} x + y + z = -3 & (1) \\ 2x - 2y - z = -7 & (2) \\ -3x + y + 5z = 5 & (3) \end{cases}$

Multiply both sides of equation (1) by -2 and add the result to equation (2).

$$-2x - 2y - 2z = 6$$
$$\underline{2x - 2y - z = -7}$$
$$-4y - 3z = -1$$

Multiply both sides of equation (1) by 3 and add the result to equation (3).

$$3x + 3y + 3z = -9$$
$$\underline{-3x + y + 5z = 5}$$
$$4y + 8z = -4$$

Rewriting the system, we have

$$\begin{cases} x + y + z = -3 & (1) \\ -4y - 3z = -1 & (2) \\ 4y + 8z = -4 & (3) \end{cases}$$

Add equations (2) and (3).

$$-4y - 3z = -1$$
$$\underline{4y + 8z = -4}$$
$$5z = -5$$

Once again rewriting the system, we have

$$\begin{cases} x + y + z = -3 & (1) \\ -4y - 3z = -1 & (2) \\ 5z = -5 & (3) \end{cases}$$

Solving equation (3) for z, we obtain

$$5z = -5$$
$$z = -1$$

Back-substituting -1 for z in equation (2), we obtain

$$-4y - 3(-1) = -1$$
$$-4y + 3 = -1$$
$$-4y = -4$$
$$y = 1$$

Back-substituting 1 for y and -1 for z in equation (1), we obtain

$$x + 1 + (-1) = -3$$
$$x = -3$$

The solution is the ordered triple $(-3,\ 1, -1)$.

3. $\begin{cases} 2x \quad\ \ - 4z = -7 & (1) \\ x + 6y \quad\ = 5 & (2) \\ \quad\ 2y - z = 2 & (3) \end{cases}$

Multiply both sides of equation (2) by -2 and add the result to equation (1).

$$-2x - 12y \quad\quad = -10$$
$$\underline{2x \quad\quad - 4z = -7}$$
$$-12y - 4z = -17$$

Rewriting the system, we have

$$\begin{cases} 2x \quad\ \ - 4z = -7 & (1) \\ -12y - 4z = -17 & (2) \\ \quad\ 2y - z = 2 & (3) \end{cases}$$

Multiply both sides of equation (3) by 6 and add the result to equation (2).

QC – 49

$$12y - 6z = 12$$
$$-12y - 4z = -17$$
$$\overline{-10z = -5}$$

Once again rewriting the system, we have
$$\begin{cases} 2x \quad\;\; -4z = -7 & (1) \\ -12y - 4z = -17 & (2) \\ \quad\;\; -10z = -5 & (3) \end{cases}$$

Solving equation (3) for z, we obtain
$$-10z = -5$$
$$z = \frac{-5}{-10} = \frac{1}{2}$$

Back-substituting $\frac{1}{2}$ for z in equation (2), we

obtain
$$-12y - 4\left(\frac{1}{2}\right) = -17$$
$$-12y - 2 = -17$$
$$-12y = -15$$
$$y = \frac{-15}{-12} = \frac{5}{4}$$

Back-substituting $\frac{1}{2}$ for z in equation (1), we

obtain
$$2x - 4\left(\frac{1}{2}\right) = -7$$
$$2x - 2 = -7$$
$$2x = -5$$
$$x = -\frac{5}{2}$$

The solution is the ordered triple $\left(-\frac{5}{2}, \frac{5}{4}, \frac{1}{2}\right)$.

4. $\begin{cases} x - y + 2z = -7 & (1) \\ -2x + y - 3z = 5 & (2) \\ x - 2y + 3z = 2 & (3) \end{cases}$

Multiply both sides of equation (1) by 2 and add the result to equation (2).
$$2x - 2y + 4z = -14$$
$$-2x + y - 3z = 5$$
$$\overline{-y + z = -9}$$

Multiply both sides of equation (1) by -1 and add the result to equation (3).
$$-x + y - 2z = 7$$
$$x - 2y + 3z = 2$$
$$\overline{-y + z = 9}$$

Rewriting the system, we have
$$\begin{cases} x - y + 2z = -7 & (1) \\ \quad -y + z = -9 & (2) \\ \quad -y + z = 9 & (3) \end{cases}$$

Multiply both sides of equation (2) by -1 and add the result to equation (3).
$$y - z = 9$$
$$-y + z = 9$$
$$\overline{0 = 18}$$

Once again rewriting the system, we have
$$\begin{cases} x - y + 2z = -7 & (1) \\ \quad -y + z = -9 & (2) \\ \quad\quad 0 = 18 & (3) \quad \text{False} \end{cases}$$

Equation (3) is a false statement (contradiction). Therefore, the system is inconsistent. The solution set is $\varnothing$ or $\{ \ \}$.

5. $\begin{cases} x - y + 3z = 2 & (1) \\ -x + 2y - 5z = -3 & (2) \\ 2x - y + 4z = 3 & (3) \end{cases}$

Add equations (1) and (2).
$$x - y + 3z = 2$$
$$-x + 2y - 5z = -3$$
$$\overline{y - 2z = -1}$$

Multiply both sides of equation (1) by -2 and add the result to equation (3).
$$-2x + 2y - 6z = -4$$
$$2x - y + 4z = 3$$
$$\overline{y - 2z = -1}$$

Rewriting the system, we have
$$\begin{cases} x - y + 3z = 2 & (1) \\ \quad y - 2z = -1 & (2) \\ \quad y - 2z = -1 & (3) \end{cases}$$

Multiply both sides of equation (2) by -1 and add the result to equation (3).
$$-y + 2z = 1$$
$$y - 2z = -1$$
$$\overline{0 = 0}$$

Once again rewriting the system, we have
$$\begin{cases} x - y + 3z = 2 & (1) \\ \quad y - 2z = -1 & (2) \\ \quad\quad 0 = 0 & (3) \quad \text{True} \end{cases}$$

Thus, the system is dependent and has an infinite number of solutions.

Solve equation (2) for y.

$y = 2z - 1$

Substituting $2z - 1$ for y in equation (1), we obtain

$$x - (2z - 1) + 3z = 2$$
$$x - 2z + 1 + 3z = 2$$
$$x + z + 1 = 2$$
$$x + z = 1$$
$$x = -z + 1$$

The solution to the system is

$\{(x, y, z) | x = -z + 1, y = 2z - 1, z \text{ is any real number}\}$.

6. Let x represent the number of 21-inch mowers, let y represent the number of 24-inch mowers, and let z represent the number of 40-inch riding mowers.

$$\begin{cases} 2x + 3y + 4z = 81 & (1) \\ 3x + 3y + 4z = 95 & (2) \\ x + y + 2z = 35 & (3) \end{cases}$$

Multiply both sides of equation (3) by -2 and add the result to equation (1).

$$\begin{aligned} -2x - 2y - 4z &= -70 \\ 2x + 3y + 4z &= 81 \\ \hline y &= 11 \end{aligned}$$

Multiply both sides of equation (3) by -3 and add the result to equation (2).

$$\begin{aligned} -3x - 3y - 6z &= -105 \\ 3x + 3y + 4z &= 95 \\ \hline -2z &= -10 \end{aligned}$$

Rewriting the system, we have

$$\begin{cases} 2x + 3y + 4z = 81 & (1) \\ y = 11 & (2) \\ -2z = -10 & (3) \end{cases}$$

From equation (2), we know $y = 11$. Solving equation (3) for z, we obtain

$$-2z = -10$$
$$z = 5$$

Substituting 11 for y and 5 for z and 11 in equation (1), we obtain

$$2x + 3(11) + 4(5) = 81$$
$$2x + 33 + 20 = 81$$
$$2x + 53 = 81$$
$$2x = 28$$
$$x = 14$$

The company can manufacture 14 twenty-one-inch mowers, 11 twenty-four-inch mowers, and 5 forty-inch rider mowers.

4.4 Quick Checks

1. In the augmented matrix, the first column represents the coefficients on the x variable. The second column represents the coefficients on the y variable. The vertical line signifies the equal signs. The third column represents the constants to the right of the equal sign.

$$\begin{bmatrix} 3 & -1 & | & -10 \\ -5 & 2 & | & 0 \end{bmatrix}$$

2. The system

$$\begin{cases} x + 2y - 2z = 11 \\ -x - 2z = 4 \\ 4x - y + z - 3 = 0 \end{cases}$$

gets rearranged as

$$\begin{cases} x + 2y - 2z = 11 \\ -x + 0y - 2z = 4 \\ 4x - y + z = 3 \end{cases}$$

Thus, the augmented matrix is

$$\begin{bmatrix} 1 & 2 & -2 & | & 11 \\ -1 & 0 & -2 & | & 4 \\ 4 & -1 & 1 & | & 3 \end{bmatrix}.$$

3. Since the augmented matrix has two rows, it represents a system of two equations. Because there are two columns to the left of the vertical bar, the system has two variables. If we call the variables x and y, the system of equations is

$$\begin{cases} x - 3y = 7 \\ -2x + 5y = -3 \end{cases}$$

4. Since the augmented matrix has three rows, it represents a system of three equations. Because there are three columns to the left of the vertical bar, the system has three variables. If we call the variables x, y, and z, the system of equations is

$$\begin{cases} x - 3y + 2z = 4 \\ 3x - z = -1 \\ -x + 4y = 0 \end{cases}$$

5. $\begin{bmatrix} 1 & -2 & | & 5 \\ -4 & 5 & | & -11 \end{bmatrix}$ $\qquad (R_2 = 4r_1 + r_2)$

$$= \begin{bmatrix} 1 & -2 & | & 5 \\ 4(1) + (-4) & 4(-2) + 5 & | & 4(5) + (-11) \end{bmatrix}$$

$$= \begin{bmatrix} 1 & -2 & | & 5 \\ 0 & -3 & | & 9 \end{bmatrix}$$

QC – 51

6. We want a 0 in row 1, column 2. We accomplish this by multiplying row 2 by -5 and adding the result to row 1. That is, we apply the row operation $R_1 = -5r_2 + r_1$.

$$\begin{bmatrix} 1 & 5 & | & 13 \\ 0 & 1 & | & 2 \end{bmatrix} \qquad (R_1 = -5r_2 + r_1)$$

$$= \begin{bmatrix} -5(0)+1 & -5(1)+5 & | & -5(2)+13 \\ 0 & 1 & | & 2 \end{bmatrix}$$

$$= \begin{bmatrix} 1 & 0 & | & 3 \\ 0 & 1 & | & 2 \end{bmatrix}$$

7. Write the augmented matrix of the system and then put it in row echelon form.

$$\begin{bmatrix} 2 & -4 & | & 20 \\ 3 & 1 & | & 16 \end{bmatrix} \qquad \left(R_1 = \frac{1}{2} r_1 \right)$$

$$= \begin{bmatrix} 1 & -2 & | & 10 \\ 3 & 1 & | & 16 \end{bmatrix} \qquad \left(R_2 = -3r_1 + r_2 \right)$$

$$= \begin{bmatrix} 1 & -2 & | & 10 \\ 0 & 7 & | & -14 \end{bmatrix} \qquad \left(R_2 = \frac{1}{7} r_2 \right)$$

$$= \begin{bmatrix} 1 & -2 & | & 10 \\ 0 & 1 & | & -2 \end{bmatrix}$$

From row 2, we have that $y = -2$. Row 1 represents the equation $x - 2y = 10$. Back-substitute -2 for y and solve for x.

$$x - 2(-2) = 10$$
$$x + 4 = 10$$
$$x = 6$$

The solution is the ordered pair $(6, -2)$.

8. Write the augmented matrix of the system and then put it in row echelon form.

$$\begin{bmatrix} 1 & -1 & 2 & | & 7 \\ 2 & -2 & 1 & | & 11 \\ -3 & 1 & -3 & | & -14 \end{bmatrix} \quad \left(\begin{matrix} R_2 = -2r_1 + r_2 \\ R_3 = 3r_1 + r_3 \end{matrix} \right)$$

$$= \begin{bmatrix} 1 & -1 & 2 & | & 7 \\ 0 & 0 & -3 & | & -3 \\ 0 & -2 & 3 & | & 7 \end{bmatrix} \quad (\text{Interchange } r_1 \text{ and } r_2)$$

$$= \begin{bmatrix} 1 & -1 & 2 & | & 7 \\ 0 & -2 & 3 & | & 7 \\ 0 & 0 & -3 & | & -3 \end{bmatrix} \quad \left(\begin{matrix} R_2 = -\frac{1}{2} r_2 \\ R_3 = -\frac{1}{3} r_3 \end{matrix} \right)$$

$$= \begin{bmatrix} 1 & -1 & 2 & | & 7 \\ 0 & 1 & -\frac{3}{2} & | & -\frac{7}{2} \\ 0 & 0 & 1 & | & 1 \end{bmatrix}$$

Write the system of equations that corresponds to the row-echelon matrix

$$\begin{cases} x - y + 2z = 7 & (1) \\ y - \dfrac{3}{2} z = -\dfrac{7}{2} & (2) \\ z = 1 & (3) \end{cases}$$

Substituting 1 for z in equation (2), we obtain

$$y - \frac{3}{2}(1) = -\frac{7}{2}$$
$$y - \frac{3}{2} = -\frac{7}{2}$$
$$y = -\frac{4}{2} = -2$$

Substituting 1 for z and -2 for y in equation (1), we obtain

$$x - (-2) + 2(1) = 7$$
$$x + 2 + 2 = 7$$
$$x + 4 = 7$$
$$x = 3$$

The solution is the ordered triple $(3, -2, 1)$.

9. Write the augmented matrix of the system and then put it in row echelon form.

$$\begin{bmatrix} 1 & 1 & -3 & | & 8 \\ 2 & 3 & -10 & | & 19 \\ -1 & -2 & 7 & | & -11 \end{bmatrix} \quad \left(\begin{matrix} R_2 = -2r_1 + r_2 \\ R_3 = r_1 + r_3 \end{matrix} \right)$$

$$= \begin{bmatrix} 1 & 1 & -3 & | & 8 \\ 0 & 1 & -4 & | & 3 \\ 0 & -1 & 4 & | & -3 \end{bmatrix} \quad (R_3 = r_2 + r_3)$$

$$= \begin{bmatrix} 1 & 1 & -3 & | & 8 \\ 0 & 1 & -4 & | & 3 \\ 0 & 0 & 0 & | & 0 \end{bmatrix}$$

Write the system of equations that corresponds to the row-echelon matrix.

$$\begin{cases} x + y - 3z = 8 & (1) \\ y - 4z = 3 & (2) \\ 0 = 0 & (3) \end{cases}$$

The statement $0 = 0$ in equation (3) indicates that the system is dependent and has an infinite number of solutions.

Solve equation (2) for y.

$$y - 4z = 3$$
$$y = 4z + 3$$

Substituting $4z+3$ for y in equation (1), we obtain

$$x+(4z+3)-3z=8$$
$$x+z+3=8$$
$$x=-z+5$$

The solution to the system is

$$\{(x,y,z)\,|\,x=-z+5, y=4z+3, z \text{ is any real number}\}.$$

10. Write the augmented matrix of the system and then put it in row echelon form.

$$\begin{bmatrix} -1 & 2 & -1 & | & 5 \\ 2 & 1 & 4 & | & 3 \\ 3 & -1 & 5 & | & 0 \end{bmatrix} \qquad (R_1=-1\cdot r_1)$$

$$=\begin{bmatrix} 1 & -2 & 1 & | & -5 \\ 2 & 1 & 4 & | & 3 \\ 3 & -1 & 5 & | & 0 \end{bmatrix} \qquad \begin{pmatrix} R_2=-2r_1+r_2 \\ R_3=-3r_1+r_3 \end{pmatrix}$$

$$=\begin{bmatrix} 1 & -2 & 1 & | & -5 \\ 0 & 5 & 2 & | & 13 \\ 0 & 5 & 2 & | & 15 \end{bmatrix} \qquad \left(R_2=\frac{1}{5}r_2\right)$$

$$=\begin{bmatrix} 1 & -2 & 1 & | & -5 \\ 0 & 1 & \frac{2}{5} & | & \frac{13}{5} \\ 0 & 5 & 2 & | & 15 \end{bmatrix} \qquad (R_3=-5r_2+r_3)$$

$$=\begin{bmatrix} 1 & -2 & 1 & | & -5 \\ 0 & 1 & \frac{2}{5} & | & \frac{13}{5} \\ 0 & 0 & 0 & | & 2 \end{bmatrix}$$

Write the system of equations that corresponds to the row-echelon matrix.

$$\begin{cases} x-2y+z=-5 & (1) \\ y+\dfrac{2}{5}z=\dfrac{13}{5} & (2) \\ 0=2 & (3) \end{cases}$$

The statement $0=2$ in equation (3) indicates that the system is inconsistent. The system has no solution. The solution set is $\varnothing$ or $\{\ \}$.

4.5 Quick Checks

1. $\begin{vmatrix} 5 & 3 \\ 4 & 6 \end{vmatrix} = 5(6)-4(3)=30-12=18$

2. $\begin{vmatrix} -2 & -5 \\ 1 & 7 \end{vmatrix} = -2(7)-1(-5)=-14+5=-9$

3. $D=\begin{vmatrix} 3 & 2 \\ -2 & -1 \end{vmatrix}=3(-1)-(-2)(2)=-3+4=1$

$D_x=\begin{vmatrix} 1 & 2 \\ 1 & -1 \end{vmatrix}=1(-1)-1(2)=-1-2=-3$

$D_y=\begin{vmatrix} 3 & 1 \\ -2 & 1 \end{vmatrix}=3(1)-(-2)(1)=3+2=5$

$x=\dfrac{D_x}{D}=\dfrac{-3}{1}=-3$; $y=\dfrac{D_y}{D}=\dfrac{5}{1}=5$

Thus, the solution is the ordered pair $(-3,\,5)$.

4. $D=\begin{vmatrix} 4 & -2 \\ -6 & 3 \end{vmatrix}=4(3)-(-6)(-2)=12-12=0$

Since $D=0$, Cramer's Rule does not apply.

5. $\begin{vmatrix} 2 & -3 & 5 \\ 0 & 4 & -1 \\ 3 & 8 & -7 \end{vmatrix}=2\begin{vmatrix} 4 & -1 \\ 8 & -7 \end{vmatrix}-(-3)\begin{vmatrix} 0 & -1 \\ 3 & -7 \end{vmatrix}+5\begin{vmatrix} 0 & 4 \\ 3 & 8 \end{vmatrix}$

$=2[4(-7)-8(-1)]+3[0(-7)-3(-1)]+5[0(8)-3(4)]$

$=2(-28+8)+3(0+3)+5(0-12)$

$=2(-20)+3(3)+5(-12)$

$=-40+9-60$

$=-91$

6. $D=\begin{vmatrix} 1 & -1 & 3 \\ 4 & 3 & 1 \\ -2 & 0 & 5 \end{vmatrix}$

$=1\begin{vmatrix} 3 & 1 \\ 0 & 5 \end{vmatrix}-(-1)\begin{vmatrix} 4 & 1 \\ -2 & 5 \end{vmatrix}+3\begin{vmatrix} 4 & 3 \\ -2 & 0 \end{vmatrix}$

$=1[3(5)-0(1)]-(-1)[4(5)-(-2)(1)]+$
$\qquad 3[4(0)-(-2)(3)]$

$=1(15-0)-(-1)(20+2)+3(0+6)$

$=1(15)-(-1)(22)+3(6)$

$=15+22+18$

$=55$

$D_x=\begin{vmatrix} -2 & -1 & 3 \\ 9 & 3 & 1 \\ 7 & 0 & 5 \end{vmatrix}$

$=-2\begin{vmatrix} 3 & 1 \\ 0 & 5 \end{vmatrix}-(-1)\begin{vmatrix} 9 & 1 \\ 7 & 5 \end{vmatrix}+3\begin{vmatrix} 9 & 3 \\ 7 & 0 \end{vmatrix}$

$=-2[3(5)-0(1)]-(-1)[9(5)-7(1)]+$
$\qquad 3[9(0)-7(3)]$

$=-2(15-0)-(-1)(45-7)+3(0-21)$

$=-2(15)-(-1)(38)+3(-21)$

$=-30+38-63$

$=-55$

QC – 53

$$D_y = \begin{vmatrix} 1 & -2 & 3 \\ 4 & 9 & 1 \\ -2 & 7 & 5 \end{vmatrix}$$

$$= 1\begin{vmatrix} 9 & 1 \\ 7 & 5 \end{vmatrix} - (-2)\begin{vmatrix} 4 & 1 \\ -2 & 5 \end{vmatrix} + 3\begin{vmatrix} 4 & 9 \\ -2 & 7 \end{vmatrix}$$

$$= 1[9(5) - 7(1)] - (-2)[4(5) - (-2)(1)] +$$
$$3[4(7) - (-2)(9)]$$

$$= 1(45 - 7) - (-2)(20 + 2) + 3(28 + 18)$$

$$= 1(38) - (-2)(22) + 3(46)$$

$$= 38 + 44 + 138$$

$$= 220$$

$$D_z = \begin{vmatrix} 1 & -1 & -2 \\ 4 & 3 & 9 \\ -2 & 0 & 7 \end{vmatrix}$$

$$= 1\begin{vmatrix} 3 & 9 \\ 0 & 7 \end{vmatrix} - (-1)\begin{vmatrix} 4 & 9 \\ -2 & 7 \end{vmatrix} + (-2)\begin{vmatrix} 4 & 3 \\ -2 & 0 \end{vmatrix}$$

$$= 1[3(7) - 0(9)] - (-1)[4(7) - (-2)(9)] +$$
$$(-2)[4(0) - (-2)(3)]$$

$$= 1(21 - 0) - (-1)(28 + 18) + (-2)(0 + 6)$$

$$= 1(21) - (-1)(46) + (-2)(6)$$

$$= 21 + 46 - 12$$

$$= 55$$

$$x = \frac{D_x}{D} = \frac{-55}{55} = -1 \; ; \; y = \frac{D_y}{D} = \frac{220}{55} = 4 \; ;$$

$$z = \frac{D_z}{D} = \frac{55}{55} = 1$$

Thus, the solution is the ordered triple $(-1, 4, 1)$.

4.6 Quick Checks

1. $\begin{cases} -4x + y < -5 & (1) \\ 2x - 5y < 10 & (2) \end{cases}$

   a. Let $x = 1$ and $y = 2$ in both inequalities (1) and (2).

   Inequality (1): $-4(1) + 2 \overset{?}{<} -5$

   $$-4 + 2 \overset{?}{<} -5$$

   $$-2 \not< -5$$

   Inequality (2): $2(1) - 5(2) \overset{?}{<} 10$

   $$2 - 10 \overset{?}{<} 10$$

   $$-8 < 10$$

   The inequality $-4x + y < -5$ is not true when $x = 1$ and $y = 2$, so $(1, 2)$ is not a solution.

   b. Let $x = 3$ and $y = 1$ in both inequalities (1) and (2).

   Inequality (1): $-4(3) + 1 \overset{?}{<} -5$

   $$-12 + 1 \overset{?}{<} -5$$

   $$-11 < -5$$

   Inequality (2): $2(3) - 5(1) \overset{?}{<} 10$

   $$6 - 5 \overset{?}{<} 10$$

   $$1 < 10$$

   These values satisfy both inequalities, so the ordered pair $(3, 1)$ is a solution.

2. $\begin{cases} 2x + y \le 5 \\ -x + y \ge -4 \end{cases}$

   First, graph the inequality $2x + y \le 5$. To do so, replace the inequality symbol with an equal sign to obtain $2x + y = 5$. Because the inequality is non-strict, graph $2x + y = 5$ $(y = -2x + 5)$ using a solid line.

   Test Point: $(0, 0)$: $2(0) + 0 \overset{?}{\le} 5$

   $$0 \le 5$$

   Therefore, the half-plane containing $(0, 0)$ is the solution set of $2x + y \le 5$.

   Second, graph the inequality $-x + y \ge -4$. To do so, replace the inequality symbol with an equal sign to obtain $-x + y = -4$. Because the inequality is non-strict, graph $-x + y = -4$ $(y = x - 4)$ using a solid line.

   Test Point: $(0, 0)$: $-(0) + 0 \overset{?}{\ge} -4$

   $$0 \ge -4$$

   Therefore, the half-plane containing $(0, 0)$ is the solution set of $-x + y \ge -4$.

   The overlapping shaded region (that is, the shaded region in the graph below) is the solution to the system of linear inequalities.

3. $\begin{cases} 3x+y>-2 \\ 2x+3y<3 \end{cases}$

First, graph the inequality $3x+y>-2$. To do so, replace the inequality symbol with an equal sign to obtain $3x+y=-2$. Because the inequality is strict, graph $3x+y=-2$ $(y=-3x-2)$ using a dashed line.

Test Point: $(0,0)$: $3(0)+0\overset{?}{>}-2$
$$0>-2$$

Therefore, the half-plane containing $(0,0)$ is the solution set of $3x+y>-2$.

Second, graph the inequality $2x+3y<3$. To do so, replace the inequality symbol with an equal sign to obtain $2x+3y=3$. Because the inequality is strict, graph $2x+3y=3$ $\left(y=-\dfrac{2}{3}x+1\right)$ using a dashed line.

Test Point: $(0,0)$: $-2(0)+3(0)\overset{?}{<}3$
$$0<3$$

Therefore, the half-plane containing $(0,0)$ is the solution set of $2x+3y<3$.

The overlapping shaded region (that is, the shaded region in the graph below) is the solution to the system of linear inequalities.

4. $\begin{cases} -2x+3y\ge 9 \\ 6x-9y\ge 9 \end{cases}$

First, graph the inequality $-2x+3y\ge 9$. To do so, replace the inequality symbol with an equal sign to obtain $-2x+3y=9$. Because the inequality is non-strict, graph $-2x+3y\ge 9$ $\left(y=\dfrac{2}{3}x+3\right)$ using a solid line.

Test Point: $(0,0)$: $-2(0)+3(0)\overset{?}{\ge}9$
$$0\not\ge 9$$

Therefore, the half-plane not containing $(0,0)$ is the solution set of $-2x+3y\ge 9$.

Second, graph the inequality $6x-9y\ge 9$. To do so, replace the inequality symbol with an equal sign to obtain $6x-9y=9$. Because the inequality is non-strict, graph $6x-9y=9$ $\left(y=\dfrac{2}{3}x-1\right)$ using a solid line.

Test Point: $(0,0)$: $6(0)-9(0)\overset{?}{\ge}9$
$$0\not\ge 9$$

Therefore, the half-plane not containing $(0,0)$ is the solution set of $6x-9y\ge 9$.

Because no overlapping region results, there are no points in the Cartesian plane that satisfy both inequalities. The system has no solution, so the solution set is $\varnothing$ or $\{\,\}$.

5. $\begin{cases} x+y\le 6 \\ 2x+y\le 10 \\ x\ge 0 \\ y\ge 0 \end{cases}$

First, graph the inequality $x+y\le 6$. To do so, replace the inequality symbol with an equal sign to obtain $x+y=6$. Because the inequality is non-strict, graph $x+y=6$ $(y=-x+6)$ using a solid line.

Test Point: $(0,0)$: $0+0\overset{?}{\le}6$
$$0\le 6$$

Therefore, the half-plane containing $(0,0)$ is the solution set of $x+y\le 6$.

Next, graph the inequality $2x+y\le 10$. To do so, replace the inequality symbol with an equal sign to obtain $2x+y=10$. Because the inequality is non-strict, graph $2x+y=10$ $(y=-2x+10)$ using a solid line.

Test Point: $(0,0)$: $2(0)+0\overset{?}{\leq}10$

$\qquad\qquad\qquad 0\leq10$

Therefore, the half-plane containing $(0,0)$ is the solution set of $2x+y\leq10$.

The two inequalities $x\geq0$ and $y\geq0$ require that the graph be in quadrant I.

The overlapping shaded region (that is, the shaded region in the graph below) is the solution to the system of linear inequalities.

The graph is bounded. The four corner points of the bounded region are $(0, 0)$, $(5, 0)$, $(4, 2)$, and $(0, 6)$.

6. Let x represent the amount to be invested in Treasury notes and let y represent the amount to be invested in corporate bonds. Now, Jack and Mary have at most \$25,000 to invest, so $x+y\leq25,000$. The amount invested in Treasury notes must be at least \$10,000, so $x\geq10,000$. The amount to be invested in corporate bonds must be no more than \$15,000, so $y\leq15,000$. They cannot invest a negative amount in corporate bonds, so we have the non-negativity constraint $y\geq0$. Thus, we have the following system:

$$\begin{cases} x+y\leq25,000 \\ x\geq10,000 \\ y\leq15,000 \\ y\geq0 \end{cases}$$

To graph the system, begin with the inequality $x+y\leq25,000$. To do so, replace the inequality symbol with an equal sign to obtain $x+y=25,000$. Because the inequality is non-strict, graph $x+y=25,000$ $(y=-x+25,000)$ using a solid line.

Test Point: $(0,0)$: $0+0\overset{?}{\leq}25,000$

$\qquad\qquad\qquad 0\leq25,000$

Thus, the solution set of $x+y\leq25,000$ is the half-plane containing $(0,0)$.

The inequality $x\geq10,000$ requires that the graph be to the right of the vertical line $x=10,000$.

The inequality $y\leq15,000$ requires that the graph be below the horizontal line $y=15,000$.

The inequality $y\geq0$ requires that the graph be above the x-axis.

The overlapping shaded region (that is, the shaded region in the graph below) is the solution to the system of linear inequalities.

The corner points of the bounded region are $(10000, 15000)$, $(10000, 0)$, and $(25000, 0)$.

Getting Ready for Chapter 5 – Quick Checks

1. $5^2 \cdot 5 = 5^{2+1} = 5^3 = 125$

2. $(-3)^2 \cdot (-3)^3 = (-3)^{2+3} = (-3)^5 = -243$

3. $y^4 \cdot y^3 = y^{4+3} = y^7$

4. $(5x^2) \cdot (-2x^5) = 5 \cdot (-2) \cdot x^2 \cdot x^5$
   $$= -10x^{2+5}$$
   $$= -10x^7$$

5. $(6y^3) \cdot (-y^2) = 6 \cdot (-1) \cdot y^3 \cdot y^2$
   $$= -6y^{3+2}$$
   $$= -6y^5$$

6. $\dfrac{5^6}{5^4} = 5^{6-4} = 5^2 = 25$

7. $\dfrac{y^8}{y^6} = y^{8-6} = y^2$

8. $\dfrac{16a^6}{10a^5} = \dfrac{8 \cdot 2}{5 \cdot 2} \cdot \dfrac{a^6}{a^5} = \dfrac{8}{5} \cdot a^{6-5} = \dfrac{8}{5}a$

9. $\dfrac{-24b^5}{16b^3} = \dfrac{-3 \cdot 8}{2 \cdot 8} \cdot \dfrac{b^5}{b^3} = \dfrac{-3}{2} \cdot b^{5-3} = -\dfrac{3}{2}b^2$

10. $5^{-3} = \dfrac{1}{5^3} = \dfrac{1}{125}$

11. $5z^{-7} = 5 \cdot \dfrac{1}{z^7} = \dfrac{5}{z^7}$

12. $\dfrac{1}{x^{-4}} = x^4$

13. $\dfrac{5}{y^{-3}} = 5y^3$

14. $-4^0 = -1 \cdot 4^0 = -1 \cdot 1 = -1$

15. $(-10)^0 = 1$

16. $\left(\dfrac{4}{3}\right)^{-2} = \left(\dfrac{3}{4}\right)^2 = \dfrac{3}{4} \cdot \dfrac{3}{4} = \dfrac{9}{16}$

17. $\left(-\dfrac{1}{4}\right)^{-3} = (-4)^3 = (-4) \cdot (-4) \cdot (-4) = -64$

18. $\left(\dfrac{3}{x}\right)^{-2} = \left(\dfrac{x}{3}\right)^2 = \dfrac{x}{3} \cdot \dfrac{x}{3} = \dfrac{x^{1+1}}{9} = \dfrac{x^2}{9}$

19. $\dfrac{5}{2^{-2}} = 5 \cdot 2^2 = 5 \cdot 4 = 20$

20. $6^3 \cdot 6^{-5} = 6^{3+(-5)} = 6^{-2} = \dfrac{1}{6^2} = \dfrac{1}{36}$

21. $\dfrac{10^{-3}}{10^{-5}} = 10^{-3-(-5)} = 10^{-3+5} = 10^2 = 100$

22. $(4x^2y^3) \cdot (5xy^{-4}) = 4 \cdot 5 \cdot x^2 \cdot x \cdot y^3 \cdot y^{-4}$
    $$= 20x^{2+1}y^{3+(-4)}$$
    $$= 20x^3 y^{-1}$$
    $$= \dfrac{20x^3}{y}$$

23. $\left(\dfrac{3}{4}a^3b\right) \cdot \left(\dfrac{8}{9}a^{-2}b^3\right) = \dfrac{3}{4} \cdot \dfrac{8}{9} \cdot a^3 \cdot a^{-2} \cdot b \cdot b^3$
    $$= \dfrac{3 \cdot 4 \cdot 2}{4 \cdot 3 \cdot 3} \cdot a^{3+(-2)}b^{1+3}$$
    $$= \dfrac{2}{3}a^1 b^4$$
    $$= \dfrac{2}{3}ab^4$$

24. $\dfrac{-24b^5}{16b^{-3}} = \dfrac{-24}{16} \cdot \dfrac{b^5}{b^{-3}}$
    $$= \dfrac{-3 \cdot 8}{2 \cdot 8} \cdot b^{5-(-3)}$$
    $$= \dfrac{-3}{2} \cdot b^{5+3}$$
    $$= -\dfrac{3}{2}b^8$$

25. $\dfrac{50s^2t}{15s^5t^{-4}} = \dfrac{50}{15} \cdot \dfrac{s^2}{s^5} \cdot \dfrac{t}{t^{-4}}$

$\quad = \dfrac{10 \cdot 5}{3 \cdot 5} \cdot s^{2-5} \cdot t^{1-(-4)}$

$\quad = \dfrac{10}{3} s^{-3} t^{1+4}$

$\quad = \dfrac{10t^5}{3s^3}$

26. $\left(2^2\right)^3 = 2^{2 \cdot 3} = 2^6 = 64$

27. $\left(5^8\right)^0 = 5^{8 \cdot 0} = 5^0 = 1$

28. $\left[(-4)^3\right]^2 = (-4)^{3 \cdot 2} = (-4)^6 = 4096$

29. $\left(a^3\right)^5 = a^{3 \cdot 5} = a^{15}$

30. $\left(z^3\right)^{-6} = z^{3 \cdot (-6)} = z^{-18} = \dfrac{1}{z^{18}}$

31. $\left(s^{-3}\right)^{-7} = s^{(-3) \cdot (-7)} = s^{21}$

32. $(5y)^3 = 5^3 \cdot y^3 = 125y^3$

33. $(6y)^0 = 6^0 \cdot y^0 = 1 \cdot 1 = 1$

34. $\left(3x^2\right)^4 = 3^4 \cdot \left(x^2\right)^4$

$\quad = 81x^{2 \cdot 4}$

$\quad = 81x^8$

35. $\left(4a^3\right)^{-2} = 4^{-2} \cdot \left(a^3\right)^{-2}$

$\quad = \dfrac{1}{4^2} \cdot a^{3 \cdot (-2)}$

$\quad = \dfrac{1}{16} a^{-6}$

$\quad = \dfrac{1}{16a^6}$

36. $\left(\dfrac{z}{3}\right)^4 = \dfrac{z^4}{3^4} = \dfrac{z^4}{81}$

37. $\left(\dfrac{x}{2}\right)^{-5} = \left(\dfrac{2}{x}\right)^5 = \dfrac{2^5}{x^5} = \dfrac{32}{x^5}$

38. $\left(\dfrac{x^2}{y^3}\right)^4 = \dfrac{\left(x^2\right)^4}{\left(y^3\right)^4} = \dfrac{x^{2 \cdot 4}}{y^{3 \cdot 4}} = \dfrac{x^8}{y^{12}}$

39. $\left(\dfrac{3a^{-2}}{b^4}\right)^3 = \dfrac{3^3 \cdot \left(a^{-2}\right)^3}{\left(b^4\right)^3}$

$\quad = \dfrac{27a^{(-2) \cdot 3}}{b^{4 \cdot 3}}$

$\quad = \dfrac{27a^{-6}}{b^{12}}$

$\quad = \dfrac{27}{a^6 b^{12}}$

40. $\dfrac{\left(3x^2y\right)^2}{12xy^{-2}} = \dfrac{3^2 \cdot \left(x^2\right)^2 \cdot y^2}{12xy^{-2}}$

$\quad = \dfrac{9x^4 y^2}{12xy^{-2}}$

$\quad = \dfrac{3 \cdot 3}{3 \cdot 4} \cdot x^{4-1} \cdot y^{2-(-2)}$

$\quad = \dfrac{3x^3 y^4}{4}$

41. $\left(3ab^3\right)^3 \cdot \left(6a^2b^2\right)^{-2}$

$\quad = \left(3^3 \cdot a^3 \cdot \left(b^3\right)^3\right) \cdot \left(6^{-2} \cdot \left(a^2\right)^{-2} \cdot \left(b^2\right)^{-2}\right)$

$\quad = \left(27a^3b^9\right) \cdot \left(\dfrac{1}{36} a^{-4}b^{-4}\right)$

$\quad = \dfrac{27}{36} a^{3+(-4)} b^{9+(-4)}$

$\quad = \dfrac{3 \cdot 9}{4 \cdot 9} a^{-1}b^5$

$\quad = \dfrac{3b^5}{4a}$

42. $\left(\dfrac{2x^2y^{-1}}{x^{-2}y^2}\right)^2 \cdot \left(\dfrac{4x^3y^2}{xy^{-2}}\right)^{-1}$

$= \left(2x^{2-(-2)}y^{-1-2}\right)^2 \cdot \left(4x^{3-1}y^{2-(-2)}\right)^{-1}$

$= \left(2x^4y^{-3}\right)^2 \cdot \left(4x^2y^4\right)^{-1}$

$= \left(2^2 \cdot \left(x^4\right)^2 \cdot \left(y^{-3}\right)^2\right) \cdot \left(4^{-1} \cdot \left(x^2\right)^{-1} \cdot \left(y^4\right)^{-1}\right)$

$= \left(4x^8y^{-6}\right) \cdot \left(\dfrac{1}{4}x^{-2}y^{-4}\right)$

$= \dfrac{4}{4}x^{8+(-2)}y^{-6+(-4)}$

$= x^6y^{-10}$

$= \dfrac{x^6}{y^{10}}$

43. Because 532 is greater than 1, we move the decimal point to the left. We move it two places to the left until it is between the 5 and the 3.
$532 = 5.32 \times 10^2$

44. Because the absolute value of $-1,230,000$ is greater than 1, we move the decimal point to the left. We move it six places to the left until it is between the 1 and the 2.
$-1,230,000 = -1.23 \times 10^6$

45. Because the absolute value of 0.034 is less than 1, we move the decimal point to the right. We move it two places to the right until it is between the 3 and the 4.
$0.034 = 3.4 \times 10^{-2}$

46. Because the absolute value of -0.0000845 is less than 1, we move the decimal point to the right. We move it five places to the right until it is between the 8 and the 4.
$-0.0000845 = -8.45 \times 10^{-5}$

47. The exponent on 10 is 2 so we move the decimal point 2 places to the right.
$5 \times 10^2 = 5.00 \times 10^2 = 500$

48. The exponent on 10 is 5 so we move the decimal point 5 places to the right.
$9.1 \times 10^5 = 9.10000 \times 10^5 = 910,000$

49. The exponent on 10 is -4 so we move the decimal point 4 places to the left.
$1.8 \times 10^{-4} = 00001.8 \times 10^{-4} = 0.00018$

50. The exponent on 10 is -6 so we move the decimal point 6 places to the left.
$1 \times 10^{-6} = 0000001 \times 10^{-6} = 0.000001$

51. $\left(3 \times 10^3\right) \cdot \left(2 \times 10^5\right) = (3 \cdot 2) \times \left(10^3 \cdot 10^5\right)$

$= 6 \times 10^8$

52. $\left(2 \times 10^{-4}\right) \cdot \left(4 \times 10^{-7}\right) = (2 \cdot 4) \times \left(10^{-4} \cdot 10^{-7}\right)$

$= 8 \times 10^{-11}$

53. $\left(6 \times 10^{-5}\right) \cdot \left(4 \times 10^8\right) = (6 \cdot 4) \times \left(10^{-5} \cdot 10^8\right)$

$= 24 \times 10^3$

$= \left(2.4 \times 10^1\right) \times 10^3$

$= 2.4 \times 10^4$

54. $\dfrac{6 \times 10^8}{3 \times 10^6} = \dfrac{6}{3} \times \dfrac{10^8}{10^6} = 2 \times 10^2$

55. $\dfrac{6.8 \times 10^{-8}}{3.4 \times 10^{-5}} = \dfrac{6.8}{3.4} \times \dfrac{10^{-8}}{10^{-5}}$

$= 2 \times 10^{-8-(-5)}$

$= 2 \times 10^{-3}$

56. $\dfrac{4.8 \times 10^7}{9.6 \times 10^3} = \dfrac{4.8}{9.6} \times \dfrac{10^7}{10^3}$

$= 0.5 \times 10^4$

$= \left(5 \times 10^{-1}\right) \times 10^4$

$= 5 \times 10^3$

57. $\dfrac{3 \times 10^{-5}}{8 \times 10^7} = \dfrac{3}{8} \times \dfrac{10^{-5}}{10^7}$

$= 0.375 \times 10^{-12}$

$= \left(3.75 \times 10^{-1}\right) \times 10^{-12}$

$= 3.75 \times 10^{-13}$

58. $(8,000,000) \cdot (30,000) = \left(8 \times 10^6\right) \cdot \left(3 \times 10^4\right)$

$\qquad = (8 \cdot 3) \times \left(10^6 \cdot 10^4\right)$

$\qquad = 24 \times 10^{10}$

$\qquad = \left(2.4 \times 10^1\right) \times 10^{10}$

$\qquad = 2.4 \times 10^{11}$

$\qquad = 240,000,000,000$

59. $\dfrac{0.000000012}{0.000004} = \dfrac{1.2 \times 10^{-8}}{4 \times 10^{-6}}$

$\qquad = \dfrac{1.2}{4} \times \dfrac{10^{-8}}{10^{-6}}$

$\qquad = 0.3 \times 10^{-2}$

$\qquad = \left(3 \times 10^{-1}\right) \times 10^{-2}$

$\qquad = 3 \times 10^{-3}$

$\qquad = 0.003$

60. $(25,000,000) \cdot (0.00003)$

$\qquad = \left(2.5 \times 10^7\right) \cdot \left(3 \times 10^{-5}\right)$

$\qquad = (2.5 \cdot 3) \times \left(10^7 \cdot 10^{-5}\right)$

$\qquad = 7.5 \times 10^2$

$\qquad = 750$

61. $\dfrac{0.000039}{13,000,000} = \dfrac{3.9 \times 10^{-5}}{1.3 \times 10^7}$

$\qquad = \dfrac{3.9}{1.3} \times \dfrac{10^{-5}}{10^7}$

$\qquad = 3 \times 10^{-12}$

$\qquad = 0.000000000003$

Chapter 5 – Quick Checks

5.1 Quick Checks

1. $8x^5$ is a monomial because it is in the form ax^k where $k \geq 0$. The coefficient is $a = 8$ and the degree is $k = 5$.

2. $5x^{-2}$ is not a monomial because the exponent of the variable is -2 and -2 is not a nonnegative integer.

3. 12 is a monomial because it is in the form ax^k where $k \geq 0$. The coefficient is $a = 12$ and the degree is $k = 0$.

4. $x^{1/3}$ is not a monomial because the exponent of the variable is $\frac{1}{3}$ and $\frac{1}{3}$ is not a nonnegative integer.

5. $3x^5 y^2$ is a monomial because the exponents of the variables are nonnegative integers. The coefficient is 3 and the degree is $n = 5 + 2 = 7$.

6. $-2m^3 n$ is a monomial because the exponents of the variables are nonnegative integers. The coefficient is -2 and the degree is $n = 3 + 1 = 4$.

7. $4ab^{1/2}$ is not a monomial because the exponent $\frac{1}{2}$ is not an integer.

8. $-xy$ is a monomial because the exponents of the variables are nonnegative integers (both are 1 in this case). The coefficient is -1 and the degree is $n = 1 + 1 = 2$.

9. $-3x^3 + 7x^2 - x + 5$ is a polynomial with degree $n = 3$.

10. $5z^{-1} + 3$ is not a polynomial because the exponent on the first term, -1, is negative.

11. $\dfrac{x-1}{x+1}$ is not a polynomial because it is the quotient of two polynomials and the polynomial in the denominator has degree greater than 0.

12. $\dfrac{3x^2 - 9x + 27}{3} = x^2 - 3x + 9$ is a polynomial. The degree is $n = 2$.

13. $5p^3 q - 8pq^2 + pq$ is a polynomial with degree $n = 3 + 1 = 4$.

14. $\left(2x^2 - 3x + 1\right) + \left(4x^2 + 5x - 3\right)$
$= 2x^2 - 3x + 1 + 4x^2 + 5x - 3$
$= 2x^2 + 4x^2 - 3x + 5x + 1 - 3$
$= (2+4)x^2 + (-3+5)x + (1-3)$
$= 6x^2 + 2x - 2$

15. $\left(5w^4 - 3w^3 + w - 8\right) + \left(-2w^4 + w^3 - 7w^2 + 3\right)$
$= 5w^4 - 3w^3 + w - 8 - 2w^4 + w^3 - 7w^2 + 3$
$= 5w^4 - 2w^4 - 3w^3 + w^3 - 7w^2 + w - 8 + 3$
$= (5-2)w^4 + (-3+1)w^3 - 7w^2 + w + (-8+3)$
$= 3w^4 - 2w^3 - 7w^2 + w - 5$

16. $\left(8x^2 y + 2x^2 y^2 - 7xy^2\right) + \left(-3x^2 y + 5x^2 y^2 + 3xy^2\right)$
$= 8x^2 y + 2x^2 y^2 - 7xy^2 - 3x^2 y + 5x^2 y^2 + 3xy^2$
$= 8x^2 y - 3x^2 y + 2x^2 y^2 + 5x^2 y^2 - 7xy^2 + 3xy^2$
$= (8-3)x^2 y + (2+5)x^2 y^2 + (-7+3)xy^2$
$= 5x^2 y + 7x^2 y^2 - 4xy^2$

17. $\left(5x^3 - 6x^2 + x + 9\right) - \left(4x^3 + 10x^2 - 6x + 7\right)$
$= 5x^3 - 6x^2 + x + 9 - 4x^3 - 10x^2 + 6x - 7$
$= 5x^3 - 4x^3 - 6x^2 - 10x^2 + x + 6x + 9 - 7$
$= (5-4)x^3 + (-6-10)x^2 + (1+6)x + (9-7)$
$= x^3 - 16x^2 + 7x + 2$

18. $\left(8y^3 - 5y^2 + 3y + 1\right) - \left(-3y^3 + 6y + 8\right)$
$= 8y^3 - 5y^2 + 3y + 1 + 3y^3 - 6y - 8$
$= 8y^3 + 3y^3 - 5y^2 + 3y - 6y + 1 - 8$
$= (8+3)y^3 - 5y^2 + (3-6)y + (1-8)$
$= 11y^3 - 5y^2 - 3y - 7$

19. $\left(8x^2 y + 2x^2 y^2 - 7xy^2\right) - \left(-3x^2 y + 5x^2 y^2 + 3xy^2\right)$
$= 8x^2 y + 2x^2 y^2 - 7xy^2 + 3x^2 y - 5x^2 y^2 - 3xy^2$
$= 8x^2 y + 3x^2 y + 2x^2 y^2 - 5x^2 y^2 - 7xy^2 - 3xy^2$
$= (8+3)x^2 y + (2-5)x^2 y^2 + (-7-3)xy^2$
$= 11x^2 y - 3x^2 y^2 - 10xy^2$

20. $g(x) = -2x^3 + 7x + 1$

   a. $g(0) = -2(0)^3 + 7(0) + 1$
           $= 0 + 0 + 1$
           $= 1$

   b. $g(2) = -2(2)^3 + 7(2) + 1$
           $= -2(8) + 7(2) + 1$
           $= -16 + 14 + 1$
           $= -1$

   c. $g(-3) = -2(-3)^3 + 7(-3) + 1$
           $= -2(-27) + 7(-3) + 1$
           $= 54 - 21 + 1$
           $= 34$

21. a. For 1994 we have $t = 0$.

$$F(t) = 0.13t^2 - 2.48t + 58.93$$
$$F(0) = 0.13(0)^2 - 2.48(0) + 58.93$$
$$= 0 - 0 + 58.93$$
$$= 58.93$$

In 1994, the fertility rate for women 15-19 years of age was approximately 58.93 births per 1,000 women.

   b. For 2008, we have $t = 14$.

$$F(t) = 0.13t^2 - 2.48t + 58.93$$
$$F(14) = 0.13(14)^2 - 2.48(14) + 58.93$$
$$= 0.13(196) - 2.48(14) + 58.93$$
$$= 25.48 - 34.72 + 58.93$$
$$= 49.69$$

In 2008, the fertility rate for women 15-19 years of age is estimated to be 49.69 births per 1,000 women.

22. $f(x) = 3x^2 - x + 1$ and $g(x) = -x^2 + 5x - 6$

   a. $(f + g)(x) = f(x) + g(x)$
             $= \left(3x^2 - x + 1\right) + \left(-x^2 + 5x - 6\right)$
             $= 3x^2 - x + 1 - x^2 + 5x - 6$
             $= 3x^2 - x^2 - x + 5x + 1 - 6$
             $= 2x^2 + 4x - 5$

   b. $(f - g)(x) = f(x) - g(x)$
             $= \left(3x^2 - x + 1\right) - \left(-x^2 + 5x - 6\right)$
             $= 3x^2 - x + 1 + x^2 - 5x + 6$
             $= 3x^2 + x^2 - x - 5x + 1 + 6$
             $= 4x^2 - 6x + 7$

   c. Because $(f + g)(x) = 2x^2 + 4x - 5$, we have
$$(f + g)(1) = 2(1)^2 + 4(1) - 5$$
$$= 2(1) + 4(1) - 5$$
$$= 2 + 4 - 5$$
$$= 1$$

   d. Because $(f - g)(x) = 4x^2 - 6x + 7$, we have
$$(f - g)(-2) = 4(-2)^2 - 6(-2) + 7$$
$$= 4(4) - 6(-2) + 7$$
$$= 16 + 12 + 7$$
$$= 35$$

23. a. The revenue function will remain the same, so we have

$$R(x) = 12x$$

Both the variable and fixed costs will change. Therefore, our new cost function will be

$$C(x) = 8x + 1250$$

The profit function is given by

$$P(x) = R(x) - C(x)$$
$$= (12x) - (8x + 1250)$$
$$= 12x - 8x - 1250$$
$$= 4x - 1250$$

The new profit function will be

$$P(x) = 4x - 1250.$$

   b. $P(x) = 4x - 1250$
      $P(800) = 4(800) - 1250$
             $= 3200 - 1250$
             $= 1950$

If the company manufactures and sells 800 calculators, its profit will be $1950.

5.2 Quick Checks

1. $\left(3x^5\right)\cdot\left(2x^2\right)=(3\cdot2)\left(x^5\cdot x^2\right)$
$$=6x^{5+2}$$
$$=6x^7$$

2. $\left(-7a^3b^2\right)\cdot\left(3ab^4\right)=(-7\cdot3)\left(a^3\cdot a\right)\left(b^2\cdot b^4\right)$
$$=-21a^{3+1}b^{2+4}$$
$$=-21a^4b^6$$

3. $\left(\dfrac{2}{3}x^4\right)\cdot\left(\dfrac{15}{8}x\right)=\left(\dfrac{2}{3}\cdot\dfrac{15}{8}\right)\left(x^4\cdot x\right)$
$$=\dfrac{5}{4}x^{4+1}$$
$$=\dfrac{5}{4}x^5$$

4. $-3(x+2)=-3\cdot x+(-3)\cdot2$
$$=-3x-6$$

5. $5x\left(x^2+3x+2\right)=5x\cdot x^2+5x\cdot3x+5x\cdot2$
$$=5x^3+15x^2+10x$$

6. $2xy\left(3x^2-5xy+2y^2\right)$
$$=2xy\cdot3x^2-2xy\cdot5xy+2xy\cdot2y^2$$
$$=6x^3y-10x^2y^2+4xy^3$$

7. $\dfrac{3}{4}y^2\left(\dfrac{4}{3}y^2+\dfrac{2}{9}y+\dfrac{16}{3}\right)$
$$=\dfrac{3}{4}y^2\cdot\dfrac{4}{3}y^2+\dfrac{3}{4}y^2\cdot\dfrac{2}{9}y+\dfrac{3}{4}y^2\cdot\dfrac{16}{3}$$
$$=\left(\dfrac{3}{4}\cdot\dfrac{4}{3}\right)y^2\cdot y^2+\left(\dfrac{3}{4}\cdot\dfrac{2}{9}\right)y^2\cdot y+\left(\dfrac{3}{4}\cdot\dfrac{16}{3}\right)y^2$$
$$=y^4+\dfrac{1}{6}y^3+4y^2$$

8. $(x+4)(x+1)=x\cdot x+x\cdot1+4\cdot x+4\cdot1$
$$=x^2+x+4x+4$$
$$=x^2+5x+4$$

9. $(3v+5)(2v-3)=3v\cdot2v-3v\cdot3+5\cdot2v-5\cdot3$
$$=6v^2-9v+10v-15$$
$$=6v^2+v-15$$

10. $(2a-b)(a+5b)=2a\cdot a+2a\cdot5b-b\cdot a-b\cdot5b$
$$=2a^2+10ab-ab-5b^2$$
$$=2a^2+9ab-5b^2$$

11. $(2y-3)\left(y^2+4y+5\right)$
$$=2y\cdot y^2+2y\cdot4y+2y\cdot5-3\cdot y^2-3\cdot4y-3\cdot5$$
$$=2y^3+8y^2+10y-3y^2-12y-15$$
$$=2y^3+5y^2-2y-15$$

12. $\left(z^2-3z+2\right)\left(2z^2+z+6\right)$
$$=z^2\cdot2z^2+z^2\cdot z+z^2\cdot6-3z\cdot2z^2-3z\cdot z$$
$$\qquad-3z\cdot6+2\cdot2z^2+2\cdot z+2\cdot6$$
$$=2z^4+z^3+6z^2-6z^3-3z^2-18z$$
$$\qquad+4z^2+2z+12$$
$$=2z^4-5z^3+7z^2-16z+12$$

13. $(5y+2)(5y-2)=(5y)^2-(2)^2$
$$=25y^2-4$$

14. $\left(7y+2z^3\right)\left(7y-2z^3\right)=(7y)^2-\left(2z^3\right)^2$
$$=49y^2-4z^6$$

15. $(z-8)^2=z^2-2\cdot z\cdot8+8^2$
$$=z^2-16z+64$$

16. $(6p+5)^2=(6p)^2+2\cdot6p\cdot5+5^2$
$$=36p^2+60p+25$$

17. $(4a-3b)^2=(4a)^2-2\cdot(4a)\cdot(3b)+(3b)^2$
$$=16a^2-24ab+9b^2$$

18. $f(x)=5x-3;\ g(x)=x^2+3x+1$

  a. $f(2)=5(2)-3\qquad g(2)=(2)^2+3(2)+1$
$$\qquad=10-3\qquad\qquad=4+6+1$$
$$\qquad=7\qquad\qquad\qquad=11$$
$$f(2)\cdot g(2)=7\cdot11=77$$

  b. $(f\cdot g)(x)$
$$=f(x)\cdot g(x)$$
$$=(5x-3)\left(x^2+3x+1\right)$$
$$=5x\cdot x^2+5x\cdot3x+5x\cdot1-3\cdot x^2-3\cdot3x-3\cdot1$$
$$=5x^3+15x^2+5x-3x^2-9x-3$$
$$=5x^3+12x^2-4x-3$$

  c. $(f\cdot g)(2)=5(2)^3+12(2)^2-4(2)-3$
$$=5(8)+12(4)-4(2)-3$$
$$=40+48-8-3$$
$$=77$$

QC – 63

19. $f(x) = x^2 - 2x$

    a. $f(x-3) = (x-3)^2 - 2(x-3)$
$$= x^2 - 2 \cdot x \cdot 3 + 3^2 - 2 \cdot x + 2 \cdot 3$$
$$= x^2 - 6x + 9 - 2x + 6$$
$$= x^2 - 8x + 15$$

    b. $f(x+h) - f(x)$
$$= \left[(x+h)^2 - 2(x+h) \right] - \left[x^2 - 2x \right]$$
$$= \left[x^2 + 2xh + h^2 - 2x - 2h \right] - \left[x^2 - 2x \right]$$
$$= x^2 + 2xh + h^2 - 2x - 2h - x^2 + 2x$$
$$= 2xh + h^2 - 2h$$

5.3 Quick Checks

1. $\dfrac{9p^4 - 12p^3 + 3p^2}{3p} = \dfrac{9p^4}{3p} - \dfrac{12p^3}{3p} + \dfrac{3p^2}{3p}$
$$= \dfrac{9}{3}p^{4-1} - \dfrac{12}{3}p^{3-1} + \dfrac{3}{3}p^{2-1}$$
$$= 3p^3 - 4p^2 + p$$

2. $\dfrac{14m^4 - 10m^3 + 2m^2}{2m^2}$
$$= \dfrac{14m^4}{2m^2} - \dfrac{10m^3}{2m^2} + \dfrac{2m^2}{2m^2}$$
$$= \dfrac{14}{2}m^{4-2} - \dfrac{10}{2}m^{3-2} + \dfrac{2}{2}m^{2-2}$$
$$= 7m^2 - 5m + 1$$

3. $\dfrac{x^4 y^4 + 8x^2 y^2 - 4xy}{4x^3 y}$
$$= \dfrac{x^4 y^4}{4x^3 y} + \dfrac{8x^2 y^2}{4x^3 y} - \dfrac{4xy}{4x^3 y}$$
$$= \dfrac{1}{4}x^{4-3}y^{4-1} + \dfrac{8}{4}x^{2-3}y^{2-1} - \dfrac{4}{4}x^{1-3}y^{1-1}$$
$$= \dfrac{1}{4}xy^3 + 2x^{-1}y - x^{-2}$$
$$= \dfrac{xy^3}{4} + \dfrac{2y}{x} - \dfrac{1}{x^2}$$

4.
$$\begin{array}{r} x^2 + 7x - 3 \\ x-4 \overline{\smash{)}\, x^3 + 3x^2 - 31x + 21} \end{array}$$

$$\dfrac{-\left(x^3 - 4x^2\right)}{ 7x^2 - 31x}$$
$$\dfrac{-\left(7x^2 - 28x\right)}{ -3x + 21}$$
$$\dfrac{-(-3x + 12)}{9}$$

$$\dfrac{x^3 + 3x^2 - 31x + 21}{x-4} = x^2 + 7x - 3 + \dfrac{9}{x-4}$$

Check:
$$(x-4)\left(x^2 + 7x - 3\right) + 9$$
$$= x^3 + 7x^2 - 3x - 4x^2 - 28x + 12 + 9$$
$$= x^3 + 3x^2 - 31x + 21$$
so our answer checks.

5.
$$\begin{array}{r} x^2 + 5x + 4 \\ 2x-3 \overline{\smash{)}\, 2x^3 + 7x^2 - 7x - 12} \end{array}$$

$$\dfrac{-\left(2x^3 - 3x^2\right)}{ 10x^2 - 7x}$$
$$\dfrac{-\left(10x^2 - 15x\right)}{ 8x - 12}$$
$$\dfrac{-(8x - 12)}{0}$$

$$\dfrac{2x^3 + 7x^2 - 7x - 12}{2x-3} = x^2 + 5x + 4$$

Check:
$$(2x-3)\left(x^2 + 5x + 4\right)$$
$$= 2x^3 + 10x^2 + 8x - 3x^2 - 15x - 12$$
$$= 2x^3 + 7x^2 - 7x - 12$$
so our answer checks.

QC – 64

6.

$$
x^2 - 2 \overline{\smash{\big)}\ x^5 - 5x^4 - 2x^3 + 12x^2 + 2} \quad\underset{}{\overset{x^3 - 5x^2 + 2}{}}
$$

$$
\underline{-\left(x^5 \qquad -2x^3\right)}
$$

$$
-5x^4 \qquad +12x^2
$$

$$
\underline{-\left(-5x^4 \qquad +10x^2\right)}
$$

$$
2x^2 + 2
$$

$$
\underline{-\left(2x^2 - 4\right)}
$$

$$
6
$$

$$
\frac{2 + 12x^2 - 2x^3 - 5x^4 + x^5}{x^2 - 2} = x^3 - 5x^2 + 2 + \frac{6}{x^2 - 2}
$$

Check:

$$
\left(x^2 - 2\right)\left(x^3 - 5x^2 + 2\right) + 6
$$

$$
= x^5 - 5x^4 + 2x^2 - 2x^3 + 10x^2 - 4 + 6
$$

$$
= x^5 - 5x^4 - 2x^3 + 12x^2 + 2
$$

so our answer checks.

7. The divisor is $x - 2$ so $c = 2$.

$$
\begin{array}{r|rrr}
2 & 2 & 1 & -7 & -13 \\
  &   & 4 & 10 & 6 \\
\hline
  & 2 & 5 & 3 & -7
\end{array}
$$

$$
\frac{2x^3 + x^2 - 7x - 13}{x - 2} = 2x^2 + 5x + 3 - \frac{7}{x - 2}
$$

8. The divisor is $x + 3$ so $c = -3$.

$$
\begin{array}{r|rrrrr}
-3 & 1 & 8 & 15 & -2 & -6 \\
   &   & -3 & -15 & 0 & 6 \\
\hline
   & 1 & 5 & 0 & -2 & 0
\end{array}
$$

$$
\frac{x^4 + 8x^3 + 15x^2 - 2x - 6}{x + 3} = x^3 + 5x^2 - 2
$$

9. $f(x) = 3x^4 - 4x^3 - 3x^2 + 10x - 5$; $g(x) = x^2 - 2$

a.

$$
x^2 - 2 \overline{\smash{\big)}\ 3x^4 - 4x^3 - 3x^2 + 10x - 5} \quad\overset{3x^2 - 4x + 3}{}
$$

$$
\underline{-\left(3x^4 \qquad -6x^2\right)}
$$

$$
-4x^3 + 3x^2 + 10x
$$

$$
\underline{-\left(-4x^3 \qquad +8x\right)}
$$

$$
3x^2 + 2x - 5
$$

$$
\underline{-\left(3x^2 \qquad -6\right)}
$$

$$
2x + 1
$$

Thus, $\left(\dfrac{f}{g}\right)(x) = 3x^2 - 4x + 3 + \dfrac{2x + 1}{x^2 - 2}$.

b.

$$
\left(\frac{f}{g}\right)(3) = 3(3)^2 - 4(3) + 3 + \frac{2(3) + 1}{(3)^2 - 2}
$$

$$
= 3(9) - 4(3) + 3 + \frac{6 + 1}{9 - 2}
$$

$$
= 27 - 12 + 3 + \frac{7}{7}
$$

$$
= 19
$$

10. $f(x) = 3x^3 + 10x^2 - 9x - 4$

a. The divisor is $x - 2$ so the Remainder Theorem says that the remainder is $f(2)$.

$$
f(2) = 3(2)^3 + 10(2)^2 - 9(2) - 4
$$

$$
= 3(8) + 10(4) - 9(2) - 4
$$

$$
= 24 + 40 - 18 - 4
$$

$$
= 42
$$

When $f(x) = 3x^3 + 10x^2 - 9x - 4$ is divided by $x - 2$, the remainder is 42.

b. The divisor is $x + 4 = x - (-4)$, so the Remainder Theorem says that the remainder is $f(-4)$.

$$
f(-4) = 3(-4)^3 + 10(-4)^2 - 9(-4) - 4
$$

$$
= 3(-64) + 10(16) - 9(-4) - 4
$$

$$
= -192 + 160 + 36 - 4
$$

$$
= 0
$$

When $f(x) = 3x^3 + 10x^2 - 9x - 4$ is divided by $x + 4$, the remainder is 0.

11. $f(x) = 2x^3 - 9x^2 - 6x + 5$

   a. $f(-2) = 2(-2)^3 - 9(-2)^2 - 6(-2) + 5$

          $= 2(-8) - 9(4) - 6(-2) + 5$

          $= -16 - 36 + 12 + 5$

          $= -35$

   Since $f(c) = f(-2) \neq 0$, we know that

   $x - c = x + 2$ is not a factor of $f(x)$.

   b. $f(5) = 2(5)^3 - 9(5)^2 - 6(5) + 5$

          $= 2(125) - 9(25) - 6(5) + 5$

          $= 250 - 225 - 30 + 5$

          $= 0$

   Since $f(c) = f(5) = 0$, we know that

   $x - c = x - 5$ is a factor of $f(x)$.

$$5\overline{)2 \quad -9 \quad -6 \quad 5}$$
$$\underline{ \quad 10 \quad 5 \quad -5}$$
$$2 \quad 1 \quad -1 \quad 0$$

   $f(x) = (x - 5)(2x^2 + x - 1)$

5.4 Quick Checks

1. Look at the coefficients first. The largest number that divides into 5 and 15 evenly is 5, so 5 is part of the GCF. Because 15 does not have a variable factor, the GCF is 5.

2. Look at the coefficients first. The largest number that divides into 4, 10, and 12 evenly is 2, so 2 is part of the GCF. Now look at the variable expressions, z^3, z^2, and z. We choose the variable expression with the smallest exponent. The GCF is $2z$.

3. Look at the coefficients first. The largest number that divides into 3, 9, and 12 evenly is 3, so 3 is part of the GCF. Now look at each variable in the expressions. The smallest exponent on x is 1, so x is part of the GCF. The smallest exponent on y is 3, so y^3 is part of the GCF. The GCF is $3xy^3$.

4. First we find that the GCF is $7z$. Next we rewrite each term as the product of the GCF and a remaining factor, then factor out the GCF.
$7z^2 - 14z = 7z \cdot z - 7z \cdot 2 = 7z(z - 2)$

5. First we find that the GCF is $2y$. Next we rewrite each term as the product of the GCF and a remaining factor, then factor out the GCF.
$6y^3 - 14y^2 + 10y = 2y \cdot 3y^2 - 2y \cdot 7y + 2y \cdot 5$

          $= 2y(3y^2 - 7y + 5)$

6. First we find that the GCF is $2m^2n^2$. Next we rewrite each term as the product of the GCF and a remaining factor, then factor out the GCF.
$2m^4n^2 + 8m^3n^4 - 6m^2n^5$
$= 2m^2n^2 \cdot m^2 + 2m^2n^2 \cdot 4mn^2 - 2m^2n^2 \cdot 3n^3$
$= 2m^2n^2(m^2 + 4mn^2 - 3n^3)$

7. First we find that the GCF is $-5y$. Next we rewrite each term as the product of the GCF and a remaining factor, then factor out the GCF.
$-5y^2 + 10y = -5y \cdot y + (-5y) \cdot (-2) = -5y(y - 2)$

8. First we find that the GCF is $-3a$. Next we rewrite each term as the product of the GCF and a remaining factor, then factor out the GCF.
$-3a^3 + 6a^2 - 12a$
$= -3a \cdot a^2 + (-3a) \cdot (-2a) + (-3a) \cdot (4)$
$= -3a(a^2 - 2a + 4)$

9. First we find that the GCF is $a - 3$. Next we rewrite each term as the product of the GCF and a remaining factor, then factor out the GCF.
$4a(a - 3) + 3(a - 3) = (a - 3) \cdot 4a + (a - 3) \cdot 3$

          $= (a - 3)(4a + 3)$

10. First we find that the GCF is $w - 5$. Next we rewrite each term as the product of the GCF and a remaining factor, then factor out the GCF.
$(w + 2)(w - 5) + (2w + 1)(w - 5)$
$= (w - 5) \cdot (w + 2) + (w - 5) \cdot (2w + 1)$
$= (w - 5)(w + 2 + 2w + 1)$
$= (w - 5)(3w + 3)$

Both terms in the second factor have a common factor of 3. Thus,
$(w + 2)(w - 5) + (2w + 1)(w - 5) = 3(w - 5)(w + 1)$

11. $5x + 5y + bx + by = (5x + 5y) + (bx + by)$
$$= 5(x + y) + b(x + y)$$
$$= (x + y)(5 + b)$$
$$= (x + y)(b + 5)$$

12. $w^3 - 3w^2 + 4w - 12 = (w^3 - 3w^2) + (4w - 12)$
$$= w^2(w - 3) + 4(w - 3)$$
$$= (w - 3)(w^2 + 4)$$

13. $6z^2 + 2z + 9z + 3 = (6z^2 + 2z) + (9z + 3)$
$$= 2z(3z + 1) + 3(3z + 1)$$
$$= (3z + 1)(2z + 3)$$

14. $2x^2 + x - 10x - 5 = (2x^2 + x) + (-10x - 5)$
$$= x(2x + 1) + (-5)(2x + 1)$$
$$= (2x + 1)(x - 5)$$

5.5 Quick Checks

1. $y^2 + 9y + 18$

We are looking for two factors of $c = 18$ whose sum is $b = 9$. Since both c and b are positive, the two factors must both be positive.

Factors	1,18	2,9	3,6
Sum	19	11	9

$y^2 + 9y + 18 = (y + 6)(y + 3)$

2. $p^2 + 14p + 24$

We are looking for two factors of $c = 24$ whose sum is $b = 14$. Since both c and b are positive, the two factors must both be positive.

Factors	1,24	2,12	3,8	4,6
Sum	25	14	11	10

$p^2 + 14p + 24 = (p + 2)(p + 12)$

3. $q^2 - 6q + 8$

We are looking for two factors of $c = 8$ whose sum is $b = -6$. Since c is positive the factors have the same sign, and since b is negative both factors are negative.

Factors	-1,-8	-2,-4
Sum	-9	-6

$q^2 - 6q + 8 = (q - 4)(q - 2)$

4. $x^2 - 8x + 12$

We are looking for two factors of $c = 12$ whose sum is $b = -8$. Since c is positive the factors have the same sign, and since b is negative the two factors are negative.

Factors	-1,-12	-2,-6	-3,-4
Sum	-13	-8	-7

$x^2 - 8x + 12 = (x - 2)(x - 6)$

5. $w^2 - 4w - 21$

We are looking for two factors of $c = -21$ whose sum is $b = -4$. Since c is negative, the two factors will have opposite signs. Since b is negative, the factor with the larger absolute value will be negative.

Factors	-21,1	-7,3
Sum	-20	-4

$w^2 - 4w - 21 = (w - 7)(w + 3)$

6. $q^2 - 9q - 36$

We are looking for two factors of $c = -36$ whose sum is $b = -9$. Since c is negative, the two factors will have opposite signs. Since b is negative, the factor with the larger absolute value will be negative.

Factors	-36,1	-18,2	-12,3	-9,4	-6,6
Sum	-35	-16	-9	-5	0

$q^2 - 9q - 36 = (q - 12)(q + 3)$

7. $t^2 - 5t + 8$

We are looking for two factors of $c = 8$ whose sum is $b = -5$. Since c is positive the factors have the same sign, and since b is negative the two factors are negative.

Factors	-1,-8	-2,-4
Sum	-9	-6

None of the possible factors yield the desire sum, so $t^2 - 5t + 8$ is prime.

QC – 67

8. $2x^3 - 12x^2 - 54x$

First we factor out the GCF.

$2x^3 - 12x^2 - 54x = 2x\left(x^2 - 6x - 27\right)$

We are looking for two factors of $c = -27$ whose sum is $b = -6$. Since c is negative, the factors will have opposite signs. Since b is negative, the factor with the larger absolute value will be negative.

Factors	$-27, 1$	$-9, 3$
Sum	-26	-6

$2x^3 - 12x^2 - 54x = 2x\left(x^2 - 6x - 27\right)$
$\qquad\qquad\qquad = 2x(x-9)(x+3)$

9. $-3z^2 - 21z - 30$

Begin by factoring out the GCF.

$-3z^2 - 21z - 30 = -3\left(z^2 + 7z + 10\right)$

We are looking for two factors of $c = 10$ whose sum is $b = 7$. Since both c and b are positive, the two factors will be positive.

Factors	$1, 10$	$2, 5$
Sum	11	7

$-3z^2 - 21z - 30 = -3\left(z^2 + 7z + 10\right)$
$\qquad\qquad\qquad = -3(z+5)(z+2)$

10. $x^2 + 8xy + 15y^2$

We are looking for two factors of $c = 15$ whose sum is $b = 8$. Since c and b are both positive, the two factors will be positive.

Factors	$1, 15$	$3, 5$
Sum	16	8

$x^2 + 8xy + 15y^2 = (x + 3y)(x + 5y)$

11. $m^2 + mn - 20n^2$

We are looking for two factors of $c = -20$ whose sum is $b = 1$. Since c is negative, the factors will have opposite signs. Since b is positive, the factor with the larger absolute value will be positive.

Factors	$-1, 20$	$-2, 10$	$-4, 5$
Sum	19	8	1

$m^2 + mn - 20n^2 = (m - 4n)(m + 5n)$

12. $6x^2 + 11x + 3$

There are no common factors, so $a = 6, b = 11, c = 3$. We find that $a \cdot c = 6 \cdot 3 = 18$. Therefore, we are looking for two factors of 18 whose sum is $b = 11$. Since the product and the sum are both positive, both factors must be positive and neither can be greater than 11.

factor 1	factor 2	sum	
3	6	9	too small
2	9	11	← okay

$6x^2 + 11x + 3 = 6x^2 + 2x + 9x + 3$
$\qquad\qquad = \left(6x^2 + 2x\right) + (9x + 3)$
$\qquad\qquad = 2x(3x + 1) + 3(3x + 1)$
$\qquad\qquad = (3x + 1)(2x + 3)$

13. $2b^2 + 7b - 15$

There are no common factors, so $a = 2$, $b = 7$, and $c = -15$. Thus, $a \cdot c = 2 \cdot (-15) = -30$. We are looking for two factors of -30 whose sum is $b = 7$. Since the product is negative, the two factors will have opposite signs. Since the sum is positive, the factor with the larger absolute value will be positive.

factor 1	factor 2	sum	
-2	15	13	too big
-5	6	1	too small
-3	10	7	← okay

$2b^2 + 7b - 15 = 2b^2 - 3b + 10b - 15$
$\qquad\qquad = \left(2b^2 - 3b\right) + (10b - 15)$
$\qquad\qquad = b(2b - 3) + 5(2b - 3)$
$\qquad\qquad = (2b - 3)(b + 5)$

14. $8x^2 + 14x + 5$

First note that there are no common factors and that $a = 8$, $b = 14$, and $c = 5$.

Since c is positive the signs in our factors will be the same. Since b is positive, the two signs will be positive. We will consider factorizations with this form:

$(\_\_x + \_\_)(\_\_x + \_\_)$.

Since $a = 8$ can be factored as $1 \cdot 8$ and $2 \cdot 4$, we have the following forms:

$(x + \_\_)(8x + \_\_)$
$(2x + \_\_)(4x + \_\_)$

$|c| = |5| = 5$ can be factored as $1 \cdot 5$. This gives us the following possibilities:

$$(x+1)(8x+5) \rightarrow 8x^2 +13x+5$$

$$(2x+1)(4x+5) \rightarrow 8x^2 +14x+5$$

$$(x+5)(8x+1) \rightarrow 8x^2 +41x+5$$

$$(2x+5)(4x+1) \rightarrow 8x^2 +22x+5$$

The correct factorization is

$$8x^2 +14x+5 = (2x+1)(4x+5).$$

15. $12y^2 +32y-35$

First note that there are no common factors and that $a=12$, $b=32$, and $c=-35$.

Since c is negative, the signs in our factors will be opposites. We will consider factorizations with this form:

$$(\_\,y+\_\,)(\_\,y-\_\,).$$

If our choice results in a middle term with the wrong sign, we simply switch the signs of the factors.

Since $a=12$ can be factored as $1\cdot12$, $2\cdot6$, and $3\cdot4$, we have the following forms:

$$(y+\_\,)(12y-\_\,)$$

$$(2y+\_\,)(6y-\_\,)$$

$$(3y+\_\,)(4y-\_\,)$$

$|c| = |-35| = 35$ can be factored as $1\cdot35$ and $5\cdot7$. This gives us the following possibilities:

$$(y+1)(12y-35) \rightarrow 12y^2 -23y-35$$

$$(2y+1)(6y-35) \rightarrow 12y^2 -64y-35$$

$$(3y+1)(4y-35) \rightarrow 12y^2 -101y-35$$

$$(y+5)(12y-7) \rightarrow 12y^2 +53y-35$$

$$(2y+5)(6y-7) \rightarrow 12y^2 +16y-35$$

$$(3y+5)(4y-7) \rightarrow 12y^2 -y-35$$

$$(y+35)(12y-1) \rightarrow 12y^2 +419y-35$$

$$(2y+35)(6y-1) \rightarrow 12y^2 +208y-35$$

$$(3y+35)(4y-1) \rightarrow 12y^2 +137y-35$$

$$(y+7)(12y-5) \rightarrow 12y^2 +79y-35$$

$$(2y+7)(6y-5) \rightarrow 12y^2 +32y-35$$

$$(3y+7)(4y-5) \rightarrow 12y^2 +13y-35$$

The correct factorization is

$$12y^2 +32y-35 = (2y+7)(6y-5)$$

16. $30x^2 +7xy-2y^2$

First note that there are no common factors and that $a=30$, $b=7$, and $c=-2$.

Since c is negative, the signs in our factors will be opposites. We will consider factorizations of the form:

$$(\_\,x+\_\,y)(\_\,x-\_\,y).$$

If our choice results in a middle term with the wrong sign, we simply switch the signs of the factors.

Since $a=30$ can be factored as $1\cdot30$, $2\cdot15$, $3\cdot10$, and $5\cdot6$, we have the following forms:

$$(x+\_\,y)(30x-\_\,y)$$

$$(2x+\_\,y)(15x-\_\,y)$$

$$(3x+\_\,y)(10x-\_\,y)$$

$$(5x+\_\,y)(6x-\_\,y)$$

$|c| = |-2| = 2$ can be factored as $1\cdot2$. Since the original expression had no common factors, the binomials we select cannot have a common factor. This gives us the following possibilities:

$$(x+2y)(30x-y) \rightarrow 30x^2 +59xy-2y^2$$

$$(2x+y)(15x-2y) \rightarrow 30x^2 +11xy-2y^2$$

$$(3x+2y)(10x-y) \rightarrow 30x^2 +17xy-2y^2$$

$$(5x+2y)(6x-y) \rightarrow 30x^2 +7xy-2y^2$$

The correct factorization is

$$30x^2 +7xy-2y^2 = (5x+2y)(6x-y).$$

17. $-6y^2 +23y+4$

Begin by factoring out -1.

$$-6y^2 +23y+4 = -(6y^2 -23y-4)$$

Focusing on the reduced trinomial, we have $a=6$, $b=-23$, and $c=-4$. Thus, $a\cdot c = 6\cdot(-4) = -24$. We are looking for two factors of -24 whose sum is $b=-23$. Since the product is negative, the two factors have opposite signs. Since the sum is negative, the factor with the larger absolute value will be negative.

factor 1	factor 2	sum	
−8	3	−5	too big
−12	2	−10	too big
−24	1	−23	← okay

$$-6y^2 + 23y + 4 = -\left(6y^2 - 23y - 4\right)$$
$$= -\left(6y^2 - 24y + y - 4\right)$$
$$= -\left[\left(6y^2 - 24y\right) + (y - 4)\right]$$
$$= -\left[6y(y-4) + 1(y-4)\right]$$
$$= -(y-4)(6y+1)$$

18. $-9x^2 - 21xy - 10y^2$

Begin by factoring out -1.

$$-9x^2 - 21xy - 10y^2 = -\left(9x^2 + 21xy + 10y^2\right)$$

Focusing on the reduced trinomial, we have $a = 9$, $b = 21$, and $c = 10$. Thus, $a \cdot c = 9 \cdot 10 = 90$. We are looking for two factors of 90 whose sum is $b = 21$. Since the product is positive, the two factors have the same sign. Since the sum is also positive, the factors will both be positive.

factor 1	factor 2	sum	
3	30	33	too big
9	10	19	too small
6	15	21	← okay

$$-9x^2 - 21xy - 10y^2$$
$$= -\left(9x^2 + 21xy + 10y^2\right)$$
$$= -\left(9x^2 + 6xy + 15xy + 10y^2\right)$$
$$= -\left[\left(9x^2 + 6xy\right) + \left(15xy + 10y^2\right)\right]$$
$$= -\left[3x(3x+2y) + 5y(3x+2y)\right]$$
$$= -(3x+2y)(3x+5y)$$

19. $y^4 - 2y^2 - 24$

Let $u = y^2$. Then $u^2 = \left(y^2\right)^2 = y^4$ and we get

$$y^4 - 2y^2 - 24 = \left(y^2\right)^2 - 2\left(y^2\right) - 24$$
$$= u^2 - 2u - 24$$
$$= (u-6)(u+4)$$
$$= \left(y^2-6\right)\left(y^2+4\right)$$

20. $4(x-3)^2 + 5(x-3) - 6$

Let $u = x - 3$. Then $u^2 = (x-3)^2$ and we get

$$4(x-3)^2 + 5(x-3) - 6$$
$$= 4u^2 + 5u - 6$$
$$= (4u-3)(u+2)$$
$$= (4(x-3)-3)((x-3)+2)$$
$$= (4x-12-3)(x-3+2)$$
$$= (4x-15)(x-1)$$

5.6 Quick Checks

1. $x^2 - 18x + 81 = x^2 - 2 \cdot 9 \cdot x + 9^2$
$$= (x-9)^2$$

2. $4x^2 + 20xy + 25y^2 = (2x)^2 + 2 \cdot 2x \cdot 5y + (5y)^2$
$$= (2x+5y)^2$$

3. $18p^4 - 84p^2 + 98 = 2\left(9p^4 - 42p^2 + 49\right)$
$$= 2\left(\left(3p^2\right)^2 - 2 \cdot \left(3p^2\right) \cdot 7 + 7^2\right)$$
$$= 2\left(3p^2 - 7\right)^2$$

4. $z^2 - 16 = z^2 - 4^2$
$$= (z-4)(z+4)$$

5. $16m^2 - 81n^2 = (4m)^2 - (9n)$
$$= (4m-9n)(4m+9n)$$

6. $4a^2 - 9b^4 = (2a)^2 - \left(3b^2\right)^2$
$$= \left(2a-3b^2\right)\left(2a+3b^2\right)$$

7. $3b^4 - 48 = 3\left(b^4 - 16\right)$
$$= 3\left(\left(b^2\right)^2 - 4^2\right)$$
$$= 3\left(b^2 - 4\right)\left(b^2 + 4\right)$$
$$= 3\left(b^2 - 2^2\right)\left(b^2 + 4\right)$$
$$= 3(b-2)(b+2)\left(b^2 + 4\right)$$

8. $p^2 - 8p + 16 - q^2 = \left(p^2 - 8p + 16\right) - q^2$

$\qquad = \left(p^2 - 2 \cdot 4 \cdot p + 4^2\right) - q^2$

$\qquad = (p-4)^2 - q^2$

$\qquad = (p-4-q)(p-4+q)$

9. $z^3 + 64 = z^3 + 4^4$

$\qquad = (z+4)\left(z^2 - 4 \cdot z + 4^2\right)$

$\qquad = (z+4)\left(z^2 - 4z + 16\right)$

10. $125p^3 - 216q^6$

$= (5p)^3 - \left(6q^2\right)^3$

$= \left(5p - 6q^2\right)\left((5p)^2 + 5p \cdot 6q^2 + \left(6q^2\right)^2\right)$

$= \left(5p - 6q^2\right)\left(25p^2 + 30pq^2 + 36q^4\right)$

11. $32m^3 + 500n^6$

$= 4\left(8m^3 + 125n^6\right)$

$= 4\left((2m)^3 + \left(5n^2\right)^3\right)$

$= 4\left(2m + 5n^2\right)\left((2m)^2 - 2m \cdot 5n^2 + \left(5n^2\right)^2\right)$

$= 4\left(2m + 5n^2\right)\left(4m^2 - 10mn^2 + 25n^4\right)$

12. $(x+1)^3 - 27x^3$

$= (x+1)^3 - (3x)^3$

$= (x+1-3x)\left((x+1)^2 + (x+1) \cdot 3x + (3x)^2\right)$

$= (-2x+1)\left(x^2 + 2x + 1 + 3x^2 + 3x + 9x^2\right)$

$= (-2x+1)\left(13x^2 + 5x + 1\right)$

5.7 Quick Checks

1. $2p^2q - 8pq^2 - 90q^3 = 2q\left(p^2 - 4pq - 45q^2\right)$

$\qquad = 2q(p - 9q)(p + 5q)$

2. $-45x^2y + 66xy + 27y = -3y\left(15x^2 - 22x - 9\right)$

$\qquad = -3y(3x + 1)(5x - 9)$

3. $81x^2 - 100y^2 = (9x)^2 - (10y)^2$

$\qquad = (9x - 10y)(9x + 10y)$

4. $-3m^2n + 147n = -3n\left(m^2 - 49\right)$

$\qquad = -3n\left(m^2 - 7^2\right)$

$\qquad = -3n(m - 7)(m + 7)$

5. $p^2 - 16pq + 64q^2 = p^2 - 2 \cdot p \cdot 8q + (8q)^2$

$\qquad = (p - 8q)^2$

6. $20x^2 + 60x + 45 = 5\left(4x^2 + 12x + 9\right)$

$\qquad = 5\left((2x)^2 + 2 \cdot 2x \cdot 3 + 3^2\right)$

$\qquad = 5(2x + 3)^2$

7. $64y^3 - 125 = (4y)^3 - 5^3$

$\qquad = (4y - 5)\left((4y)^2 + 4y \cdot 5 + 5^2\right)$

$\qquad = (4y - 5)\left(16y^2 + 20y + 25\right)$

8. $-16m^3 - 2n^3 = -2\left(8m^3 + n^3\right)$

$\qquad = -2\left((2m)^3 + n^3\right)$

$\qquad = -2(2m + n)\left((2m)^2 - 2m \cdot n + n^2\right)$

$\qquad = -2(2m + n)\left(4m^2 - 2mn + n^2\right)$

9. $10z^2 - 15z + 35 = 5\left(2z^2 - 3z + 7\right)$

Using $a = 2$, $b = -3$, and $c = 7$, we get $a \cdot c = 2 \cdot 7 = 14$. We are looking for two factors of 14 whose sum is $b = -3$. There are no such factors, so the above factorization is complete.

10. $6xy^2 + 81x^3 = 3x\left(2y^2 + 27x^2\right)$

The expression in parentheses cannot be factored any further.

11. $2x^3 + 5x^2 + 4x + 10 = \left(2x^3 + 5x^2\right) + (4x + 10)$

$\qquad = x^2(2x + 5) + 2(2x + 5)$

$\qquad = (2x + 5)\left(x^2 + 2\right)$

$\qquad = \left(x^2 + 2\right)(2x + 5)$

QC – 71

12. $9x^3 + 3x^2 - 9x - 3 = 3(3x^3 + x^2 - 3x - 1)$
$$= 3((3x^3 + x^2) + (-3x - 1))$$
$$= 3(x^2(3x + 1) - 1(3x + 1))$$
$$= 3(3x + 1)(x^2 - 1)$$
$$= 3(3x + 1)(x - 1)(x + 1)$$

13. $4x^2 + 4xy + y^2 - 81 = (4x^2 + 4xy + y^2) - 81$
$$= ((2x)^2 + 2 \cdot 2x \cdot y + y^2) - 81$$
$$= (2x + y)^2 - 9^2$$
$$= (2x + y - 9)(2x + y + 9)$$

14. $16 - m^2 - 8mn - 16n^2$
$$= 16 - (m^2 + 8mn + 16n^2)$$
$$= 16 - (m^2 + 2 \cdot m \cdot 4n + (4n)^2)$$
$$= 4^2 - (m + 4n)^2$$
$$= (4 - (m + 4n))(4 + (m + 4n))$$
$$= (4 - m - 4n)(4 + m + 4n)$$

5.8 Quick Checks

1. $x(x + 7) = 0$
$x = 0$ or $x + 7 = 0$
$\qquad\qquad\quad x = -7$
Check: $(-7)(-7 + 7) \overset{?}{=} 0$
$\qquad\qquad (-7)(0) \overset{?}{=} 0$
$\qquad\qquad\quad 0 = 0$ ✓
The solution set is $\{-7, 0\}$.

2. $(x - 3)(4x + 3) = 0$
$x - 3 = 0$ or $4x + 3 = 0$
$\quad x = 3$ $\qquad\qquad 4x = -3$
$\qquad\qquad\qquad\qquad x = -\dfrac{3}{4}$

Check:
$(3 - 3)(4(3) + 3) \overset{?}{=} 0$
$\qquad\quad 0(15) \overset{?}{=} 0$
$\qquad\qquad\quad 0 = 0$ ✓
$\left(-\dfrac{3}{4} - 3\right)\left(4\left(-\dfrac{3}{4}\right) + 3\right) \overset{?}{=} 0$
$\qquad\qquad \left(-\dfrac{15}{4}\right)(0) \overset{?}{=} 0$
$\qquad\qquad\qquad\quad 0 = 0$ ✓
The solution set is $\left\{-\dfrac{3}{4}, 3\right\}$.

3. $\quad p^2 - 5p + 6 = 0$
$(p - 3)(p - 2) = 0$
$p - 3 = 0$ or $p - 2 = 0$
$\quad p = 3$ $\qquad\qquad p = 2$
Check:
$(2)^2 - 5(2) + 6 \overset{?}{=} 0$
$\qquad 4 - 10 + 6 \overset{?}{=} 0$
$\qquad\qquad\quad 0 = 0$ ✓
$(3)^2 - 5(3) + 6 \overset{?}{=} 0$
$\qquad 9 - 15 + 6 \overset{?}{=} 0$
$\qquad\qquad\quad 0 = 0$ ✓
The solution set is $\{2, 3\}$.

4. $\qquad 3t^2 - 14t = 5$
$\quad 3t^2 - 14t - 5 = 0$
$(3t + 1)(t - 5) = 0$
$3t + 1 = 0$ or $t - 5 = 0$
$\quad 3t = -1$ $\qquad\qquad t = 5$
$\quad t = -\dfrac{1}{3}$
Check:
$3\left(-\dfrac{1}{3}\right)^2 - 14\left(-\dfrac{1}{3}\right) \overset{?}{=} 5$
$\qquad\qquad \dfrac{1}{3} + \dfrac{14}{3} \overset{?}{=} 5$
$\qquad\qquad\qquad\quad 5 = 5$ ✓
$3(5)^2 - 14(5) \overset{?}{=} 5$
$\qquad 75 - 70 \overset{?}{=} 5$
$\qquad\qquad\quad 5 = 5$ ✓
The solution set is $\left\{-\dfrac{1}{3}, 5\right\}$.

5. $4y^2 + 8y + 3 = y^2 - 1$

$3y^2 + 8y + 4 = 0$

$(3y + 2)(y + 2) = 0$

$3y + 2 = 0$ or $y + 2 = 0$

$3y = -2$ $\qquad$ $y = -2$

$y = -\dfrac{2}{3}$

Check:

$4(-2)^2 + 8(-2) + 3 \overset{?}{=} (-2)^2 - 1$

$16 - 16 + 3 \overset{?}{=} 4 - 1$

$3 = 3$ ✓

$4\left(-\dfrac{2}{3}\right)^2 + 8\left(-\dfrac{2}{3}\right) + 3 \overset{?}{=} \left(-\dfrac{2}{3}\right)^2 - 1$

$\dfrac{16}{9} - \dfrac{16}{3} + 3 \overset{?}{=} \dfrac{4}{9} - 1$

$-\dfrac{5}{9} = -\dfrac{5}{9}$ ✓

The solution set is $\left\{-2, -\dfrac{2}{3}\right\}$.

6. $x(x + 3) = -2$

$x^2 + 3x = -2$

$x^2 + 3x + 2 = 0$

$(x + 1)(x + 2) = 0$

$x + 1 = 0$ or $x + 2 = 0$

$x = -1$ $\qquad$ $x = -2$

Check:

$(-2)(-2 + 3) \overset{?}{=} -2$

$-2(1) \overset{?}{=} -2$

$-2 = -2$ ✓

$(-1)(-1 + 3) \overset{?}{=} -2$

$(-1)(2) \overset{?}{=} -2$

$-2 = -2$ ✓

The solution set is $\{-2, -1\}$.

7. $(x - 3)(x + 5) = 9$

$x^2 - 3x + 5x - 15 = 9$

$x^2 + 2x - 24 = 0$

$(x + 6)(x - 4) = 0$

$x + 6 = 0$ or $x - 4 = 0$

$x = -6$ $\qquad$ $x = 4$

Check:

$(-6 - 3)(-6 + 5) \overset{?}{=} 9$

$(-9)(-1) \overset{?}{=} 9$

$9 = 9$ ✓

$(4 - 3)(4 + 5) \overset{?}{=} 9$

$(1)(9) \overset{?}{=} 9$

$9 = 9$ ✓

The solution set is $\{-6, 4\}$.

8. $y^3 - y^2 - 9y + 9 = 0$

$(y^3 - y^2) + (-9y + 9) = 0$

$y^2(y - 1) - 9(y - 1) = 0$

$(y - 1)(y^2 - 9) = 0$

$(y - 1)(y - 3)(y + 3) = 0$

$y - 1 = 0$ or $y - 3 = 0$ or $y + 3 = 0$

$y = 1$ $\qquad$ $y = 3$ $\qquad$ $y = -3$

Check:

$(-3)^3 - (-3)^2 - 9(-3) + 9 \overset{?}{=} 0$

$-27 - 9 + 27 + 9 \overset{?}{=} 0$

$0 = 0$ ✓

$(1)^3 - (1)^2 - 9(1) + 9 \overset{?}{=} 0$

$1 - 1 - 9 + 9 \overset{?}{=} 0$

$0 = 0$ ✓

$(3)^3 - (3)^2 - 9(3) + 9 \overset{?}{=} 0$

$27 - 9 - 27 + 9 \overset{?}{=} 0$

$0 = 0$ ✓

The solution set is $\{-3, 1, 3\}$.

9. $g(x) = x^2 - 8x + 3$

a. $\qquad g(x) = 12$

$x^2 - 8x + 3 = 12$

$x^2 - 8x - 9 = 0$

$(x - 9)(x + 1) = 0$

$x - 9 = 0$ or $x + 1 = 0$

$x = 9$ $\qquad$ $x = -1$

The solution set is $\{-1, 9\}$. The points

$(-1, 12)$ and $(9, 12)$ are on the graph of g.

b.
$$g(x) = -4$$
$$x^2 - 8x + 3 = -4$$
$$x^2 - 8x + 7 = 0$$
$$(x-7)(x-1) = 0$$
$$x - 7 = 0 \quad \text{or} \quad x - 1 = 0$$
$$x = 7 \qquad\qquad x = 1$$

The solution set is $\{1, 7\}$. The points $(1, -4)$ and $(7, -4)$ are on the graph of g.

10.
$$h(x) = 2x^2 + 3x - 20$$
$$h(x) = 0$$
$$2x^2 + 3x - 20 = 0$$
$$(2x - 5)(x + 4) = 0$$
$$2x - 5 = 0 \quad \text{or} \quad x + 4 = 0$$
$$2x = 5 \qquad\qquad x = -4$$
$$x = \frac{5}{2}$$

The zeros are -4 and $\frac{5}{2}$; the x-intercepts are also -4 and $\frac{5}{2}$.

11. Let w = the width of the plot. Then the length is given by $w + 6$.
$$A = \text{length} \cdot \text{width}$$
$$= (w + 6) \cdot w$$
$$135 = w(w + 6)$$
$$135 = w^2 + 6w$$
$$0 = w^2 + 6w - 135$$
$$0 = (w + 15)(w - 9)$$
$$w + 15 = 0 \quad \text{or} \quad w - 9 = 0$$
$$w = -15 \qquad\qquad w = 9$$

Since the width must be positive, we discard the negative solution. The width is 9 miles and the length is $9 + 6 = 15$ miles.

12. Let x = the number of boxes ordered. The price per box is then given by $100 - (x - 30) = 130 - x$.
$$\text{Cost} = \text{price} \cdot \text{quantity}$$
$$4200 = (130 - x)x$$
$$4200 = 130x - x^2$$
$$x^2 - 130x + 4200 = 0$$
$$(x - 60)(x - 70) = 0$$
$$x - 60 = 0 \quad \text{or} \quad x - 70 = 0$$
$$x = 60 \qquad\qquad x = 70$$

Since the number of boxes ordered must be between 30 and 65, we discard the second solution. The customer ordered 60 boxes of CDs.

13. $s(t) = -16t^2 + 160t$

a.
$$s(t) = 384$$
$$-16t^2 + 160t = 384$$
$$16t^2 - 160t + 384 = 0$$
$$t^2 - 10t + 24 = 0$$
$$(t - 4)(t - 6) = 0$$
$$t - 4 = 0 \quad \text{or} \quad t - 6 = 0$$
$$t = 4 \qquad\qquad t = 6$$

The rocket will be 384 feet above the ground after 4 seconds and after 6 seconds.

b.
$$s(t) = 0$$
$$-16t^2 + 160t = 0$$
$$t^2 - 10t = 0$$
$$t(t - 10) = 0$$
$$t = 0 \quad \text{or} \quad t - 10 = 0$$
$$t = 10$$

The rocket will strike the ground after 10 seconds.

Getting Ready for Chapter 6 – Quick Checks

1. $\dfrac{13\cdot 5}{13\cdot 6}=\dfrac{\cancel{13}^{1}\cdot 5}{\cancel{13}_{1}\cdot 6}=\dfrac{5}{6}$

2. $\dfrac{80}{12}=\dfrac{20\cdot 4}{3\cdot 4}=\dfrac{20\cdot \cancel{4}^{1}}{3\cdot \cancel{4}_{1}}=\dfrac{20}{3}$

3. $\dfrac{5}{7}\left(-\dfrac{21}{10}\right)=-\dfrac{5}{7}\cdot\dfrac{3\cdot 7}{2\cdot 5}=-\dfrac{\cancel{5}^{1}}{\cancel{7}_{1}}\cdot\dfrac{3\cdot \cancel{7}^{1}}{2\cdot \cancel{5}_{1}}=-\dfrac{3}{2}$

4. $\dfrac{35}{15}\cdot\dfrac{3}{14}=\dfrac{5\cdot 7}{3\cdot 5}\cdot\dfrac{3}{2\cdot 7}=\dfrac{\cancel{5}^{1}\cdot \cancel{7}^{1}}{\cancel{3}_{1}\cdot \cancel{5}_{1}}\cdot\dfrac{\cancel{3}^{1}}{2\cdot \cancel{7}_{1}}=\dfrac{1}{2}$

5. $\dfrac{\frac{4}{5}}{\frac{12}{25}}=\dfrac{4}{5}\cdot\dfrac{25}{12}=\dfrac{\cancel{4}^{1}}{\cancel{5}_{1}}\cdot\dfrac{\cancel{5}^{1}\cdot 5}{\cancel{4}_{1}\cdot 3}=\dfrac{5}{3}$

6. $\dfrac{24}{35}\div\left(-\dfrac{8}{7}\right)=-\dfrac{24}{35}\cdot\dfrac{7}{8}$

$=-\dfrac{8\cdot 3}{5\cdot 7}\cdot\dfrac{7}{8}$

$=-\dfrac{\cancel{8}^{1}\cdot 3}{5\cdot \cancel{7}_{1}}\cdot\dfrac{\cancel{7}^{1}}{\cancel{8}_{1}}$

$=-\dfrac{3}{5}$

7. $\dfrac{11}{12}+\dfrac{5}{12}=\dfrac{11+5}{12}=\dfrac{16}{12}=\dfrac{4\cdot 4}{4\cdot 3}=\dfrac{4}{3}$

8. $\dfrac{3}{18}-\dfrac{13}{18}=\dfrac{3-13}{18}=\dfrac{-10}{18}=-\dfrac{2\cdot 5}{2\cdot 9}=-\dfrac{5}{9}$

9. $25=5\cdot 5$

$15=3\cdot 5$

$\text{LCD}=3\cdot 5\cdot 5=75$

$\dfrac{3}{25}=\dfrac{3}{25}\cdot\dfrac{3}{3}=\dfrac{9}{75}$

$\dfrac{2}{15}=\dfrac{2}{15}\cdot\dfrac{5}{5}=\dfrac{10}{75}$

10. $18=2\cdot 3\cdot 3$

$63=3\cdot 3\cdot 7$

$\text{LCD}=2\cdot 3\cdot 3\cdot 7=126$

$\dfrac{5}{18}=\dfrac{5}{18}\cdot\dfrac{7}{7}=\dfrac{35}{126}$

$-\dfrac{1}{63}=-\dfrac{1}{63}\cdot\dfrac{2}{2}=-\dfrac{2}{126}$

11. $4=2\cdot 2$

5 is prime

$\text{LCD}=2\cdot 2\cdot 5=20$

$\dfrac{3}{4}+\dfrac{1}{5}=\dfrac{3}{4}\cdot\dfrac{5}{5}+\dfrac{1}{5}\cdot\dfrac{4}{4}$

$=\dfrac{15}{20}+\dfrac{4}{20}=\dfrac{15+4}{20}$

$=\dfrac{19}{20}$

12. $20=2\cdot 2\cdot 5$

$15=3\cdot 5$

$\text{LCD}=2\cdot 2\cdot 3\cdot 5=60$

$\dfrac{3}{20}+\dfrac{2}{15}=\dfrac{3}{20}\cdot\dfrac{3}{3}+\dfrac{2}{15}\cdot\dfrac{4}{4}$

$=\dfrac{9}{60}+\dfrac{8}{60}=\dfrac{9+8}{60}$

$=\dfrac{17}{60}$

13. $14=2\cdot 7$

$21=3\cdot 7$

$\text{LCD}=2\cdot 3\cdot 7=42$

$\dfrac{5}{14}-\dfrac{11}{21}=\dfrac{5}{14}\cdot\dfrac{3}{3}-\dfrac{11}{21}\cdot\dfrac{2}{2}$

$=\dfrac{15}{42}-\dfrac{22}{42}=\dfrac{15-22}{42}$

$=-\dfrac{7}{42}=-\dfrac{1\cdot 7}{6\cdot 7}$

$=-\dfrac{1}{6}$

Chapter 6 – Quick Checks

6.1 Quick Checks

1. We need to find all values of x that cause the denominator $x+6$ to equal 0.

$x+6=0$

$x=-6$

Thus, the domain of $\dfrac{x-4}{x+6}$ is $\{x \mid x \neq -6\}$.

2. We need to find all values of x that cause the denominator $z^2+3z-28$ to equal 0.

$z^2+3z-28=0$

$(z+7)(x-4)=0$

$z+7=0$ or $z-4=0$

$z=-7$ or $z=4$

Thus, the domain of $\dfrac{z^2-9}{z^2+3z-28}$ is $\{z \mid z \neq -4, z \neq 7\}$.

3. $\dfrac{x^2-7x+12}{x^2+4x-21}=\dfrac{(x-3)(x-4)}{(x-3)(x+7)}$

$=\dfrac{\cancel{(x-3)}(x-4)}{\cancel{(x-3)}(x+7)}=\dfrac{x-4}{x+7}$

4. $\dfrac{z^3-64}{2z^2-3z-20}=\dfrac{(z-4)(z^2+4z+16)}{(2z+5)(z-4)}$

$=\dfrac{\cancel{(z-4)}(z^2+4z+16)}{(2z+5)\cancel{(z-4)}}$

$=\dfrac{z^2+4z+16}{2z+5}$

5. $\dfrac{3w^2+13w-10}{2-3w}=\dfrac{(3w-2)(w+5)}{-1(3w-2)}$

$=\dfrac{\cancel{(3w-2)}(w+5)}{-1\cancel{(3w-2)}}$

$=\dfrac{w+5}{-1}=-(w+5)$

6. $\dfrac{p^2-9}{p^2+5p+6} \cdot \dfrac{3p^2-p-2}{2p-6}$

$=\dfrac{(p-3)(p+3)}{(p+2)(p+3)} \cdot \dfrac{(3p+2)(p-1)}{2(p-3)}$

$=\dfrac{\cancel{(p-3)}\cancel{(p+3)}}{(p+2)\cancel{(p+3)}} \cdot \dfrac{(3p+2)(p-1)}{2\cancel{(p-3)}}$

$=\dfrac{(3p+2)(p-1)}{2(p+2)}$

7. $\dfrac{2x+8}{2x^2+11x+12} \cdot \dfrac{2x^2-3x-9}{6-2x}$

$=\dfrac{2(x+4)}{(2x+3)(x+4)} \cdot \dfrac{(2x+3)(x-3)}{-1 \cdot 2(x-3)}$

$=\dfrac{\cancel{2}\cancel{(x+4)}}{\cancel{(2x+3)}\cancel{(x+4)}} \cdot \dfrac{\cancel{(2x+3)}\cancel{(x-3)}}{-1 \cdot \cancel{2}\cancel{(x-3)}}$

$=\dfrac{1}{-1}=-1$

8. $\dfrac{m^2+2mn+n^2}{2m^2+3mn+n^2} \cdot \dfrac{2m^2-5mn-3n^2}{3n-m}$

$=\dfrac{(m+n)(m+n)}{(2m+n)(m+n)} \cdot \dfrac{(2m+n)(m-3n)}{-1(m-3n)}$

$=\dfrac{\cancel{(m+n)}(m+n)}{\cancel{(2m+n)}\cancel{(m+n)}} \cdot \dfrac{\cancel{(2m+n)}\cancel{(m-3n)}}{-1\cancel{(m-3n)}}$

$=\dfrac{m+n}{-1}=-(m+n)$

9. $\dfrac{\dfrac{12a^4}{5b^2}}{\dfrac{4a^2}{15b^5}}=\dfrac{12a^4}{5b^2} \cdot \dfrac{15b^5}{4a^2}$

$=\dfrac{\overset{3}{\cancel{12}} \cdot \cancel{a^4} \cdot a^2}{\cancel{5} \cdot \cancel{b^2}} \cdot \dfrac{\overset{3}{\cancel{15}} \cdot \cancel{b^5} \cdot b^3}{\cancel{4} \cdot \cancel{a^2}}=9a^2b^3$

10. $\dfrac{\dfrac{m^2-5m}{m-7}}{\dfrac{2m}{m^2-6m-7}} = \dfrac{m^2-5m}{m-7}\cdot\dfrac{m^2-6m-7}{2m}$

$\qquad = \dfrac{m(m-5)}{m-7}\cdot\dfrac{(m-7)(m+1)}{2\cdot m}$

$\qquad = \dfrac{\cancel{m}(m-5)}{\cancel{m-7}}\cdot\dfrac{\cancel{(m-7)}(m+1)}{2\cdot \cancel{m}}$

$\qquad = \dfrac{(m-5)(m+1)}{2}$

11. We need to find all values of x that cause the denominator x^2+x-30 to equal 0.

$x^2+x-30=0$

$(x+6)(x-5)=0$

$x+6=0 \quad$ or $\quad x-5=0$

$\quad x=-6 \quad$ or $\qquad x=5$

Thus, the domain of $R(x)=\dfrac{2x}{x^2+x-30}$ is

$\left\{x\,\middle|\,x\ne-6, x\ne 5\right\}$.

12. a. $R(x)=f(x)\cdot g(x)$

$\qquad = \dfrac{x^2-4x-5}{3x-5}\cdot\dfrac{3x^2+4x-15}{x^2-2x-15}$

$\qquad = \dfrac{(x-5)(x+1)}{3x-5}\cdot\dfrac{(3x-5)(x+3)}{(x-5)(x+3)}$

$\qquad = \dfrac{\cancel{(x-5)}(x+1)}{\cancel{3x-5}}\cdot\dfrac{\cancel{(3x-5)}\cancel{(x+3)}}{\cancel{(x-5)}\cancel{(x+3)}}$

$\qquad = x+1$

The domain of $f(x)$ is $\left\{x\,\middle|\,x\ne\dfrac{5}{3}\right\}$.

The domain of $g(x)$ is $\{x\mid x\ne-3, x\ne 5\}$.

Therefore, the domain of $R(x)$ is

$\left\{x\,\middle|\,x\ne-3, x\ne\dfrac{5}{3}, x\ne 5\right\}$.

b. $H(x)=\dfrac{f(x)}{h(x)} = \dfrac{\dfrac{x^2-4x-5}{3x-5}}{\dfrac{4x^2+7x+3}{9x^2-15x}}$

$\qquad = \dfrac{x^2-4x-5}{3x-5}\cdot\dfrac{9x^2-15x}{4x^2+7x+3}$

$\qquad = \dfrac{(x-5)(x+1)}{3x-5}\cdot\dfrac{3x(3x-5)}{(4x+3)(x+1)}$

$\qquad = \dfrac{(x-5)\cancel{(x+1)}}{\cancel{3x-5}}\cdot\dfrac{3x\cancel{(3x-5)}}{(4x+3)\cancel{(x+1)}}$

$\qquad = \dfrac{3x(x-5)}{4x+3}$

The domain of $f(x)$ is $\left\{x\,\middle|\,x\ne\dfrac{5}{3}\right\}$.

The domain of $h(x)$ is $\left\{x\,\middle|\,x\ne 0, x\ne\dfrac{5}{3}\right\}$.

Because the denominator of $H(x)$ cannot equal 0, we must exclude those values of x such that

$4x^2+7x+3=0$. These values are $x=-\dfrac{3}{4}$ and

$x=-1$. Therefore, the domain of $H(x)$ is

$\left\{x\,\middle|\,x\ne-1, x\ne-\dfrac{3}{4}, x\ne 0, x\ne\dfrac{5}{3}\right\}$.

6.2 Quick Checks

1. $\dfrac{x^2-3x-1}{x-2}+\dfrac{x^2-2x+3}{x-2} = \dfrac{x^2-3x-1+\left(x^2-2x+3\right)}{x-2}$

$\qquad = \dfrac{2x^2-5x+2}{x-2}$

$\qquad = \dfrac{(2x-1)(x-2)}{x-2}$

$\qquad = \dfrac{(2x-1)\cancel{(x-2)}}{\cancel{x-2}}$

$\qquad = 2x-1$

2. $\dfrac{4x+3}{x+5}-\dfrac{x-6}{x+5} = \dfrac{4x+3-(x-6)}{x+5}$

$\qquad = \dfrac{4x+3-x+6}{x+5}$

$\qquad = \dfrac{3x+9}{x+5} \quad$ or $\quad \dfrac{3(x+3)}{x+5}$

3. $\dfrac{4x}{x-5}+\dfrac{3}{5-x} = \dfrac{4x}{x-5}+\dfrac{3}{-1(x-5)}$

$\qquad = \dfrac{4x}{x-5}+\dfrac{-3}{x-5} = \dfrac{4x-3}{x-5}$

4. $8x^2y = 2^3\cdot x^2\cdot y$

$12xy^3 = 2^2\cdot 3\cdot x\cdot y^3$

$\text{LCD} = 2^3\cdot 3\cdot x^2\cdot y^3 = 24x^2y^3$

5. $x^2 - 5x - 14 = (x+2)(x-7)$

$x^2 + 4x + 4 = (x+2)^2$

$LCD = (x+2)^2(x-7)$

6. $10a = 2 \cdot 5 \cdot a$

$15a^2 = 3 \cdot 5 \cdot a^2$

$LCD = 2 \cdot 3 \cdot 5 \cdot a^2 = 30a^2$

$\dfrac{3}{10a} + \dfrac{4}{15a^2} = \dfrac{3}{10a} \cdot \dfrac{3a}{3a} + \dfrac{4}{15a^2} \cdot \dfrac{2}{2}$

$\qquad\qquad = \dfrac{9a}{30a^2} + \dfrac{8}{30a^2} = \dfrac{9a+8}{30a^2}$

7. $x-1$

$x+2$

$LCD = (x-1)(x+2)$

$\dfrac{3x}{x-1} + \dfrac{x+5}{x+2} = \dfrac{3x}{x-1} \cdot \dfrac{x+2}{x+2} + \dfrac{x+5}{x+2} \cdot \dfrac{x-1}{x-1}$

$\qquad\qquad = \dfrac{3x^2+6x}{(x-1)(x+2)} + \dfrac{x^2+4x-5}{(x-1)(x+2)}$

$\qquad\qquad = \dfrac{3x^2+6x+\left(x^2+4x-5\right)}{(x-1)(x+2)}$

$\qquad\qquad = \dfrac{4x^2+10x-5}{(x-1)(x+2)}$

8. $2x^2 + 7x + 6 = (2x+3)(x+2)$

$x^2 + 6x + 8 = (x+2)(x+4)$

$LCD = (2x+3)(x+2)(x+4)$

$\dfrac{x-1}{2x^2+7x+6} + \dfrac{x-1}{x^2+6x+8}$

$= \dfrac{x-1}{(2x+3)(x+2)} + \dfrac{x-1}{(x+2)(x+4)}$

$= \dfrac{x-1}{(2x+3)(x+2)} \cdot \dfrac{x+4}{x+4} + \dfrac{x-1}{(x+2)(x+4)} \cdot \dfrac{2x+3}{2x+3}$

$= \dfrac{x^2+3x-4}{(2x+3)(x+2)(x+4)} + \dfrac{2x^2+x-3}{(2x+3)(x+2)(x+4)}$

$= \dfrac{x^2+3x-4+\left(2x^2+x-3\right)}{(2x+3)(x+2)(x+4)}$

$= \dfrac{3x^2+4x-7}{(2x+3)(x+2)(x+4)}$

$= \dfrac{(3x+7)(x-1)}{(2x+3)(x+2)(x+4)}$

9. $2x^2 + x - 6 = (2x-3)(x+2)$

$x^2 + 4x + 4 = (x+2)^2$

$LCD = (2x-3)(x+2)^2$

$\dfrac{3x+4}{2x^2+x-6} - \dfrac{x-1}{x^2+4x+4}$

$= \dfrac{3x+4}{(2x-3)(x+2)} - \dfrac{x-1}{(x+2)^2}$

$= \dfrac{3x+4}{(2x-3)(x+2)} \cdot \dfrac{x+2}{x+2} - \dfrac{x-1}{(x+2)^2} \cdot \dfrac{2x-3}{2x-3}$

$= \dfrac{3x^2+10x+8}{(2x-3)(x+2)^2} - \dfrac{2x^2-5x+3}{(2x-3)(x+2)^2}$

$= \dfrac{3x^2+10x+8-\left(2x^2-5x+3\right)}{(2x-3)(x+2)^2}$

$= \dfrac{3x^2+10x+8-2x^2+5x-3}{(2x-3)(x+2)^2}$

$= \dfrac{x^2+15x+5}{(2x-3)(x+2)^2}$

10. $x^2 - 4 = (x-2)(x+2)$

$x-2$

$x+2$

$LCD = (x-2)(x+2)$

$\dfrac{4}{x^2-4} - \dfrac{x+3}{x-2} + \dfrac{x+3}{x+2}$

$= \dfrac{4}{(x-2)(x+2)} - \dfrac{x+3}{x-2} + \dfrac{x+3}{x+2}$

$= \dfrac{4}{(x-2)(x+2)} - \dfrac{x+3}{x-2} \cdot \dfrac{x+2}{x+2} + \dfrac{x+3}{x+2} \cdot \dfrac{x-2}{x-2}$

$= \dfrac{4}{(x-2)(x+2)} - \dfrac{x^2+5x+6}{(x-2)(x+2)} + \dfrac{x^2+x-6}{(x-2)(x+2)}$

$= \dfrac{4-\left(x^2+5x+6\right)+x^2+x-6}{(x-2)(x+2)}$

$= \dfrac{4-x^2-5x-6+x^2+x-6}{(x-2)(x+2)}$

$= \dfrac{-4x-8}{(x-2)(x+2)}$

$= \dfrac{-4(x+2)}{(x-2)(x+2)}$

$= \dfrac{-4}{x-2}$

6.3 Quick Checks

1. Write the numerator of the complex rational expression as a single rational expression. Note that the LCD of the rational expressions in the numerator is $4z$.

$$\frac{z}{4}-\frac{4}{z}=\frac{z}{4}\cdot\frac{z}{z}-\frac{4}{z}\cdot\frac{4}{4}=\frac{z^2}{4z}-\frac{16}{4z}=\frac{z^2-16}{4z}$$

The denominator of the complex rational expression is already a single rational expression: $\dfrac{z+4}{16}$.

Rewrite the complex rational expression using the single rational expressions and simplify.

$$\frac{\dfrac{z}{4}-\dfrac{4}{z}}{\dfrac{z+4}{16}}=\frac{\dfrac{z^2-16}{4z}}{\dfrac{z+4}{16}}=\frac{z^2-16}{4z}\cdot\frac{16}{z+4}$$

$$=\frac{(z-4)(z+4)}{4z}\cdot\frac{16}{z+4}$$

$$=\frac{(z-4)\,\cancel{(z+4)}}{\cancel{4}z}\cdot\frac{\overset{4}{\cancel{16}}}{\cancel{z+4}}=\frac{4(z-4)}{z}$$

2. Write the numerator of the complex rational expression as a single rational expression. Note that the LCD of the rational expressions in the numerator is $(x+1)(x+2)$.

$$\frac{2x}{x+1}-\frac{x^2-3}{x^2+3x+2}=\frac{2x}{x+1}-\frac{x^2-3}{(x+1)(x+2)}$$

$$=\frac{2x}{x+1}\cdot\frac{x+2}{x+2}-\frac{x^2-3}{(x+1)(x+2)}$$

$$=\frac{2x^2+4x}{(x+1)(x+2)}-\frac{x^2-3}{(x+1)(x+2)}$$

$$=\frac{2x^2+4x-\left(x^2-3\right)}{(x+1)(x+2)}$$

$$=\frac{2x^2+4x-x^2+3}{(x+1)(x+2)}$$

$$=\frac{x^2+4x+3}{(x+1)(x+2)}$$

Write the denominator of the complex rational expression as a single rational expression. Note that the LCD of the rational expressions in the denominator is $x+2$.

$$4+\frac{4}{x+2}=4\cdot\frac{x+2}{x+2}+\frac{4}{x+2}$$

$$=\frac{4x+8}{x+2}+\frac{4}{x+2}=\frac{4x+12}{x+2}=\frac{4(x+3)}{x+2}$$

Rewrite the complex rational expression using the single rational expressions and simplify.

$$\frac{\dfrac{2x}{x+1}-\dfrac{x^2-3}{x^2+3x+2}}{4+\dfrac{4}{x+2}}=\frac{\dfrac{x^2+4x+3}{(x+1)(x+2)}}{\dfrac{4(x+3)}{x+2}}$$

$$=\frac{x^2+4x+3}{(x+1)(x+2)}\cdot\frac{x+2}{4(x+3)}$$

$$=\frac{(x+1)(x+3)}{(x+1)(x+2)}\cdot\frac{x+2}{4(x+3)}$$

$$=\frac{\cancel{(x+1)}\cancel{(x+3)}}{\cancel{(x+1)}\cancel{(x+2)}}\cdot\frac{\cancel{x+2}}{4\cancel{(x+3)}}$$

$$=\frac{1}{4}$$

3. The LCD of all the denominators in the complex rational expression is $16z$.

$$\frac{\dfrac{z}{4}-\dfrac{4}{z}}{\dfrac{z+4}{16}}=\frac{\dfrac{z}{4}-\dfrac{4}{z}}{\dfrac{z+4}{16}}\cdot\frac{16z}{16z}=\frac{\dfrac{z}{4}\cdot16z-\dfrac{4}{z}\cdot16z}{\dfrac{z+4}{16}\cdot16z}$$

$$=\frac{\dfrac{z}{\cancel{4}}\cdot\overset{4}{\cancel{16}}z-\dfrac{4}{\cancel{z}}\cdot16\cancel{z}}{\dfrac{z+4}{\cancel{16}}\cdot\cancel{16}z}$$

$$=\frac{4z^2-64}{z(z+4)}=\frac{4(z-4)(z+4)}{z(z+4)}$$

$$=\frac{4(z-4)\cancel{(z+4)}}{z\cancel{(z+4)}}=\frac{4(z-4)}{z}$$

4. The LCD of all the denominators in the complex rational expression is $(x+5)(x+1)$.

$$\frac{\dfrac{x+2}{x+5}-\dfrac{x+2}{x+1}}{\dfrac{2x+1}{x+1}-1}=\frac{\dfrac{x+2}{x+5}-\dfrac{x+2}{x+1}}{\dfrac{2x+1}{x+1}-1}\cdot\frac{(x+5)(x+1)}{(x+5)(x+1)}$$

$$=\frac{\dfrac{x+2}{x+5}\cdot(x+5)(x+1)-\dfrac{x+2}{x+1}\cdot(x+5)(x+1)}{\dfrac{2x+1}{x+1}\cdot(x+5)(x+1)-1\cdot(x+5)(x+1)}$$

$$=\frac{\dfrac{x+2}{\cancel{x+5}}\cdot\cancel{(x+5)}(x+1)+\dfrac{x+2}{\cancel{x+1}}\cdot(x+5)\cancel{(x+1)}}{\dfrac{2x+1}{\cancel{x+1}}\cdot(x+5)\cancel{(x+1)}-1\cdot(x+5)(x+1)}$$

$$=\frac{(x+2)(x+1)-(x+2)(x+5)}{(2x+1)(x+5)-(x+5)(x+1)}$$

$$=\frac{(x+2)\left[x+1-(x+5)\right]}{(x+5)\left[2x+1-(x+1)\right]}$$

$$=\frac{(x+2)\left[x+1-x-5\right]}{(x+5)\left[2x+1-x-1\right]}$$

$$=\frac{(x+2)(-4)}{(x+5)x}=\frac{-4(x+2)}{x(x+5)}$$

5. Rewrite the expression so that it does not contain any negative exponents.

$$\frac{3a^{-1}+b^{-1}}{9a^{-2}-b^{-2}}=\frac{\dfrac{3}{a}+\dfrac{1}{b}}{\dfrac{9}{a^2}-\dfrac{1}{b^2}}$$

Using Method 1, begin by writing the numerator of the complex rational expression as a single rational expression. Note that the LCD of the rational expressions in the numerator is ab.

$$\frac{3}{a}+\frac{1}{b}=\frac{3}{a}\cdot\frac{b}{b}+\frac{1}{b}\cdot\frac{a}{a}=\frac{3b}{ab}+\frac{a}{ab}=\frac{3b+a}{ab}$$

Next, write the denominator of the complex rational expression as a single rational expression. Note that the LCD of the rational expressions in the denominator is a^2b^2.

$$\frac{9}{a^2}-\frac{1}{b^2}=\frac{9}{a^2}\cdot\frac{b^2}{b^2}-\frac{1}{b^2}\cdot\frac{a^2}{a^2}$$

$$=\frac{9b^2}{a^2b^2}-\frac{a^2}{a^2b^2}=\frac{9b^2-a^2}{a^2b^2}$$

Rewrite the complex rational expression using the single rational expressions and simplify.

$$\frac{\dfrac{3}{a}+\dfrac{1}{b}}{\dfrac{9}{a^2}-\dfrac{1}{b^2}}=\frac{\dfrac{3b+a}{ab}}{\dfrac{9b^2-a^2}{a^2b^2}}=\frac{3b+a}{ab}\cdot\frac{a^2b^2}{9b^2-a^2}$$

$$=\frac{3b+a}{ab}\cdot\frac{a^2b^2}{(3b-a)(3b+a)}$$

$$=\frac{\cancel{3b+a}}{\cancel{ab}}\cdot\frac{\overset{ab}{\cancel{a^2b^2}}}{(3b-a)\cancel{(3b+a)}}$$

$$=\frac{ab}{3b-a}$$

Using Method 2, the LCD of all the denominators in the complex rational expression is a^2b^2.

$$\frac{3a^{-1}+b^{-1}}{9a^{-2}-b^{-2}}=\frac{\dfrac{3}{a}+\dfrac{1}{b}}{\dfrac{9}{a^2}-\dfrac{1}{b^2}}=\frac{\dfrac{3}{a}+\dfrac{1}{b}}{\dfrac{9}{a^2}-\dfrac{1}{b^2}}\cdot\frac{a^2b^2}{a^2b^2}$$

$$=\frac{\dfrac{3}{a}\cdot a^2b^2+\dfrac{1}{b}\cdot a^2b^2}{\dfrac{9}{a^2}\cdot a^2b^2-\dfrac{1}{b^2}\cdot a^2b^2}$$

$$=\frac{3ab^2+a^2b}{9b^2-a^2}$$

$$=\frac{ab(3b+a)}{(3b-a)(3b+a)}$$

$$=\frac{ab\cancel{(3b+a)}}{(3b-a)\cancel{(3b+a)}}$$

$$=\frac{ab}{3b-a}$$

6.4 Quick Checks

1.
$$\frac{x-4}{x^2+4}=\frac{3}{3x+2}$$

$$(x^2+4)(3x+2)\left(\frac{x-4}{x^2+4}\right)=(x^2+4)(3x+2)\left(\frac{3}{3x+2}\right)$$

$$(3x+2)(x-4)=3(x^2+4)$$

$$3x^2-10x-8=3x^2+12$$

$$-10x-8=12$$

$$-10x=20$$

$$x=-2$$

QC – 80

Check:

$$\frac{-2-4}{(-2)^2+4} \overset{?}{=} \frac{3}{3(-2)+2}$$

$$\frac{-2-4}{4+4} \overset{?}{=} \frac{3}{-6+2}$$

$$\frac{-6}{8} \overset{?}{=} \frac{3}{-4}$$

$$-\frac{3}{4} = -\frac{3}{4} \leftarrow \text{True}$$

The solution checks, so the solution set is $\{-2\}$.

2.
$$\frac{5}{x}+\frac{1}{4}=\frac{3}{2x}-\frac{3}{2}$$

$$4x\left(\frac{5}{x}+\frac{1}{4}\right)=4x\left(\frac{3}{2x}-\frac{3}{2}\right)$$

$$4x\cdot\frac{5}{x}+4x\cdot\frac{1}{4}=4x\cdot\frac{3}{2x}-4x\cdot\frac{3}{2}$$

$$20+x=6-6x$$

$$20+7x=6$$

$$7x=-14$$

$$x=-2$$

Check:

$$\frac{5}{-2}+\frac{1}{4} \overset{?}{=} \frac{3}{2(-2)}-\frac{3}{2}$$

$$-\frac{5}{2}+\frac{1}{4} \overset{?}{=} \frac{3}{-4}-\frac{3}{2}$$

$$-\frac{10}{4}+\frac{1}{4} \overset{?}{=} -\frac{3}{4}-\frac{6}{4}$$

$$-\frac{9}{4}=-\frac{9}{4} \leftarrow \text{True}$$

Both solutions check, so the solution set is $\{-2\}$.

3. First, we find the domain of the variable, x.
$x^2+5x+4=(x+1)(x+4)$, so $x\neq-1, x\neq-4$ in the first term.
$x^2-3x-4=(x+1)(x-4)$, so $x\neq-1, x\neq4$ in the second term.
$x^2-16=(x+4)(x-4)$, so $x\neq-4, x\neq4$ in the third term.

$$\frac{3}{x^2+5x+4}+\frac{2}{x^2-3x-4}=\frac{4}{x^2-16}$$

$$\frac{3}{(x+1)(x+4)}+\frac{2}{(x+1)(x-4)}=\frac{4}{(x+4)(x-4)}$$

$$(x+1)(x+4)(x-4)\left(\frac{3}{(x+1)(x+4)}+\frac{2}{(x+1)(x-4)}\right)=$$

$$(x+1)(x+4)(x-4)\left(\frac{4}{(x+4)(x-4)}\right)$$

$$3(x-4)+2(x+4)=4(x+1)$$

$$3x-12+2x+8=4x+4$$

$$5x-4=4x+4$$

$$x-4=4$$

$$x=8$$

Check:

$$\frac{3}{8^2+5(8)+4}+\frac{2}{8^2-3(8)-4} \overset{?}{=} \frac{4}{8^2-16}$$

$$\frac{3}{108}+\frac{2}{36} \overset{?}{=} \frac{4}{48}$$

$$\frac{3}{108}+\frac{6}{108} \overset{?}{=} \frac{1}{12}$$

$$\frac{9}{108} \overset{?}{=} \frac{1}{12}$$

$$\frac{1}{12}=\frac{1}{12} \leftarrow \text{True}$$

The solution set is $\{8\}$.

4. First, we find the domain of the variable, z.
$z^2+2z-3=(z-1)(z+3)$, so $z\neq-3, z\neq1$ in the first term.
$z^2+z-2=(z-1)(z+2)$, so $z\neq-2, z\neq1$ in the second term.
$z^2+5z+6=(z+2)(z+3)$, so $z\neq-3, z\neq-2$ in the third term.

$$\frac{5}{z^2+2z-3}-\frac{3}{z^2+z-2}=\frac{1}{z^2+5z+6}$$

$$\frac{5}{(z-1)(z+3)}-\frac{3}{(z-1)(z+2)}=\frac{1}{(z+2)(z+3)}$$

$$(z-1)(z+2)(z+3)\left(\frac{5}{(z-1)(z+3)}-\frac{3}{(z-1)(z+2)}\right)=$$

$$(z-1)(z+2)(z+3)\left(\frac{1}{(z+2)(z+3)}\right)$$

$$5(z+2)-3(z+3)=z-1$$

$$5z+10-3z-9=z-1$$

$$2z+1=z-1$$

$$z+1=-1$$

$$z=-2$$

Notice that $z=-2$ is not in the domain of the variable z. Therefore, there is no solution to the equation, and the solution set is $\varnothing$ or $\{\ \}$.

5. First, we find the domain of the variable, z.

$z+4$, so $z \neq -4$ in the first term.

$z-3$, so $z \neq 3$ in the second term.

$z^2 + z - 12 = (z+4)(z-3)$, so $z \neq -4, z \neq 3$ in the third term.

$$\frac{z+1}{z+4} + \frac{z+1}{z-3} = \frac{z^2+z+16}{z^2+z-12}$$

$$\frac{z+1}{z+4} + \frac{z+1}{z-3} = \frac{z^2+z+16}{(z+4)(z-3)}$$

$$(z+4)(z-3)\left(\frac{z+1}{z+4} + \frac{z+1}{z-3}\right)$$

$$= (z+4)(z-3)\left(\frac{z^2+z+16}{(z+4)(z-3)}\right)$$

$$(z-3)(z+1) + (z+4)(z+1) = z^2 + z + 16$$

$$z^2 - 2z - 3 + z^2 + 5z + 4 = z^2 + z + 16$$

$$2z^2 + 3z + 1 = z^2 + z + 16$$

$$z^2 + 2z - 15 = 0$$

$$(z+5)(z-3) = 0$$

$$z+5 = 0 \quad \text{or} \quad z-3 = 0$$

$$z = -5 \quad \text{or} \quad z = 3$$

Since $z = 3$ is not in the domain of the variable, it is an extraneous solution.

Check $z = -5$:

$$\frac{-5+1}{-5+4} + \frac{-5+1}{-5-3} \overset{?}{=} \frac{(-5)^2 + (-5) + 16}{(-5)^2 + (-5) - 12}$$

$$\frac{-4}{-1} + \frac{-4}{-8} \overset{?}{=} \frac{25 + (-5) + 16}{25 + (-5) - 12}$$

$$4 + \frac{1}{2} \overset{?}{=} \frac{36}{8}$$

$$\frac{9}{2} = \frac{9}{2} \quad \leftarrow \text{True}$$

The solution checks, so the solution set is $\{-5\}$.

6.
$$f(x) = 1$$
$$2x - \frac{3}{x} = 1$$
$$x\left(2x - \frac{3}{x}\right) = x \cdot 1$$
$$2x^2 - 3 = x$$
$$2x^2 - x - 3 = 0$$
$$(2x-3)(x+1) = 0$$

$$2x - 3 = 0 \quad \text{or} \quad x + 1 = 0$$

$$x = \frac{3}{2} \quad \text{or} \quad x = -1$$

The solution set is $\left\{-1, \frac{3}{2}\right\}$. Thus, $f(-1) = 1$ and $f\left(\frac{3}{2}\right) = 1$, so the points $(-1, 1)$ and $\left(\frac{3}{2}, 1\right)$ are on the graph of f.

7.
$$C(t) = 4$$
$$\frac{50t}{t^2 + 6} = 4$$
$$(t^2 + 6)\left(\frac{50t}{t^2 + 6}\right) = (t^2 + 6) \cdot 4$$
$$50t = 4t^2 + 24$$
$$-4t^2 + 50t - 24 = 0$$
$$-2(2t - 1)(t - 12) = 0$$

$$2t - 1 = 0 \quad \text{or} \quad t - 12 = 0$$

$$t = \frac{1}{2} \quad \text{or} \quad t = 12$$

The concentration of the drug will be 4 milligrams per liter after $\frac{1}{2}$ hour and after 12 hours.

6.5 Quick Checks

1. $\dfrac{x-7}{x+3} \geq 0$

The rational expression will equal 0 when $x = 7$. It is undefined when $x = -3$. Thus, we separate the real number line into the intervals $(-\infty, -3)$, $(-3, 7)$, and $(7, \infty)$. Determine where the numerator and denominator are positive and negative and where the quotient is positive and negative.

Interval	$(-\infty, -3)$	-3	$(-3, 7)$	7	$(7, \infty)$
$x - 7$	Neg	Neg	Neg	0	Pos
$x + 3$	Neg	0	Pos	Pos	Pos
$\dfrac{x-7}{x+3}$	Pos	Undef	Neg	0	Pos

The rational function is undefined at $x = -3$, so -3 is not part of the solution. The inequality is non-strict, so 7 is part of the solution. Now, $\dfrac{x-7}{x+3}$ is greater than zero where the quotient is positive. The solution is $\{x \mid x < -3 \text{ or } x \geq 7\}$ in set-builder notation; the solution is $(-\infty, -3) \cup [7, \infty)$ in interval notation.

2.

$$\frac{4x+5}{x+2} < 3$$

$$\frac{4x+5}{x+2} - 3 < 0$$

$$\frac{4x+5}{x+2} - \frac{3(x+2)}{x+2} < 0$$

$$\frac{4x+5-3x-6}{x+2} < 0$$

$$\frac{x-1}{x+2} < 0$$

The rational expression will equal 0 when $x = 1$. It is undefined when $x = -2$. Thus, we separate the real number line into the intervals $(-\infty, -2)$, $(-2, 1)$, and $(1, \infty)$. Determine where the numerator and denominator are positive and negative and where the quotient is positive and negative.

Interval	$(-\infty, -2)$	-2	$(-2, 1)$	1	$(1, \infty)$
$x - 1$	Neg	Neg	Neg	0	Pos
$x + 2$	Neg	0	Pos	Pos	Pos
$\dfrac{x-1}{x+2}$	Pos	Undef	Neg	0	Pos

The rational function is undefined at $x = -2$, so -2 is not part of the solution. The inequality is strict, so 1 is not part of the solution. Now, $\dfrac{x-1}{x+2}$ is less than zero where the quotient is negative. The solution is $\{x \mid -2 < x < 1\}$ in set-builder notation; the solution is $(-2, 1)$ in interval notation.

6.6 Quick Checks

1. **a.**
$$Y = \frac{G}{1-b}$$
$$(1-b)Y = (1-b)\left(\frac{G}{1-b}\right)$$
$$Y - Yb = G$$
$$Y = G + Yb$$
$$Y - G = Yb$$
$$\frac{Y-G}{Y} = b \quad \text{or} \quad b = \frac{Y-G}{Y}$$

b. Substitute $G = \$100$ billion and $Y = \$1,000$ billion into $b = \dfrac{Y-G}{Y}$.

$$b = \frac{1,000 \text{ billion} - 100 \text{ billion}}{1000 \text{ billion}}$$
$$= \frac{900 \text{ billion}}{1000 \text{ billion}} = 0.9$$

2.
$$\frac{AB}{AC} = \frac{DE}{DF}$$
$$\frac{3x}{8} = \frac{6}{x}$$
$$8x\left(\frac{3x}{8}\right) = 8x\left(\frac{6}{x}\right)$$
$$3x^2 = 48$$
$$3x^2 - 48 = 0$$
$$3(x+4)(x-4) = 0$$
$$x + 4 = 0 \quad \text{or} \quad x - 4 = 0$$
$$x = -4 \quad \text{or} \quad x = 4$$

Since the length of DF cannot be negative, we discard $x = -4$ and keep $x = 4$. The length of AB is $3x = 3 \cdot 4 = 12$.

In summary, $AB = 12$ and $DF = 4$.

3. Let p represent the population of the United States in 2005.

$$\frac{20}{100,000} = \frac{59,850}{x}$$
$$100,000x\left(\frac{20}{100,000}\right) = 100,000x\left(\frac{59,850}{x}\right)$$
$$20x = 5,985,000,000$$
$$x = \frac{5,985,000,000}{20}$$
$$x = 299,250,000$$

In 2005, the population of the United States was 299,250,000 people.

4. Let t represent the time required to fill the pool using the two hoses together.

$$\begin{pmatrix}\text{Part done} \\ \text{by Juan and} \\ \text{Maria's hose} \\ \text{in 1 hour}\end{pmatrix} + \begin{pmatrix}\text{Part done by} \\ \text{the neighbor's} \\ \text{hose in 1 hour}\end{pmatrix} = \begin{pmatrix}\text{Part done} \\ \text{together} \\ \text{in 1 hour}\end{pmatrix}$$

$$\frac{1}{30} + \frac{1}{24} = \frac{1}{t}$$

$$120t\left(\frac{1}{30}+\frac{1}{24}\right) = 120t\left(\frac{1}{t}\right)$$

$$4t + 5t = 120$$

$$9t = 120$$

$$t = \frac{120}{9}$$

$$t = \frac{40}{3} = 13\frac{1}{3}$$

Using both hoses, it will take $\dfrac{40}{3}$ hours, or 13 hours and 20 minutes, to fill the pool.

5. Let t represent the time required to fill the pool.

$$\begin{pmatrix}\text{Portion of} \\ \text{pool filled in} \\ \text{1 minute by} \\ \text{the air pump}\end{pmatrix} - \begin{pmatrix}\text{Portion of} \\ \text{air released} \\ \text{from the pool} \\ \text{in 1 minute}\end{pmatrix} = \begin{pmatrix}\text{Portion of} \\ \text{pool filled in} \\ \text{1 minute with} \\ \text{valve open}\end{pmatrix}$$

$$\frac{1}{20} - \frac{1}{50} = \frac{1}{t}$$

$$100t\left(\frac{1}{20}-\frac{1}{50}\right) = 100t\left(\frac{1}{t}\right)$$

$$5t - 2t = 100$$

$$3t = 100$$

$$t = \frac{100}{3} \approx 33.3$$

To fill the pool with the valve open, it will take $\dfrac{100}{3} = 33\frac{1}{3}$ minutes or 33 minutes, 20 seconds.

6. Let x represent the speed of the canoe in still water.

	Distance (miles)	Rate (mph)	Time (hours)
Upstream	12	$x-2$	$\dfrac{12}{x-2}$
Downstream	12	$x+2$	$\dfrac{12}{x+2}$

Trip up + Trip down = 8

$$\frac{12}{x-2} + \frac{12}{x+2} = 8$$

$$(x-2)(x+2)\left(\frac{12}{x-2}+\frac{12}{x+2}\right) = (x-2)(x+2)\cdot 8$$

$$12(x+2) + 12(x-2) = 8\left(x^2-4\right)$$

$$12x + 24 + 12x - 24 = 8\left(x^2-4\right)$$

$$24x = 8\left(x^2-4\right)$$

$$3x = x^2 - 4$$

$$0 = x^2 - 3x - 4$$

$$0 = (x+1)(x-4)$$

$$x+1 = 0 \quad \text{or} \quad x-4 = 0$$

$$x = -1 \quad \text{or} \quad x = 4$$

We disregard -1 because the speed of the canoe must be positive. Thus, the speed of the canoe in still water is 4 miles per hour.

7. a. $V = \dfrac{k}{l}$

$$500 = \frac{k}{30}$$

$$k = 500(30) = 15,000$$

Thus, the function that relates the rate of vibration to the length of the string is

$$V(l) = \frac{15,000}{l}.$$

b. $V(50) = \dfrac{15,000}{50} = 300$

The rate of vibration is 300 oscillations per second.

8. Let K represent the kinetic energy, m represent the mass, and v represent the velocity. Then,

$$K = kmv^2$$

$$4455 = k \cdot 110 \cdot 9^2$$

$$4455 = 8910k$$

$$\frac{1}{2} = k$$

Thus, $K = \dfrac{1}{2}mv^2$.

For $m = 140$ and $v = 5$, $K = \dfrac{1}{2}(140)(5)^2 = 1750$.

The kinetic energy of a 140 kg lineman running at 5 meters per second is 1750 joules.

9. $R = \dfrac{kl}{d^2}$

$1.24 = \dfrac{k \cdot 432}{4^2}$

$1.24 = \dfrac{432k}{16}$

$1.24 = 27k$

$k = \dfrac{1.24}{27} \approx 0.0459$

Thus, $R = \dfrac{0.0459l}{d^2}$.

For $l = 282$ and $d = 3$, $R = \dfrac{0.0459(282)}{3^2} \approx 1.44$.

The resistance is approximately 1.44 ohms when the length of the wire is 282 feet and the diameter is 3 millimeters.

Getting Ready for Chapter 7 – Quick Checks

1. $\sqrt{81} = 9$ because $9^2 = 81$.

2. $\sqrt{900} = 30$ because $30^2 = 900$.

3. $\sqrt{\dfrac{1}{4}} = \dfrac{1}{2}$ because $\left(\dfrac{1}{2}\right)^2 = \dfrac{1}{4}$.

4. $\sqrt{0.16} = 0.4$ because $(0.4)^2 = 0.16$

5. $\left(\sqrt{13}\right)^2 = 13$ because $\left(\sqrt{c}\right)^2 = c$ if $c \geq 0$.

6. $5\sqrt{9} = 5\sqrt{3^2} = 5 \cdot 3 = 15$

7. $\sqrt{36 + 64} = \sqrt{100} = \sqrt{10^2} = 10$

8. $\sqrt{36} + \sqrt{64} = \sqrt{6^2} + \sqrt{8^2} = 6 + 8 = 14$

9. $\sqrt{25 - 4 \cdot 3 \cdot (-2)} = \sqrt{25 + 24} = \sqrt{49} = \sqrt{7^2} = 7$

10. $\sqrt{400}$ is rational because $20^2 = 400$. Thus, $\sqrt{400} = 20$.

11. $\sqrt{40}$ is irrational because 40 is not a perfect square. There is no rational number whose square is 40. Using a calculator, we find $\sqrt{40} \approx 6.32$.

12. $\sqrt{-25}$ is not a real number. There is no real number whose square is -25.

13. $-\sqrt{196}$ is a rational number because $14^2 = 196$. Thus, $-\sqrt{196} = -14$.

14. $\sqrt{(-14)^2} = |-14| = 14$

15. $\sqrt{z^2} = |z|$

16. $\sqrt{(2x+3)^2} = |2x+3|$

17. $\sqrt{p^2 - 12p + 36} = \sqrt{(p-6)^2} = |p-6|$

Chapter 7 – Quick Checks

7.1 Quick Checks

1. $\sqrt[3]{125} = 5$ since $5^3 = 125$.

2. $\sqrt[4]{81} = 3$ since $3^4 = 81$.

3. $\sqrt[3]{-216} = -6$ since $(-6)^3 = -216$.

4. $\sqrt[4]{-32}$ is not a real number.

5. $\sqrt[5]{\dfrac{1}{32}} = \dfrac{1}{2}$ since $\left(\dfrac{1}{2}\right)^5 = \dfrac{1}{32}$.

6. $\sqrt[3]{50} \approx 3.68$

```
³√(50)
        3.684031499
```

7. $\sqrt[4]{80} \approx 2.99$

```
4×√(80)
        2.990697562
```

8. $\sqrt[5]{40} \approx 2.09$

```
5×√(40)
        2.091279105
```

9. Because the index is even, we have
$\sqrt[4]{5^4} = |5| = 5$.

10. Because the index is even, we have $\sqrt[6]{z^6} = |z|$.

11. Because the index is odd, we have
$\sqrt[7]{(3x-2)^7} = 3x - 2$.

12. Because the index is even, we have
$\sqrt[8]{(-2)^8} = |-2| = 2$.

13. Because the index is odd, we have
$\sqrt[5]{\dfrac{-32}{243}} = \sqrt[5]{\left(\dfrac{-2}{3}\right)^5} = -\dfrac{2}{3}$.

14. $25^{1/2} = \sqrt{25} = \sqrt{5^2} = 5$

15. $(-27)^{1/3} = \sqrt[3]{-27} = \sqrt[3]{(-3)^3} = -3$

16. $-64^{1/2} = -\sqrt{64} = -\sqrt{8^2} = -8$

17. $(-64)^{1/2} = \sqrt{-64}$ is not a real number.

18. $b^{1/2} = \sqrt{b}$

19. $\sqrt[5]{8b} = (8b)^{1/5}$

20. $\sqrt[8]{\dfrac{mn^5}{3}} = \left(\dfrac{mn^5}{3}\right)^{1/8}$

21. $16^{3/2} = \left(\sqrt{16}\right)^3 = 4^3 = 64$

22. $27^{2/3} = \left(\sqrt[3]{27}\right)^2 = 3^2 = 9$

23. $-16^{3/4} = -\left(\sqrt[4]{16}\right)^3 = -2^3 = -8$

24. $(-64)^{2/3} = \left(\sqrt[3]{-64}\right)^2 = (-4)^2 = 16$

25. $(-25)^{5/2} = \left(\sqrt{-25}\right)^5$ is not a real number.

26. $50^{2/3} \approx 13.57$

```
50^(2/3)
        13.57208808
```

27. $40^{0.15} \approx 1.74$

```
40^0.15
        1.739037707
```

28. $\sqrt[8]{a^3} = \left(a^3\right)^{1/8} = a^{3/8}$

29. $\left(\sqrt[4]{12ab^3}\right)^9 = \left(\left(12ab^3\right)^{1/4}\right)^9 = \left(12ab^3\right)^{9/4}$

30. $81^{-1/2} = \dfrac{1}{81^{1/2}} = \dfrac{1}{\sqrt{81}} = \dfrac{1}{9}$

31. $\dfrac{1}{8^{-2/3}} = 8^{2/3} = \left(\sqrt[3]{8}\right)^2 = 2^2 = 4$

32. $\left(13x\right)^{-3/2} = \dfrac{1}{\left(13x\right)^{3/2}}$

7.2 Quick Checks

1. $5^{3/4} \cdot 5^{1/6} = 5^{\frac{3}{4}+\frac{1}{6}} = 5^{\frac{9}{12}+\frac{2}{12}} = 5^{\frac{11}{12}}$

2. $\dfrac{32^{6/5}}{32^{3/5}} = 32^{\frac{6}{5}-\frac{3}{5}} = 32^{3/5} = \left(\sqrt[5]{32}\right)^3 = 2^3 = 8$

3. $\left(100^{3/8}\right)^{4/3} = 100^{\frac{3}{8}\cdot\frac{4}{3}} = 100^{1/2} = \sqrt{100} = 10$

4. $\left(a^{3/2} \cdot b^{5/4}\right)^{2/3} = a^{\frac{3}{2}\cdot\frac{2}{3}} \cdot b^{\frac{5}{4}\cdot\frac{2}{3}} = ab^{5/6}$

5. $\left(8x^{3/4}y^{-1}\right)^{2/3} = 8^{2/3}\left(x^{3/4}\right)^{2/3}\left(y^{-1}\right)^{2/3}$

$= 4x^{\frac{3}{4}\cdot\frac{2}{3}}y^{-1\cdot\frac{2}{3}}$

$= 4x^{1/2}y^{-2/3}$

$= \dfrac{4x^{1/2}}{y^{2/3}}$

6. $\left(\dfrac{25x^{1/2}y^{3/4}}{x^{-3/4}y}\right)^{1/2} = \left(25x^{\frac{1}{2}-\left(-\frac{3}{4}\right)}y^{\frac{3}{4}-1}\right)^{1/2}$

$= \left(25x^{5/4}y^{-1/4}\right)^{1/2}$

$= 25^{1/2}\left(x^{5/4}\right)^{1/2}\left(y^{-1/4}\right)^{1/2}$

$= 5x^{\frac{5}{4}\cdot\frac{1}{2}}y^{-\frac{1}{4}\cdot\frac{1}{2}}$

$= 5x^{5/8}y^{-1/8}$

$= \dfrac{5x^{5/8}}{y^{1/8}}$

7. $8\left(125a^{3/4}b^{-1}\right)^{2/3} = 8\cdot 125^{2/3}\left(a^{3/4}\right)^{2/3}\left(b^{-1}\right)^{2/3}$

$= 8\cdot 25a^{\frac{3}{4}\cdot\frac{2}{3}}b^{-1\cdot\frac{2}{3}}$

$= 200a^{1/2}b^{-2/3}$

$= \dfrac{200a^{1/2}}{b^{2/3}}$

8. $\sqrt[10]{36^5} = \left(36^5\right)^{1/10} = 36^{5\cdot\frac{1}{10}} = 36^{1/2} = \sqrt{36} = 6$

9. $\sqrt[4]{16a^8b^{12}} = \left(16a^8b^{12}\right)^{1/4}$

$= 16^{1/4}\left(a^8\right)^{1/4}\left(b^{12}\right)^{1/4}$

$= 2a^{8\cdot\frac{1}{4}}b^{12\cdot\frac{1}{4}}$

$= 2a^2b^3$

10. $\dfrac{\sqrt[3]{x^2}}{\sqrt[4]{x}} = \dfrac{x^{2/3}}{x^{1/4}} = x^{\frac{2}{3}-\frac{1}{4}} = x^{5/12} = \sqrt[12]{x^5}$

11. $\sqrt[4]{\sqrt[3]{a^2}} = \sqrt[4]{a^{2/3}} = \left(a^{2/3}\right)^{1/4} = a^{\frac{2}{3}\cdot\frac{1}{4}} = a^{1/6} = \sqrt[6]{a}$

12. $8x^{3/2} + 3x^{1/2}\left(4x+3\right) = 8x^{\frac{2}{2}+\frac{1}{2}} + 3x^{1/2}\left(4x+3\right)$

$= 8x\cdot x^{1/2} + 3x^{1/2}\left(4x+3\right)$

$= x^{1/2}\left(8x + 3\left(4x+3\right)\right)$

$= x^{1/2}\left(8x+12x+9\right)$

$= x^{1/2}\left(20x+9\right)$

13. $9x^{1/3} + x^{-2/3}\left(3x+1\right) = 9x^{\frac{3}{3}-\frac{2}{3}} + x^{-2/3}\left(3x+1\right)$

$= 9x\cdot x^{-2/3} + x^{-2/3}\left(3x+1\right)$

$= x^{-2/3}\left(9x + \left(3x+1\right)\right)$

$= x^{-2/3}\left(12x+1\right)$

$= \dfrac{12x+1}{x^{2/3}}$

7.3 Quick Checks

1. $\sqrt{11} \cdot \sqrt{7} = \sqrt{11 \cdot 7} = \sqrt{77}$

2. $\sqrt[4]{6} \cdot \sqrt[4]{7} = \sqrt[4]{6 \cdot 7} = \sqrt[4]{42}$

3. $\sqrt{x-5} \cdot \sqrt{x+5} = \sqrt{(x-5)(x+5)} = \sqrt{x^2 - 25}$

4. $\sqrt[7]{5p} \cdot \sqrt[7]{4p^3} = \sqrt[7]{5p \cdot 4p^3} = \sqrt[7]{20p^4}$

5. $\sqrt{48} = \sqrt{16 \cdot 3} = \sqrt{16} \cdot \sqrt{3} = 4\sqrt{3}$

6. $4\sqrt[3]{54} = 4\sqrt[3]{27 \cdot 2} = 4\sqrt[3]{27} \cdot \sqrt[3]{2} = 4 \cdot 3\sqrt[3]{2} = 12\sqrt[3]{2}$

7. $\sqrt{200a^2} = \sqrt{200} \cdot \sqrt{a^2}$
$= \sqrt{100 \cdot 2} \cdot \sqrt{a^2}$
$= \sqrt{100} \cdot \sqrt{2} \cdot \sqrt{a^2}$
$= 10\sqrt{2}\,|a| \quad \text{or} \quad 10|a|\sqrt{2}$

8. $\sqrt[4]{40}$ cannot be simplified further.

9. $\dfrac{6+\sqrt{45}}{3} = \dfrac{6+\sqrt{9 \cdot 5}}{3} = \dfrac{6+\sqrt{9} \cdot \sqrt{5}}{3}$
$= \dfrac{6+3\sqrt{5}}{3} = \dfrac{3(2+\sqrt{5})}{3}$
$= 2+\sqrt{5}$

10. $\dfrac{-2+\sqrt{32}}{4} = \dfrac{-2+\sqrt{16 \cdot 2}}{4} = \dfrac{-2+\sqrt{16} \cdot \sqrt{2}}{4}$
$= \dfrac{-2+4\sqrt{2}}{4} = \dfrac{2(-1+2\sqrt{2})}{4}$
$= \dfrac{-1+2\sqrt{2}}{2}$

11. $\sqrt{75a^6} = \sqrt{25 \cdot 3 \cdot a^6}$
$= \sqrt{25} \cdot \sqrt{3} \cdot \sqrt{a^6}$
$= \sqrt{25} \cdot \sqrt{3} \cdot \sqrt{(a^3)^2}$
$= 5\sqrt{3} \cdot a^3$
$= 5a^3\sqrt{3}$

12. $\sqrt{18a^5} = \sqrt{9 \cdot 2 \cdot a^4 \cdot a}$
$= \sqrt{9} \cdot \sqrt{2} \cdot \sqrt{a^4} \cdot \sqrt{a}$
$= \sqrt{9} \cdot \sqrt{2} \cdot \sqrt{(a^2)^2} \cdot \sqrt{a}$
$= 3\sqrt{2} \cdot a^2\sqrt{a}$
$= 3a^2\sqrt{2a}$

13. $\sqrt[3]{128x^6 y^{10}} = \sqrt[3]{64 \cdot 2 \cdot x^6 \cdot y^9 \cdot y}$
$= \sqrt[3]{64} \cdot \sqrt[3]{2} \cdot \sqrt[3]{x^6} \cdot \sqrt[3]{y^9} \cdot \sqrt[3]{y}$
$= \sqrt[3]{64} \cdot \sqrt[3]{2} \cdot \sqrt[3]{(x^2)^3} \cdot \sqrt[3]{(y^3)^3} \cdot \sqrt[3]{y}$
$= 4x^2 y^3 \sqrt[3]{2y}$

14. $\sqrt[4]{16a^5 b^{11}} = \sqrt[4]{16 \cdot a^4 \cdot a \cdot b^8 \cdot b^3}$
$= \sqrt[4]{16} \cdot \sqrt[4]{a^4} \cdot \sqrt[4]{a} \cdot \sqrt[4]{b^8} \cdot \sqrt[4]{b^3}$
$= \sqrt[4]{16} \cdot \sqrt[4]{a^4} \cdot \sqrt[4]{a} \cdot \sqrt[4]{(b^2)^4} \cdot \sqrt[4]{b^3}$
$= 2ab^2 \sqrt[4]{ab^3}$

15. $\sqrt{6} \cdot \sqrt{8} = \sqrt{6 \cdot 8}$
$= \sqrt{48}$
$= \sqrt{16 \cdot 3}$
$= \sqrt{16} \cdot \sqrt{3}$
$= 4\sqrt{3}$

16. $\sqrt[3]{12a^2} \cdot \sqrt[3]{10a^4} = \sqrt[3]{12a^2 \cdot 10a^4}$
$= \sqrt[3]{120a^6}$
$= \sqrt[3]{8 \cdot 15 \cdot a^6}$
$= \sqrt[3]{8} \cdot \sqrt[3]{a^6} \cdot \sqrt[3]{15}$
$= 2a^2 \sqrt[3]{15}$

17. $4\sqrt[3]{8a^2 b^5} \cdot \sqrt[3]{6a^2 b^4} = 4\sqrt[3]{8a^2 b^5 \cdot 6a^2 b^4}$
$= 4\sqrt[3]{48a^4 b^9}$
$= 4\sqrt[3]{8 \cdot 6 \cdot a^3 \cdot a \cdot b^9}$
$= 4\sqrt[3]{8} \cdot \sqrt[3]{6} \cdot \sqrt[3]{a^3} \cdot \sqrt[3]{a} \cdot \sqrt[3]{b^9}$
$= 4 \cdot 2ab^3 \cdot \sqrt[3]{6a}$
$= 8ab^3 \sqrt[3]{6a}$

18. $\sqrt{\dfrac{13}{49}} = \dfrac{\sqrt{13}}{\sqrt{49}} = \dfrac{\sqrt{13}}{7}$

19. $\sqrt[3]{\dfrac{27p^3}{8}} = \dfrac{\sqrt[3]{27p^3}}{\sqrt[3]{8}} = \dfrac{3p}{2}$

20. $\sqrt[4]{\dfrac{3q^4}{16}} = \dfrac{\sqrt[4]{3q^4}}{\sqrt[4]{16}} = \dfrac{q\sqrt[4]{3}}{2}$

21. $\dfrac{\sqrt{12a^5}}{\sqrt{3a}} = \sqrt{\dfrac{12a^5}{3a}} = \sqrt{4a^4} = 2a^2$

22. $\dfrac{\sqrt[3]{-24x^2}}{\sqrt[3]{3x^{-1}}} = \sqrt[3]{\dfrac{-24x^2}{3x^{-1}}} = \sqrt[3]{-8x^3} = -2x$

23. $\dfrac{\sqrt[3]{250a^5b^{-2}}}{\sqrt[3]{2ab}} = \sqrt[3]{\dfrac{250a^5b^{-2}}{2ab}}$

$\qquad = \sqrt[3]{125a^4b^{-3}}$

$\qquad = \sqrt[3]{\dfrac{125a^4}{b^3}}$

$\qquad = \dfrac{5a\sqrt[3]{a}}{b}$

24. $\sqrt[4]{5} \cdot \sqrt[3]{3} = 5^{1/4} \cdot 3^{1/3}$

$\qquad = 5^{3/12} \cdot 3^{4/12}$

$\qquad = \left(5^3\right)^{1/12} \cdot \left(3^4\right)^{1/12}$

$\qquad = \left[\left(5^3\right)\left(3^4\right)\right]^{1/12}$

$\qquad = \left(10{,}125\right)^{1/12}$

$\qquad = \sqrt[12]{10{,}125}$

25. $\sqrt{10} \cdot \sqrt[3]{12} = 10^{1/2} \cdot 12^{1/3}$

$\qquad = 10^{3/6} \cdot 12^{2/6}$

$\qquad = \left(10^3\right)^{1/6} \cdot \left(12^2\right)^{1/6}$

$\qquad = \left[\left(10^3\right)\left(12^2\right)\right]^{1/6}$

$\qquad = \left(2^3 \cdot 5^3 \cdot 4^2 \cdot 3^2\right)^{1/6}$

$\qquad = \left(2^3 \cdot 5^3 \cdot 2^4 \cdot 3^2\right)^{1/6}$

$\qquad = \left(2^7 \cdot 5^3 \cdot 3^2\right)^{1/6}$

$\qquad = 2\left(2 \cdot 5^3 \cdot 3^2\right)^{1/6}$

$\qquad = 2\left(2250\right)^{1/6}$

$\qquad = 2\sqrt[6]{2250}$

7.4 Quick Checks

1. $9\sqrt{13y} + 4\sqrt{13y} = (9+4)\sqrt{13y} = 13\sqrt{13y}$

2. $\sqrt[4]{5} + 9\sqrt[4]{5} - 3\sqrt[4]{5} = (1+9-3)\sqrt[4]{5} = 7\sqrt[4]{5}$

3. $4\sqrt{18} - 3\sqrt{8} = 4 \cdot \sqrt{9} \cdot \sqrt{2} - 3 \cdot \sqrt{4} \cdot \sqrt{2}$

$\qquad = 4 \cdot 3\sqrt{2} - 3 \cdot 2\sqrt{2}$

$\qquad = 12\sqrt{2} - 6\sqrt{2}$

$\qquad = (12-6)\sqrt{2}$

$\qquad = 6\sqrt{2}$

4. $-5x\sqrt[3]{54x} + 7\sqrt[3]{2x^4}$

$\qquad = -5x \cdot \sqrt[3]{27} \cdot \sqrt[3]{2x} + 7 \cdot \sqrt[3]{x^3} \cdot \sqrt[3]{2x}$

$\qquad = -5x \cdot 3\sqrt[3]{2x} + 7x \cdot \sqrt[3]{2x}$

$\qquad = -15x\sqrt[3]{2x} + 7x\sqrt[3]{2x}$

$\qquad = (-15+7)x\sqrt[3]{2x}$

$\qquad = -8x\sqrt[3]{2x}$

5. $7\sqrt{10} - 6\sqrt{3}$ cannot be simplified further.

6. $\sqrt[3]{8z^4} - 2z\sqrt[3]{-27z} + \sqrt[3]{125z}$

$= \sqrt[3]{8z^3} \cdot \sqrt[3]{z} - 2z \cdot \sqrt[3]{-27} \cdot \sqrt[3]{z} + \sqrt[3]{125} \cdot \sqrt[3]{z}$

$= 2z\sqrt[3]{z} + -2z(-3)\sqrt[3]{z} + 5\sqrt[3]{z}$

$= 2z\sqrt[3]{z} + 6z\sqrt[3]{z} + 5\sqrt[3]{z}$

$= (2z + 6z + 5)\sqrt[3]{z}$

$= (8z + 5)\sqrt[3]{z}$

7. $\sqrt{25m} - 3\sqrt[4]{m^2} = \sqrt{25m} - 3m^{2/4}$

$= \sqrt{25m} - 3m^{1/2}$

$= \sqrt{25m} - 3\sqrt{m}$

$= \sqrt{25} \cdot \sqrt{m} - 3\sqrt{m}$

$= 5\sqrt{m} - 3\sqrt{m}$

$= (5 - 3)\sqrt{m}$

$= 2\sqrt{m}$

8. $\sqrt{6}(3 - 5\sqrt{6}) = \sqrt{6} \cdot 3 - 5\sqrt{6} \cdot \sqrt{6}$

$= 3\sqrt{6} - 5\sqrt{36}$

$= 3\sqrt{6} - 5 \cdot 6$

$= 3\sqrt{6} - 30$

$= 3(\sqrt{6} - 10)$

9. $\sqrt[3]{12}(3 - \sqrt[3]{2}) = \sqrt[3]{12} \cdot 3 - \sqrt[3]{12} \cdot \sqrt[3]{2}$

$= 3\sqrt[3]{12} - \sqrt[3]{24}$

$= 3\sqrt[3]{12} - 2\sqrt[3]{3}$

10. $(2 - 7\sqrt{3})(5 + 4\sqrt{3})$

$= 2 \cdot 5 + 2 \cdot 4\sqrt{3} - 7\sqrt{3} \cdot 5 - 7\sqrt{3} \cdot 4\sqrt{3}$

$= 10 + 8\sqrt{3} - 35\sqrt{3} - 28\sqrt{9}$

$= 10 - 27\sqrt{3} - 28 \cdot 3$

$= 10 - 27\sqrt{3} - 84$

$= -74 - 27\sqrt{3}$

11. $\left(5\sqrt{2} + \sqrt{3}\right)^2 = \left(5\sqrt{2} + \sqrt{3}\right)\left(5\sqrt{2} + \sqrt{3}\right)$

$= \left(5\sqrt{2}\right)^2 + 2\left(5\sqrt{2}\right)\left(\sqrt{3}\right) + \left(\sqrt{3}\right)^2$

$= 25\sqrt{4} + 10\sqrt{6} + \sqrt{9}$

$= 25 \cdot 2 + 10\sqrt{6} + 3$

$= 50 + 10\sqrt{6} + 3$

$= 53 + 10\sqrt{6}$

12. $\left(\sqrt{7} - 3\sqrt{2}\right)^2 = \left(\sqrt{7} - 3\sqrt{2}\right)\left(\sqrt{7} - 3\sqrt{2}\right)$

$= \left(\sqrt{7}\right)^2 - 2\left(\sqrt{7}\right)\left(3\sqrt{2}\right) + \left(3\sqrt{2}\right)^2$

$= \sqrt{49} - 6\sqrt{14} + 9\sqrt{4}$

$= 7 - 6\sqrt{14} + 9 \cdot 2$

$= 7 - 6\sqrt{14} + 18$

$= 25 - 6\sqrt{14}$

13. $\left(\sqrt{3} + \sqrt{2}\right)\left(\sqrt{3} - \sqrt{2}\right) = \left(\sqrt{3}\right)^2 - \left(\sqrt{2}\right)^2$

$= \sqrt{9} - \sqrt{4}$

$= 3 - 2$

$= 1$

7.5 Quick Checks

1. $\dfrac{1}{\sqrt{3}} = \dfrac{1}{\sqrt{3}} \cdot \dfrac{\sqrt{3}}{\sqrt{3}} = \dfrac{\sqrt{3}}{\sqrt{9}} = \dfrac{\sqrt{3}}{3}$

2. $\dfrac{\sqrt{5}}{\sqrt{8}} = \dfrac{\sqrt{5}}{2\sqrt{2}} = \dfrac{\sqrt{5}}{2\sqrt{2}} \cdot \dfrac{\sqrt{2}}{\sqrt{2}} = \dfrac{\sqrt{10}}{2\sqrt{4}} = \dfrac{\sqrt{10}}{2 \cdot 2} = \dfrac{\sqrt{10}}{4}$

3. $\dfrac{5}{\sqrt{10x}} = \dfrac{5}{\sqrt{10x}} \cdot \dfrac{\sqrt{10x}}{\sqrt{10x}}$

$= \dfrac{5\sqrt{10x}}{\sqrt{100x^2}}$

$= \dfrac{5\sqrt{10x}}{10x}$

$= \dfrac{\sqrt{10x}}{2x}$

4. $\dfrac{4}{\sqrt[3]{3}} = \dfrac{4}{\sqrt[3]{3}} \cdot \dfrac{\sqrt[3]{3^2}}{\sqrt[3]{3^2}} = \dfrac{4\sqrt[3]{9}}{\sqrt[3]{27}} = \dfrac{4\sqrt[3]{9}}{3}$

5. $\sqrt[3]{\dfrac{3}{20}} = \dfrac{\sqrt[3]{3}}{\sqrt[3]{20}} = \dfrac{\sqrt[3]{3}}{\sqrt[3]{2^2 \cdot 5}} \cdot \dfrac{\sqrt[3]{2 \cdot 5^2}}{\sqrt[3]{2 \cdot 5^2}}$

$= \dfrac{\sqrt[3]{150}}{\sqrt[3]{1000}}$

$= \dfrac{\sqrt[3]{150}}{10}$

6. $\dfrac{3}{\sqrt[4]{p}} = \dfrac{3}{\sqrt[4]{p}} \cdot \dfrac{\sqrt[4]{p^3}}{\sqrt[4]{p^3}} = \dfrac{3\sqrt[4]{p^3}}{p}$

7. $\dfrac{4}{\sqrt{3}+1} = \dfrac{4}{\sqrt{3}+1} \cdot \dfrac{\sqrt{3}-1}{\sqrt{3}-1}$

$= \dfrac{4(\sqrt{3}-1)}{(\sqrt{3}+1)(\sqrt{3}-1)}$

$= \dfrac{4(\sqrt{3}-1)}{(\sqrt{3})^2 - 1^2}$

$= \dfrac{4(\sqrt{3}-1)}{3-1}$

$= \dfrac{4(\sqrt{3}-1)}{2}$

$= 2(\sqrt{3}-1)$

8. $\dfrac{\sqrt{2}}{\sqrt{6}-\sqrt{2}} = \dfrac{\sqrt{2}}{\sqrt{6}-\sqrt{2}} \cdot \dfrac{\sqrt{6}+\sqrt{2}}{\sqrt{6}+\sqrt{2}}$

$= \dfrac{\sqrt{2}(\sqrt{6}+\sqrt{2})}{(\sqrt{6}-\sqrt{2})(\sqrt{6}+\sqrt{2})}$

$= \dfrac{\sqrt{2}(\sqrt{6}+\sqrt{2})}{(\sqrt{6})^2 - (\sqrt{2})^2}$

$= \dfrac{\sqrt{12}+\sqrt{4}}{6-2}$

$= \dfrac{2\sqrt{3}+2}{4}$

$= \dfrac{2(\sqrt{3}+1)}{4}$

$= \dfrac{\sqrt{3}+1}{2}$

9. $\dfrac{\sqrt{5}+4}{\sqrt{5}-\sqrt{2}} = \dfrac{\sqrt{5}+4}{\sqrt{5}-\sqrt{2}} \cdot \dfrac{\sqrt{5}+\sqrt{2}}{\sqrt{5}+\sqrt{2}}$

$= \dfrac{(\sqrt{5}+4)(\sqrt{5}+\sqrt{2})}{(\sqrt{5}-\sqrt{2})(\sqrt{5}+\sqrt{2})}$

$= \dfrac{\sqrt{25}+\sqrt{10}+4\sqrt{5}+4\sqrt{2}}{(\sqrt{5})^2 - (\sqrt{2})^2}$

$= \dfrac{5+\sqrt{10}+4\sqrt{5}+4\sqrt{2}}{5-2}$

$= \dfrac{5+\sqrt{10}+4\sqrt{5}+4\sqrt{2}}{3}$

7.6 Quick Checks

1. $f(x) = \sqrt{3x+7}$

   a. $f(3) = \sqrt{3(3)+7} = \sqrt{9+7} = \sqrt{16} = 4$

   b. $f(7) = \sqrt{3(7)+7} = \sqrt{21+7} = \sqrt{28} = 2\sqrt{7}$

2. $g(x) = \sqrt[3]{2x+7}$

   a. $g(-4) = \sqrt[3]{2(-4)+7} = \sqrt[3]{-8+7} = \sqrt[3]{-1} = -1$

   b. $g(10) = \sqrt[3]{2(10)+7} = \sqrt[3]{20+7} = \sqrt[3]{27} = 3$

3. $H(x) = \sqrt{x+6}$

   The function tells us to take the square root of $x+6$. We can only take the square root of numbers that are greater than or equal to 0. Thus, we need
   $x+6 \geq 0$
   $\quad x \geq -6$
   The domain of H is $\{x \mid x \geq -6\}$ or the interval $[-6, \infty)$.

4. $g(t) = \sqrt[5]{3t-1}$

   The function tells us to take the fifth root of $3t-1$. Since we can take the fifth root of any real number, the domain of g is all real numbers $\{t \mid t \text{ is any real number}\}$ or the interval $(-\infty, \infty)$.

5. $F(m) = \sqrt[4]{6-3m}$

The function tells us to take the fourth root of $6-3m$. We can only take the fourth root of numbers that are greater than or equal to 0. Thus, we need

$6-3m \geq 0$

$-3m \geq -6$

$m \leq 2$

The domain of F is $\{m \mid m \leq 2\}$ or the interval $(-\infty, 2]$.

6. $f(x) = \sqrt{x+3}$

a. The function tells us to take the square root of $x+3$. We can only take the square root of numbers that are greater than or equal to 0. Thus, we need

$x+3 \geq 0$

$x \geq -3$

The domain of f is $\{x \mid x \geq -3\}$ or the interval $[-3, \infty)$.

b.

x	$f(x) = \sqrt{x+3}$	(x, y)
-3	$f(-3)\sqrt{-3+3} = 0$	$(-3, 0)$
-2	$f(-2) = \sqrt{-2+3} = 1$	$(-2, 1)$
1	$f(1) = \sqrt{1+3} = 2$	$(1, 2)$
6	$f(6) = \sqrt{6+3} = 3$	$(6, 3)$

c. Based on the graph, the range is $\{y \mid y \geq 0\}$ or the interval $[0, \infty)$.

7. $G(x) = \sqrt[3]{x} - 1$

a. The function tells us to take the cube root of x and then subtract 1. We can take the cube root of any real number so the domain is all real numbers, $\{x \mid x$ is any real number$\}$ or the interval $(-\infty, \infty)$.

b.

x	$G(x) = \sqrt[3]{x} - 1$	(x, y)
-8	$G(-8) = \sqrt[3]{-8} - 1 = -3$	$(-8, -3)$
-1	$G(-1) = \sqrt[3]{-1} - 1 = -2$	$(-1, -2)$
0	$G(0) = \sqrt[3]{0} - 1 = -1$	$(0, -1)$
1	$G(1) = \sqrt[3]{1} - 1 = 0$	$(1, 0)$
8	$G(8) = \sqrt[3]{8} - 1 = 1$	$(8, 1)$

c. Based on the graph, the range is all real numbers, $\{y \mid y$ is any real number$\}$ or the interval $(-\infty, \infty)$.

7.7 Quick Checks

1. $\sqrt{3x+1} - 4 = 0$

$\sqrt{3x+1} = 4$

$\left(\sqrt{3x+1}\right)^2 = 4^2$

$3x+1 = 16$

$3x+1-1 = 16-1$

$3x = 15$

$\dfrac{3x}{3} = \dfrac{15}{3}$

$x = 5$

Check:

$\sqrt{3(5)+1} \overset{?}{=} 4$

$\sqrt{15+1} \overset{?}{=} 4$

$\sqrt{16} \overset{?}{=} 4$

$4 = 4 \checkmark$

The solution set is $\{5\}$.

QC – 93

2.
$$\sqrt{6x+4} - 5 = 3$$
$$\sqrt{6x+4} - 5 + 5 = 3 + 5$$
$$\sqrt{6x+4} = 8$$
$$\left(\sqrt{6x+4}\right)^2 = 8^2$$
$$6x + 4 = 64$$
$$6x + 4 - 4 = 64 - 4$$
$$6x = 60$$
$$\frac{6x}{6} = \frac{60}{6}$$
$$x = 10$$

Check:
$$\sqrt{6(10)+4} - 5 \overset{?}{=} 3$$
$$\sqrt{64} - 5 \overset{?}{=} 3$$
$$8 - 5 \overset{?}{=} 3$$
$$3 = 3 \checkmark$$
The solution set is $\{10\}$.

3.
$$\sqrt{2x+3} + 8 = 6$$
$$\sqrt{2x+3} + 8 - 8 = 6 - 8$$
$$\sqrt{2x+3} = -2$$
$$\left(\sqrt{2x+3}\right)^2 = (-2)^2$$
$$2x + 3 = 4$$
$$2x + 3 - 3 = 4 - 3$$
$$2x = 1$$
$$\frac{2x}{2} = \frac{1}{2}$$
$$x = \frac{1}{2}$$

Check:
$$\sqrt{2\left(\frac{1}{2}\right)+3} + 8 \overset{?}{=} 6$$
$$\sqrt{4} + 8 \overset{?}{=} 6$$
$$2 + 8 \overset{?}{=} 6$$
$$10 \neq 6$$
The solution does not check. Since there are no other possible solutions, the equation has no real solution.

4.
$$\sqrt{2x+1} = x - 1$$
$$\left(\sqrt{2x+1}\right)^2 = (x-1)^2$$
$$2x + 1 = x^2 - 2x + 1$$
$$x^2 - 4x = 0$$
$$x(x-4) = 0$$
$$x = 0 \quad \text{or} \quad x - 4 = 0$$
$$x = 4$$

Check:
$$\sqrt{2(0)+1} \overset{?}{=} 0 - 1 \qquad \sqrt{2(4)+1} \overset{?}{=} 4 - 1$$
$$\sqrt{1} \overset{?}{=} -1 \qquad\qquad \sqrt{9} \overset{?}{=} 3$$
$$1 \neq -1 \qquad\qquad\quad 3 = 3 \checkmark$$
The solution set is $\{4\}$.

5.
$$\sqrt[3]{6x+3} - 4 = -1$$
$$\sqrt[3]{6x+3} - 4 + 4 = -1 + 4$$
$$\sqrt[3]{6x+3} = 3$$
$$\left(\sqrt[3]{6x+3}\right)^3 = 3^3$$
$$6x + 3 = 27$$
$$6x + 3 - 3 = 27 - 3$$
$$6x = 24$$
$$\frac{6x}{6} = \frac{24}{6}$$
$$x = 4$$

Check:
$$\sqrt[3]{6(4)+3} - 4 \overset{?}{=} -1$$
$$\sqrt[3]{27} - 4 \overset{?}{=} -1$$
$$3 - 4 \overset{?}{=} -1$$
$$-1 = -1 \checkmark$$
The solution set is $\{4\}$.

6. $(2x-3)^{1/3} - 7 = -4$

$(2x-3)^{1/3} - 7 + 7 = -4 + 7$

$(2x-3)^{1/3} = 3$

$\left[(2x-3)^{1/3}\right]^3 = 3^3$

$2x - 3 = 27$

$2x - 3 + 3 = 27 + 3$

$2x = 30$

$\dfrac{2x}{2} = \dfrac{30}{2}$

$x = 15$

Check:

$(2(15)-3)^{1/3} - 7 \overset{?}{=} -4$

$(27)^{1/3} - 7 \overset{?}{=} -4$

$3 - 7 \overset{?}{=} -4$

$-4 = -4 \ \checkmark$

The solution set is $\{15\}$.

7. $\sqrt[3]{m^2 + 4m + 4} = \sqrt[3]{2m+7}$

$\left(\sqrt[3]{m^2 + 4m + 4}\right)^3 = \left(\sqrt[3]{2m+7}\right)^3$

$m^2 + 4m + 4 = 2m + 7$

$m^2 + 4m + 4 - 2m - 7 = 2m + 7 - 2m - 7$

$m^2 + 2m - 3 = 0$

$(m+3)(m-1) = 0$

$m + 3 = 0 \quad \text{or} \quad m - 1 = 0$

$m = -3 \qquad\qquad m = 1$

Check:

$\sqrt[3]{(-3)^2 + 4(-3) + 4} \overset{?}{=} \sqrt[3]{2(-3)+7}$

$\sqrt[3]{9 - 12 + 4} \overset{?}{=} \sqrt[3]{-6+7}$

$\sqrt[3]{1} \overset{?}{=} \sqrt[3]{1}$

$1 = 1 \ \checkmark$

$\sqrt[3]{(1)^2 + 4(1) + 4} \overset{?}{=} \sqrt[3]{2(1)+7}$

$\sqrt[3]{1 + 4 + 4} \overset{?}{=} \sqrt[3]{2+7}$

$\sqrt[3]{9} = \sqrt[3]{9} \ \checkmark$

The solution set is $\{-3, 1\}$

8. $\sqrt{2x+1} - \sqrt{x+4} = 1$

$\sqrt{2x+1} = 1 + \sqrt{x+4}$

$\left(\sqrt{2x+1}\right)^2 = \left(1 + \sqrt{x+4}\right)^2$

$2x + 1 = 1 + 2\sqrt{x+4} + \left(\sqrt{x+4}\right)^2$

$2x + 1 = 1 + 2\sqrt{x+4} + x + 4$

$2x + 1 = 5 + x + 2\sqrt{x+4}$

$x - 4 = 2\sqrt{x+4}$

$(x-4)^2 = \left(2\sqrt{x+4}\right)^2$

$x^2 - 8x + 16 = 4(x+4)$

$x^2 - 8x + 16 = 4x + 16$

$x^2 - 12x = 0$

$x(x-12) = 0$

$x = 0 \quad \text{or} \quad x - 12 = 0$

$x = 12$

Check:

$\sqrt{2(0)+1} - \sqrt{0+4} \overset{?}{=} 1 \qquad \sqrt{2(12)+1} - \sqrt{(12)+4} \overset{?}{=} 1$

$\sqrt{1} - \sqrt{4} \overset{?}{=} 1 \qquad\qquad \sqrt{25} - \sqrt{16} \overset{?}{=} 1$

$1 - 2 \overset{?}{=} 1 \qquad\qquad\qquad 5 - 4 \overset{?}{=} 1$

$-1 \neq 1 \qquad\qquad\qquad\qquad 1 = 1 \ \checkmark$

The solution set is $\{12\}$.

9. a. $T = 2\pi\sqrt{\dfrac{L}{32}}$

$\dfrac{T}{2\pi} = \sqrt{\dfrac{L}{32}}$

$\left(\dfrac{T}{2\pi}\right)^2 = \left(\sqrt{\dfrac{L}{32}}\right)^2$

$\dfrac{T^2}{4\pi^2} = \dfrac{L}{32}$

$L = \dfrac{32T^2}{4\pi^2}$

$L = \dfrac{8T^2}{\pi^2}$

b. $L = \dfrac{8T^2}{\pi^2} = \dfrac{8(2\pi)^2}{\pi^2} = \dfrac{8 \cdot 4\pi^2}{\pi^2} = 32 \text{ feet}$.

7.8 Quick Checks

1. $\sqrt{-36} = \sqrt{36\cdot(-1)} = \sqrt{36}\cdot\sqrt{-1} = 6i$

2. $\sqrt{-5} = \sqrt{5\cdot(-1)} = \sqrt{5}\cdot\sqrt{-1} = \sqrt{5}\,i$

3. $\sqrt{-12} = \sqrt{12\cdot(-1)} = \sqrt{12}\cdot\sqrt{-1} = 2\sqrt{3}\,i$

4. $4+\sqrt{-100} = 4+\sqrt{100\cdot(-1)}$
   $= 4+\sqrt{100}\cdot\sqrt{-1}$
   $= 4+10i$

5. $-2-\sqrt{-8} = -2-\sqrt{8\cdot(-1)}$
   $= -2-\sqrt{8}\cdot\sqrt{-1}$
   $= -2-2\sqrt{2}\,i$

6. $\dfrac{6-\sqrt{-72}}{3} = \dfrac{6-\sqrt{72\cdot(-1)}}{3}$
   $= \dfrac{6-\sqrt{72}\cdot\sqrt{-1}}{3}$
   $= \dfrac{6-6\sqrt{2}\,i}{3}$
   $= \dfrac{3\left(2-2\sqrt{2}\,i\right)}{3}$
   $= 2-2\sqrt{2}\,i$

7. $(4+6i)+(-3+5i) = 4+6i-3+5i$
   $= (4-3)+(6+5)i$
   $= 1+11i$

8. $(4-2i)-(-2+7i) = 4-2i+2-7i$
   $= (4+2)+(-2-7)i$
   $= 6-9i$

9. $\left(4-\sqrt{-4}\right)+\left(-7+\sqrt{-9}\right) = (4-2i)+(-7+3i)$
   $= 4-2i-7+3i$
   $= (4-7)+(-2+3)i$
   $= -3+i$

10. $3i(5-4i) = 3i\cdot5-3i\cdot4i$
    $= 15i-12i^2$
    $= 15i-12(-1)$
    $= 12+15i$

11. $(-2+5i)(4-2i) = -2\cdot4-2\cdot(-2i)+5i\cdot4-5i\cdot2i$
    $= -8+4i+20i-10i^2$
    $= -8+24i-10(-1)$
    $= 2+24i$

12. $\sqrt{-9}\cdot\sqrt{-36} = 3i\cdot6i = 18i^2 = -18$

13. $\left(2+\sqrt{-36}\right)\left(4-\sqrt{-25}\right)$
    $= (2+6i)(4-5i)$
    $= 2\cdot4-2\cdot5i+6i\cdot4-6i\cdot5i$
    $= 8-10i+24i-30i^2$
    $= 8+14i-30(-1)$
    $= 38+14i$

14. $(3-8i)(3+8i) = 3^2-(8i)^2$
    $= 9-64i^2$
    $= 9-64(-1)$
    $= 73$

15. $(-2+5i)(-2-5i) = (-2)^2-(5i)^2$
    $= 4-25i^2$
    $= 4-25(-1)$
    $= 29$

16. $\dfrac{-4+i}{3i} = \dfrac{-4+i}{3i}\cdot\dfrac{3i}{3i} = \dfrac{-12i+3i^2}{9i^2}$
    $= \dfrac{-12i-3}{-9} = \dfrac{-3}{-9}+\dfrac{-12}{-9}i$
    $= \dfrac{1}{3}+\dfrac{4}{3}i$

17. $\dfrac{4+3i}{1-3i} = \dfrac{4+3i}{1-3i} \cdot \dfrac{1+3i}{1+3i}$

$\qquad = \dfrac{(4+3i)(1+3i)}{(1-3i)(1+3i)}$

$\qquad = \dfrac{4+12i+3i+9i^2}{1-9i^2}$

$\qquad = \dfrac{4+15i-9}{1+9}$

$\qquad = \dfrac{-5+15i}{10}$

$\qquad = -\dfrac{5}{10} + \dfrac{15}{10}i$

$\qquad = -\dfrac{1}{2} + \dfrac{3}{2}i$

18. $i^{43} = i^{40} \cdot i^3$

$\qquad = \left(i^4\right)^{10} \cdot i^3$

$\qquad = (1)^{10} \cdot (-i)$

$\qquad = -i$

19. $i^{98} = i^{96} \cdot i^2$

$\qquad = \left(i^4\right)^{24} \cdot i^2$

$\qquad = (1)^{24} \cdot (-1)$

$\qquad = -1$

Chapter 8 – Quick Checks

8.1 Quick Checks

1. $p^2 = 48$
   $p = \pm\sqrt{48}$
   $p = \pm 4\sqrt{3}$
   The solution set is $\left\{-4\sqrt{3},\ 4\sqrt{3}\right\}$.

2. $3b^2 = 75$
   $b^2 = 25$
   $b = \pm\sqrt{25}$
   $b = \pm 5$
   The solution set is $\{-5,\ 5\}$.

3. $s^2 - 81 = 0$
   $s^2 = 81$
   $s = \pm\sqrt{81}$
   $s = \pm 9$
   The solution set is $\{-9,\ 9\}$.

4. $d^2 = -72$
   $d = \pm\sqrt{-72}$
   $d = \pm 6\sqrt{2}\, i$
   The solution set is $\left\{-6\sqrt{2}\, i,\ 6\sqrt{2}\, i\right\}$.

5. $3q^2 + 27 = 0$
   $3q^2 = -27$
   $q^2 = -9$
   $q = \pm\sqrt{-9}$
   $q = \pm 3i$
   The solution set is $\{-3i,\ 3i\}$.

6. $(y+3)^2 = 100$
   $y+3 = \pm\sqrt{100}$
   $y+3 = \pm 10$
   $y = -3 \pm 10$
   $y = -3 - 10$ or $y = -3 + 10$
   $y = -13$ or $y = 7$
   The solution set is $\{-13,\ 7\}$.

7. $(q-5)^2 + 20 = 4$
   $(q-5)^2 = -16$
   $q-5 = \pm\sqrt{-16}$
   $q-5 = \pm 4i$
   $q = 5 \pm 4i$
   The solution set is $\{5-4i,\ 5+4i\}$.

8. Start: $p^2 + 14p$

   Add: $\left(\dfrac{1}{2} \cdot 14\right)^2 = 49$

   Result: $p^2 + 14p + 49$

   Factored Form: $\left(p+7\right)^2$

9. Start: $w^2 + 3w$

   Add: $\left(\dfrac{1}{2} \cdot 3\right)^2 = \dfrac{9}{4}$

   Result: $w^2 + 3w + \dfrac{9}{4}$

   Factored Form: $\left(w + \dfrac{3}{2}\right)^2$

10. $b^2 + 2b - 8 = 0$
    $b^2 + 2b = 8$
    $b^2 + 2b + \left(\dfrac{1}{2} \cdot 2\right)^2 = 8 + \left(\dfrac{1}{2} \cdot 2\right)^2$
    $b^2 + 2b + 1 = 8 + 1$
    $(b+1)^2 = 9$
    $b+1 = \pm\sqrt{9}$
    $b+1 = \pm 3$
    $b = -1 \pm 3$
    $b = -4$ or $b = 2$
    The solution set is $\{-4,\ 2\}$.

11.
$$2q^2 + 6q - 1 = 0$$
$$\frac{2q^2 + 6q - 1}{2} = \frac{0}{2}$$
$$q^2 + 3q - \frac{1}{2} = 0$$
$$q^2 + 3q \quad = \frac{1}{2}$$
$$q^2 + 3q + \left[\frac{1}{2} \cdot 3\right]^2 = \frac{1}{2} + \left[\frac{1}{2} \cdot 3\right]^2$$
$$q^2 + 3q + \frac{9}{4} = \frac{1}{2} + \frac{9}{4}$$
$$\left(q + \frac{3}{2}\right)^2 = \frac{11}{4}$$
$$q + \frac{3}{2} = \pm\sqrt{\frac{11}{4}}$$
$$q + \frac{3}{2} = \pm\frac{\sqrt{11}}{2}$$
$$q = -\frac{3}{2} \pm \frac{\sqrt{11}}{2}$$

The solution set is $\left\{\dfrac{-3}{2} - \dfrac{\sqrt{11}}{2},\ \dfrac{-3}{2} + \dfrac{\sqrt{11}}{2}\right\}$, or

$$\left\{\frac{-3 - \sqrt{11}}{2},\ \frac{-3 + \sqrt{11}}{2}\right\}.$$

12. $c^2 = a^2 + b^2$
$$c^2 = 3^2 + 4^2$$
$$= 9 + 16$$
$$= 25$$
$$c = \sqrt{25}$$
$$= 5$$
The hypotenuse is 5 units long.

13. $c^2 = a^2 + b^2$
$$c^2 = 6^2 + 6^2$$
$$= 36 + 36$$
$$= 72$$
$$c = \sqrt{72}$$
$$= 6\sqrt{2}$$
The hypotenuse is $6\sqrt{2}$ units long.

14. Let d represent the unknown distance.

Since the line of sight and the two lines drawn from the center of Earth form a right triangle, we know $\text{Hypotenuse}^2 = \text{Leg}^2 + \text{Leg}^2$. We also know $200 \text{ feet} = \dfrac{200}{5280} \text{ mile}$, so the hypotenuse is $\left(3960 + \dfrac{200}{5280}\right)$ miles. Since one leg is the line of sight, d, and the other leg is 3960 miles, we have that

$$d^2 + 3960^2 = \left(3960 + \frac{200}{5280}\right)^2$$
$$d^2 = \left(3960 + \frac{200}{5280}\right)^2 - 3960^2$$
$$d^2 \approx 300.001435$$
$$d \approx \sqrt{300.001435}$$
$$\approx 17.32$$

The sailor can see approximately 17.32 miles.

8.2 Quick Checks

1. $2x^2 - 3x - 9 = 0$
For this equation, $a = 2$, $b = -3$, and $c = -9$.
$$x = \frac{-(-3) \pm \sqrt{(-3)^2 - 4(2)(-9)}}{2(2)}$$
$$= \frac{3 \pm \sqrt{9 + 72}}{4}$$
$$= \frac{3 \pm \sqrt{81}}{4}$$
$$= \frac{3 \pm 9}{4}$$
$$x = \frac{3 - 9}{4} \quad \text{or} \quad x = \frac{3 + 9}{4}$$
$$= \frac{-6}{4} \quad \text{or} \quad = \frac{12}{4}$$
$$= -\frac{3}{2} \quad \text{or} \quad = 3$$

The solution set is $\left\{-\dfrac{3}{2},\ 3\right\}$.

2. $2x^2 + 7x = 4$

$2x^2 + 7x - 4 = 0$

For this equation, $a = 2$, $b = 7$, and $c = -4$.

$$x = \frac{-7 \pm \sqrt{7^2 - 4(2)(-4)}}{2(2)}$$

$$= \frac{-7 \pm \sqrt{49 + 32}}{4}$$

$$= \frac{-7 \pm \sqrt{81}}{4}$$

$$= \frac{-7 \pm 9}{4}$$

$$x = \frac{-7 - 9}{4} \quad \text{or} \quad x = \frac{-7 + 9}{4}$$

$$= \frac{-16}{4} \quad \text{or} \quad = \frac{2}{4}$$

$$= -4 \quad \text{or} \quad = \frac{1}{2}$$

The solution set is $\left\{ -4, \frac{1}{2} \right\}$.

3. $4z^2 + 1 = 8z$

$4z^2 - 8z + 1 = 0$

For this equation, $a = 4$, $b = -8$, and $c = 1$.

$$z = \frac{-(-8) \pm \sqrt{(-8)^2 - 4(4)(1)}}{2(4)}$$

$$= \frac{8 \pm \sqrt{64 - 16}}{8}$$

$$= \frac{8 \pm \sqrt{48}}{8}$$

$$= \frac{8 \pm 4\sqrt{3}}{8}$$

$$= \frac{8}{8} \pm \frac{4\sqrt{3}}{8}$$

$$= 1 \pm \frac{\sqrt{3}}{2}$$

The solution set is $\left\{ 1 - \frac{\sqrt{3}}{2}, 1 + \frac{\sqrt{3}}{2} \right\}$.

4. $4w + \dfrac{25}{w} = 20$

$$w \left(4w + \frac{25}{w} \right) = w(20)$$

$$4w^2 + 25 = 20w$$

$$4w^2 - 20w + 25 = 0$$

For this equation, $a = 4$, $b = -20$, and $c = 25$.

$$w = \frac{-(-20) \pm \sqrt{(-20)^2 - 4(4)(25)}}{2(4)}$$

$$= \frac{20 \pm \sqrt{400 - 400}}{8}$$

$$= \frac{20 \pm \sqrt{0}}{8}$$

$$= \frac{20}{8}$$

$$= \frac{5}{2}$$

The solution set is $\left\{ \frac{5}{2} \right\}$.

5. $z^2 + 2z + 26 = 0$

For this equation, $a = 1$, $b = 2$, and $c = 26$.

$$z = \frac{-2 \pm \sqrt{2^2 - 4(1)(26)}}{2(1)}$$

$$= \frac{-2 \pm \sqrt{4 - 104}}{2}$$

$$= \frac{-2 \pm \sqrt{-100}}{2}$$

$$= \frac{-2 \pm 10i}{2}$$

$$= \frac{-2}{2} \pm \frac{10i}{2}$$

$$= -1 \pm 5i$$

The solution set is $\{ -1 - 5i, \ -1 + 5i \}$.

6. $2z^2 + 5z + 4 = 0$

For this equation, $a = 2$, $b = 5$, and $c = 4$.

$b^2 - 4ac = 5^2 - 4(2)(4) = 25 - 32 = -7$

Because $b^2 - 4ac = -7$ is negative, the quadratic equation will have two complex solutions that are not real. The solutions will be complex conjugates of each other.

7. $4y^2 + 12y = -9$

$4y^2 + 12y + 9 = 0$

For this equation, $a = 4$, $b = 12$, and $c = 9$.

$b^2 - 4ac = 12^2 - 4(4)(9) = 144 - 144 = 0$

Because $b^2 - 4ac = 0$, the quadratic equation will have one repeated real solution.

QC – 100

8. $2x^2 - 4x + 1 = 0$

For this equation, $a = 2$, $b = -4$, and $c = 1$.

$b^2 - 4ac = (-4)^2 - 4(2)(1) = 16 - 8 = 8$

Because $b^2 - 4ac = 8$ is positive, but not a perfect square, the quadratic equation will have two irrational solutions.

9. $5n^2 - 45 = 0$

Because this equation has no linear term, solve by using the square root method.

$5n^2 = 45$

$n^2 = 9$

$n = \pm\sqrt{9}$

$\quad = \pm 3$

The solution set is $\{-3, 3\}$.

10. $-2y^2 + 5y - 6 = 0$

$2y^2 - 5y + 6 = 0$

Because this equation does not easily factor, solve by using the quadratic formula. For this equation, $a = 2$, $b = -5$, and $c = 6$.

$y = \dfrac{-(-5) \pm \sqrt{(-5)^2 - 4(2)(6)}}{2(2)}$

$\quad = \dfrac{5 \pm \sqrt{25 - 48}}{4}$

$\quad = \dfrac{5 \pm \sqrt{-23}}{4}$

$\quad = \dfrac{5 \pm \sqrt{23}\,i}{4}$

The solution set is $\left\{ \dfrac{5 - \sqrt{23}\,i}{4}, \dfrac{5 + \sqrt{23}\,i}{4} \right\}$ or

$\left\{ \dfrac{5}{4} - \dfrac{\sqrt{23}}{4}i, \dfrac{5}{4} + \dfrac{\sqrt{23}}{4}i \right\}$.

11. $\quad 3w^2 + 2w = 5$

$3w^2 + 2w - 5 = 0$

Because this equation factors easily, solve by factoring.

$(3w + 5)(w - 1) = 0$

$3w + 5 = 0 \quad$ or $\quad w - 1 = 0$

$3w = -5 \quad$ or $\quad\quad w = 1$

$w = -\dfrac{5}{3}$

The solution set is $\left\{ -\dfrac{5}{3}, 1 \right\}$.

12. a. $\quad\quad\quad\quad R(x) = 600$

$-0.005x^2 + 4x = 600$

$-0.005x^2 + 4x - 600 = 0$

For this equation, $a = -0.005$, $b = 4$, and $c = -600$.

$x = \dfrac{-4 \pm \sqrt{4^2 - 4(-0.005)(-600)}}{2(-0.005)}$

$\quad = \dfrac{-4 \pm \sqrt{4}}{-0.01}$

$\quad = \dfrac{-4 \pm 2}{-0.01}$

$x = \dfrac{-6}{-0.01} \quad$ or $\quad x = \dfrac{-2}{-0.01}$

$\quad = 600 \quad\quad$ or $\quad\quad = 200$

If revenue is to be $600 per day, then either 200 or 600 DVDs must be rented.

b. $\quad\quad\quad\quad R(x) = 800$

$-0.005x^2 + 4x = 800$

$-0.005x^2 + 4x - 800 = 0$

For this equation, $a = -0.005$, $b = 4$, and $c = -800$.

$x = \dfrac{-4 \pm \sqrt{4^2 - 4(-0.005)(-800)}}{2(-0.005)}$

$\quad = \dfrac{-4 \pm \sqrt{0}}{-0.01}$

$\quad = \dfrac{-4 \pm 0}{-0.01}$

$x = \dfrac{-4}{-0.01} = 400$

If revenue is to be $800 per day, then 400 DVDs must be rented.

13. Let w represent the width of the rectangle. Then $w + 14$ will represent the length.

$w^2 + (w + 14)^2 = 34^2$

$w^2 + w^2 + 28w + 196 = 1156$

$2w^2 + 28w - 960 = 0$

$w^2 + 14w - 480 = 0$

$(w - 16)(w + 30) = 0$

$w - 16 = 0 \quad$ or $\quad w + 30 = 0$

$w = 16 \quad$ or $\quad\quad\quad w = -30$

We disregard $w = -30$ because w represents the width of the rectangle, which must be positive. Thus, $w = 16$ is the only viable answer. Now, $w + 14 = 16 + 14 = 30$. Thus, the dimensions of the rectangle are 16 meters by 30 meters.

8.3 Quick Checks

1.
$$x^4 - 13x^2 + 36 = 0$$
$$\left(x^2\right)^2 - 13\left(x^2\right) + 36 = 0$$

Let $u = x^2$.
$$u^2 - 13u + 36 = 0$$
$$(u-4)(u-9) = 0$$

$u - 4 = 0$	or	$u - 9 = 0$
$u = 4$	or	$u = 9$
$x^2 = 4$	or	$x^2 = 9$
$x = \pm\sqrt{4}$	or	$x = \pm\sqrt{9}$
$x = \pm 2$	or	$x = \pm 3$

Check:
$$x = -2: \ (-2)^4 - 13(-2)^2 + 36 \overset{?}{=} 0$$
$$16 - 13 \cdot 4 + 36 \overset{?}{=} 0$$
$$16 - 52 + 36 \overset{?}{=} 0$$
$$0 = 0 \ \checkmark$$

$$x = 2: \ 2^4 - 13(2)^2 + 36 \overset{?}{=} 0$$
$$16 - 13 \cdot 4 + 36 \overset{?}{=} 0$$
$$16 - 52 + 36 \overset{?}{=} 0$$
$$0 = 0 \ \checkmark$$

$$x = -3: \ (-3)^4 - 13(-3)^2 + 36 \overset{?}{=} 0$$
$$81 - 13 \cdot 9 + 36 \overset{?}{=} 0$$
$$81 - 117 + 36 \overset{?}{=} 0$$
$$0 = 0 \ \checkmark$$

$$x = 3: \ 3^4 - 13(3)^2 + 36 \overset{?}{=} 0$$
$$81 - 13 \cdot 9 + 36 \overset{?}{=} 0$$
$$81 - 117 + 36 \overset{?}{=} 0$$
$$0 = 0 \ \checkmark$$

All check; the solution set is $\{-3, -2, 2, 3\}$.

2.
$$p^4 - 7p^2 = 18$$
$$p^4 - 7p^2 - 18 = 0$$
$$\left(p^2\right)^2 - 7\left(p^2\right) - 18 = 0$$

Let $u = p^2$.
$$u^2 - 7u - 18 = 0$$
$$(u+2)(u-9) = 0$$

$u + 2 = 0$	or	$u - 9 = 0$
$u = -2$	or	$u = 9$
$p^2 = -2$	or	$p^2 = 9$
$p = \pm\sqrt{-2}$	or	$p = \pm\sqrt{9}$
$p = \pm\sqrt{2}\,i$	or	$p = \pm 3$

Check:
$$p = -\sqrt{2}\,i: \ \left(\sqrt{2}\,i\right)^4 - 7\left(\sqrt{2}\,i\right)^2 \overset{?}{=} 18$$
$$4i^4 - 7 \cdot 2i^2 \overset{?}{=} 18$$
$$4(1) - 7 \cdot 2(-1) \overset{?}{=} 18$$
$$4 - 7 \cdot 2(-1) \overset{?}{=} 18$$
$$4 + 14 \overset{?}{=} 18$$
$$18 = 18 \ \checkmark$$

$$p = \sqrt{2}\,i: \ \left(-\sqrt{2}\,i\right)^4 - 7\left(-\sqrt{2}\,i\right)^2 \overset{?}{=} 18$$
$$4i^4 - 7 \cdot 2i^2 \overset{?}{=} 18$$
$$4(1) - 7 \cdot 2(-1) \overset{?}{=} 18$$
$$4 - 7 \cdot 2(-1) \overset{?}{=} 18$$
$$4 + 14 \overset{?}{=} 18$$
$$18 = 18 \ \checkmark$$

$$p = -3: \ (-3)^4 - 7(-3)^2 \overset{?}{=} 18$$
$$81 - 7 \cdot 9 \overset{?}{=} 18$$
$$81 - 63 \overset{?}{=} 18$$
$$18 = 18 \ \checkmark$$

$$p = 3: \ 3^4 - 7(3)^2 \overset{?}{=} 18$$
$$81 - 7 \cdot 9 \overset{?}{=} 18$$
$$81 - 63 \overset{?}{=} 18$$
$$18 = 18 \ \checkmark$$

All check; the solution set is
$$\left\{-\sqrt{2}\,i, \ \sqrt{2}\,i, \ -3, \ 3\right\}.$$

3. $\left(p^2-2\right)^2 -9\left(p^2-2\right)+14=0$

Let $u = p^2 - 2$.

$u^2 - 9u + 14 = 0$

$(u-2)(u-7)=0$

$u-2=0 \quad$ or $\quad u-7=0$

$u=2 \quad$ or $\quad u=7$

$p^2-2=2 \quad$ or $\quad p^2-2=7$

$p^2=4 \quad$ or $\quad p^2=9$

$p=\pm\sqrt{4} \quad$ or $\quad p=\pm\sqrt{9}$

$p=\pm2 \quad$ or $\quad p=\pm3$

Check:

$p=-2: \quad \left((-2)^2-2\right)^2 -9\left((-2)^2-2\right)+14\overset{?}{=}0$

$\left(4-2\right)^2 -9(4-2)+14\overset{?}{=}0$

$2^2-9\cdot2+14\overset{?}{=}0$

$4-18+14\overset{?}{=}0$

$0=0 \checkmark$

$p=2: \quad \left(2^2-2\right)^2 -9\left(2^2-2\right)+14\overset{?}{=}0$

$\left(4-2\right)^2 -9(4-2)+14\overset{?}{=}0$

$2^2-9\cdot2+14\overset{?}{=}0$

$4-18+14\overset{?}{=}0$

$0=0 \checkmark$

$p=-3: \quad \left((-3)^2-2\right)^2 -9\left((-3)^2-2\right)+14\overset{?}{=}0$

$\left(9-2\right)^2 -9(9-2)+14\overset{?}{=}0$

$7^2-9\cdot7+14\overset{?}{=}0$

$49-63+14\overset{?}{=}0$

$0=0 \checkmark$

$p=3: \quad \left(3^2-2\right)^2 -9\left(3^2-2\right)+14\overset{?}{=}0$

$\left(9-2\right)^2 -9(9-2)+14\overset{?}{=}0$

$7^2-9\cdot7+14\overset{?}{=}0$

$49-63+14\overset{?}{=}0$

$0=0 \checkmark$

All check; the solution set is $\{-3,-2,\ 2,\ 3\}$.

4. $2\left(2z^2-1\right)^2 +5\left(2z^2-1\right)-3=0$

Let $u = 2z^2 - 1$.

$2u^2 + 5u - 3 = 0$

$(2u-1)(u+3)=0$

$2u-1=0 \quad$ or $\quad u+3=0$

$u=\dfrac{1}{2} \quad$ or $\quad u=-3$

$2z^2-1=\dfrac{1}{2} \quad$ or $\quad 2z^2-1=-3$

$2z^2=\dfrac{3}{2} \quad$ or $\quad 2z^2=-2$

$z^2=\dfrac{3}{4} \quad$ or $\quad z^2=-1$

$z=\pm\sqrt{\dfrac{3}{4}} \quad$ or $\quad z=\pm\sqrt{-1}$

$z=\pm\dfrac{\sqrt{3}}{2} \quad$ or $\quad z=\pm i$

Check:

$z=-\dfrac{\sqrt{3}}{2}: \quad 2\left(2\left(-\dfrac{\sqrt{3}}{2}\right)^2-1\right)^2 +5\left(2\left(-\dfrac{\sqrt{3}}{2}\right)^2-1\right)-3\overset{?}{=}0$

$2\left(2\left(\dfrac{3}{4}\right)-1\right)^2 +5\left(2\left(\dfrac{3}{4}\right)-1\right)-3\overset{?}{=}0$

$2\left(\dfrac{3}{2}-1\right)^2 +5\left(\dfrac{3}{2}-1\right)-3\overset{?}{=}0$

$2\left(\dfrac{1}{2}\right)^2 +5\left(\dfrac{1}{2}\right)-3\overset{?}{=}0$

$2\left(\dfrac{1}{4}\right) +5\left(\dfrac{1}{2}\right)-3\overset{?}{=}0$

$\dfrac{1}{2}+\dfrac{5}{2}-3\overset{?}{=}0$

$0=0 \checkmark$

$z=\dfrac{\sqrt{3}}{2}: \quad 2\left(2\left(\dfrac{\sqrt{3}}{2}\right)^2-1\right)^2 +5\left(2\left(\dfrac{\sqrt{3}}{2}\right)^2-1\right)-3\overset{?}{=}0$

$2\left(2\left(\dfrac{3}{4}\right)-1\right)^2 +5\left(2\left(\dfrac{3}{4}\right)-1\right)-3\overset{?}{=}0$

$2\left(\dfrac{3}{2}-1\right)^2 +5\left(\dfrac{3}{2}-1\right)-3\overset{?}{=}0$

$2\left(\dfrac{1}{2}\right)^2 +5\left(\dfrac{1}{2}\right)-3\overset{?}{=}0$

$2\left(\dfrac{1}{4}\right) +5\left(\dfrac{1}{2}\right)-3\overset{?}{=}0$

$\dfrac{1}{2}+\dfrac{5}{2}-3\overset{?}{=}0$

$0=0 \checkmark$

$z = -i:\ 2\left(2(-i)^2 - 1\right)^2 + 5\left(2(-i)^2 - 1\right) - 3 \overset{?}{=} 0$

$2\left(2i^2 - 1\right)^2 + 5\left(2i^2 - 1\right) - 3 \overset{?}{=} 0$

$2\left(2(-1) - 1\right)^2 + 5\left(2(-1) - 1\right) - 3 \overset{?}{=} 0$

$2(-2-1)^2 + 5(-2-1) - 3 \overset{?}{=} 0$

$2(-3)^2 + 5(-3) - 3 \overset{?}{=} 0$

$2(9) + 5(-3) - 3 \overset{?}{=} 0$

$18 - 15 - 3 \overset{?}{=} 0$

$0 = 0\ \checkmark$

$z = i:\ \ \ 2\left(2i^2 - 1\right)^2 + 5\left(2i^2 - 1\right) - 3 \overset{?}{=} 0$

$2\left(2(-1) - 1\right)^2 + 5\left(2(-1) - 1\right) - 3 \overset{?}{=} 0$

$2(-2-1)^2 + 5(-2-1) - 3 \overset{?}{=} 0$

$2(-3)^2 + 5(-3) - 3 \overset{?}{=} 0$

$2(9) + 5(-3) - 3 \overset{?}{=} 0$

$18 - 15 - 3 \overset{?}{=} 0$

$0 = 0\ \checkmark$

All check; the solution set is $\left\{ -\dfrac{\sqrt{3}}{2},\ \dfrac{\sqrt{3}}{2}, -i,\ i \right\}$.

5. $3w - 14\sqrt{w} + 8 = 0$

$3\left(\sqrt{w}\right)^2 - 14\left(\sqrt{w}\right) + 8 = 0$

Let $u = \sqrt{w}$.

$3u^2 - 14u + 8 = 0$

$(3u - 2)(u - 4) = 0$

$3u - 2 = 0\ \ \ \ $ or $\ \ u - 4 = 0$

$u = \dfrac{2}{3}\ \ \ \ $ or $\ \ \ \ u = 4$

$\sqrt{w} = \dfrac{2}{3}\ \ \ \ $ or $\ \ \ \ \sqrt{w} = 4$

$w = \left(\dfrac{2}{3}\right)^2\ \ $ or $\ \ \ \ w = 4^2$

$w = \dfrac{4}{9}\ \ \ \ $ or $\ \ \ \ w = 16$

Check:

$w = \dfrac{4}{9}:\ 3\left(\dfrac{4}{9}\right) - 14\sqrt{\dfrac{4}{9}} + 8 \overset{?}{=} 0$

$\dfrac{4}{3} - 14 \cdot \dfrac{2}{3} + 8 \overset{?}{=} 0$

$\dfrac{4}{3} - \dfrac{28}{3} + 8 \overset{?}{=} 0$

$0 = 0\ \checkmark$

$w = 16:\ 3(16) - 14\sqrt{16} + 8 \overset{?}{=} 0$

$48 - 14 \cdot 4 + 8 \overset{?}{=} 0$

$48 - 56 + 8 \overset{?}{=} 0$

$0 = 0\ \checkmark$

Both check; the solution set is $\left\{ \dfrac{4}{9},\ 16 \right\}$.

6. $2q - 9\sqrt{q} - 5 = 0$

$2\left(\sqrt{q}\right)^2 - 9\left(\sqrt{q}\right) - 5 = 0$

Let $u = \sqrt{q}$.

$2u^2 - 9u - 5 = 0$

$(2u + 1)(u - 5) = 0$

$2u + 1 = 0\ \ \ $ or $\ \ u - 5 = 0$

$u = -\dfrac{1}{2}\ $ or $\ \ \ \ \ u = 5$

$\sqrt{q} = -\dfrac{1}{2}\ \ \ \ $ or $\ \ \ \sqrt{q} = 5$

$q = \left(-\dfrac{1}{2}\right)^2\ $ or $\ \ \ \ \ q = 5^2$

$q = \dfrac{1}{4}\ \ \ \ $ or $\ \ \ \ \ q = 25$

Check:

$q = \dfrac{1}{4}:\ 2\left(\dfrac{1}{4}\right) - 9\sqrt{\dfrac{1}{4}} - 5 \overset{?}{=} 0$

$\dfrac{1}{2} - 9 \cdot \dfrac{1}{2} - 5 \overset{?}{=} 0$

$\dfrac{1}{2} - \dfrac{9}{2} - 5 \overset{?}{=} 0$

$-9 \neq 0\ \ \boldsymbol{\times}$

$q = 25:\ 2(25) - 9\sqrt{25} - 5 \overset{?}{=} 0$

$50 - 9 \cdot 5 - 5 \overset{?}{=} 0$

$50 - 45 - 5 \overset{?}{=} 0$

$0 = 0\ \checkmark$

$q = \dfrac{1}{4}$ does not check; the solution set is $\{25\}$.

7. $5x^{-2} + 12x^{-1} + 4 = 0$

$5\left(x^{-1}\right)^2 + 12\left(x^{-1}\right) + 4 = 0$

Let $u = x^{-1}$.

$5u^2 + 12u + 4 = 0$

$(5u + 2)(u + 2) = 0$

$5u + 2 = 0 \quad$ or $\quad u + 2 = 0$

$u = -\dfrac{2}{5} \quad$ or $\quad u = -2$

$x^{-1} = -\dfrac{2}{5} \quad$ or $\quad x^{-1} = -2$

$\dfrac{1}{x} = -\dfrac{2}{5} \quad$ or $\quad \dfrac{1}{x} = -2$

$x = -\dfrac{5}{2} \quad$ or $\quad x = -\dfrac{1}{2}$

Check:

$x = -\dfrac{5}{2}: \quad 5\left(-\dfrac{5}{2}\right)^{-2} + 12\left(-\dfrac{5}{2}\right)^{-1} + 4 \overset{?}{=} 0$

$5\left(-\dfrac{2}{5}\right)^2 + 12\left(-\dfrac{2}{5}\right) + 4 \overset{?}{=} 0$

$5\left(\dfrac{4}{25}\right) + 12\left(-\dfrac{2}{5}\right) + 4 \overset{?}{=} 0$

$\dfrac{4}{5} - \dfrac{24}{5} + 4 \overset{?}{=} 0$

$0 = 0 \checkmark$

$x = -\dfrac{1}{2}: \quad 5\left(-\dfrac{1}{2}\right)^{-2} + 12\left(-\dfrac{1}{2}\right)^{-1} + 4 \overset{?}{=} 0$

$5(-2)^2 + 12(-2) + 4 \overset{?}{=} 0$

$5(4) + 12(-2) + 4 \overset{?}{=} 0$

$20 - 24 + 4 \overset{?}{=} 0$

$0 = 0 \checkmark$

Both check; the solution set is $\left\{-\dfrac{5}{2}, -\dfrac{1}{2}\right\}$.

8. $p^{2/3} - 4p^{1/3} - 5 = 0$

$\left(p^{1/3}\right)^2 - 4\left(p^{1/3}\right) - 5 = 0$

Let $u = p^{1/3}$.

$u^2 - 4u - 5 = 0$

$(u + 1)(u - 5) = 0$

$u + 1 = 0 \quad$ or $\quad u - 5 = 0$

$u = -1 \quad$ or $\quad u = 5$

$p^{1/3} = -1 \quad$ or $\quad p^{1/3} = 5$

$\left(p^{1/3}\right)^3 = (-1)^3 \quad$ or $\quad \left(p^{1/3}\right)^3 = 5^3$

$p = -1 \quad$ or $\quad p = 125$

Check:

$p = -1: \quad (-1)^{2/3} - 4\cdot(-1)^{1/3} - 5 \overset{?}{=} 0$

$\left(\sqrt[3]{-1}\right)^2 - 4\left(\sqrt[3]{-1}\right) - 5 \overset{?}{=} 0$

$(-1)^2 - 4(-1) - 5 \overset{?}{=} 0$

$1 + 4 - 5 \overset{?}{=} 0$

$0 = 0 \checkmark$

$p = 125: \quad (125)^{2/3} - 4\cdot(125)^{1/3} - 5 \overset{?}{=} 0$

$\left(\sqrt[3]{125}\right)^2 - 4\left(\sqrt[3]{125}\right) - 5 \overset{?}{=} 0$

$(5)^2 - 4(5) - 5 \overset{?}{=} 0$

$25 - 20 - 5 \overset{?}{=} 0$

$0 = 0 \checkmark$

Both check; the solution set is $\{-1, 125\}$.

8.4 Quick Checks

1. Begin with the graph of $y = x^2$, then shift the graph up 5 unit to obtain the graph of $f(x) = x^2 + 5$.

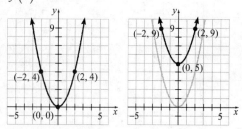

2. Begin with the graph of $y = x^2$, then shift the graph down 2 units to obtain the graph of $f(x) = x^2 - 2$.

QC – 105

3. Begin with the graph of $y = x^2$, then shift the graph to the left 5 units to obtain the graph of $f(x) = (x+5)^2$.

4. Begin with the graph of $y = x^2$, then shift the graph to the right 1 unit to obtain the graph of $f(x) = (x-1)^2$.

5. Begin with the graph of $y = x^2$, then shift the graph 3 units to the right to obtain the graph of $y = (x-3)^2$. Shift this graph up 2 units to obtain the graph of $f(x) = (x-3)^2 + 2$.

6. Begin with the graph of $y = x^2$, then shift the graph 1 unit to the left to obtain the graph of $y = (x+1)^2$. Shift this graph down 4 units to obtain the graph of $f(x) = (x+1)^2 - 4$.

7. Begin with the graph of $y = x^2$, then vertically stretch the graph by a factor of 3 (multiply each y-coordinate by 3) to obtain the graph of $f(x) = 3x^2$.

8. Begin with the graph of $y = x^2$, then multiply the y-coordinates by $-\dfrac{1}{4}$ to obtain the graph of $f(x) = -\dfrac{1}{4}x^2$.

9. Begin with the graph of $y = x^2$, then shift the graph 2 units to the left to obtain the graph of $y = (x+2)^2$. Multiply the y-coordinates by -3 to obtain the graph of $y = -3(x+2)^2$. Lastly, shift the graph up 1 unit to obtain the graph of $f(x) = -3(x+2)^2 + 1$.

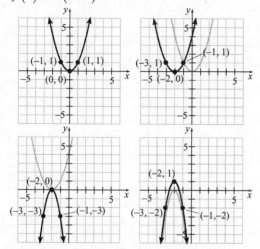

The domain is $\{x \mid x$ is and real number$\}$ or, using interval notation, $(-\infty, \infty)$. The range is $\{y \mid y \le 1\}$ or using interval notation $(-\infty, 1]$.

10. Use completing the square to write the function in the form $y = a(x-h)^2 + k$.

$$f(x) = 2x^2 - 8x + 5$$
$$= (2x^2 - 8x) + 5$$
$$= 2(x^2 - 4x) + 5$$
$$= 2(x^2 - 4x + 4) + 5 - 8$$
$$= 2(x-2)^2 - 3$$

Begin with the graph of $y = x^2$, then shift the graph right 2 units to obtain the graph of $y = (x-2)^2$. Vertically stretch this graph by a factor of 2 (multiply the y-coordinates by 2) to obtain the graph of $y = 2(x-2)^2$. Lastly, shift the graph down 3 units to obtain the graph of $f(x) = 2(x-2)^2 - 3$.

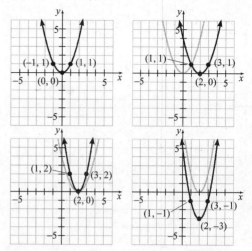

The domain is $\{x \mid x$ is and real number$\}$ or, using interval notation, $(-\infty, \infty)$. The range is $\{y \mid y \ge -3\}$ or, using interval notation, $[-3, \infty)$.

11. Consider the form $f(x) = a(x-h)^2 + k$. From the graph, we know that the vertex is $(-1, 2)$. So $h = -1$ and $k = 2$, and we have that
$$f(x) = a(x-(-1))^2 + 2$$
$$f(x) = a(x+1)^2 + 2$$
The graph also passes through the point $(0, 1)$ which means that $f(0) = 1$. Substituting these values into the functon, we can solve for a:
$$f(x) = a(x+1)^2 + 2$$
$$1 = a(0+1)^2 + 2$$
$$1 = a(1)^2 + 2$$
$$1 = a + 2$$
$$-1 = a$$
The quadratic function is $f(x) = -(x+1)^2 + 2$.

8.5 Quick Checks

1. For the function $f(x) = x^2 - 4x - 12$, we see that $a = 1$, $b = -4$, and $c = -12$. The parabola opens up because $a = 1 > 0$. The x-coordinate of the vertex is $x = -\dfrac{b}{2a} = -\dfrac{(-4)}{2(1)} = 2$. The y-coordinate of the vertex is

QC – 107

$$f\left(-\frac{b}{2a}\right) = f(2)$$
$$= (2)^2 - 4(2) - 12$$
$$= 4 - 8 - 12$$
$$= -16$$

Thus, the vertex is $(2, -16)$ and the axis of symmetry is the line $x = 2$.
The y-intercept is
$$f(0) = (0)^2 - 4(0) - 12 = -12.$$

Now, $b^2 - 4ac = (-4)^2 - 4(1)(-12) = 64 > 0$.
The parabola will have two distinct x-intercepts. We find these by solving
$$f(x) = 0$$
$$x^2 - 4x - 12 = 0$$
$$(x - 6)(x + 2) = 0$$
$$x - 6 = 0 \text{ or } x + 2 = 0$$
$$x = 6 \text{ or } \quad x = -2$$

Finally, the y-intercept point, $(0, -12)$, is two units to the left of the axis of symmetry. Therefore, if we move two units to the right of the axis of symmetry, we obtain the point $(4, -12)$ which must also be on the graph.

2. For the function $f(x) = -3x^2 + 12x - 7$, we see that $a = -3$, $b = 12$, and $c = -7$. The parabola opens down because $a = -3 < 0$. The x-coordinate of the vertex is
$$x = -\frac{b}{2a} = -\frac{12}{2(-3)} = 2.$$ The y-coordinate of the vertex is
$$f\left(-\frac{b}{2a}\right) = f(2)$$
$$= -3(2)^2 + 12(2) - 7$$
$$= -12 + 24 - 7$$
$$= 5$$

Thus, the vertex is $(2, 5)$ and the axis of

symmetry is the line $x = 2$. The y-intercept is
$$f(0) = -3(0)^2 + 12(0) - 7 = -7.$$

Now, $b^2 - 4ac = 12^2 - 4(-3)(-7) = 60 > 0$.
The parabola will have two distinct x-intercepts. We find these by solving
$$f(x) = 0$$
$$-3x^2 + 12x - 7 = 0$$
$$x = \frac{-12 \pm \sqrt{60}}{2(-3)}$$
$$= \frac{-12 \pm 2\sqrt{15}}{-6}$$
$$= \frac{6 \pm \sqrt{15}}{3}$$
$$x \approx 0.71 \text{ or } x \approx 3.29$$

Finally, the y-intercept point, $(0, -7)$, is two units to the left of the axis of symmetry. Therefore, if we move two units to the right of the axis of symmetry, we obtain the point $(4, -7)$ which must also be on the graph.

3. For the function $f(x) = x^2 + 6x + 9$, we see that $a = 1$, $b = 6$, and $c = 9$. The parabola opens up because $a = 1 > 0$. The x-coordinate of the vertex is $x = -\frac{b}{2a} = -\frac{6}{2(1)} = -3$. The y-coordinate of the vertex is
$$f\left(-\frac{b}{2a}\right) = f(-3)$$
$$= (-3)^2 + 6(-3) + 9$$
$$= 9 - 18 + 9$$
$$= 0$$

Thus, the vertex is $(-3, \ 0)$ and the axis of symmetry is the line $x = -3$. The y-intercept is $f(0) = 0^2 + 6(0) + 9 = 9$. Now,
$b^2 - 4ac = 6^2 - 4(1)(9) = 36 - 36 = 0$. Since the discriminant is 0, the x-coordinate of the

vertex is the only x-intercept, $x = -3$. Finally, the y-intercept point, $(0, 9)$, is three units to the right of the axis of symmetry. Therefore, if we move three units to the left of the axis of symmetry, we obtain the point $(-6, 9)$ which must also be on the graph.

4. For the function $G(x) = -3x^2 + 9x - 8$, we see that $a = -3$, $b = 9$, and $c = -8$. The parabola opens down because $a = -3 < 0$. The x-coordinate of the vertex is

    $$x = -\frac{b}{2a} = -\frac{9}{2(-3)} = \frac{9}{6} = \frac{3}{2}.$$

    The y-coordinate of the vertex is

    $$G\left(-\frac{b}{2a}\right) = G\left(\frac{3}{2}\right)$$

    $$= -3\left(\frac{3}{2}\right)^2 + 9\left(\frac{3}{2}\right) - 8$$

    $$= -\frac{27}{4} + \frac{27}{2} - 8$$

    $$= -\frac{5}{4}$$

    Thus, the vertex is $\left(\frac{3}{2}, -\frac{5}{4}\right)$ and the axis of symmetry is the line $x = \frac{3}{2}$. The y-intercept is $G(0) = -3(0)^2 + 9(0) - 8 = -8$. Now, $b^2 - 4ac = 9^2 - 4(-3)(-8) = 81 - 96 = -15$. Since the discriminant is negative, there are no x-intercepts. Finally, the y-intercept point, $(0, -8)$, is three-halves units to the left of the axis of symmetry. Therefore, if we move three-halves units to the right of the axis of symmetry, we obtain the point $(3, -8)$ which must also be on the graph.

5. If we compare $f(x) = 2x^2 - 8x + 1$ to $f(x) = ax^2 + bx + c$, we find that $a = 2$, $b = -8$, and $c = 1$. Because $a > 0$, we know the graph will open up, so the function will have a minimum value. The minimum value occurs at

    $$x = -\frac{b}{2a} = -\frac{(-8)}{2(2)} = 2.$$

    The minimum value of the function is

    $$f\left(-\frac{b}{2a}\right) = f(2) = 2(2)^2 - 8(2) + 1 = -7.$$ So, the minimum value is -7 and it occurs when $x = 2$.

6. If we compare $G(x) = -x^2 + 10x + 8$ to $G(x) = ax^2 + bx + c$, we find that $a = -1$, $b = 10$, and $c = 8$. Because $a < 0$, we know the graph will open down, so the function will have a maximum value. The maximum value occurs

    at $x = -\frac{b}{2a} = -\frac{10}{2(-1)} = 5.$

    The maximum value of the function is

    $$G\left(-\frac{b}{2a}\right) = G(5) = -5^2 + 10(5) + 8 = 33.$$ So, the maximum value is 33 and it occurs when $x = 5$.

7. **a.** We first recognize that the revenue function is a quadratic function whose graph opens down since $a = -0.5 < 0$. This means that the function indeed has a maximum value. The maximum value occurs when

    $$p = -\frac{b}{2a} = -\frac{75}{2(-0.5)} = 75.$$

    The revenue will be maximized when the calculators are sold at a price of $75.

    b. The maximum revenue is obtained by evaluating the revenue function at the price found in part (a).

    $$R(75) = -0.5(75)^2 + 75(75) = 2812.5$$

    The maximum daily revenue is $2812.50.

8. Let l = length and w = width.
The area of a rectangle is given by $A = l \cdot w$.
Before we can work on maximizing the area, we need to get the function in terms of one independent variable.
The 1000 yards of fence will form the perimeter of the rectangle. That is, we have
$2l + 2w = 1000$.
We can solve this equation for l and substitute the result in the area equation.

$2l + 2w = 1000$

$l + w = 500$

$l = 500 - w$

Thus, the area equation becomes
$A = l \cdot w$

$\quad = (500 - w) \cdot w$

$\quad = -w^2 + 500w$

The area function is a quadratic function whose graph opens down since $a = -1 < 0$. This means that the function indeed has a maximum. This occurs when $w = -\dfrac{b}{2a} = -\dfrac{500}{2(-1)} = 250$.

The maximum area can be found by substituting this value for w in the area function.
$A = -250^2 + 500(250) = 62{,}500$ square yards

Since $l = 500 - w$ and $w = 250$, the length will be $l = 500 - 250 = 250$ yards.

The rectangular field will have a maximum area of 62,500 square yards when the field measures 250 yards by 250 yards.

9. Let x represent the number of boxes in excess of 30. Revenue is price times quantity. If 30 boxes of CDs are sold, the revenue will be $100(30)$.

If 31 boxes of CDs are sold, the revenue will be $99(31)$. If 32 boxes of CDs are sold, the revenue will be $98(32)$. In general, if x boxes in excess of 30 are sold, then the number of boxes will be $30 + x$, and the price per box will be $100 - x$. Thus, revenue will be
$R(x) = (100 - x)(30 + x)$

$\quad = 3000 + 100x - 30x - x^2$

$\quad = -x^2 + 70x + 3000$

Now, this revenue function is a quadratic function whose graph opens down since $a = -1 < 0$. This means that the function indeed has a maximum value. The maximum value

occurs when $x = -\dfrac{b}{2a} = -\dfrac{70}{2(-1)} = 35$.

The maximum revenue will be
$R(35) = -35^2 + 70(35) + 3000 = 4225$.

Now recall that x is the number of boxes in excess of 30. Therefore, $30 + 30 = 65$ boxes of CDs should be sold in order to maximize revenue. The maximum revenue will be $4,225.

8.6 Quick Checks

1. We graph $f(x) = x^2 + 3x - 10$. We see that $a = 1$, $b = 3$, and $c = -10$. The parabola opens up because $a = 1 > 0$. The x-coordinate of the vertex is $x = -\dfrac{b}{2a} = -\dfrac{3}{2(1)} = -\dfrac{3}{2}$. The y-coordinate of the vertex is

$f\left(-\dfrac{b}{2a}\right) = f\left(-\dfrac{3}{2}\right)$

$\quad = \left(-\dfrac{3}{2}\right)^2 + 3\left(-\dfrac{3}{2}\right) - 10$

$\quad = \dfrac{9}{4} - \dfrac{9}{2} - 10$

$\quad = -\dfrac{49}{4}$

Thus, the vertex is $\left(-\dfrac{3}{2}, -\dfrac{49}{4}\right)$ and the axis of symmetry is the line $x = -\dfrac{3}{2}$.

The y-intercept is $f(0) = 0^2 + 3(0) - 10 = -10$.
Now, $b^2 - 4ac = 3^2 - 4(1)(-10) = 49 > 0$. The parabola will have two distinct x-intercepts. We find these by solving
$\qquad f(x) = 0$

$\qquad x^2 + 3x - 10 = 0$

$\quad (x + 5)(x - 2) = 0$

$\quad x + 5 = 0 \quad$ or $\quad x - 2 = 0$

$\qquad x = -5 \quad$ or $\qquad x = 2$

Finally, the y-intercept point, $(0, -10)$, is three-haves units to the right of the axis of symmetry. Therefore, if we move three-halves units to the left of the axis of symmetry, we obtain the point $(-3, -10)$ which must also be on the graph.

From the graph, we can see that
$f(x) = x^2 + 3x - 10$ is greater than 0 for $x < -5$
or $x > 2$. Because the inequality is non-strict,
we include the x-intercepts in the solution. So,
the solution is $\{x | x \le -5 \text{ or } x \ge 2\}$ using set-
builder notation; the solution is
$(-\infty, -5] \cup [2, \infty)$ using interval notation.

2. $x^2 + 3x - 10 \ge 0$

Solve: $x^2 + 3x - 10 = 0$
$$(x - 2)(x + 5) = 0$$
$$x - 2 = 0 \quad \text{or} \quad x + 5 = 0$$
$$x = 2 \quad \text{or} \quad x = -5$$

Determine where each factor is positive and
negative and where the product of these factors
is positive and negative.

Interval	$(-\infty, -5)$	-5	$(-5, 2)$	2	$(2, \infty)$
$x - 2$	Neg	Neg	Neg	0	Pos
$x + 5$	Neg	0	Pos	Pos	Pos
$(x-2)(x+5)$	Pos	0	Neg	0	Pos

The inequality is non-strict, so -5 and 2 are part
of the solution. Now, $(x - 2)(x + 5)$ is greater
than zero where the product is positive. The
solution is $\{x | x \le -5 \text{ or } x \ge 2\}$ in set-builder
notation; the solution is $(-\infty, -5] \cup [2, \infty)$ in
interval notation.

3.
$$-x^2 > 2x - 24$$
$$0 > x^2 + 2x - 24$$
$$x^2 + 2x - 24 < 0$$

Solve: $x^2 + 2x - 24 = 0$
$$(x - 4)(x + 6) = 0$$
$$x - 4 = 0 \quad \text{or} \quad x + 6 = 0$$
$$x = 4 \quad \text{or} \quad x = -6$$

Determine where each factor is positive and
negative and where the product of these factors
is positive and negative.

Interval	$(-\infty, -6)$	-6	$(-6, 4)$	4	$(4, \infty)$
$x - 4$	Neg	Neg	Neg	0	Pos
$x + 6$	Neg	0	Pos	Pos	Pos
$(x-4)(x+6)$	Pos	0	Neg	0	Pos

The inequality is strict, so -6 and 4 are not part
of the solution. Now, $(x + 6)(x - 4)$ is less than
zero where the product is negative. The solution
is $\{x | -6 < x < 4\}$ in set-builder notation; the
solution is $(-6, 4)$ in interval notation.

4.
$$3x^2 > -x + 5$$
$$3x^2 + x - 5 > 0$$

Graphical Method:
To graph $f(x) = 3x^2 + x - 5$, we notice that
$a = 3$, $b = 1$, and $c = -5$. The parabola opens
up because $a = 3 > 0$. The x-coordinate of the
vertex is $x = -\dfrac{b}{2a} = -\dfrac{1}{2(3)} = -\dfrac{1}{6}$. The y-
coordinate of the vertex is
$$f\left(-\frac{b}{2a}\right) = f\left(-\frac{1}{6}\right)$$
$$= 3\left(-\frac{1}{6}\right)^2 + \left(-\frac{1}{6}\right) - 5$$
$$= -\frac{61}{12}$$

Thus, the vertex is $\left(-\dfrac{1}{6}, -\dfrac{61}{12}\right)$ and the axis of

symmetry is the line $x = -\dfrac{1}{6}$. The y-intercept is

$$f(0) = 3(0)^2 + 0 - 5 = -5.$$

QC – 111

Now, $b^2 - 4ac = 1^2 - 4(3)(-5) = 61 > 0$. The parabola will have two distinct x-intercepts. We find these by solving

$$f(x) = 0$$

$$3x^2 + x - 5 = 0$$

$$x = \frac{-1 \pm \sqrt{61}}{2(3)}$$

$$= \frac{-1 \pm \sqrt{61}}{6}$$

$$x \approx -1.47 \quad \text{or} \quad x \approx 1.14$$

From the graph, we can see that $f(x) = 3x^2 + x - 5$ is greater than 0 for

$x < \dfrac{-1 - \sqrt{61}}{6}$ or $x > \dfrac{-1 + \sqrt{61}}{6}$. Because the inequality is strict, we do not include the x-intercepts in the solution. So, the solution is

$\left\{ x \middle| x < \dfrac{-1 - \sqrt{61}}{6} \text{ or } x > \dfrac{-1 + \sqrt{61}}{6} \right\}$ using set-builder notation; the solution is

$\left(-\infty, \dfrac{-1 - \sqrt{61}}{6} \right) \cup \left(\dfrac{-1 + \sqrt{61}}{6}, \infty \right)$ using interval notation.

Algebraic Method:

Solve: $3x^2 + x - 5 = 0$

$$x = \frac{-1 \pm \sqrt{61}}{2(3)}$$

$$= \frac{-1 + \sqrt{61}}{6}$$

$$x \approx -1.47 \quad \text{or} \quad x \approx 1.14$$

Determine where each factor is positive and negative and where the product of these factors is positive and negative.

Interval	$(-\infty, -1.47)$		$(-1.47, 1.14)$		$(1.14, \infty)$
	$\dfrac{-1-\sqrt{61}}{6}$		$\dfrac{-1+\sqrt{61}}{6}$		
$x - \left(\dfrac{-1-\sqrt{61}}{6} \right)$	Neg	0	Pos	Pos	Pos
$x - \left(\dfrac{-1+\sqrt{61}}{6} \right)$	Neg	Neg	Neg	0	Pos
$\left[x - \left(\dfrac{-1-\sqrt{61}}{6} \right) \right]\left[x - \left(\dfrac{-1+\sqrt{61}}{6} \right) \right]$	Pos	0	Neg	0	Pos

The inequality is strict, so $\dfrac{-1 - \sqrt{61}}{6}$ and $\dfrac{-1 + \sqrt{61}}{6}$ are not part of the solution. Now,

$\left[x - \left(\dfrac{-1 - \sqrt{61}}{6} \right) \right]\left[x - \left(\dfrac{-1 + \sqrt{61}}{6} \right) \right]$ is greater than zero where the product is positive. So, the solution is $\left\{ x \middle| x < \dfrac{-1 - \sqrt{61}}{6} \text{ or } x > \dfrac{-1 + \sqrt{61}}{6} \right\}$ using set-builder notation; the solution is $\left(-\infty, \dfrac{-1 - \sqrt{61}}{6} \right) \cup \left(\dfrac{-1 + \sqrt{61}}{6}, \infty \right)$ using interval notation.

Chapter 9 – Quick Checks

9.1 Quick Checks

1. $f(x) = 4x - 3$; $g(x) = x^2 + 1$

  a. $g(2) = (2)^2 + 1 = 4 + 1 = 5$

    $f(5) = 4(5) - 3 = 20 - 3 = 17$

    $(f \circ g)(2) = f(g(2)) = f(5) = 17$

  b. $f(2) = 4(2) - 3 = 8 - 3 = 5$

    $g(5) = (5)^2 + 1 = 25 + 1 = 26$

    $(g \circ f)(2) = g(f(2)) = g(5) = 26$

  c. $f(-3) = 4(-3) - 3 = -12 - 3 = -15$

    $f(-15) = 4(-15) - 3 = -60 - 3 = -63$

    $(f \circ f)(-3) = f(f(-3)) = f(-15) = -63$

2. $f(x) = x^2 - 3x + 1$; $g(x) = 3x + 2$

  a. $(f \circ g)(x) = f(g(x))$

    $= (3x + 2)^2 - 3(3x + 2) + 1$

    $= 9x^2 + 12x + 4 - 9x - 6 + 1$

    $= 9x^2 + 3x - 1$

  b. $(g \circ f)(x) = g(f(x))$

    $= 3(x^2 - 3x + 1) + 2$

    $= 3x^2 - 9x + 3 + 2$

    $= 3x^2 - 9x + 5$

  c. $(f \circ g)(-2) = 9(-2)^2 + 3(-2) - 1$

    $= 9(4) + 3(-2) - 1$

    $= 36 - 6 - 1$

    $= 29$

3. Since the two friends (inputs) Max and Yolanda share the same birthday (output) of November 8, this function is not one-to-one.

4. The function is one-to-one because there are no two distinct inputs that correspond to the same output.

5. The graph fails the horizontal line test. For example, the line $y = -1$ will intersect the graph of f in four places. Therefore, the function is not one-to-one.

6. The graph passes the horizontal line test because every horizontal line will intersect the graph of f exactly once. Thus, the function is one-to-one.

7. The inverse of the one-to-one function is:

Right Tibia	Right Humerus
36.05	→ 24.80
35.57	→ 24.59
34.58	→ 24.29
34.20	→ 23.81
34.73	→ 24.87

The domain of the inverse function is {36.05, 35.57, 34.58, 34.20, 34.73}. The range of the inverse function is {24.80, 24.59, 24.29, 23.81, 24.87}.

8. To obtain the inverse, we switch the x- and y-coordinates: $\{(3,-3),(2,-2),(1,-1),(0,0),(-1,1)\}$

The domain of the inverse function is $\{3, 2, 1, 0, -1\}$. The range of the inverse function is $\{-3, -2, -1, 0, 1\}$.

9. To plot the inverse, switch the x- and y-coordinates of each point and connect the corresponding points. The graph of the function (shaded) and the line $y = x$ (dashed) are included for reference.

10. $g(x) = 5x - 1$

    $y = 5x - 1$

    $x = 5y - 1$

    $x + 1 = 5y$

    $\dfrac{x + 1}{5} = y$

    $g^{-1}(x) = \dfrac{x + 1}{5}$

Check: $g\left(g^{-1}(x)\right) = 5\left(\dfrac{x+1}{5}\right) - 1 = x + 1 - 1 = x$

    $g^{-1}\left(g(x)\right) = \dfrac{(5x - 1) + 1}{5} = \dfrac{5x}{5} = x$

QC – 113

11. $f(x) = x^5 + 3$

$$y = x^5 + 3$$

$$x = y^5 + 3$$

$$x - 3 = y^5$$

$$\sqrt[5]{x-3} = y$$

$$f^{-1}(x) = \sqrt[5]{x-3}$$

Check:

$$f\left(f^{-1}(x)\right) = \left(\sqrt[5]{x-3}\right)^5 + 3 = x - 3 + 3 = x$$

$$f^{-1}\left(f(x)\right) = \sqrt[5]{x^5 + 3 - 3} = \sqrt[5]{x^5} = x$$

9.2 Quick Checks

1. a. $2^{1.7} \approx 3.249009585$

b. $2^{1.73} \approx 3.317278183$

c. $2^{1.732} \approx 3.321880096$

d. $2^{1.7321} \approx 3.32211036$

e. $2^{\sqrt{3}} \approx 3.321997085$

2. Locate some points on the graph of $f(x) = 4^x$.

x	$f(x) = 4^x$	$(x, f(x))$
-2	$f(-2) = 4^{-2} = \dfrac{1}{4^2} = \dfrac{1}{16}$	$\left(-2, \dfrac{1}{16}\right)$
-1	$f(-1) = 4^{-1} = \dfrac{1}{4^1} = \dfrac{1}{4}$	$\left(-1, \dfrac{1}{4}\right)$
0	$f(0) = 4^0 = 1$	$(0, 1)$
1	$f(1) = 4^1 = 4$	$(1, 4)$

Plot the points and connect them with a smooth curve.

The domain of f is all real numbers or, using interval notation, $(-\infty, \infty)$. The range of f is $\{y \mid y > 0\}$ or , using interval notation, $(0, \infty)$.

3. Locate some points on the graph of $f(x) = \left(\dfrac{1}{4}\right)^x$.

x	$f(x) = \left(\dfrac{1}{4}\right)^x$	$(x, f(x))$
-1	$f(-1) = \left(\dfrac{1}{4}\right)^{-1} = 4^1 = 4$	$(-1, 4)$
0	$f(0) = \left(\dfrac{1}{4}\right)^0 = 1$	$(0, 1)$
1	$f(1) = \left(\dfrac{1}{4}\right)^1 = \dfrac{1}{4}$	$\left(1, \dfrac{1}{4}\right)$
2	$f(2) = \left(\dfrac{1}{4}\right)^2 = \dfrac{1}{16}$	$\left(2, \dfrac{1}{16}\right)$

Plot the points and connect them with a smooth curve.

The domain of f is all real numbers or, using interval notation, $(-\infty, \infty)$. The range of f is $\{y \mid y > 0\}$ or , using interval notation, $(0, \infty)$.

4. Locate some points on the graph of $f(x) = 2^{x-1}$.

x	$f(x) = 2^{x-1}$	$(x, f(x))$
-1	$f(-1) = 2^{-1-1} = 2^{-2} = \dfrac{1}{2^2} = \dfrac{1}{4}$	$\left(-1, \dfrac{1}{4}\right)$
0	$f(0) = 2^{0-1} = 2^{-1} = \dfrac{1}{2^1} = \dfrac{1}{2}$	$\left(0, \dfrac{1}{2}\right)$
1	$f(1) = 2^{1-1} = 2^0 = 1$	$(1, 1)$
2	$f(2) = 2^{2-1} = 2^1 = 2$	$(2, 2)$
3	$f(3) = 2^{3-1} = 2^2 = 4$	$(3, 4)$
4	$f(4) = 2^{4-1} = 2^3 = 8$	$(4, 8)$

Plot the points and connect them with a smooth curve.

The domain of f is all real numbers or, using interval notation, $(-\infty, \infty)$. The range of f is $\{y \mid y > 0\}$ or, using interval notation, $(0, \infty)$.

5. Locate some points on the graph of $f(x) = 3^x + 1$.

x	$f(x) = 3^x + 1$	$(x, f(x))$
-2	$f(-2) = 3^{-2} + 1 = \dfrac{1}{9} + 1 = \dfrac{10}{9}$	$\left(-2, \dfrac{10}{9}\right)$
-1	$f(-1) = 3^{-1} + 1 = \dfrac{1}{3} + 1 = \dfrac{4}{3}$	$\left(-1, \dfrac{4}{3}\right)$
0	$f(0) = 3^0 + 1 = 1 + 1 = 2$	$(0, 2)$
1	$f(1) = 3^1 + 1 = 3 + 1 = 4$	$(1, 4)$
2	$f(2) = 3^2 + 1 = 9 + 1 = 10$	$(2, 10)$

Plot the points and connect them with a smooth curve.

The domain of f is all real numbers or, using interval notation, $(-\infty, \infty)$. The range of f is $\{y \mid y > 1\}$ or, using interval notation, $(1, \infty)$.

6. $5^{x-4} = 5^{-1}$
$\quad x - 4 = -1$
$\qquad x = 3$
The solution set is $\{3\}$.

7. $3^{x+2} = 81$
$\quad 3^{x+2} = 3^4$
$\quad x + 2 = 4$
$\qquad x = 2$
The solution set is $\{2\}$.

8. $\quad e^{x^2} = e^x \cdot e^{4x}$
$\quad e^{x^2} = e^{5x}$
$\quad x^2 = 5x$
$\quad x^2 - 5x = 0$
$\quad x(x - 5) = 0$
$\quad x = 0 \quad \text{or} \quad x - 5 = 0$
$\qquad\qquad\qquad x = 5$
The solution set is $\{0,\ 5\}$.

9. $\quad \dfrac{2^{x^2}}{8} = 2^{2x}$
$\quad \dfrac{2^{x^2}}{2^3} = 2^{2x}$
$\quad 2^{x^2 - 3} = 2^{2x}$
$\quad x^2 - 3 = 2x$
$\quad x^2 - 2x - 3 = 0$
$\quad (x+1)(x-3) = 0$
$\quad x + 1 = 0 \quad \text{or} \quad x - 3 = 0$
$\quad x = -1 \quad \text{or} \qquad x = 3$
The solution set is $\{-1,\ 3\}$.

10. a. $F(10) = 1 - e^{-0.25(10)} \approx 0.918$.
    The likelihood that a person will arrive within 10 minutes of 3:00 P.M. is 0.918, or 91.8%.

    b. $F(25) = 1 - e^{-0.25(25)} \approx 0.998$.
    The likelihood that a person will arrive within 25 minutes of 3:00 P.M. is 0.998, or 99.8%.

11. a. $A(10) = 10\left(\dfrac{1}{2}\right)^{10/18.72} \approx 6.91$.
    After 10 days, approximately 6.91 grams of thorium-227 will be left in the sample.

    b. $A(18.72) = 10\left(\dfrac{1}{2}\right)^{18.72/18.72} = 5$.
    After 18.72 days, 5 grams of thorium-227 will be left in the sample.

    c. $A(74.88) = 10\left(\dfrac{1}{2}\right)^{74.88/18.72} = 0.625$.
    After 74.88 days, 0.625 gram of thorium-227 will be left in the sample.

    d. $A(100) = 10\left(\dfrac{1}{2}\right)^{100/18.72} \approx 0.247$.
    After 100 days, approximately 0.247 gram of thorium-227 will be left in the sample.

12. We use the compound interest formula with $P = \$2000$, $r = 0.12$, and $n = 12$, so that

$$A = 2000\left(1 + \frac{0.12}{12}\right)^{12t}$$

$$= 2000(1 + 0.01)^{12t}$$

$$= 2000(1.01)^{12t}$$

    a. The value of the account after $t = 1$ years is

$$A = 2000(1.01)^{12(1)}$$

$$= 2000(1.01)^{12} \approx \$2,253.65$$

    b. The value of the account after $t = 15$ years is

$$A = 2000(1.01)^{12(15)}$$

$$= 2000(1.01)^{180} \approx \$11,991.60$$

    c. The value of the account after $t = 30$ years is

$$A = 2000(1.01)^{12(30)}$$

$$= 2000(1.01)^{360} \approx \$71,899.28$$

9.3 Quick Checks

1. If $4^3 = w$, then $3 = \log_4 w$.

2. If $p^{-2} = 8$, then $-2 = \log_p 8$.

3. If $5^b = 125$, then $b = \log_5 125$.

4. If $y = \log_2 16$, then $2^y = 16$.

5. If $5 = \log_a 20$, then $a^5 = 20$.

6. If $-3 = \log_5 z$, then $5^{-3} = z$.

7. Let $y = \log_5 25$. Then,

$$5^y = 25$$
$$5^y = 5^2$$
$$y = 2$$

Thus, $\log_5 25 = 2$.

8. Let $y = \log_2 \frac{1}{8}$. Then,

$$2^y = \frac{1}{8}$$

$$2^y = \frac{1}{2^3} = 2^{-3}$$

$$y = -3$$

Thus, $\log_2 \frac{1}{8} = -3$.

9. $g(25)$ means to evaluate $\log_5 x$ at $x = 25$. So, we want to know the value of $\log_5 25$.

Let $y = \log_5 25$. Then,

$$5^y = 25$$
$$5^y = 5^2$$
$$y = 2$$

Thus, $g(25) = 2$.

10. $g\left(\frac{1}{5}\right)$ means to evaluate $\log_5 x$ at $x = \frac{1}{5}$. So, we want to know the value of $\log_5\left(\frac{1}{5}\right)$.

Let $y = \log_5\left(\frac{1}{5}\right)$. Then,

$$5^y = \frac{1}{5}$$

$$5^y = 5^{-1}$$

$$y = -1$$

Thus, $g\left(\frac{1}{5}\right) = -1$.

11. The domain of $g(x) = \log_8(x+3)$ is the set of all real numbers x such that

$$x + 3 > 0$$
$$x > -3$$

Thus, the domain of $g(x) = \log_8(x+3)$ is $\{x \mid x > -3\}$ or, using interval notation, $(-3, \infty)$.

12. The domain of $F(x) = \log_2(5 - 2x)$ is the set of all real numbers x such that

$$5 - 2x > 0$$
$$-2x > -5$$
$$x < \frac{-5}{-2}$$
$$x < \frac{5}{2}$$

Thus, the domain of $F(x) = \log_2(5 - 2x)$ is $\left\{x \mid x < \frac{5}{2}\right\}$ or, using interval notation, $\left(-\infty, \frac{5}{2}\right)$.

13. Rewrite $y = f(x) = \log_4 x$ as $x = 4^y$. Locate some points on the graph of $x = 4^y$.

y	$x = 4^y$	(x, y)
-2	$x = 4^{-2} = \dfrac{1}{4^2} = \dfrac{1}{16}$	$\left(\dfrac{1}{16}, -2\right)$
-1	$x = 4^{-1} = \dfrac{1}{4^1} = \dfrac{1}{4}$	$\left(\dfrac{1}{4}, -1\right)$
0	$x = 4^0 = 1$	$(1, 0)$
1	$x = 4^1 = 4$	$(4, 1)$

Plot the points and connect them with a smooth curve.

The domain of f is $\{x \mid x > 0\}$ or, using interval notation, $(0, \infty)$. The range of f is all real numbers or, using interval notation, $(-\infty, \infty)$.

14. Rewrite $y = f(x) = \log_{1/4} x$ as $x = \left(\dfrac{1}{4}\right)^y$. Locate some points on the graph of $x = \left(\dfrac{1}{4}\right)^y$.

y	$x = \left(\dfrac{1}{4}\right)^y$	(x, y)
-1	$x = \left(\dfrac{1}{4}\right)^{-1} = 4^1 = 4$	$(4, -1)$
0	$x = \left(\dfrac{1}{4}\right)^0 = 1$	$(1, 0)$
1	$x = \left(\dfrac{1}{4}\right)^1 = \dfrac{1}{4}$	$\left(\dfrac{1}{4}, 1\right)$
2	$x = \left(\dfrac{1}{4}\right)^2 = \dfrac{1}{16}$	$\left(\dfrac{1}{16}, 2\right)$

Plot the points and connect them with a smooth curve.

The domain of f is $\{x \mid x > 0\}$ or, using interval notation, $(0, \infty)$. The range of f is all real numbers or, using interval notation, $(-\infty, \infty)$.

15. $\log 1400 \approx 3.146$

16. $\ln 4.8 \approx 1.569$

17. $\log 0.3 \approx -0.523$

18. $\log_3(5x+1) = 4$
$$5x + 1 = 3^4$$
$$5x + 1 = 81$$
$$5x = 80$$
$$x = 16$$

Check: $\log_3(5 \cdot 16 + 1) \overset{?}{=} 4$
$$\log_3(80 + 1) \overset{?}{=} 4$$
$$\log_3(81) \overset{?}{=} 4$$
$$4 = 4 \checkmark$$

The solution set is $\{16\}$.

19. $\log_x 16 = 2$
$$x^2 = 16$$
$$x = \pm\sqrt{16}$$
$$x = \pm 4$$

Since the base of a logarithm must always be positive, we know that $a = -4$ is extraneous. We check the potential solution $x = 4$.

Check: $\log_4 16 \overset{?}{=} 2$
$$2 = 2 \checkmark$$

The solution set is $\{4\}$.

20. $\ln x = -2$

$x = e^{-2}$

Check: $\ln e^{-2} \overset{?}{=} -2$

$-2 = -2$ ✓

The solution set is $\{e^{-2}\}$.

21. $\log(x - 20) = 4$

$x - 20 = 10^4$

$x - 20 = 10,000$

$x = 10,020$

Check: $\log(10,020 - 20) \overset{?}{=} 4$

$\log(10,000) \overset{?}{=} 4$

$4 = 4$ ✓

The solution set is $\{10,020\}$.

22. We evaluate $L(x) = 10\log \dfrac{x}{10^{-12}}$ at $x = 10^{-2}$.

$L(10^{-2}) = 10\log \dfrac{10^{-2}}{10^{-12}}$

$= 10\log 10^{-2-(-12)}$

$= 10\log 10^{10}$

$= 10(10)$

$= 100$

The loudness of an MP3 player on "full blast" is 100 decibels.

9.4 Quick Checks

1. $\log_5 1 = 0$

2. $\ln 1 = 0$

3. $\log_4 4 = 1$

4. $\log 10 = 1$

5. $12^{\log_{12} \sqrt{2}} = \sqrt{2}$

6. $10^{\log 0.2} = 0.2$

7. $\log_8 8^{1.2} = 1.2$

8. $\log 10^{-4} = -4$

9. $\log_4(9 \cdot 5) = \log_4 9 + \log_4 5$

10. $\log(5w) = \log 5 + \log w$

11. $\log_7\left(\dfrac{9}{5}\right) = \log_7 9 - \log_7 5$

12. $\ln\left(\dfrac{p}{3}\right) = \ln p - \ln 3$

13. $\log_2\left(\dfrac{3m}{n}\right) = \log_2(3m) - \log_2 n$

$= \log_2 3 + \log_2 m - \log_2 n$

14. $\ln\left(\dfrac{q}{3p}\right) = \ln q - \ln(3p)$

$= \ln q - (\ln 3 + \ln p)$

$= \ln q - \ln 3 - \ln p$

15. $\log_2 5^{1.6} = 1.6\log_2 5$

16. $\log b^5 = 5\log b$

17. $\log_4(a^2 b) = \log_4 a^2 + \log_4 b$

$= 2\log_4 a + \log_4 b$

18. $\log_3\left(\dfrac{9m^4}{\sqrt[3]{n}}\right) = \log_3(9m^4) - \log_3 \sqrt[3]{n}$

$= \log_3(3^2 m^4) - \log_3 n^{1/3}$

$= \log_3 3^2 + \log_3 m^4 - \log_3 n^{1/3}$

$= 2 + 4\log_3 m - \dfrac{1}{3}\log_3 n$

19. $\log_8 4 + \log_8 16 = \log_8(4 \cdot 16)$

$= \log_8 64$

$= 2$

20. $\log_3(x + 4) - \log_3(x - 1) = \log_3\left(\dfrac{x + 4}{x - 1}\right)$

21. $\log_5 x - 3\log_5 2 = \log_5 x - \log_5 2^3$

$= \log_5 x - \log_5 8$

$= \log_5 \dfrac{x}{8}$

22. $\log_2(x+1)+\log_2(x+2)-2\log_2 x$

$=\log_2\big[(x+1)(x+2)\big]-\log_2 x^2$

$=\log_2\big(x^2+3x+2\big)-\log_2 x^2$

$=\log_2\left(\dfrac{x^2+3x+2}{x^2}\right)$

23. Using common logarithms:

$\log_3 32=\dfrac{\log 32}{\log 3}\approx 3.155$

24. Using natural logarithms:

$\log_{\sqrt{2}}\sqrt{7}=\dfrac{\ln\sqrt{7}}{\ln\sqrt{2}}\approx 2.807$

9.5 Quick Checks

1. $2\log_4 x=\log_4 9$

$\log_4 x^2=\log_4 9$

$x^2=9$

$x=\pm\sqrt{9}$

$x=\pm 3$

The apparent solution $x=-3$ is extraneous because the argument of a logarithm must be positive. The solution set is $\{3\}$.

2. $\log_4(x-6)+\log_4 x=2$

$\log_4\big[x(x-6)\big]=2$

$\log_4\big(x^2-6x\big)=2$

$x^2-6x=4^2$

$x^2-6x=16$

$x^2-6x-16=0$

$(x+2)(x-8)=0$

$x+2=0\quad\text{or}\quad x-8=0$

$x=-2\quad\text{or}\qquad x=8$

The apparent solution $x=-2$ is extraneous because it causes the argument of a logarithm to be negative. The solution set is $\{8\}$.

3. $2^x=11$

$\log 2^x=\log 11$

$x\log 2=\log 11$

$x=\dfrac{\log 11}{\log 2}\approx 3.459$

The solution set is $\left\{\dfrac{\log 11}{\log 2}\right\}\approx\{3.459\}$. If we had taken the natural logarithm of both sides, the solution set would be $\left\{\dfrac{\ln 11}{\ln 2}\right\}\approx\{3.459\}$.

4. $5^{2x}=3$

$\log 5^{2x}=\log 3$

$2x\log 5=\log 3$

$x=\dfrac{\log 3}{2\log 5}\approx 0.341$

The solution set is $\left\{\dfrac{\log 3}{2\log 5}\right\}\approx\{0.341\}$. If we had taken the natural logarithm of both sides, the solution set would be $\left\{\dfrac{\ln 3}{2\ln 5}\right\}\approx\{0.341\}$.

5. $e^{2x}=5$

$\ln e^{2x}=\ln 5$

$2x=\ln 5$

$x=\dfrac{\ln 5}{2}\approx 0.805$

The solution set is $\left\{\dfrac{\ln 5}{2}\right\}\approx\{0.805\}$.

6. $3e^{-4x}=20$

$e^{-4x}=\dfrac{20}{3}$

$\ln e^{-4x}=\ln\left(\dfrac{20}{3}\right)$

$-4x=\ln\left(\dfrac{20}{3}\right)$

$x=\dfrac{\ln\left(\dfrac{20}{3}\right)}{-4}\approx -0.474$

The solution set is $\left\{\dfrac{\ln\left(20/3\right)}{-4}\right\}\approx\{-0.474\}$.

7. a. We need to determine the time until $A = 9$ grams. So we solve the equation

$$9 = 10\left(\frac{1}{2}\right)^{t/18.72}$$

$$0.9 = \left(\frac{1}{2}\right)^{t/18.72}$$

$$\log 0.9 = \log\left(\frac{1}{2}\right)^{t/18.72}$$

$$\log 0.9 = \frac{t}{18.72}\log\left(\frac{1}{2}\right)$$

$$\frac{18.72 \cdot \log 0.9}{\log\left(\frac{1}{2}\right)} = t$$

So, $t = \dfrac{18.72 \cdot \log 0.9}{\log\left(\frac{1}{2}\right)} \approx 2.85$ days.

Thus, 9 grams of thorium-227 will be left after approximately 2.85 days.

b. We need to determine the time until $A = 3$ grams. So we solve the equation

$$3 = 10\left(\frac{1}{2}\right)^{t/18.72}$$

$$0.3 = \left(\frac{1}{2}\right)^{t/18.72}$$

$$\log 0.3 = \log\left(\frac{1}{2}\right)^{t/18.72}$$

$$\log 0.3 = \frac{t}{18.72}\log\left(\frac{1}{2}\right)$$

$$\frac{18.72 \cdot \log 0.3}{\log\left(\frac{1}{2}\right)} = t$$

So, $t = \dfrac{18.72 \cdot \log 0.3}{\log\left(\frac{1}{2}\right)} \approx 32.52$ days.

Thus, 3 grams of thorium-227 will be left after approximately 32.52 days.

8. We first write the model with the parameters $P = 2000$, $r = 0.06$, and $n = 12$ to obtain

$$A = 2000\left(1 + \frac{0.06}{12}\right)^{12t}, \text{ or } A = 2000(1.005)^{12t}.$$

a. We need to determine the time until $A = \$3000$, so we solve the equation

$$3000 = 2000(1.005)^{12t}$$

$$1.5 = (1.005)^{12t}$$

$$\log 1.5 = \log(1.005)^{12t}$$

$$\log 1.5 = 12t\log 1.005$$

$$\frac{\log 1.5}{12\log 1.005} = t$$

So, $t = \dfrac{\log 1.5}{12\log 1.005} \approx 6.77$. Thus, after approximately 6.77 years (6 years, 9 months), the account will be worth \$3000.

b. We need to determine the time until $A = \$4000$, so we solve the equation

$$4000 = 2000(1.005)^{12t}$$

$$2 = (1.005)^{12t}$$

$$\log 2 = \log(1.005)^{12t}$$

$$\log 2 = 12t\log 1.005$$

$$\frac{\log 2}{12\log 1.005} = t$$

So, $t = \dfrac{\log 2}{12\log 1.005} \approx 11.58$. Thus, after approximately 11.58 years (11 years, 7 months), the account will be worth \$4000.

Chapter 10 – Quick Checks

10.1 Quick Checks

1. Using the distance formula with $P_1 = (3,\ 8)$ and $P_2 = (0,\ 4)$, the length is

$$d(P_1, P_2) = \sqrt{(x_2 - x_1)^2 + (y_2 - y_1)^2}$$
$$= \sqrt{(0-3)^2 + (4-8)^2}$$
$$= \sqrt{(-3)^2 + (-4)^2}$$
$$= \sqrt{9 + 16}$$
$$= \sqrt{25}$$
$$= 5$$

2. Using the distance formula with $P_1 = (-2, -5)$ and $P_2 = (4,\ 7)$, the length is

$$d(P_1, P_2) = \sqrt{(x_2 - x_1)^2 + (y_2 - y_1)^2}$$
$$= \sqrt{(4 - (-2))^2 + (7 - (-5))^2}$$
$$= \sqrt{6^2 + 12^2}$$
$$= \sqrt{36 + 144}$$
$$= \sqrt{180}$$
$$= 6\sqrt{5} \approx 13.42$$

3. **a.**

b. $d(A, B) = \sqrt{(4 - (-2))^2 + (2 - (-1))^2}$
$$= \sqrt{6^2 + 3^2}$$
$$= \sqrt{36 + 9}$$
$$= \sqrt{45}$$
$$= 3\sqrt{5}$$

$d(B, C) = \sqrt{(0 - 4)^2 + (10 - 2)^2}$
$$= \sqrt{(-4)^2 + 8^2}$$
$$= \sqrt{16 + 64}$$
$$= \sqrt{80}$$
$$= 4\sqrt{5}$$

$d(A, C) = \sqrt{(0 - (-2))^2 + (10 - (-1))^2}$
$$= \sqrt{2^2 + 11^2}$$
$$= \sqrt{4 + 121}$$
$$= \sqrt{125}$$
$$= 5\sqrt{5}$$

c. To determine if triangle ABC is a right triangle, we check to see if

$$[d(A,B)]^2 + [d(B,C)]^2 \overset{?}{=} [d(A,C)]^2$$
$$\left(3\sqrt{5}\right)^2 + \left(4\sqrt{5}\right)^2 \overset{?}{=} \left(5\sqrt{5}\right)^2$$
$$9 \cdot 5 + 16 \cdot 5 \overset{?}{=} 25 \cdot 5$$
$$45 + 80 \overset{?}{=} 125$$
$$125 = 125 \leftarrow \text{True}$$

Therefore, triangle ABC is a right triangle.

d. The length of the "base" of the triangle is $d(A, B) = 3\sqrt{5}$ and the length of the "height" of the triangle is $d(B, C) = 4\sqrt{5}$.

Thus, the area of triangle ABC is

$$\text{Area} = \frac{1}{2} \cdot \text{base} \cdot \text{height} = \frac{1}{2} \cdot 3\sqrt{5} \cdot 4\sqrt{5} = 30$$

square units.

4. $M = \left(\dfrac{x_1 + x_2}{2}, \dfrac{y_1 + y_2}{2} \right)$
$$= \left(\frac{3 + 0}{2}, \frac{8 + 4}{2} \right)$$
$$= \left(\frac{3}{2}, \frac{12}{2} \right)$$
$$= \left(\frac{3}{2}, 6 \right)$$

5. $M = \left(\dfrac{x_1 + x_2}{2}, \dfrac{y_1 + y_2}{2} \right)$
$$= \left(\frac{-2 + 4}{2}, \frac{-5 + 10}{2} \right)$$
$$= \left(\frac{2}{2}, \frac{5}{2} \right)$$
$$= \left(1, \frac{5}{2} \right)$$

10.2 Quick Checks

1. We are given that $h = 2$, $k = 4$, and $r = 5$.
   Thus, the equation of the circle is
   $$(x - h)^2 + (y - k)^2 = r^2$$
   $$(x - 2)^2 + (y - 4)^2 = 5^2$$
   $$(x - 2)^2 + (y - 4)^2 = 25$$

2. We are given that $h = -2$, $k = 0$, and $r = \sqrt{2}$.
   Thus, the equation of the circle is
   $$(x - h)^2 + (y - k)^2 = r^2$$
   $$(x - (-2))^2 + (y - 0)^2 = \left(\sqrt{2}\right)^2$$
   $$(x + 2)^2 + y^2 = 2$$

3. $(x - 3)^2 + (y - 1)^2 = 4$
   $(x - 3)^2 + (y - 1)^2 = 2^2$
   The center is $(h, k) = (3, 1)$; the radius is $r = 2$.

4. $$(x + 5)^2 + y^2 = 16$$
   $$(x - (-5))^2 + (y - 0)^2 = 4^2$$
   The center is $(h, k) = (-5, 0)$; the radius is $r = 4$.

5. $$x^2 + y^2 - 6x - 4y + 4 = 0$$
   $$(x^2 - 6x) + (y^2 - 4y) = -4$$
   $$(x^2 - 6x + 9) + (y^2 - 4y + 4) = -4 + 9 + 4$$
   $$(x - 3)^2 + (y - 2)^2 = 9$$
   $$(x - 3)^2 + (y - 2)^2 = 3^2$$
   The center is $(h, k) = (3, 2)$; the radius is $r = 3$.

6. $$2x^2 + 2y^2 - 16x + 4y - 38 = 0$$
   $$\frac{2x^2 + 2y^2 - 16x + 4y - 38}{2} = \frac{0}{2}$$
   $$x^2 + y^2 - 8x + 2y - 19 = 0$$
   $$(x^2 - 8x) + (y^2 + 2y) = 19$$
   $$(x^2 - 8x + 16) + (y^2 + 2y + 1) = 19 + 16 + 1$$
   $$(x - 4)^2 + (y + 1)^2 = 36$$
   $$(x - 4)^2 + (y - (-1))^2 = 6^2$$
   The center is $(h, k) = (4, -1)$; the radius is $r = 6$.

10.3 Quick Checks

1. Notice that $y^2 = 8x$ is of the form $y^2 = 4ax$, where $4a = 8$, so that $a = 2$. Now, the graph of an equation of the form $y^2 = 4ax$ will be a parabola that opens to the right with the vertex at the origin, focus at $(a, 0)$, and directrix of $x = -a$. Thus, the graph of $y^2 = 8x$ is a parabola that opens to the right with vertex $(0, 0)$, focus $(2, 0)$, and directrix $x = -2$. To help graph the parabola, we plot the two points on the graph above and below the focus. Let $x = 2$:
   $$y^2 = 8(2)$$
   $$y^2 = 16$$
   $$y = \pm 4$$
   The points $(2, -4)$ and $(2, 4)$ are on the graph.

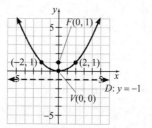

2. Notice that $y^2 = -20x$ is of the form $y^2 = -4ax$, where $-4a = -20$, so that $a = 5$. Now, the graph of an equation of the form $y^2 = -4ax$ will be a parabola that opens to the left with the vertex at the origin, focus at $(-a, 0)$, and directrix of $x = a$. Thus, the graph of $y^2 = -20x$ is a parabola that opens to the left with vertex $(0,0)$, focus $(-5, 0)$, and directrix $x = 5$. To help graph the parabola, we plot the two points on the graph above and below the focus. Let $x = 5$:

$$y^2 = -20(-5)$$
$$y^2 = 100$$
$$y = \pm 10$$

The points $(-5, -10)$ and $(-5, 10)$ are on the graph.

3. Notice that $x^2 = 4y$ is of the form $x^2 = 4ay$, where $4a = 4$, so that $a = 1$. Now, the graph of an equation of the form $x^2 = 4ay$ will be a parabola that opens up with the vertex at the origin, focus at $(0, a)$, and directrix of $y = -a$. Thus, the graph of $x^2 = 4y$ is a parabola that opens up with vertex $(0,0)$, focus $(0, 1)$, and directrix $y = -1$. To help graph the parabola, we plot the two points on the graph to the left and to the right of the focus. Let $y = 1$:

$$x^2 = 4(1)$$
$$x^2 = 4$$
$$x = \pm 2$$

The points $(-2, 1)$ and $(2, 1)$ are on the graph.

4. Notice that $x^2 = -12y$ is of the form $x^2 = -4ay$, where $-4a = -12$, so that $a = 3$. Now, the graph of an equation of the form $x^2 = -4ay$ will be a parabola that opens down with the vertex at the origin, focus at $(0, -a)$, and directrix of $y = a$. Thus, the graph of $x^2 = -12y$ is a parabola that opens down with vertex $(0,0)$, focus $(0, -3)$, and directrix $y = 3$. To help graph the parabola, we plot the two points on the graph to the left and to the right of the focus. Let $y = -3$:

$$x^2 = -12(-3)$$
$$x^2 = 36$$
$$x = \pm 6$$

The points $(-6, -3)$ and $(6, -3)$ are on the graph.

5. The distance from the vertex $(0,0)$ to the focus $(0, -8)$ is $a = 8$. Because the focus lies on the negative y-axis, we know that the parabola will open down and the axis of symmetry is the y-axis. This means the equation of the parabola is of the form $x^2 = -4ay$ with $a = 8$:

$$x^2 = -4(8)y$$
$$x^2 = -32y$$

The directrix is the line $y = 8$. To help graph the parabola, we plot the two points on the graph to the left and right of the focus. Let $y = -8$:

$$x^2 = -32(-8) = 256$$
$$x = \pm 16$$

The points $(-16, -8)$ and $(16, -8)$ are on the graph.

QC – 123

6. The vertex is at the origin and the axis of symmetry is the x-axis, so the parabola either opens left or right. Because the graph contains the point $(3, 2)$, which is in quadrant I, the parabola must open right. Therefore, the equation of the parabola is of the form $y^2 = 4ax$. Now $y = 2$ when $x = 3$, so

$$y^2 = 4ax$$
$$2^2 = 4a(3)$$
$$4 = 12a$$
$$a = \frac{4}{12} = \frac{1}{3}$$

The equation of the parabola is

$$y^2 = 4\left(\frac{1}{3}\right)x$$
$$y^2 = \frac{4}{3}x$$

With $a = \frac{1}{3}$, we know that the focus is $\left(\frac{1}{3},\ 0\right)$ and the directrix is the line $x = -\frac{1}{3}$. To help graph the parabola, we plot the two points on the graph to the left and right of the focus. Let $x = \frac{1}{3}$:

$$y^2 = \frac{4}{3}\left(\frac{1}{3}\right)$$
$$y^2 = \frac{4}{9}$$
$$y = \pm\frac{2}{3}$$

The points $\left(\frac{1}{3}, -\frac{2}{3}\right)$ and $\left(\frac{1}{3},\ \frac{2}{3}\right)$ are on the graph.

7. We complete the square in y to write the equation in standard form:

$$y^2 - 4y - 12x - 32 = 0$$
$$y^2 - 4y = 12x + 32$$
$$y^2 - 4y + 4 = 12x + 32 + 4$$
$$y^2 - 4y + 4 = 12x + 36$$
$$(y - 2)^2 = 12(x + 3)$$

Notice that the equation is of the form $(y - k)^2 = 4a(x - h)$. The graph is a parabola that opens right with vertex $(h,\ k) = (-3,\ 2)$. Since $4a = 12$, we have that $a = 3$. The focus is $(h + a,\ k) = (-3 + 3,\ 2) = (0,\ 2)$, and the directrix is $x = h - a = -3 - 3 = -6$. To help graph the parabola, we plot the two points on the graph above and below the focus. Let $x = 0$:

$$(y - 2)^2 = 12(0 + 3)$$
$$(y - 2)^2 = 12(3)$$
$$(y - 2)^2 = 36$$
$$y - 2 = \pm 6$$
$$y = 2 \pm 6$$
$$y = -4 \text{ or } y = 8$$

The points $(0, -4)$ and $(0,\ 8)$ are on the graph.

8. The receiver should be located at the focus of the satellite dish, so we need to find where the focus of the satellite dish is. To solve this problem, we draw a parabola on a Cartesian plane so that the vertex is the origin and the focus is on the positive y-axis. The width of the parabola is 4 feet, and the depth is 6 inches $= 0.5$ feet. Therefore, we know two points on the graph of the parabola: $(-2, 0.5)$ and $(2, 0.5)$.

The equation of the parabola has the form $x^2 = 4ay$. Since $(2, 0.5)$ is a point on the graph, we have

$$2^2 = 4a(0.5)$$
$$4 = 2a$$
$$2 = a$$

The receiver should be located 2 feet from the base of the dish along its axis of symmetry.

10.4 Quick Checks

1. $\dfrac{x^2}{9} + \dfrac{y^2}{4} = 1$

The larger number, 9, is in the denominator of the x^2-term. This means that the major axis is the x-axis and that the equation of the ellipse is of the form $\dfrac{x^2}{a^2} + \dfrac{y^2}{b^2} = 1$, so that $a^2 = 9$ and $b^2 = 4$. The center of the ellipse is $(0,0)$. Because $b^2 = a^2 - c^2$, or $c^2 = a^2 - b^2$, we have that $c^2 = 9 - 4 = 5$, so that $c = \pm\sqrt{5}$. Since the major axis is the x-axis, the foci are $\left(-\sqrt{5}, 0\right)$ and $\left(\sqrt{5}, 0\right)$. To find the x-intercepts (vertices), let $y = 0$; to find the y-intercepts, let $x = 0$:

x-intercepts:

$$\dfrac{x^2}{9} + \dfrac{0^2}{4} = 1$$
$$\dfrac{x^2}{9} = 1$$
$$x^2 = 9$$
$$x = \pm 3$$

y-intercepts:

$$\dfrac{0^2}{9} + \dfrac{y^2}{4} = 1$$
$$\dfrac{y^2}{4} = 1$$
$$y^2 = 4$$
$$y = \pm 2$$

The intercepts are $(-3,0)$, $(3,0)$, $(0,-2)$, and $(0,2)$.

2. $\dfrac{x^2}{16} + \dfrac{y^2}{36} = 1$

The larger number, 36, is in the denominator of the y^2-term. This means that the major axis is the y-axis and that the equation of the ellipse is of the form $\dfrac{x^2}{b^2} + \dfrac{y^2}{a^2} = 1$, so that $a^2 = 36$ and $b^2 = 16$. The center of the ellipse is $(0,0)$. Because $b^2 = a^2 - c^2$, or $c^2 = a^2 - b^2$, we have that $c^2 = 36 - 16 = 20$, so that $c = \pm\sqrt{20} = \pm 2\sqrt{5}$. Since the major axis is the y-axis, the foci are $\left(0, -2\sqrt{5}\right)$ and $\left(0, 2\sqrt{5}\right)$. To find the x-intercepts, let $y = 0$; to find the y-intercepts (vertices), let $x = 0$:

x-intercepts:

$$\dfrac{x^2}{16} + \dfrac{0^2}{36} = 1$$
$$\dfrac{x^2}{16} = 1$$
$$x^2 = 16$$
$$x = \pm 4$$

y-intercepts:

$$\dfrac{0^2}{16} + \dfrac{y^2}{36} = 1$$
$$\dfrac{y^2}{36} = 1$$
$$y^2 = 36$$
$$y = \pm 6$$

The intercepts are $(-4,0)$, $(4,0)$, $(0,-6)$, and $(0,6)$.

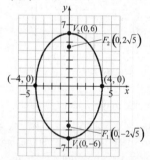

3. The given focus $(0, 3)$ and the given vertex $(0, 7)$ lie on the y-axis. Thus, the major axis is the y-axis, and the equation of the ellipse is of the form $\dfrac{x^2}{b^2} + \dfrac{y^2}{a^2} = 1$. The distance from the center of the ellipse to the vertex is $a = 7$ units. The distance from the center of the ellipse to the focus is $c = 3$ units. Because $b^2 = a^2 - c^2$, we have that $b^2 = 7^2 - 3^2 = 49 - 9 = 40$. So, the equation of the ellipse is $\dfrac{x^2}{40} + \dfrac{y^2}{49} = 1$.

To help graph the ellipse, find the x-intercepts:

Let $y = 0$: $\dfrac{x^2}{40} + \dfrac{0^2}{49} = 1$

$$\dfrac{x^2}{40} = 1$$
$$x^2 = 40$$
$$x = \pm\sqrt{40} = \pm 2\sqrt{10}$$

The x-intercepts are $\left(-2\sqrt{10}, 0\right)$ and $\left(2\sqrt{10}, 0\right)$.

4.
$$9x^2 + y^2 + 54x - 2y + 73 = 0$$
$$9x^2 + y^2 + 54x - 2y + 73 = 0$$
$$9x^2 + 54x + y^2 - 2y = -73$$
$$9\left(x^2 + 6x\right) + \left(y^2 - 2y\right) = -73$$
$$9\left(x^2 + 6x + 9\right) + \left(y^2 - 2y + 1\right) = -73 + 9(9) + 1$$
$$9\left(x+3\right)^2 + \left(y-1\right)^2 = 9$$
$$\dfrac{9\left(x+3\right)^2 + \left(y-1\right)^2}{9} = \dfrac{9}{9}$$
$$\dfrac{\left(x+3\right)^2}{1} + \dfrac{\left(y-1\right)^2}{9} = 1$$

The center of the ellipse is $(h,k) = (-3,1)$.
Because the larger number, 9, is the denominator of the y^2-term, the major axis is parallel to the y-axis. Because $a^2 = 9$ and $b^2 = 1$, we have that $c^2 = a^2 - b^2 = 9 - 1 = 8$. The vertices are $a = 3$ units below and above the center at $V_1(-3,-2)$ and $V_2(-3,4)$. The foci are $c = \sqrt{8} = 2\sqrt{2}$ units below and above the center at $F_1\left(-3,\ 1-2\sqrt{2}\right)$ and $F_2\left(-3,\ 1+2\sqrt{2}\right)$. We plot the points $b = 1$ unit to the left and right of the center point at $(-4,\ 1)$ and $(-2,\ 1)$.

5. To solve the problem, we draw the ellipse on a Cartesian plane so that the center of the ellipse is at the origin and the major axis is along the x-axis. The equation of the ellipse is of the form $\dfrac{x^2}{a^2} + \dfrac{y^2}{b^2} = 1$. Since the length of the hall is 100 feet, the distance from the center of the room to each vertex is $a = \dfrac{100}{2} = 50$ feet. The distance from the center of the room to each focus is $c = 30$ feet.

Now, because $b^2 = a^2 - c^2$, we have that $b^2 = 50^2 - 30^2 = 2500 - 900 = 1600$. Thus, the equation that describes the room is
$$\dfrac{x^2}{2500} + \dfrac{y^2}{1600} = 1.$$
The height of the room at its center is $b = \sqrt{1600} = 40$ feet.

10.5 Quick Checks

1. $\dfrac{x^2}{36} - \dfrac{y^2}{64} = 1$

Notice the equation is of the form $\dfrac{x^2}{a^2} - \dfrac{y^2}{b^2} = 1$.

Because the x^2-term is first, the transverse axis is the x-axis and the hyperbola opens left and right. The center of the hyperbola is the origin. We have that $a^2 = 36$ and $b^2 = 64$. Because $c^2 = a^2 + b^2$, we have that $c^2 = 36 + 64 = 100$, so that $c = \sqrt{100} = 10$. The vertices are $(\pm a, 0) = (\pm 6, 0)$, and the foci are $(\pm c, 0) = (\pm 10, 0)$. To help graph the hyperbola, we plot the points on the graph above and below the foci. Let $x = \pm 10$:
$$\dfrac{\left(\pm 10\right)^2}{36} - \dfrac{y^2}{64} = 1$$
$$\dfrac{100}{36} - \dfrac{y^2}{64} = 1$$
$$\dfrac{25}{9} - \dfrac{y^2}{64} = 1$$

$$-\frac{y^2}{64} = -\frac{16}{9}$$

$$y^2 = \frac{1024}{9}$$

$$y = \pm\frac{32}{3}$$

The points above and below the foci are

$$\left(-10, -\frac{32}{3}\right), \left(-10, \frac{32}{3}\right), \left(10, -\frac{32}{3}\right), \text{ and}$$

$$\left(10, \frac{32}{3}\right).$$

2. $\dfrac{y^2}{9} - \dfrac{x^2}{16} = 1$

Notice the equation is of the form $\dfrac{y^2}{a^2} - \dfrac{x^2}{b^2} = 1$.

Because the y^2-term is first, the transverse axis
is the y-axis and the hyperbola opens up and
down. The center of the hyperbola is the origin.
We have that $a^2 = 9$ and $b^2 = 16$. Because
$c^2 = a^2 + b^2$, we have that $c^2 = 9 + 16 = 25$, so
that $c = \sqrt{25} = 5$. The vertices are
$(0, \pm a) = (0, \pm 3)$, and the foci are
$(0, \pm c) = (0, \pm 5)$. To help graph the hyperbola,
we plot the points on the graph to the left and
right of the foci. Let $y = \pm 5$:

$$\frac{(\pm 5)^2}{9} - \frac{x^2}{16} = 1$$

$$\frac{25}{9} - \frac{x^2}{16} = 1$$

$$-\frac{x^2}{16} = -\frac{16}{9}$$

$$x^2 = \frac{256}{9}$$

$$x = \pm\frac{16}{3}$$

The points to the left and right of the foci are

$$\left(-\frac{16}{3}, -5\right), \left(-\frac{16}{3}, 5\right), \left(\frac{16}{3}, -5\right), \text{ and } \left(\frac{16}{3}, 5\right).$$

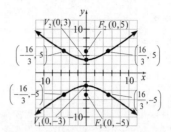

3. The given vertices $(\pm 4, 0)$ and focus $(6, 0)$ all lie
on the x-axis. Thus, the transverse axis is the x-
axis and the hyperbola opens left and right. The
center of the hyperbola is the midpoint between the
two vertices. Therefore, the center is $(0,0)$ and
the equation of the hyperbola is of the form
$\dfrac{x^2}{a^2} - \dfrac{y^2}{b^2} = 1$. Now, the distance from the center
$(0,0)$ to each vertex is $a = 4$ units. Likewise, the
distance from the center to the given focus $(6, 0)$
is $c = 6$ units. Also, $b^2 = c^2 - a^2$, so
$b^2 = 6^2 - 4^2 = 36 - 16 = 20$. Thus, the equation of
the hyperbola is $\dfrac{x^2}{16} - \dfrac{y^2}{20} = 1$.

To help graph the hyperbola, we first find the focus
that was not given. Since the center is at $(0,0)$
and since one focus is at $(6, 0)$, the other focus
must be at $(-6, 0)$. Next, plot the points on the
graph to the left and right of the foci. Let $x = \pm 6$:

$$\frac{(\pm 6)^2}{16} - \frac{y^2}{20} = 1$$

$$\frac{36}{16} - \frac{y^2}{20} = 1$$

$$\frac{9}{4} - \frac{y^2}{20} = 1$$

$$-\frac{y^2}{20} = -\frac{5}{4}$$

$$y^2 = 25$$

$$y = \pm 5$$

The points to the left and right of the foci are
$(-6, -5)$, $(-6, 5)$, $(6, -5)$, and $(6, 5)$.

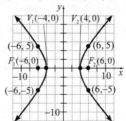

4. $x^2 - 9y^2 = 9$

$$\frac{x^2 - 9y^2}{9} = \frac{9}{9}$$

$$\frac{x^2}{9} - \frac{y^2}{1} = 1$$

Notice that the equation is of the form

$\dfrac{x^2}{a^2} - \dfrac{y^2}{b^2} = 1$. The center of the hyperbola is

$(0,0)$. Because the x^2-term is first, the hyperbola opens left and right. The transverse axis is along the x-axis. We have that $a^2 = 9$ and $b^2 = 1$. Because $c^2 = a^2 + b^2$, we have that $c^2 = 9 + 1 = 10$, so that $c = \sqrt{10}$. The vertices are $(\pm a, 0) = (\pm 3, 0)$, and the foci are $(\pm c, 0) = \left(\pm\sqrt{10}, 0\right)$. The asymptotes are of the form $y = -\dfrac{b}{a}x$ and $y = \dfrac{b}{a}x$. Since $a = 3$ and $b = 1$, the equations of the asymptotes are $y = -\dfrac{1}{3}x$ and $y = \dfrac{1}{3}x$. To help graph the hyperbola, we form the rectangle using the points $(\pm a, 0) = (\pm 3, 0)$ and $(0, \pm b) = (0, \pm 1)$. The diagonals are the asymptotes.

5. $\dfrac{y^2}{16} - \dfrac{x^2}{9} = 1$

Notice the equation is of the form $\dfrac{y^2}{a^2} - \dfrac{x^2}{b^2} = 1$.

Because the y^2-term is first, the transverse is along the y-axis and the hyperbola opens up and down. The center of the hyperbola is $(0,0)$. We have that $a^2 = 16$ and $b^2 = 9$. Because $c^2 = a^2 + b^2$, we have that $c^2 = 16 + 9 = 25$, so that $c = \sqrt{25} = 5$. The vertices are $(0, \pm a) = (0, \pm 4)$, and the foci are $(0, \pm c) = (0, \pm 5)$. The asymptotes are of the form $y = -\dfrac{a}{b}x$ and $y = \dfrac{a}{b}x$. Since $a = 4$ and $b = 3$, the equations of the asymptotes

are $y = -\dfrac{4}{3}x$ and $y = \dfrac{4}{3}x$. To help graph the hyperbola, we form the rectangle using the points $(0, \pm a) = (0, \pm 4)$ and $(\pm b, 0) = (\pm 3, 0)$. The diagonals are the asymptotes.

10.6 Quick Checks

1. $\begin{cases} 2x + y = -1 \\ x^2 - y = 4 \end{cases}$

First, graph each equation in the system.

The system apparently has two solutions. Now solve the first equation for y: $y = -2x - 1$.

Substitute the result for y into the second equation:

$$x^2 - (-2x - 1) = 4$$

$$x^2 + 2x + 1 = 4$$

$$x^2 + 2x - 3 = 0$$

$$(x - 1)(x + 3) = 0$$

$$x = 1 \text{ or } x = -3$$

Substitute these x-values into the first equation to find the corresponding y-values:

$x = 1$: $2(1) + y = -1$

$$2 + y = -1$$

$$y = -3$$

$x = -3$: $2(-3) + y = -1$

$$-6 + y = -1$$

$$y = 5$$

Both pairs check, so the solutions are $(-3, 5)$ and $(1, -3)$.

2. $\begin{cases} 2x + y = 0 \\ (x-4)^2 + (y+2)^2 = 9 \end{cases}$

First, graph each equation in the system.

The system apparently has two solutions. Now solve the first equation for y: $y = -2x$.

Substitute the result for y into the second equation:

$$(x-4)^2 + (-2x+2)^2 = 9$$
$$x^2 - 8x + 16 + 4x^2 - 8x + 4 = 9$$
$$5x^2 - 16x + 11 = 0$$
$$(5x-11)(x-1) = 0$$
$$x = \frac{11}{5} \quad \text{or} \quad x = 1$$

Substitute these x-values into the first equation to find the corresponding y-values:

$$x = \frac{11}{5}: \ 2\left(\frac{11}{5}\right) + y = 0$$
$$\frac{22}{5} + y = 0$$
$$y = -\frac{22}{5}$$
$$x = 1: \ 2(1) + y = 0$$
$$2 + y = 0$$
$$y = -2$$

Both pairs check, so the solutions are $(1, -2)$ and $\left(\frac{11}{5}, -\frac{22}{5}\right)$.

3. $\begin{cases} x^2 + y^2 = 16 \\ x^2 - 2y = 8 \end{cases}$

First, graph each equation in the system.

The system apparently has three solutions. Now multiply the second equation by -1 and add the result to the first equation:

$$\begin{array}{r} x^2 + y^2 = 16 \\ -x^2 + 2y = -8 \\ \hline y^2 + 2y = 8 \end{array}$$
$$y^2 + 2y - 8 = 0$$
$$(y+4)(y-2) = 0$$
$$y = -4 \quad \text{or} \quad y = 2$$

Substitute these y-values into the first equation to find the corresponding x-values:

$$y = -4: \ x^2 + (-4)^2 = 16$$
$$x^2 + 16 = 16$$
$$x^2 = 0$$
$$x = 0$$
$$y = 2: \ x^2 + 2^2 = 16$$
$$x^2 + 4 = 16$$
$$x^2 = 12$$
$$x = \pm\sqrt{12} = \pm 2\sqrt{3}$$

All three pairs check, so the solutions are $(0, -4)$, $\left(-2\sqrt{3}, \ 2\right)$ and $\left(2\sqrt{3}, \ 2\right)$.

4. $\begin{cases} x^2 - y = -4 \\ x^2 + y^2 = 9 \end{cases}$

First, graph each equation in the system.

The system apparently has no solution. Now multiply the first equation by -1 and add the result to the second equation:

$$\begin{array}{r} -x^2 + y = 4 \\ x^2 + y^2 = 9 \\ \hline y^2 + y = 13 \end{array}$$
$$y^2 + y - 13 = 0$$
$$y = \frac{-1 \pm \sqrt{1^2 - 4(1)(-13)}}{2(1)}$$
$$= \frac{-1 \pm \sqrt{53}}{2}$$

Substitute these y-values into the first equation to find the corresponding x-values:

$$y = \frac{-1-\sqrt{53}}{2}: \quad x^2 - \left(\frac{-1-\sqrt{53}}{2}\right) = -4$$

$$x^2 = -4 + \left(\frac{-1-\sqrt{53}}{2}\right)$$

$$x^2 = \frac{-9-\sqrt{53}}{2}$$

$$x = \pm\sqrt{\frac{-9-\sqrt{53}}{2}} \quad \text{(not real)}$$

$$y = \frac{-1+\sqrt{53}}{2}: \quad x^2 - \left(\frac{-1+\sqrt{53}}{2}\right) = -4$$

$$x^2 = -4 + \left(\frac{-1+\sqrt{53}}{2}\right)$$

$$x^2 = \frac{-9+\sqrt{53}}{2}$$

$$x = \pm\sqrt{\frac{-9+\sqrt{53}}{2}} \quad \text{(not real)}$$

Since both *y*-values result in non-real *x*-values (because the values under each of the radicals are negative), the system of equations is inconsistent. The solution set is $\varnothing$.

Chapter 11 – Quick Checks

11.1 Quick Checks

1. $a_n = 2n - 3$

   $a_1 = 2(1) - 3 = 2 - 3 = -1$

   $a_2 = 2(2) - 3 = 4 - 3 = 1$

   $a_3 = 2(3) - 3 = 6 - 3 = 3$

   $a_4 = 2(4) - 3 = 8 - 3 = 5$

   $a_5 = 2(5) - 3 = 10 - 3 = 7$

   The first five terms of the sequence are -1, 1, 3, 5, and 7.

2. $b_n = (-1)^n \cdot 4n$

   $b_1 = (-1)^1 \cdot 4(1) = -4$

   $b_2 = (-1)^2 \cdot 4(2) = 8$

   $b_3 = (-1)^3 \cdot 4(3) = -12$

   $b_4 = (-1)^4 \cdot 4(4) = 16$

   $b_5 = (-1)^5 \cdot 4(5) = -20$

   The first five terms of the sequence are -4, 8, -12, 16, and -20.

3. $5, 7, 9, 11, \ldots$

   The terms are consecutive odd numbers with the first term being 5. We can write the terms as follows:

   $5 = 2(1) + 3$

   $7 = 2(2) + 3$

   $9 = 2(3) + 3$

   $11 = 2(4) + 3$

   Notice that each term is 3 more than twice the term number. A formula for the nth term is given by $a_n = 2n + 3$.

4. $\dfrac{1}{2}, -\dfrac{1}{3}, \dfrac{1}{4}, -\dfrac{1}{5}, \ldots$

   The terms alternate sign with the first term being positive. So, $(-1)^{n+1}$ must be part of the formula.

   Each term is a fraction with a numerator of 1 and a denominator that is 1 more than the term number. A formula for the nth term is given by

   $b_n = (-1)^{n+1} \cdot \dfrac{1}{n+1}$.

5. $\displaystyle\sum_{i=1}^{3}(4i - 1) = (4 \cdot 1 - 1) + (4 \cdot 2 - 1) + (4 \cdot 3 - 1)$

   $= 4 - 1 + 8 - 1 + 12 - 1$

   $= 21$

6. $\displaystyle\sum_{i=1}^{5}(i^3 + 1) = (1^3 + 1) + (2^3 + 1) + (3^3 + 1)$

   $\qquad\qquad\quad + (4^3 + 1) + (5^3 + 1)$

   $= (1 + 1) + (8 + 1) + (27 + 1)$

   $\qquad + (64 + 1) + (125 + 1)$

   $= 2 + 9 + 28 + 65 + 126$

   $= 230$

7. $1 + 4 + 9 + \ldots + 144$

   Notice that each term is a perfect square. We can rewrite the sum as $1^2 + 2^2 + 3^2 + \ldots + 12^2$. Thus, the sum has 12 terms, each of the form i^2.

   $1 + 4 + 9 + \ldots + 144 = \displaystyle\sum_{i=1}^{12} i^2$

8. Begin by writing the first term as $\dfrac{1}{1}$. We notice that each term is a fraction with a numerator of 1 and a denominator that is a power of 2. We can write the sum as

   $\dfrac{1}{2^0} + \dfrac{1}{2^1} + \dfrac{1}{2^2} + \ldots + \dfrac{1}{2^5}$

   The exponent on 2 in the denominator is always 1 less than the term number. Thus, the sum has 6 terms, each of the form $\dfrac{1}{2^{i-1}}$.

   $1 + \dfrac{1}{2} + \dfrac{1}{4} + \ldots + \dfrac{1}{32} = \displaystyle\sum_{i=1}^{6}\left(\dfrac{1}{2^{i-1}}\right)$

11.2 Quick Checks

1. $-1-(-3) = -1+3 = 2$
   $1-(-1) = 1+1 = 2$
   $3-1 = 2$
   $5-3 = 2$
   The sequence $-3, -1, 1, 3, 5, \ldots$ is arithmetic because the difference between consecutive terms is constant. The first term is $a = -3$ and the common difference is $d = 2$.

2. $9-3 = 6, \ 27-9 = 18, \ 81-27 = 54$
   The sequence is not arithmetic because the difference between consecutive terms is not constant.

3. $a_n - a_{n-1} = [3n-8] - [3(n-1)-8]$
   $\qquad\qquad = [3n-8] - [3n-11]$
   $\qquad\qquad = 3n-8-3n+11$
   $\qquad\qquad = 3$
   The sequence is arithmetic because the difference between consecutive terms is constant. The first term is $a = a_1 = 3(1)-8 = -5$ and the common difference is $d = 3$.

4. $b_n - b_{n-1} = \left[n^2 - 1\right] - \left[(n-1)^2 - 1\right]$
   $\qquad\qquad = \left[n^2-1\right] - \left[n^2-2n+1-1\right]$
   $\qquad\qquad = \left[n^2-1\right] - \left[n^2-2n\right]$
   $\qquad\qquad = n^2-1-n^2+2n$
   $\qquad\qquad = 2n-1$
   The sequence is not arithmetic because the difference between consecutive terms is not constant.

5. $c_n - c_{n-1} = [5-2n] - [5-2(n-1)]$
   $\qquad\qquad = [5-2n] - [5-2n+2]$
   $\qquad\qquad = [5-2n] - [7-2n]$
   $\qquad\qquad = 5-2n-7+2n$
   $\qquad\qquad = -2$
   The sequence is arithmetic because the difference between consecutive terms is constant. The first term is $a = c_1 = 5-2(1) = 3$ and the common difference is $d = -2$.

6. **a.** We have that $a_5 = 25$ and $d = 6$.
   $a_n = a+(n-1)d$
   $a_5 = a+(5-1)d$
   $25 = a+4(6)$
   $25 = a+24$
   $1 = a$
   Therefore, the nth term of the sequence is given by
   $a_n = 1+(n-1)(6) = 1+6n-6$
   $a_n = 6n-5$

   b. $a_{14} = 6(14)-5 = 84-5 = 79$

7. **a.** We are given $a_5 = 7$ and $a_{13} = 31$. The nth term of an arithmetic sequence is given by $a_n = a+(n-1)d$. Therefore, we have
   $\begin{cases} a_5 = a+(5-1)d & \text{or} \\ a_{13} = a+(13-1)d \end{cases}$
   $\begin{cases} 7 = a+4d & (1) \\ 31 = a+12d & (2) \end{cases}$
   This is a system of linear equations in a and d. We can solve the system by using elimination. Subtract equation (2) from equation (1) to obtain
   $-24 = -8d$
   $\ \ 3 = d$
   Let $d = 3$ in equation (1) and solve for a.
   $7 = a+4(3)$
   $7 = a+12$
   $-5 = a$
   The first term is $a = -5$ and the common difference is $d = 3$.

   b. A formula for the nth term is
   $a_n = a+(n-1)d = -5+(n-1)(3)$
   $\qquad = -5+3n-3$
   $a_n = 3n-8$

8. We have $a = 5$ and $d = 2$, and wish to find S_{100}.
   $S_n = \dfrac{n}{2}\left[2a+(n-1)d\right]$
   $S_{100} = \dfrac{100}{2}\left[2(5)+(100-1)(2)\right] = 50\left[10+198\right]$
   $\qquad = 50(208) = 10,400$

9. The first term is $a = 1$ and the common difference is $d = 5 - 1 = 4$. We wish to find S_{70}.

$$S_n = \frac{n}{2}\left[2a + (n-1)d\right]$$
$$S_{70} = \frac{70}{2}\left[2(1) + (70-1)(4)\right]$$
$$= 35\left[2 + 276\right]$$
$$= 35(278)$$
$$= 9,730$$

10. We have $a = 4$ and $a_{50} = 298$, and wish to find the sum of the first 50 terms, S_{50}.

$$S_n = \frac{n}{2}\left[a + a_n\right]$$
$$S_{50} = \frac{50}{2}\left[a + a_{50}\right]$$
$$= \frac{50}{2}\left[4 + 298\right]$$
$$= 25(302)$$
$$= 7,550$$

11. $a_n = -3n + 100$

$$a = a_1 = -3(1) + 100 = 97$$
$$a_{75} = -3(75) + 100 = -125$$
$$S_n = \frac{n}{2}\left[a + a_n\right]$$
$$S_{75} = \frac{75}{2}\left[a + a_{75}\right]$$
$$S_{75} = \frac{75}{2}\left[97 + (-125)\right]$$
$$= \frac{75}{2}(-28)$$
$$= -1,050$$

12. If we let a_n = the number of seats in the nth row, then we have an arithmetic sequence with first term $a = 20$ and common difference $d = 2$. Thus, the total number of seats in the 30 rows is given by S_{30}.

$$S_n = \frac{n}{2}\left[2a + (n-1)d\right]$$
$$S_{30} = \frac{30}{2}\left[2a + (30-1)d\right] = 15\left[2(20) + 29(2)\right]$$
$$= 15(98) = 1,470$$

There are 1,470 seats in the 30 rows.

11.3 Quick Checks

1. $\dfrac{8}{4} = 2$, $\dfrac{16}{8} = 2$, $\dfrac{32}{16} = 2$, $\dfrac{64}{32} = 2$

The sequence is geometric because the ratio of consecutive terms is constant. The first term is $a = 4$ and the common ratio is $r = 2$.

2. $\dfrac{10}{5} = 2$, $\dfrac{16}{10} = \dfrac{8}{5}$

The sequence is not geometric because the ratio of consecutive terms is not constant.

3. $\dfrac{3}{9} = \dfrac{1}{3}$, $\dfrac{1}{3}$, $\dfrac{\frac{1}{3}}{1} = \dfrac{1}{3}$, $\dfrac{\frac{1}{9}}{\frac{1}{3}} = \dfrac{1}{9} \cdot 3 = \dfrac{1}{3}$

The sequence is geometric because the ratio of consecutive terms is constant. The first term is $a = 9$ and the common ratio is $r = \dfrac{3}{9} = \dfrac{1}{3}$.

4. $\dfrac{a_n}{a_{n-1}} = \dfrac{5^n}{5^{n-1}} = \dfrac{5 \cdot 5^{n-1}}{5^{n-1}} = 5$

The sequence is geometric because the ratio of consecutive terms is constant. The first term is $a = a_1 = 5^1 = 5$ and the common ratio is $r = 5$.

5. $\dfrac{b_n}{b_{n-1}} = \dfrac{n^2}{(n-1)^2} = \dfrac{n^2}{n^2 - 2n + 1}$

The sequence is not geometric because the ratio of consecutive terms is not constant.

6. $\dfrac{c_n}{c_{n-1}} = \dfrac{5\left(\frac{2}{3}\right)^n}{5\left(\frac{2}{3}\right)^{n-1}} = \dfrac{5 \cdot \frac{2}{3} \cdot \left(\frac{2}{3}\right)^{n-1}}{5\left(\frac{2}{3}\right)^{n-1}} = \dfrac{2}{3}$

The sequence is geometric because the ratio of consecutive terms is constant. The first term is $a = a_1 = 5\left(\dfrac{2}{3}\right)^1 = \dfrac{10}{3}$ and the common ratio is $r = \dfrac{2}{3}$.

7. The nth term of a geometric sequence is given by $a_n = a \cdot r^{n-1}$. We are given $a = 5$ and $r = 2$. Therefore, a formula for the nth term of the sequence is $a_n = 5 \cdot 2^{n-1}$.

$$a_9 = 5 \cdot 2^{9-1} = 5 \cdot 2^8 = 5(256) = 1,280$$

QC – 133

8. The nth term of a geometric sequence is given by $a_n = a \cdot r^{n-1}$. We are given that the first term is $a = 50$ and the common ratio is $r = \frac{25}{50} = \frac{1}{2}$. Therefore, a formula for the nth term of the sequence is $a_n = 50 \cdot \left(\frac{1}{2}\right)^{n-1}$.

$$a_9 = 50 \cdot \left(\frac{1}{2}\right)^{9-1} = 50 \cdot \left(\frac{1}{2}\right)^{8} = \frac{50}{256}$$

$$= \frac{25}{128} = 0.1953125$$

9. We wish to find the sum of the first 13 terms of a geometric sequence with first term $a = 3$ and common ratio $r = \frac{6}{3} = 2$.

$$S_n = a \cdot \frac{1-r^n}{1-r}$$

$$S_{13} = 3 \cdot \frac{1-2^{13}}{1-2} = 3(8191) = 24{,}573$$

10. We wish to find the sum of the first 10 terms of a geometric sequence with first term $a = 8\left(\frac{1}{2}\right)^1 = 4$ and common ratio $r = \frac{1}{2}$.

$$S_n = a \cdot \frac{1-r^n}{1-r}$$

$$S_{10} = 4 \cdot \frac{1-\left(\frac{1}{2}\right)^{10}}{1-\frac{1}{2}} = 4\left(\frac{\frac{1023}{1024}}{\frac{1}{2}}\right) = 4\left(\frac{1023}{512}\right)$$

$$= \frac{1023}{128} = 7.9921875$$

11. This is an infinite geometric series with $a = 10$ and $r = \frac{\frac{5}{2}}{10} = \frac{5}{2} \cdot \frac{1}{10} = \frac{1}{4}$. Since the common ratio is between -1 and 1, we can use the formula for the sum of an infinite geometric series to find

$$S_\infty = \frac{a}{1-r}$$

$$S_\infty = \frac{10}{1-\frac{1}{4}} = \frac{10}{\frac{3}{4}} = 10 \cdot \frac{4}{3} = \frac{40}{3}$$

12. This is an infinite geometric series with $a = a_1 = \left(\frac{1}{3}\right)^1 = \frac{1}{3}$ and $r = \frac{1}{3}$. Since the common ratio is between -1 and 1, we can use the formula for the sum of an infinite geometric series to find

$$S_\infty = \frac{a}{1-r}$$

$$S_\infty = \frac{\frac{1}{3}}{1-\frac{1}{3}} = \frac{\frac{1}{3}}{\frac{2}{3}} = \frac{1}{3} \cdot \frac{3}{2} = \frac{1}{2}$$

13. The line over the 2 indicates that the 2 repeats indefinitely. That is, we can write
$$0.\overline{2} = 0.2 + 0.02 + 0.002 + 0.0002 + \ldots$$
This is an infinite geometric series with $a = 0.2$ and common ratio $r = 0.1$. Since the common ratio is between -1 and 1, we can use the formula for the sum of a geometric series to find that
$$0.\overline{2} = 0.2 + 0.02 + 0.002 + 0.0002 + \ldots$$

$$= \frac{0.2}{1-0.1}$$

$$= \frac{0.2}{0.9}$$

$$= \frac{2}{9}$$

14. The total impact of the $500 tax rebate on the U.S. economy is
$$\$500 + \$500(0.95) + \$500(0.95)^2 + \$500(0.95)^3 + \ldots$$
This is an infinite geometric series with first term $a = 500$ and common ratio $r = 0.95$. The sum of this series is
$$\$500 + \$500(0.95) + \$500(0.95)^2 + \ldots$$

$$= \frac{\$500}{1-0.95}$$

$$= \frac{\$500}{0.05}$$

$$= \$10{,}000$$

The U.S. economy will grow by $10,000 because of the child tax credit to Roberta.

15. This is an ordinary annuity with $n = 4 \cdot 30 = 120$ payments with deposits of $P = \$500$. The interest rate per payment period is

$i = \dfrac{0.08}{4} = 0.02$. This gives

$$A = 500\left[\dfrac{(1+0.02)^{120} - 1}{0.02}\right]$$

$$= 500(488.258152)$$

$$= 244{,}129.08$$

After 30 years, the IRA will be worth $244,129.08.

11.4 Quick Checks

1. $9! = 9 \cdot 8 \cdot 7 \cdot 6 \cdot 5 \cdot 4 \cdot 3 \cdot 2 \cdot 1 = 362{,}880$

2. $\dfrac{7!}{3!} = \dfrac{7 \cdot 6 \cdot 5 \cdot 4 \cdot 3!}{3!} = 7 \cdot 6 \cdot 5 \cdot 4 = 840$

3. $\dbinom{7}{1} = \dfrac{7!}{1! \cdot (7-1)!} = \dfrac{7!}{6!} = \dfrac{7 \cdot 6!}{6!} = 7$

4. $\dbinom{6}{3} = \dfrac{6!}{3! \cdot (6-3)!} = \dfrac{6 \cdot 5 \cdot 4 \cdot 3!}{3! \cdot 3!} = \dfrac{6 \cdot 5 \cdot 4}{3 \cdot 2 \cdot 1} = 20$

5. $(x+2)^4 = \dbinom{4}{0}x^4 + \dbinom{4}{1}2^1 \cdot x^{4-1} + \dbinom{4}{2}2^2 \cdot x^{4-2} + \dbinom{4}{3}2^3 \cdot x^{4-3} + \dbinom{4}{4}2^4$

$$= 1 \cdot x^4 + 4 \cdot 2 \cdot x^3 + 6 \cdot 4 \cdot x^2 + 4 \cdot 8 \cdot x + 1 \cdot 16$$

$$= x^4 + 8x^3 + 24x^2 + 32x + 16$$

6. $(2p-1)^5$

$$= \left(2p + (-1)\right)^5$$

$$= \dbinom{5}{0}(2p)^5 + \dbinom{5}{1}(-1)^1 \cdot (2p)^{5-1} + \dbinom{5}{2}(-1)^2 \cdot (2p)^{5-2} + \dbinom{5}{3}(-1)^3 \cdot (2p)^{5-3} + \dbinom{5}{4}(-1)^4 \cdot (2p)^{5-4} + \dbinom{5}{5}(-1)^5$$

$$= 1 \cdot (2p)^5 + 5 \cdot (-1) \cdot (2p)^4 + 10 \cdot (-1)^2 \cdot (2p)^3 + 10 \cdot (-1)^3 \cdot (2p)^2 + 5 \cdot (-1)^4 \cdot (2p) + 1 \cdot (-1)^5$$

$$= 32p^5 + 5(-1)\left(16p^4\right) + 10(1)\left(8p^3\right) + 10(-1)\left(4p^2\right) + 5(1)(2p) + 1(-1)$$

$$= 32p^5 - 80p^4 + 80p^3 - 40p^2 + 10p - 1$$

Chapter R

R.1 Exercises

Answers will vary

R.2 Exercises

1. set

3. rational

5. True. The order of the elements in a list does not matter.

7. False. If a number is rational, it cannot be irrational and vice-versa.

9. True. The set of rational numbers is a subset of the set of real numbers.

11. No; if a number is rational, it cannot be irrational and vice-versa.
    No; every real number, when written in decimal form, will either terminate (rational), have a repeating block (rational), or neither terminate nor repeat (irrational).

13. Answers will vary.

15. If A is a subset of B, then all the elements that are in set A are also in set B. Thus B is a subset of B. If A is a proper subset of B, then all the elements that are in set A are also elements in set B, but there are elements in B that are not in set A. Thus, B is not a proper subset of B.

17. If the digit *after* the specified final digit is 4 or less, then truncating and rounding will yield the same decimal approximation.

19. $\{0,1,2,3,4,5\}$

21. $\{-2,-1,0,1,2,3,4\}$

23. $\varnothing$ or $\{\ \}$

25. The statement $B \subseteq C$ is true since all the elements of B are also elements of C.

27. In order for B to be a proper subset of D, it must be the case that all the elements that are in B are also elements in D. In addition, there must be elements that are in D that are not in B. Because $B = D$, this statement is false.

29. The statement $B = D$ is true because sets B and D have the same elements.

31. The statement $\varnothing \subset C$ is true because the empty set is a subset of every set, and the set C is not empty.

33. $\dfrac{1}{2} \notin \{x \mid x \text{ is an integer}\}$

35. $\pi \in \{x \mid x \text{ is a real number}\}$

37. **a.** 4

    b. $-5, 4$

    c. $-5, 4, \dfrac{4}{3}, -\dfrac{7}{5}, 5.\overline{1}$

    d. π

    e. $-5, 4, \dfrac{4}{3}, -\dfrac{7}{5}, 5.\overline{1}, \pi$

39. **a.** 100

    b. $100, -64$

    c. $100, -5.423, \dfrac{8}{7}, -64$

    d. $\sqrt{2} + 4$

    e. $100, -5.423, \dfrac{8}{7}, \sqrt{2} + 4, -64$

41. **a.** To truncate, we remove all digits after the fourth decimal place. So, 19.93483 truncated to four decimal places is 19.9348.

    b. To round to four decimal places, we first examine the digit in the fifth decimal place and then truncate. Since the fifth decimal place contains a 3, we do not change the digit in the fourth decimal place by 1. Thus, 19.93483 rounded to four decimal places is 19.9348.

43. a. To truncate, we remove all digits after the first decimal place. So, 0.06345 truncated to one decimal place is 0.0.

b. To round to one decimal place, we first examine the digit in the second decimal place and then truncate. Since the second decimal place contains a 6, we increase the digit in the first decimal place by 1. Thus, 0.06345 rounded to one decimal place is 0.1.

45.

47. $-5 < -3$ since -5 is further to the left on a real number line.

49. $\frac{3}{2} = 1.5$ since $\frac{3}{2}$ and 1.5 are at the same point on a real number line.

51. $\frac{1}{3} > 0.3$ since $\frac{1}{3}$ is further to the right on a real number line.

53. $0 - 282 = -282$
Since sea level is an elevation of 0 ft, Death Valley has an elevation of -282 feet.

55. $-\$0.04$
The value of Tellabs common stock fell $0.04 during the fourth quarter of 2002.

57. $66 - 72 = -6$
A score of 66 is 6 under par.

59. Answers will vary. One possible starting point:
http://scienceworld.wolfram.com/biography/Pythagoras.html

61. Answers will vary. One possible starting point:
http://itech.fgcu.edu/faculty/clindsey/mhf4404/archimedes/archimedes.html

63. Rounded: $\frac{8}{7} \approx 1.143$

Truncated: $\frac{8}{7} \approx 1.142$

```
8/7
         1.142857143
```

R.3 Exercises

1. factors

3. negative, *or* opposite; reciprocal

5. True

7. 0 is the additive inverse of 0.

9. Multiplication is distributive on a sum, but not on a product.

11. No, the order of subtraction is important. For example:
$7 - 5 \neq 5 - 7$
$2 \neq -2$

13. No, the order of division is important. For example:
$12 \div 4 \neq 4 \div 12$
$3 \neq \frac{1}{3}$

15. a. $-\left(\frac{9}{5}\right) = -\frac{9}{5}$
The additive inverse of $\frac{9}{5}$ is $-\frac{9}{5}$.

b. $\frac{1}{9/5} = \frac{5}{9}$
The multiplicative inverse of $\frac{9}{5}$ is $\frac{5}{9}$.

c. $\frac{1}{9/5} = \frac{5}{9}$
The reciprocal of $\frac{9}{5}$ is $\frac{5}{9}$.

17. a. $-(-15) = 15$
The additive inverse of -15 is 15.

b. $\frac{1}{(-15)} = -\frac{1}{15}$
The multiplicative inverse of -15 is $-\frac{1}{15}$.

c. $\frac{1}{-15} = -\frac{1}{15}$
The reciprocal of -15 is $-\frac{1}{15}$.

19. a. $-\left(\dfrac{4}{3}\right) = -\dfrac{4}{3}$

The additive inverse of $\dfrac{4}{3}$ is $-\dfrac{4}{3}$.

b. $\dfrac{1}{4/3} = \dfrac{3}{4}$

The multiplicative inverse of $\dfrac{4}{3}$ is $\dfrac{3}{4}$.

c. $\dfrac{1}{4/3} = \dfrac{3}{4}$

The reciprocal of $\dfrac{4}{3}$ is $\dfrac{3}{4}$.

21. a. $-(8) = -8$

The additive inverse of 8 is -8.

b. $\dfrac{1}{(8)} = \dfrac{1}{8}$

The multiplicative inverse of 8 is $\dfrac{1}{8}$.

c. $\dfrac{1}{(8)} = \dfrac{1}{8}$

The reciprocal of 8 is $\dfrac{1}{8}$.

23. a. $-(-4) = 4$

The additive inverse of -4 is 4.

b. $\dfrac{1}{(-4)} = -\dfrac{1}{4}$

The multiplicative inverse of -4 is $-\dfrac{1}{4}$.

c. $\dfrac{1}{(-4)} = -\dfrac{1}{4}$

The reciprocal of -4 is $-\dfrac{1}{4}$.

25. a. $-\left(\dfrac{2}{5}\right) = -\dfrac{2}{5}$

The additive inverse of $\dfrac{2}{5}$ is $-\dfrac{2}{5}$.

b. $\dfrac{1}{(2/5)} = \dfrac{5}{2}$

The multiplicative inverse of $\dfrac{2}{5}$ is $\dfrac{5}{2}$.

c. $\dfrac{1}{(2/5)} = \dfrac{5}{2}$

The reciprocal of $\dfrac{2}{5}$ is $\dfrac{5}{2}$.

27. $2(x+4) = 2 \cdot x + 2 \cdot 4 = 2x + 8$

29. $3(z+2) = 3 \cdot z + 3 \cdot 2 = 3z + 6$

31. $(x-10) \cdot 3 = x \cdot 3 - 10 \cdot 3 = 3x - 30$

33. $\dfrac{3}{4}(8x-10) = \dfrac{3}{4} \cdot 8x - \dfrac{3}{4} \cdot 10 = \dfrac{24x}{4} - \dfrac{30}{4} = 6x - \dfrac{15}{2}$

35. $\dfrac{4 \cdot z}{20} = \dfrac{4 \cdot z}{4 \cdot 5} = \dfrac{\cancel{4} \cdot z}{\cancel{4} \cdot 5} = \dfrac{z}{5}$

37. $\dfrac{30}{25} = \dfrac{5 \cdot 6}{5 \cdot 5} = \dfrac{\cancel{5} \cdot 6}{\cancel{5} \cdot 5} = \dfrac{6}{5}$

39. $8 + 7 = 15$

41. $12 - 5 = 12 + (-5) = 7$

43. $|13 - 16| = |13 + (-16)| = |-3| = 3$

45. $4.3 - 6.8 = 4.3 + (-6.8) = -2.5$

47. $4 \cdot (-8) = -(4 \cdot 8) = -32$

49. $-6 \cdot (-14) = 6 \cdot 14 = 84$

51. $\dfrac{3}{4} \cdot \dfrac{20}{9} = \dfrac{3 \cdot 20}{4 \cdot 9} = \dfrac{3 \cdot 4 \cdot 5}{4 \cdot 3 \cdot 3} = \dfrac{\cancel{3} \cdot \cancel{4} \cdot 5}{\cancel{4} \cdot \cancel{3} \cdot 3} = \dfrac{5}{3}$

53. $\dfrac{2}{3} \cdot \left(-\dfrac{9}{14}\right) = -\dfrac{2}{3} \cdot \dfrac{9}{14} = -\dfrac{2 \cdot 3 \cdot 3}{3 \cdot 2 \cdot 7} = -\dfrac{\cancel{2} \cdot \cancel{3} \cdot 3}{\cancel{3} \cdot \cancel{2} \cdot 7} = -\dfrac{3}{7}$

55. $\dfrac{7}{4} \div \dfrac{21}{8} = \dfrac{7}{4} \cdot \dfrac{8}{21} = \dfrac{7 \cdot 8}{4 \cdot 21} = \dfrac{7 \cdot 2 \cdot 4}{4 \cdot 3 \cdot 7} = \dfrac{\cancel{7} \cdot 2 \cdot \cancel{4}}{\cancel{4} \cdot 3 \cdot \cancel{7}} = \dfrac{2}{3}$

SSM – 3

57. $\dfrac{\frac{2}{5}}{\frac{8}{25}} = \dfrac{2}{5} \cdot \dfrac{25}{8} = \dfrac{2 \cdot 25}{5 \cdot 8} = \dfrac{2 \cdot 5 \cdot 5}{5 \cdot 4 \cdot 2} = \dfrac{\cancel{2} \cdot \cancel{5} \cdot 5}{\cancel{5} \cdot 4 \cdot \cancel{2}} = \dfrac{5}{4}$

59. $-\dfrac{5}{12} + \dfrac{7}{12} = \dfrac{-5+7}{12} = \dfrac{2}{12} = \dfrac{2}{2 \cdot 6} = \dfrac{\cancel{2}}{\cancel{2} \cdot 6} = \dfrac{1}{6}$

61. $LCD = 5 \cdot 3 \cdot 7 \cdot 2 = 210$

$\dfrac{8}{15} + \dfrac{9}{14} = \dfrac{8}{15} \cdot \dfrac{14}{14} + \dfrac{9}{14} \cdot \dfrac{15}{15}$

$= \dfrac{112}{210} + \dfrac{135}{210}$

$= \dfrac{112 + 135}{210}$

$= \dfrac{247}{210}$

63. $LCD = 7 \cdot 6 \cdot 5 = 210$

$\dfrac{41}{42} - \dfrac{8}{35} = \dfrac{41}{42} \cdot \dfrac{5}{5} - \dfrac{8}{35} \cdot \dfrac{6}{6}$

$= \dfrac{205}{210} - \dfrac{48}{210}$

$= \dfrac{205 - 48}{210}$

$= \dfrac{205 + (-48)}{210}$

$= \dfrac{157}{210}$

65. $5 \div \dfrac{15}{4} = \dfrac{5}{1} \cdot \dfrac{4}{15} = \dfrac{5 \cdot 4}{15} = \dfrac{5 \cdot 4}{5 \cdot 3} = \dfrac{\cancel{5} \cdot 4}{\cancel{5} \cdot 3} = \dfrac{4}{3}$

67. $|6.2 - 9.5| = |6.2 + (-9.5)| = |-3.3| = 3.3$

69. $-|-8 \cdot (4)| = -|-32| = -(32) = -32$

71. $\left| -\dfrac{1}{2} - \dfrac{4}{5} \right| = \left| -\left(\dfrac{1}{2} + \dfrac{4}{5} \right) \right| = \dfrac{1}{2} + \dfrac{4}{5}$

$= \dfrac{1}{2} \cdot \dfrac{5}{5} + \dfrac{4}{5} \cdot \dfrac{2}{2} = \dfrac{5}{10} + \dfrac{8}{10}$

$= \dfrac{5 + 8}{10} = \dfrac{13}{10}$

73. $\left| -\dfrac{5}{6} - \dfrac{3}{10} \right| = \left| -\left(\dfrac{5}{6} + \dfrac{3}{10} \right) \right| = \dfrac{5}{6} + \dfrac{3}{10}$

$= \dfrac{5}{6} \cdot \dfrac{5}{5} + \dfrac{3}{10} \cdot \dfrac{3}{3}$

$= \dfrac{25}{30} + \dfrac{9}{30} = \dfrac{34}{30} = \dfrac{17 \cdot 2}{15 \cdot 2}$

$= \dfrac{17 \cdot \cancel{2}}{15 \cdot \cancel{2}} = \dfrac{17}{15}$

75. $\dfrac{21}{32} + (-5) = \dfrac{21}{32} + \left(\dfrac{-5}{1} \cdot \dfrac{32}{32} \right) = \dfrac{21}{32} + \left(\dfrac{-160}{32} \right)$

$= \dfrac{21 + (-160)}{32} = \dfrac{-139}{32} = -\dfrac{139}{32}$

77. $\dfrac{\frac{2}{3}}{6} = \dfrac{2}{3} \cdot \dfrac{1}{6} = \dfrac{2}{3 \cdot 6} = \dfrac{2}{3 \cdot 2 \cdot 3} = \dfrac{\cancel{2}}{3 \cdot \cancel{2} \cdot 3} = \dfrac{1}{9}$

79. $5 \cdot 3 = 3 \cdot 5$
Commutative Property of Multiplication

81. $5 \cdot \dfrac{1}{5} = 1$
Multiplicative Inverse Property

83. $\dfrac{42}{10} = \dfrac{21}{5}$
Reduction Property

85. $3 + (4 + 5) = (3 + 4) + 5$
Associative Property of Addition

87. $69 - 42 = 69 + (-42) = 27$

The difference in age of the oldest and youngest president at the time of inauguration is 27 years.

89. $(4 + (-3)) + 8 = 1 + 8 = 9$

The Bears gained a total of 9 yards in the first 3 plays. Since 9 is less than 10, they did not obtain a first down.

91. $20,320 - (-282) = 20,320 + 282 = 20,602$

The difference between the highest and lowest elevation is 20,602 feet.

93. Multiplying two numbers, say a and b, means that we add the number a a total of b times. On a number line, we would start at 0 and move to the right a units (since a is positive) a total of b times. Since we keep moving to the right, the end result will be positive. For example, $5 \cdot 3$ means we would add the number 5 three times. That is, $5 \cdot 3 = 5 + 5 + 5 = 15$

On a number line we would get:

95. a. $\dfrac{1}{1} = 1$, $\dfrac{2}{1} = 2$, $\dfrac{3}{2} = 1.5$, $\dfrac{5}{3} \approx 1.666667$,

$\dfrac{8}{5} = 1.6$, $\dfrac{13}{8} = 1.625$, $\dfrac{21}{13} \approx 1.615385$,

$\dfrac{34}{21} \approx 1.619048$, $\dfrac{55}{34} \approx 1.617647$,

$\dfrac{89}{55} \approx 1.618182$, $\dfrac{144}{89} \approx 1.617978$, ...

b. The ratios approach a number that is roughly equivalent to 1.618. The golden ratio is

$\dfrac{1 + \sqrt{5}}{2} \approx 1.61803398875...$

c. Answers will vary. One possible source is http://www.mcs.surrey.ac.uk/Personal/R.Kn ott/Fibonacci/fib.html

97. $d(P, Q) = |6 - (-2)| = |6 + 2| = |8| = 8$

99. $d(P, Q) = |1.6 - (-9.3)| = |1.6 + 9.3|$
$= |10.9| = 10.9$

101. $d(P, Q) = \left| 6 - \left(-\dfrac{7}{5} \right) \right| = \left| 6 + \dfrac{7}{5} \right| = \left| \dfrac{6}{1} \cdot \dfrac{5}{5} + \dfrac{7}{5} \right|$

$= \left| \dfrac{30}{5} + \dfrac{7}{5} \right| = \left| \dfrac{37}{5} \right| = \dfrac{37}{5}$

103. $\left\{ \pm 6, \pm 3, \pm 2, \pm \dfrac{3}{2}, \pm 1, \pm \dfrac{1}{2} \right\}$

105.

107.

109.

111.

113.

R.4 Exercises

1. base; exponent; power

3. False.
$-7^4 = -(7 \cdot 7 \cdot 7 \cdot 7) = -7 \cdot 7 \cdot 7 \cdot 7$

5. In the first problem, order of operations says that multiplication is done before addition.
$2 + 3 \cdot 4 = 2 + 12 = 14$
In the second problem, what is inside grouping symbols must be done before multiplication.
$(2 + 3) \cdot 4 = 5 \cdot 4 = 20$

7. Answers will vary.

9. $4^2 - 3^2 = 16 - 9 = 7$

11. $3 \cdot 2 + 9 = 6 + 9 = 15$

13. $4 + 2 \cdot (6 - 2) = 4 + 2 \cdot (4) = 4 + 8 = 12$

15. $-2\left[10 - (3 - 7)\right] = -2\left[10 - (-4)\right] = -2\left[10 + 4\right]$
$$= -2\left[14\right] = -28$$

17. $\dfrac{5 - (-7)}{4} = \dfrac{5 + 7}{4} = \dfrac{12}{4} = \dfrac{\cancel{4} \cdot 3}{\cancel{4} \cdot 1} = 3$

19. $\left|3 \cdot 2 - 4 \cdot 5\right| = \left|6 - 20\right| = \left|-14\right| = 14$

21. $12 \cdot \dfrac{2}{3} - 5 \cdot 2 = \dfrac{24}{3} - 10 = 8 - 10 = -2$

23. $3 \cdot \left[2 + 3 \cdot (1 + 5)\right] = 3 \cdot \left[2 + 3 \cdot (6)\right] = 3 \cdot \left[2 + 18\right]$
$$= 3 \cdot \left[20\right] = 60$$

25. $\left(3^2 - 3\right)\left(3 - (-3)^3\right) = (9 - 3)\left(3 - (-27)\right)$
$$= (6)(3 + 27)$$
$$= (6)(30) = 180$$

27. $\left|3 \cdot \left(6 - 3^2\right)\right| = \left|3 \cdot (6 - 9)\right| = \left|3 \cdot (-3)\right| = \left|-9\right| = 9$

29. $\left|4 \cdot \left[2 \cdot 5 + (-3) \cdot 4\right]\right| = \left|4 \cdot \left[10 + (-12)\right]\right|$
$$= \left|4 \cdot [-2]\right| = \left|-8\right| = 8$$

31. $\dfrac{2 \cdot 5 + 15}{2^2 + 3 \cdot 2} = \dfrac{2 \cdot 5 + 15}{4 + 3 \cdot 2} = \dfrac{10 + 15}{4 + 6} = \dfrac{25}{10} = \dfrac{\cancel{5} \cdot 5}{\cancel{5} \cdot 2} = \dfrac{5}{2}$

33. $\dfrac{2 \cdot (4 + 8)}{3 + 3^2} = \dfrac{2 \cdot (12)}{3 + 3^2} = \dfrac{2(12)}{3 + 9} = \dfrac{24}{3 + 9}$
$$= \dfrac{24}{12} = \dfrac{\cancel{12} \cdot 2}{\cancel{12} \cdot 1} = 2$$

35. $\dfrac{6 \cdot \left[12 - 3 \cdot (5 - 2)\right]}{5 \cdot \left[21 - 2 \cdot (4 + 5)\right]} = \dfrac{6 \cdot \left[12 - 3 \cdot 3\right]}{5 \cdot \left[21 - 2 \cdot 9\right]} = \dfrac{6 \cdot \left[12 - 9\right]}{5 \cdot \left[21 - 18\right]}$
$$= \dfrac{6 \cdot 3}{5 \cdot 3} = \dfrac{6 \cdot \cancel{3}}{5 \cdot \cancel{3}} = \dfrac{6}{5}$$

37. $\left(\dfrac{2}{3}\right)^2 \cdot \left(\dfrac{1 + 2^3}{2^3 - 2}\right) = \left(\dfrac{4}{9}\right)\left(\dfrac{1 + 8}{8 - 2}\right) = \left(\dfrac{4}{9}\right)\left(\dfrac{9}{6}\right)$
$$= \dfrac{\cancel{2} \cdot 2 \cdot \cancel{9}}{\cancel{9} \cdot 3 \cdot \cancel{2}} = \dfrac{2}{3}$$

39. $\dfrac{3^3 - 2^4 \cdot 3}{4 \cdot \left(3^2 - 2 \cdot 3\right)} = \dfrac{27 - 16 \cdot 3}{4 \cdot (9 - 2 \cdot 3)} = \dfrac{27 - 48}{4 \cdot (9 - 6)}$
$$= \dfrac{-21}{4 \cdot 3} = -\dfrac{21}{12} = -\dfrac{\cancel{3} \cdot 7}{\cancel{3} \cdot 4} = -\dfrac{7}{4}$$

41. $\dfrac{2 \cdot 4 - 5}{4^2 + (-2)^3} + \dfrac{3^2}{2^3} = \dfrac{2 \cdot 4 - 5}{16 - 8} + \dfrac{9}{8} = \dfrac{8 - 5}{16 - 8} + \dfrac{9}{8}$
$$= \dfrac{3}{8} + \dfrac{9}{8} = \dfrac{3 + 9}{8} = \dfrac{12}{8} = \dfrac{\cancel{4} \cdot 3}{\cancel{4} \cdot 2} = \dfrac{3}{2}$$

43. $\dfrac{\dfrac{2 \cdot 3 + 3^2}{2 \cdot 5 - 8} + \dfrac{4}{3}}{\dfrac{7 \cdot (5 - 3)}{14 - 2^3}} = \dfrac{\dfrac{2 \cdot 3 + 9}{2 \cdot 5 - 8} + \dfrac{4}{3}}{\dfrac{7 \cdot (5 - 3)}{14 - 8}} = \dfrac{\dfrac{2 \cdot 3 + 9}{2 \cdot 5 - 8} + \dfrac{4}{3}}{\dfrac{7 \cdot (2)}{14 - 8}}$

$$= \dfrac{\dfrac{6 + 9}{10 - 8} + \dfrac{4}{3}}{14} = \dfrac{\dfrac{15}{2} + \dfrac{4}{3}}{14}$$

$$= \dfrac{\dfrac{15}{2} \cdot \dfrac{3}{3} + \dfrac{4}{3} \cdot \dfrac{2}{2}}{\dfrac{14}{6}} = \dfrac{\dfrac{45}{6} + \dfrac{8}{6}}{\dfrac{14}{6}} = \dfrac{\dfrac{45 + 8}{6}}{\dfrac{14}{6}}$$

$$= \dfrac{\dfrac{53}{6}}{\dfrac{14}{6}} = \dfrac{53}{6} \cdot \dfrac{6}{14} = \dfrac{53 \cdot \cancel{6}}{14 \cdot \cancel{6}} = \dfrac{53}{14}$$

45. $3 \cdot (7 - 2) = 15$

47. $3 + 5 \cdot (6 - 3) = 18$

49. $2 \cdot 3.1416 \cdot 5^2 + 2 \cdot 3.1416 \cdot 5 \cdot 12$
$$= 3.1416\left(2 \cdot 5^2 + 2 \cdot 5 \cdot 12\right)$$
$$= 3.1416(2 \cdot 25 + 2 \cdot 5 \cdot 12)$$
$$= 3.1416(50 + 120)$$
$$= 3.1416(170)$$
$$\approx 534.07$$
The surface area of the cylinder is about 534.07 square inches.

51. $-16 \cdot 3^2 + 50 \cdot 3 = -16 \cdot 9 + 50 \cdot 3$
$$= -144 + 150$$
$$= 6$$
After 3 seconds, the height of the ball is 6 feet.

53. We can only cancel like factors. Here 2 is an addend of both the numerator and denominator, but it is not a factor of either.

55. Answers will vary.

57. $\dfrac{(105-100)^2 + (80-100)^2 + (115-100)^2 + (95-100)^2 + (105-100)^2}{4} = \dfrac{(5)^2 + (-20)^2 + (15)^2 + (-5)^2 + (5)^2}{4}$
$$= \frac{25 + 400 + 225 + 25 + 25}{4}$$
$$= \frac{700}{4} = 175$$

59. $\dfrac{4}{5} - \left(\dfrac{2}{3}\right)^2 = \dfrac{4}{5} - \dfrac{4}{9} = \dfrac{36}{45} - \dfrac{20}{45} = \dfrac{16}{45}$

```
(4/5)-(2/3)²▶Fra
c
          16/45
```

61. $\dfrac{4^2 + 1}{13} = \dfrac{16 + 1}{13} = \dfrac{17}{13}$

```
(4²+1)/13▶Frac
          17/13
```

63. $\dfrac{3.5^3}{1.3^2} - 6.2^3 = \dfrac{42.875}{1.69} - 238.328 \approx -212.96$

```
(3.5³/1.3²)-6.2³
▶Frac
      -212.9581775
```

65. $4.3\left[9.3^2 - 4(34.2 + 18.5)\right]$
$$= 4.3\left[86.49 - 4(52.7)\right]$$
$$= 4.3\left[86.49 - 210.8\right]$$
$$= 4.3\left[-124.31\right] = -534.533 \approx -534.53$$

```
4.3(9.3²-4(34.2+
18.5))▶Frac
      -534533/1000
-534533/1000
          -534.533
```

R.5 Exercises

1. variable

3. term

5. True

7. Answers will vary. A *factor* is one of at least two expressions that are multiplied together. A *term* is an expression that is written as a product or quotient. Terms are added (or subtracted) while factors are multiplied.

9. $4x + 3$
$$4(2) + 3 = 8 + 3 = 11$$

11. $x^2 + 5x - 3$
$$(-2)^2 + 5(-2) - 3 = 4 - 10 - 3 = -6 - 3 = -9$$

13. $-z^2 + 4$
$$-(5)^2 + 4 = -25 + 4 = -21$$

15. $\dfrac{2w}{w^2 + 2w + 1}$
$$\frac{2(3)}{(3)^2 + 2(3) + 1} = \frac{6}{9 + 6 + 1} = \frac{6}{16} = \frac{3 \cdot \cancel{2}}{8 \cdot \cancel{2}} = \frac{3}{8}$$

17. $\dfrac{v^2 + 2v + 1}{v^2 + 3v + 2}$
$$\frac{(5)^2 + 2(5) + 1}{(5)^2 + 3(5) + 2} = \frac{25 + 10 + 1}{25 + 15 + 2} = \frac{36}{42} = \frac{\cancel{6} \cdot 6}{\cancel{6} \cdot 7} = \frac{6}{7}$$

19. $|5x-4|$

$|5(-5)-4|=|-25-4|=|-29|=29$

21. $|15y+10|$

$\left|15\left(-\dfrac{3}{5}\right)+10\right|=\left|-\dfrac{45}{5}+10\right|=|-9+10|=|1|=1$

23. $\dfrac{(x+2)^2}{|4x-10|}$

$\dfrac{((1)+2)^2}{|4(1)-10|}=\dfrac{3^2}{|4-10|}=\dfrac{9}{|-6|}=\dfrac{9}{6}=\dfrac{\cancel{3}\cdot 3}{\cancel{3}\cdot 2}=\dfrac{3}{2}$

25. $3x-2x=(3-2)x=1x=x$

27. $-4z-2z+3=(-4-2)z+3=-6z+3$

29. $13z+2-14z-7=13z-14z+2-7$
$=(13-14)z+(2-7)$
$=-1z+(-5)=-z-5$

31. $\dfrac{3}{4}x+\dfrac{1}{6}x=\left(\dfrac{3}{4}+\dfrac{1}{6}\right)x=\left(\dfrac{9}{12}+\dfrac{2}{12}\right)x=\dfrac{11}{12}x$

33. $2x+3x^2-5x+x^2=3x^2+x^2+2x-5x$
$=(3+1)x^2+(2-5)x$
$=4x^2-3x$

35. $-1.3x-3.4+2.9x+3.4=-1.3x+2.9x-3.4+3.4$
$=(-1.3+2.9)x+0$
$=1.6x$

37. $3x-2-x+3-5x=3x-x-5x-2+3$
$=(3-1-5)x+(-2+3)$
$=-3x+1$

39. $-2(5x-4)-(4x+1)=-10x+8-4x-1$
$=-10x-4x+8-1$
$=(-10-4)x+(8-1)$
$=-14x+7$

41. $5(z+2)-6z=5z+10-6z$
$=5z-6z+10$
$=(5-6)z+10$
$=-z+10$

43. $\dfrac{2}{5}(5x-10)+\dfrac{1}{4}(8x+4)$

$=\dfrac{2}{5}\cdot 5x-\dfrac{2}{5}\cdot 10+\dfrac{1}{4}\cdot 8x+\dfrac{1}{4}\cdot 4$
$=2x-4+2x+1=2x+2x-4+1$
$=(2+2)x+(-4+1)$
$=4x-3$

45. $2(v-3)+5(2v-1)=2v-6+10v-5$
$=2v+10v-6-5$
$=(2+10)v+(-6-5)$
$=12v-11$

47. $\dfrac{3}{5}(10x+4)-\dfrac{8x+3}{2}=\dfrac{3}{5}(10x+4)-\dfrac{1}{2}(8x+3)$

$=\dfrac{3}{5}\cdot 10x+\dfrac{3}{5}\cdot 4-\dfrac{1}{2}\cdot 8x-\dfrac{1}{2}\cdot 3$
$=6x+\dfrac{12}{5}-4x-\dfrac{3}{2}=6x-4x+\dfrac{12}{5}-\dfrac{3}{2}$
$=(6-4)x+\left(\dfrac{12}{5}-\dfrac{3}{2}\right)=2x+\left(\dfrac{24}{10}-\dfrac{15}{10}\right)$
$=2x+\dfrac{9}{10}$

49. $\dfrac{5}{6}\left(\dfrac{3}{10}x-\dfrac{2}{5}\right)+\dfrac{2}{3}\left(\dfrac{1}{6}x+\dfrac{1}{2}\right)$

$=\dfrac{5}{6}\cdot\dfrac{3}{10}x-\dfrac{5}{6}\cdot\dfrac{2}{5}+\dfrac{2}{3}\cdot\dfrac{1}{6}x+\dfrac{2}{3}\cdot\dfrac{1}{2}$
$=\dfrac{\cancel{5}\cdot\cancel{3}}{2\cdot\cancel{3}\cdot\cancel{5}\cdot 2}x-\dfrac{\cancel{5}\cdot\cancel{2}}{3\cdot\cancel{2}\cdot\cancel{5}}+\dfrac{\cancel{2}}{3\cdot\cancel{2}\cdot 3}x+\dfrac{\cancel{2}}{3\cdot\cancel{2}}$
$=\dfrac{1}{4}x-\dfrac{1}{3}+\dfrac{1}{9}x+\dfrac{1}{3}$
$=\dfrac{1}{4}x+\dfrac{1}{9}x-\dfrac{1}{3}+\dfrac{1}{3}$
$=\left(\dfrac{1}{4}+\dfrac{1}{9}\right)x=\left(\dfrac{9}{36}+\dfrac{4}{36}\right)x$
$=\dfrac{13}{36}x$

51. $4.3(1.2x-2.3)+9.3x-5.6$
$=5.16x-9.89+9.3x-5.6$
$=5.16x+9.3x-9.89-5.6$
$=(5.16+9.3)x+(-9.89-5.6)$
$=14.46x-15.49$

53. $6.2(x-1.4)-5.4(3.2x-0.6)$
$= 6.2x - 8.68 - 17.28x + 3.24$
$= 6.2x - 17.28x - 8.68 + 3.24$
$= (6.2 - 17.28)x + (-8.68 + 3.24)$
$= -11.08x - 5.44$

55. $5 + x$

57. $4z$

59. $y - 7$

61. $2(t + 4)$

63. $5x - 3$

65. $\dfrac{y}{3} + 6x$

67. We need to determine whether the value of the variable causes division by 0. That is, we need to determine if the value makes $x - 5 = 0$.

   a. When $x = 5$, we have $x - 5 = 5 - 5 = 0$, so 5 is **not** in the domain of the variable.

   b. When $x = -1$, we have $x - 5 = -1 - 5 = -6$, so -1 is in the domain of the variable.

   c. When $x = -4$, we have $x - 5 = -4 - 5 = -9$, so -4 is in the domain of the variable.

   d. When $x = 0$, we have $x - 5 = 0 - 5 = -5$, so 0 is in the domain of the variable.

69. We need to determine whether the value of the variable causes division by 0. That is, we need to determine if the value makes $x + 5 = 0$.

   a. When $x = 5$, we have $x + 5 = 5 + 5 = 10$, so 5 is in the domain of the variable.

   b. When $x = -1$, we have $x + 5 = -1 + 5 = 4$, so -1 is in the domain of the variable.

   c. When $x = -4$, we have $x + 5 = -4 + 5 = 1$, so -4 is in the domain of the variable.

   d. When $x = 0$, we have $x + 5 = 0 + 5 = 5$, so 0 is in the domain of the variable.

71. We need to determine whether the value of the variable causes division by 0. That is, we need to determine if the value makes $x^2 - 5x = 0$.

   a. When $x = 5$, we have $x^2 - 5x = (5)^2 - 5(5) = 25 - 25 = 0$, so 5 is **not** in the domain of the variable.

   b. When $x = -1$, we have $x^2 - 5x = (-1)^2 - 5(-1) = 1 + 5 = 6$, so -1 is in the domain of the variable.

   c. When $x = -4$, we have $x^2 - 5x = (-4)^2 - 5(-4) = 16 + 20 = 36$, so -4 is in the domain of the variable.

   d. When $x = 0$, we have $x^2 - 5x = (0)^2 - 5(0) = 0 - 0 = 0$, so 0 is **not** in the domain of the variable.

73. For $s = 1$ inch, $s^3 = (1)^3 = 1$ cubic inch.

   For $s = 2$ inches, $s^3 = (2)^3 = 8$ cubic inches.

   For $s = 3$ inches, $s^3 = (3)^3 = 27$ cubic inches.

   For $s = 4$ inches, $s^3 = (4)^3 = 64$ cubic inches.

75. a. For $t = 0$:
$-16(0)^2 + 75(0) = 0 + 0 = 0$ ft
For $t = 1$:
$-16(1)^2 + 75(1) = -16 + 75 = 59$ ft
For $t = 2$:
$-16(2)^2 + 75(2) = -16(4) + 75(2)$
$\qquad\qquad\qquad = -64 + 150 = 86$ ft
For $t = 3$:
$-16(3)^2 + 75(3) = -16(9) + 75(3)$
$\qquad\qquad\qquad = -144 + 225 = 81$ ft
For $t = 4$:
$-16(4)^2 + 75(4) = -16(16) + 75(4)$
$\qquad\qquad\qquad = -256 + 300 = 44$ ft

   b. The ball begins on the ground. When it is hit, it rises in the air (for somewhere around 2 seconds) and then begins to fall back towards the ground.

77. Let $x = $ Bob's age in years .

Tony's age is expressed as $x + 5$.
When $x = 13$, $x + 5 = 13 + 5 = 18$. When Bob is
13 years old, Tony is 18 years old.

79. Let $p = $ the original price in dollars .

"half off regular price" is $p - \dfrac{1}{2} p = \dfrac{1}{2} p$

The discounted price can be expressed as $\dfrac{1}{2} p$.

When $p = 900$, $\dfrac{1}{2} p = \dfrac{1}{2}(900) = 450$. When the

original price is \$900, the discount price is \$450.

81. $Z = \dfrac{X - \mu}{\sigma}$

When $X = 120, \mu = 100$, and $\sigma = 15$, we have

$$Z = \frac{X - \mu}{\sigma} = \frac{120 - 100}{15} = \frac{20}{15} = \frac{\cancel{5} \cdot 4}{\cancel{5} \cdot 3} = \frac{4}{3}$$

83. Answers may vary. One possible answer is:
"Twice a number z decreased by 5"

85. Answers may vary. One possible answer is:
"Twice the difference of a number z and 5"

87. Answers may vary. One possible answer is:
"One-half the sum of a number z and 3"

89. a. $-4x + 3$ when $x = 0$.

```
0→X: -4X+3
                3
```

b. $-4x + 3$ when $x = -3$.

```
-3→X: -4X+3
               15
```

91. a. $4x^2 - 8x + 3$ when $x = 5$.

```
5→X: 4X²-8X+3
              63
```

b. $4x^2 - 8x + 3$ when $x = -2$.

```
-2→X: 4X²-8X+3
               35
```

93. a. $\dfrac{3z - 1}{z^2 + 1}$ when $z = -2$.

```
-2→Z: (3Z-1)/(Z²+
1)►Frac
             -7/5
```

b. $\dfrac{3z - 1}{z^2 + 1}$ when $z = 8$.

```
8→Z: (3Z-1)/(Z²+1
)►Frac
            23/65
```

95. a. $|-9x + 5|$ when $x = 8$.

```
8→X: abs(-9X+5)
               67
```

b. $|-9x + 5|$ when $x = -3$.

```
-3→X: abs(-9X+5)
               32
```

97. The calculator displays an error message because
$x = 5$ makes the denominator equal to 0.

```
5→X: (2X+1)/(X-5)     ERR:DIVIDE BY 0
                      1◼Quit
                      2:Goto
```

Chapter 1

1.1 Preparing for Linear Equations

1. The additive inverse of 5 is -5 because $5 + (-5) = 0$.

2. The multiplicative inverse of -3 is $-\dfrac{1}{3}$ because
$$(-3) \cdot \left(-\frac{1}{3}\right) = 1.$$

3. $\dfrac{1}{5} \cdot 5x = \dfrac{5 \cdot x}{5} = \dfrac{\cancel{5} \cdot x}{\cancel{5}} = x$

4. $8 = 2 \cdot 2 \cdot 2$
   $12 = 2 \cdot 2 \cdot 3$
   The common factors are 2 and 2. The remaining factors are 2 and 3.
   $LCD = 2 \cdot 2 \cdot 2 \cdot 3 = 24$

5. $6(z - 2) = 6 \cdot z - 6 \cdot 2 = 6z - 12$

6. The coefficient of $-4x$ is -4.

7. $4(y - 2) - y + 5 = 4y - 8 - y + 5$
   $= 4y - y - 8 + 5$
   $= 3y - 3$

8. $-5(x + 3) - 8$
   $-5((-2) + 3) - 8 = -5(1) - 8$
   $= -5 - 8$
   $= -13$

9. Since division by 0 is undefined, we need to determine if the value for the variable makes $x + 3 = 0$.
   When $x = 3$, we have $x + 3 = (3) + 3 = 6$, so 3 is in the domain of the variable.
   When $x = -3$, we have $x + 3 = (-3) + 3 = 0$, so -3 is **not** in the domain of the variable.

1.1 Exercises

1. equivalent equations

3. conditional equation

5. False. Such an equation is called an identity.

7. $4(x + 1) - 2$ is an expression and $4(x + 1) = 2$ is an equation. In general, an equation can be distinguished from an algebraic expression by the presence of an equal sign.

9. $8x - 10 = 6$
   Let $x = -2$ in the equation.
   $8(-2) - 10 \overset{?}{=} 6$
   $-16 - 10 \overset{?}{=} 6$
   $-26 \neq 6$
   $x = -2$ is **not** a solution to the equation.
   Let $x = 1$ in the equation.
   $8(1) - 10 \overset{?}{=} 6$
   $8 - 10 \overset{?}{=} 6$
   $-2 \neq 6$
   $x = 1$ is **not** a solution to the equation.
   Let $x = 2$ in the equation.
   $8(2) - 10 \overset{?}{=} 6$
   $16 - 10 \overset{?}{=} 6$
   $6 = 6$ ✓
   $x = 2$ is a solution to the equation.

11. $5m - 3 = -3m + 5$
    Let $m = -2$ in the equation.
    $5(-2) - 3 \overset{?}{=} -3(-2) + 5$
    $-10 - 3 \overset{?}{=} 6 + 5$
    $-13 \neq 11$
    $m = -2$ is **not** a solution to the equation.
    Let $m = 1$ in the equation.
    $5(1) - 3 \overset{?}{=} -3(1) + 5$
    $5 - 3 \overset{?}{=} -3 + 5$
    $2 = 2$ ✓
    $m = 1$ is a solution to the equation.

Let $m = 3$ in the equation.

$$5(3) - 3 \stackrel{?}{=} -3(3) + 5$$

$$15 - 3 \stackrel{?}{=} -9 + 5$$

$$12 \neq -4$$

$m = 3$ is **not** a solution to the equation.

13. $4(x-1) = 3x + 1$

Let $x = -1$ in the equation.

$$4((-1)-1) \stackrel{?}{=} 3(-1) + 1$$

$$4(-2) \stackrel{?}{=} -3 + 1$$

$$-8 \neq -2$$

$x = -1$ is **not** a solution to the equation.

Let $x = 2$ in the equation.

$$4((2)-1) \stackrel{?}{=} 3(2) + 1$$

$$4(1) \stackrel{?}{=} 6 + 1$$

$$4 \neq 7$$

$x = 2$ is **not** a solution to the equation.

Let $x = 5$ in the equation.

$$4((5)-1) \stackrel{?}{=} 3(5) + 1$$

$$4(4) \stackrel{?}{=} 15 + 1$$

$$16 = 16 \checkmark$$

$x = 5$ is a solution to the equation.

15. $3x + 1 = 7$

$$3x + 1 - 1 = 7 - 1$$

$$3x = 6$$

$$\frac{3x}{3} = \frac{6}{3}$$

$$x = 2$$

Check:

$$3(2) + 1 \stackrel{?}{=} 7$$

$$6 + 1 \stackrel{?}{=} 7$$

$$7 = 7 \checkmark$$

This is a conditional equation.

Solution set: $\{2\}$

17. $5x + 4 = 14$

$$5x + 4 - 4 = 14 - 4$$

$$5x = 10$$

$$\frac{5x}{5} = \frac{10}{5}$$

$$x = 2$$

Check:

$$5(2) + 4 \stackrel{?}{=} 14$$

$$10 + 4 \stackrel{?}{=} 14$$

$$14 = 14 \checkmark$$

This is a conditional equation.

Solution set: $\{2\}$

19. $4z + 3 = 2$

$$4z + 3 - 3 = 2 - 3$$

$$4z = -1$$

$$\frac{4z}{4} = \frac{-1}{4}$$

$$z = -\frac{1}{4}$$

Check:

$$4\left(-\frac{1}{4}\right) + 3 \stackrel{?}{=} 2$$

$$-1 + 3 \stackrel{?}{=} 2$$

$$2 = 2 \checkmark$$

This is a conditional equation.

Solution set: $\left\{-\frac{1}{4}\right\}$

21. $-3w + 2w + 5 = -4$

$$-w + 5 = -4$$

$$-w + 5 - 5 = -4 - 5$$

$$-w = -9$$

$$-1(-w) = -1(-9)$$

$$w = 9$$

Check:

$$-3(9) + 2(9) + 5 \stackrel{?}{=} -4$$

$$-27 + 18 + 5 \stackrel{?}{=} -4$$

$$-4 = -4 \checkmark$$

This is a conditional equation.

Solution set: $\{9\}$

23.
$$3m + 4 = 2m - 5$$
$$3m + 4 - 4 = 2m - 5 - 4$$
$$3m = 2m - 9$$
$$3m - 2m = 2m - 9 - 2m$$
$$m = -9$$

Check:
$$3(-9) + 4 \overset{?}{=} 2(-9) - 5$$
$$-27 + 4 \overset{?}{=} -18 - 5$$
$$-23 = -23 \checkmark$$

This is a conditional equation.
Solution set: $\{-9\}$

25.
$$5x + 2 - 2x + 3 = 7x + 2 - x + 5$$
$$5x - 2x + 2 + 3 = 7x - x + 2 + 5$$
$$3x + 5 = 6x + 7$$
$$3x + 5 - 5 = 6x + 7 - 5$$
$$3x = 6x + 2$$
$$3x - 6x = 6x + 2 - 6x$$
$$-3x = 2$$
$$\frac{-3x}{-3} = \frac{2}{-3}$$
$$x = -\frac{2}{3}$$

Check:
$$5\left(-\frac{2}{3}\right) + 2 - 2\left(-\frac{2}{3}\right) + 3 \overset{?}{=} 7\left(-\frac{2}{3}\right) + 2 - \left(-\frac{2}{3}\right) + 5$$
$$-\frac{10}{3} + 2 + \frac{4}{3} + 3 \overset{?}{=} -\frac{14}{3} + 2 + \frac{2}{3} + 5$$
$$-\frac{6}{3} + 5 \overset{?}{=} -\frac{12}{3} + 7$$
$$-2 + 5 \overset{?}{=} -4 + 7$$
$$3 = 3 \checkmark$$

This is a conditional equation.
Solution set: $\left\{-\frac{2}{3}\right\}$

27.
$$3(x + 2) = -6$$
$$3x + 6 = -6$$
$$3x + 6 - 6 = -6 - 6$$
$$3x = -12$$
$$\frac{3x}{3} = \frac{-12}{3}$$
$$x = -4$$

Check:
$$3(-4 + 2) \overset{?}{=} -6$$
$$3(-2) \overset{?}{=} -6$$
$$-6 = -6 \checkmark$$

This is a conditional equation.
Solution set: $\{-4\}$

29.
$$4(x + 1) = 4x$$
$$4x + 4 = 4x$$
$$4x - 4x + 4 = 4x - 4x$$
$$4 = 0$$

This statement is a contradiction. The equation has no solution.
Solution set: $\{\ \}$ or $\varnothing$

31.
$$4m + 1 - 6m = 2(m + 3) - 4m$$
$$-2m + 1 = 2m + 6 - 4m$$
$$-2m + 1 = -2m + 6$$
$$-2m + 1 + 2m = -2m + 6 + 2m$$
$$1 = 6$$

This statement is a contradiction. The equation has no solution.
Solution set: $\{\ \}$ or $\varnothing$

33.
$$2(y + 1) - 3(y - 2) = 5y + 8 - 6y$$
$$2y + 2 - 3y + 6 = 8 - y$$
$$8 - y = 8 - y$$
$$8 - y + y = 8 - y + y$$
$$8 = 8$$

This statement is an identity. All real numbers are solutions.
Solution set: $\{y \mid y \text{ is a real number}\}$ or $\mathbb{R}$

35.
$$\frac{4y}{5} - \frac{14}{15} = \frac{y}{3}$$
$$15\left(\frac{4y}{5} - \frac{14}{15}\right) = 15\left(\frac{y}{3}\right)$$
$$15 \cdot \frac{4y}{5} - 15 \cdot \frac{14}{15} = 15 \cdot \frac{y}{3}$$
$$12y - 14 = 5y$$
$$12y - 14 - 12y = 5y - 12y$$
$$-14 = -7y$$
$$\frac{-14}{-7} = \frac{-7y}{-7}$$
$$2 = y \quad \text{or} \quad y = 2$$

Check:
$$\frac{4(2)}{5} - \frac{14}{15} \overset{?}{=} \frac{(2)}{3}$$
$$\frac{8}{5} - \frac{14}{15} \overset{?}{=} \frac{2}{3}$$
$$\frac{24}{15} - \frac{14}{15} \overset{?}{=} \frac{2}{3}$$
$$\frac{10}{15} \overset{?}{=} \frac{2}{3}$$
$$\frac{2}{3} = \frac{2}{3} \checkmark$$

This is a conditional equation.
Solution set: $\{2\}$

37.
$$\frac{x}{4} + \frac{3x}{10} = -\frac{33}{20}$$
$$20\left(\frac{x}{4} + \frac{3x}{10}\right) = 20\left(-\frac{33}{20}\right)$$
$$20 \cdot \frac{x}{4} + 20 \cdot \frac{3x}{10} = -33$$
$$5x + 6x = -33$$
$$11x = -33$$
$$\frac{11x}{11} = \frac{-33}{11}$$
$$x = -3$$

Check:
$$\frac{(-3)}{4} + \frac{3(-3)}{10} \overset{?}{=} -\frac{33}{20}$$
$$-\frac{3}{4} - \frac{9}{10} \overset{?}{=} -\frac{33}{20}$$
$$-\frac{15}{20} - \frac{18}{20} \overset{?}{=} -\frac{33}{20}$$
$$-\frac{33}{20} = -\frac{33}{20} \checkmark$$

This is a conditional equation.
Solution set: $\{-3\}$

39.
$$3p - \frac{p}{4} = \frac{11p}{4} + 1$$
$$4\left(3p - \frac{p}{4}\right) = 4\left(\frac{11p}{4} + 1\right)$$
$$4 \cdot 3p - 4 \cdot \frac{p}{4} = 4 \cdot \frac{11p}{4} + 4 \cdot 1$$
$$12p - p = 11p + 4$$
$$11p = 11p + 4$$
$$11p - 11p = 11p + 4 - 11p$$
$$0 = 1$$

This statement is a contradiction. The equation has no solution.
Solution set: $\{\ \}$ or $\varnothing$

41.
$$\frac{4x+3}{9} - \frac{2x+1}{2} = \frac{1}{6}$$
$$18\left(\frac{4x+3}{9}\right) - 18\left(\frac{2x+1}{2}\right) = 18\left(\frac{1}{6}\right)$$
$$2(4x+3) - 9(2x+1) = 3$$
$$8x + 6 - 18x - 9 = 3$$
$$-10x - 3 = 3$$
$$-10x - 3 + 3 = 3 + 3$$
$$-10x = 6$$
$$\frac{-10x}{-10} = \frac{6}{-10}$$
$$x = -\frac{3}{5}$$

Check: $\dfrac{4\left(-\dfrac{3}{5}\right)+3}{9}-\dfrac{2\left(-\dfrac{3}{5}\right)+1}{2}\overset{?}{=}\dfrac{1}{6}$

$$\dfrac{-\dfrac{12}{5}+\dfrac{15}{5}}{9}-\dfrac{-\dfrac{6}{5}+\dfrac{5}{5}}{2}\overset{?}{=}\dfrac{1}{6}$$

$$\dfrac{\dfrac{3}{5}}{9}+\dfrac{\dfrac{1}{5}}{2}\overset{?}{=}\dfrac{1}{6}$$

$$\dfrac{3}{5}\cdot\dfrac{1}{9}+\dfrac{1}{5}\cdot\dfrac{1}{2}\overset{?}{=}\dfrac{1}{6}$$

$$\dfrac{1}{15}+\dfrac{1}{10}\overset{?}{=}\dfrac{1}{6}$$

$$30\left(\dfrac{1}{15}\right)+30\left(\dfrac{1}{10}\right)\overset{?}{=}30\left(\dfrac{1}{6}\right)$$

$$2+3\overset{?}{=}5$$

$$5=5 \checkmark$$

This is a conditional equation.

Solution set: $\left\{-\dfrac{3}{5}\right\}$

43. $\dfrac{2x+1}{2}-\dfrac{x+1}{5}=\dfrac{23}{10}$

$$10\left(\dfrac{2x+1}{2}-\dfrac{x+1}{5}\right)=10\cdot\dfrac{23}{10}$$

$$5(2x+1)-2(x+1)=23$$

$$10x+5-2x-2=23$$

$$8x+3=23$$

$$8x+3-3=23-3$$

$$8x=20$$

$$\dfrac{8x}{8}=\dfrac{20}{8}$$

$$x=\dfrac{5}{2}$$

Check: $\dfrac{2\left(\dfrac{5}{2}\right)+1}{2}-\dfrac{\left(\dfrac{5}{2}\right)+1}{5}\overset{?}{=}\dfrac{23}{10}$

$$\dfrac{5+1}{2}-\dfrac{\dfrac{7}{2}}{5}\overset{?}{=}\dfrac{23}{10}$$

$$\dfrac{6}{2}-\dfrac{7}{10}\overset{?}{=}\dfrac{23}{10}$$

$$3-\dfrac{7}{10}\overset{?}{=}\dfrac{23}{10}$$

$$\dfrac{30}{10}-\dfrac{7}{30}\overset{?}{=}\dfrac{23}{10}$$

$$\dfrac{23}{10}=\dfrac{23}{10} \checkmark$$

This is a conditional equation.

Solution set: $\left\{\dfrac{5}{2}\right\}$

45. $0.5x-3.2=-1.7$

$$10(0.5x-3.2)=10(-1.7)$$

$$5x-32=-17$$

$$5x-32+32=-17+32$$

$$5x=15$$

$$\dfrac{5x}{5}=\dfrac{15}{5}$$

$$x=3$$

Check:

$$0.5(3)-3.2\overset{?}{=}-1.7$$

$$1.5-3.2\overset{?}{=}-1.7$$

$$-1.7=-1.7 \checkmark$$

This is a conditional equation.

Solution set: $\{3\}$

47. $0.14x+2.23=0.09x+1.98$

$$100(0.14x+2.23)=100(0.09x+1.98)$$

$$14x+223=9x+198$$

$$14x+223-223=9x+198-223$$

$$14x=9x-25$$

$$14x-9x=9x-25-9x$$

$$5x=-25$$

$$\dfrac{5x}{5}=\dfrac{-25}{5}$$

$$x=-5$$

Check: $0.14(-5)+2.23\overset{?}{=}0.09(-5)+1.98$

$$-0.7+2.23\overset{?}{=}-0.45+1.98$$

$$1.53=1.53 \checkmark$$

This is a conditional equation.

Solution set: $\{-5\}$

49. $0.4(z+1)-0.7z=-0.1z+0.7-0.2z-0.3$

$$0.4z+0.4-0.7z=-0.3z+0.4$$

$$-0.3z+0.4=-0.3z+0.4$$

$$-0.3z+0.4-0.4=-0.3z+0.4-0.4$$

$$-0.3z=-0.3z$$

$$-0.3z+0.3z=-0.3z+0.3z$$

$$0=0$$

This is an identity.

Solution set: $\{z\,|\,z \text{ is a real number}\}$ or $\mathbb{R}$

51. $\dfrac{1}{3}(2x-3)+2=\dfrac{5}{6}(x+3)-\dfrac{11}{12}$

$12\left[\dfrac{1}{3}(2x-3)+2\right]=12\left[\dfrac{5}{6}(x+3)-\dfrac{11}{12}\right]$

$\qquad 4(2x-3)+24=10(x+3)-11$

$\qquad 8x-12+24=10x+30-11$

$\qquad 8x+12=10x+19$

$\quad 8x+12-12=10x+19-12$

$\qquad\qquad 8x=10x+7$

$\quad 8x-10x=10x+7-10x$

$\qquad\qquad -2x=7$

$\qquad\qquad \dfrac{-2x}{-2}=\dfrac{7}{-2}$

$\qquad\qquad x=-\dfrac{7}{2}$

Check:

$\dfrac{1}{3}\left(2\left(-\dfrac{7}{2}\right)-3\right)+2\overset{?}{=}\dfrac{5}{6}\left(-\dfrac{7}{2}+3\right)-\dfrac{11}{12}$

$\dfrac{1}{3}(-7-3)+2\overset{?}{=}\dfrac{5}{6}\left(-\dfrac{1}{2}\right)-\dfrac{11}{12}$

$\dfrac{1}{3}(-10)+2\overset{?}{=}-\dfrac{5}{12}-\dfrac{11}{12}$

$-\dfrac{10}{3}+\dfrac{6}{3}\overset{?}{=}-\dfrac{16}{12}$

$-\dfrac{4}{3}=-\dfrac{4}{3}\ \checkmark$

This is a conditional equation.

Solution set: $\left\{-\dfrac{7}{2}\right\}$

53. $\quad 7y-8=-7$

$7y-8+8=-7+8$

$\qquad 7y=1$

$\qquad \dfrac{7y}{7}=\dfrac{1}{7}$

$\qquad y=\dfrac{1}{7}$

Check: $\quad 7\left(\dfrac{1}{7}\right)-8\overset{?}{=}-7$

$\qquad\qquad 1-8\overset{?}{=}-7$

$\qquad\qquad -7=-7\checkmark$

This is a conditional equation.

Solution set: $\left\{\dfrac{1}{7}\right\}$

55. $4a+3-2a+4=5a-7+a$

$\qquad 2a+7=6a-7$

$2a+7-7=6a-7-7$

$\qquad 2a=6a-14$

$2a-6a=6a-14-6a$

$\qquad -4a=-14$

$\qquad \dfrac{-4a}{-4}=\dfrac{-14}{-4}$

$\qquad a=\dfrac{7}{2}$

Check:

$4\left(\dfrac{7}{2}\right)+3-2\left(\dfrac{7}{2}\right)+4\overset{?}{=}5\left(\dfrac{7}{2}\right)-7+\dfrac{7}{2}$

$14+3-7+4\overset{?}{=}\dfrac{35}{2}-7+\dfrac{7}{2}$

$21-7\overset{?}{=}\dfrac{42}{2}-7$

$14\overset{?}{=}21-7$

$14=14\checkmark$

This is a conditional equation.

Solution set: $\left\{\dfrac{7}{2}\right\}$

57. $\qquad 4(p+3)=3(p-2)+p+18$

$\qquad 4p+12=3p-6+p+18$

$\qquad 4p+12=4p+12$

$4p+12-4p=4p+12-4p$

$\qquad 12=12$

This statement is an identity. The solution set is all real numbers.

Solution set: $\{p\,|\,p$ is any real number$\}$ or $\mathbb{R}$

59. $4b-3(b+1)-b=5(b-1)-5b$

$\qquad 4b-3b-3-b=5b-5-5b$

$\qquad\qquad -3=-5$

This statement is a contradiction. The equation has no solution.

Solution set: $\{\ \}$ or $\varnothing$

61. $\dfrac{m+1}{4}+\dfrac{5}{6}=\dfrac{2m-1}{12}$

$12\left(\dfrac{m+1}{4}+\dfrac{5}{6}\right)=12\left(\dfrac{2m-1}{12}\right)$

$3(m+1)+10=2m-1$

$3m+3+10=2m-1$

$3m+13=2m-1$

$3m+13-13=2m-1-13$

$3m=2m-14$

$3m-2m=2m-14-2m$

$m=-14$

Check:

$\dfrac{-14+1}{4}+\dfrac{5}{6}=\dfrac{2(-14)-1}{12}$

$\dfrac{-13}{4}+\dfrac{5}{6}=\dfrac{-28-1}{12}$

$\dfrac{-39}{12}+\dfrac{10}{12}=\dfrac{-29}{12}$

$\dfrac{-29}{12}=\dfrac{-29}{12}$ ✓

This is a conditional equation.
Solution set: $\{-14\}$

63. $0.3x-1.3=0.5x-0.7$

$0.3x-1.3+1.3=0.5x-0.7+1.3$

$0.3x=0.5x+0.6$

$0.3x-0.5x=0.5x+0.6-0.5x$

$-0.2x=0.6$

$\dfrac{-0.2x}{-0.2}=\dfrac{0.6}{-0.2}$

$x=-3$

Check:

$0.3(-3)-1.3\overset{?}{=}0.5(-3)-0.7$

$-0.9-1.3\overset{?}{=}-1.5-0.7$

$-2.2=-2.2$ ✓

This is a conditional equation.
Solution set: $\{-3\}$

(Note: Alternatively, we could have started by multiplying both sides of the equation by 10 to clear the decimals.)

65. $-0.8(x+1)=0.2(x+4)$

$-0.8x-0.8=0.2x+0.8$

$-0.8x-0.8+0.8=0.2x+0.8+0.8$

$-0.8x=0.2x+1.6$

$-0.8x-0.2x=0.2x+1.6-0.2x$

$-1.0x=1.6$

$\dfrac{-1.0x}{-1.0}=\dfrac{1.6}{-1.0}$

$x=-1.6$

Check: $-0.8(-1.6+1)\overset{?}{=}0.2(-1.6+4)$

$-0.8(-0.6)\overset{?}{=}0.2(2.4)$

$0.48=0.48$ ✓

This is a conditional equation.
Solution set: $\{-1.6\}$

(Note: Alternatively, we could have started by multiplying both sides of the equation by 10 to clear the decimals.)

67. $\dfrac{1}{4}(x-4)+3=\dfrac{1}{3}(2x+6)-\dfrac{5}{6}$

$12\left[\dfrac{1}{4}(x-4)+3\right]=12\left[\dfrac{1}{3}(2x+6)-\dfrac{5}{6}\right]$

$3(x-4)+36=4(2x+6)-10$

$3x-12+36=8x+24-10$

$3x+24=8x+14$

$3x+24-24=8x+14-24$

$3x=8x-10$

$3x-8x=8x-10-8x$

$-5x=-10$

$\dfrac{-5x}{-5}=\dfrac{-10}{-5}$

$x=2$

Check: $\frac{1}{4}(2-4)+3 \overset{?}{=} \frac{1}{3}(2(2)+6)-\frac{5}{6}$

$\frac{1}{4}(-2)+3 \overset{?}{=} \frac{1}{3}(10)-\frac{5}{6}$

$-\frac{1}{2}+3 \overset{?}{=} \frac{1}{3}(10)-\frac{5}{6}$

$-\frac{1}{2}+\frac{6}{2} \overset{?}{=} \frac{20}{6}-\frac{5}{6}$

$\frac{5}{2} \overset{?}{=} \frac{15}{6}$

$\frac{5}{2} = \frac{5}{2}$ ✓

This is a conditional equation.

Solution set: $\{2\}$

69. $ax+3=15$

Let $x=-3$: $\quad a(-3)+3=15$

$-3a+3=15$

$-3a+3-3=15-3$

$-3a=12$

$\frac{-3a}{-3}=\frac{12}{-3}$

$a=-4$

Check: $\quad -4x+3=15$

$-4x+3-3=15-3$

$-4x=12$

$\frac{-4x}{-4}=\frac{12}{-4}$

$x=-3$

71. $a(x-1)=3(x-1)$

To have the solution set be all real numbers, we need both sides of the linear equation to be identical. This can be achieved by letting $a=3$.

73. We need to set the denominator equal to 0 and solve the resulting equation.

$2x+1=0$

$2x+1-1=0-1$

$2x=-1$

$\frac{2x}{2}=\frac{-1}{2}$

$x=-\frac{1}{2}$

Check:

$2\left(-\frac{1}{2}\right)+1\overset{?}{=}0$

$-1+1\overset{?}{=}0$

$0=0$ ✓

We must exclude $x=-\frac{1}{2}$ from the domain.

75. We need to set the denominator equal to 0 and solve the resulting equation.

$4x-3=0$

$4x-3+3=0+3$

$4x=3$

$\frac{4x}{4}=\frac{3}{4}$

$x=\frac{3}{4}$

Check:

$4\left(\frac{3}{4}\right)-3\overset{?}{=}0$

$3-3\overset{?}{=}0$

$0=0$ ✓

We must exclude $x=\frac{3}{4}$ from the domain.

77. We need to set the denominator equal to 0 and solve the resulting equation.

$3(x+1)-6=0$

$3x+3-6=0$

$3x-3=0$

$3x-3+3=0+3$

$3x=3$

$\frac{3x}{3}=\frac{3}{3}$

$x=1$

Check:

$3(1+1)-6\overset{?}{=}0$

$3(2)-6\overset{?}{=}0$

$6-6\overset{?}{=}0$

$0=0$ ✓

We must exclude $x=1$ from the domain.

79.
$$25 = \frac{2000}{12} \cdot r$$
$$\frac{12}{2000} \cdot 25 = \frac{12}{2000} \cdot \frac{2000}{12} \cdot r$$
$$\frac{300}{2000} = r$$
$$0.15 = r$$
The card's annual interest rate is 0.15 or 15%.

81.
$$2335 = 0.15(x - 7300) + 730$$
$$2335 = 0.15x - 1095 + 730$$
$$2335 = 0.15x - 365$$
$$2335 + 365 = 0.15x - 365 + 365$$
$$2700 = 0.15x$$
$$\frac{2700}{0.15} = \frac{0.15x}{0.15}$$
$$18,000 = x$$
You earned $18,000 in 2005.

83. Answers will vary. One possibility:
One solution: $3x + 2 = 2x - 7$
No solution: $4x - 3 = 4x + 5$
Identity: $3x + 2 = 3x + 2$
In both the no solution case and the identity case, the variable terms will cancel out leaving a constant on each side of the equation. If the constants are the same, then you have an identity. If they differ, then there is no solution. If the variable terms do not cancel when put on the same side, then there will be one solution.

1.2 Preparing for Problem Solving

1. $12 + z$
The keyword 'sum' indicates addition.

2. $4x$
The keyword 'product' indicates multiplication.

3. $y - 87$
The keywords 'decreased by' indicate subtraction. Since order matters here, we subtract the quantity after the keywords.

4. $\dfrac{z}{12}$
The keyword 'quotient' indicates division. The first quantity is the numerator and the second quantity is the denominator.

5. $4(x + 7)$
The keyword 'times' indicates multiplication and the keyword 'sum' indicates addition. Because the statement says 'times the sum' we multiply 4 by the entire sum, not just the x.

6. $4x + 7$
The keyword 'times' indicates multiplication and the keyword 'sum' indicates addition. After the keywords 'sum of', we look for the two quantities to add. These are separated by the keyword 'and'. Thus, the first addend is 'four times a number x' while the second addend is the number '7'.

1.2 Exercises

1. mathematical modeling

3. True

5. Answers will vary. Mathematical modeling is related to problem solving in that it requires us to use information, tools (mathematical formulas), and our own skills to solve math related problems.

7. Categories: Direct Translation, Mixtures, Geometry, Uniform Motion, and Work Problems.
Two types of mixture problems are interest and blends.

9. Let x = desired result
$$x = 0.25(40) = 10$$
25% of 40 is 10.

11. Let x = original amount .
$$12 = 0.3x$$
$$\frac{12}{0.3} = \frac{0.3x}{0.3}$$
$$40 = x$$
12 is 30% of 40.

13. Let x = percent as a decimal.

$$30 = x \cdot 80$$
$$30 = 80x$$
$$\frac{30}{80} = \frac{80x}{80}$$
$$.375 = x$$

30 is 37.5% of 80.

15.
$$x + 12 = 20$$
$$x + 12 - 12 = 20 - 12$$
$$x = 8$$

17.
$$2 \cdot (y + 3) = 16$$
$$2y + 6 = 16$$
$$2y = 10$$
$$\frac{2y}{2} = \frac{10}{2}$$
$$y = 5$$

19.
$$w - 22 = 3w$$
$$-22 = 2w$$
$$\frac{-22}{2} = \frac{2w}{2}$$
$$-11 = w$$

21.
$$4x = 2x + 14$$
$$2x = 14$$
$$\frac{2x}{2} = \frac{14}{2}$$
$$x = 7$$

23.
$$0.8x = x + 5$$
$$-0.2x = 5$$
$$\frac{-0.2x}{-0.2} = \frac{5}{-0.2}$$
$$x = -25$$

25. First number: x
Second number: $2x$
$$x + 2x = 39$$
$$3x = 39$$
$$\frac{3x}{3} = \frac{39}{3}$$
$$x = 13$$

Check:
$$13 + 2(13) = 13 + 26 = 39$$

The two numbers are 13 and 26.

27. First of the consecutive integers: x
Second consecutive integer: $x + 1$
Third consecutive integer: $x + 2$
$$x + (x + 1) + (x + 2) = 75$$
$$x + x + 1 + x + 2 = 75$$
$$3x + 3 = 75$$
$$3x + 3 - 3 = 75 - 3$$
$$3x = 72$$
$$\frac{3x}{3} = \frac{72}{3}$$
$$x = 24$$

Check:
$$24 + (24 + 1) + (24 + 2) = 24 + 25 + 26 = 75$$

The integers are 24, 25, and 26.

29. Let x = score on Kendra's final exam.
$$\frac{84 + 78 + 64 + 88 + 2x}{6} = 80$$
$$\frac{314 + 2x}{6} = 80$$
$$6 \cdot \frac{314 + 2x}{6} = 6 \cdot 80$$
$$314 + 2x = 480$$
$$314 + 2x - 314 = 480 - 314$$
$$2x = 166$$
$$\frac{2x}{2} = \frac{166}{2}$$
$$x = 83$$

Check:
$$\frac{84 + 78 + 64 + 88 + 2(83)}{6} = \frac{314 + 166}{6} = \frac{480}{6} = 80$$

Kendra needs an 83 on her final exam to have an average of 80.

31. Let x = number of pages printed.
HP printer cost: $180 + 0.03x$
Brother printer cost: $230 + 0.01x$
$$180 + 0.03x = 230 + 0.01x$$
$$180 + 0.03x - 180 = 230 + 0.01x - 180$$
$$0.03x = 0.01x + 50$$
$$0.03x - 0.01x = 0.01x + 50 - 0.01x$$
$$0.02x = 50$$
$$\frac{0.02x}{0.02} = \frac{50}{0.02}$$
$$x = 2500$$

Check:

$$180 + 0.03(2500) \overset{?}{=} 230 + 0.01(2500)$$

$$180 + 75 \overset{?}{=} 230 + 25$$

$$255 = 255 \checkmark$$

Jacob would need to print 2500 pages for the cost to be the same for the two printers.

33. Let x = amount that Connor receives.

Olivia: $\dfrac{3}{4}x$

Avery: $\dfrac{1}{4}x$

$$x + \frac{3}{4}x + \frac{1}{4}x = 800,000$$

$$2x = 800,000$$

$$\frac{2x}{2} = \frac{800,000}{2}$$

$$x = 400,000$$

Check:

$$400,000 + \frac{3}{4}(400,000) + \frac{1}{4}(400,000) \overset{?}{=} 800,000$$

$$400,000 + 300,000 + 100,000 \overset{?}{=} 800,000$$

$$800,000 = 800,000 \checkmark$$

Connor: $400,000; Olivia: $300,000; Avery: $100,000.

35. Let x = total of final bill.

$$599 + 0.029 \cdot 599 = x$$

$$599 + 17.371 = x$$

$$616.371 = x$$

The final bill will be $616.37.

37. Let x = dealer's cost.

$$x + 0.15x = 25,800$$

$$1.15x = 25,800$$

$$\frac{1.15x}{1.15} = \frac{25,800}{1.15}$$

$$x \approx 22434.78$$

Check:

$$22434.78 + 0.15(22434.78)$$

$$= 22434.78 + 3365.217$$

$$= 25,799.997$$

The dealer's cost is about $22,434.78.

39. Let x = original price of memory card.

Discount price: $x - 0.2x = 0.8x$

$$0.8x = 13.60$$

$$\frac{0.8x}{0.8} = \frac{13.60}{0.8}$$

$$x = 17$$

Check:

$$0.8(17) \overset{?}{=} 13.6$$

$$13.6 = 13.6 \checkmark$$

The memory cards originally cost $17.

41. Let x = weight in pounds of Nissan Altima.

Mazda 6s: $x + 20$

Honda Accord EX: $x + 70$

$$x + (x + 20) + (x + 70) = 10,050$$

$$x + x + 20 + x + 70 = 10,050$$

$$3x + 90 = 10,050$$

$$3x + 90 - 90 = 10,050 - 90$$

$$3x = 9960$$

$$\frac{3x}{3} = \frac{9960}{3}$$

$$x = 3320$$

The Nissan Altima weighs 3320 pounds, the Mazda 6s weighs 3340 pounds, and the Honda Accord EX weighs 3390 pounds.

Check:

$$3320 + 3340 + 3390 = 10,050$$

43. Let x = total yards rushed by Raiders.

Bucs: $x + 90$

$$x + (x + 90) = 560$$

$$x + x + 90 = 560$$

$$2x + 90 = 560$$

$$2x + 90 - 90 = 560 - 90$$

$$2x = 470$$

$$\frac{2x}{2} = \frac{470}{2}$$

$$x = 235$$

Check: $235 + (235 + 90) = 235 + 325 = 560$

The Raiders rushed for 235 yards.

45. Let x = amount that Adam will receive .
Krissy: $x + 3000$

$$x + (x + 3000) = 20,000$$
$$x + x + 3000 = 20,000$$
$$2x + 3000 = 20,000$$
$$2x + 3000 - 3000 = 20,000 - 3000$$
$$2x = 17,000$$
$$\frac{2x}{2} = \frac{17,000}{2}$$
$$x = 8500$$

Check:
$$8500 + (8500 + 3000) = 8500 + 11,500 = 20,000$$
Adam will get $8500 and Krissy will get $11,500.

47. Let x = amount invested in stocks .

Bonds: $\frac{3}{5}x$

$$x + \frac{3}{5}x = 24,000$$
$$\frac{8}{5}x = 24,000$$
$$\frac{5}{8} \cdot \frac{8}{5}x = \frac{5}{8} \cdot 24,000$$
$$x = 15,000$$

Check:
$$15,000 + \frac{3}{5}(15,000) = 15,000 + 9000 = 24,000$$
You should invest $15,000 in stocks and $9,000 in bonds.

49. Let I = interest charge after one month .

$$I = Prt = (2500)(0.14)\left(\frac{1}{12}\right) \approx 29.17$$

The interest charge after one month will be $29.17.

Check:
$$\left(\frac{29.17}{2500}\right) \cdot 12 = (0.011668) \cdot 12 = 0.140016$$

51. Let x = amount loaned at 6% .
Amount at 11%: $500,000 - x$

$$0.06x + 0.11(500,000 - x) = 43,750$$
$$0.06x + 55,000 - 0.11x = 43,750$$
$$-0.05x + 55,000 = 43,750$$
$$-0.05x = -11,250$$
$$\frac{-0.05x}{-0.05} = \frac{-11,250}{-0.05}$$
$$x = 225,000$$
The bank loaned $225,000 at 6% interest.

53. Let x = the amount invested in bonds.
Amount in stocks: $25,000 - x$
Here we need the simple interest formula $I = P \cdot r \cdot t$. We need to add the interest from each investment after $t = 1$ year.

$$0.05x + 0.09(25,000 - x) = 1875$$
$$0.05x + 2250 - 0.09x = 1875$$
$$2250 - 0.04x = 1875$$
$$2250 - 0.04x - 2250 = 1875 - 2250$$
$$-0.04x = -375$$
$$\frac{-0.04x}{-0.04} = \frac{-375}{-0.04}$$
$$x = 9375$$

Pedro should invest $9375 in the 5% bond and $25,000 - 9,375 = \$15,625$ in the 9% stock fund.

Check:
$$0.05(9375) + 0.09(15,625) \overset{?}{=} 1875$$
$$468.75 + 1406.25 \overset{?}{=} 1875$$
$$1875 = 1875 \checkmark$$

55. Let x = pounds of coffee A . Since there will be a total of 50 pounds of coffee, you must add $50 - x$ pounds of coffee B.

57. Let d = number of dimes .

Quarters: $47 - d$

$$0.1(d) + 0.25(47 - d) = 9.50$$
$$0.1d + 11.75 - 0.25d = 9.50$$
$$-0.15d + 11.75 = 9.50$$
$$-0.15d = -2.25$$
$$\frac{-0.15d}{-0.15} = \frac{-2.25}{-0.15}$$
$$d = 15$$

Check:

$$0.1(15) + 0.25(32) = 1.5 + 8 = 9.5$$

Bobby has 15 dimes and 32 quarters saved.

59. Let x = grams of pure gold .

12 karat: $72 - x$

18k gold = 12k gold + pure gold

$$(\%) \cdot (\text{grams}) = (\%) \cdot (\text{grams}) + (\%) \cdot (\text{grams})$$
$$\frac{18}{24}(72) = \frac{12}{24}(72 - x) + \frac{24}{24}(x)$$
$$54 = 36 - \frac{1}{2}x + x$$
$$54 = 36 + \frac{1}{2}x$$
$$18 = \frac{1}{2}x$$
$$2 \cdot 18 = 2 \cdot \frac{1}{2}x$$
$$36 = x$$

36 grams of pure gold should be mixed with 36 grams of 12 karat gold.

Check:

$$36 - \frac{1}{2}(36) + 36 = 36 - 18 + 36 = 54$$

61. Let x = time spent running (hours) .

Bicycle: $4 - x$

For this problem we will need the distance traveled formula: $d = r \cdot t$.

tot. dist. = dist. run + dist. biked

tot. dist. = $(\text{run rate})(\text{time}) + (\text{bike rate})(\text{time})$

$$62 = 8(x) + 20(4 - x)$$
$$62 = 8x + 80 - 20x$$
$$62 = 80 - 12x$$
$$-18 = -12x$$
$$\frac{-18}{-12} = \frac{-12x}{-12}$$
$$1.5 = x$$

Check:

$$8(1.5) + 20(4 - 1.5) = 12 + 20(2.5) = 12 + 50 = 62$$

We now know that the time spent running is 1.5 hours and the time spent biking is 2.5 hours. However, the question asked for distances. We can use the distance traveled formula here.

Run: distance = $8(1.5) = 12$ miles

Bike: distance = $20(2.5) = 50$ miles

The race consists of running for 12 miles and biking for 50 miles.

63. Let x = speed of slower car (mph) .

Faster car: $10 + x$

tot. dist. = slow dist. + fast dist.

$$455 = x(3.5) + (10 + x)(3.5)$$
$$455 = 3.5x + 35 + 3.5x$$
$$455 = 7x + 35$$
$$420 = 7x$$
$$\frac{420}{7} = \frac{7x}{7}$$
$$60 = x$$

Check:

$$60(3.5) + 70(3.5) = 210 + 245 = 455$$

The slow car is traveling at 60 mph while the faster car travels at 70 mph.

65. Let t = time in hours

Speed of slow boat: 25 mph

Speed of fast boat: 25 + 12 = 37 mph

tot. dist. = slow boat dist. + fast boat dist.

$$155 = 25t + 37t$$
$$155 = 62t$$
$$\frac{155}{62} = t$$
$$2.5 = t$$

Check:

$$25(2.5) + 37(2.5) = 62.5 + 92.5 = 155$$

The boats will be 155 miles apart after 2.5 hours.

67. Let $x =$ speed of slower person (mph).

Speed of faster person: $2.0 + x$

tot. dist. = slow dist. + fast dist.

$$15 = x(1.5) + (2 + x)(1.5)$$
$$15 = 1.5x + 3 + 1.5x$$
$$15 = 3x + 3$$
$$12 = 3x$$
$$\frac{12}{3} = x$$
$$4 = x$$

Check:

$$4(1.5) + 6(1.5) = 6 + 9 = 15$$

One person is walking at a rate of 4 miles per hour and the other is walking at a rate of 6 miles per hour.

69. Written answers will vary.

Algebraic:

Let $x =$ distance to Florida (miles).

When thinking about this problem, we are assuming that the distance to Florida is the same as the distance back. We will again need the distance traveled formula: $d = r \cdot t$

Also note that $t = \dfrac{d}{r}$ (this is used to express the times of travel to and from Florida). This gives us the following:

$$\text{avg. speed} = \frac{\text{total distance traveled}}{\text{total time of travel}}$$
$$= \frac{\text{dist. to} + \text{dist. from}}{\text{time to} + \text{time from}}$$
$$= \frac{x + x}{\dfrac{x}{50} + \dfrac{x}{60}} = \frac{2x}{\dfrac{6x}{300} + \dfrac{5x}{300}} = \frac{2x}{\dfrac{11x}{300}}$$
$$= \frac{2x}{1} \cdot \frac{300}{11x} = \frac{600}{11} \approx 54.55$$

The average speed of the trip to Florida and back is roughly 54.55 miles per hour.

71. Answers will vary. One possibility:

"Payton has DSL service and gets a 5% discount for bundling this service with her local phone service. If her discounted monthly rate for DSL is $60, how much would she pay without the discount?"

73. Start by noting that you and the train travel for the same amount of time. We also need the distance traveled formula: $d = r \cdot t$

Distance traveled by train:

$$\frac{20 \text{ miles}}{1 \text{ hr}} \cdot 1 \text{ min} \cdot \frac{1 \text{ hr}}{60 \text{ min}} = \frac{1}{3} \text{ mile}$$

Distance traveled by you:

$$\frac{2 \text{ miles}}{1 \text{ hr}} \cdot 1 \text{ min} \cdot \frac{1 \text{ hr}}{60 \text{ min}} = \frac{1}{30} \text{ mile}$$

Since you went from the front of the train to the back, the difference in the distances traveled is the length of the train.

$$\frac{1}{3} - \frac{1}{30} = \frac{10}{30} - \frac{1}{30} = \frac{9}{30} = \frac{3}{10} = 0.3$$

The train is 0.3 miles long, or 1584 feet.

From a physical point of view, the situation would be the same as if you were standing still and the train was traveling at 18 mph (20-2). We know the rate (18 mph) and we know the time ($1 \text{ min} = \dfrac{1}{60}$ hr). Using the distance traveled formula we get:

$$d = r \cdot t = 18\left(\frac{1}{60}\right) = 0.3 \text{ miles}$$

The train is 0.3 miles long, or 1584 feet.

1.3 Preparing for Formulas

1. a. To round to three decimal places, we first examine the digit in the fourth decimal place and then truncate. Since the fourth decimal place contains a 4, we do not change the digit in the third decimal place. Thus, 3.00343 rounded to three decimal places is 3.003.

b. To truncate, we remove all digits after the third decimal place. So, 3.00343 truncated to three decimal places is 3.003.

2. a. To round to two decimal places, we first examine the digit in the third decimal place and then truncate. Since the third decimal place contains a 7, we increase the digit in the second decimal place by 1. Thus, 14.957 rounded to two decimal places is 14.96.

b. To truncate, we remove all digits after the second decimal place. So, 14.957 truncated to two decimal places is 14.95.

1.3 Exercises

1. formula

3. golden rectangles

5. True

7. $F = m \cdot a$

9. $V = \dfrac{4}{3}\pi r^3$

11. $d = r \cdot t$

$$\frac{d}{t} = \frac{r \cdot t}{t}$$

$$\frac{d}{t} = r$$

13. $y - y_1 = m(x - x_1)$

$$\frac{y - y_1}{x - x_1} = \frac{m(x - x_1)}{(x - x_1)}$$

$$\frac{y - y_1}{x - x_1} = m$$

15. $Z = \dfrac{x - \mu}{\sigma}$

$$\sigma \cdot Z = \sigma \cdot \frac{x - \mu}{\sigma}$$

$$\sigma Z = x - \mu$$

$$\sigma Z + \mu = x - \mu + \mu$$

$$\mu + \sigma Z = x$$

17. $F = G\dfrac{m_1 m_2}{r^2}$

$$r^2 \cdot F = r^2 \cdot G\frac{m_1 m_2}{r^2}$$

$$r^2 F = Gm_1 m_2$$

$$\frac{r^2 F}{Gm_2} = \frac{Gm_1 m_2}{Gm_2}$$

$$\frac{r^2 F}{Gm_2} = m_1$$

19. $A = P + P \cdot r \cdot t$

$$A = P(1 + rt)$$

$$\frac{A}{1 + rt} = \frac{P(1 + rt)}{1 + rt}$$

$$\frac{A}{1 + rt} = P$$

21. $C = \dfrac{5}{9}(F - 32)$

$$\frac{9}{5} \cdot C = \frac{9}{5} \cdot \frac{5}{9}(F - 32)$$

$$\frac{9}{5}C = F - 32$$

$$\frac{9}{5}C + 32 = F - 32 + 32$$

$$\frac{9}{5}C + 32 = F$$

23. $2x + y = 13$

$$2x + y - 2x = 13 - 2x$$

$$y = 13 - 2x \text{ or } y = -2x + 13$$

25. $9x - 3y = 15$

$$9x - 3y - 9x = 15 - 9x$$

$$-3y = 15 - 9x$$

$$\frac{-3y}{-3} = \frac{15 - 9x}{-3}$$

$$y = -5 + 3x \text{ or } y = 3x - 5$$

27. $4x + 3y = 13$

$$4x + 3y - 4x = 13 - 4x$$

$$3y = 13 - 4x$$

$$\frac{3y}{3} = \frac{13 - 4x}{3}$$

$$y = \frac{13}{3} - \frac{4}{3}x \text{ or } y = -\frac{4}{3}x + \frac{13}{3}$$

29. $\dfrac{1}{2}x + \dfrac{1}{6}y = 2$

$$6\left(\frac{1}{2}x + \frac{1}{6}y\right) = 6(2)$$

$$3x + y = 12$$

$$3x + y - 3x = 12 - 3x$$

$$y = 12 - 3x \text{ or } y = -3x + 12$$

SSM – 25

31. a.
$$V = \pi r^2 h$$
$$\frac{V}{\pi r^2} = \frac{\pi r^2 h}{\pi r^2}$$
$$\frac{V}{\pi r^2} = h$$

b. $h = \dfrac{V}{\pi r^2} = \dfrac{32\pi}{\pi(2)^2} = \dfrac{32}{4} = 8$ inches

The height of the cylinder is 8 inches.

33. a.
$$M = -0.711A + 206.3$$
$$M - 206.3 = -0.711A + 206.3 - 206.3$$
$$M - 206.3 = -0.711A$$
$$\frac{M - 206.3}{-0.711} = \frac{-0.711A}{-0.711}$$
$$\frac{206.3 - M}{0.711} = A$$

b. $A = \dfrac{206.3 - M}{0.711} = \dfrac{206.3 - 160}{0.711}$

$$= \frac{46.3}{0.711} \approx 65.12$$

An individual whose maximum heart rate is 160 should be about 65 years old.

35. a.
$$A = P(1+r)^t$$
$$\frac{A}{(1+r)^t} = \frac{P(1+r)^t}{(1+r)^t}$$
$$\frac{A}{(1+r)^t} = P$$

b. $P = \dfrac{A}{(1+r)^t} = \dfrac{5000}{(1+0.04)^5} = \dfrac{5000}{1.04^5} \approx 4109.64$

Roughly $4109.64 should be deposited today to have $5000 in 5 years in an account that pays 4% annual interest.

37. Let x = measure of smaller angle (degrees).
Larger angle: $x + 30$
$$x + (x + 30) = 180$$
$$x + x + 30 = 180$$
$$2x + 30 = 180$$
$$2x + 30 - 30 = 180 - 30$$
$$2x = 150$$
$$\frac{2x}{2} = \frac{150}{2}$$
$$x = 75$$

The smaller angle measures $75°$ and its supplement measures $105°$.

39. Let y = measure of the smaller angle (degrees).
Larger angle: $10 + 3y$
$$y + (10 + 3y) = 90$$
$$y + 10 + 3y = 90$$
$$4y + 10 = 90$$
$$4y + 10 - 10 = 90 - 10$$
$$4y = 80$$
$$\frac{4y}{4} = \frac{80}{4}$$
$$y = 20$$

The smaller angle measures $20°$ and its complement measures $70°$.

41. Let l = length of the window (feet).
width: $w = l + 3$
$$P = 2l + 2w$$
$$26 = 2l + 2(l + 3)$$
$$26 = 2l + 2l + 6$$
$$26 = 4l + 6$$
$$26 - 6 = 4l + 6 - 6$$
$$20 = 4l$$
$$\frac{20}{4} = \frac{4l}{4}$$
$$5 = l$$

The window is 5 feet long and 8 feet wide.

43. We can start by finding the length, s, of one side of the square given that $P = 40$.

$$\frac{P}{4} = s$$

$$\frac{40}{4} = s$$

$10 \text{ inches} = s$

The circle with the largest area will have a diameter equal to the length of one side of the square. Since the diameter is twice the radius, r, of the circle, we have

$2r = 10$ or $r = 5$

The radius of the desired circle is 5 inches.

$$A = \pi r^2 = \pi (5)^2 = 25\pi \approx 78.54 \text{ in}^2$$

The area of the circle is 25π square inches (roughly 78.54 square inches).

45. Let x = measure of the first angle (degrees).

Second angle: $x + 15$

Third angle: $x + 45$

$$x + (x+15) + (x+45) = 180$$

$$x + x + 15 + x + 45 = 180$$

$$3x + 60 = 180$$

$$3x + 60 - 60 = 180 - 60$$

$$3x = 120$$

$$\frac{3x}{3} = \frac{120}{3}$$

$$x = 40$$

The first angle measures $40°$, the second measures $55°$, and the third measures $85°$.

47. a. Let w = width of patio in feet.

Length: $l = w + 5$

$$P = 2l + 2w$$

$$80 = 2(w+5) + 2w$$

$$80 = 2w + 10 + 2w$$

$$80 = 4w + 10$$

$$80 - 10 = 4w + 10 - 10$$

$$70 = 4w$$

$$\frac{70}{4} = \frac{4w}{4}$$

$$17.5 = w$$

The patio is 17.5 ft wide and 22.5 ft long.

b. $h = 4 \; \cancel{\text{in}} \cdot \dfrac{1 \text{ ft}}{12 \; \cancel{\text{in}}} = \dfrac{1}{3} \text{ ft}$

$$V = l \cdot w \cdot h$$

$$V = (22.5)(17.5)\left(\tfrac{1}{3}\right)$$

$$V = 131.25 \text{ cubic feet}$$

You would need to purchase 131.25 cubic feet of cement.

49. a. Notice that the edge of the deck forms a large circle and the pool forms a smaller circle that sits inside the larger circle. We can subtract the area covered by the pool from the area of the larger circle to obtain the area of the deck. Since the diameter of the pool is 25 ft, the radius must be 12.5 ft.

Area of pool:

$$A = \pi r^2 = \pi (12.5)^2 = 156.25\pi \text{ sq. feet}$$

Area of large circle:

$$A = \pi(12.5+3)^2 = \pi(15.5)^2$$

$$= 240.25\pi \text{ sq. feet}$$

Area of deck:

$$A = 240.25\pi - 156.25\pi$$

$$= 84\pi \approx 263.89 \text{ sq. feet}$$

The deck has an area of 84π square feet (roughly 264 square feet).

b. The fence would go on the perimeter of the deck so we need the circumference of the large circle.

$$C = 2\pi r = 2\pi(15.5) = 31\pi \text{ feet} \approx 97.39 \text{ feet}$$

It would require roughly 97.39 feet of fencing to encircle the pool.

c. $31\pi(25) = 775\pi \approx 2434.73$

The fence would cost about \$2434.73.

1.4 Preparing for Linear Inequalities

1. $3 < 6$ because 6 is further to the right on a real number line.

2. $-3 > -6$ because -3 is further to the right on a real number line.

3. $\dfrac{1}{2} = 0.5$ because both numbers are at the same point on a real number line.

4. $\frac{2}{3} = \frac{10}{15} > \frac{9}{15} = \frac{3}{5}$ because $\frac{2}{3}$ is further to the right on a real number line.

5. False; strict inequalities are either $<$ or $>$.

6. $\{x \mid x$ is a digit that is divisible by 3$\}$

1.4 Exercises

1. closed interval

3. left endpoint; right endpoint

5. True. Since $a < b$, if we multiply both sides of the inequality by c (where $c < 0$) we need to switch the direction of the inequality.

7. The use of a square bracket in interval notation implies that the endpoint is included in the solution interval. The infinity symbol represents unbounded behavior and is not a number. Therefore, it can never be 'included' in a solution interval. Both ∞ and $-\infty$ require parentheses in interval notation. The proper notation would be $[4, \infty)$.

9. $x - 4 \le 2$
$x - 4 + 4 \le 2 + 4$
$x \le 6$
$\{x \mid x \le 6\}; (-\infty, 6]$

11. $6x < 24$
$\frac{6x}{6} < \frac{24}{6}$
$x < 4$
$\{x \mid x < 4\}; (-\infty, 4)$

13. $-7x < 21$
$\frac{-7x}{-7} > \frac{21}{-7}$
$x > -3$
$\{x \mid x > -3\}; (-3, \infty)$

15. $\frac{4}{15}x > \frac{8}{5}$
$\frac{15}{4} \cdot \frac{4}{15}x > \frac{15}{4} \cdot \frac{8}{5}$
$x > 6$
$\{x \mid x > 6\}; (6, \infty)$

17. $3x + 2 > 11$
$3x + 2 - 2 > 11 - 2$
$3x > 9$
$\frac{3x}{3} > \frac{9}{3}$
$x > 3$
$\{x \mid x > 3\}; (3, \infty)$

19. $-3x + 1 > 13$
$-3x + 1 - 1 > 13 - 1$
$-3x > 12$
$\frac{-3x}{-3} < \frac{12}{-3}$
$x < -4$
$\{x \mid x < -4\}; (-\infty, -4)$

21. $6x + 5 \le 3x + 2$
$6x + 5 - 5 \le 3x + 2 - 5$
$6x \le 3x - 3$
$6x - 3x \le 3x - 3 - 3x$
$3x \le -3$
$\frac{3x}{3} \le \frac{-3}{3}$
$x \le -1$
$\{x \mid x \le -1\}; (-\infty, -1]$

23.
$$-3x+1 < 2x+11$$
$$-3x+1-1 < 2x+11-1$$
$$-3x < 2x+10$$
$$-3x-2x < 2x+10-2x$$
$$-5x < 10$$
$$\frac{-5x}{-5} > \frac{10}{-5}$$
$$x > -2$$
$$\{x \mid x > -2\}; \; (-2, \infty)$$

25.
$$3(x-3) < 2(x+4)$$
$$3x-9 < 2x+8$$
$$3x-9+9 < 2x+8+9$$
$$3x < 2x+17$$
$$3x-2x < 2x+17-2x$$
$$x < 17$$
$$\{x \mid x < 17\}; \; (-\infty, 17)$$

27.
$$4(x+1)-2x \ge 5(x-2)+2$$
$$4x+4-2x \ge 5x-10+2$$
$$2x+4 \ge 5x-8$$
$$2x+4-4 \ge 5x-8-4$$
$$2x \ge 5x-12$$
$$2x-5x \ge 5x-12-5x$$
$$-3x \ge -12$$
$$\frac{-3x}{-3} \le \frac{-12}{-3}$$
$$x \le 4$$
$$\{x \mid x \le 4\}; \; (-\infty, 4]$$

29.
$$0.5x+4 \le 0.2x-5$$
$$0.5x+4-4 \le 0.2x-5-4$$
$$0.5x \le 0.2x-9$$
$$0.5x-0.2x \le 0.2x-9-0.2x$$
$$0.3x \le -9$$
$$\frac{0.3x}{0.3} \le \frac{-9}{0.3}$$
$$x \le -30$$
$$\{x \mid x \le -30\}; \; (-\infty, -30]$$

31.
$$\frac{3x+1}{4} < \frac{1}{2}$$
$$4\left(\frac{3x+1}{4}\right) < 4\left(\frac{1}{2}\right)$$
$$3x+1 < 2$$
$$3x+1-1 < 2-1$$
$$3x < 1$$
$$\frac{3x}{3} < \frac{1}{3}$$
$$x < \frac{1}{3}$$
$$\left\{x \mid x < \frac{1}{3}\right\}; \; \left(-\infty, \frac{1}{3}\right)$$

33.
$$\frac{1}{2}(x-4) > \frac{3}{4}(2x+1)$$
$$4 \cdot \frac{1}{2}(x-4) > 4 \cdot \frac{3}{4}(2x+1)$$
$$2(x-4) > 3(2x+1)$$
$$2x-8 > 6x+3$$
$$2x > 6x+11$$
$$-4x > 11$$
$$\frac{-4x}{-4} < \frac{11}{-4}$$
$$x < -\frac{11}{4}$$
$$\left\{x \mid x < -\frac{11}{4}\right\}; \; \left(-\infty, -\frac{11}{4}\right)$$

35. $\dfrac{3}{5} - x > \dfrac{5}{3}$

$\dfrac{3}{5} - x - \dfrac{3}{5} > \dfrac{5}{3} - \dfrac{3}{5}$

$-x > \dfrac{25}{15} - \dfrac{9}{15}$

$-x > \dfrac{16}{15}$

$-1(-x) < -1\left(\dfrac{16}{15}\right)$

$x < -\dfrac{16}{15}$

$\left\{x \mid x < -\dfrac{16}{15}\right\}; \left(-\infty, -\dfrac{16}{15}\right)$

37. $-5(x-3) \geq 3\big[4 - (x+4)\big]$

$-5x + 15 \geq 3[4 - x - 4]$

$-5x + 15 \geq 3(-x)$

$-5x + 15 \geq -3x$

$-5x \geq -3x - 15$

$-2x \geq -15$

$\dfrac{-2x}{-2} \leq \dfrac{-15}{-2}$

$x \leq \dfrac{15}{2}$

$\left\{x \mid x \leq \dfrac{15}{2}\right\}; \left(-\infty, \dfrac{15}{2}\right]$

39. $4(3x-1) - 5(x+4) \geq 3\big[2 - (x+3)\big] - 6x$

$12x - 4 - 5x - 20 \geq 3[2 - x - 3] - 6x$

$7x - 24 \geq 3[-1 - x] - 6x$

$7x - 24 \geq -3 - 3x - 6x$

$7x - 24 \geq -3 - 9x$

$7x \geq 21 - 9x$

$16x \geq 21$

$\dfrac{16x}{16} \geq \dfrac{21}{16}$

$x \geq \dfrac{21}{16}$

$\left\{x \mid x \geq \dfrac{21}{16}\right\}; \left[\dfrac{21}{16}, \infty\right)$

41. $\dfrac{2}{3}(4x-1) - \dfrac{4}{9}(x-4) > \dfrac{5}{12}(2x+3)$

$36 \cdot \dfrac{2}{3}(4x-1) - 36 \cdot \dfrac{4}{9}(x-4) > 36 \cdot \dfrac{5}{12}(2x+3)$

$24(4x-1) - 16(x-4) > 15(2x+3)$

$96x - 24 - 16x + 64 > 30x + 45$

$80x + 40 > 30x + 45$

$80x > 30x + 5$

$50x > 5$

$\dfrac{50x}{50} > \dfrac{5}{50}$

$x > \dfrac{1}{10}$

$\left\{x \mid x > \dfrac{1}{10}\right\}; \left(\dfrac{1}{10}, \infty\right)$

43. $\dfrac{4x-3}{3} < 3$

$3 \cdot \dfrac{4x-3}{3} < 3 \cdot 3$

$4x - 3 < 9$

$4x < 12$

$\dfrac{4x}{4} < \dfrac{12}{4}$

$x < 3$

$\{x \mid x < 3\}; (-\infty, 3)$

45. $\dfrac{2}{3}x < \dfrac{1}{4}(2x+3)$

$12 \cdot \dfrac{2}{3}x < 12 \cdot \dfrac{1}{4}(2x+3)$

$8x < 3(2x+3)$

$8x < 6x+9$

$2x < 9$

$\dfrac{2x}{2} < \dfrac{9}{2}$

$x < \dfrac{9}{2}$

$\left\{ x \mid x < \dfrac{9}{2} \right\}$; $\left(-\infty, \dfrac{9}{2} \right)$

47. $y+8 > -7$

$y+8-8 > -7-8$

$y > -15$

$\{ y \mid y > -15 \}$; $(-15, \infty)$

49. $-3a \le -21$

$\dfrac{-3a}{-3} \ge \dfrac{-21}{-3}$

$a \ge 7$

$\{ a \mid a \ge 7 \}$; $[7, \infty)$

51. $13x - 5 > 10x - 6$

$13x - 5 + 5 > 10x - 6 + 5$

$13x > 10x - 1$

$13x - 10x > 10x - 1 - 10x$

$3x > -1$

$\dfrac{3x}{3} > \dfrac{-1}{3}$

$x > -\dfrac{1}{3}$

$\left\{ x \mid x > -\dfrac{1}{3} \right\}$; $\left(-\dfrac{1}{3}, \infty \right)$

53. $4(x+2) \le 3(x-2)$

$4x + 8 \le 3x - 6$

$4x + 8 - 8 \le 3x - 6 - 8$

$4x \le 3x - 14$

$4x - 3x \le 3x - 14 - 3x$

$x \le -14$

$\{ x \mid x \le -14 \}$; $(-\infty, -14]$

55. $3(4-3x) > 6 - 5x$

$12 - 9x > 6 - 5x$

$12 - 9x - 12 > 6 - 5x - 12$

$-9x > -5x - 6$

$-9x + 5x > -5x - 6 + 5x$

$-4x > -6$

$\dfrac{-4x}{-4} < \dfrac{-6}{-4}$

$x < \dfrac{3}{2}$

$\left\{ x \mid x < \dfrac{3}{2} \right\}$; $\left(-\infty, \dfrac{3}{2} \right)$

57. $2[4-3(x+1)] \le -4x+8$

$2[4-3x-3] \le -4x+8$

$2[1-3x] \le -4x+8$

$2 - 6x \le -4x+8$

$-6x \le -4x+6$

$-2x \le 6$

$\dfrac{-2x}{-2} \ge \dfrac{6}{-2}$

$x \ge -3$

$\{ x \mid x \ge -3 \}$; $[-3, \infty)$

59.
$$\frac{x}{2}+\frac{3}{4}\ge\frac{3}{8}$$
$$8\cdot\frac{x}{2}+8\cdot\frac{3}{4}\ge 8\cdot\frac{3}{8}$$
$$4x+6\ge 3$$
$$4x\ge -3$$
$$\frac{4x}{4}\ge\frac{-3}{4}$$
$$x\ge -\frac{3}{4}$$
$$\left\{x\mid x\ge -\frac{3}{4}\right\};\ \left[-\frac{3}{4},\infty\right)$$

61.
$$2x+5\ge 13$$
$$2x+5-5\ge 13-5$$
$$2x\ge 8$$
$$\frac{2x}{2}\ge\frac{8}{2}$$
$$x\ge 4$$
$$\{x\mid x\ge 4\};\ [4,\infty)$$

63.
$$4z-3\le 9$$
$$4z-3+3\le 9+3$$
$$4z\le 12$$
$$\frac{4z}{4}\le\frac{12}{4}$$
$$z\le 3$$
$$\{z\mid z\le 3\};\ (-\infty,3]$$

65. Let $x=$ score on final exam.
$$90+83+95+90+x\ge 540$$
$$358+x\ge 540$$
$$358+x-358\ge 540-358$$
$$x\ge 182$$
Jackie must earn at least 182 points on the final exam to earn an *A* in Mr. Ruffatto's class.

67. Let $x=$ number of hamburgers.
$$22+17+10x\le 69$$
$$39+10x\le 69$$
$$39+10x-39\le 69-39$$
$$10x\le 30$$
$$\frac{10x}{10}\le\frac{30}{10}$$
$$x\le 3$$
You can order no more than 3 hamburgers to keep the fat content to no more than 69 grams.

69. Let $x=$ cargo weight.
$$150(179)+x\le 45,686$$
$$26,850+x\le 45,686$$
$$26,850+x-26,850\le 45,686-26,850$$
$$x\le 18,836$$
The plane can carry up to 18,836 pounds of luggage and cargo.

71.
$$19.25t+585.72>1000$$
$$19.25t+585.72-585.72>1000-585.72$$
$$19.25t>414.28$$
$$\frac{19.25t}{19.25}>\frac{414.28}{19.25}$$
$$t>\frac{414.28}{19.25}\approx 21.52$$
The monthly benefit will exceed $1000 in 2012.

73. Let $x=$ value of computer systems sold
$$34,000+0.012x\ge 100,000$$
$$34,000+0.012x-34,000\ge 100,000-34,000$$
$$0.012x\ge 66,000$$
$$\frac{0.012x}{0.012}\ge\frac{66,000}{0.012}$$
$$x\ge\frac{66,000}{0.012}=5,500,000$$
Susan will need to sell at least $5,500,000 in computer systems to earn $100,000.

75.
$$S > D$$
$$-200 + 10p > 1000 - 20p$$
$$-200 + 10p - 1000 > 1000 - 20p - 1000$$
$$-1200 + 10p > -20p$$
$$-1200 + 10p - 10p > -20p - 10p$$
$$-1200 > -30p$$
$$\frac{-1200}{-30} < \frac{-30p}{-30}$$
$$40 < p$$

Supply will exceed demand when the price is greater than $40.

77. $3(x+2) + 2x > 5(x+1)$
$$3x + 6 + 2x > 5x + 5$$
$$5x + 6 > 5x + 5$$
$$5x + 6 - 6 > 5x + 5 - 6$$
$$5x > 5x - 1$$
$$5x - 5x > 5x - 1 - 5x$$
$$0 > -1$$

This statement is an identity. All real numbers are solutions.

79. Answers may vary. The direction, or sense, of an inequality changes if you multiply or divide both sides by a negative number, or if you take the reciprocal of both sides. For example,

$$5 < 8 \rightarrow -2 \cdot 5 > -2 \cdot 8 \qquad \frac{1}{5} < \frac{1}{2} \rightarrow \frac{1}{\frac{1}{5}} > \frac{1}{\frac{1}{2}}$$
$$-10 > -16 \qquad\qquad\qquad 5 > 2$$

Putting the Concepts Together (Sections 1.1-1.4)

1. a. Let $x = -3$ in the equation.
$$5(2(-3) - 3) + 1 \overset{?}{=} 2(-3) - 6$$
$$5(-6 - 3) + 1 \overset{?}{=} -6 - 6$$
$$5(-9) + 1 \overset{?}{=} -12$$
$$-45 + 1 \overset{?}{=} -12$$
$$-44 \neq -12$$
$x = -3$ is **not** a solution to the equation.

b. Let $x = 1$ in the equation.
$$5(2(1) - 3) + 1 \overset{?}{=} 2(1) - 6$$
$$5(2 - 3) + 1 \overset{?}{=} 2 - 6$$
$$5(-1) + 1 \overset{?}{=} -4$$
$$-5 + 1 \overset{?}{=} -4$$
$$-4 = -4$$
$x = 1$ is a solution to the equation.

2. $3(2x - 1) + 6 = 5x - 2$
$$6x - 3 + 6 = 5x - 2$$
$$6x + 3 = 5x - 2$$
$$6x + 3 - 5x = 5x - 2 - 5x$$
$$x + 3 = -2$$
$$x + 3 - 3 = -2 - 3$$
$$x = -5$$
Solution set: $\{-5\}$

3.
$$\frac{7}{3}x + \frac{4}{5} = \frac{5x + 12}{15}$$
$$15\left(\frac{7}{3}x + \frac{4}{5}\right) = 15\left(\frac{5x + 12}{15}\right)$$
$$35x + 12 = 5x + 12$$
$$35x + 12 - 12 = 5x + 12 - 12$$
$$35x = 5x$$
$$35x - 5x = 5x - 5x$$
$$30x = 0$$
$$\frac{30x}{30} = \frac{0}{30}$$
$$x = 0$$
Solution set: $\{0\}$

4. $5 - 2(x+1) + 4x = 6(x+1) - (3+4x)$
$$5 - 2x - 2 + 4x = 6x + 6 - 3 - 4x$$
$$3 + 2x = 2x + 3$$
These expressions are equivalent, so the statement is an identity.

5. Let x represent the number. $x - 3 = \frac{1}{2}x + 2$

6. Let x represent the number.
$$\frac{x}{2} < x + 5$$

7. Let x = liters of 20% solution.

Amount of 40% solution: $16 - x$ liters

tot. acid = acid from 20% + acid from 40%

$$(\%)(\text{liters}) = (\%)(\text{liters}) + (\%)(\text{liters})$$

$$0.35(16) = 0.2(x) + 0.4(16 - x)$$

$$5.6 = 0.2x + 6.4 - 0.4x$$

$$5.6 = 6.4 - 0.2x$$

$$5.6 - 6.4 = 6.4 - 0.2x - 6.4$$

$$-0.8 = -0.2x$$

$$\frac{-0.8}{-0.2} = \frac{-0.2x}{-0.2}$$

$$4 = x$$

The chemist needs to mix 4 liters of the 20% solution with 12 liters of the 40% solution.

8. Let t = time of travel in hours.

$d = r \cdot t$

total distance = dist. for car 1 + dist. for car 2

$$255 = 30(t) + 45(t)$$

$$255 = 75t$$

$$\frac{255}{75} = \frac{75t}{75}$$

$$3.4 = t$$

After 3.4 hours, the two cars will be 255 miles apart.

9.
$$3x - 2y = 4$$

$$3x - 2y - 3x = 4 - 3x$$

$$-2y = -3x + 4$$

$$\frac{-2y}{-2} = \frac{-3x + 4}{-2}$$

$$y = \frac{-3x}{-2} + \frac{4}{-2}$$

$$y = \frac{3}{2}x - 2$$

10.
$$A = P + Prt$$

$$A - P = P + Prt - P$$

$$A - P = Prt$$

$$\frac{A - P}{Pt} = \frac{Prt}{Pt}$$

$$\frac{A - P}{Pt} = r \quad \text{or} \quad r = \frac{A - P}{Pt}$$

11. a.
$$V = \pi r^2 h$$

$$\frac{V}{\pi r^2} = \frac{\pi r^2 h}{\pi r^2}$$

$$\frac{V}{\pi r^2} = h \quad \text{or} \quad h = \frac{V}{\pi r^2}$$

b. $h = \dfrac{V}{\pi r^2} = \dfrac{294\pi}{\pi(7)^2} = \dfrac{294}{49} = 6$ inches .

12. a. Interval: $(-3, \infty)$

Graph:

b. Interval: $(2, 5]$

Graph:

13. a. Inequality: $x \le -1.5$

Graph:

b. Inequality: $-3 < x \le 1$

Graph:

14.
$$2x + 3 \le 4x - 9$$

$$2x + 3 - 3 \le 4x - 9 - 3$$

$$2x \le 4x - 12$$

$$2x - 4x \le 4x - 12 - 4x$$

$$-2x \le -12$$

$$\frac{-2x}{-2} \ge \frac{-12}{-2}$$

$$x \ge 6$$

Interval: $[6, \infty)$

15. $-3 > 3x - (x+5)$

$-3 > 3x - x - 5$

$-3 > 2x - 5$

$-3 + 5 > 2x - 5 + 5$

$2 > 2x$

$\dfrac{2}{2} > \dfrac{2x}{2}$

$1 > x \quad \text{or} \quad x < 1$

Interval: $(-\infty, 1)$

16. $x - 9 \le x + 3(2 - x)$

$x - 9 \le x + 6 - 3x$

$x - 9 \le -2x + 6$

$x - 9 + 2x \le -2x + 6 + 2x$

$3x - 9 \le 6$

$3x - 9 + 9 \le 6 + 9$

$3x \le 15$

$\dfrac{3x}{3} \le \dfrac{15}{3}$

$x \le 5$

Interval: $(-\infty, 5]$

17. Let x = number of children at the party.

$75 + 5x \le 125$

$75 + 5x - 75 \le 125 - 75$

$5x \le 50$

$\dfrac{5x}{5} \le \dfrac{50}{5}$

$x \le 10$

Including Logan, there can be at most 10 children at the party. Therefore, Logan can invite at most 9 children to the party.

1.5 Preparing for Compound Inequalities

1. $\{x \mid -2 \le x \le 4, \ x \text{ is an integer}\}$

$\{-2, -1, 0, 1, 2, 3, 4\}$

2. $\{x \mid 0 < x < 3, \ x \text{ is an integer}\}$

$\{1, 2\}$

1.5 Exercises

1. intersection

3. compound inequality

5. False. The symbol for the union of two sets is $\cup$ while the symbol for intersection is $\cap$.

7. The inequality implies that 4 is less than 2 which is not true. There is no real number, x, such that $x > 4$ and $x < 2$.

9. To be a solution, $x = 3$ must satisfy both inequalities.

$$3x + 1 \overset{?}{>} 4 \qquad\qquad 2x - 3 \overset{?}{<} 7$$

$$3(3) + 1 \overset{?}{>} 4 \qquad\qquad 2(3) - 3 \overset{?}{<} 7$$

$$10 > 4 \ \checkmark \qquad\qquad 3 < 7 \ \checkmark$$

Since $x = 3$ makes both statements true, it is a solution.

11. $A \cup B = \{1, 4, 5, 6, 7, 8, 9\}$

13. $A \cap B = \{5, 7, 9\}$

15. $B \cap C = \varnothing \ \text{or} \ \{\ \}$

17. a. $A \cap B = \{x \mid -2 < x \le 5\}$

Interval: $(-2, 5]$

b. $A \cup B = \{x \mid x \text{ is a real number}\}$

Interval: $(-\infty, \infty)$

19. a. $E \cap F = \varnothing \ \text{or} \ \{\ \}$

b. $E \cup F = \{x \mid x < -1 \ \text{or} \ x > 3\}$

Interval: $(-\infty, -1) \cup (3, \infty)$

SSM – 35

21. $x < 3$ and $x \geq -2$

Solution set: $\{x \mid -2 \leq x < 3\}$

Interval: $[-2, 3)$

23. $x < -2$ or $x > 3$

Solution set: $\{x \mid x < -2 \text{ or } x > 3\}$

Interval: $(-\infty, -2) \cup (3, \infty)$

25. $4x - 4 < 0$ and $-5x + 1 \leq -9$

$\qquad 4x < 4 \qquad\qquad -5x \leq -10$

$\qquad\quad x < 1 \qquad\qquad\quad x \geq 2$

We need $x < 1$ and $x \geq 2$.

Solution set: $\varnothing$ or $\{\ \}$

27. $4x - 3 < 5$ and $-5x + 3 > 13$

$\qquad 4x < 8 \qquad\qquad -5x > 10$

$\qquad\quad x < 2 \qquad\qquad\quad x < -2$

We need $x < 2$ and $x < -2$.

Solution set: $\{x \mid x < -2\}$

Interval: $(-\infty, -2)$

29. $-4x - 1 < 3$ and $-x - 2 > 3$

$\qquad -4x < 4 \qquad\qquad -x > 5$

$\qquad\quad x > -1 \qquad\qquad x < -5$

We need $x > -1$ and $x < -5$.

Solution set: $\varnothing$ or $\{\ \}$

31. $x - 2 < -4$ or $x + 3 > 8$

$\qquad x < -2 \qquad\qquad x > 5$

We need $x < -2$ or $x > 5$.

Solution set: $\{x \mid x < -2 \text{ or } x > 5\}$

Interval: $(-\infty, -2) \cup (5, \infty)$

33. $6(x - 2) < 12$ or $4(x + 3) > 12$

$\qquad 6x - 12 < 12 \qquad\quad 4x + 12 > 12$

$\qquad\quad 6x < 24 \qquad\qquad\quad 4x > 0$

$\qquad\quad\ \ x < 4 \qquad\qquad\qquad x > 0$

We need $x < 4$ or $x > 0$.

Solution set: $\{x \mid x \text{ is a real number}\}$

Interval: $(-\infty, \infty)$

35. $-8x + 6x - 2 > 0$ or $5x > 3x + 8$

$\qquad -2x - 2 > 0 \qquad\qquad 2x > 8$

$\qquad\quad -2x > 2 \qquad\qquad\quad x > 4$

$\qquad\qquad x < -1$

We need $x < -1$ or $x > 4$.

Solution set: $\{x \mid x < -1 \text{ or } x > 4\}$

Interval: $(-\infty, -1) \cup (4, \infty)$

37. $\qquad -3 \leq 5x + 2 < 17$

$-3 - 2 \leq 5x + 2 - 2 < 17 - 2$

$\qquad -5 \leq 5x < 15$

$\qquad \dfrac{-5}{5} \leq \dfrac{5x}{5} < \dfrac{15}{5}$

$\qquad -1 \leq x < 3$

Solution set: $\{x \mid -1 \leq x < 3\}$

Interval: $[-1, 3)$

39. $\qquad -3 \leq 6x + 1 \leq 10$

$-3 - 1 \leq 6x + 1 - 1 \leq 10 - 1$

$\qquad -4 \leq 6x \leq 9$

$\qquad \dfrac{-4}{6} \leq \dfrac{6x}{6} \leq \dfrac{9}{6}$

$\qquad -\dfrac{2}{3} \leq x \leq \dfrac{3}{2}$

Solution set: $\left\{ x \mid -\dfrac{2}{3} \leq x \leq \dfrac{3}{2} \right\}$

Interval: $\left[-\dfrac{2}{3}, \dfrac{3}{2} \right]$

41. $2x + 5 \le -1$ or $\dfrac{4}{3}x - 3 > 5$

$2x \le -6$

$x \le -3$ $\dfrac{4}{3}x > 8$

$4x > 24$

$x > 6$

We need $x \le -3$ or $x > 6$.

Solution set: $\{x \mid x \le -3 \text{ or } x > 6\}$

Interval: $(-\infty, -3] \cup (6, \infty)$

43. $3 \le -5x + 7 < 12$

$3 - 7 \le -5x + 7 - 7 < 12 - 7$

$-4 \le -5x < 5$

$\dfrac{-4}{-5} \ge \dfrac{-5x}{-5} > \dfrac{5}{-5}$

$\dfrac{4}{5} \ge x > -1$ or $-1 < x \le \dfrac{4}{5}$

Solution set: $\left\{x \mid -1 < x \le \dfrac{4}{5}\right\}$

Interval: $\left(-1, \dfrac{4}{5}\right]$

45. $-1 \le \dfrac{1}{2}x - 1 \le 3$

$-1 + 1 \le \dfrac{1}{2}x - 1 + 1 \le 3 + 1$

$0 \le \dfrac{1}{2}x \le 4$

$2(0) \le 2 \cdot \dfrac{1}{2}x \le 2 \cdot 4$

$0 \le x \le 8$

Solution set: $\{x \mid 0 \le x \le 8\}$

Interval: $[0, 8]$

47. $3 \le -2x - 1 \le 11$

$3 + 1 \le -2x - 1 + 1 \le 11 + 1$

$4 \le -2x \le 12$

$\dfrac{4}{-2} \ge \dfrac{-2x}{-2} \ge \dfrac{12}{-2}$

$-2 \ge x \ge -6$ or $-6 \le x \le -2$

Solution set: $\{x \mid -6 \le x \le -2\}$

Interval: $[-6, -2]$

49. $\dfrac{1}{2}x < 3$ or $\dfrac{3x - 1}{2} > 4$

$x < 6$ $3x - 1 > 8$

$3x > 9$

$x > 3$

We need $x < 6$ or $x > 3$.

Solution set: $\{x \mid x \text{ is a real number}\}$

Interval: $(-\infty, \infty)$

51. $\dfrac{2}{3}x + \dfrac{1}{2} < \dfrac{5}{6}$ and $-\dfrac{1}{5}x + 1 < \dfrac{3}{10}$

$6\left(\dfrac{2}{3}x + \dfrac{1}{2}\right) < 6\left(\dfrac{5}{6}\right)$ $10\left(-\dfrac{1}{5}x + 1\right) < 10\left(\dfrac{3}{10}\right)$

$4x + 3 < 5$ $-2x + 10 < 3$

$4x < 2$ $-2x < -7$

$x < \dfrac{1}{2}$ $x > \dfrac{7}{2}$

We need $x < \dfrac{1}{2}$ and $x > \dfrac{7}{2}$.

Solution set: $\varnothing$ or $\{\ \}$

53. $-2 < \dfrac{3x+1}{2} \le 8$

$2(-2) < 2\left(\dfrac{3x+1}{2}\right) \le 2(8)$

$-4 < 3x+1 \le 16$

$-4-1 < 3x+1-1 \le 16-1$

$-5 < 3x \le 15$

$\dfrac{-5}{3} < \dfrac{3x}{3} \le \dfrac{15}{3}$

$-\dfrac{5}{3} < x \le 5$

Solution set: $\left\{x \middle| -\dfrac{5}{3} < x \le 5\right\}$

Interval: $\left(-\dfrac{5}{3}, 5\right]$

55. $-8 \le -2(x+1) < 6$

$-8 \le -2x-2 < 6$

$-8+2 \le -2x-2+2 < 6+2$

$-6 \le -2x < 8$

$\dfrac{-6}{-2} \ge \dfrac{-2x}{-2} > \dfrac{8}{-2}$

$3 \ge x > -4 \quad \text{or} \quad -4 < x \le 3$

Solution set: $\{x \mid -4 < x \le 3\}$

Interval: $(-4, 3]$

57. $3(x-1)+5 < 2 \quad \text{or} \quad -2(x-3) < 1$

$3x-3+5 < 2 \qquad -2x+6 < 1$

$3x+2 < 2 \qquad\qquad -2x < -5$

$3x < 0 \qquad\qquad\qquad x > \dfrac{5}{2}$

$x < 0$

We need $x < 0$ or $x > \dfrac{5}{2}$.

Solution set: $\left\{x \middle| x < 0 \text{ or } x > \dfrac{5}{2}\right\}$

Interval: $(-\infty, 0) \cup \left(\dfrac{5}{2}, \infty\right)$

59. $3a+5 < 5 \qquad \text{and} \qquad -2a+1 \le 7$

$3a+5-5 < 5-5 \qquad -2a+1-1 \le 7-1$

$3a < 0 \qquad\qquad\qquad -2a \le 6$

$\dfrac{3a}{3} < \dfrac{0}{3} \qquad\qquad \dfrac{-2a}{-2} \ge \dfrac{6}{-2}$

$a < 0 \qquad\qquad\qquad a \ge -3$

We need $a < 0$ and $a \ge -3$.

Solution set: $\{a \mid -3 \le a < 0\}$

Interval: $[-3, 0)$

61. $5(x+2) < 20 \qquad \text{or} \qquad 4(x-4) > -20$

$\dfrac{5(x+2)}{5} < \dfrac{20}{5} \qquad \dfrac{4(x-4)}{4} > \dfrac{-20}{4}$

$x+2 < 4 \qquad\qquad x-4 > -5$

$x+2-2 < 4-2 \qquad x-4+4 > -5+4$

$x < 2 \qquad\qquad\qquad x > -1$

We need $x < 2$ or $x > -1$.

Solution set: $\{x \mid x \text{ is a real number}\}$

Interval: $(-\infty, \infty)$

63. $-4 \le 3x+2 \le 10$

$-4-2 \le 3x+2-2 \le 10-2$

$-6 \le 3x \le 8$

$\dfrac{-6}{3} \le \dfrac{3x}{3} \le \dfrac{8}{3}$

$-2 \le x \le \dfrac{8}{3}$

Solution set: $\left\{x \middle| -2 \le x \le \dfrac{8}{3}\right\}$

Interval: $\left[-2, \dfrac{8}{3}\right]$

SSM – 38

65. $2x+7<-13$ or $5x-3>7$

$\quad 2x+7-7<-13-7 \qquad 5x-3+3>7+3$

$\qquad\quad 2x<-20 \qquad\qquad 5x>10$

$\qquad\quad \dfrac{2x}{2}<\dfrac{-20}{2} \qquad\qquad \dfrac{5x}{5}>\dfrac{10}{5}$

$\qquad\qquad x<-10 \qquad\qquad\quad x>2$

We need $x<-10$ or $x>2$.

Solution set: $\{x\,|\,x<-10 \text{ or } x>2\}$

Interval: $(-\infty,-10)\cup(2,\infty)$

67. $5<3x-1<14$

$5+1<3x-1+1<14+1$

$\quad 6<3x<15$

$\quad \dfrac{6}{3}<\dfrac{3x}{3}<\dfrac{15}{3}$

$\quad 2<x<5$

Solution set: $\{x\,|\,2<x<5\}$

Interval: $(2,5)$

69. $\dfrac{x}{3}\le-1$ or $\dfrac{4x-1}{2}>7$

$3\cdot\dfrac{x}{3}\le3\cdot(-1) \qquad 2\cdot\dfrac{4x-1}{2}>2\cdot7$

$\quad x\le-3 \qquad\qquad\quad 4x-1>14$

$\qquad\qquad\qquad\qquad 4x-1+1>14+1$

$\qquad\qquad\qquad\qquad\quad 4x>15$

$\qquad\qquad\qquad\qquad\quad \dfrac{4x}{4}>\dfrac{15}{4}$

$\qquad\qquad\qquad\qquad\qquad x>\dfrac{15}{4}$

We need $x\le-3$ or $x>\dfrac{15}{4}$.

Solution set: $\left\{x\,|\,x\le-3 \text{ or } x>\dfrac{15}{4}\right\}$

Interval: $(-\infty,-3]\cup\left(\dfrac{15}{4},\infty\right)$

71. $-3\le-2(x+1)<8$

$\quad -3\le-2x-2<8$

$-3+2\le-2x-2+2<8+2$

$\quad -1\le-2x<10$

$\quad \dfrac{-1}{-2}\ge\dfrac{-2x}{-2}>\dfrac{10}{-2}$

$\quad \dfrac{1}{2}\ge x>-5 \quad \text{or} \quad -5<x\le\dfrac{1}{2}$

Solution set: $\left\{x\,|\,-5<x\le\dfrac{1}{2}\right\}$

Interval: $\left(-5,\dfrac{1}{2}\right]$

73. $-3<x<4$

$-3+4<x+4<4+4$

$\quad 1<x+4<8$

We need $a=1$ and $b=8$.

75. $4<x<10$

$3\cdot4<3\cdot x<3\cdot10$

$\quad 12<3x<30$

We need $a=12$ and $b=30$.

77. $-2<x<6$

$3\cdot(-2)<3\cdot x<3\cdot6$

$\quad -6<3x<18$

$-6+5<3x+5<18+5$

$\quad -1<3x+5<23$

We need $a=-1$ and $b=23$.

79. Let $x=$ systolic blood pressure .

$\quad 90<x<140$

81. Let x = final exam score.

$$80 \leq \frac{74 + 86 + 77 + 89 + 2x}{6} \leq 89$$

$$80 \leq \frac{326 + 2x}{6} \leq 89$$

$$6 \cdot 80 \leq 6 \cdot \frac{326 + 2x}{6} \leq 6 \cdot 89$$

$$480 \leq 326 + 2x \leq 534$$

$$480 - 326 \leq 326 + 2x - 326 \leq 534 - 326$$

$$154 \leq 2x \leq 208$$

$$\frac{154}{2} \leq \frac{2x}{2} \leq \frac{208}{2}$$

$$77 \leq x \leq 104$$

Joanna needs to score at least a 77 on the final. That is, $77 \leq x \leq 100$ (assuming 100 is the max score, otherwise $77 \leq x \leq 104$).

83. Let x = weekly wages.

$$600 \leq x \leq 700$$

$$600 - 517 \leq x - 517 \leq 700 - 517$$

$$83 \leq x - 517 \leq 183$$

$$0.28(83) \leq 0.28(x - 517) \leq 0.28(183)$$

$$23.24 \leq 0.28(x - 517) \leq 51.24$$

$$23.24 + 69.6 \leq 0.28(x - 517) + 69.6 \leq 51.24 + 69.6$$

$$92.84 \leq 0.28(x - 517) + 69.6 \leq 120.84$$

The amount withheld ranges between \$92.84 and \$120.84, inclusive.

85. Let x = number of therms.

$$157.73 \leq 1.15855(x - 70) + 65.05 \leq 175.11$$

$$92.68 \leq 1.15855(x - 70) \leq 110.06$$

$$\frac{92.68}{1.15855} \leq x - 70 \leq \frac{110.06}{1.15855}$$

$$\frac{92.68}{1.15855} + 70 \leq x \leq \frac{110.06}{1.15855} + 70$$

$$150 \leq x \leq 165 \text{ (approx.)}$$

The gas usage ranged from 150 to 165 therms.

87. Step 1:

$$a < b$$

$$a + a < a + b$$

$$2a < a + b$$

$$\frac{2a}{2} < \frac{a + b}{2}$$

$$a < \frac{a + b}{2}$$

Step 2:

$$a < b$$

$$a + b < b + b$$

$$a + b < 2b$$

$$\frac{a + b}{2} < \frac{2b}{2}$$

$$\frac{a + b}{2} < b$$

Step 3:

Since $a < \frac{a + b}{2}$ and $\frac{a + b}{2} < b$, it follows that

$$a < \frac{a + b}{2} < b.$$

89. $2x + 1 \leq 5x + 7 \leq x - 5$

We can rewrite the inequality as

$2x + 1 \leq 5x + 7$ and $5x + 7 \leq x - 5$

$2x + 1 \leq 5x + 7$	$5x + 7 \leq x - 5$
$2x + 1 - 5x \leq 5x + 7 - 5x$	$5x + 7 - x \leq x - 5 - x$
$-3x + 1 \leq 7$	$4x + 7 \leq -5$
$-3x + 1 - 1 \leq 7 - 1$	$4x + 7 - 7 \leq -5 - 7$
$-3x \leq 6$	$4x \leq -12$
$\frac{-3x}{-3} \geq \frac{6}{-3}$	$\frac{4x}{4} \leq \frac{-12}{4}$
$x \geq -2$	$x \leq -3$

Therefore, we need $x \geq -2$ AND $x \leq -3$. Since $-2 > -3$, there are no values for x that can satisfy both inequalities. Thus, the solution set is $\{\ \}$ or $\varnothing$.

91.

$$4x + 1 > 2(2x + 1)$$

$$4x + 1 > 4x + 2$$

$$4x + 1 - 4x > 4x + 2 - 4x$$

$$1 > 2$$

This is a contradiction. There is no solution. If, during simplification, the variable terms all cancel out and a contradiction results, then there is no solution to the inequality.

93. If $x < 2$ then $x - 2 < 2 - 2 \Rightarrow x - 2 < 0$. When multiplying both sides of the inequality by $x - 2$ in the second step, the direction of the inequality must switch.

1.6 Preparing for Absolute Value Equations and Inequalities

1. $|3| = 3$ because the distance from 0 to 3 on a real number line is 3 units.

2. $|-4| = 4$ because the distance from 0 to -4 on a real number line is 4 units.

3. $|-1.6| = 1.6$ because the distance from 0 to -1.6 on a real number line is 1.6 units.

4. $|0| = 0$ because the distance from 0 to 0 on a real number line is 0 units.

5. The distance between 0 and 5 on a real number line can be expressed as $|5|$.

6. The distance between 0 and -8 on a real number line can be expressed as $|-8|$.

1.6 Exercises

1. $u = a$ or $u = -a$

3. $a < 0$

5. False. Since $|x| \geq 0$ for all x and $0 > -2$, we have that $|x| \geq 0 > -2$ for all x.

7. $|x| = 10$
   $x = 10$ or $x = -10$
   Solution set: $\{-10, 10\}$

9. $|y - 3| = 4$
   $y - 3 = 4$ or $y - 3 = -4$
   $y = 7$ or $y = -1$
   Solution set: $\{-1, 7\}$

11. $|-3x + 5| = 8$
    $-3x + 5 = 8$ or $-3x + 5 = -8$
    $-3x = 3$ or $-3x = -13$
    $x = -1$ or $x = \dfrac{13}{3}$
    Solution set: $\left\{-1, \dfrac{13}{3}\right\}$

13. $|y| - 7 = -2$
    $|y| = 5$
    $y = 5$ or $y = -5$
    Solution set: $\{-5, 5\}$

15. $|2x + 3| - 5 = 3$
    $|2x + 3| = 8$
    $2x + 3 = 8$ or $2x + 3 = -8$
    $2x = 5$ or $2x = -11$
    $x = \dfrac{5}{2}$ or $x = -\dfrac{11}{2}$
    Solution set: $\left\{-\dfrac{11}{2}, \dfrac{5}{2}\right\}$

17. $-2|x - 3| + 10 = -4$
    $-2|x - 3| = -14$
    $|x - 3| = 7$
    $x - 3 = 7$ or $x - 3 = -7$
    $x = 10$ or $x = -4$
    Solution set: $\{-4, 10\}$

19. $|-3x| - 5 = -5$

$$|-3x| = 0$$
$$-3x = 0$$
$$x = 0$$

Solution set: $\{0\}$

21. $\left|\dfrac{3x-1}{4}\right| = 2$

$$\dfrac{3x-1}{4} = 2 \ \text{ or } \ \dfrac{3x-1}{4} = -2$$
$$3x - 1 = 8 \ \text{ or } \ 3x - 1 = -8$$
$$3x = 9 \ \text{ or } \ 3x = -7$$
$$x = 3 \ \text{ or } \ x = -\dfrac{7}{3}$$

Solution set: $\left\{-\dfrac{7}{3}, 3\right\}$

23. $|3x + 2| = |2x - 5|$

$$3x + 2 = 2x - 5 \ \text{ or } \ 3x + 2 = -(2x - 5)$$
$$3x = 2x - 7 \ \text{ or } \ 3x + 2 = -2x + 5$$
$$x = -7 \ \text{ or } \ 3x = -2x + 3$$
$$x = -7 \ \text{ or } \ 5x = 3$$
$$x = -7 \ \text{ or } \ x = \dfrac{3}{5}$$

Solution set: $\left\{-7, \dfrac{3}{5}\right\}$

25. $|8 - 3x| = |2x - 7|$

$$8 - 3x = 2x - 7 \ \text{ or } \ 8 - 3x = -(2x - 7)$$
$$-3x = 2x - 15 \ \text{ or } \ 8 - 3x = -2x + 7$$
$$-5x = -15 \ \text{ or } \ -3x = -2x - 1$$
$$x = 3 \ \text{ or } \ -x = -1$$
$$x = 3 \ \text{ or } \ x = 1$$

Solution set: $\{1, 3\}$

27. $|4y - 7| = |9 - 4y|$

$$4y - 7 = 9 - 4y \ \text{ or } \ 4y - 7 = -(9 - 4y)$$
$$4y = 16 - 4y \ \text{ or } \ 4y - 7 = -9 + 4y$$
$$8y = 16 \ \text{ or } \ 4y = -2 + 4y$$
$$y = 2 \ \text{ or } \ 0 \ne -2$$

Solution set: $\{2\}$

29. $|x| < 9$

$$-9 < x < 9$$

Solution set: $\{x \mid -9 < x < 9\}$

Interval: $(-9, 9)$

31. $|x - 4| \le 7$

$$-7 \le x - 4 \le 7$$
$$-3 \le x \le 11$$

Solution set: $\{x \mid -3 \le x \le 11\}$

Interval: $[-3, 11]$

33. $|3x + 1| < 8$

$$-8 < 3x + 1 < 8$$
$$-9 < 3x < 7$$
$$-3 < x < \dfrac{7}{3}$$

Solution set: $\left\{x \mid -3 < x < \dfrac{7}{3}\right\}$

Interval: $\left(-3, \dfrac{7}{3}\right)$

35. $|6x + 5| < -1$

No solution. Absolute value is never negative.

Solution set: $\varnothing$ or $\{ \ \}$

37. $|y-5| > 2$

$y - 5 < -2$ or $y - 5 > 2$

$y < 3$ or $y > 7$

Solution set: $\{y \mid y < 3 \text{ or } y > 7\}$

Interval: $(-\infty, 3) \cup (7, \infty)$

39. $|-4x - 3| \geq 5$

$-4x - 3 \leq -5$ or $-4x - 3 \geq 5$

$-4x \leq -2$ or $-4x \geq 8$

$x \geq \dfrac{1}{2}$ or $x \leq -2$

Solution set: $\left\{ x \mid x \leq -2 \text{ or } x \geq \dfrac{1}{2} \right\}$

Interval: $(-\infty, -2] \cup \left[\dfrac{1}{2}, \infty \right)$

41. $2|y| + 3 > 1$

$2|y| > -2$

$|y| > -1$

Since $|y| \geq 0 > -1$ for all y, all real numbers are solutions.

Solution set: $\{y \mid y \text{ is a real number}\}$

Interval: $(-\infty, \infty)$

43. $2|x - 3| + 3 < 9$

$2|x - 3| < 6$

$|x - 3| < 3$

$-3 < x - 3 < 3$

$0 < x < 6$

Solution set: $\{x \mid 0 < x < 6\}$

Interval: $(0, 6)$

45. $|-5x - 3| > -3$

Since absolute value is always ≥ 0, this inequality is true for all real numbers.

Solution set: $\{x \mid x \text{ is a real number}\}$

Interval: $(-\infty, \infty)$

47. $|2 - 5x| + 3 < 10$

$|2 - 5x| < 7$

$-7 < 2 - 5x < 7$

$-9 < -5x < 5$

$\dfrac{9}{5} > x > -1$ or $-1 < x < \dfrac{9}{5}$

Solution set: $\left\{ x \mid -1 < x < \dfrac{9}{5} \right\}$

Interval: $\left(-1, \dfrac{9}{5} \right)$

49. $|-2x + 1| > 1$

$-2x + 1 < -1$ or $-2x + 1 > 1$

$-2x < -2$ or $-2x > 0$

$x > 1$ or $x < 0$

Solution set: $\{x \mid x < 0 \text{ or } x > 1\}$

Interval: $(-\infty, 0) \cup (1, \infty)$

51. $|1 - 2x| \geq |-5|$

$|1 - 2x| \geq 5$

$1 - 2x \leq -5$ or $1 - 2x \geq 5$

$-2x \leq -6$ or $-2x \geq 4$

$x \geq 3$ or $x \leq -2$

Solution set: $\{x \mid x \leq -2 \text{ or } x \geq 3\}$

Interval: $(-\infty, -2] \cup [3, \infty)$

53. $|(2x-3)-1| < 0.01$

$\quad |2x-3-1| < 0.01$

$\quad\quad |2x-4| < 0.01$

$\quad\quad -0.01 < 2x-4 < 0.01$

$\quad\quad 3.99 < 2x < 4.01$

$\quad\quad 1.995 < x < 2.005$

Solution set: $\{x \mid 1.995 < x < 2.005\}$

Interval: $(1.995, 2.005)$

55. $|x| > 5$

$\quad x < -5 \text{ or } x > 5$

Solution set: $\{x \mid x < -5 \text{ or } x > 5\}$

Interval: $(-\infty, -5) \cup (5, \infty)$

57. $|2x+5| = 3$

$\quad 2x+5 = 3 \text{ or } 2x+5 = -3$

$\quad 2x = -2 \text{ or } 2x = -8$

$\quad x = -1 \text{ or } x = -4$

Solution set: $\{-4, -1\}$

59. $7|x| = 35$

$\quad |x| = 5$

$\quad x = 5 \text{ or } x = -5$

Solution set: $\{-5, 5\}$

61. $|5x+2| \le 8$

$\quad -8 \le 5x+2 \le 8$

$\quad -10 \le 5x \le 6$

$\quad -2 \le x \le \dfrac{6}{5}$

Solution set: $\left\{ x \mid -2 \le x \le \dfrac{6}{5} \right\}$

Interval: $\left[-2, \dfrac{6}{5} \right]$

63. $|-2x+3| = -4$

No solution. Absolute value is never negative.

Solution set: $\varnothing$ or $\{\ \}$

65. $|3x+2| \ge 5$

$\quad 3x+2 \le -5 \text{ or } 3x+2 \ge 5$

$\quad\quad 3x \le -7 \text{ or } 3x \ge 3$

$\quad\quad x \le -\dfrac{7}{3} \text{ or } x \ge 1$

Solution set: $\left\{ x \mid x \le -\dfrac{7}{3} \text{ or } x \ge 1 \right\}$

Interval: $\left(-\infty, -\dfrac{7}{3} \right] \cup [1, \infty)$

67. $|3x-2| + 7 > 9$

$\quad |3x-2| > 2$

$\quad 3x-2 < -2 \text{ or } 3x-2 > 2$

$\quad\quad 3x < 0 \text{ or } 3x > 4$

$\quad\quad x < 0 \text{ or } x > \dfrac{4}{3}$

Solution set: $\left\{ x \mid x < 0 \text{ or } x > \dfrac{4}{3} \right\}$

Interval: $(-\infty, 0) \cup \left(\dfrac{4}{3}, \infty \right)$

69. $|5x+3| = |3x+5|$

$\quad 5x+3 = 3x+5 \text{ or } 5x+3 = -(3x+5)$

$\quad\quad 5x = 3x+2 \text{ or } 5x+3 = -3x-5$

$\quad\quad 2x = 2 \text{ or } 8x = -8$

$\quad\quad x = 1 \text{ or } x = -1$

Solution set: $\{-1, 1\}$

71. $|4x+7| + 6 < 5$

$\quad |4x+7| < -1$

Since absolute value is always nonnegative, that is ≥ 0, this inequality has no solution.

Solution set: $\varnothing$ or $\{\ \}$

73. $\left|\dfrac{x-2}{4}\right| = \left|\dfrac{2x+1}{6}\right|$

$\dfrac{x-2}{4} = \dfrac{2x+1}{6}$ or $\dfrac{x-2}{4} = -\dfrac{2x+1}{6}$

$12 \cdot \dfrac{x-2}{4} = 12 \cdot \dfrac{2x+1}{6}$ or $12 \cdot \dfrac{x-2}{4} = 12 \cdot \dfrac{-2x-1}{6}$

$3x-6 = 4x+2$ or $3x-6 = -4x-2$

$3x = 4x+8$ or $3x = -4x+4$

$-x = 8$ or $7x = 4$

$x = -8$ or $x = \dfrac{4}{7}$

Solution set: $\left\{-8, \dfrac{4}{7}\right\}$

75. $|5-x| < 3$

$-3 < 5-x < 3$

$-8 < -x < -2$

$8 > x > 2$ or $2 < x < 8$

Solution set: $\{x \mid 2 < x < 8\}$

Interval: $(2,8)$

77. $|2x-(-6)| > 3$

$|2x+6| > 3$

$2x+6 < -3$ or $2x+6 > 3$

$2x < -9$ or $2x > -3$

$x < -\dfrac{9}{2}$ or $x > -\dfrac{3}{2}$

Solution set: $\left\{x \mid x < -\dfrac{9}{2} \text{ or } x > -\dfrac{3}{2}\right\}$

Interval: $\left(-\infty, -\dfrac{9}{2}\right) \cup \left(-\dfrac{3}{2}, \infty\right)$

79. $|x-5.7| \le 0.0005$

$-0.0005 \le x-5.7 \le 0.0005$

$5.6995 \le x \le 5.7005$

The acceptable rod lengths are between 5.6995 inches and 5.7005 inches, inclusive.

81. $\left|\dfrac{x-100}{15}\right| > 1.96$

$\dfrac{x-100}{15} < -1.96$ or $\dfrac{x-100}{15} > 1.96$

$x-100 < -29.4$ or $x-100 > 29.4$

$x < 70.6$ or $x > 129.4$

An unusual IQ score would be less than 70.6 or greater than 129.4.

83. $|2x-3|+1 = 0$ has no solution because the absolute value, when isolated, is equal to a negative number which is not possible.

85. $|4x+3|+3 < 0$ has the empty set as the solution set because the absolute value, when isolated, is less than a negative number (-3). Since absolute values are always nonnegative, this is not possible.

87. $|x|-x = 5$

$|x| = x+5$

$x = x+5$ or $x = -(x+5)$

$0 = 5$ or $x = -x-5$

$2x = -5$

$x = -\dfrac{5}{2}$

We also need $x+5 \ge 0$ so the absolute value is not negative. This means we need $x \ge -5$ so the solution above works. Solution set: $\left\{-\dfrac{5}{2}\right\}$

89. $z+|-z| = 4$

$|-z| = 4-z$

$-z = 4-z$ or $-z = -(4-z)$

$0 = 4$ or $-z = -4+z$

$-2z = -4$

$z = 2$

We also need $4-z \ge 0$ so the absolute value is not negative. This means we need $z \le 4$ so the solution above works. Solution set: $\{2\}$

91. $|4x+1| = x-2$

$4x+1 = x-2$ or $4x+1 = -(x-2)$

$\quad 4x = x-3$ or $4x+1 = -x+2$

$\quad 3x = -3$ or $4x = -x+1$

$\quad\quad x = -1$ or $5x = 1$

$\quad\quad x = -1$ or $x = \dfrac{1}{5}$

We also need $x-2 \geq 0$ so that the absolute value is not negative. This means we need $x \geq 2$ so neither solution above works.

Check:

$$|4(-1)+1| \overset{?}{=} (-1)-2 \qquad \left|4\left(\dfrac{1}{5}\right)+1\right| \overset{?}{=} \dfrac{1}{5}-2$$

$$|-4+1| \overset{?}{=} -3 \qquad\qquad \left|\dfrac{4}{5}+1\right| \overset{?}{=} -\dfrac{9}{5}$$

$$|-3| \overset{?}{=} -3 \qquad\qquad\quad \left|\dfrac{9}{5}\right| \overset{?}{=} -\dfrac{9}{5}$$

$$3 \neq -3 \qquad\qquad\qquad \dfrac{9}{5} \neq -\dfrac{9}{5}$$

Solution set: $\varnothing$ or $\{\ \}$

93. $|x+5| = -(x+5)$

Since we have $|u| = -u$, we need $u \leq 0$ so the absolute value will not be negative. Thus, we can say that $x+5 \leq 0$ or $x \leq -5$.

Solution set: $\{x \mid x \leq -5\}$

Interval: $(-\infty, -5]$

Chapter 1 Review

1. $3x-4 = 6+x$

Let $x = 5$ in the equation.

$$3(5)-4 \overset{?}{=} 6+(5)$$

$$15-4 \overset{?}{=} 11$$

$$11 = 11 \checkmark$$

$x = 5$ is a solution to the equation.

Let $x = 6$ in the equation.

$$3(6)-4 \overset{?}{=} 6+(6)$$

$$18-4 \overset{?}{=} 12$$

$$14 \neq 12$$

$x = 6$ is **not** a solution to the equation.

2. $-1-4x = 2(3-2x)-7$

Let $x = -2$ in the equation.

$$-1-4(-2) \overset{?}{=} 2(3-2(-2))-7$$

$$-1+8 \overset{?}{=} 2(3+4)-7$$

$$7 \overset{?}{=} 2(7)-7$$

$$7 \overset{?}{=} 14-7$$

$$7 = 7 \checkmark$$

$x = -2$ is a solution to the equation.

Let $x = -1$ in the equation.

$$-1-4(-1) \overset{?}{=} 2(3-2(-1))-7$$

$$-1+4 \overset{?}{=} 2(3+2)-7$$

$$3 \overset{?}{=} 2(5)-7$$

$$3 \overset{?}{=} 10-7$$

$$3 = 3 \checkmark$$

$x = -1$ is a solution to the equation.

3. $4y-(1-y)+5 = -6-2(3y-5)-2y$

Let $y = -2$ in the equation.

$$4(-2)-(1-(-2))+5 \overset{?}{=} -6-2(3(-2)-5)-2(-2)$$

$$-8-(3)+5 \overset{?}{=} -6-2(-6-5)+4$$

$$-11+5 \overset{?}{=} -2-2(-11)$$

$$-6 \neq 20$$

$y = -2$ is **not** a solution to the equation.

Let $y = 0$ in the equation.

$$4(0)-(1-0)+5 \overset{?}{=} -6-2(3(0)-5)-2(0)$$

$$0-1+5 \overset{?}{=} -6-2(-5)-0$$

$$4 \overset{?}{=} -6+10$$

$$4 = 4 \checkmark$$

$y = 0$ is a solution to the equation.

4. $\dfrac{w-7}{3} - \dfrac{w}{4} = -\dfrac{7}{6}$

Let $w = -14$ in the equation.

$\dfrac{-14-7}{3} - \dfrac{-14}{4} \overset{?}{=} -\dfrac{7}{6}$

$\dfrac{-21}{3} + \dfrac{14}{4} \overset{?}{=} -\dfrac{7}{6}$

$-7 + \dfrac{7}{2} \overset{?}{=} -\dfrac{7}{6}$

$-\dfrac{7}{2} \ne -\dfrac{7}{6}$

$w = -14$ is **not** a solution to the equation.

Let $w = 7$ in the equation.

$\dfrac{7-7}{3} - \dfrac{7}{4} \overset{?}{=} -\dfrac{7}{6}$

$0 - \dfrac{7}{4} \overset{?}{=} -\dfrac{7}{6}$

$-\dfrac{7}{4} \ne -\dfrac{7}{6}$

$w = 7$ is **not** a solution to the equation.

5. $2w + 9 = 15$

$2w + 9 - 9 = 15 - 9$

$2w = 6$

$\dfrac{2w}{2} = \dfrac{6}{2}$

$w = 3$

Check: $2(3) + 9 \overset{?}{=} 15$

$6 + 9 \overset{?}{=} 15$

$15 = 15$ ✓

This is a conditional equation. Solution set: $\{3\}$

6. $-4 = 8 - 3y$

$-4 - 8 = 8 - 3y - 8$

$-12 = -3y$

$\dfrac{-12}{-3} = \dfrac{-3y}{-3}$

$4 = y$

Check: $-4 \overset{?}{=} 8 - 3(4)$

$-4 \overset{?}{=} 8 - 12$

$-4 = -4$ ✓

This is a conditional equation. Solution set: $\{4\}$

7. $2x + 5x - 1 = 20$

$7x - 1 = 20$

$7x - 1 + 1 = 20 + 1$

$7x = 21$

$x = 3$

Check: $2(3) + 5(3) - 1 \overset{?}{=} 20$

$6 + 15 - 1 \overset{?}{=} 20$

$20 = 20$ ✓

This is a conditional equation. Solution set: $\{3\}$

8. $7x + 5 - 8x = 13$

$-x + 5 = 13$

$-x + 5 - 5 = 13 - 5$

$-x = 8$

$x = -8$

Check: $7(-8) + 5 - 8(-8) \overset{?}{=} 13$

$-56 + 5 + 64 \overset{?}{=} 13$

$13 = 13$ ✓

This is a conditional equation. Solution set $\{-8\}$

9. $-2(x - 4) = 8 - 2x$

$-2x + 8 = 8 - 2x$

$-2x + 8 - 8 = 8 - 2x - 8$

$-2x = -2x$

$-2x + 2x = -2x + 2x$

$0 = 0$

This statement is an identity. The equation is true for all real numbers. Solution set: $\{x \mid x \text{ is a real number}\}$, or $\mathbb{R}$

10. $3(2r + 1) - 5 = 9(r - 1) - 3r$

$6r + 3 - 5 = 9r - 9 - 3r$

$6r - 2 = 6r - 9$

$6r - 2 + 2 = 6r - 9 + 2$

$6r = 6r - 7$

$6r - 6r = 6r - 7 - 6r$

$0 = -7$

This statement is a contradiction. The equation has no solution. Solution set: $\{\ \}$ or $\varnothing$

11.
$$\frac{2y+3}{4} - \frac{y}{2} = 5$$
$$4\left(\frac{2y+3}{4}\right) - 4\left(\frac{y}{2}\right) = 4(5)$$
$$2y+3-2y = 20$$
$$3 = 20$$

This statement is a contradiction. The equation has no solution. Solution set: $\{\ \}$ or $\varnothing$

12.
$$\frac{x}{3} + \frac{2x}{5} = \frac{x-20}{15}$$
$$15\left(\frac{x}{3}\right) + 15\left(\frac{2x}{5}\right) = 15\left(\frac{x-20}{15}\right)$$
$$5x+6x = x-20$$
$$11x = x-20$$
$$11x-x = x-20-x$$
$$10x = -20$$
$$\frac{10x}{10} = \frac{-20}{10}$$
$$x = -2$$

Check:
$$\frac{-2}{3} + \frac{2(-2)}{5} \overset{?}{=} \frac{(-2)-20}{15}$$
$$-\frac{2}{3} - \frac{4}{5} \overset{?}{=} -\frac{22}{15}$$
$$-\frac{10}{15} - \frac{12}{15} \overset{?}{=} -\frac{22}{15}$$
$$-\frac{22}{15} = -\frac{22}{15} \ \checkmark$$

This is a conditional equation.
Solution set: $\{-2\}$

13.
$$0.2(x-6)+1.75 = 4.25+0.1(3x+10)$$
$$0.2x-1.2+1.75 = 4.25+0.3x+1$$
$$0.2x+0.55 = 5.25+0.3x$$
$$0.2x-0.3x+0.55 = 5.25+0.3x-0.3x$$
$$-0.1x+0.55 = 5.25$$
$$-0.1x+0.55-0.55 = 5.25-0.55$$
$$-0.1x = 4.7$$
$$\frac{-0.1x}{-0.1} = \frac{4.7}{-0.1}$$
$$x = -47$$

Check:
$$0.2(-47-6)+1.75 \overset{?}{=} 4.25+0.1(3(-47)+10)$$
$$0.2(-53)+1.75 \overset{?}{=} 4.25+0.1(-141+10)$$
$$-10.6+1.75 \overset{?}{=} 4.25+0.1(-131)$$
$$-8.85 \overset{?}{=} 4.25-13.1$$
$$-8.85 = -8.85 \ \checkmark$$

This is a conditional equation.
Solution set: $\{-47\}$

(Note: Alternatively, we could have started by multiplying both sides of the equation by 100 to clear the decimals.)

14.
$$2.1w-3(2.4-0.2w) = 0.9(3w-5)-2.7$$
$$2.1w-7.2+0.6w = 2.7w-4.5-2.7$$
$$2.7w-7.2 = 2.7w-7.2$$
$$0 = 0$$

This statement is an identity. The equation is true for all real numbers. Solution set:
$\{w \mid w \text{ is a real number}\}$, or $\mathbb{R}$

(Note: Alternatively, we could have started by multiplying both sides of the equation by 10 to clear the decimals.)

15. We need to set the denominator equal to 0 and solve the resulting equation.
$$2x+3 = 0$$
$$2x+3-3 = 0-3$$
$$2x = -3$$
$$\frac{2x}{2} = \frac{-3}{2}$$
$$x = -\frac{3}{2}$$

Check:
$$2\left(-\frac{3}{2}\right)+3 \overset{?}{=} 0$$
$$-3+3 \overset{?}{=} 0$$
$$0 = 0 \ \checkmark$$

Solution set: $\left\{-\frac{3}{2}\right\}$. Thus, $x = -\frac{3}{2}$ must be excluded from the domain.

16. We need to set the denominator equal to 0 and solve the resulting equation.

$$6(x-1)+3=0$$
$$6x-6+3=0$$
$$6x-3=0$$
$$6x-3+3=0+3$$
$$6x=3$$
$$\frac{6x}{6}=\frac{3}{6}$$
$$x=\frac{1}{2}$$

Check:
$$6\left(\tfrac{1}{2}-1\right)+3\overset{?}{=}0$$
$$6\left(-\tfrac{1}{2}\right)+3\overset{?}{=}0$$
$$-3+3\overset{?}{=}0$$
$$0=0\ \checkmark$$

Solution set: $\left\{\tfrac{1}{2}\right\}$. Thus, $x=\tfrac{1}{2}$ must be excluded from the domain.

17.
$$2370=0.06(x-9000)+315$$
$$2370=0.06x-540+315$$
$$2370=0.06x-225$$
$$2370+225=0.06x-225+225$$
$$2595=0.06x$$
$$\frac{2595}{0.06}=\frac{0.06x}{0.06}$$
$$43{,}250=x$$

Her Missouri taxable income was $43,250.

18. $x+4(x-10)=69.75$
$$x+4x-40=69.75$$
$$5x-40=69.75$$
$$5x-40+40=69.75+40$$
$$5x=109.75$$
$$\frac{5x}{5}=\frac{109.75}{5}$$
$$x=21.95$$

The regular club price for a DVD is $21.95.

19. Let x = the number.
$$3x+7=22$$

20. Let x = the number.
$$x-3=\frac{x}{2}$$

21. Let x = the number.
$$0.2x=x-12$$

22. Let x = the number.
$$6x=2x-4$$

23. Let x = Payton's age.
Shawn's age: $x+8$
$$x+(x+8)=18$$
$$2x+8=18$$
$$2x+8-8=18-8$$
$$2x=10$$
$$\frac{2x}{2}=\frac{10}{2}$$
$$x=5$$
Payton is 5 years old and Shawn is 13 years old.

24. Let x = the first odd integer.
Second odd integer: $x+2$
Third odd integer: $x+4$
Fourth odd integer: $x+6$
Fifth odd integer: $x+8$
$$x+(x+2)+(x+4)+(x+6)+(x+8)=125$$
$$5x+20=125$$
$$5x+20-20=125-20$$
$$5x=105$$
$$\frac{5x}{5}=\frac{105}{5}$$
$$x=21$$
The five odd integers are 21, 23, 25, 27, and 29.

25. Let x = the final exam score.
$$\frac{85+81+84+77+2x}{6}=80$$
$$\frac{327+2x}{6}=80$$
$$6\cdot\frac{327+2x}{6}=6\cdot80$$
$$327+2x=480$$
$$327+2x-327=480-327$$
$$2x=153$$
$$\frac{2x}{2}=\frac{153}{2}$$
$$x=76.5$$
Logan needs to get a score of 76.5 on the final exam to have an average of 80.

26. Here we can use the simple interest formula $I = P \cdot r \cdot t$. Remember that t is in years and that the interest rate should be written as a decimal.

$$I = 3200(0.0425)\left(\frac{1}{12}\right)$$

$$I = \frac{34}{3} \approx 11.33$$

After 1 month, Cherie will accrue about $11.33 in interest.

27. Let x = the original price.
Discount: $0.3x$

sale price = original price − discount

$$94.50 = x - 0.3x$$
$$94.50 = 0.7x$$
$$\frac{94.50}{0.7} = \frac{0.7x}{0.7}$$
$$135 = x$$

The original price of the sleeping bag was $135.00.

28. Let x = the federal minimum wage.
Increase: $0.65x$
$$8.50 = x + 0.65x$$
$$8.50 = 1.65x$$
$$\frac{8.50}{1.65} = \frac{1.65x}{1.65}$$
$$5.15 \approx x$$

The federal minimum wage was $5.15 (per hour).

29. Let x = pounds of blueberries.
Strawberries: $12 - x$

tot. rev. = rev. from b.b. + rev. from s.b.

$$(\text{price})(\text{lbs}) = (\text{price})(\text{lbs}) + (\text{price})(\text{lbs})$$
$$(12.95)(12) = (10.95)(x) + (13.95)(12 - x)$$
$$155.4 = 10.95x + 167.4 - 13.95x$$
$$155.4 = 167.4 - 3x$$
$$155.4 - 167.4 = 167.4 - 3x - 167.4$$
$$-12 = -3x$$
$$\frac{-12}{-3} = \frac{-3x}{-3}$$
$$4 = x$$

The store should mix 4 pounds of chocolate covered blueberries with 8 pounds of chocolate covered strawberries.

30. Let x = pounds of baseball gum.
Soccer gum: $10 - x$

tot. rev. = rev. from b.b. + rev. from s.b.

$$(\text{price})(\text{lbs}) = (\text{price})(\text{lbs}) + (\text{price})(\text{lbs})$$
$$(3.75)(10) = (3.50)(x) + (4.50)(10 - x)$$
$$37.5 = 3.5x + 45 - 4.5x$$
$$37.5 = 45 - x$$
$$37.5 - 45 = 45 - x - 45$$
$$-7.5 = -x$$
$$7.5 = x$$

The store should mix 7.5 pounds of baseball gumballs with 2.5 pounds of soccer gumballs.

31. Let x = amount invested at 8%.
Amount at 18%: $8000 - x$

tot. return = ret. from 8% + ret. from 18%

$$(\%)(\$) = (\%)(\$) + (\%)(\$)$$
$$(0.12)(8000) = (0.08)(x) + (0.18)(8000 - x)$$
$$960 = 0.08x + 1440 - 0.18x$$
$$960 = 1440 - 0.1x$$
$$960 - 1440 = 1440 - 0.1x - 1440$$
$$-480 = -0.1x$$
$$\frac{-480}{-0.1} = \frac{-0.1x}{-0.1}$$
$$4800 = x$$

Angie should invest $4800 at 8% and $3200 at 18% to achieve a 12% return.

32. Let x = liters drained = liters added.
We can write the following equation for the amount of antifreeze:

final amt = amt now − amt. drain + amt add

$$(\%)(\text{L}) = (\%)(\text{L}) - (\%)(\text{L}) + (\%)(\text{L})$$
$$(0.5)(10.1) = (0.3)(10.1) - (0.3)(x) + (1.0)(x)$$
$$5.05 = 3.03 - 0.3x + x$$
$$5.05 = 3.03 + 0.7x$$
$$5.05 - 3.03 = 3.03 + 0.7x - 3.03$$
$$2.02 = 0.7x$$
$$\frac{2.02}{0.7} = \frac{0.7x}{0.7}$$
$$2.89 \approx x$$

About 2.89 liters would need to be drained and replaced with pure antifreeze.

33. For this problem, we will need the distance traveled formula: $d = r \cdot t$.

Let x = miles driven at 60 mph.

Miles at 70 mph: $300 - x$

tot. time = time at 60 mph + time at 70 mph

$$4.5 = \frac{x}{60} + \frac{300 - x}{70}$$

$$420(4.5) = 420\left(\frac{x}{60} + \frac{300 - x}{70}\right)$$

$$1890 = 7x + 1800 - 6x$$

$$1890 = x + 1800$$

$$1890 - 1800 = x + 1800 - 1800$$

$$90 = x$$

Josh drove 90 miles at 60 miles per hour and 210 miles at 70 miles per hour.

34. For this problem, we will need the distance traveled formula: $d = r \cdot t$

We also need to note that 50 minutes is $\frac{5}{6}$ of an hour.

Let x = speed of the F14.

Speed of F15: $x + 200$.

tot. dist. = dist. of F14 + dist. of F15

$$2200 = \frac{5}{6}x + \frac{5}{6}(x + 200)$$

$$2200 = \frac{5}{6}x + \frac{5}{6}x + \frac{500}{3}$$

$$2200 = \frac{5}{3}x + \frac{500}{3}$$

$$3(2200) = 3\left(\frac{5}{3}x + \frac{500}{3}\right)$$

$$6600 = 5x + 500$$

$$6600 - 500 = 5x + 500 - 500$$

$$6100 = 5x$$

$$\frac{6100}{5} = \frac{5x}{5}$$

$$1220 = x$$

The F14 is traveling at a speed of 1220 miles per hour and the F15 is traveling at a speed of 1420 miles per hour.

35.
$$y = \frac{k}{x}$$

$$y \cdot x = \frac{k}{x} \cdot x$$

$$xy = k$$

$$\frac{xy}{y} = \frac{k}{y}$$

$$x = \frac{k}{y}$$

36.
$$F = \frac{9}{5}C + 32$$

$$F - 32 = \frac{9}{5}C + 32 - 32$$

$$F - 32 = \frac{9}{5}C$$

$$\frac{5}{9}(F - 32) = \frac{5}{9}\left(\frac{9}{5}C\right)$$

$$\frac{5}{9}(F - 32) = C$$

37.
$$P = 2L + 2W$$

$$P - 2L = 2L + 2W - 2L$$

$$P - 2L = 2W$$

$$\frac{P - 2L}{2} = \frac{2W}{2}$$

$$\frac{P - 2L}{2} = W$$

38.
$$\rho = m_1 v_1 + m_2 v_2$$

$$\rho - m_1 v_1 = m_1 v_1 + m_2 v_2 - m_1 v_1$$

$$\rho - m_1 v_1 = m_2 v_2$$

$$\frac{\rho - m_1 v_1}{v_2} = \frac{m_2 v_2}{v_2}$$

$$\frac{\rho - m_1 v_1}{v_2} = m_2$$

39. $PV = nRT$

$$\frac{PV}{nR} = \frac{nRT}{nR}$$

$$\frac{PV}{nR} = T$$

40.
$$S = 2LW + 2LH + 2WH$$

$$S - 2LH = 2LW + 2LH + 2WH - 2LH$$

$$S - 2LH = 2LW + 2WH$$

$$S - 2LH = W(2L + 2H)$$

$$\frac{S - 2LH}{2L + 2H} = \frac{W(2L + 2H)}{2L + 2H}$$

$$\frac{S - 2LH}{2L + 2H} = W$$

41.
$$3x + 4y = 2$$

$$3x + 4y - 3x = 2 - 3x$$

$$4y = -3x + 2$$

$$\frac{4y}{4} = \frac{-3x + 2}{4}$$

$$y = -\frac{3}{4}x + \frac{1}{2}$$

42.
$$-5x + 4y = 10$$
$$-5x + 4y + 5x = 10 + 5x$$
$$4y = 5x + 10$$
$$\frac{4y}{4} = \frac{5x + 10}{4}$$
$$y = \frac{5}{4}x + \frac{5}{2}$$

43.
$$4.8x - 1.2y = 6$$
$$4.8x - 1.2y - 4.8x = 6 - 4.8x$$
$$-1.2y = -4.8x + 6$$
$$\frac{-1.2y}{-1.2} = \frac{-4.8x + 6}{-1.2}$$
$$y = 4x - 5$$

44.
$$\frac{2}{5}x + \frac{1}{3}y = 8$$
$$\frac{2}{5}x + \frac{1}{3}y - \frac{2}{5}x = 8 - \frac{2}{5}x$$
$$\frac{1}{3}y = -\frac{2}{5}x + 8$$
$$3\left(\frac{1}{3}y\right) = 3\left(-\frac{2}{5}x + 8\right)$$
$$y = -\frac{6}{5}x + 24$$

45. $C = \frac{5}{9}(3221.6 - 32)$

$C = \frac{5}{9}(3189.6)$

$C = 1772$

The melting point of platinum is $1772°C$.

46. Let x = the measure of the congruent angle.
Third angle: $x - 30$
$$x + x + (x - 30) = 180$$
$$3x - 30 = 180$$
$$3x - 30 + 30 = 180 + 30$$
$$3x = 210$$
$$\frac{3x}{3} = \frac{210}{3}$$
$$x = 70$$
The angles measure $70°, 70°,$ and $40°$.

47. Let w = width of the window in feet.
Length: $l = w + 8$
$$2l + 2w = P$$
$$2(w + 8) + 2w = 76$$
$$2w + 16 + 2w = 76$$
$$4w + 16 = 76$$
$$4w + 16 - 16 = 76 - 16$$
$$4w = 60$$
$$\frac{4w}{4} = \frac{60}{4}$$
$$w = 15$$
$$l = w + 8 = 15 + 8 = 23$$
The window measures 15 feet by 23 feet.

48. a.
$$C = 2.95 + 0.04x$$
$$C - 2.95 = 2.95 + 0.04x - 2.95$$
$$C - 2.95 = 0.04x$$
$$\frac{C - 2.95}{0.04} = \frac{0.04x}{0.04}$$
$$25C - 73.75 = x \quad \text{or} \quad x = 25C - 73.75$$

b. $x = 25(20) - 73.75$

$x = 500 - 73.75$

$x = 426.25$

Debbie can talk for 426 minutes in one month and not spend more than $20 on long distance.

49. Let x = thickness in feet.
$$V = l \cdot w \cdot h$$
$$80 = 12 \cdot 18 \cdot x$$
$$80 = 216x$$
$$\frac{80}{216} = \frac{216x}{216}$$
$$\frac{10}{27} = x \quad \text{or} \quad x \approx 0.37$$

The patio will be $\frac{10}{27}$ of a foot thick (i.e. about 4.44 inches).

50. a.
$$A = \pi s(R + r)$$
$$\frac{A}{\pi s} = \frac{\pi s(R + r)}{\pi s}$$
$$\frac{A}{\pi s} = R + r$$
$$\frac{A}{\pi s} - R = r \quad \text{or} \quad r = \frac{A - \pi Rs}{\pi s}$$

b. $r = \dfrac{10\pi - \pi(3)(2)}{\pi(2)}$

$r = \dfrac{10-6}{2}$

$r = \dfrac{4}{2} = 2$

The radius of the top of the frustum is 2 feet.

51. a.
$C = 23.121 + 0.05947(x - 300)$

$C = 23.121 + 0.05947x - 17.841$

$C = 5.28 + 0.05947x$

$C - 5.28 = 5.28 + 0.05947x - 5.28$

$C - 5.28 = 0.05947x$

$\dfrac{C - 5.28}{0.05947} = \dfrac{0.05947x}{0.05947}$

$x = \dfrac{C - 5.28}{0.05947}$

b. $x = \dfrac{115.30 - 5.28}{0.05947}$

$x = \dfrac{110.02}{0.05947}$

$x \approx 1850$

Approximately 1850 kwh were used.

52. Let x = the measure of the angle.
Complement: $90 - x$
Supplement: $180 - x$
$(90 - x) + (180 - x) = 150$

$90 - x + 180 - x = 150$

$270 - 2x = 150$

$270 - 2x - 270 = 150 - 270$

$-2x = -120$

$\dfrac{-2x}{-2} = \dfrac{-120}{-2}$

$x = 60$

The angle measures $60°$.

53. $2 < x \le 7$
Interval: $(2, 7]$

54. $x > -2$
Interval: $(-2, \infty)$

55. $(-\infty, 4]$
Inequality: $x \le 4$

56. $[-1, 3)$
Inequality: $-1 \le x < 3$

57.
$5 \le x \le 9$

$2 \cdot 5 \le 2 \cdot x \le 2 \cdot 9$

$10 \le 2x \le 18$

$10 - 3 \le 2x - 3 \le 18 - 3$

$7 \le 2x - 3 \le 15$

Therefore, $a = 7$ and $b = 15$.

58.
$-2 < x < 0$

$3(-2) < 3(x) < 3(0)$

$-6 < 3x < 0$

$-6 + 5 < 3x + 5 < 0 + 5$

$-1 < 3x + 5 < 5$

Therefore, $a = -1$ and $b = 5$.

59.
$3x + 12 \le 0$

$3x + 12 - 12 \le 0 - 12$

$3x \le -12$

$\dfrac{3x}{3} \le \dfrac{-12}{3}$

$x \le -4$

Solution set: $\{x \mid x \le -4\}$

Interval: $(-\infty, -4]$

Graph:

60.
$$2 < 1 - 3x$$
$$2 - 1 < 1 - 3x - 1$$
$$1 < -3x$$
$$\frac{1}{-3} > \frac{-3x}{-3}$$
$$-\frac{1}{3} > x \ \text{ or } \ x < -\frac{1}{3}$$

Solution set: $\left\{ x \mid x < -\frac{1}{3} \right\}$

Interval: $\left(-\infty, -\frac{1}{3} \right)$

Graph:

61.
$$-7 \le 3(h+1) - 8$$
$$-7 \le 3h + 3 - 8$$
$$-7 \le 3h - 5$$
$$-7 + 5 \le 3h - 5 + 5$$
$$-2 \le 3h$$
$$\frac{-2}{3} \le \frac{3h}{3}$$
$$-\frac{2}{3} \le h \ \text{ or } \ h \ge -\frac{2}{3}$$

Solution set: $\left\{ h \mid h \ge -\frac{2}{3} \right\}$

Interval: $\left[-\frac{2}{3}, \infty \right)$

Graph:

62.
$$-7x - 8 < -22$$
$$-7x - 8 + 8 < -22 + 8$$
$$-7x < -14$$
$$\frac{-7x}{-7} > \frac{-14}{-7}$$
$$x > 2$$

Solution set: $\left\{ x \mid x > 2 \right\}$

Interval: $(2, \infty)$

Graph:

63.
$$3(p-2) + (5-p) > 2 - (p-3)$$
$$3p - 6 + 5 - p > 2 - p + 3$$
$$2p - 1 > 5 - p$$
$$2p + p - 1 > 5 - p + p$$
$$3p - 1 > 5$$
$$3p - 1 + 1 > 5 + 1$$
$$3p > 6$$
$$\frac{3p}{3} > \frac{6}{3}$$
$$p > 2$$

Solution set: $\left\{ p \mid p > 2 \right\}$

Interval: $(2, \infty)$

Graph:

64.
$$2(x+1) + 1 > 2(x-2)$$
$$2x + 2 + 1 > 2x - 4$$
$$2x + 3 > 2x - 4$$
$$2x + 3 - 2x > 2x - 4 - 2x$$
$$3 > -4$$

This statement is true for all real numbers.

Solution set: $\left\{ x \mid \text{ any real number} \right\}$

Interval: $(-\infty, \infty)$

Graph:

65.
$$5(x-1) - 7x > 2(2-x)$$
$$5x - 5 - 7x > 4 - 2x$$
$$-2x - 5 > 4 - 2x$$
$$-2x - 5 + 2x > 4 - 2x + 2x$$
$$-5 > 4 \quad \text{false}$$

This statement is false for all real numbers. The inequality has no solutions.

Solution set: $\{ \ \}$ or $\varnothing$

66.
$$0.03x + 0.10 > 0.52 - 0.07x$$
$$0.03x + 0.10 - 0.10 > 0.52 - 0.07x - 0.10$$
$$0.03x > 0.42 - 0.07x$$
$$0.03x + 0.07x > 0.42 - 0.07x + 0.07x$$
$$0.1x > 0.42$$
$$\frac{0.1x}{0.1} > \frac{0.42}{0.1}$$
$$x > 4.2$$
Solution set: $\{x \mid x > 4.2\}$

Interval: $(4.2, \infty)$

Graph:

67.
$$-\frac{4}{9}w + \frac{7}{12} < \frac{5}{36}$$
$$36\left(-\frac{4}{9}w + \frac{7}{12}\right) < 36\left(\frac{5}{36}\right)$$
$$-16w + 21 < 5$$
$$-16w + 21 - 21 < 5 - 21$$
$$-16w < -16$$
$$\frac{-16w}{-16} > \frac{-16}{-16}$$
$$w > 1$$
Solution set: $\{w \mid w > 1\}$

Interval: $(1, \infty)$

Graph:

68.
$$\frac{2}{5}y - 20 > \frac{2}{3}y + 12$$
$$15\left(\frac{2}{5}y - 20\right) > 15\left(\frac{2}{3}y + 12\right)$$
$$6y - 300 > 10y + 180$$
$$6y - 300 - 10y > 10y + 180 - 10y$$
$$-4y - 300 > 180$$
$$-4y - 300 + 300 > 180 + 300$$
$$-4y > 480$$
$$\frac{-4y}{-4} < \frac{480}{-4}$$
$$y < -120$$
Solution set: $\{y \mid y < -120\}$

Interval: $(-\infty, -120)$

Graph:

69. Let x = number of people attending.
$$7.5x + 150 \le 600$$
$$7.5x + 150 - 150 \le 600 - 150$$
$$7.5x \le 450$$
$$\frac{7.5x}{7.5} \le \frac{450}{7.5}$$
$$x \le 60$$
To stay within budget, no more than 60 people can attend the banquet.

70. Let x = number of miles driven daily (average)
Miles charged: $x - 150$
$$43.46 + 0.25(x - 150) \le 60$$
$$43.46 + 0.25x - 37.5 \le 60$$
$$0.25x + 5.96 \le 60$$
$$0.25x + 5.96 - 5.96 \le 60 - 5.96$$
$$0.25x \le 54.04$$
$$\frac{0.25x}{0.25} \le \frac{54.04}{0.25}$$
$$x \le 216.16$$
To stay within budget, you can drive an average of 216 miles per day.

71. Let x = number of candy bars sold.
$$1.0x > 50 + 0.6x$$
$$1.0x - 0.6x > 50 + 0.6x - 0.6x$$
$$0.4x > 50$$
$$\frac{0.4x}{0.4} > \frac{50}{0.4}$$
$$x > 125$$
The band must sell more than 125 candy bars to make a profit.

72. Let x = number of DVDs purchased.
$$24.95 + 9.95(x - 1) \le 72$$
$$24.95 + 9.95x - 9.95 \le 72$$
$$15 + 9.95x \le 72$$
$$15 + 9.95x - 15 \le 72 - 15$$
$$9.95x \le 57$$
$$\frac{9.95x}{9.95} \le \frac{57}{9.95}$$
$$x \le \frac{57}{9.95} \approx 5.73$$
You can purchase up to 5 DVDs and still be within budget.

73. $A \cup B = \{-1, 0, 1, 2, 3, 4, 6, 8\}$

74. $A \cap C = \{2, 4\}$

75. $B \cap C = \{1, 2, 3, 4\}$

76. $A \cup C = \{1, 2, 3, 4, 6, 8\}$

77. a. $A \cap B = \{x \mid 2 < x \le 4\}$

Interval: $(2, 4]$

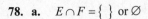

b. $A \cup B = \{x \mid x \text{ is a real number}\}$

Interval: $(-\infty, \infty)$

78. a. $E \cap F = \{\ \}$ or $\varnothing$

b. $E \cup F = \{x \mid x < -2 \text{ or } x \ge 3\}$

Interval: $(-\infty, -2) \cup [3, \infty)$

79. $x < 4$ and $x + 3 > 2$

$x > -1$

We need $x < 4$ and $x > -1$.

Solution set: $\{x \mid -1 < x < 4\}$

Interval: $(-1, 4)$

Graph:

80. $3 < 2 - x < 7$

$3 - 2 < 2 - x - 2 < 7 - 2$

$1 < -x < 5$

$-1(1) > -1(-x) > -1(5)$

$-1 > x > -5$

$-5 < x < -1$

Solution set: $\{x \mid -5 < x < -1\}$

Interval: $(-5, -1)$

Graph:

81. $x + 3 < 1$ or $x > 2$

$x < -2$

We need $x < -2$ or $x > 2$.

Solution set: $\{x \mid x < -2 \text{ or } x > 2\}$

Interval: $(-\infty, -2) \cup (2, \infty)$

Graph:

82. $x + 6 \ge 10$ or $x \le 0$

$x \ge 4$

We need $x \ge 4$ or $x \le 0$.

Solution set: $\{x \mid x \le 0 \text{ or } x \ge 4\}$

Interval: $(-\infty, 0] \cup [4, \infty)$

Graph:

83. $3x + 2 \le 5$ and $-4x + 2 \le -10$

$3x \le 3 \qquad\qquad -4x \le -12$

$x \le 1 \qquad\qquad\quad x \ge 3$

We need $x \le 1$ and $x \ge 3$.

Solution set: $\{\ \}$ or $\varnothing$

84. $1 \le 2x + 5 < 13$

$1 - 5 \le 2x + 5 - 5 < 13 - 5$

$-4 \le 2x < 8$

$\dfrac{-4}{2} \le \dfrac{2x}{2} < \dfrac{8}{2}$

$-2 \le x < 4$

Solution set: $\{x \mid -2 \le x < 4\}$

Interval: $[-2, 4)$

Graph:

85. $x - 3 \le -5$ or $2x + 1 > 7$

$x \le -2 \qquad\qquad 2x > 6$

$\qquad\qquad\qquad\quad x > 3$

We need $x \le -2$ or $x > 3$.

Solution set: $\{x \mid x \le -2 \text{ or } x > 3\}$

Interval: $(-\infty, -2] \cup (3, \infty)$

Graph:

86. $3x + 4 > -2$ or $4 - 2x \geq -6$

$\qquad$ $3x > -6$ $\qquad$ $-2x \geq -10$

$\qquad$ $x > -2$ $\qquad$ $x \leq 5$

We need $x > -2$ or $x \leq 5$.

Solution set: $\{x \mid -\infty < x < \infty\}$

Interval: $(-\infty, \infty)$

Graph:

87. $\frac{1}{3}x > 2$ or $\frac{2}{5}x < -4$

$\qquad$ $x > 6$ $\qquad$ $x < -10$

We need $x < -10$ or $x > 6$.

Solution set: $\{x \mid x < -10 \text{ or } x > 6\}$

Interval: $(-\infty, -10) \cup (6, \infty)$

Graph:

88. $x + \frac{3}{2} \geq 0$ and $-2x + \frac{3}{2} > \frac{1}{4}$

$\qquad$ $x \geq -\frac{3}{2}$ $\qquad$ $-2x > -\frac{5}{4}$

$\qquad$ $\qquad$ $\qquad$ $x < \frac{5}{8}$

We need $x \geq -\frac{3}{2}$ and $x < \frac{5}{8}$.

Solution set: $\{x \mid -\frac{3}{2} \leq x < \frac{5}{8}\}$

Interval: $\left[-\frac{3}{2}, \frac{5}{8}\right)$

Graph:

89. $70 \leq x \leq 75$

90. Let x = number of kilowatt-hours. Then, the number of kilowatt-hours *above* 300 is given by the expression $x - 300$. Therefore, we need to solve the following inequality:

$50.28 \leq 23.12 + 0.05947(x - 300) \leq 121.43$

$27.16 \leq 0.05947(x - 300) \leq 98.31$

$456.7 \leq x - 300 \leq 1653.1$

$756.7 \leq x \leq 1953.1$

The electric usage varied from roughly 756.7 kilowatt-hours up to roughly 1953.1 kilowatt-hours.

91. $|x| = 4$

$\qquad$ $x = 4$ or $x = -4$

Solution set: $\{-4, 4\}$

92. $|3x - 5| = 4$

$\qquad$ $3x - 5 = 4$ or $3x - 5 = -4$

$\qquad$ $3x = 9$ $\qquad$ $3x = 1$

$\qquad$ $x = 3$ $\qquad$ $x = \frac{1}{3}$

Solution set: $\{\frac{1}{3}, 3\}$

93. $|-y + 4| = 9$

$\qquad$ $-y + 4 = 9$ or $-y + 4 = -9$

$\qquad$ $-y = 5$ $\qquad$ $-y = -13$

$\qquad$ $y = -5$ $\qquad$ $y = 13$

Solution set: $\{-5, 13\}$

94. $-3|x + 2| - 5 = -8$

$\qquad$ $-3|x + 2| = -3$

$\qquad$ $|x + 2| = 1$

$\qquad$ $x + 2 = 1$ or $x + 2 = -1$

$\qquad$ $x = -1$ $\qquad$ $x = -3$

Solution set: $\{-3, -1\}$

95. $|2w - 7| = -3$

This equation has no solution since an absolute value can never yield a negative result.

Solution set: $\{ \ \}$ or $\varnothing$

96. $|x+3| = |3x-1|$

$x+3 = 3x-1$ or $x+3 = -(3x-1)$

$-2x = -4$ $x+3 = -3x+1$

$x = 2$ $4x = -2$

                 $x = -\frac{1}{2}$

Solution set: $\left\{-\frac{1}{2}, 2\right\}$

97. $|x| < 2$

$-2 < x < 2$

Solution set: $\{x \mid -2 < x < 2\}$

Interval: $(-2, 2)$

98. $|x| \geq \frac{7}{2}$

$x \leq -\frac{7}{2}$ or $x \geq \frac{7}{2}$

Solution set: $\left\{x \mid x \leq -\frac{7}{2} \text{ or } x \geq \frac{7}{2}\right\}$

Interval: $\left(-\infty, -\frac{7}{2}\right] \cup \left[\frac{7}{2}, \infty\right)$

99. $|x+2| \leq 3$

$-3 \leq x+2 \leq 3$

$-3-2 \leq x+2-2 \leq 3-2$

$-5 \leq x \leq 1$

Solution set: $\{x \mid -5 \leq x \leq 1\}$

Interval: $[-5, 1]$

100. $|4x-3| \geq 1$

$4x-3 \leq -1$ or $4x-3 \geq 1$

$4x \leq 2$ $4x \geq 4$

$x \leq \frac{1}{2}$ $x \geq 1$

Solution set: $\left\{x \mid x \leq \frac{1}{2} \text{ or } x \geq 1\right\}$

Interval: $\left(-\infty, \frac{1}{2}\right] \cup [1, \infty)$

101. $3|x| + 6 \geq 1$

$3|x| \geq -5$

$|x| \geq -\frac{5}{3}$

Since the result of an absolute value is always nonnegative, any real number is a solution to this inequality.

Solution set: $\{x \mid x \text{ is a real number}\}$

Interval: $(-\infty, \infty)$

102. $|7x+5| + 4 < 3$

$|7x+5| < -1$

Since the result of an absolute value is never negative, this inequality has no solutions.

Solution set: $\{\ \}$ or $\varnothing$

103. $|(x-3) - 2| \leq 0.01$

$|x-3-2| \leq 0.01$

$|x-5| \leq 0.01$

$-0.01 \leq x-5 \leq 0.01$

$-0.01+5 \leq x-5+5 \leq 0.01+5$

$4.99 \leq x \leq 5.01$

Solution set: $\{x \mid 4.99 \leq x \leq 5.01\}$

Interval: $[4.99, 5.01]$

104. $\left|\dfrac{2x-3}{4}\right| > 1$

$\dfrac{2x-3}{4} < -1$ or $\dfrac{2x-3}{4} > 1$

$2x-3 < -4$ $2x-3 > 4$

$2x < -1$ $2x > 7$

$x < -\frac{1}{2}$ $x > \frac{7}{2}$

Solution set: $\left\{x \mid x < -\frac{1}{2} \text{ or } x > \frac{7}{2}\right\}$

Interval: $\left(-\infty, -\frac{1}{2}\right) \cup \left(\frac{7}{2}, \infty\right)$

105. $|x - 0.503| \le 0.001$

$-0.001 \le x - 0.503 \le 0.001$

$0.502 \le x \le 0.504$

The acceptable diameters of the bearing are between 0.502 inches and 0.504 inches, inclusive.

106. $\left|\dfrac{x - 40}{2}\right| > 1.96$

$\dfrac{x - 40}{2} < -1.96$ or $\dfrac{x - 40}{2} > 1.96$

$x - 40 < -3.92 \qquad x - 40 > 3.92$

$\qquad x < 36.08 \qquad\qquad x > 43.92$

Tensile strengths below 36.08 lb/in^2 or above 43.92 lb/in^2 would be considered unusual.

Chapter 1 Test

1. a. Let $x = 6$ in the equation.

$$3(6 - 7) + 5 \overset{?}{=} 6 - 4$$

$$3(-1) + 5 \overset{?}{=} 2$$

$$-3 + 5 \overset{?}{=} 2$$

$$2 = 2 \ \text{true}$$

$x = 6$ is a solution to the equation.

b. Let $x = -2$ in the equation.

$$3(-2 - 7) + 5 \overset{?}{=} -2 - 4$$

$$3(-9) + 5 \overset{?}{=} -6$$

$$-27 + 5 \overset{?}{=} -6$$

$$-22 \ne -6$$

$x = -2$ is **not** a solution to the equation.

2. a. Interval: $(-4, \infty)$

b. Interval: $(3, 7]$

3. Let x represent the number.

$3x - 8 = x + 4$

4. Let x represent the number.

$\dfrac{2}{3}x + 2(x - 5) > 7$

5. $5x - (x - 2) = 6 + 2x$

$5x - x + 2 = 6 + 2x$

$4x + 2 = 6 + 2x$

$4x + 2 - 2 = 6 + 2x - 2$

$4x = 4 + 2x$

$4x - 2x = 4 + 2x - 2x$

$2x = 4$

$\dfrac{2x}{2} = \dfrac{4}{2}$

$x = 2$

Solution set: $\{2\}$

This is a conditional equation.

6. $|2x + 5| - 3 = 0$

$|2x + 5| = 3$

$2x + 5 = -3$ or $2x + 5 = 3$

$2x = -8 \qquad\qquad 2x = -2$

$x = -4 \qquad\qquad x = -1$

Solution set: $\{-4, -1\}$

This is a conditional equation.

7. $7 + (x - 3) = 3(x + 1) - 2x$

$7 + x - 3 = 3x + 3 - 2x$

$4 + x = x + 3$

$4 + x - x = x + 3 - x$

$4 = 3 \ \text{false}$

This statement is a contradiction. The equation has no solution. Solution set: $\{\ \}$ or $\varnothing$

8. $\qquad x + 2 \le 3x - 4$

$x + 2 - 3x \le 3x - 4 - 3x$

$-2x + 2 \le -4$

$-2x + 2 - 2 \le -4 - 2$

$-2x \le -6$

$\dfrac{-2x}{-2} \ge \dfrac{-6}{-2}$

$x \ge 3$

Solution set: $\{x \mid x \ge 3\}$

Interval: $[3, \infty)$

9.
$$4x+7>2x-3(x-2)$$
$$4x+7>2x-3x+6$$
$$4x+7>-x+6$$
$$4x+7+x>-x+6+x$$
$$5x+7>6$$
$$5x+7-7>6-7$$
$$5x>-1$$
$$\frac{5x}{5}>\frac{-1}{5}$$
$$x>-\frac{1}{5}$$

Solution set: $\left\{x \mid x>-\frac{1}{5}\right\}$

Interval: $\left(-\frac{1}{5},\infty\right)$

10.
$$-x+4\le x+3$$
$$-x+4-x\le x+3-x$$
$$-2x+4\le 3$$
$$-2x+4-4\le 3-4$$
$$-2x\le -1$$
$$\frac{-2x}{-2}\ge\frac{-1}{-2}$$
$$x\ge\frac{1}{2}$$

Solution set: $\left\{x \mid x\ge\frac{1}{2}\right\}$

Interval: $\left[\frac{1}{2},\infty\right)$

11. $x+2<8$ and $2x+5\ge 1$
$$x<6 \qquad 2x\ge -4$$
$$x\ge -2$$
We need $x\ge -2$ and $x<6$.

Solution set: $\{x \mid -2\le x<6\}$

Interval: $[-2,6)$

12. $x>4$ or $2(x-1)+3<-2$
$$2x-2+3<-2$$
$$2x+1<-2$$
$$2x+1-1<-2-1$$
$$2x<-3$$
$$\frac{2x}{2}<\frac{-3}{2}$$
$$x<-\frac{3}{2}$$

We need $x>4$ or $x<-\frac{3}{2}$.

Solution set: $\left\{x \mid x<-\frac{3}{2}\ \text{or}\ x>4\right\}$

Interval: $\left(-\infty,-\frac{3}{2}\right)\cup\left(4,\infty\right)$

13.
$$7x+4y=3$$
$$7x+4y-7x=3-7x$$
$$4y=-7x+3$$
$$\frac{4y}{4}=\frac{-7x+3}{4}$$
$$y=-\frac{7}{4}x+\frac{3}{4}$$

14. a. $A\cup B=\{1,3,5,6,7,9,12\}$

b. $A\cap B=\{3,9\}$

15. Let $x=$ Glen's weekly sales.
$$400+0.08x\ge 750$$
$$400+0.08x-400\ge 750-400$$
$$0.08x\ge 350$$
$$\frac{0.08x}{0.08}\ge\frac{350}{0.08}$$
$$x\ge 4375$$

Glen's weekly sales must be at least $4375 for him to earn at least $750.

16. Let $x=$ width in inches.
$$|x-60|\le 1$$
$$-1\le x-60\le 1$$
$$-1+60\le x-60+60\le 1+60$$
$$59\le x\le 61$$

The Crescent Rod can fit openings with widths between 59 inches and 61 inches.

17. Let x = number of children at the party.

$$75 + 5x = 145$$
$$75 + 5x - 75 = 145 - 75$$
$$5x = 70$$
$$\frac{5x}{5} = \frac{70}{5}$$
$$x = 14$$

There were 14 children at Payton's party.

18. Let x = the width of the sandbox.

length: $x + 2$

$$P = 2L + 2W$$
$$20 = 2(x + 2) + 2(x)$$
$$20 = 2x + 4 + 2x$$
$$20 = 4x + 4$$
$$20 - 4 = 4x + 4 - 4$$
$$16 = 4x$$
$$\frac{16}{4} = \frac{4x}{4}$$
$$4 = x$$

The sandbox has a width of 4 feet and a length of 6 feet.

19. Let x = liters of 10% solution.

Amount of 40% solution: $12 - x$ liters

tot. acid = acid from 10% + acid from 40%

$$(\%)(\text{liters}) = (\%)(\text{liters}) + (\%)(\text{liters})$$
$$0.2(12) = 0.1(x) + 0.4(12 - x)$$
$$2.4 = 0.1x + 4.8 - 0.4x$$
$$2.4 = 4.8 - 0.3x$$
$$2.4 - 4.8 = 4.8 - 0.3x - 4.8$$
$$-2.4 = -0.3x$$
$$\frac{-2.4}{-0.3} = \frac{-0.3x}{-0.3}$$
$$8 = x$$

The chemist needs to mix 8 liters of the 10% solution with 4 liters of the 40% solution.

20. Let t = time to catch up in hours.

Running time for A: $t + 0.5$

Running time for B: t

The total distance traveled by both runners will be the same when they meet. Therefore, we have

distance A = distance B

$$(\text{rate})(\text{time}) = (\text{rate})(\text{time})$$
$$8(t + 0.5) = 10(t)$$
$$8t + 4 = 10t$$
$$8t + 4 - 8t = 10t - 8t$$
$$4 = 2t$$
$$\frac{4}{2} = \frac{2t}{2}$$
$$2 = t$$

It will take contestant B two hours to catch up to contestant A.

Cumulative Review Chapters R-1

1. a. (i) 27.235
(ii) 27.236

b. (i) 1.0
(ii) 1.1

2.

3. $-|-14| = -(14) = -14$

4. $(-3) + 4 - 7 = 1 - 7 = -6$

5. $\dfrac{-3(12)}{-6} = \dfrac{-36}{-6} = 6$

6. $(-3)^4 = (-3) \cdot (-3) \cdot (-3) \cdot (-3) = 81$

7. $5 - 2(1 - 4)^3 + 5 \cdot 3 = 5 - 2(-3)^3 + 5 \cdot 3$
$$= 5 + 54 + 15 = 74$$

8. $\dfrac{2}{3} + \dfrac{1}{2} - \dfrac{1}{4} = \dfrac{8}{12} + \dfrac{6}{12} - \dfrac{3}{12} = \dfrac{8 + 6 - 3}{12} = \dfrac{11}{12}$

9. $3(2)^2 + 2(2) - 7 = 3(4) + 4 - 7 = 12 - 3 = 9$

10. $4a^2 - 6a + a^2 - 12 + 2a - 1$

$= 4a^2 + a^2 - 6a + 2a - 12 - 1$

$= 5a^2 - 4a - 13$

11. a. Evaluate the denominator when $x = -2$.

$(-2)^2 + (-2) - 2 = 4 - 2 - 2 = 0$

Since $x = -2$ makes the denominator 0, it is not in the domain.

b. Evaluate the denominator when $x = 0$.

$(0)^2 + (0) - 2 = -2$

Since $x = 0$ does not make the denominator equal 0, it is in the domain.

12. $3(x + 2) - 4(2x - 1) + 8 = 3x + 6 - 8x + 4 + 8$

$= 3x - 8x + 6 + 4 + 8$

$= -5x + 18$

13. Let $x = 3$ in the equation.

$3 - (2(3) + 3) \overset{?}{=} 5(3) - 1$

$3 - (6 + 3) \overset{?}{=} 15 - 1$

$3 - 9 \overset{?}{=} 14$

$-6 \neq 14$

$x = 3$ is **not** a solution to the equation.

14. $4x - 3 = 2(3x - 2) - 7$

$4x - 3 = 6x - 4 - 7$

$4x - 3 = 6x - 11$

$4x - 3 - 6x = 6x - 11 - 6x$

$-2x - 3 = -11$

$-2x - 3 + 3 = -11 + 3$

$-2x = -8$

$\dfrac{-2x}{-2} = \dfrac{-8}{-2}$

$x = 4$

Solution set: $\{4\}$

15. $\dfrac{x + 1}{3} = x - 4$

$3\left(\dfrac{x + 1}{3}\right) = 3(x - 4)$

$x + 1 = 3x - 12$

$x + 1 - 3x = 3x - 12 - 3x$

$-2x + 1 = -12$

$-2x + 1 - 1 = -12 - 1$

$-2x = -13$

$\dfrac{-2x}{-2} = \dfrac{-13}{-2}$

$x = \dfrac{13}{2}$

Solution set: $\left\{\dfrac{13}{2}\right\}$

16. $2|x - 1| + 2 = 9$

$2|x - 1| = 7$

$|x - 1| = \dfrac{7}{2}$

$x - 1 = -\dfrac{7}{2}$ or $x - 1 = \dfrac{7}{2}$

$x = -\dfrac{5}{2}$ $\qquad$ $x = \dfrac{9}{2}$

Solution set: $\left\{-\dfrac{5}{2}, \dfrac{9}{2}\right\}$

17. $2x - 5y = 6$

$2x - 5y - 2x = 6 - 2x$

$-5y = -2x + 6$

$\dfrac{-5y}{-5} = \dfrac{-2x + 6}{-5}$

$y = \dfrac{2}{5}x - \dfrac{6}{5}$

18. $\dfrac{x + 3}{2} \leq \dfrac{3x - 1}{4}$

$4\left(\dfrac{x + 3}{2}\right) \leq 4\left(\dfrac{3x - 1}{4}\right)$

$2x + 6 \leq 3x - 1$

$2x + 6 - 3x \leq 3x - 1 - 3x$

$-x + 6 \leq -1$

$-x + 6 - 6 \leq -1 - 6$

$-x \leq -7$

$x \geq 7$

Solution set: $\{x \mid x \geq 7\}$

Interval: $[7, \infty)$

SSM – 62

19. $|x-4| \le 3$

$$-3 \le x-4 \le 3$$
$$-3+4 \le x-4+4 \le 3+4$$
$$1 \le x \le 7$$

Solution set: $\{x \mid 1 \le x \le 7\}$

Interval: $[1,7]$

20. $|x+7| > 2$

$$x+7 < -2 \quad \text{or} \quad x+7 > 2$$
$$x < -9 \qquad\qquad x > -5$$

Solution set: $\{x \mid x < -9 \ \text{or} \ x > -5\}$

Interval: $(-\infty, -9) \cup (-5, \infty)$

21. Let x = score on final exam.

$$93 \le \frac{94+95+90+97+2x}{6} \le 100$$
$$93 \le \frac{376+2x}{6} \le 100$$
$$6(93) \le 6\left(\frac{376+2x}{6}\right) \le 6(100)$$
$$558 \le 376+2x \le 600$$
$$558-376 \le 376+2x-376 \le 600-376$$
$$182 \le 2x \le 224$$
$$\frac{182}{2} \le \frac{2x}{2} \le \frac{224}{2}$$
$$91 \le x \le 112$$

Shawn needs to score at least 91 on the final exam to earn an A (assuming the maximum score on the exam is 100).

22. Let x = weight in pounds.

$$0.2x - 2 \ge 30$$
$$0.2x-2+2 \ge 30+2$$
$$0.2x \ge 32$$
$$\frac{0.2x}{0.2} \ge \frac{32}{0.2}$$
$$x \ge 160$$

A person 62 inches tall would be considered obese if they weighed 160 pounds or more.

23. Let x = measure of the smaller angle.

Larger angle: $15+2x$

$$x+(15+2x) = 180$$
$$3x+15 = 180$$
$$3x+15-15 = 180-15$$
$$3x = 165$$
$$\frac{3x}{3} = \frac{165}{3}$$
$$x = 55$$

The angles measure $55°$ and $125°$.

24. Let h = height of cylinder in inches.

$$S = 2\pi r^2 + 2\pi rh$$
$$100 = 2\pi(2)^2 + 2\pi(2)h$$
$$100 = 8\pi + 4\pi h$$
$$100 - 8\pi = 4\pi h$$
$$h = \frac{100-8\pi}{4\pi} \approx 5.96$$

The cylinder should be about 5.96 inches tall.

25. Let x = first even integer.

Second even integer: $x+2$

Third even integer: $x+4$

$$x+(x+2) = 22+(x+4)$$
$$2x+2 = x+26$$
$$2x+2-x = x+26-x$$
$$x+2 = 26$$
$$x+2-2 = 26-2$$
$$x = 24$$

The three consecutive even integers are 24, 26, and 28.

Chapter 2

2.1 Preparing for Rectangular Coordinates and Graphs of Equations

1.

2. $3x - 5(x+2) = 4$

a. Let $x = 0$ in the equation.

$$3(0) - 5(0+2) \overset{?}{=} 4$$

$$0 - 5(2) \overset{?}{=} 4$$

$$-10 = 4 \text{ False}$$

$x = 0$ is not a solution to the equation.

b. Let $x = -3$ in the equation.

$$3(-3) - 5(-3+2) \overset{?}{=} 4$$

$$-9 - 5(-1) \overset{?}{=} 4$$

$$-9 + 5 \overset{?}{=} 4$$

$$-4 = 4 \text{ False}$$

$x = -3$ is not a solution to the equation.

c. Let $x = -7$ in the equation.

$$3(-7) - 5(-7+2) \overset{?}{=} 4$$

$$-21 - 5(-5) \overset{?}{=} 4$$

$$-21 + 25 \overset{?}{=} 4$$

$$4 = 4 \text{ True}$$

$x = -7$ is a solution to the equation.

3. a. Let $x = 0$:

$$2x^2 - 3x + 1 = 2(0)^2 - 3(0) + 1$$

$$= 0 - 0 + 1$$

$$= 1$$

b. Let $x = 2$:

$$2x^2 - 3x + 1 = 2(2)^2 - 3(2) + 1$$

$$= 2(4) - 6 + 1$$

$$= 8 - 6 + 1$$

$$= 3$$

c. Let $x = -3$:

$$2x^2 - 3x + 1 = 2(-3)^2 - 3(-3) + 1$$

$$= 2(9) + 9 + 1$$

$$= 18 + 9 + 1$$

$$= 28$$

4.

$$3x + 2y = 8$$

$$3x + 2y - 3x = 8 - 3x$$

$$2y = 8 - 3x$$

$$\frac{2y}{2} = \frac{8 - 3x}{2}$$

$$y = \frac{8}{2} - \frac{3x}{2}$$

$$y = 4 - \frac{3}{2}x \quad \text{or} \quad y = -\frac{3}{2}x + 4$$

5. $|-4| = 4$ because -4 is 4 units away from 0 on a real number line.

2.1 Exercises

1. origin

3. intercepts

5. False. The graph of an equation does not necessarily touch or cross the x-axis.

7. A graph is considered to be complete when enough is shown to indicate main features and allow the viewer to 'see' the rest of the graph as an obvious continuation of what is shown.

9. The point-plotting method is when we choose values for one variable and find the corresponding value of the other variable. The resulting ordered pairs form points that lie on the graph of the equation.

11. $A : (2,3)$; in quadrant I

$B : (-5,2)$; in quadrant II

$C : (0,-2)$; on the y-axis

$D : (-4,-3)$; in quadrant III

$E : (3,-4)$; in quadrant IV

$F : (4,0)$; on the x-axis

13. A: quadrant I; B: quadrant III; C: x-axis; D: quadrant IV; E: y-axis; F: quadrant II

15. a. Let $x = 1$ and $y = 2$.

$$2(1) + 5(2) \overset{?}{=} 12$$
$$2 + 10 \overset{?}{=} 12$$
$$12 = 12 \text{ True}$$

The point $(1, 2)$ is on the graph.

b. Let $x = -2$ and $y = 3$.

$$2(-2) + 5(3) \overset{?}{=} 12$$
$$-4 + 15 \overset{?}{=} 12$$
$$11 = 12 \text{ False}$$

The point $(-2, 3)$ is not on the graph.

c. Let $x = -4$ and $y = 4$.

$$2(-4) + 5(4) \overset{?}{=} 12$$
$$-8 + 20 \overset{?}{=} 12$$
$$12 = 12 \text{ True}$$

The point $(-4, 4)$ is on the graph.

d. Let $x = -\dfrac{3}{2}$ and $y = 3$.

$$2\left(-\dfrac{3}{2}\right) + 5(3) \overset{?}{=} 12$$
$$-3 + 15 \overset{?}{=} 12$$
$$12 = 12 \text{ True}$$

The point $\left(-\dfrac{3}{2}, 3\right)$ is on the graph.

17. a. Let $x = -2$ and $y = -15$.

$$(-15) \overset{?}{=} -2(-2)^2 + 3(-2) - 1$$
$$-15 \overset{?}{=} -2(4) - 6 - 1$$
$$-15 \overset{?}{=} -8 - 6 - 1$$
$$-15 = -15 \text{ True}$$

The point $(-2, -15)$ is on the graph.

b. Let $x = 3$ and $y = 10$.

$$(10) \overset{?}{=} -2(3)^2 + 3(3) - 1$$
$$10 \overset{?}{=} -2(9) + 9 - 1$$
$$10 \overset{?}{=} -18 + 9 - 1$$
$$10 = -10 \text{ False}$$

The point $(3, 10)$ is not on the graph.

c. Let $x = 0$ and $y = 1$.

$$(1) \overset{?}{=} -2(0)^2 + 3(0) - 1$$
$$1 \overset{?}{=} 0 + 0 - 1$$
$$1 = -1 \text{ False}$$

The point $(0, 1)$ is not on the graph.

d. Let $x = 2$ and $y = -3$.

$$(-3) \overset{?}{=} -2(2)^2 + 3(2) - 1$$
$$-3 \overset{?}{=} -2(4) + 6 - 1$$
$$-3 \overset{?}{=} -8 + 6 - 1$$
$$-3 = -3 \text{ True}$$

The point $(2, -3)$ is on the graph.

19. a. Let $x = 1$ and $y = 4$.

$$(4) \overset{?}{=} |1 - 3|$$
$$4 \overset{?}{=} |-2|$$
$$4 = 2 \text{ False}$$

The point $(1, 4)$ is not on the graph.

b. Let $x = 4$ and $y = 1$.

$$(1) \overset{?}{=} |4 - 3|$$

$$1 \overset{?}{=} |1|$$

$$1 = 1 \text{ True}$$

The point $(4,1)$ is on the graph.

c. Let $x = -6$ and $y = 9$.

$$(9) \overset{?}{=} |-6 - 3|$$

$$9 \overset{?}{=} |-9|$$

$$9 = 9 \text{ True}$$

The point $(-6,9)$ is on the graph.

d. Let $x = 0$ and $y = 3$.

$$(3) \overset{?}{=} |0 - 3|$$

$$3 \overset{?}{=} |-3|$$

$$3 = 3 \text{ True}$$

The point $(0,3)$ is on the graph.

21. The intercepts are $(-2,0)$ and $(0,3)$.

23. The intercepts are $(-2,0)$, $(1,0)$, and $(0,-4)$.

25. $y = 4x$

x	$y = 4x$	(x,y)
-2	$y = 4(-2) = -8$	$(-2,-8)$
-1	$y = 4(-1) = -4$	$(-1,-4)$
0	$y = 4(0) = 0$	$(0,0)$
1	$y = 4(1) = 4$	$(1,4)$
2	$y = 4(2) = 8$	$(2,8)$

27. $y = -\dfrac{1}{2}x$

x	$y = -\dfrac{1}{2}x$	(x,y)
-4	$y = -\dfrac{1}{2}(-4) = 2$	$(-4,2)$
-2	$y = -\dfrac{1}{2}(-2) = 1$	$(-2,1)$
0	$y = -\dfrac{1}{2}(0) = 0$	$(0,0)$
2	$y = -\dfrac{1}{2}(2) = -1$	$(2,-1)$
4	$y = -\dfrac{1}{2}(4) = -2$	$(4,-2)$

29. $y = x + 3$

x	$y = x + 3$	(x,y)
-4	$y = (-4) + 3 = -1$	$(-4,-1)$
-2	$y = (-2) + 3 = 1$	$(-2,1)$
0	$y = (0) + 3 = 3$	$(0,3)$
2	$y = (2) + 3 = 5$	$(2,5)$
4	$y = (4) + 3 = 7$	$(4,7)$

31. $y = -3x + 1$

x	$y = -3x + 1$	(x, y)
-2	$y = -3(-2) + 1 = 7$	$(-2, 7)$
-1	$y = -3(-1) + 1 = 4$	$(-1, 4)$
0	$y = -3(0) + 1 = 1$	$(0, 1)$
1	$y = -3(1) + 1 = -2$	$(1, -2)$
2	$y = -3(2) + 1 = -5$	$(2, -5)$

33. $y = \dfrac{1}{2}x - 4$

x	$y = \dfrac{1}{2}x - 4$	(x, y)
-4	$y = \dfrac{1}{2}(-4) - 4 = -6$	$(-4, -6)$
-2	$y = \dfrac{1}{2}(-2) - 4 = -5$	$(-2, -5)$
0	$y = \dfrac{1}{2}(0) - 4 = -4$	$(0, -4)$
2	$y = \dfrac{1}{2}(2) - 4 = -3$	$(2, -3)$
4	$y = \dfrac{1}{2}(4) - 4 = -2$	$(4, -2)$

35. $2x + y = 7$

$y = -2x + 7$

x	$y = -2x + 7$	(x, y)
-5	$y = -2(-5) + 7 = 17$	$(-5, 17)$
-3	$y = -2(-3) + 7 = 13$	$(-3, 13)$
0	$y = -2(0) + 7 = 7$	$(0, 7)$
3	$y = -2(3) + 7 = 1$	$(3, 1)$
5	$y = -2(5) + 7 = -3$	$(5, -3)$

37. $y = -x^2$

x	$y = -x^2$	(x, y)
-3	$y = -(-3)^2 = -9$	$(-3, -9)$
-2	$y = -(-2)^2 = -4$	$(-2, -4)$
0	$y = -(0)^2 = 0$	$(0, 0)$
2	$y = -(2)^2 = -4$	$(2, -4)$
3	$y = -(3)^2 = -9$	$(3, -9)$

39. $y = 2x^2 - 8$

x	$y = 2x^2 - 8$	(x, y)
-3	$y = 2(-3)^2 - 8 = 10$	$(-3, 10)$
-2	$y = 2(-2)^2 - 8 = 0$	$(-2, 0)$
-1	$y = 2(-1)^2 - 8 = -6$	$(-1, -6)$
0	$y = 2(0)^2 - 8 = -8$	$(0, -8)$
1	$y = 2(1)^2 - 8 = -6$	$(1, -6)$
2	$y = 2(2)^2 - 8 = 0$	$(2, 0)$
3	$y = 2(3)^2 - 8 = 10$	$(3, 10)$

41. $y = |x|$

x	$y = |x|$	(x, y)
-4	$y = |-4| = 4$	$(-4, 4)$
-2	$y = |-2| = 2$	$(-2, 2)$
0	$y = |0| = 0$	$(0, 0)$
2	$y = |2| = 2$	$(2, 2)$
4	$y = |4| = 4$	$(4, 4)$

43. $y = |x - 1|$

x	$y = |x - 1|$	(x, y)
-4	$y = |-4 - 1| = 5$	$(-4, 5)$
-1	$y = |-1 - 1| = 2$	$(-1, 2)$
0	$y = |0 - 1| = 1$	$(0, 1)$
1	$y = |1 - 1| = 0$	$(1, 0)$
3	$y = |3 - 1| = 2$	$(3, 2)$
5	$y = |5 - 1| = 4$	$(5, 4)$

45. $y = x^3$

x	$y = x^3$	(x, y)
-3	$y = (-3)^3 = -27$	$(-3, -27)$
-2	$y = (-2)^3 = -8$	$(-2, -8)$
-1	$y = (-1)^3 = -1$	$(-1, -1)$
0	$y = (0)^3 = 0$	$(0, 0)$
1	$y = (1)^3 = 1$	$(1, 1)$
2	$y = (2)^3 = 8$	$(2, 8)$
3	$y = (3)^3 = 27$	$(3, 27)$

47. $y = x^3 + 1$

x	$y = x^3 + 1$	(x, y)
-2	$y = (-2)^3 + 1 = -7$	$(-2, -7)$
-1	$y = (-1)^3 + 1 = 0$	$(-1, 0)$
0	$y = (0)^3 + 1 = 1$	$(0, 1)$
1	$y = (1)^3 + 1 = 2$	$(1, 2)$
2	$y = (2)^3 + 1 = 9$	$(2, 9)$

49. $x^2 - y = 4$

$x^2 = y + 4$

$x^2 - 4 = y$

$y = x^2 - 4$

x	$y = x^2 - 4$	(x, y)
-3	$y = (-3)^2 - 4 = 5$	$(-3, 5)$
-2	$y = (-2)^2 - 4 = 0$	$(-2, 0)$
0	$y = (0)^2 - 4 = -4$	$(0, -4)$
2	$y = (2)^2 - 4 = 0$	$(2, 0)$
3	$y = (3)^2 - 4 = 5$	$(3, 5)$

51. $x = y^2 - 1$

y	$x = y^2 - 1$	(x, y)
-2	$x = (-2)^2 - 1 = 3$	$(3, -2)$
-1	$x = (-1)^2 - 1 = 0$	$(0, -1)$
0	$x = (0)^2 - 1 = -1$	$(-1, 0)$
1	$x = (1)^2 - 1 = 0$	$(0, 1)$
2	$x = (2)^2 - 1 = 3$	$(3, 2)$

53. If $(a, 4)$ is a point on the graph, then we have

$$4 = 4(a) - 3$$
$$4 = 4a - 3$$
$$7 = 4a$$
$$\frac{7}{4} = a$$

We need $a = \frac{7}{4}$.

55. If $(3, b)$ is a point on the graph, then we have

$$b = (3)^2 - 2(3) + 1 = 9 - 6 + 1 = 4$$

We need $b = 4$.

57. **a.** According to the graph, the area of the opening will be 400 ft^2 when the width is 10 feet.

b. According to the graph, the area of the opening will have a maximum value of 625 ft^2 when the width is 25 feet.

c. The x-intercepts are $x = 0$ and $x = 50$. These values indicate that the window opening will have 0 area when the width is 0 feet or 50 feet. These values form the bounds for the width of the opening.

The y-intercept is $y = 0$. This indicates that the area of the opening will be 0 ft^2 when the width is 0 feet.

59. a. According to the graph, the Sprint PCS 500-minute plan would cost $40 for 200 minutes of talking in a month and $40 for 500 minutes of talking in a month.

   b. According to the graph, the plan would cost $800 for 2400 minutes of talking in a month.

   c. The only intercept for the graph is the y-intercept, $y = 40$. This indicates that the monthly cost will be $40 if no minutes are used. In other words, the base charge for the plan is $40 per month.

61. The set of all points of the form $(4, y)$ form a vertical line with an x-intercept of 4.

63. Answers will vary. One possible graph is below.

65. Answers will vary. One possibility:
All three points have a y-coordinate of 0. Therefore, they all lie on the horizontal line with equation $y = 0$.

67. $y = 3x - 9$

69. $y = -x^2 + 8$

71. $y + 2x^2 = 13$
$y = -2x^2 + 13$

73. $y = x^3 - 6x + 1$

2.2 Preparing for Relations

1. Inequality: $-4 \le x \le 4$
   Interval: $[-4, 4]$
   We use square brackets in interval notation because the inequalities are not strict.

2. Interval: $[2, \infty)$
   Inequality: $2 \le x < \infty$ or $x \ge 2$
   The square bracket indicates a non-strict inequality while the parenthesis indicates a strict inequality.

2.2 Exercises

1. corresponds; depends on

3. True

5. Answers will vary. A relation could be thought of as a rule that tells us what to do to a value in the domain (input value) to obtain its corresponding value in the range (output value).

7. {(USA Today, 2.1), (Wall Street Journal, 1.8), (New York Times, 1.1), (Los Angeles Times, 0.9), (Washington Post, 0.8)}

   Domain: {USA Today, Wall Street Journal, New York Times, Los Angeles Times, Washington Post}

   Range: {0.8, 0.9, 1.1, 1.8, 2.1}

9. {(Less than 9th Grade, $17261), (9th-12th Grade – No Diploma, $21737), (High School Graduate, $35744), (Associate's Degree, $49279), (Bachelor's Degree or Higher, $69804)}

   Domain: {Less than 9th Grade, 9th-12th Grade – No Diploma, High School Graduate, Associate's Degree, Bachelor's Degree or Higher}

   Range: {$17261, $21737, $35744, $49279, $69804}

11.

    Domain: $\{-3, -2, -1, 0, 1\}$

    Range: $\{4, 6, 8, 10, 12\}$

13.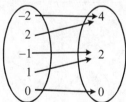

    Domain: $\{-2, -1, 0, 1, 2\}$

    Range: $\{0, 2, 4\}$

15.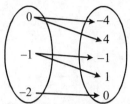

    Domain: $\{-2, -1, 0\}$

    Range: $\{-4, -1, 0, 1, 4\}$

17. Domain: $\{-3, -2, 0, 2, 3\}$

    Range: $\{-3, -1, 2, 3\}$

19. Domain: $\{x \mid -4 \le x \le 4\}$ or $[-4, 4]$

    Range: $\{y \mid -2 \le y \le 2\}$ or $[-2, 2]$

21. Domain: $\{x \mid -1 \le x \le 3\}$ or $[-1, 3]$

    Range: $\{y \mid 0 \le y \le 4\}$ or $[0, 4]$

23. Domain: $\{x \mid x \text{ is a real number}\}$ or $(-\infty, \infty)$

    Range: $\{y \mid y \ge -3\}$ or $[-3, \infty)$

25. $y = 4x$

x	$y = 4x$	(x, y)
-2	$y = 4(-2) = -8$	$(-2, -8)$
-1	$y = 4(-1) = -4$	$(-1, -4)$
0	$y = 4(0) = 0$	$(0, 0)$
1	$y = 4(1) = 4$	$(1, 4)$
2	$y = 4(2) = 8$	$(2, 8)$

Domain: $\{x \mid x \text{ is a real number}\}$ or $(-\infty, \infty)$

Range: $\{y \mid y \text{ is a real number}\}$ or $(-\infty, \infty)$

27. $y = -\dfrac{1}{2}x$

x	$y = -\dfrac{1}{2}x$	(x,y)
-4	$y = -\dfrac{1}{2}(-4) = 2$	$(-4,2)$
-2	$y = -\dfrac{1}{2}(-2) = 1$	$(-2,1)$
0	$y = -\dfrac{1}{2}(0) = 0$	$(0,0)$
2	$y = -\dfrac{1}{2}(2) = -1$	$(2,-1)$
4	$y = -\dfrac{1}{2}(4) = -2$	$(4,-2)$

Domain: $\{x \mid x \text{ is a real number}\}$ or $(-\infty,\infty)$

Range: $\{y \mid y \text{ is a real number}\}$ or $(-\infty,\infty)$

29. $y = x + 3$

x	$y = x + 3$	(x,y)
-4	$y = (-4) + 3 = -1$	$(-4,-1)$
-2	$y = (-2) + 3 = 1$	$(-2,1)$
0	$y = (0) + 3 = 3$	$(0,3)$
2	$y = (2) + 3 = 5$	$(2,5)$
4	$y = (4) + 3 = 7$	$(4,7)$

Domain: $\{x \mid x \text{ is a real number}\}$ or $(-\infty,\infty)$

Range: $\{y \mid y \text{ is a real number}\}$ or $(-\infty,\infty)$

31. $y = -3x + 1$

x	$y = -3x + 1$	(x,y)
-2	$y = -3(-2) + 1 = 7$	$(-2,7)$
-1	$y = -3(-1) + 1 = 4$	$(-1,4)$
0	$y = -3(0) + 1 = 1$	$(0,1)$
1	$y = -3(1) + 1 = -2$	$(1,-2)$
2	$y = -3(2) + 1 = -5$	$(2,-5)$

Domain: $\{x \mid x \text{ is a real number}\}$ or $(-\infty,\infty)$

Range: $\{y \mid y \text{ is a real number}\}$ or $(-\infty,\infty)$

33. $y = \dfrac{1}{2}x - 4$

x	$y = \dfrac{1}{2}x - 4$	(x,y)
-4	$y = \dfrac{1}{2}(-4) - 4 = -6$	$(-4,-6)$
-2	$y = \dfrac{1}{2}(-2) - 4 = -5$	$(-2,-5)$
0	$y = \dfrac{1}{2}(0) - 4 = -4$	$(0,-4)$
2	$y = \dfrac{1}{2}(2) - 4 = -3$	$(2,-3)$
4	$y = \dfrac{1}{2}(4) - 4 = -2$	$(4,-2)$

Domain: $\{x \mid x \text{ is a real number}\}$ or $(-\infty,\infty)$

Range: $\{y \mid y \text{ is a real number}\}$ or $(-\infty,\infty)$

35. $2x + y = 7$

$y = -2x + 7$

x	$y = -2x + 7$	(x, y)
-5	$y = -2(-5) + 7 = 17$	$(-5, 17)$
-3	$y = -2(-3) + 7 = 13$	$(-3, 13)$
0	$y = -2(0) + 7 = 7$	$(0, 7)$
3	$y = -2(3) + 7 = 1$	$(3, 1)$
5	$y = -2(5) + 7 = -3$	$(5, -3)$

Domain: $\{x \mid x \text{ is a real number}\}$ or $(-\infty, \infty)$

Range: $\{y \mid y \text{ is a real number}\}$ or $(-\infty, \infty)$

37. $y = -x^2$

x	$y = -x^2$	(x, y)
-3	$y = -(-3)^2 = -9$	$(-3, -9)$
-2	$y = -(-2)^2 = -4$	$(-2, -4)$
0	$y = -(0)^2 = 0$	$(0, 0)$
2	$y = -(2)^2 = -4$	$(2, -4)$
3	$y = -(3)^2 = -9$	$(3, -9)$

Domain: $\{x \mid x \text{ is a real number}\}$ or $(-\infty, \infty)$

Range: $\{y \mid y \leq 0\}$ or $(-\infty, 0]$

39. $y = 2x^2 - 8$

x	$y = 2x^2 - 8$	(x, y)
-3	$y = 2(-3)^2 - 8 = 10$	$(-3, 10)$
-2	$y = 2(-2)^2 - 8 = 0$	$(-2, 0)$
-1	$y = 2(-1)^2 - 8 = -6$	$(-1, -6)$
0	$y = 2(0)^2 - 8 = -8$	$(0, -8)$
1	$y = 2(1)^2 - 8 = -6$	$(1, -6)$
2	$y = 2(2)^2 - 8 = 0$	$(2, 0)$
3	$y = 2(3)^2 - 8 = 10$	$(3, 10)$

Domain: $\{x \mid x \text{ is a real number}\}$ or $(-\infty, \infty)$

Range: $\{y \mid y \geq -8\}$ or $[-8, \infty)$

41. $y = |x|$

x	$y = |x|$	(x, y)
-4	$y = |-4| = 4$	$(-4, 4)$
-2	$y = |-2| = 2$	$(-2, 2)$
0	$y = |0| = 0$	$(0, 0)$
2	$y = |2| = 2$	$(2, 2)$
4	$y = |4| = 4$	$(4, 4)$

Domain: $\{x \mid x \text{ is a real number}\}$ or $(-\infty, \infty)$

Range: $\{y \mid y \geq 0\}$ or $[0, \infty)$

43. $y = |x - 1|$

x	$y = |x-1|$	(x, y)
-4	$y = |-4-1| = 5$	$(-4, 5)$
-1	$y = |-1-1| = 2$	$(-1, 2)$
0	$y = |0-1| = 1$	$(0, 1)$
1	$y = |1-1| = 0$	$(1, 0)$
3	$y = |3-1| = 2$	$(3, 2)$
5	$y = |5-1| = 4$	$(5, 4)$

Domain: $\{x \mid x \text{ is a real number}\}$ or $(-\infty, \infty)$

Range: $\{y \mid y \geq 0\}$ or $[0, \infty)$

47. $y = x^3 + 1$

x	$y = x^3 + 1$	(x, y)
-2	$y = (-2)^3 + 1 = -7$	$(-2, -7)$
-1	$y = (-1)^3 + 1 = 0$	$(-1, 0)$
0	$y = (0)^3 + 1 = 1$	$(0, 1)$
1	$y = (1)^3 + 1 = 2$	$(1, 2)$
2	$y = (2)^3 + 1 = 9$	$(2, 9)$

Domain: $\{x \mid x \text{ is a real number}\}$ or $(-\infty, \infty)$

Range: $\{y \mid y \text{ is a real number}\}$ or $(-\infty, \infty)$

45. $y = x^3$

x	$y = x^3$	(x, y)
-3	$y = (-3)^3 = -27$	$(-3, -27)$
-2	$y = (-2)^3 = -8$	$(-2, -8)$
-1	$y = (-1)^3 = -1$	$(-1, -1)$
0	$y = (0)^3 = 0$	$(0, 0)$
1	$y = (1)^3 = 1$	$(1, 1)$
2	$y = (2)^3 = 8$	$(2, 8)$
3	$y = (3)^3 = 27$	$(3, 27)$

Domain: $\{x \mid x \text{ is a real number}\}$ or $(-\infty, \infty)$

Range: $\{y \mid y \text{ is a real number}\}$ or $(-\infty, \infty)$

49. $x^2 - y = 4$

$x^2 = y + 4$

$x^2 - 4 = y$

$y = x^2 - 4$

x	$y = x^2 - 4$	(x, y)
-3	$y = (-3)^2 - 4 = 5$	$(-3, 5)$
-2	$y = (-2)^2 - 4 = 0$	$(-2, 0)$
0	$y = (0)^2 - 4 = -4$	$(0, -4)$
2	$y = (2)^2 - 4 = 0$	$(2, 0)$
3	$y = (3)^2 - 4 = 5$	$(3, 5)$

Domain: $\{x \mid x \text{ is a real number}\}$ or $(-\infty, \infty)$

Range: $\{y \mid y \geq -4\}$ or $[-4, \infty)$

51. $x = y^2 - 1$

y	$x = y^2 - 1$	(x, y)
-2	$x = (-2)^2 - 1 = 3$	$(3, -2)$
-1	$x = (-1)^2 - 1 = 0$	$(0, -1)$
0	$x = (0)^2 - 1 = -1$	$(-1, 0)$
1	$x = (1)^2 - 1 = 0$	$(0, 1)$
2	$x = (2)^2 - 1 = 3$	$(3, 2)$

Domain: $\{x \mid x \geq -1\}$ or $[-1, \infty)$

Range: $\{y \mid y$ is a real number$\}$ or $(-\infty, \infty)$

53. a. Domain: $\{x \mid 0 \leq x \leq 50\}$ or $[0, 50]$

Range: $\{y \mid 0 \leq y \leq 625\}$ or $[0, 625]$

The window can be between 0 and 50 feet wide (inclusive) and will have an area of between 0 and 625 square feet (inclusive).

b. Answers may vary;
Assuming the window is rectangular, the perimeter is given by the equation
$P = 2l + 2w$
where l is the length and w is the width. Since the window cannot have a negative width, it is reasonable for the domain to begin with 0. If the width were greater than 50, this would require a negative value for the length in order to have a perimeter of 100 in the above equation. Since length cannot be negative, it is reasonable for the domain to stop at 50.

55. a. Domain: $\{m \mid 0 \leq m \leq 15,120\}$ or $[0, 15120]$

Range: $\{c \mid 40 \leq c \leq 5888\}$ or $[40, 5888]$

The monthly cost will be at least \$40, but no more than \$5888.

b. Answers may vary. It is not possible to talk a negative number of minutes so the lower bound of 0 makes sense. Assuming there are 21 non-weekend days in a month, we get:

$$\frac{21 \text{ days}}{1} \cdot \frac{12 \text{ hrs}}{1 \text{ day}} \cdot \frac{60 \text{ min}}{1 \text{ hr}} = 15,120$$

That is, in 21 non-weekend days there are 15,120 'anytime' minutes so this is the most someone could use in a month.

57. Actual graphs will vary but all should be horizontal lines.

Chapter 2 Putting the Concepts Together (Sections 2.1-2.2)

1. A: x-axis; B: quadrant II; C: quadrant I; D: y-axis; E: quadrant III; F: quadrant IV.

2. a. Let $x = 1$ and $y = \frac{5}{2}$.

$$\frac{5}{2} \overset{?}{=} 4(1) - \frac{3}{2}$$

$$\frac{5}{2} \overset{?}{=} 4 - \frac{3}{2}$$

$$\frac{5}{2} = \frac{5}{2} \text{ True}$$

The point $\left(1, \frac{5}{2}\right)$ is on the graph.

b. Let $x = \frac{1}{2}$ and $y = \frac{1}{2}$.

$$\frac{1}{2} \overset{?}{=} 4\left(\frac{1}{2}\right) - \frac{3}{2}$$

$$\frac{1}{2} \overset{?}{=} 2 - \frac{3}{2}$$

$$\frac{1}{2} = \frac{1}{2} \text{ True}$$

The point $\left(\frac{1}{2}, \frac{1}{2}\right)$ is on the graph.

c. Let $x = \dfrac{1}{4}$ and $y = \dfrac{1}{4}$.

$$\dfrac{1}{4} \overset{?}{=} 4\left(\dfrac{1}{4}\right) - \dfrac{3}{2}$$

$$\dfrac{1}{4} \overset{?}{=} 1 - \dfrac{3}{2}$$

$$\dfrac{1}{4} \neq -\dfrac{1}{2}$$

The point $\left(\dfrac{1}{4}, \dfrac{1}{4}\right)$ is not on the graph.

3. $y = |x| + 3$

x	$y = |x| + 3$	(x, y)
-3	$y = |-3| + 3 = 6$	$(-3, 6)$
-1	$y = |-1| + 3 = 4$	$(-1, 4)$
0	$y = |0| + 3 = 3$	$(0, 3)$
1	$y = |1| + 3 = 4$	$(1, 4)$
3	$y = |3| + 3 = 6$	$(3, 6)$

4. $y = \dfrac{1}{2}x^2 - 1$

x	$y = \dfrac{1}{2}x^2 - 1$	(x, y)
-4	$y = \frac{1}{2}(-4)^2 - 1 = 7$	$(-4, 7)$
-2	$y = \frac{1}{2}(-2)^2 - 1 = 1$	$(-2, 1)$
0	$y = \frac{1}{2}(0)^2 - 1 = -1$	$(0, -1)$
2	$y = \frac{1}{2}(2)^2 - 1 = 1$	$(2, 1)$
4	$y = \frac{1}{2}(4)^2 - 1 = 7$	$(4, 7)$

5. The intercepts are $(0, -5)$ and $(4, 0)$. The x-intercept is 4 and the y-intercept is -5.

6. a. The average selling price of a new home in January of 2003 was approximately $230,000.

b. The average selling price was highest in July of 2003 when it was approximately $248,000.

c. The average selling price increased the most between September 2002 and October 2002. The average selling price increased approximately $16,000 during that period.

7. $\{(-2, -1), (-1, 0), (0, 1), (1, 2), (2, 3)\}$

8. a. Domain: $\{x \mid -4 \le x \le 5\}$ or $[-4, 5]$

Range: $\{y \mid -6 \le y \le -1\}$ or $[-6, -1]$

b. Domain: $\{-4, -1, 0, 3, 6\}$

Range: $\{-3, -2, 2, 6\}$

9. a. $y = |x - 2| - 3$

x	$y = |x - 2| - 3$	(x, y)
-2	$y = |-2 - 2| - 3 = 1$	$(-2, 1)$
0	$y = |-0 - 2| - 3 = -1$	$(0, -1)$
2	$y = |2 - 2| - 3 = -3$	$(2, -3)$
4	$y = |4 - 2| - 3 = -1$	$(4, -1)$
6	$y = |6 - 2| - 3 = 1$	$(6, 1)$

Domain: $\{x \mid x \text{ is a real number}\}$ or $(-\infty, \infty)$

Range: $\{y \mid y \ge -3\}$ or $[-3, \infty)$

b. $y = \frac{1}{2}x^2 + 1$

x	$y = \frac{1}{2}x^2 + 1$	(x, y)
-4	$y = \frac{1}{2}(-4)^2 + 1 = 9$	$(-4, 9)$
-2	$y = \frac{1}{2}(-2)^2 + 1 = 3$	$(-2, 3)$
0	$y = \frac{1}{2}(0)^2 + 1 = 1$	$(0, 1)$
2	$y = \frac{1}{2}(2)^2 + 1 = 3$	$(2, 3)$
4	$y = \frac{1}{2}(4)^2 + 1 = 9$	$(4, 9)$

Domain: $\{x \mid x \text{ is a real number}\}$ or $(-\infty, \infty)$

Range: $\{y \mid y \geq 1\}$ or $[1, \infty)$

10. From the graph, we see that the object will be in the air from $t = 0$ seconds to $t = 3.8$ seconds (when it hits the ground). The ball reaches a maximum height of 105 feet and a minimum height of 0 feet (when it is on the ground). Therefore, we have
Domain: $\{t \mid 0 \leq t \leq 3.8\}$

Range: $\{h \mid 0 \leq h \leq 105\}$

2.3 Preparing for an Introduction to Functions

1. a. Let $x = 1$:
$$2x^2 - 5x = 2(1)^2 - 5(1) = 2 - 5 = -3$$

b. Let $x = 4$:
$$2x^2 - 5x = 2(4)^2 - 5(4)$$
$$= 2(16) - 20$$
$$= 32 - 20$$
$$= 12$$

c. Let $x = -3$:
$$2x^2 - 5x = 2(-3)^2 - 5(-3)$$
$$= 2(9) + 15$$
$$= 18 + 15$$
$$= 33$$

2. Inequality: $x \leq 5$
Interval: $(-\infty, 5]$

3. Interval: $(2, \infty)$

Set notation: $\{x \mid x > 2\}$

The inequality is strict since the parenthesis was used instead of a square bracket.

2.3 Exercises

1. function

3. argument

5. True

7. map; ordered pairs; equation; graph

9. Function. Each state corresponds to exactly one number of Representatives.
Domain: {Virginia, Nevada, New Mexico, Tennessee, Texas}
Range: {3, 9, 11, 32}

11. Not a function. The domain element 174 for horsepower corresponds to two different top speeds in the range.
Domain: {150, 174, 180|
Range: {118, 130, 140}

13. Function. There are no ordered pairs that have the same first coordinate, but different second coordinates.
Domain: $\{0, 1, 2, 3\}$

Range: $\{3, 4, 5, 6\}$

15. Function. There are no ordered pairs that have the same first coordinate, but different second coordinates.
Domain: $\{-3, 1, 4, 7\}$

Range: $\{5\}$

17. Not a function. There are two ordered pairs that have the same first coordinate, but different second coordinates.

    Domain: $\{-10, -5, 0\}$

    Range: $\{1, 2, 3, 4\}$

19. $y = 2x + 9$

    Since there is only one output y that can result from any given input x, this relation is a function.

21. $2x + y = 10$

    $y = -2x + 10$

    Since there is only one output y that can result from any given input x, this relation is a function.

23. $y = \pm 5x$

    Since a given input x can result in more than one output y, this relation is not a function.

25. $y = x^2 + 2$

    Since there is only one output y that can result from any given input x, this relation is a function.

27. $x + y^2 = 10$

    $y^2 = 10 - x$

    Since a given input x can result in more than one output y, this relation is not a function. For example, if $x = 1$ then $y = 3$ or $y = -3$.

29. Function. The graph passes the vertical line test so it is the graph of a function.

31. Not a function. The graph fails the vertical line test so it is not the graph of a function.

33. Function. The graph passes the vertical line test so it is the graph of a function.

35. Function. The graph passes the vertical line test so it is the graph of a function.

37. a. $f(0) = 2(0) + 3 = 0 + 3 = 3$

    b. $f(3) = 2(3) + 3 = 6 + 3 = 9$

    c. $f(-2) = 2(-2) + 3 = -4 + 3 = -1$

    d. $f(-x) = 2(-x) + 3 = -2x + 3$

    e. $-f(x) = -(2x + 3) = -2x - 3$

    f. $f(x + 2) = 2(x + 2) + 3 = 2x + 4 + 3 = 2x + 7$

    g. $f(2x) = 2(2x) + 3 = 4x + 3$

    h. $f(x + h) = 2(x + h) + 3 = 2x + 2h + 3$

39. a. $f(0) = -5(0) + 2 = 0 + 2 = 2$

    b. $f(3) = -5(3) + 2 = -15 + 2 = -13$

    c. $f(-2) = -5(-2) + 2 = 10 + 2 = 12$

    d. $f(-x) = -5(-x) + 2 = 5x + 2$

    e. $-f(x) = -(-5x + 2) = 5x - 2$

    f. $f(x + 2) = -5(x + 2) + 2$
    $= -5x - 10 + 2$
    $= -5x - 8$

    g. $f(2x) = -5(2x) + 2 = -10x + 2$

    h. $f(x + h) = -5(x + h) + 2$
    $= -5x - 5h + 2$

41. $f(x) = x^2 + 3$

    $f(2) = (2)^2 + 3 = 4 + 3 = 7$

43. $s(t) = -t^3 - 4t$

    $s(-2) = -(-2)^3 - 4(-2)$
    $= -(-8) + 8$
    $= 8 + 8$
    $= 16$

45. $F(x) = |x - 2|$

    $F(-3) = |(-3) - 2| = |-5| = 5$

47. $F(z) = \dfrac{z + 2}{z - 5}$

    $F(4) = \dfrac{(4) + 2}{(4) - 5} = \dfrac{6}{-1} = -6$

49. $f(x) = 4x - 6$

x	$y = f(x) = 4x - 6$	(x, y)
-2	$f(-2) = 4(-2) - 6 = -14$	$(-2, -14)$
-1	$f(-1) = 4(-1) - 6 = -10$	$(-1, -10)$
0	$f(0) = 4(0) - 6 = -6$	$(0, -6)$
1	$f(1) = 4(1) - 6 = -2$	$(1, -2)$
2	$f(2) = 4(2) - 6 = 2$	$(2, 2)$

53. $G(x) = |x - 1|$

x	$y = G(x) = |x - 1|$	(x, y)
-3	$G(-3) = |-3 - 1| = 4$	$(-3, 4)$
-1	$G(-1) = |-1 - 1| = 2$	$(-1, 2)$
1	$G(1) = |1 - 1| = 0$	$(1, 0)$
3	$G(3) = |3 - 1| = 2$	$(3, 2)$
5	$G(5) = |5 - 1| = 4$	$(5, 4)$

51. $h(x) = x^2 - 2$

x	$y = h(x) = x^2 - 2$	(x, y)
-3	$h(-3) = (-3)^2 - 2 = 7$	$(-3, 7)$
-2	$h(-2) = (-2)^2 - 2 = 2$	$(-2, 2)$
-1	$h(-1) = (-1)^2 - 2 = -1$	$(-1, -1)$
0	$h(0) = (0)^2 - 2 = -2$	$(0, -2)$
1	$h(1) = (1)^2 - 2 = -1$	$(1, -1)$
2	$h(2) = (2)^2 - 2 = 2$	$(2, 2)$
3	$h(3) = (3)^2 - 2 = 7$	$(3, 7)$

55. $g(x) = x^3$

x	$y = g(x) = x^3$	(x, y)
-3	$y = (-3)^3 = -27$	$(-3, -27)$
-2	$y = (-2)^3 = -8$	$(-2, -8)$
-1	$y = (-1)^3 = -1$	$(-1, -1)$
0	$y = (0)^3 = 0$	$(0, 0)$
1	$y = (1)^3 = 1$	$(1, 1)$
2	$y = (2)^3 = 8$	$(2, 8)$
3	$y = (3)^3 = 27$	$(3, 27)$

57. $f(x) = 3x^2 - x + C;\ f(3) = 18$

$$18 = 3(3)^2 - (3) + C$$
$$18 = 3(9) - 3 + C$$
$$18 = 27 - 3 + C$$
$$18 = 24 + C$$
$$-6 = C$$

59. $f(x) = \dfrac{2x+5}{x-A}; f(0) = -1$

$$-1 = \dfrac{2(0)+5}{0-A}$$

$$-1 = \dfrac{0+5}{0-A}$$

$$-1 = \dfrac{5}{-A}$$

$$A = 5$$

61. $A(r) = \pi r^2$

$A(4) = \pi(4)^2 = 16\pi \approx 50.27$

The area is roughly 50.27 square inches.

63. $h =$ number of hours worked

$G =$ gross salary

$G(h) = 15h$

$G(25) = 15(25) = 375$

Jackie's gross salary for 25 hours is $375.

65. a. The dependent variable is the population, P, and the independent variable is the age, a.

b. $P(20) = 0.025(20)^2 - 5.633(20) + 300.517$

$$= 0.025(400) - 112.66 + 300.517$$

$$= 10 + 187.857 = 197.857$$

The population of Americans that were 20 years of age or older in 2005 was roughly 198 million.

c. $P(0) = 0.025(0)^2 - 5.633(0) + 300.517$

$$= 300.517$$

$P(0)$ represents the entire population of the U.S. since every member of the population is at least 0 years of age. The population of the U.S. in 2005 was roughly 301 million.

67. a. The dependent variable is revenue, R, and the independent variable is price, p.

b. $R(50) = -(50)^2 + 200(50)$

$$= -2500 + 10,000$$

$$= 7500$$

Selling PDAs for $50 will yield a daily revenue of $7500 for the company.

c. $R(120) = -(120)^2 + 200(120)$

$$= -14,400 + 24,000$$

$$= 9600$$

Selling PDAs for $120 will yield a daily revenue of $9600 for the company.

69. Answers will vary.

71. $f(x) = x^2 + 3$

$f(2) = 7$

73. $F(x) = |x-2|$

$F(-3) = 5$

75. $H(x) = \sqrt{4x-3}$

$H(7) = 5$

77. $F(z) = \dfrac{z+2}{z-5}$

$F(4) = -6$

2.4 Preparing for Functions and Their Graphs

1. We need to determine whether the value of the variable causes division by 0. That is, we need to determine if the value makes $x - 5 = 0$.

   a. When $x = -1$, we have $x - 5 = -1 - 5 = -6$, so -1 is in the domain of the variable.

   b. When $x = 5$, we have $x - 5 = 5 - 5 = 0$, so 5 is not in the domain of the variable.

   c. When $x = 0$, we have $x - 5 = 0 - 5 = -5$, so 0 is in the domain of the variable.

2. $3x - 12 = 0$

   $3x - 12 + 12 = 0 + 12$

   $3x = 12$

   $\dfrac{3x}{3} = \dfrac{12}{3}$

   $x = 4$

   The solution set is $\{4\}$.

2.4 Exercises

1. $f(3) = 8$

3. domain

5. True (e.g. $f(x) = x^2 - 4$).

7. Answers will vary. The domain is basically the set of all possible input values. This set may be restricted in applications due to physical, geometric, or other constraints.

9. $f(x) = 4x + 7$

   Since each operation in the function can be performed for any real number, the domain of the function is all real numbers.
   Domain: $\{x \mid x \text{ is a real number}\}$ or $(-\infty, \infty)$

11. $F(z) = \dfrac{2z + 1}{z - 5}$

    The function tells us to divide $2z + 1$ by $z - 5$. Since division by 0 is not defined, the denominator can never equal 0. Thus, z can never equal 5.
    Domain: $\{z \mid z \neq 5\}$ or $(-\infty, 5) \cup (5, \infty)$

13. $f(x) = 3x^4 - 2x^2$

    Since each operation in the function can be performed for any real number, the domain of the function is all real numbers.
    Domain: $\{x \mid x \text{ is a real number}\}$ or $(-\infty, \infty)$

15. $G(x) = \dfrac{3x - 5}{3x + 1}$

    The function tells us to divide $3x - 5$ by $3x + 1$. Since division by 0 is not defined, the denominator can never equal 0.
    $3x + 1 = 0$

    $3x = -1$

    $x = -\dfrac{1}{3}$

    Thus, x can never equal $-\dfrac{1}{3}$.

    Domain: $\left\{ x \mid x \neq -\dfrac{1}{3} \right\}$ or $\left(-\infty, -\dfrac{1}{3} \right) \cup \left(-\dfrac{1}{3}, \infty \right)$

17. $f(x) = \dfrac{10x + 7}{3}$

    Since each operation in the function can be performed for any real number, the domain of the function is all real numbers.
    Domain: $\{x \mid x \text{ is a real number}\}$ or $(-\infty, \infty)$

19. **a.** Domain: $\{x \mid x \text{ is a real number}\}$ or $(-\infty, \infty)$
    Range: $\{y \mid y \text{ is a real number}\}$ or $(-\infty, \infty)$

    b. The intercepts are $(0, 2)$ and $(1, 0)$. The x-intercept is 1 and the y-intercept is 2.

21. **a.** Domain: $\{x \mid x \text{ is a real number}\}$ or $(-\infty, \infty)$
    Range: $\{y \mid y \geq -2.25\}$ or $[-2.25, \infty)$

    b. The intercepts are $(-2, 0), (4, 0)$ and $(0, -2)$. The x-intercepts are -2 and 4, and the y-intercept is -2.

23. **a.** Domain: $\{x \mid x \text{ is a real number}\}$ or $(-\infty, \infty)$
    Range: $\{y \mid y \text{ is a real number}\}$ or $(-\infty, \infty)$

    b. The intercepts are $(-3, 0)$, $(-1, 0)$, $(2, 0)$, and $(0, -3)$. The x-intercepts are $-3, -1$, and 2, and the y-intercept is -3.

25. a. Domain: $\{x \mid x \text{ is a real number}\}$ or $(-\infty, \infty)$
Range: $\{y \mid y \geq 0\}$ or $[0, \infty)$

b. The intercepts are $(-3, 0), (3, 0),$ and $(0, 9)$.
The x-intercepts are -3 and 3, and the y-intercept is 9.

27. a. Domain: $\{x \mid x \leq 4\}$ or $(-\infty, 4]$
Range: $\{y \mid y \leq 3\}$ or $(-\infty, 3]$

b. The intercepts are $(-2, 0)$ and $(0, 2)$. The x-intercept is -2 and the y-intercept is 2.

29. a. $f(-7) = -2$

b. $f(-3) = 3$

c. $f(6) = 2$

d. negative

e. $f(x) = 0$ for $x = \{-6, -1, 4\}$

f. Domain: $\{x \mid -7 \leq x \leq 6\}$ or $[-7, 6]$

g. Range: $\{y \mid -2 \leq y \leq 3\}$ or $[-2, 3]$

h. The x-intercepts are -6, -1, and 4.

i. The y-intercept is -1.

j. $f(x) = -2$ for $x = -7$ and 2.

k. $f(x) = 3$ for $x = -3$.

31. a. From the table, when $x = -2$ the value of the function is 3. Therefore,
$F(-2) = 3$

b. From the table, when $x = 3$ the value of the function is -6. Therefore,
$F(3) = -6$

c. From the table, $F(x) = 5$ when $x = -1$.

d. The x-intercept is the value of x that makes the function equal 0. From the table,
$F(x) = 0$ when $x = -4$. Therefore, the x-intercept is $x = -4$.

e. The y-intercept is the value of the function when $x = 0$. From the table, when $x = 0$ the value of the function is 2. Therefore, the y-intercept is $y = 2$.

33. a. $f(2) = 4(2) - 9 = 8 - 9 = -1$
Since $f(2) = -1$, the point $(2, 1)$ is not on the graph of the function.

b. $f(3) = 4(3) - 9 = 12 - 9 = 3$
The point $(3, 3)$ is on the graph.

c. $4x - 9 = 7$
$4x = 16$
$x = 4$
The point $(4, 7)$ is on the graph.

35. a. $g(4) = -\frac{1}{2}(4) + 4 = -2 + 4 = 2$
Since $g(4) = 2$, the point $(4, 2)$ is on the graph of the function.

b. $g(6) = -\frac{1}{2}(6) + 4 = -3 + 4 = 1$
The point $(6, 1)$ is on the graph.

c. $-\frac{1}{2}x + 4 = 10$
$-\frac{1}{2}x = 6$
$x = -12$
The point $(-12, 10)$ is on the graph.

37. $V(r) = \frac{4}{3}\pi r^3$
Since the radius cannot have a negative length, the domain is all nonnegative real numbers.
Domain: $\{r \mid r \geq 0\}$ or $[0, \infty)$

39. $G(h) = 22.5h$
Since Jackie cannot work a negative number of hours and she can work a maximum of 60 hours in a week, the domain is all real numbers between 0 and 60 (inclusive).
Domain: $\{h \mid 0 \leq h \leq 60\}$ or $[0, 60]$

41. $D(p) = 1200 - 10p$

A graph of the function would indicate that the domain is all real numbers. However, the context of the problem needs to be considered. It is not feasible that the price would be negative, nor that the demand for hot dogs would be negative. Thus, the domain is all real numbers between 0 and 120, inclusive.

Domain: $\{p \mid 0 \le p \le 120\}$ or $[0, 120]$

43. a. Graph (III). The height should fluctuate up and down as the person jumps. Thus, we expect to see a graph that oscillates.

b. Graph (I). Billed phone calls are generally charged per minute so the cost will continue to increase the longer you talk. Thus, we expect to see a graph that continually increases.

c. Graph (IV). As a person grows, his or her height increases until they reach adulthood at which time the height tends to stabilize. Thus, we expect to see a graph that starts increasing but then levels off.

d. Graph (V). As price increases, we expect that revenues will increase to a point. If prices get too high, few people will be able to afford the cars and little or no revenue will be generated. We would look for a graph that starts increasing but then begins to decrease.

e. Graph (II). Starting with some initial cost, we expect the value to decrease over time until it reaches 0. We expect to see a graph that is constantly decreasing but stops when it hits 0.

45.

47. Answers will vary. One possibility:

49. Answers will vary. One possibility: Starting from the person's birth weight, the individual gained weight as they grew to adulthood. As an adult, the individual's weight fluctuated a little and then started to decline slightly after middle-age.

51. Answers will vary. One possibility:

Chapter 2 Review

1. A: quadrant IV; B: quadrant III; C: y-axis; D: quadrant II; E: x-axis; F: quadrant I.

2. A: x-axis; B: quadrant I; C: quadrant III; D: quadrant II; E: quadrant IV; F: y-axis.

3. a. Let $x = 3$ and $y = 1$.

$$3(3) - 2(1) \overset{?}{=} 7$$

$$9 - 2 \overset{?}{=} 7$$

$$7 = 7 \text{ True}$$

The point $(3,1)$ is on the graph.

b. Let $x = 2$ and $y = -1$.

$$3(2) - 2(-1) \overset{?}{=} 7$$

$$6 + 2 \overset{?}{=} 7$$

$$8 = 7 \text{ False}$$

The point $(2,-1)$ is not on the graph.

c. Let $x = 4$ and $y = 0$.

$$3(4) - 2(0) \overset{?}{=} 7$$

$$12 - 0 \overset{?}{=} 7$$

$$12 = 7 \text{ False}$$

The point $(4,0)$ is not on the graph.

d. Let $x = \frac{1}{3}$ and $y = -3$.

$$3\left(\frac{1}{3}\right) - 2(-3) \overset{?}{=} 7$$

$$1 + 6 \overset{?}{=} 7$$

$$7 = 7 \text{ True}$$

The point $\left(\frac{1}{3}, -3\right)$ is on the graph.

4. a. Let $x = -1$ and $y = 3$.

$$3 \overset{?}{=} 2(-1)^2 - 3(-1) + 2$$

$$3 \overset{?}{=} 2(1) + 3 + 2$$

$$3 \overset{?}{=} 2 + 3 + 2$$

$$3 = 7 \text{ False}$$

The point $(-1,3)$ is not on the graph.

b. Let $x = 1$ and $y = 1$.

$$1 \overset{?}{=} 2(1)^2 - 3(1) + 2$$

$$1 \overset{?}{=} 2(1) - 3 + 2$$

$$1 \overset{?}{=} 2 - 3 + 2$$

$$1 = 1 \text{ True}$$

The point $(1,1)$ is on the graph.

c. Let $x = -2$ and $y = 16$.

$$16 \overset{?}{=} 2(-2)^2 - 3(-2) + 2$$

$$16 \overset{?}{=} 2(4) + 6 + 2$$

$$16 \overset{?}{=} 8 + 6 + 2$$

$$16 = 16 \text{ True}$$

The point $(-2,16)$ is on the graph.

d. Let $x = \frac{1}{2}$ and $y = \frac{3}{2}$.

$$\frac{3}{2} \overset{?}{=} 2\left(\frac{1}{2}\right)^2 - 3\left(\frac{1}{2}\right) + 2$$

$$\frac{3}{2} \overset{?}{=} 2\left(\frac{1}{4}\right) - \frac{3}{2} + 2$$

$$\frac{3}{2} \overset{?}{=} \frac{1}{2} - \frac{3}{2} + 2$$

$$\frac{3}{2} = 1 \text{ False}$$

The point $\left(\frac{1}{2}, \frac{3}{2}\right)$ is not on the graph.

5. $y = x + 2$

x	$y = x + 2$	(x, y)
-3	$y = (-3) + 2 = -1$	$(-3,-1)$
-1	$y = (-1) + 2 = 1$	$(-1,1)$
0	$y = (0) + 2 = 2$	$(0,2)$
1	$y = (1) + 2 = 3$	$(1,3)$
3	$y = (3) + 2 = 5$	$(3,5)$

6. $2x + y = 3$

$y = -2x + 3$

x	$y = -2x + 3$	(x, y)
-3	$y = -2(-3) + 3 = 9$	$(-3, 9)$
-1	$y = -2(-1) + 3 = 5$	$(-1, 5)$
0	$y = -2(0) + 3 = 3$	$(0, 3)$
1	$y = -2(1) + 3 = 1$	$(1, 1)$
3	$y = -2(3) + 3 = -3$	$(3, -3)$

7. $y = 2x^2 - 3$

x	$y = 2x^2 - 3$	(x, y)
-2	$y = 2(-2)^2 - 3 = 5$	$(-2, 5)$
-1	$y = 2(-1)^2 - 3 = -1$	$(-1, -1)$
0	$y = 2(0)^2 - 3 = -3$	$(0, -3)$
1	$y = 2(1)^2 - 3 = -1$	$(1, -1)$
2	$y = 2(2)^2 - 3 = 5$	$(2, 5)$

8. $y = -x^2 + 4$

x	$y = -x^2 + 4$	(x, y)
-3	$y = -(-3)^2 + 4 = -5$	$(-3, -5)$
-1	$y = -(-1)^2 + 4 = 3$	$(-1, 3)$
0	$y = -(0)^2 + 4 = 4$	$(0, 4)$
1	$y = -(1)^2 + 4 = 3$	$(1, 3)$
3	$y = -(3)^2 + 4 = -5$	$(3, -5)$

9. $y = -|x| - 2$

x	$y = -|x| - 2$	(x, y)
-3	$y = -|-3| - 2 = -5$	$(-3, -5)$
-1	$y = -|-1| - 2 = -3$	$(-1, -3)$
0	$y = -|0| - 2 = -2$	$(0, -2)$
1	$y = -|1| - 2 = -3$	$(1, -3)$
3	$y = -|3| - 2 = -5$	$(3, -5)$

10. $y = |x+2| - 1$

x	$y = |x+2| - 1$	(x,y)
-5	$y = |-5+2| - 1 = 2$	$(-5,2)$
-3	$y = |-3+2| - 1 = 0$	$(-3,0)$
-1	$y = |-1+2| - 1 = 0$	$(-1,0)$
0	$y = |0+2| - 1 = 1$	$(0,1)$
1	$y = |1+2| - 1 = 2$	$(1,2)$

11. $y = x^3 + 2$

x	$y = x^3 + 2$	(x,y)
-2	$y = (-2)^3 + 2 = -6$	$(-2,-6)$
-1	$y = (-1)^3 + 2 = 1$	$(-1,1)$
0	$y = (0)^3 + 2 = 2$	$(0,2)$
1	$y = (1)^3 + 2 = 3$	$(1,3)$
2	$y = (2)^3 + 2 = 10$	$(2,10)$

12. $y = -x^3 + 1$

x	$y = -x^3 + 1$	(x,y)
-2	$y = -(-2)^3 + 1 = 9$	$(-2,9)$
-1	$y = -(-1)^3 + 1 = 2$	$(-1,2)$
0	$y = -(0)^3 + 1 = 1$	$(0,1)$
1	$y = -(1)^3 + 1 = 0$	$(1,0)$
2	$y = -(2)^3 + 1 = -7$	$(2,-7)$

13. $x = y^2 + 1$

y	$x = y^2 + 1$	(x,y)
-2	$x = (-2)^2 + 1 = 5$	$(5,-2)$
-1	$x = (-1)^2 + 1 = 2$	$(2,-1)$
0	$x = (0)^2 + 1 = 1$	$(1,0)$
1	$x = (1)^2 + 1 = 2$	$(2,1)$
2	$x = (2)^2 + 1 = 5$	$(5,2)$

14. $y = \dfrac{1}{x-2}$

x	$y = \dfrac{1}{x-2}$	(x,y)
-2	$y = \dfrac{1}{-2-2} = -\dfrac{1}{4}$	$\left(-2,-\dfrac{1}{4}\right)$
0	$y = \dfrac{1}{0-2} = -\dfrac{1}{2}$	$\left(0,-\dfrac{1}{2}\right)$
1	$y = \dfrac{1}{1-2} = -1$	$(1,-1)$
3	$y = \dfrac{1}{3-2} = 1$	$(3,1)$
4	$y = \dfrac{1}{4-2} = \dfrac{1}{2}$	$\left(4,\dfrac{1}{2}\right)$
6	$y = \dfrac{1}{6-2} = \dfrac{1}{4}$	$\left(6,\dfrac{1}{4}\right)$

15. The intercepts are $(-3,0)$, $(0,-1)$, and $(0,3)$.

16. The intercepts are $(-2,0)$, $(0,0)$, and $(2,0)$.

17. a. Since 2250 is less than 3000, the monthly bill will still be $40. Using the graph, we find that when $x = 2.25$ (2250 minutes) the y-value is 40, or $40.

    b. For 12,000 minutes, we have $x = 12$. According to the graph, the monthly bill for 12,000 minutes will be about $500.

18. a. According to the graph, the winning time in the 1999 Kentucky Derby was 2:03, or 123 seconds.

    b. To find the fastest time, we look for the lowest point on the graph. The lowest point on the graph occurs for the year 2001. Therefore, the fastest winning time for the Kentucky Derby between 1995 and 2004 occurred in 2001. The winning time was roughly 2:00, or 120 seconds.

19. {(Cent, 2.500), (Nickel, 5.000), (Dime, 2.268), (Quarter, 5.670), (Half Dollar, 11.340), (Dollar, 8.100)}
Domain:
{Cent, Nickel, Dime, Quarter, Half Dollar, Dollar}
Range:
{2.268, 2.500, 5.000, 5.670, 8.100, 11.340}

20. {(70, $6.99), (90, $9.99), (120, $9.99), (128, $12.99), (446, $49.99)}
Domain:
{70, 90, 120, 128, 446}
Range:
{$6.99, $9.99, $12.99, $49.99}

21. Domain: $\{-4,-2,2,3,6\}$
    Range: $\{-9,-1,5,7,8\}$

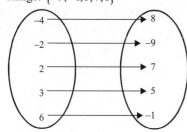

22. Domain: $\{-2,1,3,5\}$
    Range: $\{1,4,7,8\}$

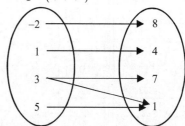

23. Domain: $\{x \mid x \text{ is a real number}\}$ or $(-\infty,\infty)$
    Range: $\{y \mid y \text{ is a real number}\}$ or $(-\infty,\infty)$

24. Domain: $\{x \mid -6 \le x \le 4\}$ or $[-6,4]$
    Range: $\{y \mid -4 \le y \le 6\}$ or $[-4,6]$

25. Domain: $\{2\}$
    Range: $\{y \mid y \text{ is a real number}\}$ or $(-\infty,\infty)$

26. Domain: $\{x \mid x \ge -1\}$ or $[-1,\infty)$
    Range: $\{y \mid y \ge -2\}$ or $[-2,\infty)$

27. $y = x + 2$

x	$y = x + 2$	(x,y)
-3	$y = (-3) + 2 = -1$	$(-3,-1)$
-1	$y = (-1) + 2 = 1$	$(-1,1)$
0	$y = (0) + 2 = 2$	$(0,2)$
1	$y = (1) + 2 = 3$	$(1,3)$
3	$y = (3) + 2 = 5$	$(3,5)$

Domain: $\{x \mid x \text{ is a real number}\}$ or $(-\infty,\infty)$
Range: $\{y \mid y \text{ is a real number}\}$ or $(-\infty,\infty)$

28. $2x + y = 3$

$y = -2x + 3$

x	$y = -2x + 3$	(x, y)
-3	$y = -2(-3) + 3 = 9$	$(-3, 9)$
-1	$y = -2(-1) + 3 = 5$	$(-1, 5)$
0	$y = -2(0) + 3 = 3$	$(0, 3)$
1	$y = -2(1) + 3 = 1$	$(1, 1)$
3	$y = -2(3) + 3 = -3$	$(3, -3)$

Domain: $\{x \mid x \text{ is a real number}\}$ or $(-\infty, \infty)$

Range: $\{y \mid y \text{ is a real number}\}$ or $(-\infty, \infty)$

29. $y = 2x^2 - 3$

x	$y = 2x^2 - 3$	(x, y)
-2	$y = 2(-2)^2 - 3 = 5$	$(-2, 5)$
-1	$y = 2(-1)^2 - 3 = -1$	$(-1, -1)$
0	$y = 2(0)^2 - 3 = -3$	$(0, -3)$
1	$y = 2(1)^2 - 3 = -1$	$(1, -1)$
2	$y = 2(2)^2 - 3 = 5$	$(2, 5)$

Domain: $\{x \mid x \text{ is a real number}\}$ or $(-\infty, \infty)$

Range: $\{y \mid y \geq -3\}$ or $[-3, \infty)$

30. $y = -x^2 + 4$

x	$y = -x^2 + 4$	(x, y)
-3	$y = -(-3)^2 + 4 = -5$	$(-3, -5)$
-1	$y = -(-1)^2 + 4 = 3$	$(-1, 3)$
0	$y = -(0)^2 + 4 = 4$	$(0, 4)$
1	$y = -(1)^2 + 4 = 3$	$(1, 3)$
3	$y = -(3)^2 + 4 = -5$	$(3, -5)$

Domain: $\{x \mid x \text{ is a real number}\}$ or $(-\infty, \infty)$

Range: $\{y \mid y \leq 4\}$ or $(-\infty, 4]$

31. $y = -|x| - 2$

x	$y = -|x| - 2$	(x, y)
-3	$y = -|-3| - 2 = -5$	$(-3, -5)$
-1	$y = -|-1| - 2 = -3$	$(-1, -3)$
0	$y = -|0| - 2 = -2$	$(0, -2)$
1	$y = -|1| - 2 = -3$	$(1, -3)$
3	$y = -|3| - 2 = -5$	$(3, -5)$

Domain: $\{x \mid x \text{ is a real number}\}$ or $(-\infty, \infty)$

Range: $\{y \mid y \leq -2\}$ or $(-\infty, -2]$

32. $y = |x+2| - 1$

x	$y = |x+2| - 1$	(x, y)
-5	$y = |-5+2| - 1 = 2$	$(-5, 2)$
-3	$y = |-3+2| - 1 = 0$	$(-3, 0)$
-1	$y = |-1+2| - 1 = 0$	$(-1, 0)$
0	$y = |0+2| - 1 = 1$	$(0, 1)$
1	$y = |1+2| - 1 = 2$	$(1, 2)$

Domain: $\{x \mid x \text{ is a real number}\}$ or $(-\infty, \infty)$

Range: $\{y \mid y \geq -1\}$ or $[-1, \infty)$

33. $y = x^3 + 2$

x	$y = x^3 + 2$	(x, y)
-2	$y = (-2)^3 + 2 = -6$	$(-2, -6)$
-1	$y = (-1)^3 + 2 = 1$	$(-1, 1)$
0	$y = (0)^3 + 2 = 2$	$(0, 2)$
1	$y = (1)^3 + 2 = 3$	$(1, 3)$
2	$y = (2)^3 + 2 = 10$	$(2, 10)$

Domain: $\{x \mid x \text{ is a real number}\}$ or $(-\infty, \infty)$

Range: $\{y \mid y \text{ is a real number}\}$ or $(-\infty, \infty)$

34. $y = -x^3 + 1$

x	$y = -x^3 + 1$	(x, y)
-2	$y = -(-2)^3 + 1 = 9$	$(-2, 9)$
-1	$y = -(-1)^3 + 1 = 2$	$(-1, 2)$
0	$y = -(0)^3 + 1 = 1$	$(0, 1)$
1	$y = -(1)^3 + 1 = 0$	$(1, 0)$
2	$y = -(2)^3 + 1 = -7$	$(2, -7)$

Domain: $\{x \mid x \text{ is a real number}\}$ or $(-\infty, \infty)$

Range: $\{y \mid y \text{ is a real number}\}$ or $(-\infty, \infty)$

35. $x = y^2 + 1$

y	$x = y^2 + 1$	(x, y)
-2	$x = (-2)^2 + 1 = 5$	$(5, -2)$
-1	$x = (-1)^2 + 1 = 2$	$(2, -1)$
0	$x = (0)^2 + 1 = 1$	$(1, 0)$
1	$x = (1)^2 + 1 = 2$	$(2, 1)$
2	$x = (2)^2 + 1 = 5$	$(5, 2)$

Domain: $\{x \mid x \geq 1\}$ or $[1, \infty)$

Range: $\{y \mid y \text{ is a real number}\}$ or $(-\infty, \infty)$

36. $y = \dfrac{1}{x-2}$

x	$y = \dfrac{1}{x-2}$	(x,y)
-2	$y = \dfrac{1}{-2-2} = -\dfrac{1}{4}$	$\left(-2, -\dfrac{1}{4}\right)$
0	$y = \dfrac{1}{0-2} = -\dfrac{1}{2}$	$\left(0, -\dfrac{1}{2}\right)$
1	$y = \dfrac{1}{1-2} = -1$	$(1,-1)$
3	$y = \dfrac{1}{3-2} = 1$	$(3,1)$
4	$y = \dfrac{1}{4-2} = \dfrac{1}{2}$	$\left(4, \dfrac{1}{2}\right)$
6	$y = \dfrac{1}{6-2} = \dfrac{1}{4}$	$\left(6, \dfrac{1}{4}\right)$

Domain: $\{x \mid x \neq 2\}$ or $(-\infty, 2) \cup (2, \infty)$

Range: $\{y \mid y \neq 0\}$ or $(-\infty, 0) \cup (0, \infty)$

37. a. Domain: $\{x \mid 0 \leq x \leq 44.64\}$ or $[0, 44.64]$

Range: $\{y \mid 40 \leq y \leq 2122\}$ or $[40, 2122]$

The monthly cost will be at least $40 but no more than $2122. The number of minutes used must be between 0 and 44,640.

b. Answers may vary. There are at most 31 days in a month. Since 31 days is equivalent to 44,640 minutes, this must be the largest value in the domain. It is not possible to talk for a negative number of minutes, so the domain should begin at 0.

38. Domain: $\{t \mid 0 \leq t \leq 4\}$ or $[0, 4]$

Range: $\{y \mid 0 \leq y \leq 121\}$ or $[0, 121]$

The ball will be in the air from 0 to 4 seconds and will reach heights from 0 feet up to a maximum of 121 feet.

39. a. Not a function. The domain element -1 corresponds to two different values in the range.

Domain: $\{-1, 5, 7, 9\}$

Range: $\{-2, 0, 2, 3, 4\}$

b. Function. Each animal corresponds to exactly one typical lifespan.
Domain: {Camel, Macaw, Deer, Fox, Tiger, Crocodile}
Range: $\{14, 22, 35, 45, 50\}$

40. a. Function. There are no ordered pairs that have the same first coordinate, but different second coordinates.
Domain: $\{-3, -2, 2, 4, 5\}$

Range: $\{-1, 3, 4, 7\}$

b. Not a function. The domain element 'Blue' corresponds to two different types of cars in the range.
Domain: {Red, Blue, Green, Black}
Range: {Camry, Taurus, Windstar, Durango}

41. $3x - 5y = 18$

$-5y = -3x + 18$

$y = \dfrac{-3x + 18}{-5}$

$y = \dfrac{3}{5}x - \dfrac{18}{5}$

Since there is only one output y that can result from any given input x, this relation is a function.

42. $x^2 + y^2 = 81$

$y^2 = 81 - x^2$

Since a given input x can result in more than one output y, this relation is not a function. For example, if $x = 0$ then $y = 9$ or $y = -9$.

43. $y = \pm 10x$

Since a given input x can result in more than one output y, this relation is not a function.

44. $y = x^2 - 14$

Since there is only one output y that can result from any given input x, this relation is a function.

45. Not a function. The graph fails the vertical line test so it is not the graph of a function.

46. Function. The graph passes the vertical line test so it is the graph of a function.

47. Function. The graph passes the vertical line test so it is the graph of a function.

48. Not a function. The graph fails the vertical line test so it is not the graph of a function.

49. a. $f(-2) = (-2)^2 + 2(-2) - 5$
$$= 4 - 4 - 5$$
$$= -5$$

b. $f(3) = (3)^2 + 2(3) - 5$
$$= 9 + 6 - 5$$
$$= 10$$

50. a. $g(0) = \dfrac{2(0)+1}{(0)-3}$
$$= \dfrac{0+1}{-3}$$
$$= -\dfrac{1}{3}$$

b. $g(2) = \dfrac{2(2)+1}{(2)-3}$
$$= \dfrac{4+1}{-1}$$
$$= -5$$

51. a. $F(5) = -2(5) + 7$
$$= -10 + 7$$
$$= -3$$

b. $F(-x) = -2(-x) + 7$
$$= 2x + 7$$

52. a. $G(7) = 2(7) + 1$
$$= 14 + 1$$
$$= 15$$

b. $G(x+h) = 2(x+h) + 1$
$$= 2x + 2h + 1$$

53. $f(x) = 2x - 5$

x	$y = f(x) = 2x - 5$	(x, y)
-1	$f(-1) = 2(-1) - 5 = -7$	$(-1, -7)$
0	$f(0) = 2(0) - 5 = -5$	$(0, -5)$
1	$f(1) = 2(1) - 5 = -3$	$(1, -3)$
2	$f(2) = 2(2) - 5 = -1$	$(2, -1)$
3	$f(3) = 2(3) - 5 = 1$	$(3, 1)$

54. $g(x) = x^2 - 3x + 2$

x	$y = g(x) = x^2 - 3x + 2$	(x, y)
-1	$g(-1) = (-1)^2 - 3(-1) + 2 = 6$	$(-1, 6)$
0	$g(0) = (0)^2 - 3(0) + 2 = 2$	$(0, 2)$
1	$g(1) = (1)^2 - 3(1) + 2 = 0$	$(1, 0)$
2	$g(2) = (2)^2 - 3(2) + 2 = 0$	$(2, 0)$
3	$g(3) = (3)^2 - 3(3) + 2 = 2$	$(3, 2)$
4	$g(4) = (4)^2 - 3(4) + 2 = 6$	$(4, 6)$

55. $h(x) = (x-1)^3 - 3$

x	$y = h(x) = (x-1)^3 - 3$	(x, y)
-1	$h(-1) = (-1-1)^3 - 3 = -11$	$(-1, -11)$
0	$h(0) = (0-1)^3 - 3 = -4$	$(0, -4)$
1	$h(1) = (1-1)^3 - 3 = -3$	$(1, -3)$
2	$h(2) = (2-1)^3 - 3 = -2$	$(2, -2)$
3	$h(3) = (3-1)^3 - 3 = 5$	$(3, 5)$

56. $f(x) = |x+1| - 4$

x	$y = f(x) = |x+1| - 4$	(x, y)
-5	$f(-5) = |-5+1| - 4 = 0$	$(-5, 0)$
-3	$f(-3) = |-3+1| - 4 = -2$	$(-3, -2)$
-1	$f(-1) = |-1+1| - 4 = -4$	$(-1, -4)$
1	$f(1) = |1+1| - 4 = -2$	$(1, -2)$
3	$f(3) = |3+1| - 4 = 0$	$(3, 0)$

57. a. The dependent variable is the population, P, and the independent variable is the number of years after 1900, t.

b. $P(110) = 0.144(110)^2 - 6.613(110) + 104.448$
$= 1119.418$
According to the model, the population of Orange County will be roughly 1,119,418 in 2010.

c. $P(-70) = 0.144(-70)^2 - 6.613(-70) + 104.448$
$= 1272.958$
According to the model, the population of Orange County was roughly 1,272,958 in 1830. This is not reasonable. (The population of the entire Florida territory was roughly 35,000 in 1830.)

58. a. The dependent variable is the annual wage, W, and the independent variable is age, a.

b. $W(30) = -0.058(30)^2 + 5.410(30) - 73.839$
$= 36.261$
According to the model, a 30-year old Wyoming resident working in the mining industry in 2000 made about $36,261 annually on average.

c. $W(16) = -0.058(16)^2 + 5.410(16) - 73.839$
$= -2.127$
$W(16)$ represents the average annual salary of a 16-year old Wyoming resident working in the mining industry in 2000. This result is unreasonable since annual salaries cannot be negative.

59. $f(x) = -\frac{3}{2}x + 5$

Since each operation in the function can be performed for any real number, the domain of the function is all real numbers.
Domain: $\{x \mid x \text{ is a real number}\}$ or $(-\infty, \infty)$

60. $g(w) = \frac{w-9}{2w+5}$

The function tells us to divide $w-9$ by $2w+5$. Since division by 0 is not defined, the denominator can never equal 0.
$2w + 5 = 0$
$2w = -5$
$w = -\frac{5}{2}$

Thus, the domain is all real numbers except $-\frac{5}{2}$.
Domain: $\left\{w \mid w \neq -\frac{5}{2}\right\}$ or $\left(-\infty, -\frac{5}{2}\right) \cup \left(-\frac{5}{2}, \infty\right)$

61. $h(t) = \dfrac{t+2}{t-5}$

The function tells us to divide $t+2$ by $t-5$. Since division by 0 is not defined, the denominator can never equal 0.

$t - 5 = 0$

$\qquad t = 5$

Thus, the domain of the function is all real numbers except 5.

Domain: $\{t \mid t \neq 5\}$ or $(-\infty, 5) \cup (5, \infty)$

62. $F(x) = \dfrac{3}{x-2}$

The function tells us to divide 3 by $x-2$. We can't divide by 0, so $x \neq 2$.

Domain: $\{x \mid x \neq 2\}$ or $(-\infty, 2) \cup (2, \infty)$

63. $G(t) = 3t^2 + 4t - 9$

Since each operation in the function can be performed for any real number, the domain of the function is all real numbers.

Domain: $\{t \mid t \text{ is a real number}\}$ or $(-\infty, \infty)$

64. $H(x) = x^4 - 2x^3 + 7$

Since each operation in the function can be performed for any real number, the domain of the function is all real numbers.

Domain: $\{x \mid x \text{ is a real number}\}$ or $(-\infty, \infty)$

65. a. Domain: $\{x \mid x \text{ is a real number}\}$ or $(-\infty, \infty)$

Range: $\{y \mid y \text{ is a real number}\}$ or $(-\infty, \infty)$

b. The intercepts are $(0, 2)$ and $(4, 0)$. The x-intercept is 4 and the y-intercept is 2.

66. a. Domain: $\{x \mid x \text{ is a real number}\}$ or $(-\infty, \infty)$

Range: $\{y \mid y \geq -3\}$ or $[-3, \infty)$

b. The intercepts are $(-2, 0)$, $(2, 0)$, and $(0, -3)$. The x-intercepts are -2 and 2, and the y-intercept is -3.

67. a. Domain: $\{x \mid x \text{ is a real number}\}$ or $(-\infty, \infty)$

Range: $\{y \mid y \text{ is a real number}\}$ or $(-\infty, \infty)$

b. The intercepts are $(0, 0)$ and $(2, 0)$. The x-intercepts are 0 and 2; the y-intercept is 0.

68. a. Domain: $\{x \mid x \geq -3\}$ or $[-3, \infty)$

Range: $\{y \mid y \geq 1\}$ or $[1, \infty)$

b. The only intercept is $(0, 3)$. There are no x-intercepts, but there is a y-intercept of 3.

69. a. Domain: $\{x \mid x \text{ is a real number}\}$ or $(-\infty, \infty)$

Range: $\{y \mid y \geq -4\}$ or $[-4, \infty)$

b. The intercepts are $(-1, 0)$, $(3, 0)$, and $(0, -2)$. The x-intercepts are -1 and 3, and the y-intercept is -2.

70. a. Domain: $\{x \mid x \text{ is a real number}\}$ or $(-\infty, \infty)$

Range: $\{y \mid y \leq 0\}$ or $(-\infty, 0]$

b. The intercepts are $(-2, 0)$, $(2, 0)$, and $(0, -4)$. The x-intercepts are -2 and 2, and the y-intercept is -4.

71. a. $h(3) = 2(3) - 7 = 6 - 7 = -1$

Since $h(3) = -1$, the point $(3, -1)$ is on the graph of the function.

b. $h(-2) = 2(-2) - 7 = -4 - 7 = -11$

The point $(-2, -11)$ is on the graph of the function.

c. $h(x) = 4$

$2x - 7 = 4$

$\qquad 2x = 11$

$\qquad x = \dfrac{11}{2}$

The point $\left(\frac{11}{2}, 4\right)$ is on the graph of h.

72. a. $g(-5) = \dfrac{3}{5}(-5) + 4 = -3 + 4 = 1$

Since $g(-5) = 1$, the point $(-5, 2)$ is not on the graph of the function.

b. $g(3) = \dfrac{3}{5}(3) + 4 = \dfrac{9}{5} + 4 = \dfrac{29}{5}$

The point $\left(3, \frac{29}{5}\right)$ is on the graph of the function.

c.　$g(x) = -2$

$$\frac{3}{5}x + 4 = -2$$

$$\frac{3}{5}x = -6$$

$$x = -10$$

The point $(-10, -2)$ is on the graph of g.

73.

74.

Chapter 2 Test

1. A: quadrant IV; B: y-axis; C: x-axis; D: quadrant I; E: quadrant III; F: quadrant II.

2. a. Let $x = -2$ and $y = 4$.

$$4 \overset{?}{=} 3(-2)^2 + (-2) - 5$$

$$4 \overset{?}{=} 3(4) - 7$$

$$4 \overset{?}{=} 12 - 7$$

$$4 = 5 \text{ False}$$

The point $(-2, 4)$ is not on the graph.

b. Let $x = -1$ and $y = -3$.

$$-3 \overset{?}{=} 3(-1)^2 + (-1) - 5$$

$$-3 \overset{?}{=} 3(1) - 6$$

$$-3 \overset{?}{=} 3 - 6$$

$$-3 = -3 \text{ True}$$

The point $(-1, -3)$ is on the graph.

c. Let $x = 2$ and $y = 9$.

$$9 \overset{?}{=} 3(2)^2 + (2) - 5$$

$$9 \overset{?}{=} 3(4) - 3$$

$$9 \overset{?}{=} 12 - 3$$

$$9 = 9 \text{ True}$$

The point $(2, 9)$ is on the graph.

3. $y = 4x - 1$

x	$y = 4x - 1$	(x, y)
-1	$y = 4(-1) - 1 = -5$	$(-1, -5)$
0	$y = 4(0) - 1 = -1$	$(0, -1)$
1	$y = 4(1) - 1 = 3$	$(1, 3)$

4. $y = 4x^2$

x	$y = 4x^2$	(x, y)
-1	$y = 4(-1)^2 = 4$	$(-1, 4)$
$-\frac{1}{2}$	$y = 4\left(-\frac{1}{2}\right)^2 = 1$	$\left(-\frac{1}{2}, 1\right)$
0	$y = 4(0)^2 = 0$	$(0, 0)$
$\frac{1}{2}$	$y = 4\left(\frac{1}{2}\right)^2 = 1$	$\left(\frac{1}{2}, 1\right)$
1	$y = 4(1)^2 = 4$	$(1, 4)$

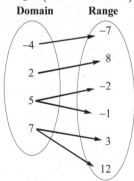

5. The intercepts are $(-3, 0)$, $(0, 1)$, and $(0, 3)$.

The x-intercept is -3 and the y-intercepts are 1 and 3.

6. a. The unemployment rate in May was about 4.9%.

b. The unemployment rate was highest in January when it was approximately 5.9%.

c. The unemployment rate was lowest in November when it was approximately 4.4%.

d. The unemployment rate gradually declined over the year except for a jump during the summer months. This might be due to recent graduates who are looking for work.

7. Domain: $\{-4, 2, 5, 7\}$

Range: $\{-7, -2, -1, 3, 8, 12\}$

8. Domain: $\left\{x \mid -\frac{5\pi}{2} \le x \le \frac{5\pi}{2}\right\}$ or $\left[-\frac{5\pi}{2}, \frac{5\pi}{2}\right]$

Range: $\{y \mid 1 \le y \le 5\}$ or $[1, 5]$

9. $y = x^2 - 3$

x	$y = x^2 - 3$	(x, y)
-2	$y = (-2)^2 - 3 = 1$	$(-2, 1)$
-1	$y = (-1)^2 - 3 = -2$	$(-1, -2)$
0	$y = (0)^2 - 3 = -3$	$(0, -3)$
1	$y = (1)^2 - 3 = -2$	$(1, -2)$
2	$y = (2)^2 - 3 = 1$	$(2, 1)$

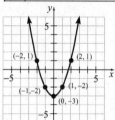

Domain: $\{x \mid x \text{ is a real number}\}$ or $(-\infty, \infty)$

Range: $\{y \mid y \ge -3\}$ or $[-3, \infty)$

10. Function. Each element in the domain corresponds to exactly one element in the range.

Domain: $\{-5, -3, 0, 2\}$

Range: $\{3, 7\}$

11. Not a function. The graph fails the vertical line test so it is not the graph of a function.

Domain: $\{x \mid x \le 3\}$ or $(-\infty, 3]$

Range: $\{y \mid y \text{ is a real number}\}$ or $(-\infty, \infty)$

12. No, $y = \pm 5x$ is not a function because a single input, x, can yield two different outputs. For example, if $x = 1$ then $y = -5$ or $y = 5$.

13. $f(x + h) = -3(x + h) + 11 = -3x - 3h + 11$

14. a. $g(-2) = 2(-2)^2 + (-2) - 1 = 2(4) - 3$
$= 8 - 3 = 5$

b. $g(0) = 2(0)^2 + (0) - 1 = 0 + 0 - 1 = -1$

c. $g(3) = 2(3)^2 + (3) - 1 = 2(9) + 2$
$= 18 + 2 = 20$

15. $f(x) = x^2 + 3$

x	$y = f(x) = x^2 + 3$	(x, y)
-2	$f(-2) = (-2)^2 + 3 = 7$	$(-2, 7)$
-1	$f(-1) = (-1)^2 + 3 = 4$	$(-1, 4)$
0	$f(0) = (0)^2 + 3 = 3$	$(0, 0)$
1	$f(1) = (1)^2 + 3 = 4$	$(1, 4)$
2	$f(2) = (2)^2 + 3 = 7$	$(2, 7)$

16. a. The dependent variable is the ticket price, P, and the independent variable is the number of years after 1989, x.

b. $P(15) = 0.13(15) + 3.76 = 5.71$

According to the model, the average ticket price in 2004 ($x = 15$) was $5.71.

17. a. The dependent variable is the number of registered climbers, N, and the independent variable is the number of years after 1960, x.

b. $N(43) = 271.4(43) + 836.83 \approx 12,507$

According to the model, there were about 12,507 registered climbers on Mt. Rainier in 2003 ($x = 43$).

c. Answers may vary. The value obtained in part (b) is much higher than the actual number. This illustrates the dangers of predicting outside the scope of given data. Beginning in 2001, Mt. Rainier began seeing a decline in the number of registered climbers which continued at least through 2003.

18. The function tells us to divide -15 by $x + 2$. Since we can't divide by zero, we need $x \neq -2$. That is, we need $x < -2$ or $x > -2$. Domain: $\{x \mid x \neq -2\}$ or the interval $(-\infty, -2) \cup (-2, \infty)$.

19. a. $h(2) = -5(2) + 12$
$= -10 + 12$
$= 2$

Since $h(2) = 2$, the point $(2, 2)$ is on the graph of the function.

b. $h(3) = -5(3) + 12$
$= -15 + 12$
$= -3$

Since $h(3) = -3$, the point $(3, -3)$ is on the graph of the function.

c. $h(x) = 0$
$-5x + 12 = 0$
$-5x = -12$
$x = \dfrac{12}{5}$

The point $\left(\dfrac{12}{5}, 0\right)$, or $(2.4, 0)$, is on the graph of h.

20. a. The car stops accelerating when the speed stops increasing. Thus, the car stops accelerating after 6 seconds.

b. The car has a constant speed when the graph is horizontal. Thus, the car maintains a constant speed for 18 seconds.

Chapter 3

3.1 Preparing for Linear Equations and Linear Functions

1.
$$3x + 12 = 0$$
$$3x + 12 - 12 = 0 - 12$$
$$3x = -12$$
$$\frac{3x}{3} = \frac{-12}{3}$$
$$x = -4$$
The solution set is $\{-4\}$.

2. $-2x + y = -4$

Let $x = 0, 1, 2,$ and 3.

$x = 0$: $-2(0) + y = -4$
 $0 + y = -4$
 $y = -4$

$x = 1$: $-2(1) + y = -4$
 $-2 + y = -4$
 $y = -2$

$x = 2$: $-2(2) + y = -4$
 $-4 + y = -4$
 $y = 0$

$x = 3$: $-2(3) + y = -4$
 $-6 + y = -4$
 $y = 2$

Thus, the points $(0, -4)$, $(1, -2)$, $(2, 0)$, and $(3, 2)$ are on the graph.

3. Yes, the equation $-2x + y = -4$ is a function. The graph passes the vertical line test.

4. $f(3) = 2(3)^2 - 5 = 2(9) - 5 = 18 - 5 = 13$

5. The domain is $\{x \mid -5 \le x \le 5\}$ or, using interval notation, $[-5, 5]$. The range is $\{y \mid -2 \le y \le 5\}$ or, using interval notation, $[-2, 5]$.

6. $f(3) = 5$ means that $y = 5$ when $x = 3$. Thus, the point $(3, 5)$ is on the graph.

3.1 Exercises

1. linear equation

3. $x = a$; a

5. TRUE.

7. Answers may vary.

First scenario: If the equation is of the form $y = mx$, then the graph will pass through the point $(0, 0)$. This means that both the x-intercept will be 0 and the y-intercept will be 0.

Second scenario: If the equation is of the form $y = -x + b$, then the graph will pass through the points $(b, 0)$ and $(0, b)$. This means that both the x-intercept is b and the y-intercept is b.

9. $x + y = 5$

Let $x = -2, -1, 0,$ and 1.

$x = -2$: $-2 + y = 5$ $\qquad$ $x = -1$: $-1 + y = 5$
 $y = 7$ $\qquad\qquad\qquad$ $y = 6$

$x = 0$: $0 + y = 5$ $\qquad\quad$ $x = 1$: $1 + y = 5$
 $y = 5$ $\qquad\qquad\qquad$ $y = 4$

Thus, the points $(-2, 7)$, $(-1, 6)$, $(0, 5)$, and $(1, 4)$ are on the graph.

11. $x - 2y = 6$

Let $x = -2,\ 0,\ 2,$ and 4.

$x = -2:\quad -2 - 2y = 6$
$\qquad\qquad -2y = 8$
$\qquad\qquad\quad y = -4$

$x = 0:\quad 0 - 2y = 6$
$\qquad\qquad -2y = 6$
$\qquad\qquad\ y = -3$

$x = 2:\quad 2 - 2y = 6$
$\qquad\qquad -2y = 4$
$\qquad\qquad\ y = -2$

$x = 4:\quad 4 - 2y = 6$
$\qquad\qquad -2y = 2$
$\qquad\qquad\ y = -1$

Thus, the points $(-2,-4)$, $(0,-3)$, $(2,-2)$, and $(4,-1)$ are on the graph.

13. $3x + 2y = 12$

Let $x = -2,\ 0,\ 2,$ and 4.

$x = -2:\quad 3(-2) + 2y = 12$
$\qquad\qquad\quad -6 + 2y = 12$
$\qquad\qquad\qquad\ 2y = 18$
$\qquad\qquad\qquad\ \ y = 9$

$x = 0:\quad 3(0) + 2y = 12$
$\qquad\qquad\qquad 2y = 12$
$\qquad\qquad\qquad\ y = 6$

$x = 2:\quad 3(2) + 2y = 12$
$\qquad\qquad\ 6 + 2y = 12$
$\qquad\qquad\qquad 2y = 6$
$\qquad\qquad\qquad\ y = 3$

$x = 4:\quad 3(4) + 2y = 12$
$\qquad\qquad 12 + 2y = 12$
$\qquad\qquad\qquad 2y = 0$
$\qquad\qquad\qquad\ y = 0$

Thus, the points $(-2,9)$, $(0,6)$, $(2,3)$, and $(4,0)$ are on the graph.

15. $\dfrac{2}{3}x + y = 6$

Let $x = -3,\ 0,\ 3,$ and 6.

$x = -3:\quad \dfrac{2}{3}(-3) + y = 6$
$\qquad\qquad\quad -2 + y = 6$
$\qquad\qquad\qquad\ y = 8$

$x = 0:\quad \dfrac{2}{3}(0) + y = 6$
$\qquad\qquad\qquad\quad y = 6$

$x = 3:\quad \dfrac{2}{3}(3) + y = 6$
$\qquad\qquad\quad 2 + y = 6$
$\qquad\qquad\qquad y = 4$

$x = 6:\quad \dfrac{2}{3}(6) + y = 6$
$\qquad\qquad\quad 4 + y = 6$
$\qquad\qquad\qquad y = 2$

Thus, the points $(-3,8)$, $(0,6)$, $(3,4)$, and $(6,2)$ are on the graph.

17. $5x - 3y = 6$

Let $x = -3,\ 0,\ 3,$ and 6.

$x = -3:\quad 5(-3) - 3y = 6$
$\qquad\qquad\ -15 - 3y = 6$
$\qquad\qquad\qquad -3y = 21$
$\qquad\qquad\qquad\quad y = -7$

$x = 0:\quad 5(0) - 3y = 6$
$$-3y = 6$$
$$y = -2$$

$x = 3:\quad 5(3) - 3y = 6$
$$15 - 3y = 6$$
$$-3y = -9$$
$$y = 3$$

$x = 6:\quad 5(6) - 3y = 6$
$$30 - 3y = 6$$
$$-3y = -24$$
$$y = 8$$

Thus, the points $(-3, -7)$, $(0, -2)$, $(3, 3)$, and $(6, 8)$ are on the graph.

19. $x + y = 3$

To find the y-intercept, let $x = 0$ and solve for y.
$x = 0:\quad 0 + y = 3$
$$y = 3$$
The y-intercept is 3, so the point $(0, 3)$ is on the graph. To find the x-intercept, let $y = 0$ and solve for x.
$y = 0:\quad x + 0 = 3$
$$x = 3$$
The x-intercept is 3, so the point $(3, 0)$ is on the graph.

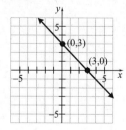

21. $3x + y = 6$

To find the y-intercept, let $x = 0$ and solve for y.
$x = 0:\quad 3(0) + y = 6$
$$0 + y = 6$$
$$y = 6$$
The y-intercept is 6, so the point $(0, 6)$ is on the graph. To find the x-intercept, let $y = 0$ and solve for x.
$y = 0:\quad 3x + 0 = 6$
$$3x = 6$$
$$x = 2$$
The x-intercept is 2, so the point $(2, 0)$ is on the graph.

23. $5x - 3y = 15$

To find the y-intercept, let $x = 0$ and solve for y.
$x = 0:\quad 5(0) - 3y = 15$
$$-3y = 15$$
$$y = -5$$
The y-intercept is -5, so the point $(0, -5)$ is on the graph. To find the x-intercept, let $y = 0$ and solve for x.
$y = 0:\quad 5x - 3(0) = 15$
$$5x = 15$$
$$x = 3$$
The x-intercept is 3, so the point $(3, 0)$ is on the graph.

25. $-3x + 2y = 7$

To find the y-intercept, let $x = 0$ and solve for y.

$x = 0$: $-3(0) + 2y = 7$

$2y = 7$

$y = \dfrac{7}{2}$

The y-intercept is $\dfrac{7}{2}$, so the point $\left(0, \dfrac{7}{2}\right)$ is on the graph. To find the x-intercept, let $y = 0$ and solve for x.

$y = 0$: $-3x + 2(0) = 7$

$-3x = 7$

$x = -\dfrac{7}{3}$

The x-intercept is $-\dfrac{7}{3}$, so the point $\left(-\dfrac{7}{3}, 0\right)$ is on the graph.

27. $\dfrac{1}{3}x - \dfrac{1}{2}y = 1$

To find the y-intercept, let $x = 0$ and solve for y.

$x = 0$: $\dfrac{1}{3}(0) - \dfrac{1}{2}y = 1$

$-\dfrac{1}{2}y = 1$

$y = -2$

The y-intercept is -2, so the point $(0, -2)$ is on the graph. To find the x-intercept, let $y = 0$ and solve for x.

$y = 0$: $\dfrac{1}{3}x - \dfrac{1}{2}(0) = 1$

$\dfrac{1}{3}x = 1$

$x = 3$

The x-intercept is 3, so the point $(3, 0)$ is on the graph.

29. $2x + y = 0$

To find the y-intercept, let $x = 0$ and solve for y.

$x = 0$: $2(0) + y = 0$

$y = 0$

The y-intercept is 0, so the point $(0, 0)$ is on the graph. To find the x-intercept, let $y = 0$ and solve for x.

$y = 0$: $2x + 0 = 0$

$2x = 0$

$x = 0$

The x-intercept is 0, so the point $(0, 0)$ is on the graph. Since the x- and y-intercepts both result in the origin, we must find other points on the graph. Let $x = -1$ and 1, and solve for y.

$x = -1$: $2(-1) + y = 0$

$-2 + y = 0$

$y = 2$

$x = 1$: $2(1) + y = 0$

$2 + y = 0$

$y = -2$

Thus, the points $(-1, 2)$ and $(1, -2)$ are also on the graph.

31. $-3x - y = 0$

To find the y-intercept, let $x = 0$ and solve for y.

$x = 0:$ $-3(0) - y = 0$

$$-y = 0$$

$$y = 0$$

The y-intercept is 0, so the point $(0,0)$ is on the graph. To find the x-intercept, let $y = 0$ and solve for x.

$y = 0:$ $-3x - 0 = 0$

$$-3x = 0$$

$$x = 0$$

The x-intercept is 0, so the point $(0,0)$ is on the graph. Since the x- and y-intercepts both result in the origin, we must find other points on the graph. Let $x = -1$ and 1, and solve for y.

$x = -1:$ $-3(-1) - y = 0$

$$3 - y = 0$$

$$3 = y$$

$x = 1:$ $-3(1) - y = 0$

$$-3 - y = 0$$

$$-3 = y$$

Thus, the points $(-1,3)$ and $(1,-3)$ are also on the graph.

33. $\dfrac{2}{3}x - \dfrac{1}{2}y = 0$

To find the y-intercept, let $x = 0$ and solve for y.

$x = 0:$ $\dfrac{2}{3}(0) - \dfrac{1}{2}y = 0$

$$-\dfrac{1}{2}y = 0$$

$$y = 0$$

The y-intercept is 0, so the point $(0,0)$ is on the graph. To find the x-intercept, let $y = 0$ and solve for x.

$y = 0:$ $\dfrac{2}{3}x - \dfrac{1}{2}(0) = 0$

$$\dfrac{2}{3}x = 0$$

$$x = 0$$

The x-intercept is 0, so the point $(0,0)$ is on the graph. Since the x- and y-intercepts both result in the origin, we must find other points on the graph. Let $x = -3$ and 3, and solve for y.

$x = -3:$ $\dfrac{2}{3}(-3) - \dfrac{1}{2}y = 0$

$$-2 - \dfrac{1}{2}y = 0$$

$$-\dfrac{1}{2}y = 2$$

$$y = -4$$

$x = 3:$ $\dfrac{2}{3}(3) - \dfrac{1}{2}y = 0$

$$2 - \dfrac{1}{2}y = 0$$

$$-\dfrac{1}{2}y = -2$$

$$y = 4$$

Thus, the points $(-3,-4)$ and $(3,4)$ are also on the graph.

35. The equation $x = 3$ will be a vertical line with x-intercept 3.

37. The equation $y = 1$ will be a horizontal line with y-intercept 1.

39. The equation $x = -5$ will be a vertical line with x-intercept -5.

41. $2y + 8 = -6$

$2y = -14$

$y = -7$

The equation $y = -7$ will be a horizontal line with y-intercept -7.

43. a. We are told that the tax function T is for adjusted gross incomes x between $7,300 and $29,700, inclusive. Thus, the domain is $\{x \mid 7,300 \le x \le 29,700\}$ or, using interval notation, $[7300, 29700]$.

b. Evaluate T at $x = 20,000$.

$T(20000) = 0.15(20000 - 7300) + 730$

$= 2635$

A single filer will pay $2635 in taxes if his or her adjusted gross income is $20,000.

c. The independent variable is adjusted gross income, x. The dependent variable is the tax bill, T.

d. Evaluate T at $x = 7300$, 18000, and 29700.

$T(7300) = 0.15(7300 - 7300) + 730$

$= 730$

$T(18000) = 0.15(18000 - 7300) + 730$

$= 2335$

$T(29700) = 0.15(29700 - 7300) + 730$

$= 4090$

Thus, the points $(7300, 730)$, $(18000, 2335)$, and $(29700, 4090)$ are on the graph.

Adjusted Gross Income ($)

e. We must solve $T(x) = 3385$.

$0.15(x - 7300) + 730 = 3385$

$0.15x - 1095 + 730 = 3385$

$0.15x - 365 = 3385$

$0.15x = 3750$

$x = 25,000$

A single filer with an adjusted gross income of $25,000 will have a tax bill of $3385.

45. a. The independent variable is the number of miles traveled, m. It would not make sense to travel a negative number of miles. Thus, the domain of C is $\{m \mid m \ge 0\}$ or, using interval notation, $[0, \infty)$.

b. $C(0) = 1.5(0) + 2 = 2$

The base fare is $2.00 before any distance is driven.

c. Evaluate C at $m = 5$.

$C(5) = 1.5(5) + 2 = 9.5$

The cab fare for a 5 mile ride is $9.50.

d. Evaluate C at $m = 0$, 10, and 20.

$C(0) = 1.5(0) + 2 = 2$

$C(10) = 1.5(10) + 2 = 17$

$C(20) = 1.5(15) + 2 = 24.5$

Thus, the points $(0,2)$, $(10,17)$, and $(15,24.5)$ are on the graph.

Distance (miles)

e. We must solve $C(m) = 13.25$.

$1.50m + 2.00 = 13.25$

$1.50m = 11.25$

$m = 7.5$

A person can travel 7.5 miles in a cab for $13.25.

47. a. The independent variable is age, a. The dependent variable is the annual cost of health insurance, H.

b. We are told in the problem that a is restricted from 15 to 90, inclusive. Thus, the domain of H is $\{a|\ 15 \le a \le 90\}$ or, using interval notation, $[15, 90]$.

c. Evaluate H at $a = 30$.

$H(30) = 22.8(30) - 117.5$

$\qquad = 566.5$

The health insurance premium of a 30 year old is $566.50.

d. Evaluate H at $a = 15$, 50, and 90.

$H(15) = 22.8(15) - 117.5$

$\qquad = 224.5$

$H(50) = 22.8(50) - 117.5$

$\qquad = 1022.5$

$H(90) = 22.8(90) - 117.5$

$\qquad = 1934.5$

Thus, the points $(15, 224.5)$, $(50, 1022.5)$, and $(90, 1934.5)$ are on the graph.

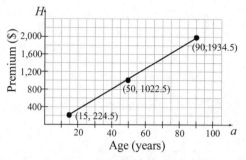

e. We must solve $H(a) = 976.9$.

$22.8a - 117.5 = 976.9$

$22.8a = 1094.4$

$\qquad a = 48$

A 48 year old individual will have a health insurance premium of $976.90.

49. a. The point $(3,1)$ is on the graph of f, so $f(3) = 1$. Thus, the solution of $f(x) = 1$ is $x = 3$.

b. The point $(-1,-3)$ is on the graph of f, so $f(-1) = -3$. Thus, the solution of $f(x) = -3$ is $x = -1$.

c. The point $(4,2)$ is on the graph of f, so $f(4) = 2$. Thus, the solution of $f(x) = 2$ is $x = 4$.

d. The intercepts of $y = f(x)$ are $(0,-2)$ and $(2,0)$. The y-intercept is -2 and the x-intercept is 2.

e. Recall that the x-intercept of a function is also called the zero of the function. Thus, the zero of $y = f(x)$ is 2.

51. The graphs of the four lines are shown below.

Answers will vary. The lines are all parallel. They all have similar slants (slopes). The y-intercept of each graph is equal to the constant term in the function being graphed.

The graph of $y = 2x + b$ will be parallel to the lines above. It will have the same slant (slope) as the lines above. The y-intercept will be b.

53. The graphs of the three lines are shown below.

Answers will vary. All three lines all pass through the origin and slant downward from left to right. The graph of $y = -x$ slants more steeply than the graph of $y = -\dfrac{1}{2}x$. The graph of $y = -2x$ slants even more steeply than that of $y = -x$.

The graph of $y = ax$, with $a < 0$, will be a line that passes through the origin and slants downward from left to right.

55. $x + y = 3$

$y = -x + 3$

57. $3x + y = 6$

$y = -3x + 6$

59. $5x - 3y = 15$

$-3y = -5x + 15$

$y = \dfrac{-5x + 15}{-3}$

$y = \dfrac{5}{3}x - 5$

61. $-3x + 2y = 7$

$2y = 3x + 7$

$y = \dfrac{3x + 7}{2}$

$y = \dfrac{3}{2}x + \dfrac{7}{2}$

63. $\dfrac{1}{3}x - \dfrac{1}{2}y = 1$

$-\dfrac{1}{2}y = -\dfrac{1}{3}x + 1$

$y = -2\left(-\dfrac{1}{3}x + 1\right)$

$y = \dfrac{2}{3}x - 2$

65. $2x + y = 0$

$y = -2x$

3.2 Preparing for Slope and Equations of Lines

1. $\dfrac{5-2}{-2-4} = \dfrac{3}{-6} = -\dfrac{1}{2}$

2. $-2(x+3) = -2 \cdot x + (-2) \cdot 3 = -2x - 6$

3.
$$4x + 3y = 15$$
$$-4x + 4x + 3y = -4x + 15$$
$$3y = -4x + 15$$
$$\dfrac{3y}{3} = \dfrac{-4x + 15}{3}$$
$$y = -\dfrac{4}{3}x + 5$$

4. For $F(z) = 4z - 3$, the independent variable is z, and the dependent variable is F.

3.2 Exercises

1. undefined

3. The slope is 5 and the y-intercept is 1.

5. TRUE

7. The only linear equation that is not a function is $x = a$, where a can be any constant.

9. A vertical line has one x-intercept, but no y-intercept.

11. Any line that is neither vertical nor horizontal.

13. a. $m = \dfrac{y_2 - y_1}{x_2 - x_1} = \dfrac{4-0}{3-0} = \dfrac{4}{3}$

b. For every 3 units of increase in x, y will increase by 4 units.

15. a. $m = \dfrac{y_2 - y_1}{x_2 - x_1} = \dfrac{-4-4}{2-(-1)} = \dfrac{-8}{3} = -\dfrac{8}{3}$

b. For every 3 units of increase in x, y will decrease by 8 units. For every 3 units of decrease in x, y will increase by 8 units.

17. $m = \dfrac{y_2 - y_1}{x_2 - x_1} = \dfrac{5-0}{1-0} = \dfrac{5}{1} = 5$

19. $m = \dfrac{y_2 - y_1}{x_2 - x_1} = \dfrac{9-1}{4-2} = \dfrac{8}{2} = 4$

21. $m = \dfrac{y_2 - y_1}{x_2 - x_1} = \dfrac{-6-3}{1-(-2)} = \dfrac{-9}{3} = -3$

23. $m = \dfrac{y_2 - y_1}{x_2 - x_1} = \dfrac{7-3}{3-(-2)} = \dfrac{4}{5}$

25. $m = \dfrac{y_2 - y_1}{x_2 - x_1} = \dfrac{2-2}{4-(-3)} = \dfrac{0}{7} = 0$

27. $m = \dfrac{y_2 - y_1}{x_2 - x_1} = \dfrac{-3-2}{10-10} = \dfrac{-5}{0} = \text{undefined}$

29. $m = \dfrac{y_2 - y_1}{x_2 - x_1} = \dfrac{\frac{11}{6} - \frac{5}{3}}{\frac{9}{4} - \frac{1}{2}} = \dfrac{\frac{11}{6} - \frac{10}{6}}{\frac{9}{4} - \frac{2}{4}} = \dfrac{\frac{1}{6}}{\frac{7}{4}} = \dfrac{1}{6} \cdot \dfrac{4}{7} = \dfrac{2}{21}$

31. $m = \dfrac{-\frac{11}{2} - \frac{14}{3}}{\frac{1}{5} - \left(-\frac{5}{4}\right)} = \dfrac{-\frac{33}{6} - \frac{28}{6}}{\frac{4}{20} + \frac{25}{20}} = \dfrac{-\frac{61}{6}}{\frac{29}{20}} = -\dfrac{61}{6} \cdot \dfrac{20}{29} = -\dfrac{610}{87}$

33. Start at $(1,2)$. Because $m = 3 = \dfrac{3}{1}$, move 1 unit to the right and 3 units up to find point $(2,5)$.

35. Start at $(-3,1)$. Because $m = -2 = -\dfrac{2}{1}$, move 1 unit to the right and 2 units down to find point $(-2,-1)$. We can also move 1 unit to the left and 2 units up to find point $(-4,3)$.

37. Start at $(-3,4)$. Because $m = \dfrac{1}{3}$, move 3 units to the right and 1 unit up to find point $(0,5)$.

39. Start at $(2,5)$. Because $m = -\dfrac{3}{2}$, move 2 unit to the right and 3 units down to find point $(4,2)$. We can also move 2 units to the left and 3 units up to find point $(0,8)$.

41. Because $m = 0$, the line is horizontal passing through the point $(1,2)$.

43. Answers will vary. One possible answer follows. We know $m = 1 = \dfrac{1}{1}$. Beginning at the point $(-3,4)$, and using a change in x of 1 and a change of y of 1, $-3+1 = -2$ and $4+1 = 5$, so $(-2,5)$ is on the line. Next, beginning at $(-2,5)$, $-2+1 = -1$ and $5+1 = 6$, so $(-1,6)$ is on the line. Now, beginning at $(-1,6)$, $-1+1 = 0$ and $6+1 = 7$, so $(0,7)$ is on the line. In summary, the points $(-2,5)$, $(-1,6)$, and $(0,7)$ will all be on the line.

45. Answers will vary. One possible answer follows. We know $m = \dfrac{5}{2}$. Beginning at the point $(-2,3)$, and using a change in x of 2 and a change of y of 5, $-2+2 = 0$ and $3+5 = 8$, so $(0,8)$ is on the line. Next, beginning at $(0,8)$, $0+2 = 2$ and $8+5 = 13$, so $(2,13)$ is on the line. Now, beginning at $(2,13)$, $2+2 = 4$ and $13+5 = 18$, so $(4,18)$ is on the line. In summary, the points $(0,8)$, $(2,13)$, and $(4,18)$ will all be on the line.

47. $m = \dfrac{y_2 - y_1}{x_2 - x_1} = \dfrac{-4-4}{-1-1} = \dfrac{-8}{-2} = 4$

$y - y_1 = m(x - x_1)$

$y - 4 = 4(x - 1)$

$y - 4 = 4x - 4$

$y = 4x$

49. $m = \dfrac{y_2 - y_1}{x_2 - x_1} = \dfrac{1-(-3)}{-4-5} = \dfrac{4}{-9} = -\dfrac{4}{9}$

$y - y_1 = m(x - x_1)$

$y - 1 = -\dfrac{4}{9}(x - (-4))$

$y - 1 = -\dfrac{4}{9}(x + 4)$

$y - 1 = -\dfrac{4}{9}x - \dfrac{16}{9}$

$y = -\dfrac{4}{9}x - \dfrac{7}{9}$

51. $m = \dfrac{y_2 - y_1}{x_2 - x_1} = \dfrac{3-3}{-4-1} = \dfrac{0}{-5} = 0$

$y - y_1 = m(x - x_1)$

$y - 3 = 0(x - 1)$

$y - 3 = 0$

$y = 3$

53. $y - y_1 = m(x - x_1)$

$y - 0 = 2(x - 0)$

$y = 2x$

55. $y - y_1 = m(x - x_1)$

$y - 1 = -3(x - (-1))$

$y - 1 = -3(x + 1)$

$y - 1 = -3x - 3$

$y = -3x - 2$

57. $y - y_1 = m(x - x_1)$

$y - 2 = \dfrac{4}{3}(x - 3)$

$y - 2 = \dfrac{4}{3}x - 4$

$y = \dfrac{4}{3}x - 2$

59. $y - y_1 = m(x - x_1)$

$$y - 4 = -\frac{5}{4}\left(x - (-2)\right)$$

$$y - 4 = -\frac{5}{4}(x + 2)$$

$$y - 4 = -\frac{5}{4}x - \frac{5}{2}$$

$$y = -\frac{5}{4}x + \frac{3}{2}$$

61. The slope is undefined, so the line is vertical and the equation is of the form $x = a$. Since the graph contains the point $(6,1)$, it must have x-intercept 6. Thus, the equation is $x = 6$.

63. $m = \dfrac{y_2 - y_1}{x_2 - x_1} = \dfrac{7 - 0}{5 - 0} = \dfrac{7}{5}$

$$y - y_1 = m(x - x_1)$$

$$y - 0 = \frac{7}{5}(x - 0)$$

$$y = \frac{7}{5}x$$

65. $m = \dfrac{y_2 - y_1}{x_2 - x_1} = \dfrac{7 - 2}{4 - 3} = \dfrac{5}{1} = 5$

$$y - y_1 = m(x - x_1)$$

$$y - 2 = 5(x - 3)$$

$$y - 2 = 5x - 15$$

$$y = 5x - 13$$

67. $m = \dfrac{y_2 - y_1}{x_2 - x_1} = \dfrac{-2 - 1}{5 - (-2)} = \dfrac{-3}{7} = -\dfrac{3}{7}$

$$y - y_1 = m(x - x_1)$$

$$y - 1 = -\frac{3}{7}\left(x - (-2)\right)$$

$$y - 1 = -\frac{3}{7}(x + 2)$$

$$y - 1 = -\frac{3}{7}x - \frac{6}{7}$$

$$y = -\frac{3}{7}x + \frac{1}{7}$$

69. $m = \dfrac{y_2 - y_1}{x_2 - x_1} = \dfrac{5 - (-3)}{-1 - (-1)} = \dfrac{8}{0} =$ undefined

Since the slope is undefined, the line is vertical and the equation is of the form $x = a$. Since the graph contains $(-1,-3)$ and $(-1,5)$, the x-intercept must be -1. Thus, the equation is $x = -1$.

71. $m = \dfrac{y_2 - y_1}{x_2 - x_1} = \dfrac{-7 - 3}{-3 - 1} = \dfrac{-10}{-4} = \dfrac{5}{2}$

$$y - y_1 = m(x - x_1)$$

$$y - 3 = \frac{5}{2}(x - 1)$$

$$y - 3 = \frac{5}{2}x - \frac{5}{2}$$

$$y = \frac{5}{2}x + \frac{1}{2}$$

73. $m = \dfrac{y_2 - y_1}{x_2 - x_1} = \dfrac{4 - 4}{-4 - 2} = \dfrac{0}{-6} = 0$

$$y - y_1 = m(x - x_1)$$

$$y - 4 = 0(x - 2)$$

$$y - 4 = 0$$

$$y = 4$$

75. $m = \dfrac{y_2 - y_1}{x_2 - x_1} = \dfrac{-\frac{1}{6} - \frac{7}{3}}{\frac{3}{4} - \frac{5}{2}} = \dfrac{-\frac{15}{6}}{-\frac{7}{4}} = \left(-\dfrac{15}{6}\right)\left(-\dfrac{4}{7}\right) = \dfrac{10}{7}$

$$y - y_1 = m(x - x_1)$$

$$y - \frac{7}{3} = \frac{10}{7}\left(x - \frac{5}{2}\right)$$

$$y - \frac{7}{3} = \frac{10}{7}x - \frac{25}{7}$$

$$y = \frac{10}{7}x - \frac{26}{21}$$

77. For $y = 2x - 1$, the slope is 2 and the y-intercept is -1. Begin at $(0,-1)$ and move to the right 1 unit and up 2 units to find point $(1,1)$.

79. For $y = -4x$, the slope is -4 and the y-intercept is 0. Begin at $(0,0)$ and move to the right 1 unit and down 4 units to find point $(1,-4)$. We can also move 1 unit to the left and 4 units up to find point $(-1,4)$.

81. $2x + y = 3$

$$y = -2x + 3$$

The slope is -2 and the y-intercept is 3. Begin at $(0,3)$ and move to the right 1 unit and down 2 units to find the point $(1,1)$. We can also move 1 unit to the left and 2 units up to find the point $(-1,5)$.

83. $4x + 2y = 8$

$$2y = -4x + 8$$

$$y = \frac{-4x + 8}{2}$$

$$y = -2x + 4$$

The slope is -2 and the y-intercept is 4. Begin at $(0,4)$ and move to the right 1 unit and down 2 units to find the point $(1,2)$. We can also move 1 unit to the left and 2 units up to find the point $(-1,6)$.

85. $x - 4y - 2 = 0$

$$-4y = -x + 2$$

$$y = \frac{-x + 2}{-4}$$

$$y = \frac{1}{4}x - \frac{1}{2}$$

The slope is $\frac{1}{4}$ and the y-intercept is $-\frac{1}{2}$.

Begin at $\left(0, -\frac{1}{2}\right)$ and move to the right 4 units

and up 1 unit to find the point $\left(4, \frac{1}{2}\right)$.

87. For $x = 3$, the slope is undefined and it has no y-intercept. It is a vertical line with x-intercept 3.

89. For $f(x) = -3x + 7$, the slope is -3 and the y-intercept is 7. Begin at $(0,7)$ and move to the right 1 unit and down 3 units to find the point $(1,4)$. We can also move 1 unit to the left and 3 units up to find the point $(-1,10)$.

91. For $h(x) = -\dfrac{5}{3}x + 4$, the slope is $-5/3$ and the y-intercept is 4. Begin at $(0,4)$ and move to the right 3 units and down 5 units to find the point $(3,-1)$. We can also move 3 units to the left and 5 units up to find the point $(-3,9)$.

93. The x-axis is a horizontal line passing through the origin. Thus, the slope is 0 and the y-intercept is 0. So, the equation of the x-axis is $y = 0x + 0$ or simply $y = 0$.

95. Since $f(2) = 6$ and $f(5) = 12$, the points $(2, 6)$ and $(5, 12)$ are on the graph of f. Thus,

$$m = \frac{y_2 - y_1}{x_2 - x_1} = \frac{12 - 6}{5 - 2} = \frac{6}{3} = 2$$

$$y - y_1 = m(x - x_1)$$

$$y - 6 = 2(x - 2)$$

$$y - 6 = 2x - 4$$

$$y = 2x + 2 \quad \text{or} \quad f(x) = 2x + 2$$

Finally, $f(-2) = 2(-2) + 2 = -4 + 2 = -2$.

97. Since $h(3) = 7$ and $h(-1) = 14$, the points $(3, 7)$ and $(-1, 14)$ are on the graph of h. Thus,

$$m = \frac{y_2 - y_1}{x_2 - x_1} = \frac{14 - 7}{-1 - 3} = \frac{7}{-4} = -\frac{7}{4}$$

$$y - y_1 = m(x - x_1)$$

$$y - 7 = -\frac{7}{4}(x - 3)$$

$$y - 7 = -\frac{7}{4}x + \frac{21}{4}$$

$$y = -\frac{7}{4}x + \frac{49}{4} \quad \text{or} \quad h(x) = -\frac{7}{4}x + \frac{49}{4}$$

Finally, $h\left(\dfrac{1}{2}\right) = -\dfrac{7}{4}\left(\dfrac{1}{2}\right) + \dfrac{49}{4} = -\dfrac{7}{8} + \dfrac{49}{4} = \dfrac{91}{8}$.

99. a.

b. Average rate of change

$$= \frac{47.5 - 50}{30 - 20}$$

$$= -0.25 \text{ heart beats per year}$$

Between ages 20 and 30, the maximum number of heartbeats (that a healthy individual should have during a 15-second time interval while exercising) decreases at a rate of 0.25 heartbeats per year.

c. Average rate of change

$$= \frac{40 - 42.5}{60 - 50}$$

$$= -0.25 \text{ heart beats per year}$$

Between ages 50 and 60, the maximum number of heartbeats (that a healthy individual should have during a 15-second time interval while exercising) decreases at a rate of 0.25 heartbeats per year.

d. Yes. The maximum number of heart beats appears to be linearly related to age. The average rate of change (slope) is constant for the data provided.

101. a.

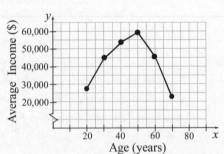

b. Average rate of change

$$= \frac{44,477 - 27,711}{30 - 20}$$

$$= \$1,676.60 \text{ per year}$$

Between ages 20 and 30, the average individual's income increases at a rate of $1,676.60 per year.

c. Average rate of change

$$= \frac{44{,}993 - 58{,}217}{60 - 50}$$

$$= -\$1{,}322.40 \text{ per year}$$

Between ages 50 and 60, the average individual's income decreases at a rate of $1,332.40 per year.

d. No. The average income is not linearly related to age. The average rate of change (slope) is not constant.

103. a. Let x represent the number of years since 1988. Then $x = 0$ represents 1988 and $x = 7$ represents 1995. Let L represent the swordfish landings (in millions of pounds).

$$m = \frac{6.3 - 10.23}{7 - 0} \approx -0.56 \text{ million pounds per year}$$

$$L - 10.23 = -0.56(x - 0)$$

$$L - 10.23 = -0.56x$$

$$L = -0.56x + 10.23$$

Using function notation, $L(x) = -0.56x + 10.23$.

b. The year 2000 corresponds to $x = 12$.

$$L(12) = -0.56(12) + 10.23 = 3.51$$

If the linear trend continues, the swordfish landings would be 3.51 million pounds in 2000.

c. The slope (-0.56) indicates that swordfish landings are decreasing at a rate of 0.56 million pounds per year.

d.

$$-0.56x + 10.23 = 2.39$$

$$-0.56x = -7.84$$

$$x = 14$$

Now, $x = 14$ correspond to the year 2002. Thus, landings of swordfish will be 2.39 million pounds in 2002.

105. a. Let x represent the weight of the diamond and C represent the cost.

$$m = \frac{4378 - 3543}{0.8 - 0.7} = \$8350 \text{ per Carat}$$

$$C - 3543 = 8350(x - 0.7)$$

$$C - 3543 = 8350x - 5845$$

$$C = 8350x - 2302$$

Using function notation, $C(x) = 8350x - 2302$.

b. $C(0.77) = 8350(0.77) - 2302 = 4127.5$

The price of a 0.77 Carat diamond would be $4127.50.

c. The slope indicates that the cost of diamonds increases at a rate of $8350 per Carat.

d.

$$8350x - 2302 = 5300$$

$$8350x = 7602$$

$$x = \frac{7602}{8350} \approx 0.91$$

A diamond weighing approximately 0.91 Carats should cost $5300.

107. a. Let x represent disposable income (in billions of dollars) and C represent personal consumption expenditures (in billions of dollars).

$$m = \frac{6728.4 - 3831.5}{7031.0 - 4293.6} \approx 1.06$$

$$C - 3831.5 = 1.06(x - 4293.6)$$

$$C - 3831.5 = 1.06x - 4551.216$$

$$C = 1.06x - 719.716$$

In function notation, $C(x) = 1.06x - 719.716$.

b. $C(7417.3) = 1.06(7417.3) - 719.716 \approx 7142.6$

In 2001, personal consumption expenditures would have been $7,142.6 billion.

c. The slope indicates that the personal consumption expenditures are increasing at a rate of approximately $1.06 per $1.00 of personal disposable income.

d.

$$1.06x - 719.716 = 7210$$

$$1.06x = 7929.716$$

$$x \approx 7480.9$$

Personal disposable income would be approximately $7,480.9 billion if personal consumption expenditures were $7,210 billion.

109. The graph shown has both a positive slope and a positive y-intercept. The only given equation that meets both of these conditions is the one in part (c), $y = 2x + 3$.

111. Graph the three equations $2x + y = -3$, $2x + y = 0$, and $2x + y = 3$ on the same Cartesian plane.

Answers may vary. The graphs of the members of the family $2x + y = C$ will be parallel lines.

113. According to the ADA codes, for every twelve units of horizontal change in the access ramp, the vertical change must be one unit or less.

115. The settings and graphs are shown below.

Answers may vary. For each graph of $y = mx + 2$, the y-intercept will be 2. For $m = 0$, the graph will be horizontal. For $m > 0$, the graph will slant upward from left to right. The slant will be steeper as m becomes larger.

Answers may vary. For $m < 0$, the graph will slant downward from left to right. The slant will be steeper as $|m|$ becomes larger.

3.3 Preparing for Parallel and Perpendicular Lines

1. The reciprocal of 3 is $\frac{1}{3}$ because $3 \cdot \frac{1}{3} = 1$.

2. The reciprocal of $-\frac{3}{5}$ is $-\frac{5}{3}$ because
$$\left(-\frac{3}{5}\right)\left(-\frac{5}{3}\right) = 1.$$

3.3 Exercises

1. slope; y-intercepts

3. FALSE. Nonvertical perpendicular lines have slopes that are *negative reciprocals* of each other.

5. No. If the two nonvertical lines have the same x-intercept but different y-intercepts, then their slopes cannot be equal. Therefore, they cannot be parallel lines.

7. **a.** Slope of parallel line: $m = 5$.

    b. Slope of perpendicular line: $m = -1/5$.

9. **a.** Slope of parallel line: $m = -5/6$.

    b. Slope of perpendicular line: $m = 6/5$

11. Parallel. The two lines have equal slopes, $m = 5$, but different y-intercepts.

13.
$$
\begin{array}{ll}
8x + y = 12 & 2x - 8y = 3 \\
\quad y = -8x + 12 & \quad -8y = -2x + 3 \\
 & \quad y = \dfrac{-2x + 3}{-8} \\
 & \quad y = \dfrac{1}{4}x - \dfrac{3}{8}
\end{array}
$$

Neither. The two slopes, $m_1 = -8$ and $m_2 = 1/4$, are not equal and are not negative reciprocals.

15.
$$
\begin{array}{ll}
-4x + 2y = 12 & x + 2y = 6 \\
\quad 2y = 4x + 12 & \quad 2y = -x + 6 \\
\quad y = \dfrac{4x + 12}{2} & \quad y = \dfrac{-x + 6}{2} \\
\quad y = 2x + 6 & \quad y = -\dfrac{1}{2}x + 3
\end{array}
$$

Perpendicular. The two slopes, $m_1 = 2$ and $m_2 = -1/2$, are negative reciprocals.

17.

$$-x+\frac{1}{3}y=\frac{1}{3} \qquad x-\frac{1}{3}y=\frac{5}{3}$$

$$3\left(-x+\frac{1}{3}y\right)=3\left(\frac{1}{3}\right) \qquad -3\left(x-\frac{1}{3}y\right)=-3\left(\frac{5}{3}\right)$$

$$-3x+y=1 \qquad -3x+y=-5$$

$$y=3x+1 \qquad y=3x-5$$

Parallel. The two lines have equal slopes, $m=3$, but different y-intercepts.

19. $m_1=\frac{5-2}{6-1}=\frac{3}{5}$; $m_2=\frac{-2-3}{1-(-2)}=\frac{-5}{3}=-\frac{5}{3}$

Perpendicular. The two slopes, $m_1=3/5$ and $m_2=-5/3$, are negative reciprocals.

21. $m_1=\frac{-3-4}{1-(-2)}=\frac{-7}{3}=-\frac{7}{3}$;

$m_2=\frac{1-(-6)}{-4-(-1)}=\frac{7}{-3}=-\frac{7}{3}$

Parallel. The two lines have equal slopes, but different y-intercepts.

23. $m_1=\frac{3-5}{1-0}=\frac{-2}{1}=-2$; $m_2=\frac{14-6}{0-(-4)}=\frac{8}{4}=2$

Neither. The two slopes are not equal and are not negative reciprocals.

25. Since line L is parallel to $y=\frac{3}{2}x$, the slope of L is $m=3/2$. From the graph, the y-intercept of L is -3. Thus, the equation of line L is $y=\frac{3}{2}x-3$.

27. Since line L is perpendicular to $y=-2x-1$, the slope of L is $m=1/2$, the negative reciprocal of -2. From the graph, the y-intercept of L is 2. Thus, the equation of line L is $y=\frac{1}{2}x+2$.

29. Since line L is perpendicular to $x=-2$ and since $x=-2$ is a vertical line, then L must be a horizontal line. From the graph, the y-intercept of L is 2. Thus, the equation of line L is $y=2$.

31. The slope of the line we seek is $m=2$, the same as the slope of $y=2x+3$. The equation of the line is

$$y-y_1=m(x-x_1)$$

$$y-1=2(x-3)$$

$$y-1=2x-6$$

$$y=2x-5$$

33. The slope of the line we seek is $m=1/2$, the negative reciprocal of the slope of $y=-2x+1$. The equation of the line is

$$y-y_1=m(x-x_1)$$

$$y-3=\frac{1}{2}(x-2)$$

$$y-3=\frac{1}{2}x-1$$

$$y=\frac{1}{2}x+2.$$

35. The line we seek is horizontal, parallel to the horizontal line $y = 1$. Now a horizontal line passing through the point $(-1, -3)$ must also pass through the point $(0, -3)$. That is, the y-intercept is -3. Thus, the equation of the line is $y = -3$.

37. The line we seek is horizontal, perpendicular to the vertical line $x = 1$. Now a horizontal line passing through the point $(1, 3)$ must also pass through the point $(0, 3)$. That is, the y-intercept is 3. Thus, the equation of the line is $y = 3$.

39. The slope of the line we seek is $m = 3$, the same as the slope of the line

$$3x - y = 2$$
$$-y = -3x + 2$$
$$y = 3x - 2.$$

Thus, the equation of the line we seek is

$$y - y_1 = m(x - x_1)$$
$$y - 5 = 3(x - 1)$$
$$y - 5 = 3x - 3$$
$$y = 3x + 2.$$

41. The slope of the line we seek is $m = 3/4$, the negative reciprocal of the slope of the line

$$4x + 3y - 1 = 0$$
$$3y = -4x + 1$$
$$y = \frac{-4x + 1}{3}$$
$$y = -\frac{4}{3}x + \frac{1}{3}.$$

Thus, the equation of the line we seek is

$$y - y_1 = m(x - x_1)$$
$$y - 1 = \frac{3}{4}(x - (-4))$$
$$y - 1 = \frac{3}{4}(x + 4)$$
$$y - 1 = \frac{3}{4}x + 3$$
$$y = \frac{3}{4}x + 4.$$

43. The slope of the line we seek is $m = -5/2$, the same as the slope of the line

$$5x + 2y = 1$$
$$2y = -5x + 1$$
$$y = \frac{-5x + 1}{2}$$
$$y = -\frac{5}{2}x + \frac{1}{2}.$$

Thus, the equation of the line we seek is

$$y - y_1 = m(x - x_1)$$
$$y - (-3) = -\frac{5}{2}(x - (-2))$$
$$y + 3 = -\frac{5}{2}(x + 2)$$
$$y + 3 = -\frac{5}{2}x - 5$$
$$y = -\frac{5}{2}x - 8.$$

45. a. $A = (1,1)$, $B = (4,3)$, $C = (2,6)$.

b. Slope of $\overline{AB} = \dfrac{3-1}{4-1} = \dfrac{2}{3}$

Slope of $\overline{BC} = \dfrac{6-3}{2-4} = \dfrac{3}{-2} = -\dfrac{3}{2}$

Because the slopes are negative reciprocals, segments $\overline{AB}$ and $\overline{BC}$ are perpendicular. Thus, triangle ABC is a right triangle.

47. a. $A = (2,2)$, $B = (7,3)$, $C = (8,6)$, $D = (3,5)$.

b. Slope of $\overline{AB} = \dfrac{3-2}{7-2} = \dfrac{1}{5}$

Slope of $\overline{BC} = \dfrac{6-3}{8-7} = \dfrac{3}{1} = 3$

Slope of $\overline{CD} = \dfrac{5-6}{3-8} = \dfrac{-1}{-5} = \dfrac{1}{5}$

Slope of $\overline{DA} = \dfrac{2-5}{2-3} = \dfrac{-3}{-1} = 3$

Because the slopes of $\overline{AB}$ and $\overline{CD}$ are equal, $\overline{AB}$ and $\overline{CD}$ are parallel. Because the slopes of $\overline{BC}$ and $\overline{DA}$ are equal, $\overline{BC}$ and $\overline{DA}$ are parallel. Thus, quadrilateral $ABCD$ is a parallelogram.

49. The line
$$4x + y = 3$$
$$y = -4x + 3$$
has a slope of -4. The line
$$Ax + 4y = 12$$
$$4y = -Ax + 12$$
$$y = \dfrac{-Ax + 12}{4}$$
$$y = -\dfrac{A}{4}x + 3$$
has a slope of $-A/4$. For the two lines to be perpendicular, the product of their slopes must be -1. Use this fact to determine the value of A:
$$-4 \cdot \left(-\dfrac{A}{4}\right) = -1$$
$$A = -1$$

51. In the graph, the two parallel lines have positive slopes. In addition, one of the lines has a positive y-intercept while the other has a negative y-intercept. The only pair of equations that meets these criteria is the pair in part (c). (Note: The graphs of each pair of equations in parts (b) and (d) are parallel, but have all positive y-intercepts. The pair of equations in part (a) are perpendicular, not parallel. The pair of equations in part (e) represents the same line.)

Putting the Concepts Together (Sections 3.1 – 3.3)

1. Find the y-intercept by letting $x = 0$ and solving for y.
$$x = 0: \quad y = -0 + 6$$
$$y = 6$$
The y-intercept is 6, so the point $(0, 6)$ is on the graph. Find the x-intercept by letting $y = 0$ and solving for x.
$$y = 0: \quad 0 = -x + 6$$
$$x = 6$$
The x-intercept is 6, so the point $(6, 0)$ is on the graph.

2. Let $x = -4, 0, 4,$ and 8.

$x = -4$: $3(-4) - 4y = 0$

$$-12 - 4y = 0$$
$$-4y = 12$$
$$y = -3$$

$x = 0$: $3(0) - 4y = 0$

$$y = 0$$

$x = 4$: $3(4) - 4y = 0$

$$12 - 4y = 0$$
$$-4y = -12$$
$$y = 3$$

$x = 8$: $3(8) - 4y = 0$

$$24 - 4y = 0$$
$$-4y = -24$$
$$y = 6$$

Thus, the points (-4, -3), (0, 0), (4, 3), and (8, 6) are on the graph.

3. Find the *y*-intercept by letting $x = 0$ and solving for *y*.

$x = 0$: $2(0) - 5y = 20$

$$-5y = 20$$
$$y = -4$$

The *y*-intercept is -4, so the point (0, -4) is on the graph. Find the *x*-intercept by letting $y = 0$ and solving for *x*.

$y = 0$: $2x - 5(0) = 20$

$$2x = 20$$
$$x = 10$$

The *x*-intercept is 10, so the point (10, 0) is on the graph.

4. Let $x = -2, 2, 6,$ and 10.

$x = -2$: $\dfrac{1}{2}(-2) - \dfrac{2}{3}y = 1$

$$-1 - \dfrac{2}{3}y = 1$$
$$-\dfrac{2}{3}y = 2$$
$$-\dfrac{3}{2}\left(-\dfrac{2}{3}y\right) = -\dfrac{3}{2}(2)$$
$$y = -3$$

$x = 2$: $\dfrac{1}{2}(2) - \dfrac{2}{3}y = 1$

$$1 - \dfrac{2}{3}y = 1$$
$$-\dfrac{2}{3}y = 0$$
$$-\dfrac{3}{2}\left(-\dfrac{2}{3}y\right) = -\dfrac{3}{2}(0)$$
$$y = 0$$

$x = 6$: $\dfrac{1}{2}(6) - \dfrac{2}{3}y = 1$

$$3 - \dfrac{2}{3}y = 1$$
$$-\dfrac{2}{3}y = -2$$
$$-\dfrac{3}{2}\left(-\dfrac{2}{3}y\right) = -\dfrac{3}{2}(-2)$$
$$y = 3$$

$x = 10$: $\dfrac{1}{2}(10) - \dfrac{2}{3}y = 1$

$$5 - \dfrac{2}{3}y = 1$$
$$-\dfrac{2}{3}y = -4$$
$$-\dfrac{3}{2}\left(-\dfrac{2}{3}y\right) = -\dfrac{3}{2}(-4)$$
$$y = 6$$

Thus, the points (-2, -3), (2, 0), (6, 3), and (10, 6) are on the graph.

5. The equation $y = 6$ will be a horizontal line with y-intercept 6.

6. For $g(x) = -\dfrac{3}{4}x + 1$, the slope is $-\dfrac{3}{4}$ and the y-intercept is 1. Begin at (0, 1) and move to the right 4 units and down 3 units to find the point (4, -2). We can also move 4 units to the left and 3 units up to find the point (-4, 4).

7. $m = \dfrac{y_2 - y_1}{x_2 - x_1} = \dfrac{7 - 5}{3 - (-1)} = \dfrac{2}{4} = \dfrac{1}{2}$;

For every 2 units of increase in x, y will increase by 1 unit.

8. We convert the equation to the form $y = mx + b$.
$$4x - 5y = 20$$
$$-5y = -4x + 20$$
$$y = \frac{-4x + 20}{-5}$$
$$y = \frac{4}{5}x - 4$$

The slope is $\dfrac{4}{5}$, and the y-intercept is -4.

9. Start at (-2, -4). Because $m = \dfrac{3}{4}$, move 4 units to the right and 3 units up to find point (2, -1).

10.

$$12x - 4y = 1 \qquad\qquad x - 3y = -12$$
$$-4y = -12x + 1 \qquad -3y = -x - 12$$
$$y = \frac{-12x + 1}{-4} \qquad y = \frac{-x - 12}{-3}$$
$$y = 3x - \frac{1}{4} \qquad\qquad y = \frac{1}{3}x + 4$$

Neither. The slopes of the two lines, 3 and 1/3, are not equal and are not negative reciprocals.

11.
$$y - y_1 = m(x - x_1)$$
$$y - (-4) = \frac{3}{2}(x - 6)$$
$$y + 4 = \frac{3}{2}x - 9$$
$$y = \frac{3}{2}x - 13$$

12. $m = \dfrac{y_2 - y_1}{x_2 - x_1} = \dfrac{-3 - 7}{4 - (-1)} = \dfrac{-10}{5} = -2$
$$y - y_1 = m(x - x_1)$$
$$y - 7 = -2(x - (-1))$$
$$y - 7 = -2x - 2$$
$$y = -2x + 5$$

13. The slope of the line we seek is $m = \dfrac{2}{3}$, the same as the slope of the line
$$2x - 3y = 12$$
$$-3y = -2x + 12$$
$$y = \frac{-2x + 12}{-3}$$
$$y = \frac{2}{3}x - 4$$

Thus, the equation of the line we seek is:
$$y - 4 = \frac{2}{3}(x - (-3))$$
$$y - 4 = \frac{2}{3}x + 2$$
$$y = \frac{2}{3}x + 6$$

14. The slope of the line we seek is $m = -\dfrac{3}{4}$, the

negative reciprocal of the line
$$4x - 3y = 3$$
$$-3y = -4x + 3$$
$$y = \frac{-4x + 3}{-3}$$
$$y = \frac{4}{3}x - 1$$

Thus, the equation of the line we seek is:
$$y - (-1) = -\frac{3}{4}(x - 4)$$
$$y + 1 = -\frac{3}{4}x + 3$$
$$y = -\frac{3}{4}x + 2$$

15. a. The total weight will be 40 pounds times the number of television sets x, plus the 5700 pounds from the weight of the van. Thus, the function is $W(x) = 40x + 5700$.

b. The independent variable is the number of television sets, x, which cannot be negative. Thus, the domain of W is $\{x \mid x \geq 0\}$ or, using interval notation, $[0, \infty)$.

c. $W(62) = 40(62) + 5700 = 8180$

If 62 televisions sets are loaded on the van, the total weight will be 8180 pounds.

d. Evaluate W at $x = 0$, 50, and 100.
$$W(0) = 40(0) + 5700 = 5700$$
$$W(50) = 40(50) + 5700 = 7700$$
$$W(100) = 40(100) + 5700 = 9700$$

Thus, the points (0, 5700), (50, 7700), and (100, 9700) are on the graph.

e. We must solve $W(x) = 8580$.
$$40x + 5700 = 8580$$
$$40x = 2880$$
$$x = 72$$
The total weight is 8580 pounds when 72 television sets are loaded on the van.

16. a.

b. Average rate of change
$$= \frac{900 - 750}{10,000 - 5,000}$$
$$= \$0.03 \text{ per dollar of sales}$$
Between monthly sales of \$5,000 and \$10,000, the earnings increase at a rate of \$0.03 for each additional dollar of sales.

c. Average rate of change
$$= \frac{1350 - 1200}{25,000 - 20,000}$$
$$= \$0.03 \text{ per dollar of sales}$$
Between monthly sales of \$20,000 and \$25,000, the earnings increase at a rate of \$0.03 for each additional dollar of sales.

d. Yes. The monthly earnings are linearly related to sales. The average rate of change (slope) is constant.

3.4 Preparing for Linear Inequalities in Two Variables

1. $3(4)+1 \overset{?}{\geq} 7$

   $12+1 \overset{?}{\geq} 7$

   $13 \geq 7 \leftarrow$ True

   Yes, $x=4$ does satisfy the inequality $3x+1 \geq 7$.

2. $-4x-3 > 9$

   $-4x-3+3 > 9+3$

   $-4x > 12$

   $\dfrac{-4x}{-4} < \dfrac{12}{-4}$

   $x < -3$

   The solution set is $\{x|x<-3\}$ or, using interval notation, $(-\infty,-3)$.

3.4 Exercises

1. half-planes

3. FALSE. The solution of a linear inequality is a half-plane.

5. Answers may vary. The solution of a linear inequality is a half-plane. In each half plane, either all of the points satisfy the inequality or no points satisfy the inequality. If a test point does not satisfy the inequality, then it must lie in the half-plane in which no points satisfy the inequality. The opposite half-plane must then contain the solutions.

7. **a.** $x=0,\ y=1 \quad 0+3(1) \overset{?}{<} 6$

   $3 < 6$ True

   So, $(0,1)$ is a solution to $x+3y<6$.

   b. $x=-2,\ y=4 \quad -2+3(4) \overset{?}{<} 6$

   $-2+12 \overset{?}{<} 6$

   $10 < 6$ False

   So, $(-2,4)$ is not a solution to $x+3y<6$.

c. $x=8,\ y=-1 \quad 8+3(-1) \overset{?}{<} 6$

   $8-3 \overset{?}{<} 6$

   $5 < 6$ True

   So, $(8,-1)$ is a solution to $x+3y<6$.

9. **a.** $x=-4,\ y=2 \quad -3(-4)+4(2) \overset{?}{\geq} 12$

   $12+8 \overset{?}{\geq} 12$

   $20 \geq 12$ True

   So, $(-4,2)$ is a solution to $-3x+4y \geq 12$.

   b. $x=0,\ y=2 \quad -3(0)+4(2) \overset{?}{\geq} 12$

   $0+8 \overset{?}{\geq} 12$

   $8 \geq 12$ False

   So, $(0,2)$ is not a solution to $-3x+4y \geq 12$.

   c. $x=0,\ y=3 \quad -3(0)+4(3) \overset{?}{\geq} 12$

   $0+12 \overset{?}{\geq} 12$

   $12 \geq 12$ True

   So, $(0,3)$ is a solution to $-3x+4y \geq 12$.

11. Replace the inequality symbol with an equal sign to obtain $y=3$. Because the inequality is strict, graph $y=3$ using a dashed line.

    Test Point: $(0,0)$: $\ 0 \overset{?}{>} 3$ False

    Therefore, $(0,0)$ is not a solution to $y>3$. Shade the half-plane that does not contain $(0,0)$.

13. Replace the inequality symbol with an equal sign to obtain $x = -2$. Because the inequality is non-strict, graph $x = -2$ using a solid line.

Test Point: $(0,0)$: $0 \overset{?}{\geq} -2$ True

Therefore, $(0,0)$ is a solution to $x \geq -2$. Shade the half-plane that contains $(0,0)$.

15. Replace the inequality symbol with an equal sign to obtain $y = 5x$. Because the inequality is strict, graph $y = 5x$ using a dashed line.

Test Point: $(1,1)$: $1 \overset{?}{<} 5(1)$

$1 \overset{?}{<} 5$ True

Therefore, $(1,1)$ is a solution to $y < 5x$. Shade the half-plane that contains $(1,1)$.

17. Replace the inequality symbol with an equal sign to obtain $y = 2x + 3$. Because the inequality is strict, graph $y = 2x + 3$ using a dashed line.

Test Point: $(0,0)$: $0 \overset{?}{>} 2(0) + 3$

$0 \overset{?}{>} 3$ False

Therefore, $(0,0)$ is not a solution to $y > 2x + 3$.

Shade the half-plane that does not contain $(0,0)$.

19. Replace the inequality symbol with an equal sign to obtain $y = \frac{1}{2}x - 5$. Because the inequality is non-strict, graph $y = \frac{1}{2}x - 5$ using a solid line.

Test Point: $(0,0)$: $0 \overset{?}{\leq} \frac{1}{2}(0) - 5$

$0 \overset{?}{\leq} -5$ False

Therefore, $(0,0)$ is not a solution to $y \leq \frac{1}{2}x - 5$.

Shade the half-plane that does not contain $(0,0)$.

21. Replace the inequality symbol with an equal sign to obtain $3x + y = 4$. Because the inequality is non-strict, graph $3x + y = 4$ $(y = -3x + 4)$ using a solid line.

Test Point: $(0,0)$: $3(0) + 0 \overset{?}{\leq} 4$

$0 \overset{?}{\leq} 4$ True

Therefore, $(0,0)$ is solution to $3x + y \leq 4$.

Shade the half-plane that contains $(0,0)$.

23. Replace the inequality symbol with an equal sign to obtain $2x + 5y = -10$. Because the inequality is non-strict, graph $2x + 5y = -10$ $\left(y = -\dfrac{2}{5}x - 2 \right)$ using a solid line.

Test Point: $(0,0)$: $2(0) + 5(0) \overset{?}{\le} -10$

$\qquad\qquad\qquad 0 \overset{?}{\le} -10 \qquad$ False

Therefore, $(0,0)$ is not a solution to $2x + 5y \le -10$.

Shade the half-plane that does not contain $(0,0)$.

25. Replace the inequality symbol with an equal sign to obtain $-4x + 6y = 24$. Because the inequality is strict, graph $-4x + 6y = 24$ $\left(y = \dfrac{2}{3}x + 4 \right)$ using a dashed line.

Test Point: $(0,0)$: $-4(0) + 6(0) \overset{?}{>} 24$

$\qquad\qquad\qquad 0 \overset{?}{>} 24 \qquad$ False

Therefore, $(0,0)$ is not a solution to $-4x + 6y > 24$. Shade the half-plane that does not contain $(0,0)$.

27. Replace the inequality symbol with an equal sign to obtain $\dfrac{x}{2} + \dfrac{y}{3} = 1$. Because the inequality is strict, graph $\dfrac{x}{2} + \dfrac{y}{3} = 1$ $\left(y = -\dfrac{3}{2}x + 3 \right)$ using a dashed line.

Test Point: $(0,0)$: $\dfrac{0}{2} + \dfrac{0}{3} \overset{?}{<} 1$

$\qquad\qquad\qquad 0 \overset{?}{<} 1 \qquad$ True

Therefore, $(0,0)$ is a solution to $\dfrac{x}{2} + \dfrac{y}{3} < 1$.

Shade the half-plane that contains $(0,0)$.

29. Replace the inequality symbol with an equal sign to obtain $\dfrac{2}{3}x - \dfrac{3}{2}y = 2$. Because the inequality is non-strict, graph $\dfrac{2}{3}x - \dfrac{3}{2}y = 2$ $\left(y = \dfrac{4}{9}x - \dfrac{4}{3} \right)$ using a solid line.

Test Point: $(0,0)$: $\dfrac{2}{3}(0) - \dfrac{3}{2}(0) \overset{?}{\ge} 2$

$\qquad\qquad\qquad 0 \overset{?}{\ge} 2 \qquad$ False

Therefore, $(0,0)$ is not a solution to $\dfrac{2}{3}x - \dfrac{3}{2}y \ge 2$. Shade the half-plane that does not contain $(0,0)$.

31. a. Let $x =$ the number of Filet-o-Fish.
Let $y =$ the number of orders of fries.
$45x + 40y \le 150$

b. $x = 2$, $y = 1$: $45(2) + 40(1) \overset{?}{\le} 150$

$\qquad\qquad\qquad 130 \overset{?}{\le} 150 \qquad$ True

Sammy can stay below his limit of 150 grams of carbohydrates by eating two Filet-o-Fish and one order of fries.

c. $x = 3$, $y = 1$: $45(3) + 40(1) \overset{?}{\leq} 150$

$175 \overset{?}{\leq} 150$ False

Sammy cannot stay below his limit of 150 grams of carbohydrates by eating three Filet-o-Fish and one order of fries.

33. a. Let x = the number Switch A assemblies.
Let y = the number Switch B assemblies.
$2x + 1.5y \leq 80$

b. $x = 24$, $y = 41$: $2(24) + 1.5(41) \overset{?}{\leq} 80$

$109.5 \overset{?}{\leq} 80$ False

Acme cannot manufacture 24 of Switch A and 41 of Switch B in a week (80 hours).

c. $x = 16$, $y = 45$: $2(16) + 1.5(45) \overset{?}{\leq} 80$

$99.5 \overset{?}{\leq} 80$ False

Acme cannot manufacture 16 of Switch A and 45 of Switch B in a week (80 hours).

35. The graph contains a line passing through the points $(0, -2)$ and $(2, 2)$. The slope of the line is $m = \dfrac{2 - (-2)}{2 - 0} = \dfrac{4}{2} = 2$. The y-intercept is -2.

Thus, the equation of the line is $y = 2x - 2$.

Because the half-plane that is shaded is above the line, our inequality will contain a "greater than." Because the line is dashed, this means that the inequality is strict. That is, our inequality will consist only of "greater than." Thus, the linear inequality is $y > 2x - 2$.

37. The graph contains a line passing through the points $(-2, 3)$ and $(2, -1)$. The slope of the line is $m = \dfrac{-1 - 3}{2 - (-2)} = \dfrac{-4}{4} = -1$. The equation of the line is

$y - (-1) = -1(x - 2)$
$y + 1 = -x + 2$
$y = -x + 1$.

Because the half-plane that is shaded is below the line, our inequality will contain a "less than." Because the line is solid, this means that the inequality is non-strict. That is, our inequality will consist of "less than or equal to." Thus, the linear inequality is $y \leq -x + 1$.

39. $y > 3$

41. $y < 5x$

43. $y > 2x + 3$

45. $y \leq \dfrac{1}{2}x - 5$

47. $3x + y \le 4$

$\quad\quad y \le -3x + 4$

49. $2x + 5y \le -10$

$\quad\quad 5y \le -2x - 10$

$\quad\quad y \le \dfrac{-2x - 10}{5}$

$\quad\quad y \le -\dfrac{2}{5}x - 2$

3.5 Preparing for Linear Inequalities in Two Variables

1. Step 1: Identify what you are looking for.
Step 2: Give names to the unknowns.
Step 3: Translate the problem into the language of mathematics
Step 4: Solve the equation(s) found in Step 3.
Step 5: Check the reasonableness to your answer
Step 6: Answer the question.

2.

3.5 Exercises

1. scatter diagram

3. $y = kx$

5. Answers will vary. The data points tend to rise from left to right at a relatively constant rate.

7. a. $y = kx$
$\quad\quad 30 = k \cdot 5$
$\quad\quad k = \dfrac{30}{5} = 6$

b. $y = 6x$

c. $y = 6(7) = 42$

9. a. $y = kx$
$\quad\quad 3 = k \cdot 7$
$\quad\quad k = \dfrac{3}{7}$

b. $y = \dfrac{3}{7}x$

c. $y = \dfrac{3}{7}(28) = 12$

11. a. $y = kx$
$\quad\quad 4 = k \cdot 8$
$\quad\quad k = \dfrac{4}{8} = \dfrac{1}{2}$

b. $y = \dfrac{1}{2}x$

c. $y = \dfrac{1}{2}(30) = 15$

13. Nonlinear

15. Linear with positive slope

17. a.

b. Answers will vary. We will use the points $(4, 1.8)$ and $(9, 2.6)$.

$$m = \frac{2.6 - 1.8}{9 - 4} = \frac{0.8}{5} = 0.16$$

$$y - 1.8 = 0.16(x - 4)$$

$$y - 1.8 = 0.16x - 0.64$$

$$y = 0.16x + 1.16$$

c.

19. a.

b. Answers will vary. We will use the points $(1.2, 8.4)$ and $(4.1, 2.4)$.

$$m = \frac{2.4 - 8.4}{4.1 - 1.2} = \frac{-6.0}{2.9} \approx -2.1$$

$$y - 8.4 = -2.1(x - 1.2)$$

$$y - 8.4 = -2.1x + 2.52$$

$$y = -2.1x + 10.92$$

c.

21. a. $B(m) = 0.05m + 8.95$

b. The number of minutes, m, is the independent variable. The amount of the bill, B, is the dependent variable.

c. Because the number minutes cannot be negative, the number of minutes must be greater than or equal to zero. That is, the implied domain is $\{m \mid m \geq 0\}$, or using interval notation $[0, \infty)$.

d. $B(300) = 0.05(300) + 8.95 = 23.95$

If 300 minutes are used, the monthly bill will be $23.95.

e. $0.05m + 8.95 = 20.95$

$$0.05m = 12$$

$$m = 240$$

If the monthly bill is $20.95, then 240 minutes were used.

f.

23. a. The computer will depreciate by

$$\frac{\$2700}{3} = \$900 \text{ per year. Thus, the slope is}$$

-900. The y-intercept will be $2700, the initial value of the computer. The linear function that represents book value, V, of the computer after x years is $V(x) = -900x + 2700$.

b. Because the computer cannot have a negative age, the age, x, must be greater than or equal to 0. After 3 years, the book value will be $V(3) = -900(3) + 2700 = 0$, and the book value cannot be negative. Therefore the implied domain of function is $\{x \mid 0 \leq x \leq 3\}$, or using interval notation $[0, 3]$.

c. $V(1) = -900(1) + 2700 = 1800$

After one year, the book value of the computer will be $1800.

d. The intercepts are $(0, 2700)$ and $(3, 0)$.

The y-intercept is 2700 and the x-intercept is 3.

e. $-900x + 2700 = 900$
$$-900x = -1800$$
$$x = 2$$

After two years, the book value of the computer will be $900.

f.

25. a. Because p varies directly with b, we know that $p = kb$ for some constant k. We know that $p = \$700.29$ when $b = \$120,000$, so,
$$700.29 = k \cdot 120000$$
$$k = 0.0058358$$
Therefore, we have $p = 0.0058358b$ or, using function notation,
$$p(b) = 0.0058358b.$$

b. $p(140,000) = 0.0058358(140,000)$
$$\approx 817.01$$
The monthly payment would be approximately $817.01 if $140,000 is borrowed.

c.

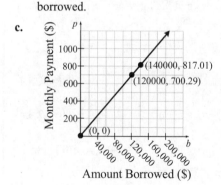

27. a. Because C varies directly with w, we know that $C = kw$ for some constant k. We know that $C = \$28$ when $w = 5$ lbs, so,
$$28 = k \cdot 5$$
$$k = 5.6$$
Therefore, we have $C = 5.6w$ or, using function notation, $C(w) = 5.6w$.

b. $C(3.5) = 5.6(3.5) = \$19.60$
The cost of 3.5 pounds of chocolate covered almonds would be $19.60.

c.

29. Because v varies directly with t, we know that $v = kt$ for some constant k. We know that $v = 64$ feet per second when $t = 2$ seconds, so
$$64 = k \cdot 2$$
$$k = 32$$
Thus, $v = 32t$ or, using function notation, $v(t) = 32t$. Finally, $v(3) = 32(3) = 96$.

Therefore, the velocity of a falling object will be 96 feet per second after 3 seconds.

31. a.

b. Linear.

c. Answers will vary. We will use the points $(2300, 4070)$ and $(3390, 5220)$.

$$m = \frac{5220 - 4070}{3390 - 2300} = \frac{1150}{1090} \approx 1.055$$
$$y - 4070 = 1.06(x - 2300)$$
$$y - 4070 = 1.06x - 2438$$
$$y = 1.06x + 1632$$

d.

7-day Strength (psi)

e. $x = 3000$: $y = 1.06(3000) + 1632$
$= 4812$

We predict that the 28-day strength will be 4812 psi if the 7-day strength is 3000 psi.

f. The slope of the line found is 1.06. This means that if the 7-day strength is increased by 1 psi, then the 28-day strength will increase by 1.06 psi.

33. a. No, the relation does not represent a function. Several *x*-coordinates are paired with multiple *y*-coordinates. For example, the *x*-coordinate 42.3 is paired with the two different *y*-coordinates 87 and 82.

b.

Number of Raisins vs Weight (grams)

c. Answers will vary. We will use the points $(42.3, 82)$ and $(42.8, 93)$.

$$m = \frac{93 - 82}{42.8 - 42.3} = \frac{11}{0.5} = 22$$

$$y - 82 = 22(x - 42.3)$$
$$y - 82 = 22x - 930.6$$
$$y = 22x - 848.6$$

d.

Weight (grams)

e. Let *N* represent the number of raisins in the box, and let *w* represent the weight (in grams) of the box of raisins.
$$N(w) = 22w - 848.6$$

f. $N(42.5) = 22(42.5) - 848.6 = 86.4$

We predict that approximately 86 raisins will be in a box weighing 42.5 grams.

g. The slope of the line found is 22 raisins per gram. This means that if the weight is to be increased by one gram, then the number of raisins must be increased by 22 raisins.

35. No, the data are not linearly related. Even though the graph of the data appears to look somewhat linear, a closer examination of the average growth rates between consecutive points shows that the function increases at a steadily increasing rate:

0 to 2.5 hours: $\dfrac{0.18 - 0.09}{2.5 - 0} = 0.036$ g/hr

2.5 to 3.5 hours: $\dfrac{0.26 - 0.18}{3.5 - 2.5} = 0.080$ g/hr

3.5 to 4.5 hours: $\dfrac{0.35 - 0.26}{4.5 - 3.5} = 0.090$ g/hr

4.5 to 6 hours: $\dfrac{0.50 - 0.35}{6 - 4.5} = 0.100$ g/hr

Population (grams) vs Time (hours)

37. a. The scatter diagram and window settings are shown below.

b. As shown below, the line of best fit is approximately $y = 0.676x + 2675.562$.

39. a. The scatter diagram and window settings are shown below.

b. As shown below, the line of best fit is approximately $y = 11.449x - 399.123$.

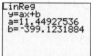

Chapter 3 Review

1. Let $x = -2, -1, 0,$ and 1.

$x = -2:$ $\quad -2 + y = 7$ $\qquad$ $x = -1:$ $\quad -1 + y = 7$
$\qquad\qquad\qquad y = 9$ $\qquad\qquad\qquad\qquad y = 8$

$x = 0:$ $\quad 0 + y = 7$ $\qquad$ $x = 1:$ $\quad 1 + y = 7$
$\qquad\qquad\qquad y = 7$ $\qquad\qquad\qquad\qquad y = 6$

Thus, the points $(-2, 9)$, $(-1, 8)$, $(0, 7)$, and $(1, 6)$ are on the graph.

2. Let $x = -2, -1, 0,$ and 1.

$x = -2:$ $\quad -2 - y = -4$ $\qquad$ $x = -1:$ $\quad -1 - y = -4$
$\qquad\qquad\qquad -y = -2$ $\qquad\qquad\qquad\qquad -y = -3$
$\qquad\qquad\qquad y = 2$ $\qquad\qquad\qquad\qquad y = 3$

$x = 0:$ $\quad 0 - y = -4$ $\qquad$ $x = 1:$ $\quad 1 - y = -4$
$\qquad\qquad\qquad -y = -4$ $\qquad\qquad\qquad\qquad -y = -5$
$\qquad\qquad\qquad y = 4$ $\qquad\qquad\qquad\qquad y = 5$

Thus, the points $(-2, 2)$, $(-1, 3)$, $(0, 4)$, and $(1, 5)$ are on the graph.

3. Let $x = -2, 0, 2,$ and 4.

$x = -2:$ $\quad 5(-2) - 2y = 6$
$\qquad\qquad\qquad -10 - 2y = 6$
$\qquad\qquad\qquad -2y = 16$
$\qquad\qquad\qquad y = -8$

$x = 0:$ $\quad 5(0) - 2y = 6$
$\qquad\qquad\qquad -2y = 6$
$\qquad\qquad\qquad y = -3$

$x = 2:$ $\quad 5(2) - 2y = 6$
$\qquad\qquad\qquad 10 - 2y = 6$
$\qquad\qquad\qquad -2y = -4$
$\qquad\qquad\qquad y = 2$

$x = 4:$ $\quad 5(4) - 2y = 6$
$\qquad\qquad\qquad 20 - 2y = 6$
$\qquad\qquad\qquad -2y = -14$
$\qquad\qquad\qquad y = 7$

Thus, the points $(-2, -8)$, $(0, -3)$, $(2, 2)$, and $(4, 7)$ are on the graph.

4. Let $x = -4, -2, 0,$ and 2.

$x = -4:$ $-3(-4) + 2y = 8$

$\qquad 12 + 2y = 8$

$\qquad 2y = -4$

$\qquad y = -2$

$x = -2:$ $-3(-2) + 2y = 8$

$\qquad 6 + 2y = 8$

$\qquad 2y = 2$

$\qquad y = 1$

$x = 0:$ $-3(0) + 2y = 8$

$\qquad 2y = 8$

$\qquad y = 4$

$x = 2:$ $-3(2) + 2y = 8$

$\qquad -6 + 2y = 8$

$\qquad 2y = 14$

$\qquad y = 7$

Thus, the points $(-4, -2)$, $(-2, 1)$, $(0, 4)$, and $(2, 7)$ are on the graph.

5. To find the *y*-intercept, let $x = 0$ and solve for *y*.

$x = 0:$ $5(0) + 3y = 30$

$\qquad 3y = 30$

$\qquad y = 10$

The *y*-intercept is 10, so $(0, 10)$ is on the graph.

To find the *x*-intercept, let $y = 0$ and solve for *x*.

$y = 0:$ $5x + 3(0) = 30$

$\qquad 5x = 30$

$\qquad x = 6$

The *x*-intercept is 6, so $(6, 0)$ is on the graph.

6. To find the *y*-intercept, let $x = 0$ and solve for *y*.

$x = 0:$ $4(0) + 3y = 0$

$\qquad 4y = 0$

$\qquad y = 0$

The *y*-intercept is 0, so the point $(0, 0)$ is on the graph. To find the *x*-intercept, let $y = 0$ and solve for *x*.

$y = 0:$ $4x + 3(0) = 0$

$\qquad 4x = 0$

$\qquad x = 0$

The *x*-intercept is 0, so the point $(0, 0)$ is on the graph. Since the *x*- and *y*-intercepts both result in the origin, we must find other points on the graph. Let $x = -3$ and 3 and solve for *y*.

$x = -3:$ $4(-3) + 3y = 0$

$\qquad -12 + 3y = 0$

$\qquad 3y = 12$

$\qquad y = 4$

$x = 3:$ $4(3) + 3y = 0$

$\qquad 12 + 3y = 0$

$\qquad 3y = -12$

$\qquad y = -4$

Thus, the points $(-3, 4)$ and $(3, -4)$ are also on the graph.

7. To find the *y*-intercept, let $x = 0$ and solve for *y*.

$x = 0:$ $\dfrac{3}{4}(0) - \dfrac{1}{2}y = 1$

$\qquad -\dfrac{1}{2}y = 1$

$\qquad y = -2$

The *y*-intercept is –2, so the point $(0, -2)$ is on the graph. To find the *x*-intercept, let $y = 0$ and solve for *x*.

$y = 0:$ $\dfrac{3}{4}x - \dfrac{1}{2}(0) = 1$

$$\dfrac{3}{4}x = 1$$

$$x = \dfrac{4}{3}$$

The x-intercept is $\dfrac{4}{3}$, so the point $\left(\dfrac{4}{3}, 0\right)$ is on the graph.

8. To find the y-intercept, let $x = 0$ and solve for y.

$x = 0:$ $4(0) + y = 8$

$$y = 8$$

The y-intercept is 8, so the point $(0,8)$ is on the graph. To find the x-intercept, let $y = 0$ and solve for x.

$y = 0:$ $4x + 0 = 8$

$$4x = 8$$

$$x = 2$$

The x-intercept is 2, so the point $(2,0)$ is on the graph.

9. The equation $x = 4$ will be a vertical line with x-intercept 4.

10. The equation $y = -8$ will be a horizontal line with y-intercept -8.

11. The equation $x = -2$ will be a vertical line with x-intercept -2.

12. The equation $y = 5$ will be a horizontal line with y-intercept 5.

13. a. The independent variable is the number of long-distance minutes used, x. It would not make sense to talk for a negative number of minutes. Thus, the domain of C is $\{x \mid x \geq 0\}$ or, using interval notation, $[0, \infty)$.

b. $C(235) = 0.07(235) + 5 = 21.45$

The cost for 235 minutes of long-distance calls during one month is $21.45.

c. Evaluate C at $x = 0$, 100, and 500.

$$C(0) = 0.07(0) + 5 = 5$$

$$C(100) = 0.07(100) + 5 = 12$$

$$C(500) = 0.07(500) + 5 = 40$$

Thus, the points $(0,5)$, $(100,12)$, and $(500,40)$ are on the graph.

Number of Minutes

d. We must solve $C(x) = 75$.

$$0.07x + 5 = 75$$
$$0.07x = 70$$
$$x = 1000$$

In one month, a person can purchase 1000 minutes of long distance for $75.

14. a. The independent variable is the number of years after purchase, x. The dependent variable is the value of the computer, V.

b. We are told that the value function V is for 0 to 5 years, inclusive. Thus, the domain is $\{x \mid 0 \le x \le 5\}$ or, using interval notation, $[0, 5]$.

c. The initial value of the computer will be the value at $x = 0$ years.
$$V(0) = 1800 - 360(0) = 1800$$
The initial value of the computer is $1800.

d. $V(2) = 1800 - 360(2) = 1080$
After 2 years, the value of the computer is $1080.

e. Evaluate V at $x = 3$, 4, and 5.
$$V(3) = 1800 - 360(3) = 720$$
$$V(4) = 1800 - 360(4) = 360$$
$$V(5) = 1800 - 360(5) = 0$$
Thus, the points $(3, 720)$, $(4, 360)$, and $(5, 0)$ are on the graph.

Number of Years

f. We must solve $V(x) = 0$.
$$1800 - 360x = 0$$
$$-360x = -1800$$
$$x = 5$$
After 5 years, the computer's value will be $0.

15. a. $m = \dfrac{y_2 - y_1}{x_2 - x_1} = \dfrac{4 - (-1)}{2 - (-2)} = \dfrac{5}{4}$

b. For every 4 units of increase in x, y will increase by 5 units.

16. a. $m = \dfrac{y_2 - y_1}{x_2 - x_1} = \dfrac{-1 - 1}{5 - (-3)} = \dfrac{-2}{8} = -\dfrac{1}{4}$

b. For every 4 units of increase in x, y will decrease by 1 unit. For every 4 units of decrease in x, y will increase by 1 unit.

17. $m = \dfrac{y_2 - y_1}{x_2 - x_1} = \dfrac{-1 - 5}{2 - (-1)} = \dfrac{-6}{3} = -2$

18. $m = \dfrac{y_2 - y_1}{x_2 - x_1} = \dfrac{-1 - 5}{0 - 4} = \dfrac{-6}{-4} = \dfrac{3}{2}$

19. a.

Year

b. Average rate of change

$$= \frac{8,712,176 - 7,897,241}{1950 - 1940}$$

$= 81,493.5$ people per year

Between 1940 and 1950, the population of Illinois increased at a rate of 81,493.5 people per year.

c. Average rate of change

$$= \frac{11,430,602 - 11,427,409}{1990 - 1980}$$

$= 319.3$ people per year

Between 1980 and 1990, the population of Illinois increased at a rate of 319.3 people per year.

d. Average rate of change

$$= \frac{12,419,293 - 11,430,602}{2000 - 1990}$$

$= 98,869.1$ people per year

Between 1990 and 2000, the population of Illinois increased at a rate of 98,869.1 people per year.

e. No. The population of Illinois is not linearly related to the year. The average rate of change (slope) is not constant.

20. a.

Year

b. Average rate of change

$$= \frac{178 - 70}{1930 - 1920}$$

$= 10.8$ community colleges per year

Between 1920 and 1930, the number of public community colleges in the U.S. increased at a rate of 10.8 colleges per year.

c. Average rate of change

$$= \frac{847 - 390}{1970 - 1960}$$

$= 45.7$ community colleges per year

Between 1960 and 1970, the number of public community colleges in the U.S. increased at a rate of 45.7 colleges per year.

d. Average rate of change

$$= \frac{1282 - 1049}{1990 - 1980}$$

$= 23.3$ community colleges per year

Between 1980 and 1990, the number of public community colleges in the U.S. increased at a rate of 23.3 colleges per year.

e. No. The number of public community colleges in the U.S. is not linearly related to the year. The average rate of change (slope) is not constant.

21. Start at $(-1, -5)$. Because $m = 4 = \dfrac{4}{1}$, move 1 unit to the right and 4 units up to find point $(0, -1)$.

22. Start at $(3, 2)$. Because $m = -\dfrac{2}{3}$, move 3 unit to the right and 2 units down to find point $(6, 0)$. We can also move 3 units to the left and 2 units up to find point $(0, 4)$.

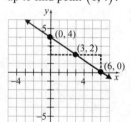

23. Because m is undefined, the line is vertical passing through the point $(2, -4)$.

24. Because $m = 0$, the line is horizontal passing through the point $(-3, 1)$.

25. $m = \dfrac{y_2 - y_1}{x_2 - x_1} = \dfrac{-1 - 3}{6 - (-2)} = \dfrac{-4}{8} = -\dfrac{1}{2}$

$y - y_1 = m(x - x_1)$

$y - (-1) = -\dfrac{1}{2}(x - 6)$

$y + 1 = -\dfrac{1}{2}x + 3$

$y = -\dfrac{1}{2}x + 2$ or $x + 2y = 4$

26. $m = \dfrac{y_2 - y_1}{x_2 - x_1} = \dfrac{6 - (-3)}{2 - (-1)} = \dfrac{9}{3} = 3$

$y - y_1 = m(x - x_1)$

$y - 6 = 3(x - 2)$

$y - 6 = 3x - 6$

$y = 3x$ or $3x - y = 0$

27. $y - y_1 = m(x - x_1)$

$y - 2 = -1(x - 3)$

$y - 2 = -x + 3$

$y = -x + 5$ or $x + y = 5$

28. $\qquad y - y_1 = m(x - x_1)$

$y - (-4) = \dfrac{3}{5}(x - (-10))$

$y + 4 = \dfrac{3}{5}(x + 10)$

$y + 4 = \dfrac{3}{5}x + 6$

$y = \dfrac{3}{5}x + 2$ or $3x - 5y = -10$

29. $m = \dfrac{y_2 - y_1}{x_2 - x_1} = \dfrac{5 - 2}{-3 - 6} = \dfrac{3}{-9} = -\dfrac{1}{3}$

$y - y_1 = m(x - x_1)$

$y - 2 = -\dfrac{1}{3}(x - 6)$

$y - 2 = -\dfrac{1}{3}x + 2$

$y = -\dfrac{1}{3}x + 4$ or $x + 3y = 12$

30. $m = \dfrac{y_2 - y_1}{x_2 - x_1} = \dfrac{3 - 3}{4 - (-2)} = \dfrac{0}{6} = 0$

$y - y_1 = m(x - x_1)$

$y - 3 = 0(x - 4)$

$y - 3 = 0$

$y = 3$

31. $m = \dfrac{y_2 - y_1}{x_2 - x_1} = \dfrac{-7 - (-1)}{1 - 4} = \dfrac{-6}{-3} = 2$

$y - y_1 = m(x - x_1)$

$y - (-7) = 2(x - 1)$

$y + 7 = 2x - 2$

$y = 2x - 9$ or $2x - y = 9$

32. $m = \dfrac{y_2 - y_1}{x_2 - x_1} = \dfrac{-1 - 2}{8 - (-1)} = \dfrac{-3}{9} = -\dfrac{1}{3}$

$y - y_1 = m(x - x_1)$

$y - (-1) = -\dfrac{1}{3}(x - 8)$

$y + 1 = -\dfrac{1}{3}x + \dfrac{8}{3}$

$y = -\dfrac{1}{3}x + \dfrac{5}{3}$ or $x + 3y = 5$

33. For $y = 4x - 6$, the slope is 4 and the y-intercept is -6. Begin at $(0, -6)$ and move to the right 1 unit and up 4 units to find point $(1, -2)$.

34. $2x + 3y = 12$

$$3y = -2x + 12$$

$$y = \frac{-2x + 12}{3}$$

$$y = -\frac{2}{3}x + 4$$

The slope is $-\frac{2}{3}$ and the y-intercept is 4. Begin at $(0,4)$ and move to the right 3 units and down 2 units to find the point $(3,2)$. We can also move 3 units to the left and 2 units up to find the point $(-3,6)$.

35. $x - y = 4$

$$-y = -x + 4$$

$$y = x - 4$$

The slope is 1 and the y-intercept is -4. Begin at $(0,-4)$ and move to the right 1 unit and up 1 unit to find the point $(1,-3)$.

36. $2x + 6y = 3$

$$6y = -2x + 3$$

$$y = \frac{-2x + 3}{6}$$

$$y = -\frac{1}{3}x + \frac{1}{2}$$

The slope is $-\frac{1}{3}$ and the y-intercept is $\frac{1}{2}$.

Begin at $\left(0, \frac{1}{2}\right)$ and move to the right 3 units

and down 1 unit to find the point $\left(3, -\frac{1}{2}\right)$. We can also move to the left 3 units and up 1 unit to find the point $\left(-3, \frac{3}{2}\right)$.

37. To find the y-intercept, find $g(0)$.

$$g(0) = 2(0) - 6 = -6$$

The y-intercept is -6, so the point $(0,-6)$ is on the graph. To find the x-intercept, solve the equation $g(x) = 0$.

$$2x - 6 = 0$$

$$2x = 6$$

$$x = 3$$

The x-intercept is 3, so the point $(3,0)$ is on the graph.

38. To find the y-intercept, find $H(0)$.

$$H(0) = -\frac{4}{3}(0) + 5 = 5$$

The y-intercept is 5, so the point $(0,5)$ is on the graph. To find the x-intercept, solve the equation $H(x) = 0$.

$$-\frac{4}{3}x + 5 = 0$$

$$-\frac{4}{3}x = -5$$

$$x = \frac{15}{4} = 3.75$$

The x-intercept is $\frac{15}{4}$, so the point $\left(\frac{15}{4}, 0\right)$ is on the graph.

39. To find the y-intercept, find $F(0)$.

$F(0) = -(0) - 3 = -3$

The y-intercept is -3, so the point $(0, -3)$ is on the graph. To find the x-intercept, solve $F(x) = 0$.

$-x - 3 = 0$

$-x = 3$

$x = -3$

The x-intercept is -3, so the point $(-3, 0)$ is on the graph.

40. To find the y-intercept, find $f(0)$.

$f(0) = \frac{3}{4}(0) - 3 = -3$

The y-intercept is -3, so the point $(0, -3)$ is on the graph. To find the x-intercept, solve $f(x) = 0$.

$\frac{3}{4}x - 3 = 0$

$\frac{3}{4}x = 3$

$x = 4$

The x-intercept is 4, so the point $(4, 0)$ is on the graph.

41. **a.** Let x represent the number of years since 1996. Then $x = 0$ represents 1996 and $x = 5$ represents 2001. Let E represent the percentage of electronically-filed returns.

$m = \dfrac{30.7 - 12.6}{5 - 0} = 3.62$ percent

$E - 12.6 = 3.62(x - 0)$

$E - 12.6 = 3.62x$

$E = 3.62x + 12.6$

In function notation, $E(x) = 3.62x + 12.6$.

b. The year 2004 corresponds to $x = 8$.

$E(8) = 3.62(8) + 12.6 = 41.56$

If the linear trend continues, 41.56% of U.S. Federal Tax Returns will be filed electronically in 2004.

c. The slope (3.62) indicates that electronically-filed tax returns are increasing at a rate of 3.62% per year.

d. $3.62x + 12.6 = 48.8$

$3.62x = 36.2$

$x = 10$

Now, $x = 10$ correspond to the year 2006. Thus, 48.8% of U.S. Federal Tax Returns will be filed electronically in the year 2006.

42. **a.** Let x represent the age of men and H represent the maximum recommended heart rate for men under stress.

$m = \dfrac{160 - 200}{60 - 20} = -1$ beats per minute per year

$H - 200 = -1(x - 20)$

$H - 200 = -x + 20$

$H = -x + 220$

In function notation, $H(x) = -x + 220$.

b. $H(45) = -(45) + 220 = 175$

The maximum recommended heart rate for a 45 year old man under stress is 175 beats per minute.

c. The slope (-1) indicates that the maximum recommended heart rate for men under stress decreases at a rate of 1 beat per minute per year.

d. $-x + 220 = 168$

$\qquad -x = -52$

$\qquad x = 52$

The maximum recommended heart rate under stress is 168 beats per minute for 52 year old men.

43. A line parallel to L will have a slope equal to the slope of L. Thus, the slope of the line parallel to L is $-\dfrac{3}{8}$.

44. A line perpendicular to L will have a slope that is the negative reciprocal to the slope of L. Thus, the slope of the line perpendicular to L is

$$\dfrac{-1}{-\dfrac{3}{8}} = -1 \cdot -\dfrac{8}{3} = \dfrac{8}{3}.$$

45.

$x - 3y = 9 \qquad\qquad 9x + 3y = -3$

$-3y = -x + 9 \qquad\quad 3y = -9x - 3$

$y = \dfrac{-x+9}{-3} \qquad\qquad y = \dfrac{-9x-3}{3}$

$y = \dfrac{1}{3}x - 3 \qquad\qquad y = -3x - 1$

Perpendicular. The two slopes, $m_1 = \dfrac{1}{3}$ and $m_2 = -3$, are negative reciprocals.

46.

$6x - 8y = 16 \qquad\qquad 3x + 4y = 28$

$-8y = -6x + 16 \qquad\quad 4y = -3x + 28$

$y = \dfrac{-6x+16}{-8} \qquad\qquad y = \dfrac{-3x+28}{4}$

$y = \dfrac{3}{4}x - 2 \qquad\qquad y = -\dfrac{3}{4}x + 7$

Neither. The two slopes are $m_1 = \dfrac{3}{4}$ and $m_2 = -\dfrac{3}{4}$. The two slopes are not equal and are not negative reciprocals.

47.

$2x - y = 3 \qquad\qquad -6x + 3y = 0$

$-y = -2x + 3 \qquad\quad 3y = 6x$

$y = \dfrac{-2x+3}{-1} \qquad\qquad y = \dfrac{6x}{3}$

$y = 2x - 3 \qquad\qquad y = 2x$

Parallel. The two lines have equal slopes, $m = 2$, but different y-intercepts.

48. Perpendicular. The line $x = 2$ is vertical, and the line $y = 2$ is horizontal. Vertical lines are perpendicular to horizontal lines.

49. The slope of the line we seek is $m = -2$, the same as the slope of $y = -2x - 5$. The equation of the line is:

$y - 2 = -2(x - 1)$

$y - 2 = -2x + 2$

$y = -2x + 4$

50. The slope of the line we seek is $m = \dfrac{5}{2}$, the same as the slope of the line

$5x - 2y = 8$

$-2y = -5x + 8$

$y = \dfrac{-5x+8}{-2}$

$y = \dfrac{5}{2}x - 4$

Thus, the equation of the line we seek is:

$y - 3 = \dfrac{5}{2}(x - 4)$

$y - 3 = \dfrac{5}{2}x - 10$

$y = \dfrac{5}{2}x - 7$

51. The line we seek is vertical, parallel to the vertical line $x = -3$. Now a vertical line passing through the point $(1, -4)$ must also pass through the point $(1, 0)$. That is, the x-intercept is 1. Thus, the equation of the line is $x = 1$.

52. The slope of the line we seek is $m = -\dfrac{1}{3}$, the negative reciprocal of the slope of $y = 3x + 7$. The equation of the line is:

$$y - 2 = -\frac{1}{3}(x - 6)$$

$$y - 2 = -\frac{1}{3}x + 2$$

$$y = -\frac{1}{3}x + 4$$

53. The slope of the line we seek is $m = \dfrac{4}{3}$, the negative reciprocal of the line
$3x + 4y = 6$

$$4y = -3x + 6$$

$$y = \frac{-3x + 6}{4}$$

$$y = -\frac{3}{4}x + \frac{3}{2}$$

Thus, the equation of the line we seek is:

$$y - (-2) = \frac{4}{3}(x - (-3))$$

$$y + 2 = \frac{4}{3}x + 4$$

$$y = \frac{4}{3}x + 2$$

54. The line we seek is horizontal, perpendicular to the vertical line $x = 2$. Now a horizontal line passing through the point $(5, -4)$ must also pass through the point $(0, -4)$. That is, the y-intercept is -4. Thus, the equation of the line is $y = -4$.

55. a. $x = 4,\ y = -2$ $\quad 5(4) + 3(-2) \overset{?}{\le} 15$

$$20 - 6 \overset{?}{\le} 15$$

$$14 \le 15 \quad \text{True}$$

So, $(4, -2)$ is a solution to $5x + 3y \le 15$.

b. $x = -6,\ y = 15$ $\quad 5(-6) + 3(15) \overset{?}{\le} 15$

$$-30 + 45 \overset{?}{\le} 15$$

$$15 \le 15 \quad \text{True}$$

So, $(-6, 15)$ is a solution to $5x + 3y \le 15$.

c. $x = 5,\ y = -1$ $\quad 5(5) + 3(-1) \overset{?}{\le} 15$

$$25 - 3 \overset{?}{\le} 15$$

$$22 \le 15 \quad \text{False}$$

So, $(5, -1)$ is not a solution to $5x + 3y \le 15$.

56. a. $x = 2,\ y = 3$ $\quad 2 - 2(3) \overset{?}{>} -4$

$$2 - 6 \overset{?}{>} -4$$

$$-4 \overset{?}{>} -4 \quad \text{False}$$

So, $(2, 3)$ is not a solution to $x - 2y > -4$.

b. $x = 5$, $y = -2$ $\quad 5 - 2(-2) \overset{?}{>} -4$

$$5 + 4 \overset{?}{>} -4$$

$$9 \overset{?}{>} -4 \quad \text{True}$$

So, $(5, -2)$ is a solution to $x - 2y > -4$.

c. $x = -1$, $y = 3$ $\quad (-1) - 2(3) \overset{?}{>} -4$

$$-1 - 6 \overset{?}{>} -4$$

$$-7 \overset{?}{>} -4 \quad \text{False}$$

So, $(-1, 3)$ is not a solution to $x - 2y > -4$.

57. Replace the inequality symbol with an equal sign to obtain $y = 3x - 2$. Because the inequality is strict, graph $y = 3x - 2$ using a dashed line.

Test Point: $(0, 0)$: $\quad 0 \overset{?}{<} 3(0) - 2$

$$0 \overset{?}{<} -2 \quad \text{False}$$

Therefore, $(0, 0)$ is not a solution to $y < 3x - 2$.
Shade the half-plane that does not contain $(0, 0)$.

58. Replace the inequality symbol with an equal sign to obtain $2x - 4y = 12$. Because the inequality is non-strict, graph $2x - 4y = 12$ $\left(y = \dfrac{1}{2}x - 3 \right)$ using a solid line.

Test Point: $(0, 0)$: $\quad 2(0) - 4(0) \overset{?}{\leq} 12$

$$0 \leq 12 \quad \text{True}$$

Therefore, $(0, 0)$ is a solution to $2x - 4y \leq 12$.
Shade the half-plane that contains $(0, 0)$.

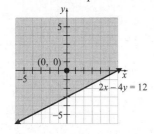

59. Replace the inequality symbol with an equal sign to obtain $3x + 4y = 20$. Because the inequality is strict, graph $3x + 4y > 20$ $\left(y = -\dfrac{3}{4}x + 5 \right)$ using a dashed line.

Test Point: $(0, 0)$: $\quad 3(0) + 4(0) \overset{?}{>} 20$

$$0 \overset{?}{>} 20 \quad \text{False}$$

Therefore, $(0, 0)$ is not a solution to $3x + 4y > 20$. Shade the half-plane that does not contain $(0, 0)$.

60. Replace the inequality symbol with an equal sign to obtain $y = 5$. Because the inequality is non-strict, graph $y = 5$ using a solid line.

Test Point: $(0, 0)$: $\quad 0 \overset{?}{>} 5 \quad \text{False}$

Therefore, $(0, 0)$ is not a solution to $y > 5$.
Shade the half-plane that does not contain $(0, 0)$.

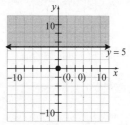

61. Replace the inequality symbol with an equal sign to obtain $2x + 3y = 0$. Because the inequality is strict, graph $2x + 3y = 0$ $\left(y = -\dfrac{2}{3}x \right)$ using a dashed line.

Test Point: $(1, 1)$: $\quad 2(1) + 3(1) \overset{?}{<} 0$

$$2 + 3 \overset{?}{<} 0$$

$$5 \overset{?}{<} 0 \quad \text{False}$$

Therefore, $(1, 1)$ is not a solution to $2x + 3x < 0$.
Shade the half-plane that does not contain $(1, 1)$.

2x + 3y = 0

62. Replace the inequality symbol with an equal sign to obtain $x = -8$. Because the inequality is non-strict, graph $x = -8$ using a solid line.

Test Point: $(0,0)$: $0 \overset{?}{>} -8$ True

Therefore, $(0,0)$ is a solution to $x > -8$. Shade the half-plane that contains $(0,0)$.

63. a. Let x = the number of movie tickets.
Let y = the number of music CDs.
$7.50x + 15y \le 60$

b. $x = 5$, $y = 2$: $7.50(5) + 15(2) \overset{?}{\le} 60$

$37.50 + 30 \overset{?}{\le} 60$

$67.50 \overset{?}{\le} 60$ False

No, Ethan cannot buy 5 movie tickets and 2 music tickets on his $60 budget.

c. $x = 2$, $y = 2$: $7.50(2) + 15(2) \overset{?}{\le} 60$

$15 + 30 \overset{?}{\le} 60$

$45 \overset{?}{\le} 60$ True

Yes, Ethan can buy 2 movie tickets and 2 music tickets on his $60 budget.

64. a. Let x = the number of candy bars.
Let y = the number of candles.
$0.50x + 2y \ge 1000$

b. $x = 500$, $y = 350$:

$0.50(500) + 2(350) \overset{?}{\ge} 1000$

$250 + 700 \overset{?}{\ge} 1000$

$950 \overset{?}{\ge} 1000$ False

No, the math club will not earn enough money for the field trip by selling 500 candy bars and 350 candles.

c. $x = 600$, $y = 400$:

$0.50(600) + 2(400) \overset{?}{\ge} 1000$

$300 + 800 \overset{?}{\ge} 1000$

$1100 \ge 1000$ True

Yes, the math club will earn enough money for the field trip by selling 600 candy bars and 400 candles.

65. a. $C(m) = 0.12m + 35$

b. The number of miles driven, m, is the independent variable. The rental cost, C, is the dependent variable.

c. Because the number of miles cannot be negative, the it must be greater than or equal to zero. That is, the implied domain is $\{m \mid m \ge 0\}$ or, using interval notation, $[0, \infty)$.

d. $C(124) = 0.12(124) + 35 = 49.88$

If 124 miles are driven during a one-day rental, the charge will be $49.88.

e. $0.12m + 35 = 67.16$

$0.12m = 32.16$

$m = 268$

If the charge for a one-day rental is $67.16, then 268 miles were driven.

f.

SSM – 138

66. a. $B(x) = 3.50x + 33.99$

b. The number of pay-per-view movies watched, x, is the independent variable. The monthly bill, B, is the dependent variable.

c. Because the number pay-per-view movies watched cannot be negative, it must be greater than or equal to zero. That is, the implied domain is $\{x \mid x \geq 0\}$ or, using interval notation, $[0, \infty)$.

d. $B(5) = 3.50(5) + 33.99 = 51.49$

If 5 pay-per-view movies are watched one month, the bill will be $51.49.

e. $3.50x + 33.99 = 58.49$
$$3.50x = 24.50$$
$$x = 7$$

If the bill one month is $58.49, then 7 pay-per-view movies were watched.

f.

67. a. The tractor will depreciate by $\dfrac{\$84,600}{12} = \$7050$ per year. Thus, the slope is -7050. The y-intercept will be $84,600, the initial value of the tractor. The linear function that represents book value, V, of the tractor after x years is $V(x) = -7050x + 84,600$.

b. Because the tractor cannot have a negative age, the age, x, must be greater than or equal to 0. After 12 years, the book value will be $V(12) = -7050(12) + 84,600 = 0$, and the book value cannot be negative. Therefore the implied domain of function is $\{x \mid 0 \leq x \leq 12\}$ or, using interval notation, $[0, 12]$.

c. $V(5) = -7050(5) + 84,600 = 49,350$

After five years, the book value of the tractor will be $49,350.

d. The intercepts are $(0, 84600)$ and $(12, 0)$. The y-intercept is 84,600 and the x-intercept is 12.

e. $-7050x + 84,600 = 28,200$
$$-7050x = -56,400$$
$$x = 8$$

After eight years, the book value of the tractor will be $28,200.

f.

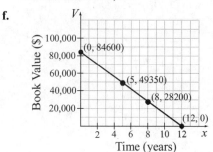

68. a. $y = kx$
$$108 = k \cdot 9$$
$$k = \frac{108}{9} = 12$$

b. $y = 12x$

c. $y = 12(4) = 48$

69. a. $y = kx$
$$11 = k \cdot 6$$
$$k = \frac{11}{6}$$

b. $y = \frac{11}{6}x$

c. $y = \frac{11}{6}(24) = 44$

70. Because recommended dosage d is directly proportional to weight w, we know that $d = kw$ for some constant k. We know that $d = 3024$ milligrams when $w = 168$ pounds, so
$$3024 = k \cdot 168$$
$$k = 18$$
Thus, $d = 18w$ or, using function notation, $d(w) = 18w$. Finally, $d(146) = 18(146) = 2628$.
Therefore, the recommended dosage for a 146 pound person is 2628 milligrams.

71. Because perimeter P varies directly with side length s, we know that $P = ks$ for some constant k. We know that $P = 32$ feet when $s = 8$ feet, so

$$32 = k \cdot 8$$
$$k = 4$$

Thus, $P = 4s$ or, using function notation, $P(s) = 4s$. Finally, $P(6) = 4(6) = 24$.

Therefore, the perimeter of a square with a side length of 6 feet is 24 feet.

72 a.

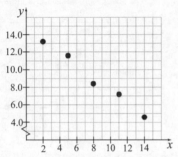

b. Answers will vary. We will use the points $(2, 13.3)$ and $(14, 4.6)$.

$$m = \frac{4.6 - 13.3}{14 - 2} = \frac{-8.7}{12} = -0.725$$
$$y - 13.3 = -0.725(x - 2)$$
$$y - 13.3 = -0.725x + 1.45$$
$$y = -0.725x + 14.75$$

c.

73. a.

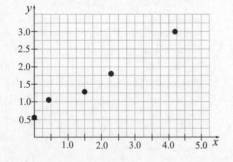

b. Answers will vary. We will use the points $(0, 0.6)$ and $(4.2, 3.0)$.

$$m = \frac{3.0 - 0.6}{4.2 - 0} = \frac{2.4}{4.2} = \frac{4}{7}$$
$$y - 0.6 = \frac{4}{7}(x - 0)$$
$$y - 0.6 = \frac{4}{7}x$$
$$y = \frac{4}{7}x + 0.6$$

c.

74. a.

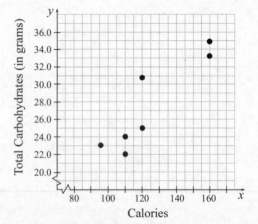

b. Approximately linear.

c. Answers will vary. We will use the points $(96, 23.2)$ and $(160, 33.3)$.

$$m = \frac{33.3 - 23.2}{160 - 96} = \frac{10.1}{64} \approx 0.158$$
$$y - 23.2 = 0.158(x - 96)$$
$$y - 23.2 = 0.158x - 15.168$$
$$y = 0.158x + 8.032$$

d.

e. $x = 140$: $y = 0.158(140) + 8.032$
$= 30.152$

We predict that a one-cup serving of cereal having 140 calories will have approximately 30.2 grams of total carbohydrates.

f. The slope of the line found is 0.158. This means that, in a one-cup serving of cereal, total carbohydrates will increase by 0.158 grams for each one-calorie increase.

75. a.

b. Approximately linear.

c. Answers will vary. We will use the points $(1, 9.25)$ and $(11, 26.50)$.

$$m = \frac{26.50 - 9.25}{11 - 1} = \frac{17.25}{10} = 1.725$$

$$y - 9.25 = 1.725(x - 1)$$
$$y - 9.25 = 1.725x - 1.725$$
$$y = 1.725x + 7.525$$

d.

e. $x = 5$: $y = 1.725(5) + 7.525$
$= 16.15$

We predict that the FedEx 2Day® price for shipping a 5-pound package will be $16.15.

f. The slope of the line found is 1.725. This means that the FedEx 2Day shipping price increases by $1.725 for each one-pound increase in the weight of a package.

Chapter 3 Test

1. Find the *y*-intercept by letting $x = 0$ and solving for *y*.

$$x = 0: \quad 0 - y = 8$$
$$-y = 8$$
$$y = -8$$

The *y*-intercept is -8, so the point (0, -8) is on the graph. Find the *x*-intercept by letting $y = 0$ and solving for *x*.

$$y = 0: \quad x - 0 = 8$$
$$x = 8$$

The *x*-intercept is 8, so the point (8, 0) is on the graph.

2. Let $x = -5, 0, 5,$ and 10.

$$x = -5: \quad 3(-5) + 5y = 0$$
$$-15 + 5y = 0$$
$$5y = 15$$
$$y = 3$$

$x = 0: \quad 3(0) + 5y = 0$

$0 + 5y = 0$

$y = 0$

$x = 5: \quad 3(5) + 5y = 0$

$15 + 5y = 0$

$5y = -15$

$y = -3$

$x = 10: \quad 3(10) + 5y = 0$

$30 + 5y = 0$

$5y = -30$

$y = -6$

Thus, the points (-5, 3), (0, 0), (5, -3), and (10, -6) are on the graph.

3. Find the y-intercept by letting $x = 0$ and solving for y.

$x = 0: \quad 3(0) + 2y = 12$

$2y = 12$

$y = 6$

The y-intercept is 6, so the point (0, 6) is on the graph. Find the x-intercept by letting $y = 0$ and solving for x.

$y = 0: \quad 3x + 2(0) = 12$

$3x = 12$

$x = 4$

The x-intercept is 4, so the point (4, 0) is on the graph.

4. Let $x = -1, \ 0, \ 1,$ and 2.

$x = -1: \quad \dfrac{3}{2}(-1) - \dfrac{1}{4}y = 1$

$-\dfrac{3}{2} - \dfrac{1}{4}y = 1$

$-4\left(-\dfrac{3}{2} - \dfrac{1}{4}y\right) = -4(1)$

$6 + y = -4$

$y = -10$

$x = 0: \quad \dfrac{3}{2}(0) - \dfrac{1}{4}y = 1$

$-\dfrac{1}{4}y = 1$

$-4\left(-\dfrac{1}{4}y\right) = -4(1)$

$y = -4$

$x = 1: \quad \dfrac{3}{2}(1) - \dfrac{1}{4}y = 1$

$\dfrac{3}{2} - \dfrac{1}{4}y = 1$

$-4\left(\dfrac{3}{2} - \dfrac{1}{4}y\right) = -4(1)$

$-6 + y = -4$

$y = 2$

$x = 2: \quad \dfrac{3}{2}(2) - \dfrac{1}{4}y = 1$

$3 - \dfrac{1}{4}y = 1$

$-\dfrac{1}{4}y = -2$

$-4\left(-\dfrac{1}{4}y\right) = -4(-2)$

$y = 8$

Thus, the points (-1, -10), (0, -4), (1, 2), and (2, 8) are on the graph.

5. The equation $x = -7$ will be a vertical line with x-intercept -7.

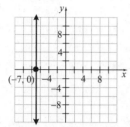

6. For $f(x) = -\dfrac{2}{3}x + 6$, the slope is $-\dfrac{2}{3}$ and the y-intercept is 6. Begin at (0, 6) and move to the right 3 units and down 2 units to find the point (3, 4). We can also move 3 units to the left and 2 units up to find the point (-3, 8).

7. $m = \dfrac{y_2 - y_1}{x_2 - x_1} = \dfrac{6 - (-2)}{-1 - 5} = \dfrac{8}{-6} = -\dfrac{4}{3}$;

For every 3 units of increase in x, y will decrease by 4 units. For every 3 units of decrease in x, y will increase by 4 units.

8. Start at (2, -4). Because $m = -\dfrac{3}{5}$, move 5 units to the right and 3 units down to find point (7, -7). We can also move 5 units to the left and 3 units up to find point (-3, -1).

9.
$$8x - 2y = 1 \qquad\qquad x + 4y = -2$$
$$-2y = -8x + 1 \qquad\quad 4y = -x - 2$$
$$y = \dfrac{-8x + 1}{-2} \qquad\quad y = \dfrac{-x - 2}{4}$$
$$y = 4x - \dfrac{1}{2} \qquad\quad y = -\dfrac{1}{4}x - \dfrac{1}{2}$$

Perpendicular. The two lines have slopes that are negative reciprocals.

10.
$$y - y_1 = m(x - x_1)$$
$$y - 1 = 4(x - (-3))$$
$$y - 1 = 4(x + 3)$$
$$y - 1 = 4x + 12$$
$$y = 4x + 13 \text{ or } 4x - y = -13$$

11. $m = \dfrac{y_2 - y_1}{x_2 - x_1} = \dfrac{7 - 1}{-3 - 6} = \dfrac{6}{-9} = -\dfrac{2}{3}$
$$y - y_1 = m(x - x_1)$$
$$y - 1 = -\dfrac{2}{3}(x - 6)$$
$$y - 1 = -\dfrac{2}{3}x + 4$$
$$y = -\dfrac{2}{3}x + 5 \text{ or } 2x + 3y = 15$$

12. The slope of the line we seek is $m = \dfrac{1}{5}$, the same as the slope of the line
$$x - 5y = 15$$
$$-5y = -x + 15$$
$$y = \dfrac{-x + 15}{-5}$$
$$y = \dfrac{1}{5}x - 3$$

Thus, the equation of the line we seek is:
$$y - (-1) = \dfrac{1}{5}(x - 10)$$
$$y + 1 = \dfrac{1}{5}x - 2$$
$$y = \dfrac{1}{5}x - 3 \text{ or } x - 5y = 15$$

13. The slope of the line we seek is $m = -\dfrac{1}{3}$, the negative reciprocal of the slope of the line
$3x - y = 4$
$$-y = -3x + 4$$
$$y = 3x - 4$$
Thus, the equation of the line we seek is:
$$y - 2 = -\frac{1}{3}(x - 6)$$
$$y - 2 = -\frac{1}{3}x + 2$$
$$y = -\frac{1}{3}x + 4 \text{ or } x + 3y = 12$$

14. a. $x = 3$, $y = -1$ $\;\; 3(3) - (-1) \overset{?}{>} 10$
$$9 + 1 \overset{?}{>} 10$$
$$10 \overset{?}{>} 10 \quad \text{False}$$
So, $(3, -1)$ is not a solution to $3x - y > 10$.

b. $x = 4$, $y = 5$ $\;\; 3(4) - 5 \overset{?}{>} 10$
$$12 - 5 \overset{?}{>} 10$$
$$7 \overset{?}{>} 10 \quad \text{False}$$
So, $(4, 5)$ is not a solution to $3x - y > 10$.

c. $x = 5$, $y = 3$ $\;\; 3(5) - 3 \overset{?}{>} 10$
$$15 - 3 \overset{?}{>} 10$$
$$12 \overset{?}{>} 10 \quad \text{True}$$
So, $(5, 3)$ is a solution to $3x - y > 10$.

15. Replace the inequality symbol with an equal sign to obtain $y = -2x + 1$. Because the inequality is non-strict, graph $y = -2x + 1$ using a solid line.

Test Point: $(0, 0)$: $\;\; 0 \overset{?}{\le} -2(0) + 1$
$$0 \overset{?}{\le} 1 \quad \text{True}$$
Therefore, $(0, 0)$ is a solution to $y \le -2x + 1$.
Shade the half-plane that contains $(0, 0)$.

16. Replace the inequality symbol with an equal sign to obtain $5x - 2y = 0$. Because the inequality is strict, graph $5x - 2y = 0$ $\left(y = \dfrac{5}{2}x \right)$ using a dashed line.

Test Point: $(1, 1)$: $\;\; 5(1) - 2(1) \overset{?}{<} 0$
$$5 - 2 \overset{?}{<} 0$$
$$3 \overset{?}{<} 0 \quad \text{False}$$
Therefore, $(1, 1)$ is not a solution to $5x - 2y < 0$.
Shade the half-plane that does not contain $(1, 1)$.

17. a. The profit is $\$30 - \$12 = \$18$ times the number of shelves sold x, minus the $\$100$ for renting the display. Thus, the function is $P(x) = 18x - 100$.

b. The independent variable is the number of shelves sold, x. Henry could not sell a negative number of shelves. Thus, the domain of P is $\{x \mid x \ge 0\}$ or, using interval notation, $[0, \infty)$.

c. $P(34) = 18(34) - 100$
$$= 512$$
If Henry sells 34 shelves, his profit will be $\$512$.

d. Evaluate P at $x = 0$, 20, and 50.
$$P(0) = 18(0) - 100$$
$$= -100$$
$$P(20) = 18(20) - 100$$
$$= 260$$
$$P(50) = 18(50) - 100$$
$$= 800$$
Thus, the points $(0, -100)$, $(20, 260)$, and $(50, 800)$ are on the graph.

Number of Shelves

e. We must solve $P(x) = 764$.

$$18x - 100 = 764$$
$$18x = 864$$
$$x = 48$$

If Henry sells 48 shelves, his profit will be $764.

18. a.

Diameter (feet)

b. Average rate of change

$$= \frac{7.07 - 0.79}{3 - 1}$$

$= 3.14$ square feet per foot

Between diameters of 1 foot and 3 feet, the area of the circle increases at a rate of 3.14 square feet per foot.

c. Average rate of change

$$= \frac{132.73 - 78.54}{13 - 10}$$

≈ 18.06 square feet per foot

Between diameters of 10 feet and 13 feet, the area of the circle increases at a rate of approximately 18.06 square feet per foot.

d. No. The area of circles is not linearly related to the diameter. The average rate of change (slope) is not constant.

19. Because recommended dosage E is directly proportional to time worked t, we know that $E = kt$ for some constant k. We know that $E = \$296.40$ when $t = 24$ hours, so

$$296.40 = k \cdot 24$$
$$k = 12.35$$

Thus, $E = 12.35t$ or, using function notation, $E(t) = 12.35t$. Finally,

$E(10) = 12.35(10) = 123.5$. Therefore, Benjamin will earn $123.50 for 10 hours of work.

20. a.

Age (months)

b. Approximately linear.

c. Answers will vary. We will use the points $(6,\ 95)$ and $(18,\ 170)$.

$$m = \frac{170 - 95}{18 - 6} = \frac{75}{12} = 6.25$$
$$y - 95 = 6.25(x - 6)$$
$$y - 95 = 6.25x - 37.5$$
$$y = 6.25x + 57.5$$

d.

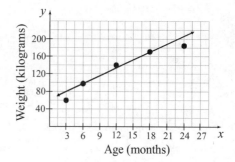

Age (months)

e. $x = 9$: $y = 6.25(9) + 57.5$
$$= 113.75$$

We predict that a nine month old Shetland pony will weigh 113.75 kilograms.

f. The slope of the line found is 6.25. This means that a Shetland pony's weight will increase by 6.25 kilograms for each one-month increase in age.

Cumulative Review Chapters R-3

1. $200 \div 25 \cdot (-2) = 8 \cdot (-2) = -16$

2. $\dfrac{3}{4} + \dfrac{1}{6} - \dfrac{2}{3} = \dfrac{9}{12} + \dfrac{2}{12} - \dfrac{8}{12}$

$\qquad = \dfrac{9 + 2 - 8}{12}$

$\qquad = \dfrac{3}{12}$

$\qquad = \dfrac{1}{4}$

3. $\dfrac{8 - 3\left(5 - 3^2\right)}{7 - 2 \cdot 6} = \dfrac{8 - 3(5 - 9)}{7 - 12}$

$\qquad = \dfrac{8 - 3(-4)}{-5}$

$\qquad = \dfrac{8 + 12}{-5}$

$\qquad = \dfrac{20}{-5}$

$\qquad = -4$

4. $(-3)^3 + 3(-3)^2 - 5(-3) - 7$

$= -27 + 3(9) - 5(-3) - 7$

$= -27 + 27 + 15 - 7$

$= 0 + 15 - 7$

$= 15 - 7$

$= 8$

5. $8m - 5m^2 - 3 + 9m^2 - 3m - 6$

$= -5m^2 + 9m^2 + 8m - 3m - 3 - 6$

$= 4m^2 + 5m - 9$

6. $8(n + 2) - 7 = 6n - 5$

$8n + 16 - 7 = 6n - 5$

$8n + 9 = 6n - 5$

$8n = 6n - 14$

$2n = -14$

$n = -7$

The solution set is $\{-7\}$.

7. $\dfrac{2}{5}x + \dfrac{1}{6} = -\dfrac{2}{3}$

$30\left(\dfrac{2}{5}x + \dfrac{1}{6}\right) = 30\left(-\dfrac{2}{3}\right)$

$12x + 5 = -20$

$12x = -25$

$x = \dfrac{-25}{12}$

The solution set is $\left\{-\dfrac{25}{12}\right\}$.

8. $\dfrac{|2x - 5|}{3} + 1 = 4$

$\dfrac{|2x - 5|}{3} = 3$

$|2x - 5| = 9$

$2x - 5 = -9 \quad$ or $\quad 2x - 5 = 9$

$\quad 2x = -4 \qquad\qquad 2x = 14$

$\quad x = -2 \qquad\qquad\ x = 7$

The solution set is $\{-2, 7\}$.

9. $A = \dfrac{1}{2}h(b + B)$

$2(A) = 2\left(\dfrac{1}{2}h(b + B)\right)$

$2A = h(b + B)$

$2A = hb + hB$

$2A - hb = hB$

$\dfrac{2A - hb}{h} = B$

$B = \dfrac{2A - hb}{h} \quad$ or $\quad B = \dfrac{2A}{h} - b$

10. $6x - 7 > -31$

$6x > -24$

$x > -4$

$\{x \mid x > -4\}$ or $(-4, \infty)$

11. $5(x-3) \geq 7(x-4)+3$

$5x-15 \geq 7x-28+3$

$5x-15 \geq 7x-25$

$5x \geq 7x-10$

$-2x \geq -10$

$x \leq 5$

$\{x \mid x \leq 5\}$ or $(-\infty, 5]$

12. $|2x+5| < 9$

$-9 < 2x+5 < 9$

$-9-5 < 2x+5-5 < 9-5$

$-14 < 2x < 4$

$\dfrac{-14}{2} < \dfrac{2x}{2} < \dfrac{4}{2}$

$-7 < x < 2$

$\{x \mid -7 < x < 2\}$ or $(-7, 2)$

13.

14. Because the *x*-coordinate -1 is paired with two different *y*-coordinates, 3 and 6, the relation is not a function.

Domain = {-1, 0, 1, 2}

Range = {-5, -2, 3, 4, 6}

15. The relation fails the vertical line test. That is, a vertical line will cross the graph in two places. Thus, the relation is not a function.

Domain = $\{x \mid 1 \leq x \leq 5\} = [1, 5]$

Range = $\{y \mid -2 \leq y \leq 5\} = [-2, 5]$

16. The relation passes the vertical line test. That is, a vertical line will only ever cross the graph in one place. Thus, the relation is a function.

Domain = {*x*|*x* is any real number} = $(-\infty, \infty)$

Range = {*y*|*y* is any real number} = $(-\infty, \infty)$

17. a. $H(1) = \dfrac{3(1)+5}{1-2} = \dfrac{3+5}{1-2} = \dfrac{8}{-1} = -8$

b.

$H\left(\dfrac{1}{2}\right) = \dfrac{3\left(\dfrac{1}{2}\right)+5}{\dfrac{1}{2}-2} = \dfrac{\dfrac{3}{2}+5}{\dfrac{1}{2}-2}$

$= \dfrac{2\left(\dfrac{3}{2}+5\right)}{2\left(\dfrac{1}{2}-2\right)} = \dfrac{3+10}{1-4} = \dfrac{13}{-3} = -\dfrac{13}{3}$

18. a. $g(-4) = 2(-4)-3 = -8-3 = -11$

b. $g(x+h) = 2(x+h)-3 = 2x+2h-3$

19. For $y = -\dfrac{1}{2}x+4$, the slope is $-\dfrac{1}{2}$ and the *y*-intercept is 4. Begin at (0, 4) and move to the right 2 units and down 1 units to find the point (2, 3). We can also move 2 units to the left and 1 units up to find the point (-2, 5).

20. $4x-5y = 15$

$-5y = -4x+15$

$y = \dfrac{-4x+15}{-5}$

$y = \dfrac{4}{5}x-3$

The slope is $\dfrac{4}{5}$ and the *y*-intercept is -3.

Begin at the point (0, -3) and move to the right 5 units and up 4 units to find the point (5, 1).

21. $m = \dfrac{y_2 - y_1}{x_2 - x_1} = \dfrac{10 - (-2)}{-6 - 3} = \dfrac{12}{-9} = -\dfrac{4}{3}$

    $y - y_1 = m(x - x_1)$

    $y - 10 = -\dfrac{4}{3}(x - (-6))$

    $y - 10 = -\dfrac{4}{3}(x + 6)$

    $y - 10 = -\dfrac{4}{3}x - 8$

    $y = -\dfrac{4}{3}x + 2$ or $4x + 3y = 6$

22. The slope of the line we seek is $m = -3$, the same as the slope of the line $y = -3x + 10$. Thus, the equation of the line we seek is:

    $y - 7 = -3(x - (-5))$

    $y - 7 = -3(x + 5)$

    $y - 7 = -3x - 15$

    $y = -3x - 8$ or $3x + y = -8$

23. Replace the inequality symbol with an equal sign to obtain $x - 3y = 12$. Because the inequality is strict, graph $x - 3y = 12$ $\left(y = \dfrac{1}{3}x - 4 \right)$ using a dashed line.

    Test Point: $(0, 0)$: $0 - 3(0) \overset{?}{>} 12$

    $\qquad\qquad\qquad\qquad 0 \overset{?}{>} 12$ False

    Therefore, $(0, 0)$ is a not a solution to $x - 3y > 12$. Shade the half-plane that does not contain $(0, 0)$.

24. **a.** The independent variable is t, the number of years after 2000. The dependent variable is C, the projected number of cell phones that will be in use that year.

b. $C(5) = 14.27(5) + 106.39 = 177.74$; $t = 5$ represents 5 years after 2000 which is the year 2005. $C(5)$ represents the projected number of cell phones that will be in use during the year 2005. That is, the function projects that 177.74 million cell phones will be in use in 2005.

c. $C(-8) = 14.27(-8) + 106.39 = -7.77$; $t = -8$ represents 8 years before 2000 which is 1992. $C(-8)$ would represent the projected number of cell phones that was in use during the year 1992. That is, the function projects that -7.77 million cell phones were in use in 1992. This result is not reasonable. The number of cell phones in use could not be negative.

25. Because the amount of total carbohydrates C is directly proportional to volume V, we know that $C = kV$ for some constant k. We know that $C = 21$ grams when $V = \dfrac{3}{4}$ cups, so

    $21 = k \cdot \dfrac{3}{4}$

    $k = \dfrac{4}{3} \cdot 21$

    $k = 28$

    Thus, $C = 28V$ or, using function notation, $C(V) = 28V$. Finally, $C(2) = 28(2) = 56$.

    Therefore, 2 cups of Peanut Butter Crunch ® will contain 56 grams of total carbohydrates.

Chapter 4

4.1 Preparing for Systems of Linear Equations in Two Variables

1. Substitute $x = 5$ and $y = 4$, and simplify:
$$2x - 3y = 2(5) - 3(4)$$
$$= 10 - 12$$
$$= -2$$

2. $2(4) - 3(-1) \overset{?}{=} 11$
$$8 + 3 \overset{?}{=} 11$$
$$11 = 11 \quad \leftarrow \text{True}$$
Yes, $(4, -1)$ is on the graph of $2x - 3y = 11$.

3. $y = 3x - 7$
Let $x = 0, 1,$ and 2.
$$x = 0: \quad y = 3(0) - 7$$
$$y = 0 - 7$$
$$y = -7$$
$$x = 1: \quad y = 3(1) - 7$$
$$y = 3 - 7$$
$$y = -4$$
$$x = 2: \quad y = 3(2) - 7$$
$$y = 6 - 7$$
$$y = -1$$
Thus, the points $(0, -7)$, $(1, -4)$, and $(2, -1)$ are on the graph.

4. The slope of the line we seek is $m = -3$, the same as the slope of $y = -3x + 1$. The equation of the line is
$$y - y_1 = m(x - x_1)$$
$$y - 3 = -3(x - 2)$$
$$y - 3 = -3x + 6$$
$$y = -3x + 9$$

5. $4x - 3y = 15$
$$-3y = -4x + 15$$
$$y = \frac{-4x + 15}{-3}$$
$$y = \frac{4}{3}x - 5$$
The slope is $\frac{4}{3}$ and the y-intercept is -5.

6. The additive inverse of 4 is -4 because $4 + (-4) = 0$.

7. $2x - 3(-3x + 1) = -36$
$$2x + 9x - 3 = -36$$
$$11x - 3 = -36$$
$$11x = -33$$
$$x = \frac{-33}{11} = -3$$
The solution set is $\{-3\}$.

4.1 Exercises

1. system of linear equations

3. consistent; dependent

5. TRUE

7. Yes. The method of elimination is preferred over the method of substitution if substitution leads to fractions.

9. The lines intersect at the point $(3, -2)$.

11. **a.** Let $x = 5, y = 3$ in both equations (1) and (2).
$$\begin{cases} 2(5) + 3 = 10 + 3 = 13 \\ -5(5) + 3(3) = -25 + 9 = -16 \neq 6 \end{cases}$$
Although these values satisfy equation (1), they do not satisfy equation (2). Therefore, the ordered pair $(5, 3)$ is not a solution of the system.

b. Let $x = 3, y = 7$ in both equations (1) and (2).
$$\begin{cases} 2(3) + 7 = 6 + 7 = 13 \\ -5(3) + 3(7) = -15 + 21 = 6 \end{cases}$$
Because these values satisfy both equations (1) and (2), the ordered pair $(3, 7)$ is a solution of the system.

13. a. Let $x = 1$, $y = 2$ in both equations (1) and (2).

$$\begin{cases} 5(1) + 2(2) = 5 + 4 = 9 \\ -10(1) - 4(2) = -10 - 8 = -18 \end{cases}$$

Because these values satisfy both equations (1) and (2), the ordered pair $(1,2)$ is a solution of the system.

b. Let $x = 2$, $y = -1/2$ in both equations (1) and (2).

$$\begin{cases} 5(2) + 2(-1/2) = 10 + (-1) = 9 \\ -10(2) - 4(-1/2) = -20 + 2 = -18 \end{cases}$$

Because these values satisfy both equations (1) and (2), the ordered pair $(2, -1/2)$ is a solution of the system.

15. The graphs of the linear equations intersect at the point $(2, -1)$. Thus, the solution is $(2, -1)$.

17. The graphs of the linear equations are parallel. Thus, the system has no solution. The solution set is $\varnothing$ or $\{ \ \}$. The system is inconsistent.

19. $\begin{cases} y = 3x & (1) \\ y = -2x + 5 & (2) \end{cases}$

The two equations are in slope-intercept form. Graph each equation and find the point of intersection.

The solution is the ordered pair $(1, 3)$.

21. $\begin{cases} y = \dfrac{1}{2}x + 1 & (1) \\ 2x - 4y = -4 & (2) \end{cases}$

Equation (2) in slope-intercept form is

$y = \dfrac{1}{2}x + 1$, which is the same as equation (1).

The two lines are coincident. The system is

dependent. The solution is $\left\{ (x,y) \middle| y = \dfrac{1}{2}x + 1 \right\}$.

23. $\begin{cases} 2x + y = 2 & (1) \\ x + 3y = -9 & (2) \end{cases}$

Equation (1) in slope-intercept form is $y = -2x + 2$. Equation (2) in slope-intercept form is $y = -\dfrac{1}{3}x - 3$. Graph each equation and find the point of intersection.

The solution is the ordered pair $(3, -4)$.

25. $\begin{cases} y = -\dfrac{1}{2}x + 1 & (1) \\ y = -2x + 10 & (2) \end{cases}$

Substituting $-\dfrac{1}{2}x + 1$ for y in equation (2), we get

$$-\dfrac{1}{2}x + 1 = -2x + 10$$

$$2\left(-\dfrac{1}{2}x + 1\right) = 2(-2x + 10)$$

$$-x + 2 = -4x + 20$$

$$3x = 18$$

$$x = 6$$

Substituting 6 for x in equation (2), we obtain

$y = -2(6) + 10 = -12 + 10 = -2$.

The solution is the ordered pair $(6, -2)$.

27. $\begin{cases} x = \dfrac{2}{3}y & (1) \\ 3x - y = -3 & (2) \end{cases}$

Substituting $\dfrac{2}{3}y$ for x in equation (2), we obtain

$3\left(\dfrac{2}{3}y\right) - y = -3$

$2y - y = -3$

$y = -3$

Substituting -3 for y in equation (1), we obtain

$x = \dfrac{2}{3}(-3) = -2$.

The solution is the ordered pair $(-2, -3)$.

29. $\begin{cases} 3x + y = 1 & (1) \\ -6x - 2y = -4 & (2) \end{cases}$

Equation (1) solved for y is $y = -3x + 1$.

Substituting $-3x + 1$ for y in equation (2), we obtain

$-6x - 2(-3x + 1) = -4$

$-6x + 6x - 2 = -4$

$-2 = -4$

The system has no solution. The solution set is $\varnothing$ or $\{\ \}$. The system is inconsistent.

31. $\begin{cases} 2x - 4y = 2 & (1) \\ x + 2y = 0 & (2) \end{cases}$

Equation (2) solved for x is $x = -2y$.

Substituting $-2y$ for x in equation (1), we obtain

$2(-2y) - 4y = 2$

$-4y - 4y = 2$

$-8y = 2$

$y = \dfrac{2}{-8} = -\dfrac{1}{4}$

Substituting $-\dfrac{1}{4}$ for y in equation (2), we obtain

$x + 2\left(-\dfrac{1}{4}\right) = 0$

$x - \dfrac{1}{2} = 0$

$x = \dfrac{1}{2}$

The solution is the ordered pair $\left(\dfrac{1}{2}, -\dfrac{1}{4}\right)$.

33. $\begin{cases} x + 3y = 6 & (1) \\ -\dfrac{x}{3} - y = -2 & (2) \end{cases}$

Equation (2) solved for y is $y = -\dfrac{x}{3} + 2$.

Substituting $-\dfrac{x}{3} + 2$ for y in equation (1), we obtain

$x + 3\left(-\dfrac{x}{3} + 2\right) = 6$

$x - x + 6 = 6$

$6 = 6$

The system is dependent. The solution is $\{(x, y) \mid x + 3y = 6\}$.

35. $\begin{cases} x + y = 10{,}000 & (1) \\ 0.05x + 0.07y = 650 & (2) \end{cases}$

Equation (1) solved for x is $x = 10{,}000 - y$.

Substituting $10{,}000 - y$ for x in equation (2), we obtain

$0.05(10{,}000 - y) + 0.07y = 650$

$500 - 0.05y + 0.07y = 650$

$0.02y + 500 = 650$

$0.02y = 150$

$y = 7500$

Substituting 7500 for y in equation (1), we obtain

$x + 7500 = 10{,}000$

$x = 2500$

The solution is the ordered pair $(2500,\ 7500)$.

37. $\begin{cases} x + y = -5 & (1) \\ -x + 2y = 14 & (2) \end{cases}$

Add equations (1) and (2).

$\begin{cases} x + y = -5 \\ -x + 2y = 14 \end{cases}$

$\overline{\qquad 3y = 9\qquad}$

$y = 3$

Substituting 3 for y in equation (1), we obtain

$x + 3 = -5$

$x = -8$

The solution is the ordered pair $(-8, 3)$.

39. $\begin{cases} x+2y=-5 & (1) \\ 3x+3y=9 & (2) \end{cases}$

Multiply both sides of equation (1) by -3, and add the result to equation (2).

$\begin{cases} -3x-6y=15 \\ \underline{3x+3y=9} \end{cases}$

$\qquad -3y=24$

$\qquad\quad y=-8$

Substituting -8 for y in equation (1), we obtain

$x+2(-8)=-5$

$\quad x-16=-5$

$\qquad\quad x=11$

The solution is the ordered pair $(11,-8)$.

41. $\begin{cases} 5x-2y=2 & (1) \\ -10x+4y=3 & (2) \end{cases}$

Multiply both sides of equation (1) by 2 and add the result to equation (2).

$\begin{cases} 10x-4y=4 \\ \underline{-10x+4y=3} \end{cases}$

$\qquad\qquad 0=7$

The system has no solution. The solution set is $\varnothing$ or $\{\ \}$. The system is inconsistent.

43. $\begin{cases} 2x+5y=-3 & (1) \\ x+\dfrac{5}{4}y=-\dfrac{1}{2} & (2) \end{cases}$

Multiply both sides of equation (2) by -4 and add the result to equation (1).

$\begin{cases} 2x+5y=-3 \\ \underline{-4x-5y=2} \end{cases}$

$-2x\qquad =-1$

$\qquad x=\dfrac{1}{2}$

Substituting $1/2$ for x in equation (1), we obtain

$2\left(\dfrac{1}{2}\right)+5y=-3$

$\quad 1+5y=-3$

$\qquad 5y=-4$

$\qquad\quad y=-\dfrac{4}{5}$

The solution is the ordered pair $\left(\dfrac{1}{2},-\dfrac{4}{5}\right)$.

45. $\begin{cases} \dfrac{1}{3}x-2y=6 & (1) \\ -\dfrac{1}{2}x+3y=-9 & (2) \end{cases}$

Multiply both sides of equation (1) by 3, multiply both sides of equation (2) by 2, and add the results.

$x-6y=18$

$-x+6y=-18$

$\qquad 0=0$

The system is dependent. The solution is

$\left\{(x,y)\ \middle|\ \dfrac{1}{3}x-2y=6\right\}$.

47. $\begin{cases} 0.05x+0.1y=5.25 & (1) \\ 0.08x-0.02y=1.2 & (2) \end{cases}$

Multiply both sides of equation (1) by 0.2, and add the result to equation (2).

$\begin{cases} 0.01x+0.02y=1.05 \\ \underline{0.08x-0.02y=1.2} \end{cases}$

$0.09x\qquad\quad =2.25$

$\qquad\qquad x=25$

Substituting 25 for x in equation (1), we obtain

$0.05(25)+0.1y=5.25$

$\quad 1.25+0.1y=5.25$

$\qquad\quad 0.1y=4$

$\qquad\qquad y=40$

The solution is the ordered pair $(25,40)$.

49. $\begin{cases} x+3y=0 & (1) \\ -2x+4y=30 & (2) \end{cases}$

Because the coefficient of x in equation (1) is 1, we use substitution to solve the system.
Equation (1) solved for x is $x=-3y$.

Substituting $-3y$ for x in equation (2), we obtain

$-2(-3y)+4y=30$

$\quad 6y+4y=30$

$\qquad 10y=30$

$\qquad\quad y=3$

Substituting 3 for y in equation (1), we obtain

$x+3(3)=0$

$\quad x+9=0$

$\qquad\quad x=-9$

The solution is the ordered pair $(-9,3)$.

51. $\begin{cases} x = 5y - 3 & (1) \\ -3x + 15y = 9 & (2) \end{cases}$

Because equation (1) is already solved for x, we use substitution to solve the system.

Substituting $5y - 3$ for x in equation (2), we obtain

$$-3(5y - 3) + 15y = 9$$
$$-15y + 9 + 15y = 9$$
$$9 = 9$$

The system is dependent. The solution is $\{(x, y) \mid x = 5y - 3\}$.

53. $\begin{cases} 2x - 4y = 18 & (1) \\ 3x + 5y = -3 & (2) \end{cases}$

Because none of variables have a coefficient of 1, we use elimination to solve the system. Multiply both sides of equation (1) by 3, multiply both sides of equation (2) by −2, and add the results.

$$\begin{cases} 6x - 12y = 54 \\ -6x - 10y = 6 \end{cases}$$
$$-22y = 60$$
$$y = \frac{60}{-22} = -\frac{30}{11}$$

Substituting $-\frac{30}{11}$ for y in equation (1), we obtain

$$2x - 4\left(-\frac{30}{11}\right) = 18$$
$$2x + \frac{120}{11} = 18$$
$$11\left(2x + \frac{120}{11}\right) = 11(18)$$
$$22x + 120 = 198$$
$$22x = 78$$
$$x = \frac{78}{22} = \frac{39}{11}$$

The solution is the ordered pair $\left(\frac{39}{11}, -\frac{30}{11}\right)$.

55. $\begin{cases} \dfrac{5}{6}x - \dfrac{1}{3}y = -5 & (1) \\ -x + \dfrac{2}{5}y = 1 & (2) \end{cases}$

Because none of the variables have a coefficient of 1, we use elimination to solve the system.

Multiply both sides of equation (1) by 6, multiply both sides of equation (2) by 5, and add the results.

$$\begin{cases} 5x - 2y = -30 \\ -5x + 2y = 5 \end{cases}$$
$$0 = -25$$

The system has no solution. The solution set is $\varnothing$ or $\{\ \}$. The system is inconsistent.

57. $\begin{cases} 2x + y = -5 & (1) \\ 5x + 3y = 1 & (2) \end{cases}$

Write each equation in slope-intercept form.

$$2x + y = -5 \qquad\qquad 5x + 3y = 1$$
$$y = -2x - 5 \qquad\qquad 3y = -5x + 1$$
$$y = \frac{-5x + 1}{3}$$
$$y = -\frac{5}{3}x + \frac{1}{3}$$

Since the equations have different slopes, the lines are neither parallel nor coincident. Thus, the system must have exactly one solution.

59. $\begin{cases} 3x - 2y = -2 & (1) \\ -6x + 4y = 4 & (2) \end{cases}$

Write each equation in slope-intercept form.

$$3x - 2y = -2 \qquad\qquad -6x + 4y = 4$$
$$-2y = -3x - 2 \qquad\qquad 4y = 6x + 4$$
$$y = \frac{-3x - 2}{-2} \qquad\qquad y = \frac{6x + 4}{4}$$
$$y = \frac{3}{2}x + 1 \qquad\qquad y = \frac{3}{2}x + 1$$

Because both equations have the same slope-intercept form, the two lines are coincident. Thus, the system is dependent and has an infinite number of solutions.

61. a. Equation of line through $(-1, 3)$ and $(3, 1)$:

$$m = \frac{1 - 3}{3 - (-1)} = \frac{-2}{4} = -\frac{1}{2}$$
$$y - 1 = -\frac{1}{2}(x - 3)$$
$$y - 1 = -\frac{1}{2}x + \frac{3}{2}$$
$$y = -\frac{1}{2}x + \frac{5}{2}$$

Equation of line through $(-2,-1)$ and $(4,5)$:

$$m = \frac{y_2 - y_1}{x_2 - x_1} = \frac{5-(-1)}{4-(-2)} = \frac{6}{6} = 1$$

$$y - 5 = 1(x - 4)$$
$$y - 5 = x - 4$$
$$y = x + 1$$

b. Solve the system formed by the equations found in part a.

$$\begin{cases} y = x + 1 & (1) \\ y = -\frac{1}{2}x + \frac{5}{2} & (2) \end{cases}$$

Substituting $x+1$ for y in equation (2), we obtain

$$x + 1 = -\frac{1}{2}x + \frac{5}{2}$$

$$2(x+1) = 2\left(-\frac{1}{2}x + \frac{5}{2}\right)$$

$$2x + 2 = -x + 5$$
$$3x = 3$$
$$x = 1$$

Substituting 1 for x in equation (1), we obtain $y = 1 + 1 = 2$.

The solution is the ordered pair $(1,\ 2)$.

63. The two lines intersect in the second quadrant. Of the choices provided, the ordered pairs $(-3,\ 1)$ and $(-1,\ 3)$ are the only ones that is in the second quadrant. Therefore, the answer is (c) and (f).

65. $\begin{cases} Ax + 3By = 2 \\ -3Ax + By = -11 \end{cases}$

Substitute 3 for x and 1 for y in the system and solve for A and B.

$$\begin{cases} A(3) + 3B(1) = 2 & \text{or} \quad 3A + 3B = 2 & (1) \\ -3A(3) + B(1) = -11 & \text{or} \quad -9A + B = -11 & (2) \end{cases}$$

Multiply equation (1) by 3 and add the result to equation (2).

$$9A + 9B = 6$$
$$-9A + B = -11$$
$$10B = -5$$

$$B = \frac{-5}{10} = -\frac{1}{2}$$

Substituting $-\frac{1}{2}$ for B in equation (2), we obtain

$$-9A + \left(-\frac{1}{2}\right) = -11$$

$$-2\left(-9A - \frac{1}{2}\right) = -2(-11)$$

$$18A + 1 = 22$$
$$18A = 21$$

$$A = \frac{21}{18} = \frac{7}{6}$$

Thus, for the system to have $x = 3$, $y = 1$ as a solution, then $A = \frac{7}{6}$ and $B = -\frac{1}{2}$.

67. Answers will vary. One possibility follows:
$$\begin{cases} x + y = 3 \\ x - y = -5 \end{cases}$$

69. $\begin{cases} y = 3x - 1 & (1) \\ y = -2x + 5 & (2) \end{cases}$

The solution is the ordered pair $(1.2,\ 2.6)$.

71. $\begin{cases} 3x - y = -1 & (1) \\ -4x + y = -3 & (2) \end{cases}$

Writing each equation in slope-intercept form, we obtain $y = 3x + 1$ and $y = 4x - 3$.

The solution is the ordered pair $(4,\ 13)$.

73. $\begin{cases} 4x - 3y = 1 & (1) \\ -8x + 6y = -2 & (2) \end{cases}$

Writing each equation in slope-intercept form, we obtain the same equation for both,

$y = \dfrac{4}{3}x - \dfrac{1}{3}$.

The two lines are coincident. The system is dependent. The solution is $\{(x, y) \mid 4x - 3y = 1\}$.

75. $\begin{cases} 2x - 3y = 2 & (1) \\ 5x + y = -2 & (2) \end{cases}$

Writing each equation in slope-intercept form,

we obtain $y = \dfrac{2}{3}x - 4$ and $y = -5x - 2$.

The solution is approximately the ordered pair $(0.35, -3.76)$.

4.2 Preparing for Problem Solving

1. Step 1: Identify what you are looking for.
   Step 2: Give names to the unknowns.
   Step 3: Translate the problem into the language of mathematics.
   Step 4: Solve the equation(s) found in Step 3.
   Step 5: Check the reasonableness of your answer.
   Step 6: Answer the question.

2. Since the total to be invested is $25,000 and the amount to be invested in stocks is s, the amount to be invested in bonds is $25,000 - s$.

3. The total interest for the year would be $0.125(\$3500) = \$437.50$. Since there are 12 months in a year, the interest that would be paid after one month would be $\dfrac{\$437.50}{12} \approx \$36.46$.

4. A linear cost function will be of the form $C(x) = mx + b$. For this problem, the variable cost is $m = \$15$ and the fixed cost is $b = \$500$. Thus, the cost function is $C(x) = 15x + 500$.

4.2 Exercises

1. Answers will vary.

3. Let x and y represent the two numbers.
   $\begin{cases} x + y = 18 & (1) \\ x - y = -2 & (2) \end{cases}$
   Adding equations (1) and (2) result in
   $2x = 16$
   $x = 8$
   Substituting 8 for x in equation (1), we obtain
   $8 + y = 18$
   $y = 10$
   The two numbers are 8 and 10.

5. Let x represent the first number and let y represent the second number.
   $\begin{cases} 2x + y = 47 & (1) \\ x + 3y = 81 & (2) \end{cases}$
   Multiply both sides of equation (2) by –2 and add the result to equation (1).
   $\begin{cases} 2x + y = 47 \\ -2x - 6y = -162 \end{cases}$
   $\overline{ -5y = -115}$
   $y = 23$
   Substituting 23 for y in equation (2), we obtain
   $x + 3(23) = 81$
   $x + 69 = 81$
   $x = 12$
   The 1st number is 12 and the 2nd number is 23.

7. Let x represent the first number and let y represent the second number.
$$\begin{cases} 2x+3y=81 & (1) \\ 3x-y=17 & (2) \end{cases}$$
Multiply both sides of equation (2) by 3 and add the result to equation (1).
$$\begin{cases} 2x+3y=81 \\ 9x-3y=51 \end{cases}$$
$$11x \qquad =132$$
$$x=12$$
Substituting 12 for x in equation (2), we obtain
$$3(12)-y=17$$
$$36-y=17$$
$$-y=-19$$
$$y=19$$
The 1st number is 12 and the 2nd number is 19.

9. **a.** $\begin{cases} R(x)=12x \\ C(x)=5.5x+9880 \end{cases}$

b. $R(x)=C(x)$
$$12x=5.5x+9880$$
$$6.5x=9880$$
$$x=1520$$

$$R(1520)=12(1520)=18,240$$
$$C(1520)=5.5(1520)+9880=18,240$$

The break-even point is $(1520, 18240)$.

11. Let x represent the flat set-up fee and let y represent the hourly rental rate.
$$\begin{cases} x+5y=235 & (1) \\ x+3y=165 & (2) \end{cases}$$
Multiply both sides of equation (2) by –1 and add the result to equation (1).

$$\begin{cases} x+5y=235 \\ -x-3y=-165 \end{cases}$$
$$2y=70$$
$$y=35$$
Substituting 35 for y in equation (2), we obtain
$$x+3(35)=165$$
$$x+105=165$$
$$x=60$$
The flat set-up fee is \$60 and the rental rate is \$35 per hour.

13. Let h represent the number of calories in a McDonald's hamburger and let c represent the number of calories in a medium Coke.
$$\begin{cases} 2h+c=770 & (1) \\ 3h+2c=1260 & (2) \end{cases}$$
Multiply both sides of equation (1) by –2 and add the result to equation (2).

$$\begin{cases} -4h-2c=-1540 \\ 3h+2c=1260 \end{cases}$$
$$-h \qquad =-280$$
$$h=280$$
Substituting 280 for h in equation (1), we obtain
$$2(280)+c=770$$
$$560+c=770$$
$$c=210$$
A McDonald's hamburger has 280 calories. A medium Coke has 210 calories.

15. Let x and y represent the length and width of the rectangle, respectively.
$$\begin{cases} 2x+2y=120 & (1) \\ x=y+20 & (2) \end{cases}$$
Substituting $y+20$ for x in equation (1), we obtain
$$2(y+20)+2y=120$$
$$2y+40+2y=120$$
$$4y+40=120$$
$$4y=80$$
$$y=20$$
Substituting 20 for y in equation (2), we obtain
$$x=20+20=40.$$
The dimensions of the rectangle are 40 meters by 20 meters.

17. Let x represent the length of one of the congruent sides and let y represent the length of the third side.

$$\begin{cases} 2x + y = 35 & (1) \\ x = 3y & (2) \end{cases}$$

Substituting $3y$ for x in equation (1), we obtain

$$2(3y) + y = 35$$
$$6y + y = 35$$
$$7y = 35$$
$$y = 5$$

Substituting 5 for y in equation (2), we obtain

$$x = 3(5) = 15.$$

The lengths of the three sides of the triangle are 15 cm, 15 cm, and 5 cm.

19. Because angles 1 and 2 are supplemental, and because angles 2 and 3 must be equal, we obtain the following system.

$$\begin{cases} (10x + 6y) + 4y = 180 & (1) \\ 4y = 7x + 2y & (2) \end{cases}$$

Simplify each equation.

$$\begin{cases} 10x + 10y = 180 & (1) \\ 7x - 2y = 0 & (2) \end{cases}$$

Divide both sides of equation (1) by 5 and add the result to equation (2).

$$\begin{cases} 2x + 2y = 36 \\ 7x - 2y = 0 \end{cases}$$
$$9x \quad\ \ = 36$$
$$x = 4$$

Substituting 4 for x in equation (2), we obtain

$$7(4) - 2y = 0$$
$$28 - 2y = 0$$
$$-2y = -28$$
$$y = 14$$

Thus, $x = 4$ and $y = 14$.

21. Because angles 1, 2, and 3 add up to $180°$, and because angles 2 and 4 are supplemental, we obtain the following system.

$$\begin{cases} (4x + 2y) + (10x + 5y) + (7x + 5y) = 180 & (1) \\ (10x + 5y) + (9x + 8y) = 180 & (2) \end{cases}$$

Simplify each equation.

$$\begin{cases} 21x + 12y = 180 & (1) \\ 19x + 13y = 180 & (2) \end{cases}$$

Multiply both sides of equation (1) by -19, multiply both sides of equation (2) by 21, and

add the results.

$$\begin{cases} -399x - 228y = -3420 \\ 399x + 273y = 3780 \end{cases}$$
$$45y = 360$$
$$y = 8$$

Substituting 8 for y in equation (2), we obtain

$$19x + 13(8) = 180$$
$$19x + 104 = 180$$
$$19x = 76$$
$$x = 4$$

Thus, $x = 4$ and $y = 8$.

23. Let s represent the amount to be invested in stocks and let b represent the amount to be invested in bonds.

$$\begin{cases} s + b = 36,000 & (1) \\ 5b = 3s & (2) \end{cases}$$

Write equation (2) in standard form.

$$\begin{cases} s + b = 36,000 & (1) \\ -3s + 5b = 0 & (2) \end{cases}$$

Multiply both sides of equation (1) by 3 and add the result to equation (2).

$$\begin{cases} 3s + 3b = 108,000 \\ -3s + 5b = 0 \end{cases}$$
$$8b = 108,000$$
$$b = 13,500$$

Substituting 13,500 for b in equation (1), we obtain

$$s + 13,500 = 36,000$$
$$s = 22,500$$

Invest \$22,500 in stocks and \$13,500 in bonds.

25. Let x represent the amount loaned at 5% per year and let y represent the amount loaned at 8% per year. We organize the information in the table below, using the interest formula:

Interest = Principal × rate × time or $I = Prt$.

	P	r	t	I
5% loan	x	0.05	1	$0.05x$
8% loan	y	0.08	1	$0.08y$
Total	750,000		1	52,500

Using the columns for Principal and Interest, we obtain the following system.

$$\begin{cases} x + y = 750,000 & (1) \\ 0.05x + 0.08y = 52,500 & (2) \end{cases}$$

Solving equation (1) for y, we obtain
$y = 750,000 - x$. Substituting $750,000 - x$ for y
in equation (2), we obtain
$$0.05x + 0.08(750,000 - x) = 52,500$$
$$0.05x + 60,000 - 0.08x = 52,500$$
$$-0.03x + 60,000 = 52,500$$
$$-0.03x = -7500$$
$$x = 250,000$$
The bank loaned $250,000 at 5%.

27. Let a represent the weight of Arabica beans to be
    used and let r represent the weight of African
    Robustas beans to be used. We organize the
    information in the table below, using the formula
    Price per pound $\times$ number of pounds = Revenue.

	Price per pound	Number of pounds	Revenue
Arabica	9.00	a	$9a$
African Robustas	11.50	r	$11.5r$
Blend	10.00	100	$10(100) = 1000$

Using the columns for Number of pounds and
Revenue, we obtain the following system.
$$\begin{cases} a + r = 100 & (1) \\ 9a + 11.5r = 1000 & (2) \end{cases}$$
Solving equation (1) for a yields $a = 100 - r$.
Substituting $100 - r$ for a in equation (2), we
obtain $9(100 - r) + 11.5r = 1000$
$$900 - 9r + 11.5r = 1000$$
$$900 + 2.5r = 1000$$
$$2.5r = 100$$
$$r = 40$$
Substituting 40 for r in equation (1) yields
$a + 40 = 100$
$\qquad a = 60$
The blend requires 60 pounds of Arabica beans
and 40 pounds of African Robustas beans.

29. Let x represent the number of milligrams of the
    first liquid and let y represent the number of
    milligrams of the second liquid to be used. Then
    the amount of vitamin C in the two liquids is
    $0.20x + 0.50y$. The amount of vitamin D in the
    two liquids is $0.30x + 0.25y$. This results in the
    following system:
    $$\begin{cases} 0.20x + 0.50y = 40 & (1) \\ 0.30x + 0.25y = 30 & (2) \end{cases}$$

Multiply both sides of equation (1) by 2,
multiply both sides of equation (2) by –4, and
add the results.
$$\begin{cases} 0.4x + y = 80 \\ -1.2x - y = -120 \end{cases}$$
$$\overline{-0.8x \qquad = -40}$$
$$x = 50$$
Substituting 50 for x in equation (1), we obtain
$$0.20(50) + 0.50y = 40$$
$$10 + 0.50y = 40$$
$$0.50y = 30$$
$$y = 60$$
To fill the prescription, 50 milligrams of the first
liquid and 60 milligrams of the second liquid
must be mixed.

31. Let x represent the speed at which Jonathon and
    Samantha can row in still water and let y
    represent the speed of the current. The rate at
    which the pair will travel downstream will be
    $x + y$, and the rate upstream will be $x - y$.
    Using the formula rate $\times$ time = distance, we
    obtain the following system:
    $$\begin{cases} (x + y) \cdot 2 = 26 & (1) \\ (x - y) \cdot 3 = 9 & (2) \end{cases}$$
    Divide both sides of equation (1) by 2, divide
    both sides of equation (2) by 3, and add the
    results.
    $$x + y = 13$$
    $$x - y = 3$$
    $$\overline{2x \qquad = 16}$$
    $$x = 8$$
    Jonathon and Samantha can row at a rate of 8
    miles per hour in still water.

33. Let t represent the time for both cars. Let d
    represent the distance traveled by the Lincoln.
    Then the distance traveled by the Infiniti is
    $d + 100$. We obtain the following system by
    utilizing the formula rate $\times$ time = distance:
    $$\begin{cases} 40t = d & (1) \\ 50t = d + 100 & (2) \end{cases}$$
    Substituting $40t$ for d in equation (2) yields
    $50t = 40t + 100$
    $\qquad 10t = 100$
    $\qquad\quad t = 10$
    Substituting 10 for t in equation (1), we obtain

$$40(10) = d$$
$$400 = d$$

The distance traveled by the Lincoln was 400 miles. The distance traveled by the Infiniti is $400 + 100 = 500$ miles. The time for both trips was 10 hours each.

35. a. $\begin{cases} S(p) = -2000 + 3000p \\ D(p) = 10,000 - 1000p \end{cases}$

b.
$$S(p) = D(p)$$
$$-2000 + 3000p = 10,000 - 1000p$$
$$-2000 + 4000p = 10,000$$
$$4000p = 12,000$$
$$p = 3$$

$$S(3) = -2000 + 3000(3) = 7000$$
$$D(3) = 10,000 - 1000(3) = 7000$$

The equilibrium price is $3. The equilibrium quantity is 7000 hot dogs.

37. a. $\begin{cases} M(t) = 0.327t + 24.24 \\ F(t) = 0.532t + 18.12 \end{cases}$

b.
$$M(t) = F(t)$$
$$0.327t + 24.24 = 0.532t + 18.12$$
$$-0.205t = -6.12$$
$$t \approx 29.9$$

The percent of male and female college graduates will be equal approximately 30 years after 1990; that is in approximately 2020.
$$M(30) = 0.327(30) + 24.24 = 34.05$$
$$F(30) = 0.532(30) + 18.12 = 34.08$$
The percent will be approximately 34%.

39. a. Let m represent the number of minutes, let A represent the cost of plan A, and let B represent the cost of plan B.
$$\begin{cases} A(m) = 8.95 + 0.05m \\ B(m) = 5.95 + 0.07m \end{cases}$$

b.

c.
$$A(m) = B(m)$$
$$8.95 + 0.05m = 5.95 + 0.07m$$
$$-0.02m = -3$$
$$m = 150$$

The number of minutes at which the two plans will cost the same is 150 minutes.

$$A(150) = 8.95 + 0.05(150) = 16.45$$
$$B(150) = 5.95 + 0.07(150) = 16.45$$

The cost of each plan at 150 minutes of calling is $16.45.

41. a. $R(x) = 60x$

b. $C(x) = 3500 + 35x$

c.

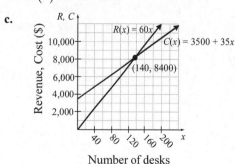

d. $R(x) = C(x)$

$\quad 60x = 3500 + 35x$

$\quad 25x = 3500$

$\quad\quad x = 140$

The number of desks at which the revenue equals cost is 140 desks.

$R(140) = 60(140) = 8400$

$C(140) = 3500 + 35(140) = 8400$

The cost and revenue for producing and selling 140 desks will both be \$8400.

43. a. and **b.** Let x represent the number of years since 1968.

c. Answers may vary. We use the points $(4,\ 20.00)$ and $(36,\ 19.79)$.

$m = \dfrac{19.79 - 20.00}{36 - 4} = \dfrac{-0.21}{32} = -0.0065625$

$y - 20.00 = -0.0065625(x - 4)$

$y - 20.00 = -0.0065625x + 0.02625$

$\quad\quad y = -0.0065625x + 20.02625$

See graph below part d.

d. Answers may vary. We use the points $(0,\ 22.50)$ and $(32,\ 21.84)$.

$m = \dfrac{21.84 - 22.50}{32 - 0} = \dfrac{-0.66}{32} = -0.020625$

$y - 22.50 = -0.020625(x - 0)$

$y - 22.50 = -0.020625x$

$\quad\quad y = -0.020625x + 22.50$

e. $-0.0065625x + 20.02625 = -0.020625x + 22.50$

$\quad 0.0140625x + 20.02625 = 22.50$

$\quad\quad 0.0140625x = 2.47375$

$\quad\quad\quad\quad x \approx 176$

Now, $1968 + 176 = 2144$ will be the year in which we predict the winning times for men and women will be equal.

Men:

$t = -0.0065625(176) + 20.02625 \approx 18.87$

Women:

$t = -0.020625(176) + 22.50 \approx 18.87$

We predict the common winning times will be approximately 18.87 seconds.

f. Answers will vary. Our prediction in part (e) is not very reliable. Neither data set is very linear, so the linear models that we found in parts (c) and (d) are suspect.

4.3 Preparing for Systems of Linear Equations in Three Variables

1. Substitute $x = 1$, $y = -2$, and $z = 3$:

$3x - 2y + 4z = 3(1) - 2(-2) + 4(3)$

$\quad\quad\quad\quad\quad = 3 + 4 + 12$

$\quad\quad\quad\quad\quad = 19$

4.3 Exercises

1. inconsistent

3. solution

5. TRUE

7. The three planes formed by the system will intersect at the point (3, 2, 5).

9. **a.** Substitute $x = 6$, $y = 2$, $z = -1$ into all three equations.

$$\begin{cases} 6+2+2(-1)=6+2-2=6 \\ -2(6)-3(2)+5(-1)=-12-6-5=-23 \neq 1 \\ 2(6)+2+3(-1)=12+2-3=11 \neq 5 \end{cases}$$

Although these values satisfy equation (1), they do not satisfy equations (2) and (3). Therefore, the ordered triple $(6, 2, -1)$ is not a solution of the system.

b. Substitute $x = -3$, $y = 5$, $z = 2$ into all thre equations).

$$\begin{cases} -3+5+2(2)=-3+5+4=6 \\ -2(-3)-3(5)+5(2)=6-15+10=1 \\ 2(-3)+5+3(2)=-6+5+6=5 \end{cases}$$

Because these values satisfy all three equations, the ordered triple $(-3, 5, 2)$ is a solution of the system.

11. $$\begin{cases} x+y+z=5 & (1) \\ -2x-3y+2z=8 & (2) \\ 3x-y-2z=3 & (3) \end{cases}$$

Multiply both sides of equation (1) by 2 and add the result to equation (2).

$$\begin{array}{r} 2x+2y+2z=10 \\ -2x-3y+2z=8 \\ \hline -y+4z=18 \quad (4) \end{array}$$

Multiply both sides of equation (1) by -3 and add the result to equation (3).

$$\begin{array}{r} -3x-3y-3z=-15 \\ 3x-y-2z=3 \\ \hline -4y-5z=-12 \quad (5) \end{array}$$

Multiply both sides of equation (4) by -4 and add the result to equation (5).

$$\begin{array}{r} 4y-16z=-72 \\ -4y-5z=-12 \\ \hline -21z=-84 \\ z=4 \end{array}$$

Substituting 4 for z in equation (4), we obtain

$$\begin{aligned} -y+4(4) &= 18 \\ -y+16 &= 18 \\ -y &= 2 \\ y &= -2 \end{aligned}$$

Substituting -2 for y and 4 for z in equation (1), we obtain

$$\begin{aligned} x+(-2)+4 &= 5 \\ x+2 &= 5 \\ x &= 3 \end{aligned}$$

The solution is the ordered triple $(3, -2, 4)$.

13. $$\begin{cases} x-3y+z=13 & (1) \\ 3x+y-4z=13 & (2) \\ -4x-4y+2z=0 & (3) \end{cases}$$

Multiply equation (1) by -3 and add the result to equation (2).

$$\begin{array}{r} -3x+9y-3z=-39 \\ 3x+y-4z=13 \\ \hline 10y-7z=-26 \quad (4) \end{array}$$

Multiply both sides of equation (1) by 4 and add the result to equation (3).

$$\begin{array}{r} 4x-12y+4z=52 \\ -4x-4y+2z=0 \\ \hline -16y+6z=52 \quad (5) \end{array}$$

Multiply equation (4) by 8, multiply equation (5) by 5, and add the results.

$$\begin{array}{r} 80y-56z=-208 \\ -80y+30z=260 \\ \hline -26z=52 \\ z=-2 \end{array}$$

Substituting -2 for z in equation (4) and solving for y, we obtain

$$\begin{aligned} 10y-7(-2) &= -26 \\ 10y+14 &= -26 \\ 10y &= -40 \\ y &= -4 \end{aligned}$$

Substituting -2 for z and -4 for y in equation (1), we obtain

$$x-3(-4)+(-2)=13$$
$$x+12-2=13$$
$$x+10=13$$
$$x=3$$

The solution is the ordered triple $(3,-4,-2)$.

15.
$$\begin{cases} 2x-y+2z=1 & (1) \\ -2x+3y-2z=3 & (2) \\ 4x-y+6z=7 & (3) \end{cases}$$

Add equations (1) and (2).
$$2x-y+2z=1$$
$$\underline{-2x+3y-2z=3}$$
$$2y=4$$
$$y=2$$

Multiply both sides of equation (2) by 2 and add the result to equation (3).
$$-4x+6y-4z=6$$
$$\underline{4x-y+6z=7}$$
$$5y+2z=13 \qquad (4)$$

Substituting 2 for y in equation (4), we obtain
$$5(2)+2z=13$$
$$10+2z=13$$
$$2z=3$$
$$z=\frac{3}{2}$$

Substituting 2 for y and $\frac{3}{2}$ for z in equation (1),

we obtain
$$2x-2+2\left(\frac{3}{2}\right)=1$$
$$2x-2+3=1$$
$$2x=0$$
$$x=0$$

The solution is the ordered triple $\left(0,\ 2,\ \frac{3}{2}\right)$.

17.
$$\begin{cases} x-4y+z=5 & (1) \\ 4x+2y+z=2 & (2) \\ -4x+y-3z=-8 & (3) \end{cases}$$

Multiply both sides of equation (1) by -4 and add the result to equation (2).
$$-4x+16y-4z=-20$$
$$\underline{4x+2y+z=2}$$
$$18y-3z=-18 \qquad (4)$$

Add equations (2) and (3).
$$4x+2y+z=2$$
$$\underline{-4x+y-3z=-8}$$
$$3y-2z=-6 \qquad (5)$$

Multiply both sides of equation (5) by -6 and add the result to equation (4).
$$-18y+12z=36$$
$$\underline{18y-3z=-18}$$
$$9z=18$$
$$z=2$$

Substituting 2 for z in equation (5), we obtain
$$3y-2(2)=-6$$
$$3y-4=-6$$
$$3y=-2$$
$$y=-\frac{2}{3}$$

Substituting $-\frac{2}{3}$ for y and 2 for z in equation

(1), we obtain
$$x-4\left(-\frac{2}{3}\right)+2=5$$
$$x+\frac{8}{3}+2=5$$
$$3\left(x+\frac{8}{3}+2\right)=3(5)$$
$$3x+8+6=15$$
$$3x=1$$
$$x=\frac{1}{3}$$

The solution is the ordered triple $\left(\frac{1}{3},-\frac{2}{3},\ 2\right)$.

19.
$$\begin{cases} x-3y=12 & (1) \\ 2y-3z=-9 & (2) \\ 2x+z=7 & (3) \end{cases}$$

Multiply both sides of equation (1) by -2 and add the result to equation (3).
$$-2x+6y=-24$$
$$\underline{2x+z=7}$$
$$6y+z=-17 \qquad (4)$$

Multiply both sides of equation (4) by 3 and add the result to equation (2).

$$18y + 3z = -51$$
$$\underline{2y - 3z = -9}$$
$$20y \quad\quad = -60$$
$$y = -3$$

Substituting -3 for y in equation (4), we obtain
$$6(-3) + z = -17$$
$$-18 + z = -17$$
$$z = 1$$

Substituting -3 for y in equation (1), we obtain
$$x - 3(-3) = 12$$
$$x + 9 = 12$$
$$x = 3$$

The solution is the ordered triple $(3, -3, 1)$.

21.
$$\begin{cases} 2y - z = -3 & (1) \\ -2x + 3y \quad = 10 & (2) \\ 4x \quad + 3z = -11 & (3) \end{cases}$$

Multiply both sides of equation (2) by 2 and add the result to equation (3).
$$-4x + 6y \quad = 20$$
$$\underline{4x \quad + 3z = -11}$$
$$6y + 3z = 9 \quad (4)$$

Multiply both sides of equation (1) by 3 and add the result to equation (4).
$$6y - 3z = -9$$
$$\underline{6y + 3z = 9}$$
$$12y = 0$$
$$y = 0$$

Substituting 0 for y in equation (1), we obtain
$$2(0) - z = -3$$
$$-z = -3$$
$$z = 3$$

Substituting 0 for y in equation (2), we obtain
$$-2x + 3(0) = 10$$
$$-2x = 10$$
$$x = -5$$

The solution is the ordered triple $(-5, 0, 3)$.

23.
$$\begin{cases} x - y + z = 5 & (1) \\ -2x + y - z = 2 & (2) \\ x - 2y + 2z = 1 & (3) \end{cases}$$

Multiply both sides of equation (1) by 2 and add the result to equation (2).
$$2x - 2y + 2z = 10$$
$$\underline{-2x + y - z = 2}$$
$$-y + z = 12 \quad (4)$$

Multiply both sides of equation (3) by 2 and add the result to equation (2).
$$2x - 4y + 4z = 2$$
$$\underline{-2x + y - z = 2}$$
$$-3y + 3z = 4 \quad (5)$$

Multiply both sides of equation (4) by -3 and add the result to equation (5).
$$3y - 3z = -36$$
$$\underline{-3y + 3z = 4}$$
$$0 = -32 \quad \text{False}$$

The system has no solution. The solution set is $\varnothing$ or $\{\ \}$. The system is inconsistent.

25.
$$\begin{cases} x - 2y + z = 5 & (1) \\ -2x + y - z = 2 & (2) \\ x - 5y - 4z = 8 & (3) \end{cases}$$

Multiply both sides of equation (1) by 2 and add the result to equation (2).
$$2x - 4y + 2z = 10$$
$$\underline{-2x + y - z = 2}$$
$$-3y + z = 12 \quad (4)$$

Multiply both sides of equation (3) by 2 and add the result to equation (2).
$$2x - 10y - 8z = 16$$
$$\underline{-2x + y - z = 2}$$
$$-9y - 9z = 18 \quad (5)$$

Multiply both sides of equation (4) by -3 and add the result to equation (5).
$$9y - 3z = -36$$
$$\underline{-9y - 9z = 18}$$
$$-12z = -18$$
$$z = \frac{-18}{-12} = \frac{3}{2}$$

Substituting $\dfrac{3}{2}$ for z in equation (4), we obtain

$$-3y+\frac{3}{2}=12$$

$$2\left(-3y+\frac{3}{2}\right)=2(12)$$

$$-6y+3=24$$

$$-6y=21$$

$$y=\frac{21}{-6}=-\frac{7}{2}$$

Substituting $-\frac{7}{2}$ for y and $\frac{3}{2}$ for z in equation (1), we obtain

$$x-2\left(-\frac{7}{2}\right)+\frac{3}{2}=5$$

$$x+7+\frac{3}{2}=5$$

$$x+\frac{17}{2}=5$$

$$x=-\frac{7}{2}$$

The solution is the ordered triple $\left(-\frac{7}{2},-\frac{7}{2},\frac{3}{2}\right)$.

27. $\begin{cases} x+2y-z=1 & (1) \\ 2x+7y+4z=11 & (2) \\ x+3y+z=4 & (3) \end{cases}$

Multiply both sides of equation (1) by -2 and add the result to equation (2).

$$\begin{array}{r} -2x-4y+2z=-2 \\ 2x+7y+4z=11 \\ \hline 3y+6z=9 \quad (4) \end{array}$$

Multiply both sides of equation (1) by -1 and add the result to equation (3).

$$\begin{array}{r} -x-2y+z=-1 \\ x+3y+z=4 \\ \hline y+2z=3 \quad (5) \end{array}$$

Multiply both sides of equation (5) by -3 and add the result to equation (4).

$$\begin{array}{r} -3y-6z=-9 \\ 3y+6z=9 \\ \hline 0=0 \quad \text{True} \end{array}$$

Thus, the system is dependent and has an infinite number of solutions.

Solve equation (5) for y.

$$y=-2z+3$$

Substituting $-2z+3$ for y in equation (1), we

obtain

$$x+2(-2z+3)-z=1$$

$$x-4z+6-z=1$$

$$x-5z+6=1$$

$$x-5z=-5$$

$$x=5z-5$$

The solution to the system is $\{(x,y,z)|x=5z-5,$ $y=-2z+3, z \text{ is any real number}\}$.

29. $\begin{cases} x+y+z=5 & (1) \\ 3x+4y+z=16 & (2) \\ -x-4y+z=-6 & (3) \end{cases}$

Add equations (1) and (3).

$$\begin{array}{r} x+y+z=5 \\ -x-4y+z=-6 \\ \hline -3y+2z=-1 \quad (4) \end{array}$$

Multiply both sides of equation (3) by 3 and add the result to equation (2).

$$\begin{array}{r} -3x-12y+3z=-18 \\ 3x+4y+z=16 \\ \hline -8y+4z=-2 \quad (5) \end{array}$$

Multiply both sides of equation (4) by -2 and add the result to equation (5).

$$\begin{array}{r} 6y-4z=2 \\ -8y+4z=-2 \\ \hline -2y=0 \\ y=0 \end{array}$$

Substituting 0 for y in equation (4), we obtain

$$-3(0)+2z=-1$$

$$2z=-1$$

$$z=-\frac{1}{2}$$

Substituting 0 for y and $-\frac{1}{2}$ for z in equation (1),

we obtain

$$x+0+\left(-\frac{1}{2}\right)=5$$

$$x=\frac{11}{2}$$

The solution is the ordered triple $\left(\frac{11}{2},\ 0,-\frac{1}{2}\right)$.

31.
$$\begin{cases} x+y+z=3 & (1) \\ -x+\dfrac{1}{2}y+z=\dfrac{1}{2} & (2) \\ -x+2y+3z=4 & (3) \end{cases}$$

Add equations (1) and (3).
$$\begin{aligned} x+y+z&=3 \\ \underline{-x+2y+3z}&=\underline{4} \\ 3y+4z&=7 \qquad (4) \end{aligned}$$

Multiply both sides of equation (1) by 2, multiply both sides of equation (2) by 2, and add the results.
$$\begin{aligned} 2x+2y+2z&=6 \\ \underline{-2x+y+2z}&=\underline{1} \\ 3y+4z&=7 \qquad (5) \end{aligned}$$

Multiply both sides of equation (4) by –1 and add the result to equation (5).
$$\begin{aligned} -3y-4z&=-7 \\ \underline{3y+4z}&=\underline{7} \\ 0&=0 \qquad \text{True} \end{aligned}$$

Thus, the system is dependent and has an infinite number of solutions.

Solve equation (5) for y.
$$\begin{aligned} 3y+4z&=7 \\ 3y&=-4z+7 \\ y&=-\frac{4}{3}z+\frac{7}{3} \end{aligned}$$

Substituting $-\dfrac{4}{3}z+\dfrac{7}{3}$ for y in equation (1), we obtain
$$\begin{aligned} x+\left(-\frac{4}{3}z+\frac{7}{3}\right)+z&=3 \\ x-\frac{1}{3}z+\frac{7}{3}&=3 \\ x&=\frac{1}{3}z+\frac{2}{3} \end{aligned}$$

The solution to the system is $\left\{(x,y,z)\Big| x=\dfrac{1}{3}z+\dfrac{2}{3},\right.$

$\left. y=-\dfrac{4}{3}z+\dfrac{7}{3}, z \text{ is any real number}\right\}$.

33. Answers will vary. One possibility follows.
For the ordered triple $(2,-1,\,3)$, evaluate the expressions $x+y+z$, $x-y+z$, and $x+y-z$:
$$x+y+z=2+(-1)+3=4$$

$$x-y+z=2-(-1)+3=6$$
$$x+y-z=2+(-1)-3=-2$$
So, the system below has the solution $(2,-1,\,3)$.
$$\begin{cases} x+y+z=4 \\ x-y+z=6 \\ x+y-z=-2 \end{cases}$$

35. a. If $f(-1)=-6$, then
$$a(-1)^2+b(-1)+c=-6 \text{ or } a-b+c=-6.$$
If $f(2)=3$, then $a(2)^2+b(2)+c=3$ or
$$4a+2b+c=3.$$

b. To find a, b, and c, we must solve the following system:
$$\begin{cases} a+b+c=4 & (1) \\ a-b+c=-6 & (2) \\ 4a+2b+c=3 & (3) \end{cases}$$

Add equations (1) and (2).
$$\begin{aligned} a+b+c&=4 \\ \underline{a-b+c}&=\underline{-6} \\ 2a\phantom{{}+b}+2c&=-2 \qquad (4) \end{aligned}$$

Multiply both sides of equation (2) by 2 and add the result to equation (3).
$$\begin{aligned} 2a-2b+2c&=-12 \\ \underline{4a+2b+c}&=\underline{3} \\ 6a\phantom{{}+2b}+3c&=-9 \qquad (5) \end{aligned}$$

Divide both sides of equation (4) by 2, divide equation (5) by –3, and add the results.
$$\begin{aligned} a+c&=-1 \\ \underline{-2a-c}&=\underline{3} \\ -a&=2 \\ a&=-2 \end{aligned}$$

Substituting –2 for a in equation (4), we obtain
$$\begin{aligned} 2(-2)+2c&=-2 \\ -4+2c&=-2 \\ 2c&=2 \\ c&=1 \end{aligned}$$

Substituting –2 for a and 1 for c in equation (1), we obtain
$$\begin{aligned} -2+b+1&=4 \\ b&=5 \end{aligned}$$

Thus, the quadratic equation that contains $(-1,-6)$, $(1,\,4)$, and $(2,\,3)$ is
$$f(x)=-2x^2+5x+1.$$

37. Rewrite the system with each equation in standard form.

$$\begin{cases} i_1 - i_2 + i_3 = 0 & (1) \\ -3i_1 \quad + 2i_3 = 3 & (2) \\ 4i_2 + 2i_3 = 22 & (3) \end{cases}$$

Multiply both sides of equation (1) by 3 and add the result to equation (2).

$$3i_1 - 3i_2 + 3i_3 = 0$$
$$\underline{-3i_1 \quad\quad + 2i_3 = 3}$$
$$-3i_2 + 5i_3 = 3 \qquad (4)$$

Multiply both sides of equation (3) by 3, multiply both sides of equation (4) by 4, and add the results.

$$12i_2 + 6i_3 = 66$$
$$\underline{-12i_2 + 20i_3 = 12}$$
$$26i_3 = 78$$
$$i_3 = 3$$

Substituting 3 for i_3 in equation (2), we obtain

$$-3i_1 + 2(3) = 3$$
$$-3i_1 + 6 = 3$$
$$-3i_1 = -3$$
$$i_1 = 1$$

Substituting 3 for i_3 and 1 for i_1 in equation (1), we obtain

$$1 - i_2 + (3) = 0$$
$$-i_2 + 4 = 0$$
$$-i_2 = -4$$
$$i_2 = 4$$

The currents are $i_1 = 1$, $i_2 = 4$, and $i_3 = 3$.

39. Let b represent the number of box seats, let r represent the number of reserved seats, and let l represent the number of lawn seats.

$$\begin{cases} b + r + l = 4100 & (1) \\ 9b + 7r + 5l = 28,400 & (2) \\ \frac{1}{2}(9b) + \frac{1}{2}(7r) + 5l = 18,300 & (3) \end{cases}$$

Simplify equation (3) and rewrite the system.

$$\frac{1}{2}(9b) + \frac{1}{2}(7r) + 5l = 18,300$$
$$4.5b + 3.5r + 5l = 18,300$$

Rewriting the system, we have

$$\begin{cases} b + r + l = 4100 & (1) \\ 9b + 7r + 5l = 28,400 & (2) \\ 4.5b + 3.5r + 5l = 18,300 & (3) \end{cases}$$

Multiply both sides of equation (1) by –9 and add the result to equation (2).

$$-9b - 9r - 9l = -36,900$$
$$\underline{9b + 7r + 5l = 28,400}$$
$$-2r - 4l = -8500 \qquad (4)$$

Multiply both sides of equation (3) by –2 and add the result to equation (2).

$$-9b - 7r - 10l = -36,600$$
$$\underline{9b + 7r + 5l = 28,400}$$
$$-5l = -8200$$
$$l = 1640$$

Substituting 1640 for l in equation (4), we obtain

$$-2r - 4(1640) = -8500$$
$$-2r - 6460 = -8500$$
$$-2r = -1940$$
$$r = 970$$

Substituting 1640 for l and 970 for r in equation (1), we obtain

$$b + 970 + 1640 = 4100$$
$$b + 2610 = 4100$$
$$b = 1490$$

There are 1490 box seats, 970 reserve seats, and 1640 lawn seats in the stadium.

41. Let c represent the number servings of Chex® cereal, let m represent the number of servings of 2% milk, and let j represent the number of servings of orange juice.

$$\begin{cases} 220c + 125m \quad\quad = 470 & \text{(sodium)} & (1) \\ 26c + 12m + 26j = 89 & \text{(carbs)} & (2) \\ c + 8m + 2j = 20 & \text{(protein)} & (3) \end{cases}$$

Multiply both sides of equation (3) by –13 and add the result to equation (2).

$$-13c - 104m - 26j = -260$$
$$\underline{26c + 12m + 26j = 89}$$
$$13c - 92m \quad\quad = -171 \qquad (4)$$

Multiply both sides of equation (1) by 13, multiply both sides of equation (4) by –220, and add the results.

$$2860c + 1625m = 6110$$
$$\underline{-2860c + 20,240m = 37,620}$$
$$21,865m = 43,730$$
$$m = 2$$

Substituting 2 for m in equation (1), we obtain

$$220c + 125(2) = 470$$
$$220c + 250 = 470$$
$$220c = 220$$
$$c = 1$$

Substituting 2 for m and 1 for c in equation (3), we obtain

$$1 + 8(2) + 2j = 20$$
$$17 + 2j = 20$$
$$2j = 3$$
$$j = 1.5$$

Nancy needs 1 serving of Chex® cereal, 2 servings of 2% milk, and 1.5 servings of orange juice.

43. Let t represent the amount to be invested in Treasury bills, let m represent the amount to be invested in municipal bonds, and let c represent the amount to be invested in corporate bonds.

$$\begin{cases} t + m + c = 25{,}000 & (1) \\ 0.03t + 0.05m + 0.09c = 1210 & (2) \\ t - c = 7000 & (3) \end{cases}$$

Multiply both sides of equation (1) by -0.05 and add the result to equation (2).

$$-0.05t - 0.05m - 0.05c = -1250$$
$$\underline{0.03t + 0.05m + 0.09c = 1210}$$
$$-0.02t \qquad\qquad + 0.04c = -40 \qquad (4)$$

Multiply both sides of equation (3) by 0.02 and add the result to equation (4).

$$0.02t - 0.02c = 140$$
$$\underline{-0.02t + 0.04c = -40}$$
$$0.02c = 100$$
$$c = 5000$$

Substituting 5000 for c in equation (3), we obtain

$$t - 5000 = 7000$$
$$t = 12{,}000$$

Substituting 5000 for c and 12,000 for t in equation (1), we obtain

$$12{,}000 + m + 5000 = 25{,}000$$
$$m + 17{,}000 = 25{,}000$$
$$m = 8000$$

Sachi should invest \$12,000 in Treasury bills, \$8000 in municipal bonds, and \$5000 in corporate bonds.

45. Let x represent the lengths of $\overline{AO}$ and $\overline{AM}$, let y represent the lengths of $\overline{OC}$ and $\overline{NC}$, and let z represent the lengths of $\overline{BM}$ and $\overline{BN}$.
Because $\overline{AO} + \overline{OC} = \overline{AC}$, $\overline{BN} + \overline{NC} = \overline{BC}$, and $\overline{AM} + \overline{MB} = \overline{AB}$, we obtain the following system..

$$\begin{cases} x + y \quad\;\; = 14 & (1) \\ x \quad\;\; + z = 6 & (2) \\ \quad\; y + z = 12 & (3) \end{cases}$$

Multiply both sides of equation (1) by -1 and add the result to equation (2).

$$-x - y \qquad = -14$$
$$\underline{x \qquad + z = 6}$$
$$-y + z = -8 \qquad (4)$$

Add equations (3) and (4).

$$y + z = 12$$
$$\underline{-y + z = -8}$$
$$2z = 4$$
$$z = 2$$

Substituting 2 for z in equation (3), we obtain

$$y + 2 = 12$$
$$y = 10$$

Substituting 2 for z in equation (2), we obtain

$$x + 2 = 6$$
$$x = 4$$

Therefore, $\overline{AM} = 4$, $\overline{BN} = 2$, and $\overline{OC} = 10$.

47.

$$\begin{cases} \dfrac{2}{5}x + \dfrac{1}{2}y - \dfrac{1}{3}z = 0 & (1) \\[2mm] \dfrac{3}{5}x - \dfrac{1}{4}y + \dfrac{1}{2}z = 10 & (2) \\[2mm] -\dfrac{1}{5}x + \dfrac{1}{4}y - \dfrac{1}{6}z = -4 & (3) \end{cases}$$

Simplify each equation and rewrite the system.

(1) $\quad 30\left(\dfrac{2}{5}x + \dfrac{1}{2}y - \dfrac{1}{3}z\right) = 30(0)$

$\qquad\qquad 12x + 15y - 10z = 0$

(2) $\quad 20\left(\dfrac{3}{5}x - \dfrac{1}{4}y + \dfrac{1}{2}z\right) = 20(10)$

$\qquad\qquad 12x - 5y + 10z = 200$

(3) $\quad 60\left(-\dfrac{1}{5}x + \dfrac{1}{4}y - \dfrac{1}{6}z\right) = 60(-4)$

$\qquad\qquad -12x + 15y - 10z = -240$

Rewriting the system, we have

$$\begin{cases} 12x+15y-10z=0 & (1) \\ 12x-5y+10z=200 & (2) \\ -12x+15y-10z=-240 & (3) \end{cases}$$

Add equations (1) and (3).

$$12x+15y-10z=0$$
$$\underline{-12x+15y-10z=-240}$$
$$30y-20z=-240 \qquad (4)$$

Add equations (2) and (3).

$$12x-5y+10z=200$$
$$\underline{-12x+15y-10z=-240}$$
$$10y =-40$$
$$y=-4$$

Substituting -4 for y in equation (4), we obtain

$$30(-4)-20z=-240$$
$$-120-20z=-240$$
$$-20z=-120$$
$$z=6$$

Substituting -4 for y and 6 for z in equation (1), we obtain

$$12x+15(-4)-10(6)=0$$
$$12x-60-60=0$$
$$12x=120$$
$$x=10$$

The solution is the ordered triple $(10,-4,6)$.

49.
$$\begin{cases} x+y+z+w=3 & (1) \\ -2x-y+3z-w=-1 & (2) \\ 2x+2y-2z+w=2 & (3) \\ -x+2y-3z+2w=12 & (4) \end{cases}$$

Add equations (1) and (4).

$$x+y+z+w=3$$
$$\underline{-x+2y-3z+2w=12}$$
$$3y-2z+3w=15 \qquad (5)$$

Add equations (2) and (3).

$$-2x-y+3z-w=-1$$
$$\underline{2x+2y-2z+w=2}$$
$$y+z =1 \qquad (6)$$

Multiply both sides of equation (1) by 2 and add the result to equation (2).

$$2x+2y+2z+2w=6$$
$$\underline{-2x-y+3z-w=-1}$$
$$y+5z+w=5 \qquad (7)$$

Multiply both sides of equation (7) by -3 and add the result to equation (5).

$$-3y-15z-3w=-15$$
$$\underline{3y-2z+3w=15}$$
$$-17z =0$$
$$z=0$$

Substituting 0 for z in equation (6), we obtain

$$y+0=1$$
$$y=1$$

Substituting 0 for z and 1 for y equation (7), we obtain

$$1+5(0)+w=5$$
$$1+w=5$$
$$w=4$$

Substituting 0 for z and 1 for y and 4 for w in equation (1), we obtain

$$x+1+0+4=3$$
$$x+5=3$$
$$x=-2$$

The solution is $(-2,1,0,4)$.

Putting the Concepts Together (Sections 4.1 – 4.3)

1. The graphs of the linear equations intersect at the point $(-3,5)$. Thus, the solution is $(-3,5)$.

2.
$$\begin{cases} 3x+y=7 & (1) \\ -2x+3y=-12 & (2) \end{cases}$$

Equation (1) in slope-intercept form is $y=-3x+7$. Equation (2) in slope-intercept form is $y=\dfrac{2}{3}x-4$. Graph each equation and find the point of intersection.

The solution is the ordered pair $(3,-2)$.

3. $\begin{cases} x = 2 - 3y & (1) \\ 3x + 10y = 5 & (2) \end{cases}$

Because equation (1) is solved for x, we use substitution to solve the system.
Substituting $2 - 3y$ for x in equation (2), we obtain

$$3(2 - 3y) + 10y = 5$$
$$6 - 9y + 10y = 5$$
$$6 + y = 5$$
$$y = -1$$

Substituting -1 for y in equation (1), we obtain
$x = 2 - 3(-1) = 2 + 3 = 5$.

The solution is the ordered pair (5, -1).

4. $\begin{cases} 4x + 3y = -1 & (1) \\ 2x - y = 3 & (2) \end{cases}$

Because the coefficient of y in equation (2) is -1, we use substitution to solve the system.
Equation (2) solved for y is $y = 2x - 3$.
Substituting $2x - 3$ for y in equation (1), we obtain

$$4x + 3(2x - 3) = -1$$
$$4x + 6x - 9 = -1$$
$$10x - 9 = -1$$
$$10x = 8$$
$$x = \frac{8}{10} = \frac{4}{5}$$

Substituting $\frac{4}{5}$ for x in equation (2), we obtain

$$2\left(\frac{4}{5}\right) - y = 3$$
$$\frac{8}{5} - y = \frac{15}{5}$$
$$-y = \frac{7}{5}$$
$$y = -\frac{7}{5}$$

The solution is the ordered pair $\left(\frac{4}{5}, \ -\frac{7}{5}\right)$.

5. $\begin{cases} x + 3y = 8 & (1) \\ \frac{1}{5}x + \frac{1}{2}y = 1 & (2) \end{cases}$

Because equation (2) contains fractions, we choose to use the elimination method to solve the system.
Multiply both sides of equation (1) by 2, multiply both side of equation (2) by -10, and

add the results.

$$\begin{array}{r} 2x + 6y = 16 \\ -2x - 5y = -10 \\ \hline y = 6 \end{array}$$

Substituting 6 for y in equation (1), we obtain

$$x + 3(6) = 8$$
$$x + 18 = 8$$
$$x = -10$$

The solution is the ordered pair (-10, 6).

6. $\begin{cases} 8x - 4y = 12 & (1) \\ -10x + 5y = -15 & (2) \end{cases}$

Because none of variables have a coefficient of 1, we use elimination to solve the system.
Multiply both sides of equation (1) by 5, multiply both sides of equation (2) by 4, and add the results.

$$\begin{array}{r} 40x - 20y = 60 \\ -40x + 20y = -60 \\ \hline 0 = 0 \quad \text{True} \end{array}$$

The system is dependent. The solution is
$\left\{ (x, \ y) \mid 8x - 4y = 12 \right\}$.

7. $\begin{cases} 2x + y + 3z = 10 & (1) \\ x - 2y + z = 10 & (2) \\ -4x + 3y + 2z = 5 & (3) \end{cases}$

Multiply both sides of equation (2) by -2 and add the result to equation (1).

$$\begin{array}{r} -2x + 4y - 2z = -20 \\ 2x + y + 3z = 10 \\ \hline 5y + z = -10 \quad (4) \end{array}$$

Multiply both sides of equation (1) by 2 and add the result to equation (3).

$$\begin{array}{r} 4x + 2y + 6z = 20 \\ -4x + 3y + 2z = 5 \\ \hline 5y + 8z = 25 \quad (5) \end{array}$$

Multiply both sides of equation (4) by -1 and add the result to equation (5).

$$\begin{array}{r} -5y - z = 10 \\ 5y + 8z = 25 \\ \hline 7z = 35 \\ z = 5 \end{array}$$

Substituting 5 for z in equation (4), we obtain

$$5y + 5 = -10$$
$$5y = -15$$
$$y = -3$$

Substituting 5 for z and -3 for y in equation (1), we obtain

$$2x+(-3)+3(5)=10$$
$$2x-3+15=10$$
$$2x+12=10$$
$$2x=-2$$
$$x=-1$$

The solution is the ordered triple (-1, -3, 5).

8. $\begin{cases} x+2y-2z=3 & (1) \\ x+3y-4z=6 & (2) \\ 4x+5y-2z=6 & (3) \end{cases}$

Multiply both sides of equation (1) by -1 and add the result to equation (2).

$$\begin{array}{r} -x-2y+2z=-3 \\ x+3y-4z=6 \\ \hline y-2z=3 \qquad (4) \end{array}$$

Multiply both sides of equation (1) by -4 and add the result to equation (3).

$$\begin{array}{r} -4x-8y+8z=-12 \\ 4x+5y-2z=6 \\ \hline -3y+6z=-6 \qquad (5) \end{array}$$

Multiply both sides of equation (4) by 3 and add the result to equation (5).

$$\begin{array}{r} 3y-6z=9 \\ -3y+6z=-6 \\ \hline 0=3 \qquad \text{False} \end{array}$$

The system has no solution. The solution set is $\varnothing$ or $\{\ \}$. The system is inconsistent.

9. Let a represent the number of adult tickets and let y represent the number of youth tickets sold.

$\begin{cases} 9a+5y=5925 & (1) \\ a+\ y=825 & (2) \end{cases}$

Multiply both sides of equation (2) by -5 and add the result to equation (1).

$$\begin{array}{r} -5a-5y=-4125 \\ 9a+5y=5925 \\ \hline 4a\ \ \ \ \ =1800 \\ a=450 \end{array}$$

Substituting 450 for a in equation (2), we obtain

$$450+y=825$$
$$y=375$$

The museum sold 450 adult tickets and 375 youth tickets.

10. Let r represent the number of orchestra seats, let m represent the number of mezzanine seats, and let b represent the number of balcony seats.

$\begin{cases} r+m+b=1200 & (1) \\ 65r+48m+35b=55,640 & (2) \\ b=m+150 & (3) \end{cases}$

Writing the equations in the system in standard form, we obtain

$\begin{cases} r+m+b=1200 & (1) \\ 65r+48m+35b=55,640 & (2) \\ m-b=-150 & (3) \end{cases}$

Multiply equation (1) by -65 and add the result to equation (2).

$$\begin{array}{r} -65r-65m-65b=-78,000 \\ 65r+48m+35b=55,640 \\ \hline -17m-30b=-22,360 \qquad (4) \end{array}$$

Multiply equation (3) by 17 and add the result to equation (4).

$$\begin{array}{r} 17m-17b=-2,550 \\ -17m-30b=-22,360 \\ \hline -47b=-24,910 \\ b=530 \end{array}$$

Substituting 530 for b in equation (3), we obtain

$$m-530=-150$$
$$m=380$$

Substituting 530 for b and 380 for m in equation (1), we obtain

$$r+380+530=1200$$
$$r+910=1200$$
$$r=290$$

The theatre contains 290 orchestra seats, 380 mezzanine seats, and 530 balcony seats.

4.4 Preparing for Using Matrices to Solve Systems

1. For the expression $4x-2y+z$, the coefficients are 4, -2, and 1.

2. $\begin{aligned} x-4y&=3 \\ x-4y+4y&=3+4y \\ x&=4y+3 \end{aligned}$

3. Substitute $x=1$, $y=-3$, and $z=2$:

$$\begin{aligned} 3x-2y+z&=3(1)-2(-3)+2 \\ &=3+6+2 \\ &=11 \end{aligned}$$

4.4 Exercises

1. matrix

3. 4; 3

5. TRUE

7. Answers will vary. One possibility follows: First, perform row operations so that the entry in row 1, column 1 is 1. Second, perform row operations so that all the entries below the 1 in row 1, column 1 are 0's. Third, perform row operations so that the entry in row 2, column 2 is 1. Make sure that the entries in column 1 remain unchanged. If it is impossible to place a 1 in row 2, column 2, then use row operations to place a 1 in row 2, column 3. (If any row with all 0's occurs, then place it in the last row of the matrix.) Once a 1 is in place, perform row operations to place 0's below it. Continue this process until the augmented matrix is in row echelon form.

9. Multiply each entry in row 2 by $\frac{1}{5}$ (or divide each entry of row 2 by 5). That is, use the row operation $R_2 = \frac{1}{5} r_2$.

11. $\begin{bmatrix} 1 & -3 & | & 2 \\ 2 & 5 & | & 1 \end{bmatrix}$

13. $\begin{bmatrix} 1 & 1 & 1 & | & 3 \\ 2 & -1 & 3 & | & 1 \\ -4 & 2 & -5 & | & -3 \end{bmatrix}$

15. Write each equation in the system in standard form.
$$\begin{cases} -x + y = 2 \\ 5x + y = -5 \end{cases}$$
Thus, the augmented matrix is
$$\begin{bmatrix} -1 & 1 & | & 2 \\ 5 & 1 & | & -5 \end{bmatrix}$$

17. Write each equation in the system in standard form.
$$\begin{cases} x \quad\;\; + z = 2 \\ 2x + y \quad\;\; = 13 \\ x - y + 4z = -4 \end{cases}$$
Thus, the augmented matrix is
$$\begin{bmatrix} 1 & 0 & 1 & | & 2 \\ 2 & 1 & 0 & | & 13 \\ 1 & -1 & 4 & | & -4 \end{bmatrix}$$

19. **a.** $\begin{bmatrix} 1 & -3 & | & 2 \\ -2 & 5 & | & 1 \end{bmatrix}$ $(R_2 = 2r_1 + r_2)$

$= \begin{bmatrix} 1 & -3 & | & 2 \\ 2(1)+(-2) & 2(-3)+5 & | & 2(2)+1 \end{bmatrix}$

$= \begin{bmatrix} 1 & -3 & | & 2 \\ 0 & -1 & | & 5 \end{bmatrix}$

b. $\begin{bmatrix} 1 & -3 & | & 2 \\ 0 & -1 & | & 5 \end{bmatrix}$ $(R_2 = -1 \cdot r_2)$

$= \begin{bmatrix} 1 & -3 & | & 2 \\ -1(0) & -1(-1) & | & -1(5) \end{bmatrix}$

$= \begin{bmatrix} 1 & -3 & | & 2 \\ 0 & 1 & | & -5 \end{bmatrix}$

21. **a.** $\begin{bmatrix} 1 & 1 & -1 & | & 4 \\ 2 & 5 & 3 & | & -3 \\ -1 & -3 & 2 & | & 1 \end{bmatrix}$ $(R_2 = -2r_1 + r_2)$

$= \begin{bmatrix} 1 & 1 & -1 & | & 4 \\ -2(1)+2 & -2(1)+5 & -2(-1)+3 & | & -2(4)+(-3) \\ -1 & -3 & 2 & | & 1 \end{bmatrix}$

$= \begin{bmatrix} 1 & 1 & -1 & | & 4 \\ 0 & 3 & 5 & | & -11 \\ -1 & -3 & 2 & | & 1 \end{bmatrix}$

b. $\begin{bmatrix} 1 & 1 & -1 & | & 4 \\ 0 & 3 & 5 & | & -11 \\ -1 & -3 & 2 & | & 1 \end{bmatrix}$ $(R_3 = r_1 + r_3)$

$= \begin{bmatrix} 1 & 1 & -1 & | & 4 \\ 0 & 3 & 5 & | & -11 \\ 1+(-1) & 1+(-3) & -1+2 & | & 4+1 \end{bmatrix}$

$= \begin{bmatrix} 1 & 1 & -1 & | & 4 \\ 0 & 3 & 5 & | & -11 \\ 0 & -2 & 1 & | & 5 \end{bmatrix}$

23. **a.** $\begin{bmatrix} 1 & 1 & 1 & | & 4 \\ 0 & 5 & 3 & | & -3 \\ 0 & -4 & 2 & | & 8 \end{bmatrix}$ $(R_2 = r_3 + r_2)$

$= \begin{bmatrix} 1 & 1 & 1 & | & 4 \\ 0+0 & -4+5 & 2+3 & | & 8+(-3) \\ 0 & -4 & 2 & | & 8 \end{bmatrix}$

$= \begin{bmatrix} 1 & 1 & 1 & | & 4 \\ 0 & 1 & 5 & | & 5 \\ 0 & -4 & 2 & | & 8 \end{bmatrix}$

b. $\begin{bmatrix} 1 & 1 & 1 & | & 4 \\ 0 & 1 & 5 & | & 5 \\ 0 & -4 & 2 & | & 8 \end{bmatrix}$ $\quad \left(R_3 = \frac{1}{2} r_3 \right)$

$= \begin{bmatrix} 1 & 1 & 1 & | & 4 \\ 0 & 1 & 5 & | & 5 \\ \frac{1}{2}(0) & \frac{1}{2}(-4) & \frac{1}{2}(2) & | & \frac{1}{2}(8) \end{bmatrix}$

$= \begin{bmatrix} 1 & 1 & 1 & | & 4 \\ 0 & 1 & 5 & | & 5 \\ 0 & -2 & 1 & | & 4 \end{bmatrix}$

25. $\begin{cases} x + 4y = -5 & (1) \\ \quad\quad y = -2 & (2) \end{cases}$

This system is consistent and independent.
Substituting -2 for y in equation (1), we obtain
$$x + 4(-2) = -5$$
$$x - 8 = -5$$
$$x = 3$$
The solution is the ordered pair $(3, -2)$.

27. $\begin{cases} x + 3y - 2z = 6 & (1) \\ \quad\quad y + 5z = -2 & (2) \\ \quad\quad\quad\quad 0 = 4 & (3) \end{cases}$

This system is inconsistent. The solution is $\varnothing$ or
$\{\ \}$.

29. $\begin{cases} x - 2y - z = 3 & (1) \\ \quad\quad y - 2z = -8 & (2) \\ \quad\quad\quad\quad z = 5 & (3) \end{cases}$

This system is consistent and independent.
Substituting 5 for z in equation (2), we obtain
$$y - 2(5) = -8$$
$$y - 10 = -8$$
$$y = 2$$
Substituting 5 for z and 2 for y in equation (1),
we obtain
$$x - 2(2) - 5 = 3$$
$$x - 4 - 5 = 3$$
$$x - 9 = 3$$
$$x = 12$$
The solution is the ordered triple $(12,\ 2,\ 5)$.

31. Write the augmented matrix of the system and
then put it in row echelon form.
$\begin{bmatrix} 1 & -3 & | & 18 \\ 2 & 1 & | & 1 \end{bmatrix}$ $\quad \left(R_2 = -2r_1 + r_2 \right)$

$= \begin{bmatrix} 1 & -3 & | & 18 \\ 0 & 7 & | & -35 \end{bmatrix}$ $\quad \left(R_2 = \frac{1}{7} r_2 \right)$

$= \begin{bmatrix} 1 & -3 & | & 18 \\ 0 & 1 & | & -5 \end{bmatrix}$

Write the system of equations that corresponds
to the row-echelon matrix
$\begin{cases} x - 3y = 18 & (1) \\ \quad\quad y = -5 & (2) \end{cases}$

This system is consistent and independent.
Substituting -5 for y in equation (1), we obtain
$$x - 3(-5) = 18$$
$$x + 15 = 18$$
$$x = 3$$
The solution is the ordered pair $(3, -5)$.

33. Write the augmented matrix of the system and
then put it in row echelon form.
$\begin{bmatrix} 2 & 4 & | & 10 \\ 1 & 2 & | & 3 \end{bmatrix}$ $\quad \left(\text{Interchange } r_1 \text{ and } r_2 \right)$

$= \begin{bmatrix} 1 & 2 & | & 3 \\ 2 & 4 & | & 10 \end{bmatrix}$ $\quad \left(R_2 = -2r_1 + r_2 \right)$

$= \begin{bmatrix} 1 & 2 & | & 3 \\ 0 & 0 & | & 4 \end{bmatrix}$

The system is inconsistent. The system has no
solution. The solution set is $\varnothing$ or $\{\ \}$.

35. Write the augmented matrix of the system and
then put it in row echelon form.
$\begin{bmatrix} 1 & -6 & | & 8 \\ 2 & 8 & | & -9 \end{bmatrix}$ $\quad \left(R_2 = -2r_1 + r_2 \right)$

$= \begin{bmatrix} 1 & -6 & | & 8 \\ 0 & 20 & | & -25 \end{bmatrix}$ $\quad \left(R_2 = \frac{1}{20} r_2 \right)$

$= \begin{bmatrix} 1 & -6 & | & 8 \\ 0 & 1 & | & -\frac{5}{4} \end{bmatrix}$

Write the system of equations that corresponds
to the row-echelon matrix
$\begin{cases} x - 6y = 8 & (1) \\ \quad\quad y = -\dfrac{5}{4} & (2) \end{cases}$

This system is consistent and independent.

Substituting $-\dfrac{5}{4}$ for y in equation (1), we obtain

$$x - 6\left(-\dfrac{5}{4}\right) = 8$$

$$x + \dfrac{15}{2} = 8$$

$$x = \dfrac{1}{2}$$

The solution is the ordered pair $\left(\dfrac{1}{2}, -\dfrac{5}{4}\right)$.

37. Write the augmented matrix of the system and then put it in row echelon form.

$$\begin{bmatrix} 4 & -1 & | & 8 \\ 2 & -\frac{1}{2} & | & 4 \end{bmatrix} \qquad \left(R_1 = \dfrac{1}{4}r_1\right)$$

$$= \begin{bmatrix} 1 & -\frac{1}{4} & | & 2 \\ 2 & -\frac{1}{2} & | & 4 \end{bmatrix} \qquad \left(R_2 = -2r_1 + r_2\right)$$

$$= \begin{bmatrix} 1 & -\frac{1}{4} & | & 2 \\ 0 & 0 & | & 0 \end{bmatrix}$$

The system is dependent. The solution to the system is $\left\{(x, y) \mid 4x - y = 8\right\}$.

39. Write the augmented matrix of the system and then put it in row echelon form.

$$\begin{bmatrix} 1 & 1 & 1 & | & 0 \\ 2 & -3 & 1 & | & 19 \\ -3 & 1 & -2 & | & -15 \end{bmatrix} \qquad \begin{pmatrix} R_2 = -2r_1 + r_2 \\ R_3 = 3r_1 + r_3 \end{pmatrix}$$

$$= \begin{bmatrix} 1 & 1 & 1 & | & 0 \\ 0 & -5 & -1 & | & 19 \\ 0 & 4 & 1 & | & -15 \end{bmatrix} \qquad \left(R_2 = -\dfrac{1}{5}r_2\right)$$

$$= \begin{bmatrix} 1 & 1 & 1 & | & 0 \\ 0 & 1 & \frac{1}{5} & | & -\frac{19}{5} \\ 0 & 4 & 1 & | & -15 \end{bmatrix} \qquad \left(R_3 = -4r_2 + r_3\right)$$

$$= \begin{bmatrix} 1 & 1 & 1 & | & 0 \\ 0 & 1 & \frac{1}{5} & | & -\frac{19}{5} \\ 0 & 0 & \frac{1}{5} & | & \frac{1}{5} \end{bmatrix} \qquad \left(R_3 = 5r_3\right)$$

$$= \begin{bmatrix} 1 & 1 & 1 & | & 0 \\ 0 & 1 & \frac{1}{5} & | & -\frac{19}{5} \\ 0 & 0 & 1 & | & 1 \end{bmatrix}$$

Write the system of equations that corresponds to the row-echelon matrix

$$\begin{cases} x + y + z = 0 & (1) \\ y + \dfrac{1}{5}z = -\dfrac{19}{5} & (2) \\ z = 1 & (3) \end{cases}$$

This system is consistent and independent. Substituting 1 for z in equation (2), we obtain

$$y + \dfrac{1}{5}(1) = -\dfrac{19}{5}$$

$$y + \dfrac{1}{5} = -\dfrac{19}{5}$$

$$y = -\dfrac{20}{4} = -4$$

Substituting 1 for z and -4 for y in equation (1), we obtain

$$x + (-4) + 1 = 0$$

$$x - 3 = 0$$

$$x = 3$$

The solution is the ordered triple $(3, -4, 1)$.

41. Write the augmented matrix of the system and then put it in row echelon form.

$$\begin{bmatrix} 2 & 1 & -1 & | & 13 \\ -1 & -3 & 2 & | & -14 \\ -3 & 2 & -3 & | & 3 \end{bmatrix} \qquad \left(\text{Interchange } r_1 \text{ and } r_2\right)$$

$$= \begin{bmatrix} -1 & -3 & 2 & | & -14 \\ 2 & 1 & -1 & | & 13 \\ -3 & 2 & -3 & | & 3 \end{bmatrix} \qquad \left(R_1 = -1 \cdot r_1\right)$$

$$= \begin{bmatrix} 1 & 3 & -2 & | & 14 \\ 2 & 1 & -1 & | & 13 \\ -3 & 2 & -3 & | & 3 \end{bmatrix} \qquad \begin{pmatrix} R_2 = -2r_1 + r_2 \\ R_3 = 3r_1 + r_3 \end{pmatrix}$$

$$= \begin{bmatrix} 1 & 3 & -2 & | & 14 \\ 0 & -5 & 3 & | & -15 \\ 0 & 11 & -9 & | & 45 \end{bmatrix} \qquad \left(R_2 = -\dfrac{1}{5}r_2\right)$$

$$= \begin{bmatrix} 1 & 3 & -2 & | & 14 \\ 0 & 1 & -\frac{3}{5} & | & 3 \\ 0 & 11 & -9 & | & 45 \end{bmatrix} \qquad \left(R_3 = -11r_2 + r_3\right)$$

$$= \begin{bmatrix} 1 & 3 & -2 & | & 14 \\ 0 & 1 & -\frac{3}{5} & | & 3 \\ 0 & 0 & -\frac{12}{5} & | & 12 \end{bmatrix} \qquad \left(R_3 = -\dfrac{5}{12}r_3\right)$$

$$= \begin{bmatrix} 1 & 3 & -2 & | & 14 \\ 0 & 1 & -\frac{3}{5} & | & 3 \\ 0 & 0 & 1 & | & -5 \end{bmatrix}$$

Write the system of equations that corresponds to the row-echelon matrix

$$\begin{cases} x+3y-2z=14 & (1) \\ \quad y-\dfrac{3}{5}z=3 & (2) \\ \qquad\qquad z=-5 & (3) \end{cases}$$

This system is consistent and independent.
Substituting –5 for z in equation (2), we obtain

$$y-\frac{3}{5}(-5)=3$$
$$y+3=3$$
$$y=0$$

Substituting –5 for z and 0 for y in equation (1),
we obtain

$$x+3(0)-2(-5)=14$$
$$x+10=14$$
$$x=4$$

The solution is the ordered triple $(4,\,0,\,-5)$.

43. Write the augmented matrix of the system and
then put it in row echelon form.

$$\begin{bmatrix} 2 & -1 & 3 & | & 1 \\ -1 & 3 & 1 & | & -4 \\ 3 & 1 & 7 & | & -2 \end{bmatrix} \qquad (\text{Interchange } r_1 \text{ and } r_2)$$

$$=\begin{bmatrix} -1 & 3 & 1 & | & -4 \\ 2 & -1 & 3 & | & 1 \\ 3 & 1 & 7 & | & -2 \end{bmatrix} \qquad (R_1=-1\cdot r_1)$$

$$=\begin{bmatrix} 1 & -3 & -1 & | & 4 \\ 2 & -1 & 3 & | & 1 \\ 3 & 1 & 7 & | & -2 \end{bmatrix} \qquad \begin{pmatrix} R_2=-2r_1+r_2 \\ R_3=-3r_1+r_3 \end{pmatrix}$$

$$=\begin{bmatrix} 1 & -3 & -1 & | & 4 \\ 0 & 5 & 5 & | & -7 \\ 0 & 10 & 10 & | & -14 \end{bmatrix} \qquad (R_3=-2r_2+r_3)$$

$$=\begin{bmatrix} 1 & -3 & -1 & | & 4 \\ 0 & 5 & 5 & | & -7 \\ 0 & 0 & 0 & | & 0 \end{bmatrix}$$

The system is dependent and has an infinite
number of solutions.
Write the system of equations that corresponds
to the row-echelon matrix

$$\begin{cases} x-3y-z=4 & (1) \\ \quad 5y+5z=-7 & (2) \\ \qquad\qquad 0=0 & (3) \end{cases}$$

Solve equation (2) for y.

$$5y+5z=-7$$
$$5y=-5z-7$$
$$y=-z-\frac{7}{5}=-z-1.4$$

Substituting $-z-1.4$ for y in equation (1), we
obtain

$$x-3(-z-1.4)-z=4$$
$$x+3z+4.2-z=4$$
$$x+2z+4.2=4$$
$$x=-2z-0.2$$

The solution to the system is $\{(x,y,z)\,|\,x=-2z-0.2,$
$y=-z-1.4,\ z$ is any real number$\}$.

45. Write the augmented matrix of the system and
then put it in row echelon form.

$$\begin{bmatrix} 3 & 1 & -4 & | & 0 \\ -2 & -3 & 1 & | & 5 \\ -1 & -5 & -2 & | & 3 \end{bmatrix} \qquad (\text{Interchange } r_1 \text{ and } r_3)$$

$$=\begin{bmatrix} -1 & -5 & -2 & | & 3 \\ -2 & -3 & 1 & | & 5 \\ 3 & 1 & -4 & | & 0 \end{bmatrix} \qquad (R_1=-1\cdot r_1)$$

$$=\begin{bmatrix} 1 & 5 & 2 & | & -3 \\ -2 & -3 & 1 & | & 5 \\ 3 & 1 & -4 & | & 0 \end{bmatrix} \qquad \begin{pmatrix} R_2=2r_1+r_2 \\ R_3=-3r_1+r_3 \end{pmatrix}$$

$$=\begin{bmatrix} 1 & 5 & 2 & | & -3 \\ 0 & 7 & 5 & | & -1 \\ 0 & -14 & -10 & | & 9 \end{bmatrix} \qquad (R_3=2r_2+r_3)$$

$$=\begin{bmatrix} 1 & 5 & 2 & | & -3 \\ 0 & 7 & 5 & | & -1 \\ 0 & 0 & 0 & | & 7 \end{bmatrix}$$

The system is inconsistent. The system has no
solution. The solution set is $\varnothing$ or $\{\ \}$.

47. Write the augmented matrix of the system and
then put it in row echelon form.

$$\begin{bmatrix} 2 & -1 & 3 & | & -1 \\ 3 & 1 & -4 & | & 3 \\ 1 & 7 & -2 & | & 2 \end{bmatrix} \qquad (\text{Interchange } r_1 \text{ and } r_3)$$

$$=\begin{bmatrix} 1 & 7 & -2 & | & 2 \\ 3 & 1 & -4 & | & 3 \\ 2 & -1 & 3 & | & -1 \end{bmatrix} \qquad \begin{pmatrix} R_2=-3r_1+r_2 \\ R_3=-2r_1+r_3 \end{pmatrix}$$

$$=\begin{bmatrix} 1 & 7 & -2 & | & 2 \\ 0 & -20 & 2 & | & -3 \\ 0 & -15 & 7 & | & -5 \end{bmatrix} \qquad \left(R_2=-\frac{1}{20}r_2\right)$$

$$=\begin{bmatrix} 1 & 7 & -2 & | & 2 \\ 0 & 1 & -\frac{1}{10} & | & \frac{3}{20} \\ 0 & -15 & 7 & | & -5 \end{bmatrix} \qquad (R_3=15r_2+r_3)$$

$$= \begin{bmatrix} 1 & 7 & -2 & | & 2 \\ 0 & 1 & -\frac{1}{10} & | & \frac{3}{20} \\ 0 & 0 & \frac{11}{2} & | & -\frac{11}{4} \end{bmatrix} \qquad \left(R_3 = \frac{2}{11} r_3 \right)$$

$$= \begin{bmatrix} 1 & 7 & -2 & | & 2 \\ 0 & 1 & -\frac{1}{10} & | & \frac{3}{20} \\ 0 & 0 & 1 & | & -\frac{1}{2} \end{bmatrix}$$

Write the system of equations that corresponds to the row-echelon matrix

$$\begin{cases} x + 7y - 2z = 2 & (1) \\ \quad y - \dfrac{1}{10}z = \dfrac{3}{20} & (2) \\ \quad\quad z = -\dfrac{1}{2} & (3) \end{cases}$$

This system is consistent and independent.

Substituting $-\dfrac{1}{2}$ for z in equation (2), we obtain

$$y - \frac{1}{10}\left(-\frac{1}{2}\right) = \frac{3}{20}$$

$$y + \frac{1}{20} = \frac{3}{20}$$

$$y = \frac{2}{20} = \frac{1}{10}$$

Substituting $-\dfrac{1}{2}$ for z and $\dfrac{1}{10}$ for y in equation (1), we obtain

$$x + 7\left(\frac{1}{10}\right) - 2\left(-\frac{1}{2}\right) = 2$$

$$x + \frac{7}{10} + 1 = 2$$

$$x + \frac{17}{10} = 2$$

$$x = \frac{3}{10}$$

The solution is the ordered triple $\left(\dfrac{3}{10}, \dfrac{1}{10}, -\dfrac{1}{2} \right)$.

49. Write the augmented matrix of the system and then put it in row echelon form.

$$\begin{bmatrix} 3 & 5 & 2 & | & 6 \\ 0 & 10 & -2 & | & 5 \\ 6 & 0 & 4 & | & 8 \end{bmatrix} \qquad \left(R_1 = \frac{1}{3} r_1 \right)$$

$$= \begin{bmatrix} 1 & \frac{5}{3} & \frac{2}{3} & | & 2 \\ 0 & 10 & -2 & | & 5 \\ 6 & 0 & 4 & | & 8 \end{bmatrix} \qquad \left(R_3 = -6r_1 + r_3 \right)$$

$$= \begin{bmatrix} 1 & \frac{5}{3} & \frac{2}{3} & | & 2 \\ 0 & 10 & -2 & | & 5 \\ 0 & -10 & 0 & | & -4 \end{bmatrix} \qquad \left(R_3 = -\frac{1}{10} r_3 \right)$$

$$= \begin{bmatrix} 1 & \frac{5}{3} & \frac{2}{3} & | & 2 \\ 0 & 10 & -2 & | & 5 \\ 0 & 1 & 0 & | & \frac{2}{5} \end{bmatrix} \qquad (\text{Interchange } r_2 \text{ and } r_3)$$

$$= \begin{bmatrix} 1 & \frac{5}{3} & \frac{2}{3} & | & 2 \\ 0 & 1 & 0 & | & \frac{2}{5} \\ 0 & 10 & -2 & | & 5 \end{bmatrix} \qquad \left(R_3 = -10r_2 + r_3 \right)$$

$$= \begin{bmatrix} 1 & \frac{5}{3} & \frac{2}{3} & | & 2 \\ 0 & 1 & 0 & | & \frac{2}{5} \\ 0 & 0 & -2 & | & 1 \end{bmatrix} \qquad \left(R_3 = -\frac{1}{2} r_3 \right)$$

$$= \begin{bmatrix} 1 & \frac{5}{3} & \frac{2}{3} & | & 2 \\ 0 & 1 & 0 & | & \frac{2}{5} \\ 0 & 0 & 1 & | & -\frac{1}{2} \end{bmatrix}$$

Write the system of equations that corresponds to the row-echelon matrix

$$\begin{cases} x + \dfrac{5}{3}y + \dfrac{2}{3}z = 2 & (1) \\ \quad y \quad\quad = \dfrac{2}{5} & (2) \\ \quad\quad z = -\dfrac{1}{2} & (3) \end{cases}$$

This system is consistent and independent.

We have $y = \dfrac{2}{5}$ and $z = -\dfrac{1}{2}$. Substituting $\dfrac{2}{5}$ for y and $-\dfrac{1}{2}$ for z in equation (1), we obtain

$$x + \frac{5}{3}\left(\frac{2}{5}\right) + \frac{2}{3}\left(-\frac{1}{2}\right) = 2$$

$$x + \frac{2}{3} - \frac{1}{3} = 2$$

$$x + \frac{1}{3} = 2$$

$$x = \frac{5}{3}$$

The solution is the ordered triple $\left(\dfrac{5}{3}, \dfrac{2}{5}, -\dfrac{1}{2} \right)$.

51. Write the augmented matrix of the system and then put it in row echelon form.

$$\begin{bmatrix} 1 & 0 & -1 & | & 3 \\ 2 & 1 & 0 & | & -3 \\ 0 & 2 & -1 & | & 7 \end{bmatrix} \quad (R_2 = -2r_1 + r_2)$$

$$= \begin{bmatrix} 1 & 0 & -1 & | & 3 \\ 0 & 1 & 2 & | & -9 \\ 0 & 2 & -1 & | & 7 \end{bmatrix} \quad (R_3 = -2r_2 + r_3)$$

$$= \begin{bmatrix} 1 & 0 & -1 & | & 3 \\ 0 & 1 & 2 & | & -9 \\ 0 & 0 & -5 & | & 25 \end{bmatrix} \quad \left(R_3 = -\frac{1}{5}r_3\right)$$

$$= \begin{bmatrix} 1 & 0 & -1 & | & 3 \\ 0 & 1 & 2 & | & -9 \\ 0 & 0 & 1 & | & -5 \end{bmatrix}$$

Write the system of equations that corresponds to the row-echelon matrix

$$\begin{cases} x & -z = 3 & (1) \\ y + 2z = -9 & (2) \\ z = -5 & (3) \end{cases}$$

This system is consistent and independent. Substituting -5 for z in equation (2), we obtain

$$y + 2(-5) = -9$$
$$y - 10 = -9$$
$$y = 1$$

Substituting -5 for z in equation (1), we obtain

$$x - (-5) = 3$$
$$x + 5 = 3$$
$$x = -2$$

The solution is the ordered triple $(-2, 1, -5)$.

53. a. If $f(1) = 0$, then $a(1)^2 + b(1) + c = 0$ or
$a + b + c = 0$.
If $f(2) = 3$, then $a(2)^2 + b(2) + c = 3$ or
$4a + 2b + c = 3$.

b. To find a, b, and c, we must solve the following system:

$$\begin{cases} a - b + c = 6 & (1) \\ a + b + c = 0 & (2) \\ 4a + 2b + c = 3 & (3) \end{cases}$$

Write the augmented matrix of the system and then put it in row echelon form.

$$\begin{bmatrix} 1 & -1 & 1 & | & 6 \\ 1 & 1 & 1 & | & 0 \\ 4 & 2 & 1 & | & 3 \end{bmatrix} \quad \begin{pmatrix} R_2 = -1r_1 + r_2 \\ R_3 = -4r_1 + r_3 \end{pmatrix}$$

$$= \begin{bmatrix} 1 & -1 & 1 & | & 6 \\ 0 & 2 & 0 & | & -6 \\ 0 & 6 & -3 & | & -21 \end{bmatrix} \quad \left(R_2 = \frac{1}{2}r_2\right)$$

$$= \begin{bmatrix} 1 & -1 & 1 & | & 6 \\ 0 & 1 & 0 & | & -3 \\ 0 & 6 & -3 & | & -21 \end{bmatrix} \quad (R_3 = -6r_2 + r_3)$$

$$= \begin{bmatrix} 1 & -1 & 1 & | & 6 \\ 0 & 1 & 0 & | & -3 \\ 0 & 0 & -3 & | & -3 \end{bmatrix} \quad \left(R_3 = -\frac{1}{3}r_3\right)$$

$$= \begin{bmatrix} 1 & -1 & 1 & | & 6 \\ 0 & 1 & 0 & | & -3 \\ 0 & 0 & 1 & | & 1 \end{bmatrix}$$

Write the system of equations that corresponds to the row-echelon matrix

$$\begin{cases} a - b + c = 6 & (1) \\ b = -3 & (2) \\ c = 1 & (3) \end{cases}$$

This system is consistent and independent. We have $b = -3$ and $c = 1$. Substituting -3 for b and 1 for c in equation (1), we obtain

$$a - (-3) + 1 = 6$$
$$a + 4 = 6$$
$$a = 2$$

Thus, the quadratic equation that contains $(-1, 6)$, $(1, 0)$, and $(2, 3)$ is

$$f(x) = 2x^2 - 3x + 1.$$

55. Let t represent the amount to be invested in Treasury bills, let m represent the amount to be invested in municipal bonds, and let c represent the amount to be invested in corporate bonds.

$$\begin{cases} t + m + c = 20{,}000 & (1) \\ 0.04t + 0.05m + 0.08c = 1{,}070 & (2) \\ t - c = 3{,}000 & (3) \end{cases}$$

Write the augmented matrix of the system and then put it in row echelon form.

$$\begin{bmatrix} 1 & 1 & 1 & | & 20{,}000 \\ 0.04 & 0.05 & 0.08 & | & 1{,}070 \\ 1 & 0 & -1 & | & 3{,}000 \end{bmatrix} \begin{pmatrix} R_2 = -0.04r_1 + r_2 \\ R_3 = -1r_1 + r_3 \end{pmatrix}$$

$$= \begin{bmatrix} 1 & 1 & 1 & | & 20{,}000 \\ 0 & 0.01 & 0.04 & | & 270 \\ 0 & -1 & -2 & | & -17{,}000 \end{bmatrix} \left(R_2 = 100r_2 \right)$$

$$= \begin{bmatrix} 1 & 1 & 1 & | & 20{,}000 \\ 0 & 1 & 4 & | & 27{,}000 \\ 0 & -1 & -2 & | & -17{,}000 \end{bmatrix} \left(R_3 = r_2 + r_3 \right)$$

$$= \begin{bmatrix} 1 & 1 & 1 & | & 20{,}000 \\ 0 & 1 & 4 & | & 27{,}000 \\ 0 & 0 & 2 & | & 10{,}000 \end{bmatrix} \left(R_3 = \frac{1}{2}r_3 \right)$$

$$= \begin{bmatrix} 1 & 1 & 1 & | & 20{,}000 \\ 0 & 1 & 4 & | & 27{,}000 \\ 0 & 0 & 1 & | & 5{,}000 \end{bmatrix}$$

Write the system of equations that corresponds
to the row-echelon matrix

$$\begin{cases} t + m + c = 20{,}000 & (1) \\ m + 4c = 27{,}000 & (2) \\ c = 5{,}000 & (3) \end{cases}$$

Substituting 5,000 for c in equation (2), we
obtain

$$m + 4(5{,}000) = 27{,}000$$
$$m + 20{,}000 = 27{,}000$$
$$m = 7{,}000$$

Substituting 5,000 for c and 7,000 for m in
equation (1), we obtain

$$t + 7{,}000 + 5{,}000 = 20{,}000$$
$$t + 12{,}000 = 20{,}000$$
$$t = 8{,}000$$

Therefore, Carissa should invest $8,000 in
Treasury bills, $7,000 in municipal bonds, and
$5,000 in corporate bonds.

57. Write the augmented matrix of the system and
then put it in reduced row echelon form.

$$\begin{bmatrix} 2 & 1 & | & 1 \\ -3 & -2 & | & -5 \end{bmatrix} \left(R_1 = 2r_1 + r_2 \right)$$

$$= \begin{bmatrix} 1 & 0 & | & -3 \\ -3 & -2 & | & -5 \end{bmatrix} \left(R_2 = 3r_1 + r_2 \right)$$

$$= \begin{bmatrix} 1 & 0 & | & -3 \\ 0 & -2 & | & -14 \end{bmatrix} \left(R_2 = -\frac{1}{2}r_2 \right)$$

$$= \begin{bmatrix} 1 & 0 & | & -3 \\ 0 & 1 & | & 7 \end{bmatrix}$$

Write the system of equations that corresponds
to the reduced row echelon matrix

$$\begin{cases} x = -3 \\ y = 7 \end{cases}$$

The solution is the ordered pair $(-3,\ 7)$.

59. Write the augmented matrix of the system and
then put it in reduced row echelon form.

$$\begin{bmatrix} 1 & 1 & 1 & | & 3 \\ 2 & 1 & -4 & | & 25 \\ -3 & 2 & 1 & | & 0 \end{bmatrix} \begin{pmatrix} R_2 = -2r_1 + r_2 \\ R_3 = 3r_1 + r_3 \end{pmatrix}$$

$$= \begin{bmatrix} 1 & 1 & 1 & | & 3 \\ 0 & -1 & -6 & | & 19 \\ 0 & 5 & 4 & | & 9 \end{bmatrix} \begin{pmatrix} R_1 = r_1 + r_2 \\ R_3 = 5r_2 + r_3 \end{pmatrix}$$

$$= \begin{bmatrix} 1 & 0 & -5 & | & 22 \\ 0 & -1 & -6 & | & 19 \\ 0 & 0 & -26 & | & 104 \end{bmatrix} \left(R_3 = -\frac{1}{26}r_3 \right)$$

$$= \begin{bmatrix} 1 & 0 & -5 & | & 22 \\ 0 & -1 & -6 & | & 19 \\ 0 & 0 & 1 & | & -4 \end{bmatrix} \begin{pmatrix} R_1 = 5r_3 + r_1 \\ R_2 = 6r_3 + r_2 \end{pmatrix}$$

$$= \begin{bmatrix} 1 & 0 & 0 & | & 2 \\ 0 & -1 & 0 & | & -5 \\ 0 & 0 & 1 & | & -4 \end{bmatrix} \left(R_2 = -1 \cdot r_2 \right)$$

$$= \begin{bmatrix} 1 & 0 & 0 & | & 2 \\ 0 & 1 & 0 & | & 5 \\ 0 & 0 & 1 & | & -4 \end{bmatrix}$$

Write the system of equations that corresponds
to the reduced row echelon matrix

$$\begin{cases} x = 2 \\ y = 5 \\ z = -4 \end{cases}$$

The solution is the ordered triple $(2,\ 5, -4)$.

61. Write the augmented matrix of the system.

$$\begin{bmatrix} 2 & 3 & | & 1 \\ -3 & -4 & | & -3 \end{bmatrix}$$

Enter the system into a 2 by 3 matrix, [A]. Then,
use the **ref(** command along with the ▶ **frac**
command to write the matrix in row echelon
form with the entries in fractional form.

```
[A]
   [[2  3  1 ]
    [-3 -4 -3]]
```
```
ref([A])▶Frac
   [[1  4/3  1 ]
    [0  1   -3]]
```

Thus, the row echelon matrix is

$$\left[\begin{array}{cc|c} 1 & \frac{4}{3} & 1 \\ 0 & 1 & -3 \end{array}\right]$$

Write the system of equations that corresponds to the row echelon matrix.

$$\begin{cases} x + \dfrac{4}{3}y = 1 & (1) \\ \qquad y = -3 & (2) \end{cases}$$

Substituting –3 for y in equation (1), we obtain

$$x + \frac{4}{3}(-3) = 1$$
$$x - 4 = 1$$
$$x = 5$$

The solution is the ordered pair $(5, -3)$.

63. Write the augmented matrix of the system.

$$\left[\begin{array}{ccc|c} 2 & 3 & -2 & -12 \\ -3 & 1 & 2 & 0 \\ 4 & 3 & -1 & 3 \end{array}\right]$$

Enter the system into a 3 by 4 matrix, [A]. Then, use the **ref(** command along with the ▸ **frac** command to write the matrix in row echelon form with the entries in fractional form. Since the entire matrix does not fit on the screen, we need to scroll right to see the rest of it.

Thus, the row echelon matrix is

$$\left[\begin{array}{ccc|c} 1 & \frac{3}{4} & -\frac{1}{4} & \frac{3}{4} \\ 0 & 1 & \frac{5}{13} & \frac{9}{13} \\ 0 & 0 & 1 & 7 \end{array}\right]$$

Write the system of equations that corresponds to the row-echelon matrix

$$\begin{cases} x + \dfrac{3}{4}y - \dfrac{1}{4}z = \dfrac{3}{4} & (1) \\ \qquad y + \dfrac{5}{13}z = \dfrac{9}{13} & (2) \\ \qquad\qquad z = 7 & (3) \end{cases}$$

Substituting 7 for z in equation (2), we obtain

$$y + \frac{5}{13}(7) = \frac{9}{13}$$
$$y + \frac{35}{13} = \frac{9}{13}$$
$$y = -\frac{26}{13} = -2$$

Substituting 7 for z and –2 for y in equation (1), we obtain

$$x + \frac{3}{4}(-2) - \frac{1}{4}(7) = \frac{3}{4}$$
$$x - \frac{3}{2} - \frac{7}{4} = \frac{3}{4}$$
$$x - \frac{13}{4} = \frac{3}{4}$$
$$x = \frac{16}{4} = 4$$

The solution is the ordered triple $(4, -2, 7)$.

4.5 Preparing for Determinants and Cramer's Rule

1. $4 \cdot 2 - 3 \cdot (-3) = 8 + 9 = 17$

2. $\dfrac{18}{6} = 3$

4.5 Exercises

1. determinants

3. square

5. FALSE. If $D = 0$ and at least one of the determinants D_x, D_y, or D_z is different from 0, then the system is inconsistent. However, if $D = 0$ and all of the determinants D_x, D_y, or D_z equal 0, then the system is consistent and dependent.

7. $x = \dfrac{D_x}{D} = \dfrac{-4}{4} = -1$; $y = \dfrac{D_y}{D} = \dfrac{8}{4} = 2$; $z = \dfrac{D_z}{D} = \dfrac{0}{4} = 0$
The solution is the ordered triple $(-1, 2, 0)$.

9. $\begin{vmatrix} 4 & 2 \\ 1 & 3 \end{vmatrix} = 4(3) - 1(2) = 12 - 2 = 10$

11. $\begin{vmatrix} -2 & -4 \\ 1 & 3 \end{vmatrix} = -2(3) - 1(-4) = -6 + 4 = -2$

13. $\begin{vmatrix} 2 & 0 & -1 \\ 3 & 8 & -3 \\ 1 & 5 & -2 \end{vmatrix} = 2\begin{vmatrix} 8 & -3 \\ 5 & -2 \end{vmatrix} - 0\begin{vmatrix} 3 & -3 \\ 1 & -2 \end{vmatrix} + (-1)\begin{vmatrix} 3 & 8 \\ 1 & 5 \end{vmatrix}$

$= 2\big[8(-2)-5(-3)\big] - 0\big[3(-2)-1(-3)\big]$
$\qquad\qquad + (-1)\big[3(5)-1(8)\big]$

$= 2(-16+15) - 0(-6+3) + (-1)(15-8)$

$= 2(-1) - 0(-3) + (-1)(7)$

$= -2 + 0 - 7$

$= -9$

15. $\begin{vmatrix} -3 & 2 & 3 \\ 0 & 5 & -2 \\ 1 & 4 & 8 \end{vmatrix} = (-3)\begin{vmatrix} 5 & -2 \\ 4 & 8 \end{vmatrix} - 2\begin{vmatrix} 0 & -2 \\ 1 & 8 \end{vmatrix} + 3\begin{vmatrix} 0 & 5 \\ 1 & 4 \end{vmatrix}$

$= -3\big[5(8)-4(-2)\big] - 2\big[0(8)-1(-2)\big]$
$\qquad\qquad + 3\big[0(4)-1(5)\big]$

$= -3(40+8) - 2(0+2) + 3(0-5)$

$= -3(48) - 2(2) + 3(-5)$

$= -144 - 4 - 15$

$= -163$

17. $\begin{vmatrix} 0 & 2 & 1 \\ 1 & -6 & -4 \\ -3 & 4 & 5 \end{vmatrix}$

$= 0\begin{vmatrix} -6 & -4 \\ 4 & 5 \end{vmatrix} - 2\begin{vmatrix} 1 & -4 \\ -3 & 5 \end{vmatrix} + 1\begin{vmatrix} 1 & -6 \\ -3 & 4 \end{vmatrix}$

$= 0\big[-6(5)-4(-4)\big] - 2\big[1(5)-(-3)(-4)\big]$
$\qquad\qquad + 1\big[1(4)-(-3)(-6)\big]$

$= 0(-30+16) - 2(5-12) + 1(4-18)$

$= 0(-14) - 2(-7) + 1(-14)$

$= 0 + 14 - 14$

$= 0$

19. $D = \begin{vmatrix} 1 & 1 \\ 1 & -1 \end{vmatrix} = 1(-1)-1(1) = -1-1 = -2$

$D_x = \begin{vmatrix} -4 & 1 \\ -12 & -1 \end{vmatrix} = -4(-1)-(-12)(1) = 4+12 = 16$

$D_y = \begin{vmatrix} 1 & -4 \\ 1 & -12 \end{vmatrix} = 1(-12)-1(-4) = -12+4 = -8$

$x = \dfrac{D_x}{D} = \dfrac{16}{-2} = -8\,;\ y = \dfrac{D_y}{D} = \dfrac{-8}{-2} = 4$

Thus, the solution is the ordered pair $(-8,\ 4)$.

21. $D = \begin{vmatrix} 2 & 3 \\ -3 & 1 \end{vmatrix} = 2(1)-(-3)(3) = 2+9 = 11$

$D_x = \begin{vmatrix} 3 & 3 \\ -10 & 1 \end{vmatrix} = 3(1)-(-10)(3) = 3+30 = 33$

$D_y = \begin{vmatrix} 2 & 3 \\ -3 & -10 \end{vmatrix} = 2(-10)-(-3)(3) = -20+9 = -11$

$x = \dfrac{D_x}{D} = \dfrac{33}{11} = 3\,;\ y = \dfrac{D_y}{D} = \dfrac{-11}{11} = -1$

Thus, the solution is the ordered pair $(3,-1)$.

23. $D = \begin{vmatrix} 3 & 4 \\ -6 & 8 \end{vmatrix} = 3(8)-(-6)(4) = 24+24 = 48$

$D_x = \begin{vmatrix} 1 & 4 \\ 4 & 8 \end{vmatrix} = 1(8)-4(4) = 8-16 = -8$

$D_y = \begin{vmatrix} 3 & 1 \\ -6 & 4 \end{vmatrix} = 3(4)-(-6)(1) = 12+6 = 18$

$x = \dfrac{D_x}{D} = \dfrac{-8}{48} = -\dfrac{1}{6}\,;\ y = \dfrac{D_y}{D} = \dfrac{18}{48} = \dfrac{3}{8}$

Thus, the solution is the ordered pair $\left(-\dfrac{1}{6},\ \dfrac{3}{8}\right)$.

25. The system in standard form is: $\begin{cases} 2x-6y=12 \\ 3x-5y=11 \end{cases}$

$D = \begin{vmatrix} 2 & -6 \\ 3 & -5 \end{vmatrix} = 2(-5)-3(-6) = -10+18 = 8$

$D_x = \begin{vmatrix} 12 & -6 \\ 11 & -5 \end{vmatrix} = 12(-5)-11(-6) = -60+66 = 6$

$D_y = \begin{vmatrix} 2 & 12 \\ 3 & 11 \end{vmatrix} = 2(11)-3(12) = 22-36 = -14$

$x = \dfrac{D_x}{D} = \dfrac{6}{8} = \dfrac{3}{4}\,;\ y = \dfrac{D_y}{D} = \dfrac{-14}{8} = -\dfrac{7}{4}$

Thus, the solution is the ordered pair $\left(\dfrac{3}{4},-\dfrac{7}{4}\right)$.

27. $D = \begin{vmatrix} 1 & -1 & 1 \\ 1 & 2 & -1 \\ 2 & 1 & 2 \end{vmatrix} = 1\begin{vmatrix} 2 & -1 \\ 1 & 2 \end{vmatrix} - (-1)\begin{vmatrix} 1 & -1 \\ 2 & 2 \end{vmatrix} + 1\begin{vmatrix} 1 & 2 \\ 2 & 1 \end{vmatrix}$

$= 1\big[2(2)-1(-1)\big] - (-1)\big[1(2)-2(-1)\big] +$
$\qquad\qquad 1\big[1(1)-2(2)\big]$

$= 1(4+1) - (-1)(2+2) + 1(1-4)$

$= 1(5) - (-1)(4) + 1(-3)$

$= 5 + 4 - 3$

$= 6$

$$D_x = \begin{vmatrix} -4 & -1 & 1 \\ 1 & 2 & -1 \\ -5 & 1 & 2 \end{vmatrix} = -4 \begin{vmatrix} 2 & -1 \\ 1 & 2 \end{vmatrix} - (-1) \begin{vmatrix} 1 & -1 \\ -5 & 2 \end{vmatrix} + 1 \begin{vmatrix} 1 & 2 \\ -5 & 1 \end{vmatrix}$$

$$= -4 \big[2(2) - 1(-1) \big] - (-1) \big[1(2) - (-5)(-1) \big]$$
$$+ 1 \big[1(1) - (-5)(2) \big]$$

$$= -4(4+1) - (-1)(2-5) + 1(1+10)$$

$$= -4(5) - (-1)(-3) + 1(11)$$

$$= -20 - 3 + 11$$

$$= -12$$

$$D_y = \begin{vmatrix} 1 & -4 & 1 \\ 1 & 1 & -1 \\ 2 & -5 & 2 \end{vmatrix} = 1 \begin{vmatrix} 1 & -1 \\ -5 & 2 \end{vmatrix} - (-4) \begin{vmatrix} 1 & -1 \\ 2 & 2 \end{vmatrix} + 1 \begin{vmatrix} 1 & 1 \\ 2 & -5 \end{vmatrix}$$

$$= 1 \big[1(2) - (-5)(-1) \big] - (-4) \big[1(2) - 2(-1) \big] +$$
$$1 \big[1(-5) - 2(1) \big]$$

$$= 1(2-5) - (-4)(2+2) + 1(-5-2)$$

$$= 1(-3) - (-4)(4) + 1(-7)$$

$$= -3 + 16 - 7$$

$$= 6$$

$$D_z = \begin{vmatrix} 1 & -1 & -4 \\ 1 & 2 & 1 \\ 2 & 1 & -5 \end{vmatrix} = 1 \begin{vmatrix} 2 & 1 \\ 1 & -5 \end{vmatrix} - (-1) \begin{vmatrix} 1 & 1 \\ 2 & -5 \end{vmatrix} + (-4) \begin{vmatrix} 1 & 2 \\ 2 & 1 \end{vmatrix}$$

$$= 1 \big[2(-5) - 1(1) \big] - (-1) \big[1(-5) - 2(1) \big] +$$
$$(-4) \big[1(1) - 2(2) \big]$$

$$= 1(-10-1) - (-1)(-5-2) + (-4)(1-4)$$

$$= 1(-11) - (-1)(-7) + (-4)(-3)$$

$$= -11 - 7 + 12$$

$$= -6$$

$$x = \frac{D_x}{D} = \frac{-12}{6} = -2 \; ; \; y = \frac{D_y}{D} = \frac{6}{6} = 1 \; ; \; z = \frac{D_z}{D} = \frac{-6}{6} = -1$$

Thus, the solution is the ordered triple $(-2, 1, -1)$.

29. $D = \begin{vmatrix} 1 & 1 & 1 \\ 5 & 2 & -3 \\ 2 & -1 & -1 \end{vmatrix} = 1 \begin{vmatrix} 2 & -3 \\ -1 & -1 \end{vmatrix} - 1 \begin{vmatrix} 5 & -3 \\ 2 & -1 \end{vmatrix} + 1 \begin{vmatrix} 5 & 2 \\ 2 & -1 \end{vmatrix}$

$$= 1 \big[2(-1) - (-1)(-3) \big] - 1 \big[5(-1) - 2(-3) \big]$$
$$+ 1 \big[5(-1) - 2(2) \big]$$

$$= 1(-2-3) - 1(-5+6) + 1(-5-4)$$

$$= 1(-5) - 1(1) + 1(-9)$$

$$= -5 - 1 - 9$$

$$= -15$$

$$D_x = \begin{vmatrix} 4 & 1 & 1 \\ 7 & 2 & -3 \\ 5 & -1 & -1 \end{vmatrix} = 4 \begin{vmatrix} 2 & -3 \\ -1 & -1 \end{vmatrix} - 1 \begin{vmatrix} 7 & -3 \\ 5 & -1 \end{vmatrix} + 1 \begin{vmatrix} 7 & 2 \\ 5 & -1 \end{vmatrix}$$

$$= 4 \big[2(-1) - (-1)(-3) \big] - 1 \big[7(-1) - 5(-3) \big] + 1 \big[7(-1) - 5(2) \big]$$

$$= 4(-2-3) - 1(-7+15) + 1(-7-10)$$

$$= 4(-5) - 1(8) + 1(-17)$$

$$= -20 - 8 - 17$$

$$= -45$$

$$D_y = \begin{vmatrix} 1 & 4 & 1 \\ 5 & 7 & -3 \\ 2 & 5 & -1 \end{vmatrix} = 1 \begin{vmatrix} 7 & -3 \\ 5 & -1 \end{vmatrix} - 4 \begin{vmatrix} 5 & -3 \\ 2 & -1 \end{vmatrix} + 1 \begin{vmatrix} 5 & 7 \\ 2 & 5 \end{vmatrix}$$

$$= 1 \big[7(-1) - 5(-3) \big] - 4 \big[5(-1) - 2(-3) \big] + 1 \big[5(5) - 2(7) \big]$$

$$= 1(-7+15) - 4(-5+6) + 1(25-14)$$

$$= 1(8) - 4(1) + 1(11)$$

$$= 8 - 4 + 11$$

$$= 15$$

$$D_z = \begin{vmatrix} 1 & 1 & 4 \\ 5 & 2 & 7 \\ 2 & -1 & 5 \end{vmatrix} = 1 \begin{vmatrix} 2 & 7 \\ -1 & 5 \end{vmatrix} - 1 \begin{vmatrix} 5 & 7 \\ 2 & 5 \end{vmatrix} + 4 \begin{vmatrix} 5 & 2 \\ 2 & -1 \end{vmatrix}$$

$$= 1 \big[2(5) - (-1)(7) \big] - 1 \big[5(5) - 2(7) \big] + 4 \big[5(-1) - 2(2) \big]$$

$$= 1(10+7) - 1(25-14) + 4(-5-4)$$

$$= 1(17) - 1(11) + 4(-9)$$

$$= 17 - 11 - 36$$

$$= -30$$

$$x = \frac{D_x}{D} = \frac{-45}{-15} = 3 \; ; \; y = \frac{D_y}{D} = \frac{15}{-15} = -1 \; ;$$

$$z = \frac{D_z}{D} = \frac{-30}{-15} = 2$$

Thus, the solution is the ordered triple $(3, -1, 2)$.

31. $D = \begin{vmatrix} 2 & 1 & -1 \\ -1 & 2 & 2 \\ 5 & 5 & -1 \end{vmatrix} = 2 \begin{vmatrix} 2 & 2 \\ 5 & -1 \end{vmatrix} - 1 \begin{vmatrix} -1 & 2 \\ 5 & -1 \end{vmatrix} + (-1) \begin{vmatrix} -1 & 2 \\ 5 & 5 \end{vmatrix}$

$$= 2 \big[2(-1) - 5(2) \big] - 1 \big[(-1)(-1) - 5(2) \big]$$
$$+ (-1) \big[(-1)(5) - 5(2) \big]$$

$$= 2(-2-10) - 1(1-10) + (-1)(-5-10)$$

$$= 2(-12) - 1(-9) + (-1)(-15)$$

$$= -24 + 9 + 15$$

$$= 0$$

Since $D = 0$, we know that Cramer's Rule does not apply and that this is not a consistent and independent system. Next, we will find D_x, D_y, and D_z in order to investigate the system further.

$$D_x = \begin{vmatrix} 4 & 1 & -1 \\ -6 & 2 & 2 \\ 6 & 5 & -1 \end{vmatrix} = 4\begin{vmatrix} 2 & 2 \\ 5 & -1 \end{vmatrix} - 1\begin{vmatrix} -6 & 2 \\ 6 & -1 \end{vmatrix} + (-1)\begin{vmatrix} -6 & 2 \\ 6 & 5 \end{vmatrix}$$

$$= 4\big[2(-1) - 5(2)\big] - 1\big[(-6)(-1) - 6(2)\big]$$
$$+ (-1)\big[(-6)(5) - 6(2)\big]$$

$$= 4(-2 - 10) - 1(6 - 12) + (-1)(-30 - 12)$$

$$= 4(-12) - 1(-6) + (-1)(-42)$$

$$= -48 + 6 + 42$$

$$= 0$$

$$D_y = \begin{vmatrix} 2 & 4 & -1 \\ -1 & -6 & 2 \\ 5 & 6 & -1 \end{vmatrix}$$

$$= 2\begin{vmatrix} -6 & 2 \\ 6 & -1 \end{vmatrix} - 4\begin{vmatrix} -1 & 2 \\ 5 & -1 \end{vmatrix} + (-1)\begin{vmatrix} -1 & -6 \\ 5 & 6 \end{vmatrix}$$

$$= 2\big[(-6)(-1) - 6(2)\big] - 4\big[(-1)(-1) - 5(2)\big]$$
$$+ (-1)\big[(-1)(6) - 5(-6)\big]$$

$$= 2(6 - 12) - 4(1 - 10) + (-1)(-6 + 30)$$

$$= 2(-6) - 4(-9) + (-1)(24)$$

$$= -12 + 36 - 24$$

$$= 0$$

$$D_z = \begin{vmatrix} 2 & 1 & 4 \\ -1 & 2 & -6 \\ 5 & 5 & 6 \end{vmatrix} = 2\begin{vmatrix} 2 & -6 \\ 5 & 6 \end{vmatrix} - 1\begin{vmatrix} -1 & -6 \\ 5 & 6 \end{vmatrix} + 4\begin{vmatrix} -1 & 2 \\ 5 & 5 \end{vmatrix}$$

$$= 2\big[2(6) - 5(-6)\big] - 1\big[(-1)(6) - 5(-6)\big]$$
$$+ 4\big[(-1)(5) - 5(2)\big]$$

$$= 2(12 + 30) - 1(-6 + 30) + 4(-5 - 10)$$

$$= 2(42) - 1(24) + 4(-15)$$

$$= 84 - 24 - 60$$

$$= 0$$

Because $D = 0$ and because all the determinants D_x, D_y, and D_z equal 0, the system is consistent and dependent. We know that there are infinitely many solutions, but we cannot yet tell what the solution set is. Next we use the augmented matrix of the system in order to determine the solution set.

$$\left[\begin{array}{ccc|c} 2 & 1 & -1 & 4 \\ -1 & 2 & 2 & -6 \\ 5 & 5 & -1 & 6 \end{array}\right] \qquad (\text{Interchange } r_1 \text{ and } r_2)$$

$$= \left[\begin{array}{ccc|c} -1 & 2 & 2 & -6 \\ 2 & 1 & -1 & 4 \\ 5 & 5 & -1 & 6 \end{array}\right] \qquad \begin{pmatrix} R_2 = 2r_1 + r_2 \\ R_3 = 5r_1 + r_3 \end{pmatrix}$$

$$= \left[\begin{array}{ccc|c} -1 & 2 & 2 & -6 \\ 0 & 5 & 3 & -8 \\ 0 & 15 & 9 & -24 \end{array}\right] \qquad \begin{pmatrix} R_1 = -1 \cdot r_1 \\ R_3 = -3r_2 + r_3 \end{pmatrix}$$

$$= \left[\begin{array}{ccc|c} 1 & -2 & -2 & 6 \\ 0 & 5 & 3 & -8 \\ 0 & 0 & 0 & 0 \end{array}\right]$$

We have confirmed that this system is dependent and has an infinite number of solutions.

Write the system of equations that corresponds to the row-echelon matrix

$$\begin{cases} x - 2y - 2z = 6 & (1) \\ 5y + 3z = -8 & (2) \\ 0 = 0 & (3) \end{cases}$$

Solve equation (2) for y.

$$5y + 3z = -8$$
$$5y = -3z - 8$$
$$y = -\frac{3}{5}z - \frac{8}{5}$$

Substituting $-\frac{3}{5}z - \frac{8}{5}$ for y in equation (1), we obtain:

$$x - 2\left(-\frac{3}{5}z - \frac{8}{5}\right) - 2z = 6$$

$$x + \frac{6}{5}z + \frac{16}{5} - 2z = 6$$

$$x - \frac{4}{5}z + \frac{16}{5} = 6$$

$$x - \frac{4}{5}z = \frac{14}{5}$$

$$x = \frac{4}{5}z + \frac{14}{5}$$

The solution to the system is $\left\{(x, y, z) \middle| x = \frac{4}{5}z + \frac{14}{5}, \right.$ $\left. y = -\frac{3}{5}z - \frac{8}{5}, z \text{ is any real number}\right\}$

33. $D = \begin{vmatrix} 3 & 1 & 1 \\ 1 & 1 & -3 \\ 4 & 3 & 1 \end{vmatrix} = 3\begin{vmatrix} 1 & -3 \\ 3 & 1 \end{vmatrix} - 1\begin{vmatrix} 1 & -3 \\ 4 & 1 \end{vmatrix} + 1\begin{vmatrix} 1 & 1 \\ 4 & 3 \end{vmatrix}$

$= 3\big[1(1) - 3(-3)\big] - 1\big[1(1) - 4(-3)\big] + 1\big[1(3) - 4(1)\big]$

$= 3(1+9) - 1(1+12) + 1(3-4)$

$= 3(10) - 1(13) + 1(-1)$

$= 30 - 13 - 1$

$= 16$

$D_x = \begin{vmatrix} 5 & 1 & 1 \\ 9 & 1 & -3 \\ 11 & 3 & 1 \end{vmatrix} = 5\begin{vmatrix} 1 & -3 \\ 3 & 1 \end{vmatrix} - 1\begin{vmatrix} 9 & -3 \\ 11 & 1 \end{vmatrix} + 1\begin{vmatrix} 9 & 1 \\ 11 & 3 \end{vmatrix}$

$= 5\big[1(1) - 3(-3)\big] - 1\big[9(1) - 11(-3)\big] + 1\big[9(3) - 11(1)\big]$

$= 5(1+9) - 1(9+33) + 1(27-11)$

$= 5(10) - 1(42) + 1(16)$

$= 50 - 42 + 16$

$= 24$

$D_y = \begin{vmatrix} 3 & 5 & 1 \\ 1 & 9 & -3 \\ 4 & 11 & 1 \end{vmatrix} = 3\begin{vmatrix} 9 & -3 \\ 11 & 1 \end{vmatrix} - 5\begin{vmatrix} 1 & -3 \\ 4 & 1 \end{vmatrix} + 1\begin{vmatrix} 1 & 9 \\ 4 & 11 \end{vmatrix}$

$= 3\big[9(1) - 11(-3)\big] - 5\big[1(1) - 4(-3)\big] + 1\big[1(11) - 4(9)\big]$

$= 3(9+33) - 5(1+12) + 1(11-36)$

$= 3(42) - 5(13) + 1(-25)$

$= 126 - 65 - 25$

$= 36$

$D_z = \begin{vmatrix} 3 & 1 & 5 \\ 1 & 1 & 9 \\ 4 & 3 & 11 \end{vmatrix} = 3\begin{vmatrix} 1 & 9 \\ 3 & 11 \end{vmatrix} - 1\begin{vmatrix} 1 & 9 \\ 4 & 11 \end{vmatrix} + 5\begin{vmatrix} 1 & 1 \\ 4 & 3 \end{vmatrix}$

$= 3\big[1(11) - 3(9)\big] - 1\big[1(11) - 4(9)\big] + 5\big[1(3) - 4(1)\big]$

$= 3(11-27) - 1(11-36) + 5(3-4)$

$= 3(-16) - 1(-25) + 5(-1)$

$= -48 + 25 - 5$

$= -28$

$x = \dfrac{D_x}{D} = \dfrac{24}{16} = \dfrac{3}{2}$; $y = \dfrac{D_y}{D} = \dfrac{36}{16} = \dfrac{9}{4}$;

$z = \dfrac{D_z}{D} = \dfrac{-28}{16} = -\dfrac{7}{4}$

The solution is the ordered triple $\left(\dfrac{3}{2}, \dfrac{9}{4}, -\dfrac{7}{4}\right)$.

35. $D = \begin{vmatrix} 2 & 0 & 1 \\ -1 & -3 & 0 \\ 1 & -2 & 1 \end{vmatrix} = 2\begin{vmatrix} -3 & 0 \\ -2 & 1 \end{vmatrix} - 0\begin{vmatrix} -1 & 0 \\ 1 & 1 \end{vmatrix} + 1\begin{vmatrix} -1 & -3 \\ 1 & -2 \end{vmatrix}$

$= 2\big[-3(1) - (-2)(0)\big] - 0\big[-1(1) - 1(0)\big]$
$\qquad\qquad + 1\big[-1(-2) - 1(-3)\big]$

$= 2(-3 - 0) - 0(-1 - 0) + 1(2+3)$

$= 2(-3) - 0(-1) + 1(5)$

$= -6 - 0 + 5$

$= -1$

$D_x = \begin{vmatrix} 27 & 0 & 1 \\ 6 & -3 & 0 \\ 27 & -2 & 1 \end{vmatrix} = 27\begin{vmatrix} -3 & 0 \\ -2 & 1 \end{vmatrix} - 0\begin{vmatrix} 6 & 0 \\ 27 & 1 \end{vmatrix} + 1\begin{vmatrix} 6 & -3 \\ 27 & -2 \end{vmatrix}$

$= 27\big[-3(1) - (-2)(0)\big] - 0\big[6(1) - 27(0)\big]$
$\qquad\qquad + 1\big[6(-2) - 27(-3)\big]$

$= 27(-3 - 0) - 0(6 - 0) + 1(-12 + 81)$

$= 27(-3) - 0(6) + 1(69)$

$= -81 - 0 + 69$

$= -12$

$D_y = \begin{vmatrix} 2 & 27 & 1 \\ -1 & 6 & 0 \\ 1 & 27 & 1 \end{vmatrix} = 2\begin{vmatrix} 6 & 0 \\ 27 & 1 \end{vmatrix} - 27\begin{vmatrix} -1 & 0 \\ 1 & 1 \end{vmatrix} + 1\begin{vmatrix} -1 & 6 \\ 1 & 27 \end{vmatrix}$

$= 2\big[6(1) - 27(0)\big] - 27\big[-1(1) - 1(0)\big]$
$\qquad\qquad + 1\big[(-1)(27) - 1(6)\big]$

$= 2(6 - 0) - 27(-1 - 0) + 1(-27 - 6)$

$= 2(6) - 27(-1) + 1(-33)$

$= 12 + 27 - 33$

$= 6$

$D_z = \begin{vmatrix} 2 & 0 & 27 \\ -1 & -3 & 6 \\ 1 & -2 & 27 \end{vmatrix}$

$= 2\begin{vmatrix} -3 & 6 \\ -2 & 27 \end{vmatrix} - 0\begin{vmatrix} -1 & 6 \\ 1 & 27 \end{vmatrix} + 27\begin{vmatrix} -1 & -3 \\ 1 & -2 \end{vmatrix}$

$= 2\big[-3(27) - (-2)(6)\big] - 0\big[-1(27) - 1(6)\big]$
$\qquad\qquad + 27\big[-1(-2) - 1(-3)\big]$

$= 2(-81 + 12) - 0(-27 - 6) + 27(2 + 3)$

$= 2(-69) - 0(-33) + 27(5)$

$= -138 - 0 + 135$

$= -3$

$x = \dfrac{D_x}{D} = \dfrac{-12}{-1} = 12$; $y = \dfrac{D_y}{D} = \dfrac{6}{-1} = -6$;

$z = \dfrac{D_z}{D} = \dfrac{-3}{-1} = 3$

The solution is the ordered triple $(12, -6, 3)$.

37. $D = \begin{vmatrix} 5 & 3 & 0 \\ -10 & 0 & 3 \\ 0 & 1 & -2 \end{vmatrix} = 5\begin{vmatrix} 0 & 3 \\ 1 & -2 \end{vmatrix} - 3\begin{vmatrix} -10 & 3 \\ 0 & -2 \end{vmatrix} + 0\begin{vmatrix} -10 & 0 \\ 0 & 1 \end{vmatrix}$

$= 5[0(-2) - 1(3)] - 3[-10(-2) - 0(3)]$
$\qquad\qquad\qquad + 0[-10(1) - 0(0)]$
$= 5(0 - 3) - 3(20 - 0) + 0(-10 - 0)$
$= 5(-3) - 3(20) + 0(-10)$
$= -15 - 60 + 0$
$= -75$

$D_x = \begin{vmatrix} 2 & 3 & 0 \\ -3 & 0 & 3 \\ -9 & 1 & -2 \end{vmatrix} = 2\begin{vmatrix} 0 & 3 \\ 1 & -2 \end{vmatrix} - 3\begin{vmatrix} -3 & 3 \\ -9 & -2 \end{vmatrix} + 0\begin{vmatrix} -3 & 0 \\ -9 & 1 \end{vmatrix}$

$= 2[0(-2) - 1(3)] - 3[-3(-2) - (-9)(3)]$
$\qquad\qquad\qquad + 0[-3(1) - (-9)(0)]$
$= 2(0 - 3) - 3(6 + 27) + 0(-3 + 0)$
$= 2(-3) - 3(33) + 0(-3)$
$= -6 - 99 + 0$
$= -105$

$D_y = \begin{vmatrix} 5 & 2 & 0 \\ -10 & -3 & 3 \\ 0 & -9 & -2 \end{vmatrix}$

$= 5\begin{vmatrix} -3 & 3 \\ -9 & -2 \end{vmatrix} - 2\begin{vmatrix} -10 & 3 \\ 0 & -2 \end{vmatrix} + 0\begin{vmatrix} -10 & -3 \\ 0 & -9 \end{vmatrix}$

$= 5[-3(-2) - (-9)(3)] - 2[-10(-2) - 0(3)]$
$\qquad\qquad\qquad + 0[-10(-9) - 0(-3)]$
$= 5(6 + 27) - 2(20 - 0) + 0(90 + 0)$
$= 5(33) - 2(20) + 0(90)$
$= 165 - 40 + 0$
$= 125$

$D_z = \begin{vmatrix} 5 & 3 & 2 \\ -10 & 0 & -3 \\ 0 & 1 & -9 \end{vmatrix} = 5\begin{vmatrix} 0 & -3 \\ 1 & -9 \end{vmatrix} - 3\begin{vmatrix} -10 & -3 \\ 0 & -9 \end{vmatrix} + 2\begin{vmatrix} -10 & 0 \\ 0 & 1 \end{vmatrix}$

$= 5[0(-9) - 1(-3)] - 3[-10(-9) - 0(-3)]$
$\qquad\qquad\qquad + 2[-10(1) - 0(0)]$
$= 5(0 + 3) - 3(90 + 0) + 2(-10 - 0)$
$= 5(3) - 3(90) + 2(-10)$
$= 15 - 270 + -20$
$= -275$

$x = \dfrac{D_x}{D} = \dfrac{-105}{-75} = \dfrac{7}{5}$; $\quad y = \dfrac{D_y}{D} = \dfrac{125}{-75} = -\dfrac{5}{3}$;

$z = \dfrac{D_z}{D} = \dfrac{-275}{-75} = \dfrac{11}{3}$

The solution is the ordered triple $\left(\dfrac{7}{5}, -\dfrac{5}{3}, \dfrac{11}{3}\right)$.

39. $\begin{vmatrix} x & 3 \\ 1 & 2 \end{vmatrix} = 7$

$x(2) - 1(3) = 7$
$2x - 3 = 7$
$2x = 10$
$x = 5$

41. $\begin{vmatrix} x & -1 & -2 \\ 1 & 0 & 4 \\ 3 & 2 & 5 \end{vmatrix} = 5$

$x\begin{vmatrix} 0 & 4 \\ 2 & 5 \end{vmatrix} - (-1)\begin{vmatrix} 1 & 4 \\ 3 & 5 \end{vmatrix} + (-2)\begin{vmatrix} 1 & 0 \\ 3 & 2 \end{vmatrix} = 5$

$x[0(5) - 2(4)] - (-1)[1(5) - 3(4)] +$
$\qquad\qquad (-2)[1(2) - 3(0)] = 5$
$x(-8) - (-1)(-7) + (-2)(2) = 5$
$-8x - 7 - 4 = 5$
$-8x - 11 = 5$
$-8x = 16$
$x = -2$

43. a. Triangle ABC is graphed below.

b. $D = \dfrac{1}{2}\begin{vmatrix} 1 & 5 & 5 \\ 1 & 1 & 6 \\ 1 & 1 & 1 \end{vmatrix} = \dfrac{1}{2}\left(1\begin{vmatrix} 1 & 6 \\ 1 & 1 \end{vmatrix} - 5\begin{vmatrix} 1 & 6 \\ 1 & 1 \end{vmatrix} + 5\begin{vmatrix} 1 & 1 \\ 1 & 1 \end{vmatrix}\right)$

$= \dfrac{1}{2}[1(1 \cdot 1 - 1 \cdot 6) - 5(1 \cdot 1 - 1 \cdot 6) + 5(1 \cdot 1 - 1 \cdot 1)]$

$= \dfrac{1}{2}[1(-5) - 5(-5) + 5(0)]$

$= \dfrac{1}{2}(-5 + 25 + 0)$

$= \dfrac{1}{2}(20)$

$= 10$

Thus, the area of triangle ABC is $|10| = 10$.

45. a. Parallelogram *ABCD* is graphed below.

b. Triangle *ABC* is formed by the points (2, 1), (7, 2), and (8, 4).

$$D = \frac{1}{2}\begin{vmatrix} 2 & 7 & 8 \\ 1 & 2 & 4 \\ 1 & 1 & 1 \end{vmatrix}$$

$$= \frac{1}{2}\left[2\begin{vmatrix} 2 & 4 \\ 1 & 1 \end{vmatrix} - 7\begin{vmatrix} 1 & 4 \\ 1 & 1 \end{vmatrix} + 8\begin{vmatrix} 1 & 2 \\ 1 & 1 \end{vmatrix} \right]$$

$$= \frac{1}{2}\left[2(2 \cdot 1 - 1 \cdot 4) - 7(1 \cdot 1 - 1 \cdot 4) + 8(1 \cdot 1 - 1 \cdot 2) \right]$$

$$= \frac{1}{2}\left[2(-2) - 7(-3) + 8(-1) \right]$$

$$= \frac{1}{2}(-4 + 21 - 8)$$

$$= \frac{1}{2}(9)$$

$$= 4.5$$

Thus, the area of triangle *ABC* is $|4.5| = 4.5$.

c. Triangle *ADC* is formed by the points (2, 1), (3, 3), and (8, 4).

$$D = \frac{1}{2}\begin{vmatrix} 2 & 3 & 8 \\ 1 & 3 & 4 \\ 1 & 1 & 1 \end{vmatrix}$$

$$= \frac{1}{2}\left[2\begin{vmatrix} 3 & 4 \\ 1 & 1 \end{vmatrix} - 3\begin{vmatrix} 1 & 4 \\ 1 & 1 \end{vmatrix} + 8\begin{vmatrix} 1 & 3 \\ 1 & 1 \end{vmatrix} \right]$$

$$= \frac{1}{2}\left[2(3 \cdot 1 - 1 \cdot 4) - 3(1 \cdot 1 - 1 \cdot 4) + 8(1 \cdot 1 - 1 \cdot 3) \right]$$

$$= \frac{1}{2}\left[2(-1) - 3(-3) + 8(-2) \right]$$

$$= \frac{1}{2}(-2 + 9 - 16)$$

$$= \frac{1}{2}(-9)$$

$$= -4.5$$

Thus, the area of triangle *ADC* is $|-4.5| = 4.5$.

d. The areas of triangle *ABC* and triangle *ADC* are equal. (That is, the diagonal of the parallelogram forms two triangles of equal area.) Thus, the area of parallelogram *ABCD* is $4.5 + 4.5 = 9$.

47. a.
$$\begin{vmatrix} x & y & 1 \\ 3 & 2 & 1 \\ 5 & 1 & 1 \end{vmatrix} = 0$$

$$x\begin{vmatrix} 2 & 1 \\ 1 & 1 \end{vmatrix} - y\begin{vmatrix} 3 & 1 \\ 5 & 1 \end{vmatrix} + 1\begin{vmatrix} 3 & 2 \\ 5 & 1 \end{vmatrix} = 0$$

$$x[2(1) - 1(1)] - y[3(1) - 5(1)] + 1[3(1) - 5(2)] = 0$$

$$x(1) - y(-2) + 1(-7) = 0$$

$$x + 2y - 7 = 0$$

$$x + 2y = 7$$

b.
$$m = \frac{y_2 - y_1}{x_2 - x_1} = \frac{1 - 2}{5 - 3} = \frac{-1}{2} = -\frac{1}{2}$$

$$y - y_1 = m(x - x_2)$$

$$y - 2 = -\frac{1}{2}(x - 3)$$

$$y - 2 = -\frac{1}{2}x + \frac{3}{2}$$

$$2y - 4 = -x + 3$$

$$x + 2y = 7$$

49. $\begin{vmatrix} 3 & -2 \\ 1 & 4 \end{vmatrix} = 3(4) - 1(-2)$

$$= 12 + 2$$

$$= 14$$

Interchanging rows 1 and 2 and recomputing the determinant, we obtain

$\begin{vmatrix} 1 & 4 \\ 3 & -2 \end{vmatrix} = 1(-2) - 3(4)$

$$= -2 - 12$$

$$= -14$$

The two determinants are opposites.
Answers may vary. In general, it is true that the value of a determinant will change signs if any two rows (or any two columns) are interchanged.

51. Using $A = D$, $B = D_x$, and $C = D_y$.

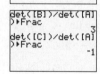

The solution is the ordered pair $(-8, 4)$.

53. Using $A = D$, $B = D_x$, and $C = D_y$.

The solution is the ordered pair $(3, -1)$.

55. Using $A = D$, $B = D_x$, $C = D_y$, and $D = D_z$.

The solution is the ordered triple $(-2, 1, -1)$.

4.6 Preparing for Systems of Linear Inequalities

1. $-3(-2) + 2 \overset{?}{\geq} 7$

$\qquad 6 + 2 \overset{?}{\geq} 7$

$\qquad\quad 8 \geq 7 \;\leftarrow\; \text{True}$

Yes, $x = -2$ does satisfy the inequality $-3x + 2 \geq 7$.

2. $\qquad -2x + 1 > 7$

$\quad -2x + 1 - 1 > 7 - 1$

$\qquad\quad -2x > 6$

$\qquad\quad \dfrac{-2x}{-2} < \dfrac{6}{-2}$

$\qquad\qquad x < -3$

The solution set is $\{x \,|\, x < -3\}$ or, using interval notation, $(-\infty, -3)$.

3. Replace the inequality symbol with an equal sign to obtain $3x + 2y = -6$. Because the inequality is strict, graph $3x + 2y = -6 \left(y = -\dfrac{3}{2}x - 3 \right)$ using a dashed line.

Test Point: $(0, 0)$: $\quad 3(0) + 2(0) \overset{?}{>} -6$

$\qquad\qquad\qquad\qquad\quad 0 + 0 \overset{?}{>} -6$

$\qquad\qquad\qquad\qquad\qquad 0 \overset{?}{>} -6 \quad \text{True}$

Therefore, $(0, 0)$ is solution to $3x + 2y > -6$.

Shade the half-plane that contains $(0, 0)$.

4.6 Exercises

1. satisfies

3. TRUE

5. Answers may vary. One possibility follows: Graph each of the linear inequalities that make up the system on the same Cartesian plane. The overlapping shaded region is the solution to the system of linear inequalities.

7. No, it is not possible for a system of linear inequalities to have the entire Cartesian plane as the solutions set. The solutions of a system of linear inequalities must make all inequalities in the system true. The solution set of one inequality alone is a half-plane. The other inequalities in the system would only restrict the solution set further. Thus, the solution set of a system of linear inequalities will be at most a half-plane.

9. **a.** Let $x = 3$ and $y = 2$ in each inequality.
$$\begin{cases} x + y = 3 + 2 = 5 \nleq 4 \\ 3x + y = 3(3) + 2 = 11 \geq 10 \end{cases}$$
The inequality $x + y \leq 4$ is not true when $x = 3$ and $y = 2$, so $(3, 2)$ is not a solution.

b. Let $x = 5$ and $y = -1$ in each inequality.
$$\begin{cases} x + y = 5 + (-1) = 4 \leq 4 \\ 3x + y = 3(5) + (-1) = 14 \geq 10 \end{cases}$$
Both inequalities are true when $x = 5$ and $y = -1$, so $(3, 2)$ is a solution.

11. **a.** Let $x = 3$ and $y = 2$ in each inequality.
$$\begin{cases} 3x + 2y = 3(3) + 2(2) = 13 \nleq 12 \\ -2x + 3y = -2(3) + 3(2) = 0 \ngtr 12 \end{cases}$$
Neither inequality is true when $x = 3$ and $y = 2$, so $(3, 2)$ is not a solution.

b. Let $x = 1$ and $y = 4$ in each inequality.
$$\begin{cases} 3x + 2y = 3(1) + 2(4) = 11 < 12 \\ -2x + 3y = -2(1) + 3(4) = 10 \ngtr 12 \end{cases}$$
The inequality $-2x + 3y > 12$ is not true when $x = 1$ and $y = 4$, so $(1, 4)$ is not a solution.

13. **a.** Let $x = 4$ and $y = 2$ in each inequality.
$$\begin{cases} x + y = 4 + 2 = 6 \leq 8 \\ 3x + y = 3(4) + 2 = 14 \nleq 12 \\ x = 4 \geq 0 \\ y = 2 \geq 0 \end{cases}$$
The inequality $3x + y \leq 12$ is not true when $x = 4$ and $y = 2$, so $(4, 2)$ is not a solution.

b. Let $x = 2$ and $y = 5$ in each inequality.
$$\begin{cases} x + y = 2 + 5 = 7 \leq 8 \\ 3x + y = 3(2) + 5 = 11 \leq 12 \\ x = 2 \geq 0 \\ y = 5 \geq 0 \end{cases}$$
All four inequalities are true when $x = 2$ and $y = 5$, so $(2, 5)$ is a solution.

15. $\begin{cases} x + y \leq 4 \\ 3x + y \geq 10 \end{cases}$

First, graph the inequality $x + y \leq 4$. To do so, replace the inequality symbol with an equal sign to obtain $x + y = 4$. Because the inequality is non-strict, graph $x + y = 4$ $(y = -x + 4)$ using a solid line.

Test Point: $(0,0)$: $0 + 0 = 0 \leq 4$

Therefore, the half-plane containing $(0,0)$ is the solution set of $x + y \leq 4$.

Second, graph the inequality $3x + y \geq 10$. To do so, replace the inequality symbol with an equal sign to obtain $3x + y = 10$. Because the inequality is non-strict, graph $3x + y = 10$ $(y = -3x + 10)$ using a solid line.

Test Point: $(0,0)$: $3(0) + 0 = 0 \ngeq 10$

Therefore, the half-plane not containing $(0,0)$ is the solution set of $3x + y \geq 10$.

The overlapping shaded region (that is, the shaded region in the graph below) is the solution to the system of linear inequalities.

SSM – 186

17. $\begin{cases} 3x+2y<12 \\ -2x+3y>12 \end{cases}$

First, graph the inequality $3x+2y<12$. To do so, replace the inequality symbol with an equal sign to obtain $3x+2y=12$. Because the inequality is strict, graph $3x+2y=12$ $\left(y=-\frac{3}{2}x+6\right)$ using a dashed line.

Test Point: $(0,0)$: $3(0)+2(0)=0<12$

Therefore, the half-plane containing $(0,0)$ is the solution set of $3x+2y<12$.

Second, graph the inequality $-2x+3y>12$. To do so, replace the inequality symbol with an equal sign to obtain $-2x+3y=12$. Because the inequality is strict, graph $-2x+3y=12$ $\left(y=\frac{2}{3}x+4\right)$ using a dashed line.

Test Point: $(0,0)$: $-2(0)+3(0)=0 \not> 12$

Therefore, the half-plane not containing $(0,0)$ is the solution set of $-2x+3y>12$.

The overlapping shaded region (that is, the shaded region in the graph below) is the solution to the system of linear inequalities.

19. $\begin{cases} x-\dfrac{1}{2}y\le 3 \\ \dfrac{3}{2}x+y>3 \end{cases}$

First, graph the inequality $x-\frac{1}{2}y\le 3$. To do so, replace the inequality symbol with an equal sign to obtain $x-\frac{1}{2}y=3$. Because the inequality is non-strict, graph $x-\frac{1}{2}y=3$ $(y=2x-6)$ using a solid line.

Test Point: $(0,0)$: $0-\frac{1}{2}(0)=0\le 3$

Therefore, the half-plane containing $(0,0)$ is the solution set of $x-\frac{1}{2}y\le 3$.

Second, graph the inequality $\frac{3}{2}x+y>3$. To do so, replace the inequality symbol with an equal sign to obtain $\frac{3}{2}x+y=3$. Because the inequality is strict, graph $\frac{3}{2}x+y=3$ $\left(y=-\frac{3}{2}x+3\right)$ using a dashed line.

Test Point: $(0,0)$: $\frac{3}{2}(0)+0=0 \not> 3$

Therefore, the half-plane not containing $(0,0)$ is the solution set of $\frac{3}{2}x+y>3$.

The overlapping shaded region (that is, the shaded region in the graph below) is the solution to the system of linear inequalities.

21. $\begin{cases} -2x+y<-8 \\ 2x-y>8 \end{cases}$

First, graph the inequality $-2x+y<-8$. To do so, replace the inequality symbol with an equal sign to obtain $-2x+y=-8$. Because the inequality is strict, graph $-2x+y=-8$ $(y=2x-8)$ using a dashed line.

Test Point: $(0,0)$: $-2(0)+0=0 \not< -8$

Therefore, the half-plane not containing $(0,0)$ is the solution set of $-2x+y<-8$.

Second, graph the inequality $2x-y>8$. To do so, replace the inequality symbol with an equal sign to obtain $2x-y=8$. Because the inequality is strict, graph $2x-y=8$ $(y=2x-8)$ using a dashed line.

Test Point: $(0,0)$: $2(0)-0=0 \not> 8$

Therefore, the half-plane not containing $(0,0)$ is the solution set of $2x - y > 8$.

The overlapping shaded region (that is, the shaded region in the graph below) is the solution to the system of linear inequalities. In this case, notice that the two inequalities that make up the system both have the exact same solution set. Therefore, the overlapping shaded region is the solution set of both individual inequalities.

23. $\begin{cases} -5x + 3y < 12 \\ 5x - 3y < 9 \end{cases}$

First, graph the inequality $-5x + 3y < 12$. To do so, replace the inequality symbol with an equal sign to obtain $-5x + 3y = 12$. Because the inequality is strict, graph $-5x + 3y = 12$

$\left(y = \dfrac{5}{3}x + 4 \right)$ using a dashed line.

Test Point: $(0,0)$: $-5(0) + 3(0) = 0 < 12$

Therefore, the half-plane containing $(0,0)$ is the solution set of $-5x + 3y < 12$.

Second, graph the inequality $5x - 3y < 9$. To do so, replace the inequality symbol with an equal sign to obtain $5x - 3y = 9$. Because the inequality is strict, graph $5x - 3y = 9$

$\left(y = \dfrac{5}{3}x - 3 \right)$ using a dashed line.

Test Point: $(0,0)$: $5(0) - 3(0) = 0 < 9$

Therefore, the half-plane containing $(0,0)$ is the solution set of $5x - 3y < 9$.

The overlapping shaded region (that is, the shaded region in the graph below) is the solution to the system of linear inequalities.

25. $\begin{cases} y \leq 8 \\ x \geq 3 \end{cases}$

First, graph the inequality $y \leq 8$. To do so, replace the inequality symbol with an equal sign to obtain $y = 8$. Because the inequality is non-strict, graph $y = 8$ using a solid line.

Test point: $(0,0)$: $0 \leq 8$

Therefore, the half-plane containing $(0,0)$ is the solution set of $y \leq 8$.

Second, graph the inequality $x \geq 3$. To do so, replace the inequality symbol with an equal sign to obtain $x = 3$. Because the inequality is non-strict, graph $x = 3$ using a solid line.

Test point: $(0,0)$: $0 \not\geq 3$

Therefore, the half-plane not containing $(0,0)$ is the solution set of $x \geq 3$.

The overlapping shaded region (that is, the shaded region in the graph below) is the solution to the system of linear inequalities.

27. $\begin{cases} x + y \leq 6 \\ 3x + y \leq 12 \\ x \geq 0 \\ y \geq 0 \end{cases}$

First, graph the inequality $x + y \leq 6$. To do so, replace the inequality symbol with an equal sign to obtain $x + y = 6$. Because the inequality is non-strict, graph $x + y = 6$ $(y = -x + 6)$ using a solid line.

Test Point: $(0,0)$: $0 + 0 = 0 \leq 6$

Therefore, the half-plane containing $(0,0)$ is the solution set of $x + y \le 6$.

Next, graph the inequality $3x + y \le 12$. To do so, replace the inequality symbol with an equal sign to obtain $3x + y = 12$. Because the inequality is non-strict, graph $3x + y = 12$ $(y = -3x + 12)$ using a solid line.

Test Point: $(0,0)$: $-3(0) + 0 = 0 \le 12$

Therefore, the half-plane containing $(0,0)$ is the solution set of $3x + y \le 12$.

The two inequalities $x \ge 0$ and $y \ge 0$ require that the graph be in quadrant I.

The overlapping shaded region (that is, the shaded region in the graph below) is the solution to the system of linear inequalities.

The graph is bounded. The four corner points of the bounded region are $(0, 0)$, $(4, 0)$, $(3, 3)$, and $(0, 6)$.

29. $\begin{cases} x + y \ge 8 \\ 4x + 2y \ge 28 \\ x \ge 0 \\ y \ge 0 \end{cases}$

First, graph the inequality $x + y \ge 8$. To do so, replace the inequality symbol with an equal sign to obtain $x + y = 8$. Because the inequality is non-strict, graph $x + y = 8$ $(y = -x + 8)$ using a solid line.

Test Point: $(0,0)$: $0 + 0 = 0 \ngeq 8$

Therefore, the half-plane not containing $(0,0)$ is the solution set of $x + y \ge 8$.

Next, graph the inequality $4x + 2y \ge 28$. To do so, replace the inequality symbol with an equal sign to obtain $4x + 2y = 28$. Because the inequality is non-strict, graph $4x + 2y = 28$ $(y = -2x + 14)$ using a solid line.

Test Point: $(0,0)$: $4(0) + 2(0) = 0 \ngeq 28$

Therefore, the half-plane not containing $(0,0)$ is the solution set of $4x + 2y \ge 28$.

The two inequalities $x \ge 0$ and $y \ge 0$ require that the graph be in quadrant I.

The overlapping shaded region (that is, the shaded region in the graph below) is the solution to the system of linear inequalities.

The graph is unbounded. The three corner points of the unbounded region are $(0, 14)$, $(6, 2)$, and $(8, 0)$.

31. $\begin{cases} 2x + 3y \le 30 \\ 3x + 2y \le 25 \\ 5x + 2y \le 35 \\ x \ge 0 \\ y \ge 0 \end{cases}$

First, graph the inequality $2x + 3y \le 30$. To do so, replace the inequality symbol with an equal sign to obtain $2x + 3y = 30$. Because the inequality is non-strict, graph $2x + 3y = 30$ $\left(y = -\dfrac{2}{3}x + 10\right)$ using a solid line.

Test Point: $(0,0)$: $2(0) + 3(0) = 0 \le 30$

Therefore, the half-plane containing $(0,0)$ is the solution set of $2x + 3y \le 30$.

Second, graph the inequality $3x + 2y \le 25$. To do so, replace the inequality symbol with an equal sign to obtain $3x + 2y = 25$. Because the inequality is non-strict, graph $3x + 2y = 25$ $\left(y = -\dfrac{3}{2}x + \dfrac{25}{2}\right)$ using a solid line.

Test Point: $(0,0)$: $3(0) + 2(0) = 0 \le 25$

Therefore, the half-plane containing $(0,0)$ is the solution set of $3x+2y \le 25$.

Third, graph the inequality $5x+2y \le 35$. To do so, replace the inequality symbol with an equal sign to obtain $5x+2y = 35$. Because the inequality is non-strict, graph $5x+2y = 35$ $\left(y=-\dfrac{5}{2}x+\dfrac{35}{2} \right)$ using a solid line.

Test Point: $(0,0)$: $5(0)+2(0)=0 \le 35$

Therefore, the half-plane containing $(0,0)$ is the solution set of $5x+2y \le 35$.

The two inequalities $x \ge 0$ and $y \ge 0$ require that the graph be in quadrant I.

The overlapping shaded region (that is, the shaded region in the graph below) is the solution to the system of linear inequalities.

The graph is bounded. The five corner points of the bounded region are $(0, 0)$, $(7, 0)$, $(5, 5)$, $(3, 8)$, and $(0, 10)$.

33. $\begin{cases} 2x+y \ge 13 \\ x+2y \ge 11 \\ x \ge 4 \\ y \ge 0 \end{cases}$

First, graph the inequality $2x+y \ge 13$. To do so, replace the inequality symbol with an equal sign to obtain $2x+y = 13$. Because the inequality is non-strict, graph $2x+y = 13$ $(y=-2x+13)$ using a solid line.

Test Point: $(0,0)$: $2(0)+0=0 \not\ge 13$

Therefore, the half-plane not containing $(0,0)$ is the solution set of $2x+y \ge 13$.

Second, graph the inequality $x+2y \ge 11$. To do so, replace the inequality symbol with an equal sign to obtain $x+2y = 11$. Because the

inequality is non-strict, graph $x+2y = 11$ $\left(y=-\dfrac{1}{2}x+\dfrac{11}{2} \right)$ using a solid line.

Test Point: $(0,0)$: $0+2(0)=0 \not\ge 11$

Therefore, the half-plane not containing $(0,0)$ is the solution set of $x+2y \ge 11$.

Third, graph the inequality $x \ge 4$. To do so, replace the inequality symbol with an equal sign to obtain $x=4$. Because the inequality is non-strict, graph $x=4$ using a solid line.

Test Point: $(0,0)$: $0 \not\ge 4$

Therefore, the half-plane not containing $(0,0)$ is the solution set of $x \ge 4$.

The inequality $y \ge 0$ requires that the graph be above the x-axis.

The overlapping shaded region (that is, the shaded region in the graph below) is the solution to the system of linear inequalities.

The graph is unbounded. The three corner points of the unbounded region are $(4, 5)$, $(5, 3)$, and $(11, 0)$.

35. a. Let x represent the number of servings of orange juice and let y represent the number of servings of cereal. Now, the amount of potassium Daria consumes must be at least 500 mg, so $450x+50y \ge 500$. The amount of protein Daria consumes must be at least 14 grams, so $2x+6y \ge 14$. Finally, Daria cannot consume negative servings of orange juice or cereal, so we have the non-negativity constraints $x \ge 0$ and $y \ge 0$.

Thus, we have the following system:

$\begin{cases} 450x+50y \ge 500 \\ 2x+6y \ge 14 \\ x \ge 0 \\ y \ge 0 \end{cases}$

b. First, graph the inequality
$450x + 50y \geq 500$. To do so, replace the inequality symbol with an equal sign to obtain $450x + 50y = 500$. Because the inequality is non-strict, graph
$450x + 50y = 500$ $(y = -9x + 10)$ using a solid line.
Test Point: $(0,0)$: $450(0) + 50(0) = 0 \ngeq 500$

Thus, the solution set of $450x + 50y \geq 500$ is the half-plane not containing $(0,0)$.

Second, graph the inequality $2x + 6y \geq 14$. To do so, replace the inequality symbol with an equal sign to obtain $2x + 6y = 14$.
Because the inequality is non-strict, graph
$2x + 6y = 14$ $\left(y = -\dfrac{1}{3}x + \dfrac{7}{3} \right)$ using a solid line.
Test Point: $(0,0)$: $2(0) + 6(0) = 0 \ngeq 14$
Thus, the solution set of $2x + 6y \geq 14$ is the half-plane not containing $(0,0)$.

The two inequalities $x \geq 0$ and $y \geq 0$ require that the graph be in quadrant I.
The overlapping shaded region (that is, the shaded region in the graph below) is the solution to the system of linear inequalities.

The three corner points of the unbounded region are $(0, 10)$, $\approx (0.88, 2.04)$ and $(7, 0)$.

37. a. Let x represent the amount to be invested in Treasury Notes and let y represent the amount to be invested in corporate bonds. Now, Jack and Mary have at most $25,000 to invest, so $x + y \leq 25,000$. They want to earn at least $1,400 per year in interest, so $0.05x + 0.08y \geq 1,400$. The amount invested in Treasury Notes must be at least $5,000, so $x \geq 5,000$. The amount to be invested in corporate bonds must be no more than $15,000, so $y \leq 15,000$. They cannot invest a negative amount in corporate bonds, so we have the non-negativity constraint $y \geq 0$. Thus, we have the following system:

$$\begin{cases} x + y \leq 25,000 \\ 0.05x + 0.08y \geq 1,400 \\ x \geq 5,000 \\ y \leq 15,000 \\ y \geq 0 \end{cases}$$

b. First, graph the inequality $x + y \leq 25,000$. To do so, replace the inequality symbol with an equal sign to obtain $x + y = 25,000$. Because the inequality is non-strict, graph
$x + y = 25,000$ $(y = -x + 25,000)$ using a solid line.
Test Point: $(0,0)$: $0 + 0 = 0 \leq 25,000$
Thus, the solution set of $x + y \leq 25,000$ is the half-plane containing $(0,0)$.

Second, graph the inequality $0.05x + 0.08y \geq 1,400$. To do so, replace the inequality symbol with an equal sign to obtain $0.05x + 0.08y = 1,400$. Because the inequality is non-strict, graph
$0.05x + 0.08y = 1,400$ $\left(y = -\dfrac{5}{8}x + 17,500 \right)$
using a solid line.
Test Point: $(0,0)$: $0.05(0) + 0.08(0) = 0 \ngeq 1,400$

Thus, the solution set of $0.05x + 0.08y \geq 1,400$ is the half-plane not containing $(0,0)$.

The inequality $x \geq 5,000$ requires that the graph be to the right of the vertical line $x = 5,000$.

The inequality $y \le 15,000$ requires that the graph be below the horizontal line $y = 15,000$.

The inequality $y \ge 0$ requires that the graph be above the *x*-axis.

The overlapping shaded region (that is, the shaded region in the graph below) is the solution to the system of linear inequalities.

The four corner points of the bounded region are $(5000, 15000)$, $(5000, 14375)$, $(20000, 5000)$, and $(10000, 15000)$.

39. The graph contains a line passing through the points $(0,4)$ and $(2,6)$. The slope of the line is

$m = \dfrac{6-4}{2-0} = \dfrac{2}{2} = 1$. The *y*-intercept is 4. Thus,

the equation of the line is $y = x + 4$. Because the shaded region is above this line, our inequality will contain a "greater than." Because the line is solid, this means that the inequality is non-strict. That is, our inequality will consist of "greater than or equal to." Thus, the linear inequality is $y \ge x + 4$.

The second line in the graph passes through the points $(0,10)$ and $(2,6)$. The slope of the line is $m = \dfrac{6-10}{2-0} = \dfrac{-4}{2} = -2$. The *y*-intercept is 10.

Thus, the equation of the line is $y = -2x + 10$.

Because the shaded region is above this line, our inequality will contain a "greater than." Because the line is solid, this means that the inequality is non-strict. That is, our inequality will consist of "greater than or equal to." Thus, the linear inequality is $y \ge -2x + 10$.

Thus, the system of linear inequalities is

$$\begin{cases} y \ge x + 4 \\ y \ge -2x + 10 \end{cases}$$

41. The graph is restricted to the first quadrant. Therefore, the system will contain the inequalities $x \ge 0$ and $y \ge 0$.

The graph contains a line passing through the points $(0,12)$ and $(4,8)$. The slope of the line is

$m = \dfrac{8-12}{4-0} = \dfrac{-4}{4} = -1$. The *y*-intercept is 12.

Thus, the equation of the line is $y = -x + 12$.

Because the shaded region is below this line, our inequality will contain a "less than." Because the line is solid, this means that the inequality is non-strict. That is, our inequality will consist of "less than or equal to." Thus, the linear inequality is $y \le -x + 12$.

The second line in the graph passes through the points $(4,8)$ and $(8,0)$. The slope of the line is

$m = \dfrac{0-8}{8-4} = \dfrac{-8}{4} = -2$. Using the point-slope

form, the equation of the second line is

$$\begin{aligned} y - y_1 &= m(x - x_1) \\ y - 0 &= -2(x - 8) \\ y &= -2x + 16 \end{aligned}$$

Because the shaded region is below this line, our inequality will contain a "less than." Because the line is solid, this means that the inequality is non-strict. That is, our inequality will consist of "less than or equal to." Thus, the linear inequality is $y \le -2x + 16$.

Thus, the system of linear inequalities is

$$\begin{cases} y \le -x + 12 \\ y \le -2x + 16 \\ x \ge 0 \\ y \ge 0 \end{cases}$$

43. $\begin{cases} x + y \le 4 & (y \le -x + 4) \\ 3x + y \ge 10 & (y \ge -3x + 10) \end{cases}$

45. $\begin{cases} 3x+2y<12 & \left(y<-\dfrac{3}{2}x+6\right) \\ -2x+3y>12 & \left(y>\dfrac{2}{3}x+4\right) \end{cases}$

47. $\begin{cases} x+y\le 6 & (y\le -x+6) \\ 3x+y\le 12 & (y\le -3x+12) \\ x\ge 0 & \\ y\ge 0 & \end{cases}$

The inequalities $x\ge 0$ and $y\ge 0$ restrict the graph to the first quadrant.

Chapter 4 Review

1. a. Let $x=3$, $y=-1$ in both equations (1) and (2).
$$\begin{cases} 3+3(-1)=3-3=0\ne -2 \\ 2(3)-(-1)=6+1=7\ne 10 \end{cases}$$
These values do not satisfy either equation. Therefore, the ordered pair (3, -1) is not a solution of the system.

b. Let $x=4$, $y=-2$ in both equations (1) and (2).
$$\begin{cases} 4+3(-2)=4-6=-2 \\ 2(4)-(-2)=8+2=10 \end{cases}$$
Because these values satisfy both equations, the ordered pair (4, -2) is a solution of the system.

2. a. Let $x=\dfrac{1}{2}$, $y=1$ in both equations (1) and (2).
$$\begin{cases} -2\left(\dfrac{1}{2}\right)+5(1)=-1+5=4 \\ 4\left(\dfrac{1}{2}\right)-5(1)=2-5=-3 \end{cases}$$
Because these values satisfy both equations, the ordered pair $\left(\dfrac{1}{2},\,1\right)$ is a solution of the system.

b. Let $x=-1$, $y=\dfrac{1}{3}$ in both equations (1) and (2).
$$\begin{cases} -2(-1)+5\left(\dfrac{1}{3}\right)=2+\dfrac{5}{3}=\dfrac{11}{3}\ne 4 \\ 4(-1)-5\left(\dfrac{1}{3}\right)=-4-\dfrac{5}{3}=-\dfrac{17}{3}\ne -3 \end{cases}$$
These values do not satisfy either equation. Therefore, the ordered pair $\left(-1,\,\dfrac{1}{3}\right)$ is not a solution of the system.

3. a. Let $x=3$, $y=6$ in both equation (1) and (2).
$$\begin{cases} 6(3)-5(6)=18-30=-12 \\ 3-6=-3 \end{cases}$$
These values satisfy both equations. Therefore, the ordered pair (3, 6) is a solution of the system.

b. Let $x=1$, $y=4$ in both equations (1) and (2).
$$\begin{cases} 6(1)-5(4)=6-20=-14\ne -12 \\ 1-4=-3 \end{cases}$$
Although these values satisfy equation (2), they do not satisfy the equation (1). Therefore, the ordered pair (1, 4) is not a solution of the system.

4. a. Let $x=3$, $y=0$ in both equations (1) and (2).
$$\begin{cases} 3(3)-0=9-0=9 \\ 8(3)+3(0)=24+0=24\ne 7 \end{cases}$$
Although these values satisfy equation (1), they do not satisfy the equation (2). Therefore, the ordered pair (3, 0) is not a solution of the system.

b. Let $x = 2$, $y = -3$ in both equations (1) and (2).

$$\begin{cases} 3(2)-(-3)=6+3=9 \\ 8(2)+3(-3)=16-9=7 \end{cases}$$

Because these values satisfy both equations, the ordered pair (2, -3) is a solution of the system.

5. The graphs of the linear equations intersect at the point (4, 2). Thus, the solution is (4, 2).

6. The graphs of the linear equations intersect at the point (2, -1). Thus, the solution is (2, -1).

7. $\begin{cases} y = -3x+1 & (1) \\ y = \dfrac{1}{2}x-6 & (2) \end{cases}$

The two equations are in slope-intercept form. Graph each equation and find the point of intersection.

The solution is the ordered pair (2, -5).

8. $\begin{cases} -2x+3y=-9 & (1) \\ 3x+y=8 & (2) \end{cases}$

Equation (1) in slope-intercept form is

$y = \dfrac{2}{3}x-3$. Equation (2) in slope-intercept form

is $y = -3x+8$. Graph each equation and find the point of intersection.

The solution is the ordered pair (3, -1).

9. $\begin{cases} y = -\dfrac{1}{3}x+2 & (1) \\ x+3y=-9 & (2) \end{cases}$

Equation (1) is already in slope-intercept form. Equation (2) in slope-intercept form is

$y = -\dfrac{1}{3}x-3$. Graph each equation.

The two lines are parallel. The system is inconsistent. The system has no solution. That is, $\varnothing$ or { }.

10. $\begin{cases} 2x-3y=0 & (1) \\ 2x-y=-4 & (2) \end{cases}$

Equation (1) in slope-intercept form is $y = \dfrac{2}{3}x$.

Equation (2) in slope-intercept form is $y = 2x+4$. Graph each equation and find the point of intersection.

The solution is the ordered pair (-3, -2).

11. $\begin{cases} y = -\dfrac{1}{4}x + 2 & (1) \\ y = 4x - 32 & (2) \end{cases}$

Substituting $-\dfrac{1}{4}x + 2$ for y in equation (2), we obtain

$$-\frac{1}{4}x + 2 = 4x - 32$$

$$-4\left(-\frac{1}{4}x + 2\right) = -4(4x - 32)$$

$$x - 8 = -16x + 128$$

$$17x = 136$$

$$x = 8$$

Substituting 8 for x in equation (2), we obtain
$y = 4(8) - 32 = 32 - 32 = 0$.

The solution is the ordered pair (8, 0).

12. $\begin{cases} y = -\dfrac{3}{4}x + 2 & (1) \\ 3x + 4y = 8 & (2) \end{cases}$

Substituting $-\dfrac{3}{4}x + 2$ for y in equation (2), we obtain

$$3x + 4\left(-\frac{3}{4}x + 2\right) = 8$$

$$3x - 3x + 8 = 8$$

$$8 = 8$$

The system is dependent. The solution is

$$\left\{ (x,\, y) \,\middle|\, y = -\frac{3}{4}x + 2 \right\}.$$

13. $\begin{cases} y = 3x - 9 & (1) \\ 4x + 3y = -1 & (2) \end{cases}$

Substituting $3x - 9$ for y in equation (2), we obtain

$$4x + 3(3x - 9) = -1$$

$$4x + 9x - 27 = -1$$

$$13x - 27 = -1$$

$$13x = 26$$

$$x = 2$$

Substituting 2 for x in equation (1), we obtain
$y = 3(2) - 9 = 6 - 9 = -3$.

The solution is the ordered pair (2, -3).

14. $\begin{cases} x - 2y = 7 & (1) \\ 3x - y = -4 & (2) \end{cases}$

Equation (1) solved for x is $x = 2y + 7$.

Substituting $2y + 7$ for x in equation (2), we obtain

$$3(2y + 7) - y = -4$$

$$6y + 21 - y = -4$$

$$5y + 21 = -4$$

$$5y = -25$$

$$y = -5$$

Substituting -5 for y in equation (1), we obtain

$$x - 2(-5) = 7$$

$$x + 10 = 7$$

$$x = -3$$

The solution is the ordered pair (-3, -5).

15. $\begin{cases} 2x - y = 9 & (1) \\ 3x + y = 11 & (2) \end{cases}$

Add equations (1) and (2).

$$2x - y = 9$$
$$\underline{3x + y = 11}$$
$$5x = 20$$
$$x = 4$$

Substituting 4 for x in equation (2), we obtain

$$3(4) + y = 11$$

$$12 + y = 11$$

$$y = -1$$

The solution is the ordered pair (4, -1).

16. $\begin{cases} -x + 3y = 4 & (1) \\ 3x - 4y = -2 & (2) \end{cases}$

Multiply both sides of equation (1) by 3 and add the result to equation (2).

$$-3x + 9y = 12$$
$$\underline{3x - 4y = -2}$$
$$5y = 10$$
$$y = 2$$

Substituting 2 for y in equation (1), we obtain

$$-x + 3(2) = 4$$

$$-x + 6 = 4$$

$$2 = x$$

The solution is the ordered pair (2, 2).

17. $\begin{cases} 2x - 4y = 8 & (1) \\ -3x + 6y = -12 & (2) \end{cases}$

Multiply both sides of equation (1) by 3, multiply both sides of equation (2) by 2, and add the results.

$6x - 12y = 24$
$-6x + 12y = -24$
$\overline{\qquad 0 = 0 \qquad}$

The system is dependent. The solution is $\{(x, y) \mid 2x - 4y = 8\}$.

18. $\begin{cases} 3x - 4y = -11 & (1) \\ 2x - 3y = -7 & (2) \end{cases}$

Multiply both sides of equation (1) by 2, multiply both sides of equation (2) by -3, and add the results.

$6x - 8y = -22$
$-6x + 9y = 21$
$\overline{\qquad y = -1 \qquad}$

Substituting -1 for y in equation (1), we obtain
$3x - 4(-1) = -11$
$\quad 3x + 4 = -11$
$\qquad 3x = -15$
$\qquad x = -5$
The solution is the ordered pair (-5, -1).

19. $\begin{cases} x + y = -4 & (1) \\ 2x - 3y = 12 & (2) \end{cases}$

Because the coefficients of x and y in equation (1) are both 1, we use substitution to solve the system.
Equation (1) solved for x is $x = -y - 4$.
Substituting $-y - 4$ for x in equation (2), we obtain
$2(-y - 4) - 3y = 12$
$\quad -2y - 8 - 3y = 12$
$\qquad -5y - 8 = 12$
$\qquad -5y = 20$
$\qquad y = -4$
Substituting -4 for y in equation (1), we obtain
$x + (-4) = -4$
$\quad x - 4 = -4$
$\qquad x = 0$
The solution is the ordered pair (0, -4).

20. $\begin{cases} 5x - 3y = 2 & (1) \\ x + 2y = -10 & (2) \end{cases}$

Because the coefficient of x in equation (2) is 1, we use substitution to solve the system.
Equation (2) solved for x is $x = -2y - 10$.
Substituting $-2y - 10$ for x in equation (1), we obtain
$5(-2y - 10) - 3y = 2$
$\quad -10y - 50 - 3y = 2$
$\qquad -13y - 50 = 2$
$\qquad -13y = 52$
$\qquad y = -4$
Substituting -4 for y in equation (2), we obtain
$x + 2(-4) = -10$
$\quad x - 8 = -10$
$\qquad x = -2$
The solution is the ordered pair (-2, -4).

21. $\begin{cases} 3x - 2y = 5 & (1) \\ 4x - 5y = 9 & (2) \end{cases}$

Because none of variables have a coefficient of 1, we use elimination to solve the system.
Multiply both sides of equation (1) by 4, multiply both sides of equation (2) by -3, and add the results.
$12x - 8y = 20$
$-12x + 15y = -27$
$\overline{\qquad 7y = -7 \qquad}$
$\qquad y = -1$
Substituting -1 for y in equation (1), we obtain
$3x - 2(-1) = 5$
$\quad 3x + 2 = 5$
$\qquad 3x = 3$
$\qquad x = 1$
The solution is the ordered pair (1, -1).

22. $\begin{cases} 12x + 20y = 21 & (1) \\ 3x - 2y = 0 & (2) \end{cases}$

Because none of variables have a coefficient of 1, we use elimination to solve the system.
Multiply both sides of equation (2) by -4 and add the result to equation (1).
$12x + 20y = 21$
$-12x + 8y = 0$
$\overline{\qquad 28y = 21 \qquad}$
$\qquad y = \dfrac{21}{28} = \dfrac{3}{4}$

Substituting $\dfrac{3}{4}$ for y in equation (1), we obtain

$$12x + 20\left(\dfrac{3}{4}\right) = 21$$
$$12x + 15 = 21$$
$$12x = 6$$
$$x = \dfrac{6}{12} = \dfrac{1}{2}$$

The solution is the ordered pair $\left(\dfrac{1}{2}, \dfrac{3}{4}\right)$.

23. $\begin{cases} 6x + 9y = -3 & (1) \\ 8x + 12y = 7 & (2) \end{cases}$

Because none of variables have a coefficient of 1, we use elimination to solve the system. Multiply both sides of equation (1) by 4, multiply both sides of equation (2) by –3, and add the results.

$$24x + 36y = -12$$
$$\underline{-24x - 36y = -21}$$
$$0 = -33$$

The system has no solution. The solution set is $\varnothing$ or $\{\ \}$. The system is inconsistent.

24. $\begin{cases} 6x + 11y = 2 & (1) \\ 5x + 8y = -3 & (2) \end{cases}$

Because none of variables have a coefficient of 1, we use elimination to solve the system. Multiply both sides of equation (1) by 5, multiply both sides of equation (2) by -6, and add the results.

$$30x + 55y = 10$$
$$\underline{-30x - 48y = 18}$$
$$7y = 28$$
$$y = 4$$

Substituting 4 for y in equation (1), we obtain
$$6x + 11(4) = 2$$
$$6x + 44 = 2$$
$$6x = -42$$
$$x = -7$$

The solution is the ordered pair (-7, 4).

25. Let x and y represent the two numbers.
$\begin{cases} x + y = 56 & (1) \\ x - y = 14 & (2) \end{cases}$

Adding equations (1) and (2) results in
$$2x = 70$$
$$x = 35$$

Substituting 35 for x in equation (1), we obtain
$$35 + y = 56$$
$$y = 21$$

The two numbers are 35 and 21.

26. Let m represent the number of males to be inducted and f represent the number of females to be inducted.
$\begin{cases} m + f = 73 & (1) \\ f = m + 11 & (2) \end{cases}$

Substituting $m + 11$ for f in equation (1), we obtain
$$m + (m + 11) = 73$$
$$2m + 11 = 73$$
$$2m = 62$$
$$m = 31$$

Substituting 31 for m in equation (2), we obtain
$$f = 31 + 11 = 42$$

The local chapter of Phi Theta Kappa will induct 31 males and 42 females.

27. Let p represent the number of calories in a slice of pepperoni pizza and s represent the number of calories in a slice of Italian sausage pizza.
$\begin{cases} 3p + 5s = 2600 & (1) \\ 4p + 2s = 1880 & (2) \end{cases}$

Multiply both sides of equation (1) by 4, multiply both sides of equation (2) by -3, and add the results.

$$12p + 20s = 10,400$$
$$\underline{-12p - 6s = -5640}$$
$$14s = 4760$$
$$s = 340$$

Substituting 340 for s in equation (1), we obtain
$$3p + 5(340) = 2600$$
$$3p + 1700 = 2600$$
$$3p = 900$$
$$p = 300$$

There are 300 calories in a slice of pepperoni pizza and 340 calories in a slice of Italian sausage pizza.

28. Let l represent the length of the rectangle and w represent the width of the rectangle.

$$\begin{cases} l = 2w - 5 & (1) \\ 2l + 2w = 68 & (2) \end{cases}$$

Substituting $2w - 5$ for l in equation (2), we obtain

$$2(2w - 5) + 2w = 68$$
$$4w - 10 + 2w = 68$$
$$6w - 10 = 68$$
$$6w = 78$$
$$w = 13$$

Substituting 13 for w in equation (1), we obtain
$$l = 2(13) - 5 = 26 - 5 = 21$$

The dimensions of the rectangle are 21 inches by 13 inches.

29. Because the sum of the measures of the three angles in a triangle must equal $180°$, we obtain the following system.

$$\begin{cases} x + y + 90 = 180 & (1) \\ y = 2x & (2) \end{cases}$$

Substituting $2x$ for y in equation (1), we obtain
$$x + 2x + 90 = 180$$
$$3x + 90 = 180$$
$$3x = 90$$
$$x = 30$$

Substituting 30 for x in equation (2), we obtain
$$y = 2(30) = 60 \, .$$

Thus, angle $x = 30°$ and angle $y = 60°$.

30. Because angles 1 and 2 are supplemental, and because angles 1 and 3 must be equal, we obtain the following system.

$$\begin{cases} (x + 4y) + (8x + 5y) = 180 & (1) \\ x + 4y = 2x + y & (2) \end{cases}$$

Simplify each equation.

$$\begin{cases} 9x + 9y = 180 & (1) \\ -x + 3y = 0 & (2) \end{cases}$$

Divide both sides of equation (1) by 9 and add the result to equation (2).

$$\begin{array}{r} x + y = 20 \\ -x + 3y = 0 \\ \hline 4y = 20 \\ y = 5 \end{array}$$

Substituting 5 for y in equation (2), we obtain
$$-x + 3(5) = 0$$
$$-x + 15 = 0$$
$$15 = x$$

Thus, $x = 15$ and $y = 5$.

31. Let n represent the number of nickels and q represent the number of quarters.

	Number of Coins	Value per Coin	Total Value
Nickels	n	0.05	$0.05n$
Quarters	q	0.25	$0.25q$
Total	40		4.40

Using the columns for Number of Coins and Total Value, we obtain the following system.

$$\begin{cases} n + q = 40 & (1) \\ 0.05n + 0.25q = 4.40 & (2) \end{cases}$$

Multiply both sides of equation (1) by -0.05 and add the result to equation (2).

$$\begin{array}{r} -0.05n - 0.05q = -2 \\ 0.05n + 0.25q = 4.40 \\ \hline 0.20q = 2.40 \\ q = 12 \end{array}$$

Substituting 12 for q in equation (1), we obtain
$$n + 12 = 40$$
$$n = 28$$

Jerome's piggy bank contains 28 nickels and 12 quarters.

32. Let x represent the number of liters of the 25%-hydrochloric-acid (HCl) solution to be used, and let y represent the number of liters of the 40%-HCl solution to be used.

	Liters of Solution	Percent HCl	Liters of HCl
25%-HCl Solution	x	25% = 0.25	$0.25x$
40%-HCl Solution	y	40% = 0.40	$0.40y$
30%-HCl Solution	12	30% = 0.30	$0.30(12) = 3.6$

Using the columns for Liters of Solution and Liters of HCl, we obtain the following system.

$$\begin{cases} x + y = 12 & (1) \\ 0.25x + 0.40y = 3.6 & (2) \end{cases}$$

Multiply both sides of equation (1) by -0.25 and add the result to equation (2).

$$\begin{array}{r} -0.25x - .25y = -3 \\ 0.25x + 0.40y = 3.6 \\ \hline 0.15y = 0.6 \\ y = 4 \end{array}$$

Substituting 4 for y in equation (1), we obtain
$$x + 4 = 12$$
$$x = 8$$
The chemist should mix 8 liters of the 25%-hydrochloric-acid solution with 4 liters of the 40%-hydrochloric-acid solution.

33. Let s represent the amount invested in stocks, and let b represent the amount invested in bonds. We organize the information in the table below, using the interest formula:

Interest = Principal × rate × time or $I = Prt$.

	P	r	t	I
Stocks	s	0.065	1	$0.065s$
Bonds	b	0.0425	1	$0.0425b$
Total	10,000		1	582.50

Using the columns for Principal and Interest, we obtain the following system.
$$\begin{cases} s + b = 10{,}000 & (1) \\ 0.065s + 0.0425b = 582.50 & (2) \end{cases}$$
Solving equation (1) for b, we obtain
$b = 10{,}000 - s$. Substituting $10{,}000 - s$ for b in equation (2), we obtain
$$0.065s + 0.0425(10{,}000 - s) = 582.50$$
$$0.065s + 425 - 0.0425s = 582.50$$
$$0.0225s + 425 = 582.50$$
$$0.0225s = 157.50$$
$$s = 7000$$
Substituting 7000 for s in equation (1), we obtain
$$7000 + b = 10{,}000$$
$$b = 3000$$
Verna invested $7000 in stocks and $3000 in bonds.

34. Let p represent the speed of the plane and let w represent the speed of the wind.
$$\begin{cases} p + w = 160 & (1) \\ p - w = 112 & (2) \end{cases}$$
Adding equations (1) and (2) results in
$$\begin{aligned} p + w &= 160 \\ p - w &= 112 \\ \hline 2p &= 272 \\ p &= 136 \end{aligned}$$
Substituting 136 for p in equation (1), we obtain
$$136 + w = 160$$
$$w = 24$$
The plane's speed is 136 miles per hour and the wind's speed is 24 miles per hour.

35. Let d represent the distance that both cars have traveled on the turnpike at the point of catch up. Let t represent the Mustang's time on the turnpike at the point of catch up. Then $t + \frac{1}{2}$ represents the Grand Am's time on the turnpike at that point. We obtain the following system by utilizing the formula rate × time = distance :
$$\begin{cases} 80t = d & (1) \\ 50\left(t + \frac{1}{2}\right) = d & (2) \end{cases}$$
Substituting $80t$ for d in equation (2) yields
$$50\left(t + \frac{1}{2}\right) = 80t$$
$$50t + 25 = 80t$$
$$-30t + 25 = 0$$
$$-30t = -25$$
$$t = \frac{-25}{-30} = \frac{5}{6}$$
Substituting $\frac{5}{6}$ for t in equation (1), we obtain
$$80\left(\frac{5}{6}\right) = d$$
$$d = \frac{200}{3} = 66\frac{2}{3}$$
It will take $\frac{5}{6}$ hours (that is, 50 minutes) for the Mustang to catch up to the Grand Am. At that time, the two cars will have traveled $66\frac{2}{3}$ miles on the turnpike.

36. Let b represent the speed of the boat in still water and let c represent the speed of the current. The rate at which the boat will travel downstream will be $b + c$, and the rate upstream will be $b - c$. Using the formula rate × time = distance , we obtain the following system:
$$\begin{cases} (b - c) \cdot 1.5 = 30 & (1) \\ (b + c) \cdot 1 = 30 & (2) \end{cases}$$
Divide both sides of equation (1) by 1.5, simplify equation (2), and add the results.
$$\begin{aligned} b - c &= 20 \\ b + c &= 30 \\ \hline 2b &= 50 \\ b &= 25 \end{aligned}$$

Substituting 25 for b in equation (2), we obtain

$$(25+c)\cdot 1 = 30$$
$$25+c = 30$$
$$c = 5$$

The speed of the boat in still water is 25 miles per hour and the speed of the current is 5 miles per hour.

37. a. $\begin{cases} M(t) = 0.056t + 3.354 \\ F(t) = 0.103t + 1.842 \end{cases}$

b.
$$M(t) = F(t)$$
$$0.056t + 3.354 = 0.103t + 1.842$$
$$-0.047t + 3.354 = 1.842$$
$$-0.047t = -1.512$$
$$t \approx 32.17$$

Male and female participation will be the same approximately 32 years after 1990, which is the year 2022.

38. a. $R(x) = 15x$

b. $C(x) = 1200 + 2.50x$

c.

d.
$$R(x) = C(x)$$
$$15x = 1200 + 2.50x$$
$$12.50x = 1200$$
$$x = 96$$
$$R(96) = 15(96) = 1440$$
$$C(96) = 1200 + 2.50(96) = 1440$$

The break-even number of pies is 96 pies. The revenue and cost of 96 pies is $1440.

39. $\begin{cases} x+y-z = 1 & (1) \\ x-y+z = 7 & (2) \\ x+2y+z = 1 & (3) \end{cases}$

Multiply both sides of equation (1) by -1 and add the result to equation (2).

$$-x-y+z = -1$$
$$\underline{x-y+z = 7}$$
$$-2y+2z = 6 \qquad (4)$$

Multiply both sides of equation (1) by -1 and add the result to equation (3).

$$-x-y+z = -1$$
$$\underline{x+2y+z = 1}$$
$$y+2z = 0 \qquad (5)$$

Divide both sides of equation (4) by 2 and add the result to equation (5).

$$-y+z = 3$$
$$\underline{y+2z = 0}$$
$$3z = 3$$
$$z = 1$$

Substituting 1 for z in equation (4), we obtain

$$-2y+2(1) = 6$$
$$-2y+2 = 6$$
$$-2y = 4$$
$$y = -2$$

Substituting -2 for y and 1 for z in equation (1), we obtain

$$x+(-2)-1 = 1$$
$$x-3 = 1$$
$$x = 4$$

The solution is the ordered triple (4, -2, 1).

40. $\begin{cases} 2x - 2y + z = -10 & (1) \\ 3x + y - 2z = 4 & (2) \\ 5x + 2y - 3z = 7 & (3) \end{cases}$

Multiply both sides of equation (1) by 2 and add the result to equation (2).

$4x - 4y + 2z = -20$
$\underline{3x + y - 2z = 4}$
$7x - 3y \quad\quad = -16 \qquad (4)$

Multiply both sides of equation (1) by 3 and add the result to equation (3).

$6x - 6y + 3z = -30$
$\underline{5x + 2y - 3z = 7}$
$11x - 4y \quad\quad = -23 \qquad (5)$

Multiply both sides of equation (4) by 4, multiply both sides of equation (5) by -3, and add the results.

$28x - 12y = -64$
$\underline{-33x + 12y = 69}$
$-5x \quad\quad = 5$
$x = -1$

Substituting -1 for x in equation (4), we obtain

$7(-1) - 3y = -16$
$-7 - 3y = -16$
$-3y = -9$
$y = 3$

Substituting -1 for x and 3 for y in equation (1), we obtain

$2(-1) - 2(3) + z = -10$
$-2 - 6 + z = -10$
$z = -2$

The solution is the ordered triple (-1, 3, -2).

41. $\begin{cases} x + 2y \quad\;\; = -1 & (1) \\ \quad\; 3y + 4z = 7 & (2) \\ 2x \quad\;\; - z = 6 & (3) \end{cases}$

Multiply both sides of equation (1) by -2 and add the result to equation (3).

$-2x - 4y \quad\;\; = 2$
$\underline{2x \quad\;\; - z = 6}$
$-4y - z = 8 \qquad (4)$

Multiply both sides of equation (4) by 4 and add the result to equation (2).

$-16y - 4z = 32$
$\underline{3y + 4z = 7}$
$-13y \quad\quad = 39$
$y = -3$

Substituting –3 for y in equation (4), we obtain

$-4(-3) - z = 8$
$12 - z = 8$
$-z = -4$
$z = 4$

Substituting –3 for y in equation (1), we obtain

$x + 2(-3) = -1$
$x - 6 = -1$
$x = 5$

The solution is the ordered triple (5, -3, 4).

42. $\begin{cases} x + 2y - 3z = -4 & (1) \\ x + y + 3z = 5 & (2) \\ 3x + 4y + 3z = 7 & (3) \end{cases}$

Add equations (1) and (2).

$x + 2y - 3z = -4$
$\underline{x + y + 3z = 5}$
$2x + 3y \quad\quad = 1 \qquad (4)$

Add equations (1) and (3).

$x + 2y - 3z = -4$
$\underline{3x + 4y + 3z = 7}$
$4x + 6y \quad\quad = 3 \qquad (5)$

Multiply both sides of equation (4) by -2 and add the result to equation (5).

$-4x - 6y = -2$
$\underline{4x + 6y = 3}$
$0 = 1 \qquad \text{False}$

The system has no solution. The solution set is $\varnothing$ or $\{\ \}$. The system is inconsistent.

43. $\begin{cases} 3x + y - 2z = 6 & (1) \\ x + y - z = -2 & (2) \\ -x - 3y + 2z = 14 & (3) \end{cases}$

Multiply both sides of equation (3) by 3 and add the result to equation (1).

$-3x - 9y + 6z = 42$
$\underline{3x + y - 2z = 6}$
$-8y + 4z = 48 \qquad (4)$

Add equations (2) and (3).

$x + y - z = -2$
$\underline{-x - 3y + 2z = 14}$
$-2y + z = 12 \qquad (5)$

Multiply both sides of equation (5) by -4 and add the result to equation (4).

$$8y - 4z = -48$$
$$-8y + 4z = 48$$
$$\overline{\ 0 = 0} \quad \text{True}$$

Thus, the system is dependent and has an infinite number of solutions.

Solve equation (5) for y.
$$-2y + z = 12$$
$$-2y = -z + 12$$
$$y = \frac{-z + 12}{-2}$$
$$y = \frac{1}{2}z - 6$$

Substituting $\frac{1}{2}z - 6$ for y in equation (2), we obtain

$$x + \left(\frac{1}{2}z - 6\right) - z = -2$$
$$x - \frac{1}{2}z - 6 = -2$$
$$x = \frac{1}{2}z + 4$$

The solution to the system is $\left\{(x, y, z) \middle| x = \frac{1}{2}z + 4, \right.$

$\left. y = \frac{1}{2}z - 6, \ z \text{ is any real number} \right\}$.

44. $\begin{cases} 9x - y + 2z = -5 & (1) \\ -3x - 4y + 4z = 3 & (2) \\ 15x + 3y - 2z = -10 & (3) \end{cases}$

Multiply both sides of equation (2) by 3 and add the result to equation (1).
$$-9x - 12y + 12z = 9$$
$$9x - y + 2z = -5$$
$$\overline{-13y + 14z = 4} \qquad (4)$$

Multiply both sides of equation (2) by 5 and add the result to equation (3).
$$-15x - 20y + 20z = 15$$
$$15x + 3y - 2z = -10$$
$$\overline{-17y + 18z = 5} \qquad (5)$$

Multiply both sides of equation (4) by 17, multiply both sides of equation (5) by -13, and add the results.

$$-221y + 238z = 68$$
$$221y - 234z = -65$$
$$\overline{4z = 3}$$
$$z = \frac{3}{4}$$

Substituting $\frac{3}{4}$ for z in equation (4), we obtain

$$-13y + 14\left(\frac{3}{4}\right) = 4$$
$$-13y + \frac{21}{2} = 4$$
$$2\left(-13y + \frac{21}{2}\right) = 2(4)$$
$$-26y + 21 = 8$$
$$-26y = -13$$
$$y = \frac{-13}{-26} = \frac{1}{2}$$

Substituting $\frac{1}{2}$ for y and $\frac{3}{4}$ for z in equation (1), we obtain

$$9x - \frac{1}{2} + 2\left(\frac{3}{4}\right) = -5$$
$$9x - \frac{1}{2} + \frac{3}{2} = -5$$
$$9x + 1 = -5$$
$$9x = -6$$
$$x = \frac{-6}{9} = -\frac{2}{3}$$

The solution is the ordered triple $\left(-\frac{2}{3}, \frac{1}{2}, \frac{3}{4}\right)$.

45. $\begin{cases} 4x - 5y + 2z = -8 & (1) \\ 3x + 7y - 3z = 21 & (2) \\ 7x - 4y + 2z = -5 & (3) \end{cases}$

Multiply both sides of equation (1) by 3, multiply both sides of equation (2) by -4, and add the results.
$$12x - 15y + 6z = -24$$
$$-12x - 28y + 12z = -84$$
$$\overline{-43y + 18z = -108} \qquad (4)$$

Multiply both sides of equation (2) by 7, multiply both sides of equation (3) by -3, and add the results.
$$21x + 49y - 21z = 147$$
$$-21x + 12y - 6z = 15$$
$$\overline{61y - 27z = 162} \qquad (5)$$

Multiply both sides of equation (4) by 3, multiply both sides of equation (5) by 2, and add the results.

$$-129y+54z=-324$$
$$122y-54z=324$$
$$\overline{-7y=0}$$
$$y=0$$

Substituting 0 for y in equation (4), we obtain
$$-43(0)+18z=-108$$
$$18z=-108$$
$$z=-6$$

Substituting 0 for y and -6 for z in equation (1), we obtain
$$4x-5(0)+2(-6)=-8$$
$$4x-0-12=-8$$
$$4x=4$$
$$x=1$$

The solution is the ordered triple (1, 0, -6).

46.
$$\begin{cases}3x-2y+5z=-7 & (1)\\ 4x+y+3z=-2 & (2)\\ 2x-3y+7z=-4 & (3)\end{cases}$$

Multiply both sides of equation (1) by 4, multiply both sides of equation (2) by -3, and add the results.
$$12x-8y+20z=-28$$
$$-12x-3y-9z=6$$
$$\overline{-11y+11z=-22}\quad (4)$$

Multiply both sides of equation (3) by -2 and add the result to equation (2).
$$-4x+6y-14z=8$$
$$4x+y+3z=-2$$
$$\overline{7y-11z=6}\quad (5)$$

Add equations (4) and (5).
$$-11y+11z=-22$$
$$7y-11z=6$$
$$\overline{-4y=-16}$$
$$y=4$$

Substituting 4 for y in equation (4), we obtain
$$-11(4)+11z=-22$$
$$-44+11z=-22$$
$$11z=22$$
$$z=2$$

Substituting 4 for y and 2 for z in equation (1), we obtain

$$3x-2(4)+5(2)=-7$$
$$3x-8+10=-7$$
$$3x+2=-7$$
$$3x=-9$$
$$x=-3$$

The solution is the ordered triple (-3, 4, 2).

47. Because the sum of the measures of the three angles in a triangle must equal $180°$, we obtain the following system.
$$\begin{cases}x+y+z=180 & (1)\\ z=2y & (2)\\ y=3x-10 & (3)\end{cases}$$

Writing the equations in the system in standard form, we obtain
$$\begin{cases}x+y+z=180 & (1)\\ 2y-z=0 & (2)\\ 3x-y=10 & (3)\end{cases}$$

Adding equations (1) and (2), we obtain
$$x+y+z=180$$
$$2y-z=0$$
$$\overline{x+3y=180}\quad (4)$$

Multiply equation (3) by 3 and add the result to equation (4).
$$9x-3y=30$$
$$x+3y=180$$
$$\overline{10x=210}$$
$$x=21$$

Substituting 21 for x in equation (3), we obtain
$$y=3(21)-10=63-10=53$$

Substituting 53 for y in equation (2), we obtain
$$z=2(53)=106$$

Thus, angle $x=21°$, angle $y=53°$, and angle $z=106°$.

48. Let b represent the number of calories in a cheeseburger, let f represent the number of calories in a medium order of fries, and let c represent the number of calories in a medium Coke.

$$\begin{cases} b+f+c=1040 & (1) \\ 2b+f+c=1400 & (2) \\ 2b+f+2c=1680 & (3) \end{cases}$$

Multiply equation (1) by -1 and add the result to equation (3).

$$\begin{array}{r} -b-f-c=-1040 \\ 2b+f+2c=1680 \\ \hline b \quad\quad +c=640 \quad (4) \end{array}$$

Multiply equation (1) by -1 and add the result to equation (2).

$$\begin{array}{r} -b-f-c=-1040 \\ 2b+f+c=1400 \\ \hline b \quad\quad =360 \end{array}$$

Substituting 360 for b in equation (4), we obtain

$$360+c=640$$
$$c=280$$

Substituting 360 for b and 280 for c in equation (1), we obtain

$$360+f+280=1040$$
$$f+640=1040$$
$$f=400$$

At Burger King, a cheeseburger contains 360 calories, a medium order of fries contains 400 calories, and a medium Coke contains 280 calories.

49. $\begin{bmatrix} 3 & 1 & | & 7 \\ 2 & 5 & | & 9 \end{bmatrix}$

50. $\begin{bmatrix} 1 & -5 & | & 14 \\ -1 & 1 & | & -3 \end{bmatrix}$

51. $\begin{bmatrix} 5 & -1 & 4 & | & 6 \\ -3 & 0 & -3 & | & -1 \\ 1 & -2 & 0 & | & 0 \end{bmatrix}$

52. $\begin{bmatrix} 8 & -1 & 3 & | & 14 \\ -3 & 5 & -6 & | & -18 \\ 7 & -4 & 5 & | & 21 \end{bmatrix}$

53. $\begin{cases} x+2y=12 \\ 3y=15 \end{cases}$

54. $\begin{cases} 3x-4y=-5 \\ -x+2y=7 \end{cases}$

55. $\begin{cases} x+3y+4z=20 \\ y-2z=-16 \\ z=7 \end{cases}$

56. $\begin{cases} -3x+7y+9z=1 \\ 4x+10y+7z=5 \\ 2x-5y-6z=-8 \end{cases}$

57. a. $\begin{bmatrix} 1 & -5 & | & 22 \\ -2 & 9 & | & -40 \end{bmatrix}$ $(R_2=2r_1+r_2)$

$$=\begin{bmatrix} 1 & -5 & | & 22 \\ 2(1)+(-2) & 2(-5)+9 & | & 2(22)+(-40) \end{bmatrix}$$

$$=\begin{bmatrix} 1 & -5 & | & 22 \\ 0 & -1 & | & 4 \end{bmatrix}$$

b. $\begin{bmatrix} 1 & -5 & | & 22 \\ 0 & -1 & | & 4 \end{bmatrix}$ $(R_2=-1\cdot r_2)$

$$=\begin{bmatrix} 1 & -5 & | & 22 \\ -1(0) & -1(-1) & | & -1(4) \end{bmatrix}$$

$$=\begin{bmatrix} 1 & -5 & | & 22 \\ 0 & 1 & | & -4 \end{bmatrix}$$

58. a. $\begin{bmatrix} 1 & -4 & | & 7 \\ 3 & -7 & | & 6 \end{bmatrix}$ $(R_2=-3r_1+r_2)$

$$=\begin{bmatrix} 1 & -4 & | & 7 \\ -3(1)+3 & -3(-4)+(-7) & | & -3(7)+6 \end{bmatrix}$$

$$=\begin{bmatrix} 1 & -4 & | & 7 \\ 0 & 5 & | & -15 \end{bmatrix}$$

b. $\begin{bmatrix} 1 & -4 & | & 7 \\ 0 & 5 & | & -15 \end{bmatrix}$ $\left(R_2=\dfrac{1}{5}r_2\right)$

$$=\begin{bmatrix} 1 & -4 & | & 7 \\ \dfrac{1}{5}(0) & \dfrac{1}{5}(5) & | & \dfrac{1}{5}(-15) \end{bmatrix}$$

$$=\begin{bmatrix} 1 & -4 & | & 7 \\ 0 & 1 & | & -3 \end{bmatrix}$$

59. a.
$$\begin{bmatrix} -1 & 2 & 1 & | & 1 \\ 2 & -1 & 3 & | & -3 \\ -1 & 5 & 6 & | & 2 \end{bmatrix} \qquad \left(R_2 = 2r_1 + r_2 \right)$$

$$= \begin{bmatrix} -1 & 2 & 1 & | & 1 \\ 2(-1)+2 & 2(2)+(-1) & 2(1)+3 & | & 2(1)+(-3) \\ -1 & 5 & 6 & | & 2 \end{bmatrix}$$

$$= \begin{bmatrix} -1 & 2 & 1 & | & 1 \\ 0 & 3 & 5 & | & -1 \\ -1 & 5 & 6 & | & 2 \end{bmatrix}$$

b.
$$\begin{bmatrix} -1 & 2 & 1 & | & 1 \\ 0 & 3 & 5 & | & -1 \\ -1 & 5 & 6 & | & 2 \end{bmatrix} \qquad \left(R_3 = -1 \cdot r_1 + r_3 \right)$$

$$= \begin{bmatrix} -1 & 2 & 1 & | & 1 \\ 0 & 3 & 5 & | & -1 \\ -1(-1)+(-1) & -1(2)+5 & -1(1)+6 & | & -1(1)+2 \end{bmatrix}$$

$$= \begin{bmatrix} -1 & 2 & 1 & | & 1 \\ 0 & 3 & 5 & | & -1 \\ 0 & 3 & 5 & | & 1 \end{bmatrix}$$

60. a.
$$\begin{bmatrix} 1 & 3 & 4 & | & 4 \\ 0 & 5 & 10 & | & -15 \\ 0 & -4 & -7 & | & 7 \end{bmatrix} \qquad \left(R_2 = -\frac{1}{5} \cdot r_2 \right)$$

$$= \begin{bmatrix} 1 & 3 & 4 & | & 4 \\ \frac{1}{5}(0) & \frac{1}{5}(5) & \frac{1}{5}(10) & | & \frac{1}{5}(-15) \\ 0 & -4 & -7 & | & 7 \end{bmatrix}$$

$$= \begin{bmatrix} 1 & 3 & 4 & | & 4 \\ 0 & 1 & 2 & | & -3 \\ 0 & -4 & -7 & | & 7 \end{bmatrix}$$

b.
$$\begin{bmatrix} 1 & 3 & 4 & | & 4 \\ 0 & 1 & 2 & | & -3 \\ 0 & -4 & -7 & | & 7 \end{bmatrix} \qquad \left(R_3 = 4r_2 + r_3 \right)$$

$$= \begin{bmatrix} 1 & 3 & 4 & | & 4 \\ 0 & 1 & 2 & | & -3 \\ 4(0)+0 & 4(1)+(-4) & 4(2)+(-7) & | & 4(-3)+7 \end{bmatrix}$$

$$= \begin{bmatrix} 1 & 3 & 4 & | & 4 \\ 0 & 1 & 2 & | & -3 \\ 0 & 0 & 1 & | & -5 \end{bmatrix}$$

61. Write the augmented matrix of the system and then put it in row echelon form.

$$\begin{bmatrix} 1 & 2 & | & 1 \\ 1 & 3 & | & -2 \end{bmatrix} \qquad \left(R_2 = -1 \cdot r_1 + r_2 \right)$$

$$= \begin{bmatrix} 1 & 2 & | & 1 \\ 0 & 1 & | & -3 \end{bmatrix}$$

Write the system of equations that corresponds to the row-echelon matrix

$$\begin{cases} x + 2y = 1 & (1) \\ y = -3 & (2) \end{cases}$$

This system is consistent and independent. Substituting -3 for y in equation (1), we obtain

$$x + 2(-3) = 1$$
$$x - 6 = 1$$
$$x = 7$$

The solution is the ordered pair (7, -3).

62. Write the augmented matrix of the system and then put it in row echelon form.

$$\begin{bmatrix} 6 & -2 & | & -7 \\ 4 & 3 & | & 17 \end{bmatrix} \qquad \left(R_1 = \frac{1}{6} r_1 \right)$$

$$= \begin{bmatrix} 1 & -\frac{1}{3} & | & -\frac{7}{6} \\ 4 & 3 & | & 17 \end{bmatrix} \qquad \left(R_2 = -4r_1 + r_2 \right)$$

$$= \begin{bmatrix} 1 & -\frac{1}{3} & | & -\frac{7}{6} \\ 0 & \frac{13}{3} & | & \frac{65}{3} \end{bmatrix} \qquad \left(R_2 = \frac{3}{13} r_2 \right)$$

$$= \begin{bmatrix} 1 & -\frac{1}{3} & | & -\frac{7}{6} \\ 0 & 1 & | & 5 \end{bmatrix}$$

Write the system of equations that corresponds to the row-echelon matrix

$$\begin{cases} x - \frac{1}{3}y = -\frac{7}{6} & (1) \\ y = 5 & (2) \end{cases}$$

This system is consistent and independent. Substituting 5 for y in equation (1), we obtain

$$x - \frac{1}{3}(5) = -\frac{7}{6}$$
$$x - \frac{5}{3} = -\frac{7}{6}$$
$$x = \frac{3}{6} = \frac{1}{2}$$

The solution is the ordered pair $\left(\frac{1}{2}, 5 \right)$.

63. Write the augmented matrix of the system and then put it in row echelon form.

$$\begin{bmatrix} 3 & 2 & | & -10 \\ 2 & -1 & | & -9 \end{bmatrix} \qquad \left(R_1 = \frac{1}{3} r_1 \right)$$

$$= \begin{bmatrix} 1 & \frac{2}{3} & | & -\frac{10}{3} \\ 2 & -1 & | & -9 \end{bmatrix} \qquad \left(R_2 = -2r_1 + r_2 \right)$$

$$= \begin{bmatrix} 1 & \frac{2}{3} & | & -\frac{10}{3} \\ 0 & -\frac{7}{3} & | & -\frac{7}{3} \end{bmatrix} \qquad \left(R_2 = -\frac{3}{7} r_2 \right)$$

$$= \begin{bmatrix} 1 & \frac{2}{3} & | & -\frac{10}{3} \\ 0 & 1 & | & 1 \end{bmatrix}$$

Write the system of equations that corresponds to the row-echelon matrix

$$\begin{cases} x + \dfrac{2}{3} y = -\dfrac{10}{3} & (1) \\ y = 1 & (2) \end{cases}$$

This system is consistent and independent.
Substituting 1 for y in equation (1), we obtain

$$x + \frac{2}{3}(1) = -\frac{10}{3}$$

$$x + \frac{2}{3} = -\frac{10}{3}$$

$$x = -\frac{12}{3} = -4$$

The solution is the ordered pair (-4, 1).

64. Write the augmented matrix of the system and then put it in row echelon form.

$$\begin{bmatrix} -3 & 9 & | & 15 \\ 5 & -15 & | & 11 \end{bmatrix} \qquad \left(R_1 = -\frac{1}{3} r_1 \right)$$

$$= \begin{bmatrix} 1 & -3 & | & -5 \\ 5 & -15 & | & 11 \end{bmatrix} \qquad \left(R_2 = -5r_1 + r_2 \right)$$

$$= \begin{bmatrix} 1 & -3 & | & -5 \\ 0 & 0 & | & 36 \end{bmatrix}$$

The system is inconsistent. The system has no solution. The solution set is $\varnothing$ or $\{\ \}$.

65. Write the augmented matrix of the system and then put it in row echelon form.

$$\begin{bmatrix} 4 & -2 & | & 6 \\ 6 & -3 & | & 9 \end{bmatrix} \qquad \left(R_1 = \frac{1}{4} r_1 \right)$$

$$= \begin{bmatrix} 1 & -\frac{1}{2} & | & \frac{3}{2} \\ 6 & -3 & | & 9 \end{bmatrix} \qquad \left(R_2 = -6r_1 + r_2 \right)$$

$$= \begin{bmatrix} 1 & -\frac{1}{2} & | & \frac{3}{2} \\ 0 & 0 & | & 0 \end{bmatrix}$$

The system is dependent. The solution to the system is $\{(x, y) \mid 4x - 2y = 6\}$.

66.
$$\begin{bmatrix} 1 & 4 & | & 4 \\ 4 & -8 & | & 7 \end{bmatrix} \qquad \left(R_2 = -4r_1 + r_2 \right)$$

$$= \begin{bmatrix} 1 & 4 & | & 4 \\ 0 & -24 & | & -9 \end{bmatrix} \qquad \left(R_2 = -\frac{1}{24} r_2 \right)$$

$$= \begin{bmatrix} 1 & 4 & | & 4 \\ 0 & 1 & | & \frac{3}{8} \end{bmatrix}$$

Write the system of equations that corresponds to the row-echelon matrix

$$\begin{cases} x + 4y = 4 & (1) \\ y = \dfrac{3}{8} & (2) \end{cases}$$

This system is consistent and independent.

Substituting $\dfrac{3}{8}$ for y in equation (1), we obtain

$$x + 4\left(\frac{3}{8} \right) = 4$$

$$x + \frac{3}{2} = 4$$

$$x = \frac{5}{2}$$

The solution is the ordered pair $\left(\dfrac{5}{2}, \dfrac{3}{8} \right)$.

67. Write the augmented matrix of the system and then put it in row echelon form.

$$\begin{bmatrix} 1 & 2 & -2 & | & -11 \\ 2 & 0 & 1 & | & -6 \\ 0 & 5 & -3 & | & -7 \end{bmatrix} \qquad \left(R_2 = -2r_1 + r_2 \right)$$

$$= \begin{bmatrix} 1 & 2 & -2 & | & -11 \\ 0 & -4 & 5 & | & 16 \\ 0 & 5 & -3 & | & -7 \end{bmatrix} \qquad \left(R_2 = -\frac{1}{4} r_2 \right)$$

$$= \begin{bmatrix} 1 & 2 & -2 & | & -11 \\ 0 & 1 & -\frac{5}{4} & | & -4 \\ 0 & 5 & -3 & | & -7 \end{bmatrix} \qquad \left(R_3 = -5r_2 + r_3 \right)$$

$$= \begin{bmatrix} 1 & 2 & -2 & | & -11 \\ 0 & 1 & -\frac{5}{4} & | & -4 \\ 0 & 0 & \frac{13}{4} & | & 13 \end{bmatrix} \qquad \left(R_3 = \frac{4}{13} r_3 \right)$$

$$= \begin{bmatrix} 1 & 2 & -2 & | & -11 \\ 0 & 1 & -\frac{5}{4} & | & -4 \\ 0 & 0 & 1 & | & 4 \end{bmatrix}$$

Write the system of equations that corresponds to the row-echelon matrix

$$\begin{cases} x+2y-2z=-11 & (1) \\ y-\dfrac{5}{4}z=-4 & (2) \\ z=4 & (3) \end{cases}$$

This system is consistent and independent.
Substituting 4 for z in equation (2), we obtain

$$y-\frac{5}{4}(4)=-4$$
$$y-5=-4$$
$$y=1$$

Substituting 4 for z and 1 for y in equation (1), we obtain

$$x+2(1)-2(4)=-11$$
$$x+2-8=-11$$
$$x-6=-11$$
$$x=-5$$

The solution is the ordered triple (-5, 1, 4).

68. Write the augmented matrix of the system and then put it in row echelon form.

$$\begin{bmatrix} 2 & -5 & 2 & | & 9 \\ -1 & 1 & -2 & | & -2 \\ -1 & -2 & -4 & | & 8 \end{bmatrix} \quad (\text{Interchange } r_1 \text{ and } r_3)$$

$$= \begin{bmatrix} -1 & -2 & -4 & | & 8 \\ -1 & 1 & -2 & | & -2 \\ 2 & -5 & 2 & | & 9 \end{bmatrix} \quad (R_1=-1\cdot r_1)$$

$$= \begin{bmatrix} 1 & 2 & 4 & | & -8 \\ -1 & 1 & -2 & | & -2 \\ 2 & -5 & 2 & | & 9 \end{bmatrix} \quad \begin{pmatrix} R_2=r_1+r_2 \\ R_3=2r_2+r_3 \end{pmatrix}$$

$$= \begin{bmatrix} 1 & 2 & 4 & | & -8 \\ 0 & 3 & 2 & | & -10 \\ 0 & -3 & -2 & | & 5 \end{bmatrix} \quad (R_3=r_2+r_3)$$

$$= \begin{bmatrix} 1 & 2 & 4 & | & -8 \\ 0 & 3 & 2 & | & -10 \\ 0 & 0 & 0 & | & -5 \end{bmatrix}$$

The system is inconsistent. The system has no solution. The solution set is $\varnothing$ or $\{\ \}$.

69. Write the augmented matrix of the system and then put it in row echelon form.

$$\begin{bmatrix} 2 & -7 & 11 & | & -5 \\ 4 & -2 & 6 & | & 2 \\ -2 & 19 & -27 & | & 17 \end{bmatrix} \quad \left(R_1=\frac{1}{2}\cdot r_1\right)$$

$$= \begin{bmatrix} 1 & -\frac{7}{2} & \frac{11}{2} & | & -\frac{5}{2} \\ 4 & -2 & 6 & | & 2 \\ -2 & 19 & -27 & | & 17 \end{bmatrix} \quad \begin{pmatrix} R_2=-4r_1+r_2 \\ R_3=2r_1+r_3 \end{pmatrix}$$

$$= \begin{bmatrix} 1 & -\frac{7}{2} & \frac{11}{2} & | & -\frac{5}{2} \\ 0 & 12 & -16 & | & 12 \\ 0 & 12 & -16 & | & 12 \end{bmatrix} \quad \left(R_2=\frac{1}{12}r_2\right)$$

$$= \begin{bmatrix} 1 & -\frac{7}{2} & \frac{11}{2} & | & -\frac{5}{2} \\ 0 & 1 & -\frac{4}{3} & | & 1 \\ 0 & 12 & -16 & | & 12 \end{bmatrix} \quad (R_3=-12r_2+r_3)$$

$$= \begin{bmatrix} 1 & -\frac{7}{2} & \frac{11}{2} & | & -\frac{5}{2} \\ 0 & 1 & -\frac{4}{3} & | & 1 \\ 0 & 0 & 0 & | & 0 \end{bmatrix}$$

The system is dependent and has an infinite number of solutions.

Write the system of equations that corresponds to the row-echelon matrix

$$\begin{cases} x-\dfrac{7}{2}y+\dfrac{11}{2}z=-\dfrac{5}{2} & (1) \\ y-\dfrac{4}{3}z=1 & (2) \\ 0=0 & (3) \end{cases}$$

Solve equation (2) for y.

$$y-\frac{4}{3}z=1$$
$$y=\frac{4}{3}z+1$$

Substituting $\dfrac{4}{3}z+1$ for y in equation (1), we obtain

$$x-\frac{7}{2}\left(\frac{4}{3}z+1\right)+\frac{11}{2}z=-\frac{5}{2}$$
$$x-\frac{14}{3}z-\frac{7}{2}+\frac{11}{2}z=-\frac{5}{2}$$
$$6\left(x-\frac{14}{3}z-\frac{7}{2}+\frac{11}{2}z\right)=6\left(-\frac{5}{2}\right)$$
$$6x-28z-21+33z=-15$$
$$6x+5z-21=-15$$
$$6x=-5z+6$$
$$x=\frac{-5z+6}{6}$$
$$x=-\frac{5}{6}z+1$$

The solution to the system is

$$\left\{(x,y,z)\left|x=-\frac{5}{6}z+1,\right.\right.$$
$$\left.y=\frac{4}{3}z+1, z \text{ is any real number}\right\}.$$

70. Write the augmented matrix of the system and then put it in row echelon form.

$$\begin{bmatrix} 5 & 3 & 7 & | & 9 \\ 3 & 5 & 4 & | & 8 \\ 1 & 3 & 3 & | & 9 \end{bmatrix} \qquad (\text{Interchange } r_1 \text{ and } r_3)$$

$$= \begin{bmatrix} 1 & 3 & 3 & | & 9 \\ 3 & 5 & 4 & | & 8 \\ 5 & 3 & 7 & | & 9 \end{bmatrix} \qquad \begin{pmatrix} R_2 = -3r_1 + r_2 \\ R_3 = -5r_1 + r_3 \end{pmatrix}$$

$$= \begin{bmatrix} 1 & 3 & 3 & | & 9 \\ 0 & -4 & -5 & | & -19 \\ 0 & -12 & -8 & | & -36 \end{bmatrix} \qquad \left(R_2 = -\frac{1}{4} r_2 \right)$$

$$= \begin{bmatrix} 1 & 3 & 3 & | & 9 \\ 0 & 1 & \frac{5}{4} & | & \frac{19}{4} \\ 0 & -12 & -8 & | & -36 \end{bmatrix} \qquad (R_3 = 12 r_2 + r_3)$$

$$= \begin{bmatrix} 1 & 3 & 3 & | & 9 \\ 0 & 1 & \frac{5}{4} & | & \frac{19}{4} \\ 0 & 0 & 7 & | & 21 \end{bmatrix} \qquad \left(R_3 = \frac{1}{7} r_3 \right)$$

$$= \begin{bmatrix} 1 & 3 & 3 & | & 9 \\ 0 & 1 & \frac{5}{4} & | & \frac{19}{4} \\ 0 & 0 & 1 & | & 3 \end{bmatrix}$$

Write the system of equations that corresponds to the row-echelon matrix

$$\begin{cases} x + 3y + 3z = 9 & (1) \\ \quad y + \frac{5}{4}z = \frac{19}{4} & (2) \\ \quad\quad z = 3 & (3) \end{cases}$$

This system is consistent and independent.
Substituting 3 for z in equation (2), we obtain

$$y + \frac{5}{4}(3) = \frac{19}{4}$$
$$y + \frac{15}{4} = \frac{19}{4}$$
$$y = 1$$

Substituting 3 for z and 1 for y in equation (1), we obtain

$$x + 3(1) + 3(3) = 9$$
$$x + 3 + 9 = 9$$
$$x + 12 = 9$$
$$x = -3$$

The solution is the ordered triple (-3, 1, 3).

71. $\begin{vmatrix} 3 & 4 \\ -1 & 2 \end{vmatrix} = 3(2) - (-1)(4) = 6 + 4 = 10$

72. $\begin{vmatrix} 2 & -3 \\ -6 & 9 \end{vmatrix} = 2(9) - (-6)(-3) = 18 - 18 = 0$

73. $\begin{vmatrix} -5 & 7 \\ -4 & 6 \end{vmatrix} = -5(6) - (-4)(7) = -30 + 28 = -2$

74. $\begin{vmatrix} -7 & 2 \\ 6 & -3 \end{vmatrix} = -7(-3) - 6(2) = 21 - 12 = 9$

75. $\begin{vmatrix} 5 & 0 & 1 \\ 2 & -3 & -1 \\ 3 & 6 & -4 \end{vmatrix} = 5\begin{vmatrix} -3 & -1 \\ 6 & -4 \end{vmatrix} - 0\begin{vmatrix} 2 & -1 \\ 3 & -4 \end{vmatrix} + 1\begin{vmatrix} 2 & -3 \\ 3 & 6 \end{vmatrix}$

$= 5[-3(-4) - 6(-1)] - 0[2(-4) - 3(-1)]$
$\qquad\qquad\qquad\qquad + 1[2(6) - 3(-3)]$
$= 5(18) - 0(-5) + 1(21)$
$= 90 + 0 + 21$
$= 111$

76. $\begin{vmatrix} 1 & -4 & 5 \\ 0 & 1 & -3 \\ 2 & -6 & 4 \end{vmatrix} = 1\begin{vmatrix} 1 & -3 \\ -6 & 4 \end{vmatrix} - (-4)\begin{vmatrix} 0 & -3 \\ 2 & 4 \end{vmatrix} + 5\begin{vmatrix} 0 & 1 \\ 2 & -6 \end{vmatrix}$

$= 1[1(4) - (-6)(-3)] + 4[0(4) - 2(-3)]$
$\qquad\qquad\qquad\qquad + 5[0(-6) - 2(1)]$
$= 1(-14) + 4(6) + 5(-2)$
$= -14 + 24 - 10$
$= 0$

77. $\begin{vmatrix} 3 & 0 & -1 \\ 2 & 6 & 7 \\ 2 & 5 & 4 \end{vmatrix} = 3\begin{vmatrix} 6 & 7 \\ 5 & 4 \end{vmatrix} - 0\begin{vmatrix} 2 & 7 \\ 2 & 4 \end{vmatrix} + (-1)\begin{vmatrix} 2 & 6 \\ 2 & 5 \end{vmatrix}$

$= 3[6(4) - 5(7)] - 0[2(4) - 2(7)]$
$\qquad\qquad\qquad\qquad - 1[2(5) - 2(6)]$
$= 3(-11) - 0(-6) - 1(-2)$
$= -33 + 0 + 2$
$= -31$

78. $\begin{vmatrix} 2 & 3 & 1 \\ 1 & -3 & -7 \\ -5 & 4 & 8 \end{vmatrix}$

$= 2\begin{vmatrix} -3 & -7 \\ 4 & 8 \end{vmatrix} - 3\begin{vmatrix} 1 & -7 \\ -5 & 8 \end{vmatrix} + 1\begin{vmatrix} 1 & -3 \\ -5 & 4 \end{vmatrix}$

$= 2[-3(8) - 4(-7)] - 3[1(8) - (-5)(-7)]$
$\qquad\qquad\qquad\qquad + 1[1(4) - (-5)(-3)]$
$= 2(4) - 3(-27) + 1(-11)$
$= 8 + 81 - 11$
$= 78$

79. $D = \begin{vmatrix} 1 & 2 \\ 2 & 3 \end{vmatrix} = 1(3) - 2(2) = 3 - 4 = -1$

$D_x = \begin{vmatrix} -1 & 2 \\ 1 & 3 \end{vmatrix} = -1(3) - 1(2) = -3 - 2 = -5$

$D_y = \begin{vmatrix} 1 & -1 \\ 2 & 1 \end{vmatrix} = 1(1) - 2(-1) = 1 + 2 = 3$

$x = \dfrac{D_x}{D} = \dfrac{-5}{-1} = 5$; $y = \dfrac{D_y}{D} = \dfrac{3}{-1} = -3$

Thus, the solution is the ordered pair (5, -3).

80. $D = \begin{vmatrix} 4 & 9 \\ -5 & 6 \end{vmatrix} = 4(6) - (-5)(9) = 24 + 45 = 69$

$D_x = \begin{vmatrix} -13 & 9 \\ 22 & 6 \end{vmatrix} = -13(6) - 22(9) = -78 - 198 = -276$

$D_y = \begin{vmatrix} 4 & -13 \\ -5 & 22 \end{vmatrix} = 4(22) - (-5)(-13) = 88 - 65 = 23$

$x = \dfrac{D_x}{D} = \dfrac{-276}{69} = -4$; $y = \dfrac{D_y}{D} = \dfrac{23}{69} = \dfrac{1}{3}$

Thus, the solution is the ordered pair $\left(-4, \dfrac{1}{3} \right)$.

81. $D = \begin{vmatrix} 4 & -1 \\ 3 & 5 \end{vmatrix} = 4(5) - 3(-1) = 20 + 3 = 23$

$D_x = \begin{vmatrix} -6 & -1 \\ 7 & 5 \end{vmatrix} = -6(5) - 7(-1) = -30 + 7 = -23$

$D_y = \begin{vmatrix} 4 & -6 \\ 3 & 7 \end{vmatrix} = 4(7) - 3(-6) = 28 + 18 = 46$

$x = \dfrac{D_x}{D} = \dfrac{-23}{23} = -1$; $y = \dfrac{D_y}{D} = \dfrac{46}{23} = 2$

Thus, the solution is the ordered pair (-1, 2).

82. $D = \begin{vmatrix} 1 & -1 \\ 2 & 1 \end{vmatrix} = 1(1) - 2(-1) = 1 + 2 = 3$

$D_x = \begin{vmatrix} 2 & -1 \\ 5 & 1 \end{vmatrix} = 2(1) - 5(-1) = 2 + 5 = 7$

$D_y = \begin{vmatrix} 1 & 2 \\ 2 & 5 \end{vmatrix} = 1(5) - 2(2) = 5 - 4 = 1$

$x = \dfrac{D_x}{D} = \dfrac{7}{3}$; $y = \dfrac{D_y}{D} = \dfrac{1}{3}$

Thus, the solution is the ordered pair $\left(\dfrac{7}{3}, \dfrac{1}{3} \right)$.

83. $D = \begin{vmatrix} 6 & 2 \\ 15 & 5 \end{vmatrix} = 6(5) - 15(2) = 30 - 30 = 0$

Because $D = 0$, Cramer's Rule does not apply. Thus, we must use a different method to solve the system. We will use elimination.

$\begin{cases} 6x + 2y = 5 & (1) \\ 15x + 5y = 8 & (2) \end{cases}$

Multiply equation (1) by 5, multiply equation (2) by -2, and add the results.

$\begin{aligned} 30x + 10y &= 25 \\ -30x - 10y &= -16 \\ \hline 0 &= 9 \end{aligned}$

The system has no solution. The solution set is $\varnothing$ or $\{\ \}$. The system is inconsistent.

84. $D = \begin{vmatrix} 12 & 1 \\ -6 & 7 \end{vmatrix} = 12(7) - (-6)(1) = 84 + 6 = 90$

$D_x = \begin{vmatrix} 6 & 1 \\ 15 & 7 \end{vmatrix} = 6(7) - 15(1) = 42 - 15 = 27$

$D_y = \begin{vmatrix} 12 & 6 \\ -6 & 15 \end{vmatrix} = 12(15) - (-6)(6) = 180 + 36 = 216$

$x = \dfrac{D_x}{D} = \dfrac{27}{90} = \dfrac{3}{10}$; $y = \dfrac{D_y}{D} = \dfrac{216}{90} = \dfrac{12}{5}$

Thus, the solution is the ordered pair $\left(\dfrac{3}{10}, \dfrac{12}{5} \right)$.

85. $D = \begin{vmatrix} 1 & -1 & 2 \\ 3 & 2 & -4 \\ 0 & 3 & 5 \end{vmatrix}$

$= 1 \begin{vmatrix} 2 & -4 \\ 3 & 5 \end{vmatrix} - (-1) \begin{vmatrix} 3 & -4 \\ 0 & 5 \end{vmatrix} + 2 \begin{vmatrix} 3 & 2 \\ 0 & 3 \end{vmatrix}$

$= 1[2(5) - 3(-4)] - (-1)[3(5) - 0(-4)]$
$\qquad\qquad\qquad + 2[3(3) - 0(2)]$

$= 1(22) - (-1)(15) + 2(9)$

$= 22 + 15 + 18$

$= 55$

$D_x = \begin{vmatrix} 9 & -1 & 2 \\ 7 & 2 & -4 \\ -1 & 3 & 5 \end{vmatrix}$

$= 9 \begin{vmatrix} 2 & -4 \\ 3 & 5 \end{vmatrix} - (-1) \begin{vmatrix} 7 & -4 \\ -1 & 5 \end{vmatrix} + 2 \begin{vmatrix} 7 & 2 \\ -1 & 3 \end{vmatrix}$

$= 9[2(5) - 3(-4)] - (-1)[7(5) - (-1)(-4)]$
$\qquad\qquad\qquad + 2[7(3) - (-1)(2)]$

$= 9(22) - (-1)(31) + 2(23)$

$= 198 + 31 + 46$

$= 275$

SSM – 209

$$D_y = \begin{vmatrix} 1 & 9 & 2 \\ 3 & 7 & -4 \\ 0 & -1 & 5 \end{vmatrix}$$

$$= 1\begin{vmatrix} 7 & -4 \\ -1 & 5 \end{vmatrix} - 9\begin{vmatrix} 3 & -4 \\ 0 & 5 \end{vmatrix} + 2\begin{vmatrix} 3 & 7 \\ 0 & -1 \end{vmatrix}$$

$$= 1[7(5) - (-1)(-4)] - 9[3(5) - 0(-4)]$$
$$+ 2[3(-1) - 0(7)]$$

$$= 1(31) - 9(15) + 2(-3)$$

$$= 31 - 135 - 6$$

$$= -110$$

$$D_z = \begin{vmatrix} 1 & -1 & 9 \\ 3 & 2 & 7 \\ 0 & 3 & -1 \end{vmatrix}$$

$$= 1\begin{vmatrix} 2 & 7 \\ 3 & -1 \end{vmatrix} - (-1)\begin{vmatrix} 3 & 7 \\ 0 & -1 \end{vmatrix} + 9\begin{vmatrix} 3 & 2 \\ 0 & 3 \end{vmatrix}$$

$$= 1[2(-1) - 3(7)] - (-1)[3(-1) - 0(7)]$$
$$+ 9[3(3) - 0(2)]$$

$$= 1(-23) - (-1)(-3) + 9(9)$$

$$= -23 - 3 + 81$$

$$= 55$$

$$x = \frac{D_x}{D} = \frac{275}{55} = 5 \; ; \; y = \frac{D_y}{D} = \frac{-110}{55} = -2 \; ;$$

$$z = \frac{D_z}{D} = \frac{55}{55} = 1$$

Thus, the solution is the ordered triple (5, -2, 1).

86. $D = \begin{vmatrix} 1 & -3 & -3 \\ 7 & 1 & -2 \\ 6 & -5 & -4 \end{vmatrix}$

$$= 1\begin{vmatrix} 1 & -2 \\ -5 & -4 \end{vmatrix} - (-3)\begin{vmatrix} 7 & -2 \\ 6 & -4 \end{vmatrix} + (-3)\begin{vmatrix} 7 & 1 \\ 6 & -5 \end{vmatrix}$$

$$= 1[1(-4) - (-5)(-2)] - (-3)[7(-4) - 6(-2)]$$
$$+ (-3)[7(-5) - 6(1)]$$

$$= 1(-14) - (-3)(-16) + (-3)(-41)$$

$$= -14 - 48 + 123$$

$$= 61$$

$$D_x = \begin{vmatrix} -5 & -3 & -3 \\ 24 & 1 & -2 \\ -9 & -5 & -4 \end{vmatrix}$$

$$= -5\begin{vmatrix} 1 & -2 \\ -5 & -4 \end{vmatrix} - (-3)\begin{vmatrix} 24 & -2 \\ -9 & -4 \end{vmatrix} + (-3)\begin{vmatrix} 24 & 1 \\ -9 & -5 \end{vmatrix}$$

$$= -5[1(-4) - (-5)(-2)] - (-3)[24(-4) - (-9)(-2)]$$
$$+ (-3)[24(-5) - (-9)(1)]$$

$$= -5(-14) - (-3)(-114) + (-3)(-111)$$

$$= 70 - 342 + 333$$

$$= 61$$

$$D_y = \begin{vmatrix} 1 & -5 & -3 \\ 7 & 24 & -2 \\ 6 & -9 & -4 \end{vmatrix}$$

$$= 1\begin{vmatrix} 24 & -2 \\ -9 & -4 \end{vmatrix} - (-5)\begin{vmatrix} 7 & -2 \\ 6 & -4 \end{vmatrix} + (-3)\begin{vmatrix} 7 & 24 \\ 6 & -9 \end{vmatrix}$$

$$= 1[24(-4) - (-9)(-2)] - (-5)[7(-4) - 6(-2)]$$
$$+ (-3)[7(-9) - 6(24)]$$

$$= 1(-114) - (-5)(-16) + (-3)(-207)$$

$$= -114 - 80 + 621$$

$$= 427$$

$$D_z = \begin{vmatrix} 1 & -3 & -5 \\ 7 & 1 & 24 \\ 6 & -5 & -9 \end{vmatrix}$$

$$= 1\begin{vmatrix} 1 & 24 \\ -5 & -9 \end{vmatrix} - (-3)\begin{vmatrix} 7 & 24 \\ 6 & -9 \end{vmatrix} + (-5)\begin{vmatrix} 7 & 1 \\ 6 & -5 \end{vmatrix}$$

$$= 1[1(-9) - (-5)(24)] - (-3)[7(-9) - 6(24)]$$
$$+ (-5)[7(-5) - 6(1)]$$

$$= 1(111) - (-3)(-207) + (-5)(-41)$$

$$= 111 - 621 + 205$$

$$= -305$$

$$x = \frac{D_x}{D} = \frac{61}{61} = 1 \; ; \; y = \frac{D_y}{D} = \frac{427}{61} = 7 \; ;$$

$$z = \frac{D_z}{D} = \frac{-305}{61} = -5$$

Thus, the solution is the ordered triple (1, 7, -5).

87. $D = \begin{vmatrix} 1 & 1 & 1 \\ 3 & 2 & 4 \\ 2 & 2 & 3 \end{vmatrix}$

$$= 1\begin{vmatrix} 2 & 4 \\ 2 & 3 \end{vmatrix} - 1\begin{vmatrix} 3 & 4 \\ 2 & 3 \end{vmatrix} + 1\begin{vmatrix} 3 & 2 \\ 2 & 2 \end{vmatrix}$$

$$= 1[2(3) - 2(4)] - 1[3(3) - 2(4)]$$
$$+ 1[3(2) - 2(2)]$$

$$= -2 - 1 + 2$$

$$= -1$$

$$D_x = \begin{vmatrix} 1 & 1 & 1 \\ -1 & 2 & 4 \\ 0 & 2 & 3 \end{vmatrix}$$

$$= 1\begin{vmatrix} 2 & 4 \\ 2 & 3 \end{vmatrix} - 1\begin{vmatrix} -1 & 4 \\ 0 & 3 \end{vmatrix} + 1\begin{vmatrix} -1 & 2 \\ 0 & 2 \end{vmatrix}$$

$$= 1[2(3) - 2(4)] - 1[-1(3) - 0(4)]$$
$$+ 1[-1(2) - 0(2)]$$

$$= -2 + 3 - 2$$

$$= -1$$

$$D_y = \begin{vmatrix} 1 & 1 & 1 \\ 3 & -1 & 4 \\ 2 & 0 & 3 \end{vmatrix}$$

$$= 1\begin{vmatrix} -1 & 4 \\ 0 & 3 \end{vmatrix} - 1\begin{vmatrix} 3 & 4 \\ 2 & 3 \end{vmatrix} + 1\begin{vmatrix} 3 & -1 \\ 2 & 0 \end{vmatrix}$$

$$= 1[-1(3)-0(4)] - 1[3(3)-2(4)]$$
$$+ 1[3(0)-2(-1)]$$

$$= -3 - 1 + 2$$

$$= -2$$

$$D_z = \begin{vmatrix} 1 & 1 & 1 \\ 3 & 2 & -1 \\ 2 & 2 & 0 \end{vmatrix}$$

$$= 1\begin{vmatrix} 2 & -1 \\ 2 & 0 \end{vmatrix} - 1\begin{vmatrix} 3 & -1 \\ 2 & 0 \end{vmatrix} + 1\begin{vmatrix} 3 & 2 \\ 2 & 2 \end{vmatrix}$$

$$= 1[2(0)-2(-1)] - 1[3(0)-2(-1)]$$
$$+ 1[3(2)-2(2)]$$

$$= 2 - 2 + 2$$

$$= 2$$

$$x = \frac{D_x}{D} = \frac{-1}{-1} = 1 \; ; \; y = \frac{D_y}{D} = \frac{-2}{-1} = 2 \; ;$$

$$z = \frac{D_z}{D} = \frac{2}{-1} = -2$$

Thus, the solution is the ordered triple (1, 2, -2).

88. $D = \begin{vmatrix} 4 & -3 & 1 \\ 4 & -2 & 3 \\ 8 & -5 & -2 \end{vmatrix}$

$$= 4\begin{vmatrix} -2 & 3 \\ -5 & -2 \end{vmatrix} - (-3)\begin{vmatrix} 4 & 3 \\ 8 & -2 \end{vmatrix} + 1\begin{vmatrix} 4 & -2 \\ 8 & -5 \end{vmatrix}$$

$$= 4[-2(-2)-(-5)(3)] - (-3)[4(-2)-8(3)]$$
$$+ 1[4(-5)-8(-2)]$$

$$= 4(19)-(-3)(-32)+1(-4)$$

$$= 76 - 96 - 4$$

$$= -24$$

$$D_x = \begin{vmatrix} -6 & -3 & 1 \\ -3 & -2 & 3 \\ -12 & -5 & -2 \end{vmatrix}$$

$$= -6\begin{vmatrix} -2 & 3 \\ -5 & -2 \end{vmatrix} - (-3)\begin{vmatrix} -3 & 3 \\ -12 & -2 \end{vmatrix} + 1\begin{vmatrix} -3 & -2 \\ -12 & -5 \end{vmatrix}$$

$$= -6[-2(-2)-(-5)(3)] - (-3)[-3(-2)-(-12)(3)]$$
$$+ 1[-3(-5)-(-12)(-2)]$$

$$= -6(19)-(-3)(42)+1(-9)$$

$$= -114 + 126 - 9$$

$$= 3$$

$$D_y = \begin{vmatrix} 4 & -6 & 1 \\ 4 & -3 & 3 \\ 8 & -12 & -2 \end{vmatrix}$$

$$= 4\begin{vmatrix} -3 & 3 \\ -12 & -2 \end{vmatrix} - (-6)\begin{vmatrix} 4 & 3 \\ 8 & -2 \end{vmatrix} + 1\begin{vmatrix} 4 & -3 \\ 8 & -12 \end{vmatrix}$$

$$= 4[-3(-2)-(-12)(3)] - (-6)[4(-2)-8(3)]$$
$$+ 1[4(-12)-8(-3)]$$

$$= 4(42)-(-6)(-32)+1(-24)$$

$$= 168 - 192 - 24$$

$$= -48$$

$$D_z = \begin{vmatrix} 4 & -3 & -6 \\ 4 & -2 & -3 \\ 8 & -5 & -12 \end{vmatrix}$$

$$= 4\begin{vmatrix} -2 & -3 \\ -5 & -12 \end{vmatrix} - (-3)\begin{vmatrix} 4 & -3 \\ 8 & -12 \end{vmatrix} + (-6)\begin{vmatrix} 4 & -2 \\ 8 & -5 \end{vmatrix}$$

$$= 4[-2(-12)-(-5)(-3)] - (-3)[4(-12)-8(-3)]$$
$$+ (-6)[4(-5)-8(-2)]$$

$$= 4(9)-(-3)(-24)+(-6)(-4)$$

$$= 36 - 72 + 24$$

$$= -12$$

$$x = \frac{D_x}{D} = \frac{3}{-24} = -\frac{1}{8} \; ; \; y = \frac{D_y}{D} = \frac{-48}{-24} = 2 \; ;$$

$$z = \frac{D_z}{D} = \frac{-12}{-24} = \frac{1}{2}$$

The solution is the ordered triple $\left(-\frac{1}{8}, \, 2, \, \frac{1}{2}\right)$.

89. $D = \begin{vmatrix} 1 & -1 & -4 \\ 4 & -3 & -3 \\ 3 & -2 & 1 \end{vmatrix}$

$$= 1\begin{vmatrix} -3 & -3 \\ -2 & 1 \end{vmatrix} - (-1)\begin{vmatrix} 4 & -3 \\ 3 & 1 \end{vmatrix} + (-4)\begin{vmatrix} 4 & -3 \\ 3 & -2 \end{vmatrix}$$

$$= 1[-3(1)-(-2)(-3)] - (-1)[4(1)-3(-3)]$$
$$+ (-4)[4(-2)-3(-3)]$$

$$= 1(-9)-(-1)(13)+(-4)(1)$$

$$= -9 + 13 - 4$$

$$= 0$$

Because $D = 0$, Cramer's Rule does not apply. Thus, we must use a different method to solve the system.

$$\begin{cases} x - y - 4z = 7 & (1) \\ 4x - 3y - 3z = 4 & (2) \\ 3x - 2y + z = -3 & (3) \end{cases}$$

Multiply both sides of equation (1) by -4 and add the result to equation (2).

$$-4x + 4y + 16z = -28$$
$$4x - 3y - 3z = 4$$
$$\overline{\qquad y + 13z = -24 \qquad (4)}$$

Multiply both sides of equation (1) by -3 and add the result to equation (3).

$$-3x + 3y + 12z = -21$$
$$3x - 2y + z = -3$$
$$\overline{\qquad y + 13z = -24 \qquad (5)}$$

Multiply both sides of equation (4) by -1 and add the result to equation (5).

$$-y - 13z = 24$$
$$y + 13z = -24$$
$$\overline{\qquad 0 = 0 \qquad \text{True}}$$

Thus, the system is dependent and has an infinite number of solutions.

Solve equation (5) for y.

$$y + 13z = -24$$
$$y = -13z - 24$$

Substituting $-13z - 24$ for y in equation (1), we obtain

$$x - (-13z - 24) - 4z = 7$$
$$x + 13z + 24 - 4z = 7$$
$$x + 9z + 24 = 7$$
$$x = -9z - 17$$

The solution to the system is

$$\{(x, y, z) \mid x = -9z - 17, y = -13z - 24, z \text{ is any real number}\}$$

90. $D = \begin{vmatrix} 1 & 1 & 0 \\ 0 & 2 & -1 \\ 5 & 0 & 1 \end{vmatrix}$

$$= 1 \begin{vmatrix} 2 & -1 \\ 0 & 1 \end{vmatrix} - 1 \begin{vmatrix} 0 & -1 \\ 5 & 1 \end{vmatrix} + 0 \begin{vmatrix} 0 & 2 \\ 5 & 0 \end{vmatrix}$$
$$= 1[2(1) - 0(-1)] - 1[0(1) - 5(-1)]$$
$$\qquad\qquad + 0[0(0) - 5(2)]$$
$$= 1(2) - 1(5) + 0(-10)$$
$$= 2 - 5 + 0$$
$$= -3$$

$D_x = \begin{vmatrix} -3 & 1 & 0 \\ -1 & 2 & -1 \\ 1 & 0 & 1 \end{vmatrix}$

$$= -3 \begin{vmatrix} 2 & -1 \\ 0 & 1 \end{vmatrix} - 1 \begin{vmatrix} -1 & -1 \\ 1 & 1 \end{vmatrix} + 0 \begin{vmatrix} -1 & 2 \\ 1 & 0 \end{vmatrix}$$

$$= -3[2(1) - 0(-1)] - 1[-1(1) - 1(-1)]$$
$$\qquad\qquad + 0[-1(0) - 1(2)]$$
$$= -3(2) - 1(0) + 0(-2)$$
$$= -6 - 0 + 0$$
$$= -6$$

$D_y = \begin{vmatrix} 1 & -3 & 0 \\ 0 & -1 & -1 \\ 5 & 1 & 1 \end{vmatrix}$

$$= 1 \begin{vmatrix} -1 & -1 \\ 1 & 1 \end{vmatrix} - (-3) \begin{vmatrix} 0 & -1 \\ 5 & 1 \end{vmatrix} + 0 \begin{vmatrix} 0 & -1 \\ 5 & 1 \end{vmatrix}$$
$$= 1[-1(1) - 1(-1)] - (-3)[0(1) - 5(-1)]$$
$$\qquad\qquad + 0[0(1) - 5(-1)]$$
$$= 1(0) - (-3)(5) + 0(5)$$
$$= 0 + 15 + 0$$
$$= 15$$

$D_z = \begin{vmatrix} 1 & 1 & -3 \\ 0 & 2 & -1 \\ 5 & 0 & 1 \end{vmatrix}$

$$= 1 \begin{vmatrix} 2 & -1 \\ 0 & 1 \end{vmatrix} - 1 \begin{vmatrix} 0 & -1 \\ 5 & 1 \end{vmatrix} + (-3) \begin{vmatrix} 0 & 2 \\ 5 & 0 \end{vmatrix}$$
$$= 1[2(1) - 0(-1)] - 1[0(1) - 5(-1)]$$
$$\qquad\qquad + (-3)[0(0) - 5(2)]$$
$$= 1(2) - 1(5) + (-3)(-10)$$
$$= 2 - 5 + 30$$
$$= 27$$

$$x = \frac{D_x}{D} = \frac{-6}{-3} = 2 \, ; \quad y = \frac{D_y}{D} = \frac{15}{-3} = -5 \, ;$$

$$z = \frac{D_z}{D} = \frac{27}{-3} = -9$$

Thus, the solution is the ordered triple (2, -5, -9).

91. a. Let $x = 5$ and $y = 2$ in each inequality.
$$\begin{cases} x - y = 5 - 2 = 3 > 2 \\ 2x + 3y = 2(5) + 3(2) = 16 > 8 \end{cases}$$
Both inequalities are true when when $x = 5$ and $y = 2$, so (5, 2) is a solution.

b. Let $x = -3$ and $y = 5$ in each inequality.
$$\begin{cases} x - y = -3 - 5 = -8 \not> 2 \\ 2x + 3y = 2(-3) + 3(5) = 9 > 8 \end{cases}$$
The inequality $x - y > 2$ is not true when $x = -3$ and $y = 5$, so (-3, 5) is not a solution.

92. a. Let $x = -1$ and $y = 2$ in each inequality.
$$\begin{cases} 7x + 3y = 7(-1) + 3(2) = -1 \leq 21 \\ -2x + y = -2(-1) + 2 = 4 \ngeq 5 \end{cases}$$
The inequality $-2x + y \geq 5$ is not true when $x = -1$ and $y = 2$, so (-1, 2) is not a solution.

b. Let $x = -3$ and $y = 4$ in each inequality.
$$\begin{cases} 7x + 3y = 7(-3) + 3(4) = -9 \leq 21 \\ -2x + y = -2(-3) + 4 = 10 \geq 5 \end{cases}$$
Both inequalities are true when $x = -3$ and $y = 4$, so (-3, 4) is a solution.

93. a. Let $x = 2$ and $y = 1$ in each inequality.
$$\begin{cases} x + 2y = 2 + 2(1) = 4 \leq 6 \\ 3x - y = 3(2) - 1 = 5 \geq 2 \\ x = 2 \geq 0 \\ y = 1 \geq 0 \end{cases}$$
All four inequalities are true when $x = 2$ and $y = 1$, so (2, 1) is a solution.

b. Let $x = 1$ and $y = 2$ in each inequality.
$$\begin{cases} x + 2y = 1 + 2(2) = 5 \leq 6 \\ 3x - y = 3(1) - 2 = 1 \ngeq 2 \\ x = 1 \geq 0 \\ y = 2 \geq 0 \end{cases}$$
The inequality $3x - y \geq 2$ is not true when $x = 1$ and $y = 2$, so (1, 2) is not a solution.

94. a. Let $x = -2$ and $y = 3$ in each inequality.
$$\begin{cases} 3x - 2y = 3(-2) - 2(3) = -12 \leq 12 \\ 2x + y = 2(-2) + 3 = -1 \leq 15 \\ x = -2 \ngeq 0 \\ y = 3 \geq 0 \end{cases}$$
The inequality $x \geq 0$ is not true when $x = -2$ and $y = 3$, so (-2, 3) is not a solution.

b. Let $x = 4$ and $y = 1$ in each inequality.
$$\begin{cases} 3x - 2y = 3(4) - 2(1) = 10 \leq 12 \\ 2x + y = 2(4) + 1 = 9 \leq 15 \\ x = 4 \geq 0 \\ y = 1 \geq 0 \end{cases}$$
All four inequalities are true when $x = 4$ and $y = 1$, so (4, 1) is a solution.

95. $\begin{cases} x + y \geq 7 \\ 2x - y \geq 5 \end{cases}$

First, graph the inequality $x + y \geq 7$. To do so, replace the inequality symbol with an equal sign to obtain $x + y = 7$. Because the inequality is non-strict, graph $x + y = 7$ $(y = -x + 7)$ using a solid line.

Test Point: $(0, 0)$: $0 + 0 = 0 \ngeq 7$

Therefore, the half-plane not containing $(0, 0)$ is the solution set of $x + y \geq 7$.

Second, graph the inequality $2x - y \geq 5$. To do so, replace the inequality symbol with an equal sign to obtain $2x - y = 5$. Because the inequality is non-strict, graph $2x - y = 5$ $(y = 2x - 5)$ using a solid line.

Test Point: $(0, 0)$: $2(0) - 0 = 0 \ngeq 5$

Therefore, the half-plane not containing $(0, 0)$ is the solution set of $2x - y \geq 5$.

The overlapping shaded region (that is, the shaded region in the graph below) is the solution to the system of linear inequalities.

96. $\begin{cases} 2x + 3y > 9 \\ x - 3y > -18 \end{cases}$

First, graph the inequality $2x + 3y > 9$. To do so, replace the inequality symbol with an equal sign to obtain $2x + 3y = 9$. Because the inequality is strict, graph $2x + 3y = 9$ $\left(y = -\dfrac{2}{3}x + 3 \right)$ using a dashed line.

Test Point: $(0, 0)$: $2(0) + 3(0) = 0 \ngtr 9$

Therefore, the half-plane not containing $(0, 0)$ is the solution set of $2x + 3y > 9$.

Second, graph the inequality $x - 3y > -18$. To do so, replace the inequality symbol with an equal sign to obtain $x - 3y = -18$. Because the inequality is strict, graph $x - 3y = -18$

$\left(y = \frac{1}{3}x + 6 \right)$ using a dashed line.

Test Point: $(0,0)$: $0 - 3(0) = 0 > -18$

Therefore, the half-plane containing $(0,0)$ is the solution set of $x - 3y > -18$.

The overlapping shaded region (that is, the shaded region in the graph below) is the solution to the system of linear inequalities.

97. $\begin{cases} x - 4y > -4 \\ x + 2y \le 8 \end{cases}$

First, graph the inequality $x - 4y > -4$. To do so, replace the inequality symbol with an equal sign to obtain $x - 4y = -4$. Because the inequality is strict, graph $x - 4y = -4$

$\left(y = \frac{1}{4}x + 1 \right)$ using a dashed line.

Test Point: $(0,0)$: $0 - 4(0) = 0 > -4$

Therefore, the half-plane containing $(0,0)$ is the solution set of $x - 4y > -4$.

Second, graph the inequality $x + 2y \le 8$. To do so, replace the inequality symbol with an equal sign to obtain $x + 2y = 8$. Because the inequality

is non-strict, graph $x + 2y = 8$ $\left(y = -\frac{1}{2}x + 4 \right)$

using a solid line.

Test Point: $(0,0)$: $0 + 2(0) = 0 \le 8$

Therefore, the half-plane containing $(0,0)$ is the solution set of $x + 2y \le 8$.

The overlapping shaded region (that is, the shaded region in the graph below) is the solution to the system of linear inequalities.

98. $\begin{cases} x - y < -2 \\ 2x - 2y > 6 \end{cases}$

First, graph the inequality $x - y < -2$. To do so, replace the inequality symbol with an equal sign to obtain $x - y = -2$. Because the inequality is strict, graph $x - y = -2$ $(y = x + 2)$ using a dashed line.

Test Point: $(0,0)$: $0 - 0 = 0 \not< -2$

Therefore, the half-plane not containing $(0,0)$ is the solution set of $x - y < -2$.

Second, graph the inequality $2x - 2y > 6$. To do so, replace the inequality symbol with an equal sign to obtain $2x - 2y = 6$. Because the inequality is strict, graph $2x - 2y = 6$

$(y = x - 3)$ using a dashed line.

Test Point: $(0,0)$: $2(0) - 2(0) = 0 \not> 6$

Therefore, the half-plane not containing $(0,0)$ is the solution set of $2x - 2y > 6$.

Notice in the graph below that the two shaded regions do not overlap. Thus, there are no points in the Cartesian plane that satisfy both inequalities. The system has no solution, so the solution set is $\varnothing$ or { }.

99. $\begin{cases} 2x - y \geq -2 \\ 2x - 3y \leq 6 \end{cases}$

First, graph the inequality $2x - y \geq -2$. To do so, replace the inequality symbol with an equal sign to obtain $2x - y = -2$. Because the inequality is non-strict, graph $2x - y = -2$ $(y = 2x + 2)$ using a solid line.

Test Point: $(0,0)$: $2(0) - 0 = 0 \geq -2$

Therefore, the half-plane containing $(0,0)$ is the solution set of $2x - y \geq -2$.

Second, graph the inequality $2x - 3y \leq 6$. To do so, replace the inequality symbol with an equal sign to obtain $2x - 3y = 6$. Because the inequality is non-strict, graph $2x - 3y = 6$ $\left(y = \dfrac{2}{3}x - 2 \right)$ using a solid line.

Test Point: $(0,0)$: $2(0) - 3(0) = 0 \leq 6$

Therefore, the half-plane containing $(0,0)$ is the solution set of $2x - 3y \leq 6$.

The overlapping shaded region (that is, the shaded region in the graph below) is the solution to the system of linear inequalities.

100. $\begin{cases} x \geq 2 \\ y < -3 \end{cases}$

First, graph the inequality $x \geq 2$. To do so, replace the inequality symbol with an equal sign to obtain $x = 2$. Because the inequality is non-strict, graph $x = 2$ using a solid line.

Test Point: $(0,0)$: $0 \not\geq 2$

Therefore, the half-plane not containing $(0,0)$ is the solution set of $x \geq 2$.

Second, graph the inequality $y < -3$. To do so, replace the inequality symbol with an equal sign to obtain $y = -3$. Because the inequality is strict, graph $y = -3$ using a dashed line.

Test Point: $(0,0)$: $0 \not< -3$

Therefore, the half-plane not containing $(0,0)$ is the solution set of $y < -3$.

The overlapping shaded region (that is, the shaded region in the graph below) is the solution to the system of linear inequalities.

101. $\begin{cases} 3x + 5y \leq 30 \\ 4x - 5y \geq 5 \\ x \leq 8 \\ y \geq 0 \end{cases}$

First, graph the inequality $3x + 5y \leq 30$. To do so, replace the inequality symbol with an equal sign to obtain $3x + 5y = 30$. Because the inequality is non-strict, graph $3x + 5y = 30$ $\left(y = -\dfrac{3}{5}x + 6 \right)$ using a solid line.

Test Point: $(0,0)$: $3(0) + 5(0) = 0 \leq 30$

Therefore, the half-plane containing $(0,0)$ is the solution set of $3x + 5y \leq 30$.

Next, graph the inequality $4x - 5y \geq 5$. To do so, replace the inequality symbol with an equal sign to obtain $4x - 5y = 5$. Because the inequality is non-strict, graph $4x - 5y = 5$ $\left(y = \dfrac{4}{5}x - 1 \right)$ using a solid line.

Test Point: $(0,0)$: $4(0) - 5(0) = 0 \not\geq 5$

Therefore, the half-plane not containing $(0,0)$ is the solution set of $4x - 5y \geq 5$.

The inequality $x \leq 8$ requires that the graph be to the left of the solid vertical line $x = 8$.

The inequality $y \geq 0$ requires that the graph be above the solid x-axis.

The overlapping shaded region (that is, the shaded region in the graph below) is the solution to the system of linear inequalities.

The graph is bounded. The four corner points of the bounded region are $(1.25, 0)$, $(8, 0)$, $(8, 1.2)$, and $(5, 3)$.

102. $\begin{cases} 3x+2y \geq 10 \\ x+2y \geq 6 \\ x \geq 0 \\ y \geq 0 \end{cases}$

First, graph the inequality $3x+2y \geq 10$. To do so, replace the inequality symbol with an equal sign to obtain $3x+2y = 10$. Because the inequality is non-strict, graph $3x+2y = 10$ $\left(y = -\dfrac{3}{2}x+5\right)$ using a solid line.

Test Point: $(0,0)$: $3(0)+2(0) = 0 \not\geq 10$

Therefore, the half-plane not containing $(0,0)$ is the solution set of $3x+2y \geq 10$.

Second, graph the inequality $x+2y \geq 6$. To do so, replace the inequality symbol with an equal sign to obtain $x+2y = 6$. Because the inequality is non-strict, graph $x+2y = 6$ $\left(y = -\dfrac{1}{2}x+3\right)$ using a solid line.

Test Point: $(0,0)$: $0+2(0) = 0 \not\geq 6$

Therefore, the half-plane not containing $(0,0)$ is the solution set of $x+2y \geq 6$.

The two inequalities $x \geq 0$ and $y \geq 0$ require that the graph be in quadrant I.

The overlapping shaded region (that is, the shaded region in the graph below) is the solution to the system of linear inequalities.

The graph is unbounded. The three corner points of the unbounded region are $(0, 5)$, $(2, 2)$, and $(6, 0)$.

103. a. Let x represent the amount to be invested at 6% interest and let y represent the amount to be invested at 8% interest. Now, Anna has at most $4000 to invest, so $x+y \leq 4000$. She wants to earn at least $275 per year in interest, so $0.06x+0.08y \geq 275$. The amount to be invested at 6% will be at least $500, so $x \geq 500$. The amount to be invested at 8% is at least $2500, so $y \geq 2500$. Thus, we have the following system:

$\begin{cases} x+y \leq 4000 \\ 0.06x+0.08y \geq 275 \\ x \geq 500 \\ y \geq 2500 \end{cases}$

b. First, graph the inequality $x+y \leq 4000$. To do so, replace the inequality symbol with an equal sign to obtain $x+y = 4000$. Because the inequality is non-strict, graph $x+y = 4000$ $(y = -x+4000)$ using a solid line.

Test Point: $(0,0)$: $0+0 = 0 \leq 4000$

Thus, the solution set of $x+y \leq 4000$ is the half-plane containing $(0,0)$.

Second, graph the inequality $0.06x+0.08y \geq 275$. To do so, replace the inequality symbol with an equal sign to obtain $0.06x+0.08y = 275$. Because the inequality is non-strict, graph $0.06x+0.08y = 275$ $\left(y = -\dfrac{3}{4}x+3437.5\right)$ using a solid line.

Test Point: $(0,0)$: $0.06(0)+0.08(0) = 0 \not\geq 275$

Thus, the solution set of $0.06x + 0.08y \geq 275$ is the half-plane not containing $(0,0)$.

The inequality $x \geq 500$ requires that the graph be to the right of the solid vertical line $x = 500$.

The inequality $y \geq 2500$ requires that the graph be above the solid horizontal line $y = 2500$.

The overlapping shaded region (that is, the shaded region in the graph below) is the solution to the system of linear inequalities.

The four corner points are (500, 3500), (500, 3062.5), (1250, 2500), and (1500, 2500).

104. a. Let x represent the number of dozens of red tulip bulbs and let y represent the number of dozens of yellow tulip bulbs. Now, Jordan has a maximum of \$144 to spend, so $6x + 4y \leq 144$. She wants at least 4 more dozens of red tulip bulbs than yellow, so $x \geq y + 4$. Finally, Jordan cannot buy a negative number of dozens of bulbs, so we have the non-negativity constraints $x \geq 0$ and $y \geq 0$. Thus, we have the following system:

$$\begin{cases} 6x + 4y \leq 144 \\ x \geq y + 4 \\ x \geq 0 \\ y \geq 0 \end{cases}$$

b. First, graph the inequality $6x + 4y \leq 144$. To do so, replace the inequality symbol with an equal sign to obtain $6x + 4y = 144$. Because the inequality is non-strict, graph

$6x + 4y = 144 \ \left(y = -\dfrac{3}{2}x + 36 \right)$ using a solid line.

Test Point: $(0,0)$: $6(0) + 4(0) = 0 \leq 144$

Thus, the solution set of $6x + 4y \leq 144$ is the half-plane containing $(0,0)$.

Second, graph the inequality $x \geq y + 4$. To do so, replace the inequality symbol with an equal sign to obtain $x = y + 4$. Because the inequality is non-strict, graph $x = y + 4$ $(y = x - 4)$ using a solid line.

Test Point: $(0,0)$: $0 \not\geq 0 + 4$

Thus, the solution set of $x \geq y + 4$ is the half-plane not containing $(0,0)$.

The two inequalities $x \geq 0$ and $y \geq 0$ require that the graph be in quadrant I.

The overlapping shaded region (that is, the shaded region in the graph below) is the solution to the system of linear inequalities.

The three corner points are (4, 0), (24, 0), and (16, 12).

Chapter 4 Test

1. $\begin{cases} 2x - y = 0 \\ 4x - 5y = 12 \end{cases}$

The graphs of the linear equations intersect at the point (-2, -4). Thus, the solution is (-2, -4).

2. $\begin{cases} 5x + 2y = -3 & (1) \\ y = 2x - 6 & (2) \end{cases}$

Because equation (2) is solved for y, we use substitution to solve the system.
Substituting $2x - 6$ for y in equation (1), we obtain

$5x + 2(2x - 6) = -3$
$\quad 5x + 4x - 12 = -3$
$\qquad\qquad 9x = 9$
$\qquad\qquad\ x = 1$

Substituting 1 for x in equation (2), we obtain

$y = 2(1) - 6 = 2 - 6 = -4$.

The solution is the ordered pair (1, -4).

3. $\begin{cases} 9x + 3y = 1 & (1) \\ x - 2y = 4 & (2) \end{cases}$

Because the coefficient of x in equation (2) is 1, we use substitution to solve the system.
Equation (2) solved for x is $x = 2y + 4$.

Substituting $2y + 4$ for x in equation (1), we obtain

$9(2y + 4) + 3y = 1$
$\quad 18y + 36 + 3y = 1$
$\qquad\qquad\quad 21y = -35$
$\qquad\qquad\qquad y = \dfrac{-35}{21} = -\dfrac{5}{3}$

Substituting $-\dfrac{5}{3}$ for y in equation (1), we obtain

$9x + 3\left(-\dfrac{5}{3}\right) = 1$
$\qquad\quad 9x - 5 = 1$
$\qquad\qquad 9x = 6$
$\qquad\qquad\ x = \dfrac{6}{9} = \dfrac{2}{3}$

The solution is the ordered pair $\left(\dfrac{2}{3}, -\dfrac{5}{3}\right)$.

4. $\begin{cases} 6x - 9y = 5 & (1) \\ 8x - 12y = 7 & (2) \end{cases}$

Because none of variables have a coefficient of 1, we use elimination to solve the system. Multiply both sides of equation (1) by 4, multiply both sides of equation (2) by -3, and add the results.

$24x - 36y = 20$
$\underline{-24x + 36y = -21}$
$\qquad\qquad 0 = -1 \qquad$ False

The system has no solution. The solution set is $\varnothing$ or $\{\ \}$. The system is inconsistent.

5. $\begin{cases} 2x + y = -4 & (1) \\ \dfrac{1}{3}x + \dfrac{1}{2}y = 2 & (2) \end{cases}$

Because equation (2) contains fractions, we choose to use the elimination method to solve the system. Multiply both sides of equation (2) by -6 and add the result to equation (1).

$-2x - 3y = -12$
$\underline{\ \ 2x + y = -4\ }$
$\qquad -2y = -16$
$\qquad\quad y = 8$

Substituting 8 for y in equation (1), we obtain

$2x + 8 = -4$
$\quad\ 2x = -12$
$\qquad x = -6$

The solution is the ordered pair (-6, 8).

6. $\begin{cases} x - 2y + 3z = 1 & (1) \\ x + y - 3z = 7 & (2) \\ 3x - 4y + 5z = 7 & (3) \end{cases}$

Multiply both sides of equation (1) by -1 and add the result to equation (2).

$-x + 2y - 3z = -1$
$\underline{\ \ x + y - 3z = 7\ }$
$\quad 3y - 6z = 6 \qquad (4)$

Multiply both sides of equation (1) by -3 and add the result to equation (3).

$-3x + 6y - 9z = -3$
$\underline{\ \ 3x - 4y + 5z = 7\ }$
$\quad 2y - 4z = 4 \qquad (5)$

Multiply both sides of equation (4) by 2, multiply both sides of equation (5) by -3, and add the results.

$$6y - 12z = 12$$
$$\underline{-6y + 12z = -12}$$
$$0 = 0 \qquad \text{True}$$

Thus, the system is dependent and has an infinite number of solutions.

Solve equation (5) for y.

$$2y - 4z = 4$$
$$2y = 4z + 4$$
$$y = \frac{4z + 4}{2}$$
$$y = 2z + 2$$

Substituting $2z + 2$ for y in equation (1), we obtain

$$x - 2(2z + 2) + 3z = 1$$
$$x - 4z - 4 + 3z = 1$$
$$x - z - 4 = 1$$
$$x = z + 5$$

The solution to the system is

$$\{(x, y, z) \mid x = z + 5,\ y = 2z + 2,\ z \text{ is any real number}\}.$$

7. $\begin{cases} 2x + 4y + 3z = 5 & (1) \\ 3x - y + 2z = 8 & (2) \\ x + y + 2z = 0 & (3) \end{cases}$

Multiply both sides of equation (3) by -2 and add the result to equation (1).

$$-2x - 2y - 4z = 0$$
$$\underline{2x + 4y + 3z = 5}$$
$$2y - z = 5 \qquad (4)$$

Multiply both sides of equation (3) by -3 and add the result to equation (2).

$$-3x - 3y - 6z = 0$$
$$\underline{3x - y + 2z = 8}$$
$$-4y - 4z = 8 \qquad (5)$$

Multiply both sides of equation (4) by 2 and add the result to equation (5).

$$4y - 2z = 10$$
$$\underline{-4y - 4z = 8}$$
$$-6z = 18$$
$$z = -3$$

Substituting -3 for z in equation (4), we obtain

$$2y - (-3) = 5$$
$$2y + 3 = 5$$
$$2y = 2$$
$$y = 1$$

Substituting -3 for z and 1 for y in equation (1), we obtain

$$2x + 4(1) + 3(-3) = 5$$
$$2x + 4 - 9 = 5$$
$$2x - 5 = 5$$
$$2x = 10$$
$$x = 5$$

The solution is the ordered triple (5, 1, -3).

8. a. $\begin{bmatrix} 1 & -3 & | & -2 \\ 2 & -4 & | & 8 \end{bmatrix}$ $\qquad (R_2 = -2r_1 + r_2)$

$$= \begin{bmatrix} 1 & -3 & | & -2 \\ -2(1)+2 & -2(-3)+(-4) & | & -2(-2)+8 \end{bmatrix}$$

$$= \begin{bmatrix} 1 & -3 & | & -2 \\ 0 & 2 & | & 12 \end{bmatrix}$$

b. $\begin{bmatrix} 1 & -3 & | & -2 \\ 0 & 2 & | & 12 \end{bmatrix}$ $\qquad \left(R_2 = \frac{1}{2}r_2\right)$

$$= \begin{bmatrix} 1 & -3 & | & -2 \\ \frac{1}{2}(0) & \frac{1}{2}(2) & | & \frac{1}{2}(12) \end{bmatrix}$$

$$= \begin{bmatrix} 1 & -3 & | & -2 \\ 0 & 1 & | & 6 \end{bmatrix}$$

9. a. $\begin{bmatrix} 1 & -2 & 1 & | & -2 \\ 3 & -5 & 2 & | & 1 \\ 0 & -4 & 5 & | & -32 \end{bmatrix}$ $\qquad (R_2 = -3r_1 + r_2)$

$$= \begin{bmatrix} 1 & -2 & 1 & | & -2 \\ -3(1)+3 & -3(-2)+(-5) & -3(1)+2 & | & -3(-2)+1 \\ 0 & -4 & 5 & | & -32 \end{bmatrix}$$

$$= \begin{bmatrix} 1 & -2 & 1 & | & -2 \\ 0 & 1 & -1 & | & 7 \\ 0 & -4 & 5 & | & -32 \end{bmatrix}$$

b. $\begin{bmatrix} 1 & -2 & 1 & | & -2 \\ 0 & 1 & -1 & | & 7 \\ 0 & -4 & 5 & | & -32 \end{bmatrix}$ $\qquad (R_3 = 4r_2 + r_3)$

$$= \begin{bmatrix} 1 & -2 & 1 & | & -2 \\ 0 & 1 & -1 & | & 7 \\ 4(0)+0 & 4(1)+(-4) & 4(-1)+5 & | & 4(7)+(-32) \end{bmatrix}$$

$$= \begin{bmatrix} 1 & -2 & 1 & | & -2 \\ 0 & 1 & -1 & | & 7 \\ 0 & 0 & 1 & | & -4 \end{bmatrix}$$

10. $\begin{cases} x - 5y = 2 & (1) \\ 2x + y = 4 & (2) \end{cases}$

Write the augmented matrix of the system and then put it in row echelon form.

$$\begin{bmatrix} 1 & -5 & | & 2 \\ 2 & 1 & | & 4 \end{bmatrix} \qquad (R_2 = -2r_1 + r_2)$$

$$= \begin{bmatrix} 1 & -5 & | & 2 \\ 0 & 11 & | & 0 \end{bmatrix} \qquad \left(R_2 = \frac{1}{11}r_2\right)$$

$$= \begin{bmatrix} 1 & -5 & | & 2 \\ 0 & 1 & | & 0 \end{bmatrix}$$

Write the system of equations that corresponds to the row-echelon matrix

$\begin{cases} x - 5y = 2 & (1) \\ y = 0 & (2) \end{cases}$

This system is consistent and independent. Substituting 0 for y in equation (1), we obtain

$$x - 5(0) = 2$$
$$x = 2$$

The solution is the ordered pair (2, 0).

11. $\begin{cases} x + 2y + z = 3 & (1) \\ 4y + 3z = 5 & (2) \\ 2x + 3y = 1 & (3) \end{cases}$

Write the augmented matrix of the system and then put it in row echelon form.

$$\begin{bmatrix} 1 & 2 & 1 & | & 3 \\ 0 & 4 & 3 & | & 5 \\ 2 & 3 & 0 & | & 1 \end{bmatrix} \qquad (R_3 = -2r_1 + r_3)$$

$$= \begin{bmatrix} 1 & 2 & 1 & | & 3 \\ 0 & 4 & 3 & | & 5 \\ 0 & -1 & -2 & | & -5 \end{bmatrix} \qquad \left(R_2 = \frac{1}{4}r_2\right)$$

$$= \begin{bmatrix} 1 & 2 & 1 & | & 3 \\ 0 & 1 & \frac{3}{4} & | & \frac{5}{4} \\ 0 & -1 & -2 & | & -5 \end{bmatrix} \qquad (R_3 = r_3 + r_2)$$

$$= \begin{bmatrix} 1 & 2 & 1 & | & 3 \\ 0 & 1 & \frac{3}{4} & | & \frac{5}{4} \\ 0 & 0 & -\frac{5}{4} & | & -\frac{15}{4} \end{bmatrix} \qquad \left(R_3 = -\frac{4}{5}r_3\right)$$

$$= \begin{bmatrix} 1 & 2 & 1 & | & 3 \\ 0 & 1 & \frac{3}{4} & | & \frac{5}{4} \\ 0 & 0 & 1 & | & 3 \end{bmatrix}$$

Write the system of equations that corresponds to the row-echelon matrix

$\begin{cases} x + 2y + z = 3 & (1) \\ y + \dfrac{3}{4}z = \dfrac{5}{4} & (2) \\ z = 3 & (3) \end{cases}$

This system is consistent and independent. Substituting 3 for z in equation (2), we obtain

$$y + \frac{3}{4}(3) = \frac{5}{4}$$
$$y + \frac{9}{4} = \frac{5}{4}$$
$$y = \frac{-4}{4} = -1$$

Substituting 3 for z and -1 for y in equation (1), we obtain

$$x + 2(-1) + 3 = 3$$
$$x - 2 + 3 = 3$$
$$x = 2$$

The solution is the ordered triple (2, -1, 3).

12. $\begin{vmatrix} 3 & -5 \\ 4 & -8 \end{vmatrix} = 3(-8) - 4(-5)$

$$= -24 + 20$$
$$= -4$$

13. $\begin{vmatrix} 0 & 1 & 2 \\ 3 & 3 & -1 \\ -2 & 1 & 2 \end{vmatrix}$

$$= 0 \begin{vmatrix} 3 & -1 \\ 1 & 2 \end{vmatrix} - 1 \begin{vmatrix} 3 & -1 \\ -2 & 2 \end{vmatrix} + 2 \begin{vmatrix} 3 & 3 \\ -2 & 1 \end{vmatrix}$$

$$= 0[3(2) - 1(-1)] - 1[3(2) - (-2)(-1)]$$
$$\qquad\qquad + 2[3(1) - (-2)(3)]$$

$$= 0(7) - 1(4) + 2(9)$$
$$= 0 - 4 + 18$$
$$= 14$$

14. $D = \begin{vmatrix} 1 & -1 \\ 5 & 3 \end{vmatrix} = 1(3) - 5(-1) = 3 + 5 = 8$

$$D_x = \begin{vmatrix} -2 & -1 \\ -8 & 3 \end{vmatrix} = -2(3) - (-8)(-1) = -6 - 8 = -14$$

$$D_y = \begin{vmatrix} 1 & -2 \\ 5 & -8 \end{vmatrix} = 1(-8) - 5(-2) = -8 + 10 = 2$$

$$x = \frac{D_x}{D} = \frac{-14}{8} = -\frac{7}{4} \;;\; y = \frac{D_y}{D} = \frac{2}{8} = \frac{1}{4}$$

Thus, the solution is the ordered pair $\left(-\dfrac{7}{4}, \dfrac{1}{4}\right)$.

15. $D = \begin{vmatrix} 1 & 1 & 1 \\ 1 & 1 & -2 \\ 4 & 2 & 3 \end{vmatrix}$

$= 1\begin{vmatrix} 1 & -2 \\ 2 & 3 \end{vmatrix} - 1\begin{vmatrix} 1 & -2 \\ 4 & 3 \end{vmatrix} + 1\begin{vmatrix} 1 & 1 \\ 4 & 2 \end{vmatrix}$

$= 1\big[1(3) - 2(-2)\big] - 1\big[1(3) - 4(-2)\big]$
$\qquad\qquad\qquad + 1\big[1(2) - 4(1)\big]$

$= 1(7) - 1(11) + 1(-2)$

$= -6$

$D_x = \begin{vmatrix} -2 & 1 & 1 \\ 1 & 1 & -2 \\ -15 & 2 & 3 \end{vmatrix}$

$= -2\begin{vmatrix} 1 & -2 \\ 2 & 3 \end{vmatrix} - 1\begin{vmatrix} 1 & -2 \\ -15 & 3 \end{vmatrix} + 1\begin{vmatrix} 1 & 1 \\ -15 & 2 \end{vmatrix}$

$= -2\big[1(3) - 2(-2)\big] - 1\big[1(3) - (-15)(-2)\big]$
$\qquad\qquad\qquad + 1\big[1(2) - (-15)(1)\big]$

$= -2(7) - 1(-27) + 1(17)$

$= -14 + 27 + 17$

$= 30$

$D_y = \begin{vmatrix} 1 & -2 & 1 \\ 1 & 1 & -2 \\ 4 & -15 & 3 \end{vmatrix}$

$= 1\begin{vmatrix} 1 & -2 \\ -15 & 3 \end{vmatrix} - (-2)\begin{vmatrix} 1 & -2 \\ 4 & 3 \end{vmatrix} + 1\begin{vmatrix} 1 & 1 \\ 4 & -15 \end{vmatrix}$

$= 1\big[1(3) - (-15)(-2)\big] - (-2)\big[1(3) - 4(-2)\big]$
$\qquad\qquad\qquad + 1\big[1(-15) - 4(1)\big]$

$= 1(-27) - (-2)(11) + 1(-19)$

$= -27 + 22 - 19$

$= -24$

$D_z = \begin{vmatrix} 1 & 1 & -2 \\ 1 & 1 & 1 \\ 4 & 2 & -15 \end{vmatrix}$

$= 1\begin{vmatrix} 1 & 1 \\ 2 & -15 \end{vmatrix} - 1\begin{vmatrix} 1 & 1 \\ 4 & -15 \end{vmatrix} + (-2)\begin{vmatrix} 1 & 1 \\ 4 & 2 \end{vmatrix}$

$= 1\big[1(-15) - 2(1)\big] - 1\big[1(-15) - 4(1)\big]$
$\qquad\qquad\qquad + (-2)\big[1(2) - 4(1)\big]$

$= 1(-17) - 1(-19) + (-2)(-2)$

$= -17 + 19 + 4$

$= 6$

$x = \dfrac{D_x}{D} = \dfrac{30}{-6} = -5$; $y = \dfrac{D_y}{D} = \dfrac{-24}{-6} = 4$;

$z = \dfrac{D_z}{D} = \dfrac{6}{-6} = -1$

Thus, the solution is the ordered triple (-5, 4, -1).

16. $\begin{cases} 2x - y > -2 \\ x - 3y < 9 \end{cases}$

First, graph the inequality $2x - y > -2$. To do so, replace the inequality symbol with an equal sign to obtain $2x - y = -2$. Because the inequality is strict, graph $2x - y = -2$ $(y = 2x + 2)$ using a dashed line.

Test Point: $(0,0)$: $2(0) - 0 = 0 > -2$

Therefore, the half-plane containing $(0,0)$ is the solution set of $2x - y > -2$.

Second, graph the inequality $x - 3y < 9$. To do so, replace the inequality symbol with an equal sign to obtain $x - 3y = 9$. Because the inequality is strict, graph $x - 3y = 9$ $\left(y = \dfrac{1}{3}x - 3\right)$ using a dashed line.

Test Point: $(0,0)$: $0 - 3(0) = 0 < 9$

Therefore, the half-plane containing $(0,0)$ is the solution set of $x - 3y < 9$.

The overlapping shaded region (that is, the shaded region in the graph below) is the solution to the system of linear inequalities.

The corner point is (-3, -4).

17. $\begin{cases} 3x + 2y \le 12 \\ x - 2y \ge -4 \\ x \ge 0 \\ y \ge 0 \end{cases}$

First, graph the inequality $3x + 2y \le 12$. To do so, replace the inequality symbol with an equal sign to obtain $3x + 2y = 12$. Because the inequality is non-strict, graph $3x + 2y = 12$ $\left(y = -\dfrac{3}{2}x + 6\right)$ using a solid line.

Test Point: $(0,0)$: $3(0) + 2(0) = 0 \le 12$

Therefore, the half-plane containing $(0,0)$ is the solution set of $3x + 2y \leq 12$.

Next, graph the inequality $x - 2y \geq -4$. To do so, replace the inequality symbol with an equal sign to obtain $x - 2y = -4$. Because the inequality is non-strict, graph $x - 2y = -4$ $\left(y = \dfrac{1}{2}x + 2\right)$ using a solid line.

Test Point: $(0,0)$: $0 - 2(0) = 0 \geq -4$

Therefore, the half-plane containing $(0,0)$ is the solution set of $x - 2y \geq -4$.

The two inequalities $x \geq 0$ and $y \geq 0$ require that the graph be in quadrant I.

The overlapping shaded region (that is, the shaded region in the graph below) is the solution to the system of linear inequalities.

The graph is bounded. The four corner points of the bounded region are (0, 0), (4, 0), (2, 3), and (0, 2).

18. Let x represent the number of twenty-five-ton bins and y represent the number of twenty-ton bins.

$$\begin{cases} x + y = 50 & (1) \\ 25x + 20y = 1160 & (2) \end{cases}$$

Equation (1) solved for y is $y = -x + 50$.

Substituting $-x + 50$ for y in equation (2), we obtain

$$25x + 20(-x + 50) = 1160$$
$$25x - 20x + 1000 = 1160$$
$$5x + 1000 = 1160$$
$$5x = 160$$
$$x = 32$$

Substituting 32 for x in equation (1), we obtain

$$32 + y = 50$$
$$y = 18$$

The warehouse contains 32 twenty-five-ton bins and 18 twenty-ton bins.

19. Because the sum of the measures of the three angles in a triangle must equal $180°$, we obtain the following system.

$$\begin{cases} x + y + z = 180 & (1) \\ z = y + 10 & (2) \\ 5x = y + z & (3) \end{cases}$$

Writing the equations in the system in standard form, we obtain

$$\begin{cases} x + y + z = 180 & (1) \\ y - z = -10 & (2) \\ 5x - y - z = 0 & (3) \end{cases}$$

Adding equations (1) and (2), we obtain

$$\begin{array}{r} x + y + z = 180 \\ y - z = -10 \\ \hline x + 2y \quad = 170 \quad (4) \end{array}$$

Adding equations (1) and (3), we obtain.

$$\begin{array}{r} x + y + z = 180 \\ 5x - y - z = 0 \\ \hline 6x \quad\quad = 180 \\ x = 30 \end{array}$$

Substituting 30 for x in equation (4), we obtain

$$30 + 2y = 170$$
$$2y = 140$$
$$y = 70$$

Substituting 30 for x and 70 for y and in equation (1), we obtain

$$30 + 70 + z = 180$$
$$100 + z = 180$$
$$z = 80$$

Thus, angle $x = 30°$, angle $y = 70°$, and angle $z = 80°$.

20. a. Margaret has a maximum of \$180 to spend, so $12x + 18y \leq 180$. She will buy no more than 13 items, so $x + y \leq 13$. Finally, Margaret cannot buy a negative number of blouses or sweaters, so we have the non-negativity constraints $x \geq 0$ and $y \geq 0$.

Thus, we have the following system:

$$\begin{cases} 12x + 18y \leq 180 \\ x + y \leq 13 \\ x \geq 0 \\ y \geq 0 \end{cases}$$

b. First, graph the inequality $12x + 18y \leq 180$.
To do so, replace the inequality symbol with
an equal sign to obtain $12x + 18y = 180$.
Because the inequality is non-strict, graph
$12x + 18y = 180$ $\left(y = -\dfrac{2}{3}x + 10 \right)$ using a
solid line.

Test Point: $(0,0)$: $12(0) + 18(0) = 0 \leq 180$

Thus, the solution set of $12x + 18y \leq 180$ is
the half-plane containing $(0, 0)$.

Second, graph the inequality $x + y \leq 13$. To
do so, replace the inequality symbol with an
equal sign to obtain $x + y = 13$. Because the
inequality is non-strict, graph $x + y = 13$
$(y = -x + 13)$ using a solid line.

Test Point: $(0,0)$: $0 + 0 = 0 \leq 13$

Thus, the solution set of $x + y \leq 13$ is the half-
plane containing $(0, 0)$.

The two inequalities $x \geq 0$ and $y \geq 0$
require that the graph be in quadrant I.

The overlapping shaded region (that is, the
shaded region in the graph below) is the
solution to the system of linear inequalities.

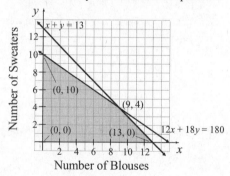

The four corner points are $(0, 0)$, $(13, 0)$,
$(9, 4)$, and $(0, 10)$.

Getting Ready for Chapter 5

1. base; exponent or power

3. $a \neq 0$

5. False; $(3a)^{-2} = \dfrac{1}{(3a)^2} = \dfrac{1}{9a^2}$

7. False; When a number is expressed in scientific notation, it is expressed as the product of a number x, $1 \le |x| < 10$, and a power of 10.

9. The expression a^{m+n} is equivalent to the expression $a^m \cdot a^n$. If either m, n, or $m+n$ is 0, then a cannot be 0 or we would have the indeterminate form 0^0. If either m, n, or $m+n$ is negative, then a cannot be 0 or we would have division by zero which is undefined. For example, $0^{-2} = \dfrac{1}{0^2} = \dfrac{1}{0} =$ undefined.

11. If the exponent, n, is 0, then neither base can equal 0 or we would have the indeterminate form 0^0. Since the product of 0 and any number is still 0, the quantity $a \cdot b$ will equal 0 if either a or b is equal to 0. This would lead to the indeterminate form 0^0 if the exponent is 0.

    If n is negative, then neither base can be 0 or we would have division by zero which is undefined. Since the product of 0 and any number is still 0, the quantity $a \cdot b$ will equal 0 if either a or b is equal to 0. This would lead to division by 0 since the negative exponent would put the quantity $a \cdot b = 0$ in the denominator.

13. Written response. Answers may vary. See Objective 1. The idea can be illustrated as follows:
    Multiply x together 7 times to get x^7
    $x \cdot x \cdot x \cdot x \cdot x \cdot x \cdot x = x^7$
    The Associative Law for Multiplication says that we can group the multiplications however we wish. Thus, we can write
    $(x \cdot x) \cdot (x \cdot x \cdot x \cdot x \cdot x) = x^7$
    Now we can write each expression in parentheses using exponents.
    $x^2 \cdot x^5 = x^7$

Notice that the bases are the same. When we multiply the two expressions on the left, we will need to add the exponents to get the result on the right.

15. Written response. Answers may vary. The idea can be illustrated as follows:
    Multiply x together 8 times to get x^8.
    $x \cdot x \cdot x \cdot x \cdot x \cdot x \cdot x \cdot x = x^8$
    The Associative Law for Multiplication says that we can group these multiplications however we wish. Group the x's in twos to get
    $(x \cdot x) \cdot (x \cdot x) \cdot (x \cdot x) \cdot (x \cdot x)$
    Remember that exponents indicate multiplication. Since we multiply x twice inside each set of parentheses, we can rewrite this as
    $(x^2) \cdot (x^2) \cdot (x^2) \cdot (x^2)$
    We again have a series of multiplications, but we are multiplying x^2 and not just x. Thus, we can write $(x^2)^4$ since x^2 is being multiplied together 4 times. Thus, the end result is that $(x^2)^4 = x^8$.

17. Written response. Answers may vary. See Objective 7.

19. $5^2 = 5 \cdot 5 = 25$

21. $-5^2 = -1 \cdot 25 = -25$

23. $-5^{-2} = -\dfrac{1}{5^2} = -\dfrac{1}{25}$

25. $8^2 \cdot 8^{-3} = 8^{2+(-3)} = 8^{-1} = \dfrac{1}{8}$

27. $\left(\dfrac{4}{9}\right)^{-2} = \left(\dfrac{9}{4}\right)^2 = \dfrac{9^2}{4^2} = \dfrac{81}{4}$

29. $(-2)^3 \cdot 4^0 = -8 \cdot 1 = -8$

31. $(-3)^2 \cdot (-3)^{-5} = (-3)^{2+(-5)}$

$\qquad = (-3)^{-3}$

$\qquad = \dfrac{1}{(-3)^3}$

$\qquad = -\dfrac{1}{27}$

33. $\dfrac{(-4)^2}{(-4)^{-1}} = (-4)^{2-(-1)}$

$\qquad = (-4)^3$

$\qquad = -64$

35. $\dfrac{2^3 \cdot 3^{-2}}{2^{-2} \cdot 3^{-4}} = 2^{3-(-2)} \cdot 3^{-2-(-4)}$

$\qquad = 2^5 \cdot 3^2$

$\qquad = 32 \cdot 9$

$\qquad = 288$

37. $z^6 \cdot z^{-2} = z^{6+(-2)} = z^4$

39. $\dfrac{y^8}{y^6} = y^{8-6} = y^2$

41. $(6x)^0 = 1 \quad (\text{assuming } x \neq 0)$

43. $\dfrac{1}{6^{-2}} = 6^2 = 36$

45. $(2s^{-2}t^4)(-5s^2t) = 2(-5)s^{-2+2}t^{4+1}$

$\qquad = -10s^0t^5$

$\qquad = -10t^5$

47. $\left(\dfrac{1}{4}xy\right) \cdot (20xy^{-2}) = \dfrac{1}{4} \cdot 20 \cdot x^{1+1}y^{1+(-2)}$

$\qquad = 5x^2y^{-1}$

$\qquad = 5x^2 \cdot \dfrac{1}{y}$

$\qquad = \dfrac{5x^2}{y}$

49. $\dfrac{16a^6}{10a^5} = \dfrac{16}{10}a^{6-5}$

$\qquad = \dfrac{8}{5}a^1$

$\qquad = \dfrac{8}{5}a$

51. $\dfrac{36x^7y^3}{9x^5y^2} = \dfrac{36}{9} \cdot x^{7-5}y^{3-2}$

$\qquad = 4x^2y$

53. $\dfrac{21a^2b}{14a^3b^{-2}} = \dfrac{21}{14} \cdot a^{2-3}b^{1-(-2)}$

$\qquad = \dfrac{3}{2}a^{-1}b^3$

$\qquad = \dfrac{3b^3}{2a}$

55. $\dfrac{6x^2y^5}{2x^3y^3} = \dfrac{6}{2} \cdot x^{2-3}y^{5-3}$

$\qquad = 3x^{-1}y^2$

$\qquad = \dfrac{3y^2}{x}$

57. $\left(x^{-2}\right)^4 = x^{-2 \cdot 4}$

$\qquad = x^{-8}$

$\qquad = \dfrac{1}{x^8}$

59. $(3x^2y)^3 = 3^3\left(x^2\right)^3 y^3$

$\qquad = 27x^{2 \cdot 3}y^3$

$\qquad = 27x^6y^3$

61. $\left(\dfrac{z}{4}\right)^3 = \dfrac{z^3}{4^3} = \dfrac{z^3}{64}$

63. $\left(3a^{-3}\right)^{-2} = 3^{-2}\left(a^{-3}\right)^{-2}$

$\qquad = \dfrac{1}{3^2} \cdot a^{-3 \cdot -2}$

$\qquad = \dfrac{1}{9}a^6$

$\qquad = \dfrac{a^6}{9}$

65. $\left(-2a^2b^3\right)^{-4} = (-2)^{-4}\left(a^2\right)^{-4}\left(b^3\right)^{-4}$

$\qquad = \dfrac{1}{(-2)^4} \cdot a^{2 \cdot -4} \cdot b^{3 \cdot -4}$

$\qquad = \dfrac{1}{16} \cdot a^{-8} \cdot b^{-12}$

$\qquad = \dfrac{1}{16} \cdot \dfrac{1}{a^8} \cdot \dfrac{1}{b^{12}}$

$\qquad = \dfrac{1}{16a^8b^{12}}$

67. $\dfrac{x^2yz^{-3}}{xy^{-4}z^2} = x^{2-1}y^{1-(-4)}z^{-3-2}$

$\qquad = xy^5z^{-5}$

$\qquad = \dfrac{xy^5}{z^5}$

69. $\dfrac{2^3 \cdot xy^{-2}}{12\left(x^2\right)^{-2}y} = \dfrac{8xy^{-2}}{12x^{2 \cdot -2}y}$

$\qquad = \dfrac{8xy^{-2}}{12x^{-4}y}$

$\qquad = \dfrac{8}{12}x^{1-(-4)}y^{-2-1}$

$\qquad = \dfrac{2}{3}x^5y^{-3}$

$\qquad = \dfrac{2x^5}{3y^3}$

71. $\left(\dfrac{15a^2b^3}{3a^{-4}b^5}\right)^{-2} = \left(5a^{2-(-4)}b^{3-5}\right)^{-2}$

$\qquad = \left(5a^6b^{-2}\right)^{-2}$

$\qquad = 5^{-2}\left(a^6\right)^{-2}\left(b^{-2}\right)^{-2}$

$\qquad = \dfrac{1}{5^2}a^{6 \cdot -2}b^{-2 \cdot -2}$

$\qquad = \dfrac{1}{25}a^{-12}b^4$

$\qquad = \dfrac{b^4}{25a^{12}}$

73. $\left(4x^4y^{-2}\right)^{-1} \cdot \left(2x^2y^{-1}\right)^2$

$\qquad = 4^{-1}\left(x^4\right)^{-1}\left(y^{-2}\right)^{-1} \cdot 2^2\left(x^2\right)^2\left(y^{-1}\right)^2$

$\qquad = \dfrac{1}{4}x^{-4}y^2 \cdot 4x^4y^{-2}$

$\qquad = \dfrac{4}{4}x^{-4+4}y^{2+(-2)}$

$\qquad = 1 \cdot x^0 \cdot y^0$

$\qquad = 1$

75. $\left(-4x^2y\right) \cdot \left(2xy^{-3}\right)^{-2} = -4x^2y \cdot 2^{-2}x^{-2}\left(y^{-3}\right)^{-2}$

$\qquad = -2^2 \cdot 2^{-2} \cdot x^2y \cdot x^{-2}y^6$

$\qquad = -2^{2+(-2)}x^{2+(-2)}y^{1+6}$

$\qquad = -2^0x^0y^7$

$\qquad = -y^7$

77. $\dfrac{(-2)^2 x^3 (yz)^2}{-4xy^{-2}z} = \dfrac{4x^3y^2z^2}{-4xy^{-2}z}$

$\qquad = \dfrac{4}{-4}x^{3-1}y^{2-(-2)}z^{2-1}$

$\qquad = -1 \cdot x^2y^4z$

$\qquad = -x^2y^4z$

79. $\dfrac{\left(3x^{-1}yz^2\right)^2}{\left(xy^{-2}z\right)^3} = \dfrac{3^2\left(x^{-1}\right)^2 y^2 \left(z^2\right)^2}{x^3\left(y^{-2}\right)^3 z^3}$

$$= \dfrac{9x^{-2}y^2z^4}{x^3 y^{-6} z^3}$$

$$= 9x^{-2-3}y^{2-(-6)}z^{4-3}$$

$$= 9x^{-5}y^8 z^1$$

$$= \dfrac{9y^8 z}{x^5}$$

81. $\dfrac{\left(6a^3b^{-2}\right)^{-1}}{\left(2a^{-2}b\right)^{-2}} \cdot \left(\dfrac{3ab^3}{2a^2b^{-3}}\right)^2$

$$= \dfrac{6^{-1}\left(a^3\right)^{-1}\left(b^{-2}\right)^{-1}}{2^{-2}\left(a^{-2}\right)^{-2}b^{-2}} \cdot \left(\dfrac{3}{2}a^{1-2}b^{3-(-3)}\right)^2$$

$$= \dfrac{2^2 a^{-3}b^2}{6a^4 b^{-2}} \cdot \left(\dfrac{3}{2}a^{-1}b^6\right)^2$$

$$= \dfrac{2}{3}a^{-3-4}b^{2-(-2)} \cdot \left(\dfrac{3}{2}\right)^2\left(a^{-1}\right)^2\left(b^6\right)^2$$

$$= \dfrac{2}{3}a^{-7}b^4 \cdot \dfrac{9}{4}a^{-2}b^{12}$$

$$= \dfrac{2}{3}\cdot\dfrac{9}{4}a^{-7+(-2)}b^{4+12}$$

$$= \dfrac{3}{2}a^{-9}b^{16}$$

$$= \dfrac{3b^{16}}{2a^9}$$

83. To write $4,500,000$ in scientific notation, we need to move the decimal point to the left 6 places. Thus, we can write 4,500,000 in scientific notation as 4.5×10^6.

85. To write $-230,000$ in scientific notation, we need to move the decimal point to the left 5 places. Thus, we can write $-230,000$ in scientific notation as -2.3×10^5.

87. To write 0.00034 in scientific notation, we need to move the decimal point to the right 4 places. Thus, we can write 0.00034 in scientific notation as 3.4×10^{-4}.

89. To write -0.0000001 in scientific notation, we need to move the decimal point to the right 7 places. Thus, we can write -0.0000001 in scientific notation as -1×10^{-7}.

91. $\left(3.4\times10^5\right)\cdot\left(2\times10^{-8}\right) = (3.4\cdot2)\times\left(10^5\cdot10^{-8}\right)$

$$= 6.8\times10^{-3}$$

93. $\left(-5.3\times10^{-4}\right)\cdot\left(2.8\times10^{-3}\right)$

$$= (-5.3\cdot2.8)\times\left(10^{-4}\cdot10^{-3}\right)$$

$$= -14.84\times10^{-7}$$

$$= -\left(1.484\times10^1\right)\times10^{-7}$$

$$= -1.484\times10^{-6}$$

95. $\dfrac{3.6\times10^{12}}{1.2\times10^7} = \dfrac{3.6}{1.2}\times\dfrac{10^{12}}{10^7}$

$$= 3.0\times10^{12-7}$$

$$= 3\times10^5$$

97. $\left(4\times10^6\right)^3 = 4^3\times\left(10^6\right)^3$

$$= 64\times10^{18}$$

$$= \left(6.4\times10^1\right)\times10^{18}$$

$$= 6.4\times10^{19}$$

99. $\dfrac{5\times10^{-6}}{8\times10^{-4}} = \dfrac{5}{8}\times\dfrac{10^{-6}}{10^{-4}}$

$$= 0.625\times10^{-6-(-4)}$$

$$= 6.25\times10^{-1}\times10^{-2}$$

$$= 6.25\times10^{-3}$$

101. $\dfrac{\left(4\times10^3\right)\left(6\times10^7\right)}{3\times10^4} = \dfrac{(4\cdot6)\times\left(10^3\cdot10^7\right)}{3\times10^4}$

$$= \dfrac{24\times10^{10}}{3\times10^4}$$

$$= \dfrac{24}{3}\times\dfrac{10^{10}}{10^4}$$

$$= 8\times10^{10-4}$$

$$= 8\times10^6$$

103.
$$\frac{\left(2\times10^{-4}\right)\left(-4.8\times10^{-6}\right)}{6\times10^3}=\frac{(2)\cdot(-4.8)\times\left(10^{-4}\cdot10^{-6}\right)}{6\times10^3}$$
$$=\frac{-9.6\times10^{-10}}{6\times10^3}$$
$$=\frac{-9.6}{6}\times\frac{10^{-10}}{10^3}$$
$$=-1.6\times10^{-10-3}$$
$$=-1.6\times10^{-13}$$

105.
$$\frac{6.2\times10^{-3}}{\left(3.1\times10^4\right)\cdot\left(2\times10^{-7}\right)}=\frac{6.2\times10^{-3}}{(3.1\cdot2)\times\left(10^4\cdot10^{-7}\right)}$$
$$=\frac{6.2\times10^{-3}}{6.2\times10^{-3}}$$
$$=1$$

107.
$$(4,000,000)\cdot(3,000,000)=\left(4\times10^6\right)\cdot\left(3\times10^6\right)$$
$$=(4\cdot3)\times\left(10^6\cdot10^6\right)$$
$$=12\times10^{12}$$
$$=\left(1.2\times10^1\right)\times10^{12}$$
$$=1.2\times10^{13}$$
$$=12,000,000,000,000$$

109.
$$(6,000)\cdot(2,000,000)=\left(6\times10^3\right)\cdot\left(2\times10^6\right)$$
$$=(6\cdot2)\times\left(10^3\cdot10^6\right)$$
$$=12\times10^9$$
$$=\left(1.2\times10^1\right)\times10^9$$
$$=1.2\times10^{10}$$
$$=12,000,000,000$$

111.
$$\frac{0.00008}{0.002}=\frac{8\times10^{-5}}{2\times10^{-3}}$$
$$=\frac{8}{2}\times\frac{10^{-5}}{10^{-3}}$$
$$=4\times10^{-5-(-3)}$$
$$=4\times10^{-2}$$
$$=0.04$$

113.
$$\frac{0.000036}{0.0009}=\frac{3.6\times10^{-5}}{9\times10^{-4}}$$
$$=\frac{3.6}{9}\times\frac{10^{-5}}{10^{-4}}$$
$$=0.4\times10^{-5-(-4)}$$
$$=\left(4\times10^{-1}\right)\times10^{-1}$$
$$=4\times10^{-2}$$
$$=0.04$$

115.
$$\frac{-60,000\cdot4,000,000}{0.008}=\frac{\left(-6\times10^4\right)\cdot\left(4\times10^6\right)}{8\times10^{-3}}$$
$$=\frac{(-6\cdot4)\times\left(10^4\cdot10^6\right)}{8\times10^{-3}}$$
$$=\frac{-24\times10^{10}}{8\times10^{-3}}$$
$$=\frac{-24}{8}\times\frac{10^{10}}{10^{-3}}$$
$$=-3\times10^{10-(-3)}$$
$$=-3\times10^{13}$$
$$=-30,000,000,000,000$$

117.
$$\frac{(0.000004)\cdot1,600,000}{(0.0008)\cdot(0.002)}=\frac{\left(4\times10^{-6}\right)\cdot\left(1.6\times10^6\right)}{\left(8\times10^{-4}\right)\cdot\left(2\times10^{-3}\right)}$$
$$=\frac{(4\cdot1.6)\times\left(10^{-6}\cdot10^6\right)}{(8\cdot2)\times\left(10^{-4}\cdot10^{-3}\right)}$$
$$=\frac{6.4\times10^0}{16\times10^{-7}}$$
$$=\frac{6.4}{16}\times10^{0-(-7)}$$
$$=0.4\times10^7$$
$$=\left(4\times10^{-1}\right)\times10^7$$
$$=4\times10^6$$
$$=4,000,000$$

119. $V=s^3$

Since each side of the cube has a length of $s=x^2$, the volume is
$$V=\left(x^2\right)^3=x^{2\cdot3}=x^6$$

The volume of the cube is x^6 cubic units.

121. $0.00001276 = 1.276 \times 10^{-5}$

The plant cell diameter is 1.276×10^{-5} meters.

123. $12,760,000 = 1.276 \times 10^{7}$

The diameter of Earth is 1.276×10^{7} meters.

125. $1 \times 10^{-9} = 0.000000001$

One nanometer is 0.000000001 meters.

127. $4 \times 10^{19} = 40,000,000,000,000,000,000$

The Rubik's Cube has
$40,000,000,000,000,000,000$ possible states.

129.
$$\frac{9.96 \times 10^{12}}{2.8 \times 10^{8}} = \frac{9.96}{2.8} \times \frac{10^{12}}{10^{8}}$$
$$\approx 3.6 \times 10^{12-8}$$
$$= 3.6 \times 10^{4}$$
$$= 36,000$$

The per capita GDP of the United States in 2000 was approximately \$36,000.

131. $d = r \cdot t$ or $t = \dfrac{d}{r}$

$$t = \frac{93,000,000}{186,000}$$
$$= \frac{9.3 \times 10^{7}}{1.86 \times 10^{5}}$$
$$= \frac{9.3}{1.86} \times 10^{7-5}$$
$$= 5 \times 10^{2}$$

It would take a beam of light 5×10^{2} seconds to reach the Earth from the Sun ($\approx$ 8.3 minutes).

133. a. pop. density $= \dfrac{2.49 \times 10^{8}}{3.54 \times 10^{6}}$
$$= \frac{2.49}{3.54} \times \frac{10^{8}}{10^{6}}$$
$$\approx 0.703 \times 10^{8-6}$$
$$= \left(7.03 \times 10^{-1}\right) \times 10^{2}$$
$$= 7.03 \times 10^{1}$$
$$= 70.3$$

The population density of the U.S. in 1990 was roughly 70.3 people per square mile. This means that, on average, each square mile of land contained about 70 people.

b. pop. density $= \dfrac{2.81 \times 10^{8}}{3.54 \times 10^{6}}$
$$= \frac{2.81}{3.54} \times \frac{10^{8}}{10^{6}}$$
$$\approx 0.794 \times 10^{8-6}$$
$$= \left(7.94 \times 10^{-1}\right) \times 10^{2}$$
$$= 7.94 \times 10^{1}$$
$$= 79.4$$

The population density of the U.S. in 2000 was roughly 79.4 people per square mile. This means that, on average, each square mile of land contained about 79 people.

c. $79.4 - 70.3 = 9.1$

The population density increased by about 9 people per square mile. This means that, on average, the number of people living on each square mile of land increased by 9, thereby making living space more crowded.

135. $\dfrac{2^{x+3}}{4} = \dfrac{2^{x+3}}{2^{2}} = 2^{x+3-2} = 2^{x+1}$

137. $3^{x} \cdot 27^{3x+1} = 3^{x} \cdot \left(3^{3}\right)^{3x+1}$
$$= 3^{x} \cdot 3^{9x+3}$$
$$= 3^{x+9x+3}$$
$$= 3^{10x+3}$$

139. $3^{x} = 5$
$$\left(3^{x}\right)^{4} = (5)^{4}$$
$$3^{4x} = 5^{4}$$
$$3^{4x} = 625$$

141. $2^{x} = 7$
$$\left(2^{x}\right)^{-4} = (7)^{-4}$$
$$2^{-4x} = 7^{-4}$$
$$2^{-4x} = \frac{1}{7^{4}}$$
$$2^{-4x} = \frac{1}{2401}$$

143. No, your friend is incorrect. He added the exponents instead of multiplying.
$$\left(x^{4}\right)^{3} = x^{4 \cdot 3} = x^{12}$$

Chapter 5

5.1 Preparing for Adding and Subtracting Polynomials

1. The coefficient is -4, the number multiplied in front of the variable expression.

2. $5x^2 - 3x + 1 - 2x^2 - 6x + 3$
   $= 5x^2 - 2x^2 - 3x - 6x + 1 + 3$
   $= (5-2)x^2 + (-3-6)x + (1+3)$
   $= 3x^2 - 9x + 4$

3. $-4(x-3) = -4 \cdot x - 4 \cdot (-3)$
   $= -4x + 12$

4. $f(x) = -4x + 3$
   $f(3) = -4(3) + 3$
   $= -12 + 3$
   $= -9$

5.1 Exercises

1. like terms

3. degree

5. True

7. Answers may vary. A *term* is any of the entities in an algebraic expression that are separated by addition or subtraction. A *monomial* is a single term expression, with the particular form $ax^m y^n$ where m and n are whole numbers.

9. A *binomial* has two terms and a *trinomial* has three terms.

11. Answers will vary. A *polynomial* is an expression and is a monomial or the sum of monomials. A *polynomial function* equates a polynomial expression to a dependent variable.

13. Coefficient: 3
    Degree: 2

15. Coefficient: -8
    Degree: $2 + 3 = 5$

17. Coefficient: $\dfrac{4}{3}$
    Degree: 6

19. Coefficient: 2
    Degree: 0

21. $2x^{-1} + 3x$ is not a polynomial because the exponent in the first term is not an integer that is greater than or equal to 0.

23. $\dfrac{4}{z-1}$ is not a polynomial because there is a variable in the denominator. The expression cannot be written in the standard form for a polynomial.

25. $5x^2 - 9x + 1$
    Yes; trinomial; degree 2; already in standard form.

27. $\dfrac{-20}{n}$ is not a polynomial because there is a variable in the denominator.

29. $3y^{1/3} + 2$ is not a polynomial because there is a fractional exponent.

31. $\dfrac{5}{8}$
    Yes; monomial; degree 0; already in standard form.

33. $5 - 8y + 2y^2$
    Yes; trinomial; degree 2; standard form is $2y^2 - 8y + 5$

35. $7x^{-1} + 4$ is not a polynomial because of the negative exponent.

37. $3x^2 y^2 + 2xy^4 + 4$
    Yes; trinomial; degree 5; standard form is $2xy^4 + 3x^2 y^2 + 4$

39. $4pqr + 2p^2 q + 3pq^{1/4}$ is not a polynomial because there is a fractional exponent.

41. $5z^3 + 8z^3 = (5+8)z^3 = 13z^3$

43. $(x^2 + 5x + 1) + (3x^2 - 2x - 3)$
$= x^2 + 5x + 1 + 3x^2 - 2x - 3$
$= x^2 + 3x^2 + 5x - 2x + 1 - 3$
$= (1+3)x^2 + (5-2)x + (1-3)$
$= 4x^2 + 3x - 2$

45. $(6p^3 - p^2 + 3p - 4) + (2p^3 - 7p + 3)$
$= 6p^3 - p^2 + 3p - 4 + 2p^3 - 7p + 3$
$= 6p^3 + 2p^3 - p^2 + 3p - 7p - 4 + 3$
$= (6+2)p^3 - p^2 + (3-7)p + (-4+3)$
$= 8p^3 - p^2 - 4p - 1$

47. $(5x^2 + 9x + 4) - (3x^2 + 5x + 1)$
$= 5x^2 + 9x + 4 - 3x^2 - 5x - 1$
$= 5x^2 - 3x^2 + 9x - 5x + 4 - 1$
$= (5-3)x^2 + (9-5)x + (4-1)$
$= 2x^2 + 4x + 3$

49. $(7s^2t^3 + st^2 - 5t - 8) - (4s^2t^3 + 5st^2 - 7)$
$= 7s^2t^3 + st^2 - 5t - 8 - 4s^2t^3 - 5st^2 + 7$
$= 7s^2t^3 - 4s^2t^3 + st^2 - 5st^2 - 5t - 8 + 7$
$= (7-4)s^2t^3 + (1-5)st^2 - 5t + (-8+7)$
$= 3s^2t^3 - 4st^2 - 5t - 1$

51. $(3 - 5x + x^2) + (-2 + 3x - 5x^2)$
$= 3 - 5x + x^2 - 2 + 3x - 5x^2$
$= x^2 - 5x^2 - 5x + 3x + 3 - 2$
$= (1-5)x^2 + (-5+3)x + (3-2)$
$= -4x^2 - 2x + 1$

53. $(6 - 2y + y^3) - (-2 + y^2 - 2y^3)$
$= 6 - 2y + y^3 + 2 - y^2 + 2y^3$
$= y^3 + 2y^3 - y^2 - 2y + 6 + 2$
$= (1+2)y^3 - y^2 - 2y + (6+2)$
$= 3y^3 - y^2 - 2y + 8$

55. $\left(\dfrac{1}{4}x^2 + \dfrac{3}{2}x + 3\right) + \left(\dfrac{1}{2}x^2 - \dfrac{1}{4}x - 2\right)$
$= \dfrac{1}{4}x^2 + \dfrac{3}{2}x + 3 + \dfrac{1}{2}x^2 - \dfrac{1}{4}x - 2$
$= \dfrac{1}{4}x^2 + \dfrac{1}{2}x^2 + \dfrac{3}{2}x - \dfrac{1}{4}x + 3 - 2$
$= \left(\dfrac{1}{4} + \dfrac{1}{2}\right)x^2 + \left(\dfrac{3}{2} - \dfrac{1}{4}\right)x + (3 - 2)$
$= \dfrac{3}{4}x^2 + \dfrac{5}{4}x + 1$

57. $(5x^2y^2 - 8x^2y + xy^2) + (3x^2y^2 + x^2y - 4xy^2)$
$= 5x^2y^2 - 8x^2y + xy^2 + 3x^2y^2 + x^2y - 4xy^2$
$= 5x^2y^2 + 3x^2y^2 - 8x^2y + x^2y + xy^2 - 4xy^2$
$= (5+3)x^2y^2 + (-8+1)x^2y + (1-4)xy^2$
$= 8x^2y^2 - 7x^2y - 3xy^2$

59. $(3x^2y + 7xy^2 + xy) - (2x^2y - 4xy^2 - xy)$
$= 3x^2y + 7xy^2 + xy - 2x^2y + 4xy^2 + xy$
$= 3x^2y - 2x^2y + 7xy^2 + 4xy^2 + xy + xy$
$= (3-2)x^2y + (7+4)xy^2 + (1+1)xy$
$= x^2y + 11xy^2 + 2xy$

61. a. $f(x) = x^2 - 4x + 1$
$f(0) = (0)^2 - 4(0) + 1$
$= 0 - 0 + 1$
$= 1$

b. $f(x) = x^2 - 4x + 1$
$f(2) = (2)^2 - 4(2) + 1$
$= 4 - 8 + 1$
$= -3$

c. $f(x) = x^2 - 4x + 1$
$f(-3) = (-3)^2 - 4(-3) + 1$
$= 9 + 12 + 1$
$= 22$

63. a. $f(x) = 2x^3 - 7x + 3$

$f(0) = 2(0)^3 - 7(0) + 3$

$= 0 - 0 + 3$

$= 3$

b. $f(x) = 2x^3 - 7x + 3$

$f(2) = 2(2)^3 - 7(2) + 3$

$= 2 \cdot 8 - 14 + 3$

$= 16 - 14 + 3$

$= 5$

c. $f(x) = 2x^3 - 7x + 3$

$f(-3) = 2(-3)^3 - 7(-3) + 3$

$= 2 \cdot -27 + 21 + 3$

$= -54 + 21 + 3$

$= -30$

65. a. $f(x) = -x^3 + 3x^2 - 2x + 3$

$f(0) = -(0)^3 + 3(0)^2 - 2(0) + 3$

$= 0 + 0 - 0 + 3$

$= 3$

b. $f(x) = -x^3 + 3x^2 - 2x + 3$

$f(2) = -(2)^3 + 3(2)^2 - 2(2) + 3$

$= -8 + 3 \cdot 4 - 4 + 3$

$= -8 + 12 - 4 + 3$

$= 3$

c. $f(x) = -x^3 + 3x^2 - 2x + 3$

$f(-3) = -(-3)^3 + 3(-3)^2 - 2(-3) + 3$

$= -(-27) + 3 \cdot 9 + 6 + 3$

$= 27 + 27 + 6 + 3$

$= 63$

67. a. $(f + g)(x) = f(x) + g(x)$

$= (2x + 5) + (-5x + 1)$

$= 2x + 5 - 5x + 1$

$= 2x - 5x + 5 + 1$

$= -3x + 6$

b. $(f - g)(x) = f(x) - g(x)$

$= (2x + 5) - (-5x + 1)$

$= 2x + 5 + 5x - 1$

$= 2x + 5x + 5 - 1$

$= 7x + 4$

c. Since $(f + g)(x) = -3x + 6$, we have

$(f + g)(2) = -3(2) + 6$

$= -6 + 6$

$= 0$

d. Since $(f - g)(x) = 7x + 4$, we have

$(f - g)(1) = 7(1) + 4$

$= 7 + 4$

$= 11$

69. a. $(f + g)(x) = f(x) + g(x)$

$= (x^2 - 5x + 3) + (2x^2 + 3)$

$= x^2 - 5x + 3 + 2x^2 + 3$

$= x^2 + 2x^2 - 5x + 3 + 3$

$= 3x^2 - 5x + 6$

b. $(f - g)(x) = f(x) - g(x)$

$= (x^2 - 5x + 3) - (2x^2 + 3)$

$= x^2 - 5x + 3 - 2x^2 - 3$

$= x^2 - 2x^2 - 5x + 3 - 3$

$= -x^2 - 5x$

c. Since $(f + g)(x) = 3x^2 - 5x + 6$, we have

$(f + g)(2) = 3(2)^2 - 5(2) + 6$

$= 3 \cdot 4 - 10 + 6$

$= 12 - 10 + 6$

$= 8$

d. Since $(f - g)(x) = -x^2 - 5x$, we have

$(f - g)(1) = -(1)^2 - 5(1)$

$= -1 - 5$

$= -6$

71. a. $(f+g)(x)=f(x)+g(x)$
$$=\left(x^3+6x^2+12x+2\right)+\left(x^3-8\right)$$
$$=x^3+6x^2+12x+2+x^3-8$$
$$=x^3+x^3+6x^2+12x+2-8$$
$$=2x^3+6x^2+12x-6$$

b. $(f-g)(x)=f(x)-g(x)$
$$=\left(x^3+6x^2+12x+2\right)-\left(x^3-8\right)$$
$$=x^3+6x^2+12x+2-x^3+8$$
$$=x^3-x^3+6x^2+12x+2+8$$
$$=6x^2+12x+10$$

c. Since $(f+g)(x)=2x^3+6x^2+12x-6$, we have
$$(f+g)(2)=2(2)^3+6(2)^2+12(2)-6$$
$$=2\cdot8+6\cdot4+24-6$$
$$=16+24+24-6$$
$$=58$$

d. Since $(f-g)(x)=6x^2+12x+10$, we have
$$(f-g)(1)=6(1)^2+12(1)+10$$
$$=6+12+10$$
$$=28$$

73. $\left(5x^3-5x+3\right)+\left(-4x^3+x^2-2x+1\right)$
$$=5x^3-5x+3-4x^3+x^2-2x+1$$
$$=5x^3-4x^3+x^2-5x-2x+3+1$$
$$=(5-4)x^3+x^2+(-5-2)x+(3+1)$$
$$=x^3+x^2-7x+4$$

75. $\left(2b^3+5b^2-b+3\right)-\left(4b^3-b^2+3b-1\right)$
$$=2b^3+5b^2-b+3-4b^3+b^2-3b+1$$
$$=2b^3-4b^3+5b^2+b^2-b-3b+3+1$$
$$=(2-4)b^3+(5+1)b^2+(-1-3)b+(3+1)$$
$$=-2b^3+6b^2-4b+4$$

77. a. If the vertex is $(2,2)$, then $x=2$.
$$A(x)=-2x^2+6x$$
$$A(2)=-2(2)^2+6(2)$$
$$=-2\cdot4+12$$
$$=-8+12$$
$$=4$$
The area of the region is 4 square units.

b. If the vertex is $(1,4)$, then $x=1$.
$$A(x)=-2x^2+6x$$
$$A(1)=-2(1)^2+6(1)$$
$$=-2+6$$
$$=4$$
The area of the region is 4 square units.

c. Since the rectangular region is in quadrant I and has one corner at the origin, the coordinates of the vertex give us the length and width of the rectangle. Since the area of a rectangle can be found by multiplying the length and width, we can just multiply the coordinates together to get the area of the region.

$(2,2)\rightarrow 2\cdot2=4$ The area is 4 square units.

$(1,4)\rightarrow 1\cdot4=4$ The area is 4 square units.

79. a. In 1991, $t=0$.
$$P(t)=0.332t^2+1.848t+97.826$$
$$P(0)=0.332(0)^2+1.848(0)+97.826$$
$$=0+0+97.826$$
$$=97.826$$
According to the model, the average price of a new single family home in 1991 was roughly \$97,826.

b. In 2010, $t=19$.
$$P(t)=0.332t^2+1.848t+97.826$$
$$P(19)=0.332(19)^2+1.848(19)+97.826$$
$$=0.332(361)+1.848(19)+97.826$$
$$=119.852+35.112+97.826$$
$$=252.79$$
According to the model, the average price of a new single family home in 2010 will be roughly \$252,790.

81. a. Profit is the difference between revenue and costs. Thus,

$$P(x) = R(x) - C(x)$$

$$= \left(-1.2x^2 + 220x\right)$$

$$\quad - \left(0.05x^3 - 2x^2 + 65x + 500\right)$$

$$= -1.2x^2 + 220x - 0.05x^3 + 2x^2 - 65x - 500$$

$$= -0.05x^3 - 1.2x^2 + 2x^2 + 220x - 65x - 500$$

$$= -0.05x^3 + 0.8x^2 + 155x - 500$$

The profit function is:

$$P(x) = -0.05x^3 + 0.8x^2 + 155x - 500$$

b. $P(15) = -0.05(15)^3 + 0.8(15)^2$

$$\quad + 155(15) - 500$$

$$= -168.75 + 180 + 2325 - 500$$

$$= 1836.25$$

If 15 cell phones are sold, there would be a profit of $1836.25.

c. $P(100) = -0.05(100)^3 + 0.8(100)^2$

$$\quad + 155(100) - 500$$

$$= -0.05(1,000,000) + 0.8(10,000)$$

$$\quad + 15,500 - 500$$

$$= -50,000 + 8000 + 15,500 - 500$$

$$= -27,000$$

If 100 cell phones are sold, the profit function yields a negative value. Thus, there would be a loss of $27,000.

83. $f(x) = 3x + 2$; $g(x) = ax - 5$

$$(f + g)(x) = (3x + 2) + (ax - 5)$$

$$= 3x + 2 + ax - 5$$

$$= 3x + ax + 2 - 5$$

$$= (3 + a)x - 3$$

Since $(f + g)(3) = 12$, we have

$$(3 + a)(3) - 3 = 12$$

$$9 + 3a - 3 = 12$$

$$3a + 6 = 12$$

$$3a = 6$$

$$a = 2$$

85. a. $(f + g)(2) = f(2) + g(2)$

$$= 2 + 1$$

$$= 3$$

b. $(f + g)(4) = f(4) + g(4)$

$$= 1 + (-3)$$

$$= -2$$

c. $(f - g)(6) = f(6) - g(6)$

$$= 0 - (1)$$

$$= -1$$

d. $(g - f)(6) = g(6) - f(6)$

$$= 1 - 0$$

$$= 1$$

87. Taxes paid to the federal government are only part of the total taxes paid. To find the remaining amount paid in other taxes, subtract the federal amount from the total amount.

$$S(x) = T(x) - F(x)$$

89. a.-c. $f(x) = 4x^2 - 7x + 1$

$$f(4) = 37$$

$$f(-2) = 31$$

$$f(6) = 103$$

91. a.-c. $f(x) = 2x^3 - 5x^2 + x + 5$

$$f(4) = 57$$

$$f(-2) = -33$$

$$f(6) = 263$$

5.2 Preparing for Multiplying Polynomials

1. $4x^2 \cdot 3x^3 = 4 \cdot 3 \cdot x^2 \cdot x^3$

$\qquad = 12x^{2+3}$

$\qquad = 12x^5$

2. $(-3x)^2 = (-3)^2 \cdot x^2 = 9x^2$

3. $4(x-5) = 4 \cdot x - 4 \cdot 5$

$\qquad = 4x - 20$

5.2 Exercises

1. $A^2 - B^2$

3. $f(x) \cdot g(x)$

5. True

7. Answers may vary.
Using the distributive law, each term of the trinomial will be multiplied by each term of the binomial. Thus, the term in the binomial with the largest degree (2) must be multiplied by the term in the trinomial with its largest degree (3) to obtain a monomial term. The degree of this term is the sum of the degrees of the terms being multiplied and will be the largest of any of the resulting monomials in the product. Thus, the degree of the polynomial will be $2 + 3 = 5$.

9. $(5xy^2)(-3x^2y^3) = (5 \cdot -3)(x \cdot x^2)(y^2 \cdot y^3)$

$\qquad = -15x^{1+2}y^{2+3}$

$\qquad = -15x^3y^5$

11. $\left(\dfrac{3}{4}yz^3\right)\left(\dfrac{20}{9}y^3z^2\right) = \left(\dfrac{3}{4} \cdot \dfrac{20}{9}\right)(y \cdot y^3)(z^3 \cdot z^2)$

$\qquad = \dfrac{5}{3}y^{1+3}z^{3+2}$

$\qquad = \dfrac{5}{3}y^4z^5$

13. $5x(x^2 + 4x + 2) = 5x \cdot x^2 + 5x \cdot 4x + 5x \cdot 2$

$\qquad = 5x^3 + 20x^2 + 10x$

15. $-4a^2b(3a^2 + 2ab - b^2)$

$\qquad = -4a^2b \cdot 3a^2 + (-4a^2b) \cdot 2ab - (-4a^2b) \cdot b^2$

$\qquad = -12a^4b - 8a^3b^2 + 4a^2b^3$

17. $\dfrac{2}{3}ab\left(\dfrac{3}{4}a^2b - \dfrac{9}{8}ab^3 + 6ab\right)$

$\qquad = \dfrac{2}{3}ab \cdot \dfrac{3}{4}a^2b - \dfrac{2}{3}ab \cdot \dfrac{9}{8}ab^3 + \dfrac{2}{3}ab \cdot 6ab$

$\qquad = \dfrac{1}{2}a^3b^2 - \dfrac{3}{4}a^2b^4 + 4a^2b^2$

19. $0.4x^2(1.2x^2 - 0.8x + 1.5)$

$\qquad = 0.4x^2 \cdot 1.2x^2 - 0.4x^2 \cdot 0.8x + 0.4x^2 \cdot 1.5$

$\qquad = 0.48x^4 - 0.32x^3 + 0.6x^2$

21. $(x+3)(x+5) = x \cdot x + x \cdot 5 + 3 \cdot x + 3 \cdot 5$

$\qquad = x^2 + 5x + 3x + 15$

$\qquad = x^2 + 8x + 15$

23. $(a+5)(a-3) = a(a-3) + 5(a-3)$

$\qquad = a \cdot a - a \cdot 3 + 5 \cdot a - 5 \cdot 3$

$\qquad = a^2 - 3a + 5a - 15$

$\qquad = a^2 + 2a - 15$

25. $(4a+3)(3a-1) = 4a \cdot 3a - 4a \cdot 1 + 3 \cdot 3a - 3 \cdot 1$

$\qquad = 12a^2 - 4a + 9a - 3$

$\qquad = 12a^2 + 5a - 3$

27. $(-3x+1)(2x+7)$

$\qquad = -3x(2x+7) + 1(2x+7)$

$\qquad = -3x \cdot 2x + (-3x) \cdot 7 + 1 \cdot 2x + 1 \cdot 7$

$\qquad = -6x^2 - 21x + 2x + 7$

$\qquad = -6x^2 - 19x + 7$

29. $(4-5x)(3+2x) = 4 \cdot 3 + 4 \cdot 2x - 5x \cdot 3 - 5x \cdot 2x$

$\qquad = 12 + 8x - 15x - 10x^2$

$\qquad = 12 - 7x - 10x^2$

$\qquad = -10x^2 - 7x + 12$

31. $\left(\dfrac{2}{3}x+2\right)\left(\dfrac{1}{2}x-4\right)$

$= \dfrac{2}{3}x \cdot \dfrac{1}{2}x - \dfrac{2}{3}x \cdot 4 + 2 \cdot \dfrac{1}{2}x - 2 \cdot 4$

$= \dfrac{1}{3}x^2 - \dfrac{8}{3}x + x - 8$

$= \dfrac{1}{3}x^2 - \dfrac{5}{3}x - 8$

33. $(4a+3b)(a-5b)$

$= 4a \cdot a - 4a \cdot 5b + 3b \cdot a - 3b \cdot 5b$

$= 4a^2 - 20ab + 3ab - 15b^2$

$= 4a^2 - 17ab - 15b^2$

35. $(x+1)(x^2+4x+2)$

$= x \cdot x^2 + x \cdot 4x + x \cdot 2 + 1 \cdot x^2 + 1 \cdot 4x + 1 \cdot 2$

$= x^3 + 4x^2 + 2x + x^2 + 4x + 2$

$= x^3 + 5x^2 + 6x + 2$

37. $(3a-2)(2a^2+a-5)$

$= 3a \cdot 2a^2 + 3a \cdot a - 3a \cdot 5 - 2 \cdot 2a^2 - 2 \cdot a - 2 \cdot(-5)$

$= 6a^3 + 3a^2 - 15a - 4a^2 - 2a + 10$

$= 6a^3 - a^2 - 17a + 10$

39. $(5z^2+3z+2)(4z+3)$

$= 5z^2 \cdot 4z + 5z^2 \cdot 3 + 3z \cdot 4z + 3z \cdot 3 + 2 \cdot 4z + 2 \cdot 3$

$= 20z^3 + 15z^2 + 12z^2 + 9z + 8z + 6$

$= 20z^3 + 27z^2 + 17z + 6$

41. $(x-3)(x^3-4x^2+2x-7)$

$= x \cdot x^3 - x \cdot 4x^2 + x \cdot 2x - x \cdot 7 - 3 \cdot x^3$
$\quad - 3 \cdot(-4x^2) - 3 \cdot 2x - 3 \cdot(-7)$

$= x^4 - 4x^3 + 2x^2 - 7x - 3x^3 + 12x^2 - 6x + 21$

$= x^4 - 7x^3 + 14x^2 - 13x + 21$

43. $(4+y)(2y^2-3+5y)$

$= 4 \cdot 2y^2 - 4 \cdot 3 + 4 \cdot 5y + y \cdot 2y^2 - y \cdot 3 + y \cdot 5y$

$= 8y^2 - 12 + 20y + 2y^3 - 3y + 5y^2$

$= 2y^3 + 13y^2 + 17y - 12$

45. $(w^2+2w+1)(2w^2-3w+1)$

$= w^2 \cdot 2w^2 - w^2 \cdot 3w + w^2 \cdot 1 + 2w \cdot 2w^2 - 2w \cdot 3w$
$\quad + 2w \cdot 1 + 1 \cdot 2w^2 - 1 \cdot 3w + 1 \cdot 1$

$= 2w^4 - 3w^3 + w^2 + 4w^3 - 6w^2 + 2w + 2w^2$
$\quad - 3w + 1$

$= 2w^4 + w^3 - 3w^2 - w + 1$

47. $(x+y)(3x^2-2xy+4y^2)$

$= x \cdot 3x^2 - x \cdot 2xy + x \cdot 4y^2 + y \cdot 3x^2$
$\quad - y \cdot 2xy + y \cdot 4y^2$

$= 3x^3 - 2x^2y + 4xy^2 + 3x^2y - 2xy^2 + 4y^3$

$= 3x^3 + x^2y + 2xy^2 + 4y^3$

49. $(2ab+5)(4a^2-2ab+b^2)$

$= 2ab \cdot 4a^2 - 2ab \cdot 2ab + 2ab \cdot b^2 + 5 \cdot 4a^2$
$\quad - 5 \cdot 2ab + 5 \cdot b^2$

$= 8a^3b - 4a^2b^2 + 2ab^3 + 20a^2 - 10ab + 5b^2$

$= 8a^3b - 4a^2b^2 + 20a^2 + 2ab^3 - 10ab + 5b^2$

51. $(x-6)(x+6) = x^2 - 6^2$

$\qquad\qquad = x^2 - 36$

53. $(a+8)^2 = a^2 + 2 \cdot a \cdot 8 + 8^2$

$\qquad\quad = a^2 + 16a + 64$

55. $(3y-1)^2 = (3y)^2 - 2 \cdot 3y \cdot 1 + 1^2$

$\qquad\quad = 9y^2 - 6y + 1$

57. $(5a+3b)(5a-3b) = (5a)^2 - (3b)^2$

$\qquad\qquad\qquad = 25a^2 - 9b^2$

59. $(8z+y)^2 = (8z)^2 + 2 \cdot 8z \cdot y + y^2$

$\qquad\quad = 64z^2 + 16zy + y^2$

$\qquad\quad$ or

$\qquad\quad = y^2 + 16yz + 64z^2$

61. $(10x-y)^2 = (10x)^2 - 2 \cdot 10x \cdot y + y^2$

$\qquad\qquad = 100x^2 - 20xy + y^2$

63. $\left(a^3+2b\right)\left(a^3-2b\right)=\left(a^3\right)^2-\left(2b\right)^2$
$$=a^6-4b^2$$

65. $\left[3x-(y+1)\right]\left[3x+(y+1)\right]$
$$=\left(3x\right)^2-\left(y+1\right)^2$$
$$=9x^2-\left(y^2+2y+1\right)$$
$$=9x^2-y^2-2y-1$$

67. $\left[2a+(b-3)\right]^2=\left(2a\right)^2+2\cdot 2a\cdot(b-3)+(b-3)^2$
$$=4a^2+4a(b-3)+\left(b^2-2\cdot b\cdot 3+3^2\right)$$
$$=4a^2+4ab-12a+b^2-6b+9$$

69. a. $(f\cdot g)(x)=f(x)\cdot g(x)$
$$=(x+4)(x-1)$$
$$=x\cdot x-x\cdot 1+4\cdot x-4\cdot 1$$
$$=x^2-x+4x-4$$
$$=x^2+3x-4$$

b. Since $(f\cdot g)(x)=x^2+3x-4$, we have
$$(f\cdot g)(3)=(3)^2+3(3)-4$$
$$=9+9-4$$
$$=14$$

71. a. $(f\cdot g)(x)=f(x)\cdot g(x)$
$$=(4x-3)(2x+5)$$
$$=4x\cdot 2x+4x\cdot 5-3\cdot 2x-3\cdot 5$$
$$=8x^2+20x-6x-15$$
$$=8x^2+14x-15$$

b. Since $(f\cdot g)(x)=8x^2+14x-15$, we have
$$(f\cdot g)(3)=8(3)^2+14(3)-15$$
$$=8\cdot 9+42-15$$
$$=72+42-15$$
$$=99$$

73. a. $(f\cdot g)(x)=f(x)\cdot g(x)$
$$=(x-2)\left(x^2+5x-3\right)$$
$$=x\cdot x^2+x\cdot 5x-x\cdot 3-2\cdot x^2$$
$$-2\cdot 5x-2\cdot(-3)$$
$$=x^3+5x^2-3x-2x^2-10x+6$$
$$=x^3+3x^2-13x+6$$

b. Since $(f\cdot g)(x)=x^3+3x^2-13x+6$, we have
$$(f\cdot g)(3)=(3)^3+3(3)^2-13(3)+6$$
$$=27+3\cdot 9-39+6$$
$$=27+27-39+6$$
$$=21$$

75. a. $f(x)=x^2+1$
$$f(x+2)=(x+2)^2+1$$
$$=x^2+2\cdot x\cdot 2+2^2+1$$
$$=x^2+4x+4+1$$
$$=x^2+4x+5$$

b. $f(x+h)-f(x)$
$$=\left[(x+h)^2+1\right]-\left[x^2+1\right]$$
$$=\left[x^2+2xh+h^2+1\right]-\left[x^2+1\right]$$
$$=x^2+2xh+h^2+1-x^2-1$$
$$=2xh+h^2$$

77. a. $f(x)=x^2+5x-2$
$$f(x+2)=(x+2)^2+5(x+2)-2$$
$$=x^2+4x+4+5x+10-2$$
$$=x^2+9x+12$$

b. $f(x+h)-f(x)$
$$=\left[(x+h)^2+5(x+h)-2\right]-\left[x^2+5x-2\right]$$
$$=\left[x^2+2xh+h^2+5x+5h-2\right]-\left[x^2+5x-2\right]$$
$$=x^2+2xh+h^2+5x+5h-2-x^2-5x+2$$
$$=2xh+5h+h^2$$

79. a.
$$f(x) = 3x^2 - x + 1$$
$$f(x+2) = 3(x+2)^2 - (x+2) + 1$$
$$= 3(x^2 + 4x + 4) - x - 2 + 1$$
$$= 3x^2 + 12x + 12 - x - 1$$
$$= 3x^2 + 11x + 11$$

b. $f(x+h) - f(x)$
$$= \left[3(x+h)^2 - (x+h) + 1\right] - \left[3x^2 - x + 1\right]$$
$$= \left[3(x^2 + 2xh + h^2) - x - h + 1\right] - \left[3x^2 - x + 1\right]$$
$$= 3x^2 + 6xh + 3h^2 - x - h + 1 - 3x^2 + x - 1$$
$$= 6xh - h + 3h^2$$

81. $5ab(a-b)^2 = 5ab(a^2 - 2 \cdot a \cdot b + b^2)$
$$= 5ab(a^2 - 2ab + b^2)$$
$$= 5ab \cdot a^2 - 5ab \cdot 2ab + 5ab \cdot b^2$$
$$= 5a^3b - 10a^2b^2 + 5ab^3$$

83. $(5y+1)(5y-1) = (5y)^2 - (1)^2$
$$= 25y^2 - 1$$

85. $(8z+3)(3z-1) = 8z \cdot 3z - 8z \cdot 1 + 3 \cdot 3z - 3 \cdot 1$
$$= 24z^2 - 8z + 9z - 3$$
$$= 24z^2 + z - 3$$

87. $(2m-3n)(4m+n) - (m-2n)^2$
$$= 2m \cdot 4m + 2m \cdot n - 3n \cdot 4m - 3n \cdot n$$
$$- \left(m^2 - 2 \cdot m \cdot 2n + (2n)^2\right)$$
$$= 8m^2 + 2mn - 12mn - 3n^2 - \left(m^2 - 4mn + 4n^2\right)$$
$$= 8m^2 - 10mn - 3n^2 - m^2 + 4mn - 4n^2$$
$$= 7m^2 - 6mn - 7n^2$$

89. $(x+3)(x^2 - 3x + 9)$
$$= x \cdot x^2 - x \cdot 3x + x \cdot 9 + 3 \cdot x^2 - 3 \cdot 3x + 3 \cdot 9$$
$$= x^3 - 3x^2 + 9x + 3x^2 - 9x + 27$$
$$= x^3 + 27$$

91. $\left(2x - \dfrac{1}{2}\right)^2 = (2x)^2 - 2 \cdot 2x \cdot \dfrac{1}{2} + \left(\dfrac{1}{2}\right)^2$
$$= 4x^2 - 2x + \dfrac{1}{4}$$

93. $(p+2)^3$
$$= (p+2)(p+2)^2$$
$$= (p+2)\left(p^2 + 2 \cdot p \cdot 2 + 2^2\right)$$
$$= (p+2)\left(p^2 + 4p + 4\right)$$
$$= p \cdot p^2 + p \cdot 4p + p \cdot 4 + 2 \cdot p^2 + 2 \cdot 4p + 2 \cdot 4$$
$$= p^3 + 4p^2 + 4p + 2p^2 + 8p + 8$$
$$= p^3 + 6p^2 + 12p + 8$$

95. $(7x - 5y + 2)(3x - 2y + 1)$
$$= 7x \cdot 3x - 7x \cdot 2y + 7x \cdot 1 - 5y \cdot 3x + 5y \cdot 2y$$
$$- 5y \cdot 1 + 2 \cdot 3x - 2 \cdot 2y + 2 \cdot 1$$
$$= 21x^2 - 14xy + 7x - 15xy + 10y^2 - 5y$$
$$+ 6x - 4y + 2$$
$$= 21x^2 - 29xy + 13x + 10y^2 - 9y + 2$$

97. $(2p-1)(p+3) + (p-3)(p+3)$
$$= 2p(p+3) - 1(p+3) + p^2 - 3^2$$
$$= 2p \cdot p + 2p \cdot 3 - 1 \cdot p - 1 \cdot 3 + p^2 - 9$$
$$= 2p^2 + 6p - p - 3 + p^2 - 9$$
$$= 3p^2 + 5p - 12$$

99. $(x+3)(x-3)(x^2 - 9) - (x+1)(x^2 - 3)$
$$= \left(x^2 - 3^2\right)\left(x^2 - 9\right) - \left[x \cdot x^2 - x \cdot 3 + 1 \cdot x^2 - 1 \cdot 3\right]$$
$$= \left(x^2 - 9\right)\left(x^2 - 9\right) - \left(x^3 - 3x + x^2 - 3\right)$$
$$= \left(x^2\right)^2 - 2\left(x^2\right)(9) + 9^2 - x^3 + 3x - x^2 + 3$$
$$= x^4 - 18x^2 + 81 - x^3 + 3x - x^2 + 3$$
$$= x^4 - x^3 - 19x^2 + 3x + 84$$

101.

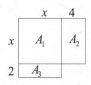

$A = A_1 + A_2 + A_3$

$\quad = x^2 + 4x + 2x$

$\quad = x^2 + 6x$

An alternate method is to note that the length is $(x+4)$ and width is $(x+2)$. The area of the corner piece that is missing is $2(4) = 8$ square units. We can multiply the length and width, then subtract off the missing area:

$A = (x+4)(x+2) - 2(4)$

$\quad = x^2 + 2x + 4x + 8 - 8$

$\quad = x^2 + 6x$

103.

	$4x$	5
x	A_1	A_2
6	A_3	A_4

$A = A_1 + A_2 + A_3 + A_4$

$\quad = 4x(x) + 5(x) + 6(4x) + 6(5)$

$\quad = 4x^2 + 5x + 24x + 30$

$\quad = 4x^2 + 29x + 30$

An alternate method is to note that the length is $(4x+5)$ and the width is $(x+6)$. Since the area of a rectangle is the product of the length and width, we would get:

$A = (4x+5)(x+6)$

$\quad = 4x^2 + 24x + 5x + 30$

$\quad = 4x^2 + 29x + 30$

Notice how the FOIL method gives each of the individual areas.

105. $A = (2x+4)(3x-1) - (x+2)(2x-5)$

$\quad = (6x^2 - 2x + 12x - 4) - (2x^2 - 5x + 4x - 10)$

$\quad = (6x^2 + 10x - 4) - (2x^2 - x - 10)$

$\quad = 6x^2 + 10x - 4 - 2x^2 + x + 10$

$\quad = 4x^2 + 11x + 6$

The area of the shaded region is $4x^2 + 11x + 6$ square units.

107. a. $A_1 = a^2;\ A_2 = ab;\ A_3 = ab;\ A_4 = b^2$

	a	b
a	A_1	A_2
b	A_3	A_4

b. $A = A_1 + A_2 + A_3 + A_4$

$\quad = a^2 + ab + ab + b^2$

$\quad = a^2 + 2ab + b^2$

c. The length of the region is $a+b$ and the width is also $a+b$.

The area of the region would be

$A = (a+b)(a+b)$

$\quad = (a+b)^2$

The result from part (b) is obtained by multiplying this expression out.

109. $(2^x + 3)(2^x - 4) = 2^x \cdot 2^x - 2^x \cdot 4 + 3 \cdot 2^x - 3 \cdot 4$

$\quad = 2^{x+x} - 2^x - 12$

$\quad = 2^{2x} - 2^x - 12$

111. $(5^y - 1)^2 = (5^y)^2 - 2 \cdot 5^y \cdot 1 + 1^2$

$\quad = 5^{2y} - 2(5^y) + 1$

5.3 Preparing for Dividing Polynomials and Synthetic Division

1. $\dfrac{15x^5}{12x^3} = \dfrac{15}{12} \cdot \dfrac{x^5}{x^3} = \dfrac{5}{4}x^{5-3} = \dfrac{5}{4}x^2$

2. $\dfrac{2}{7} + \dfrac{5}{7} = \dfrac{2+5}{7} = \dfrac{7}{7} = 1$

5.3 Exercises

1. $0;\ (x+1)\cdot(3x-1)$

3. synthetic division

5. True

7. For polynomial division we have
dividend = divisor · quotient + remainder
The dividend is the polynomial f and has degree n. Since the remainder must be 0 or a polynomial that has a lower degree than f, the degree n must be obtained from the product of the divisor and the quotient. The divisor is $x+4$ which is of degree 1 so the quotient must be of degree $n-1$.

9. Yes, $3x+4$ is a factor since the remainder is 0. We can write
$6x^3 - x^2 - 9x + 4 = (3x+4)(2x^2 - 3x + 1)$

11. $\dfrac{8x^2 + 12x}{4x} = \dfrac{8x^2}{4x} + \dfrac{12x}{4x}$
$= \dfrac{8}{4}x^{2-1} + \dfrac{12}{4}x^{1-1}$
$= 2x + 3$

13. $\dfrac{2a^3 - 15a^2 + 10a}{5a} = \dfrac{2a^3}{5a} - \dfrac{15a^2}{5a} + \dfrac{10a}{5a}$
$= \dfrac{2}{5}a^{3-1} - \dfrac{15}{5}a^{2-1} + \dfrac{10}{5}a^{1-1}$
$= \dfrac{2}{5}a^2 - 3a + 2$

15. $\dfrac{2y^3 + 6y}{4y^2} = \dfrac{2y^3}{4y^2} + \dfrac{6y}{4y^2}$
$= \dfrac{2}{4}y^{3-2} + \dfrac{6}{4}y^{1-2}$
$= \dfrac{1}{2}y + \dfrac{3}{2}y^{-1}$
$= \dfrac{y}{2} + \dfrac{3}{2y}$

17. $\dfrac{4m^2n^2 + 6m^2n - 18mn^2}{4m^2n^2}$
$= \dfrac{4m^2n^2}{4m^2n^2} + \dfrac{6m^2n}{4m^2n^2} - \dfrac{18mn^2}{4m^2n^2}$
$= \dfrac{4}{4}m^{2-2}n^{2-2} + \dfrac{6}{4}m^{2-2}n^{1-2} - \dfrac{18}{4}m^{1-2}n^{2-2}$
$= m^0n^0 + \dfrac{3}{2}m^0n^{-1} - \dfrac{9}{2}m^{-1}n^0$
$= 1 + \dfrac{3}{2n} - \dfrac{9}{2m}$

19.
$$
\begin{array}{r}
x+3 \\
x+2\overline{\smash{\big)}\,x^2 + 5x + 6} \\
\underline{-\left(x^2 + 2x\right)} \\
3x + 6 \\
\underline{-(3x + 6)} \\
0
\end{array}
$$

$\dfrac{x^2 + 5x + 6}{x + 2} = x + 3$

21.
$$
\begin{array}{r}
2x+5 \\
x-2\overline{\smash{\big)}\,2x^2 + x - 4} \\
\underline{-\left(2x^2 - 4x\right)} \\
5x - 4 \\
\underline{-(5x - 10)} \\
6
\end{array}
$$

$\dfrac{2x^2 + x - 4}{x - 2} = 2x + 5 + \dfrac{6}{x - 2}$

23.

$$
\begin{array}{r}
w+6 \\
2w-7\overline{\smash{)}2w^2+5w-49} \\
\underline{-\left(2w^2-7w\right)} \\
12w-49 \\
\underline{-(12w-42)} \\
-7
\end{array}
$$

$$\frac{2w^2+5w-49}{2w-7}=w+6-\frac{7}{2w-7}$$

25.

$$
\begin{array}{r}
x^2+5x-14 \\
x+3\overline{\smash{)}x^3+8x^2+x-42} \\
\underline{-\left(x^3+3x^2\right)} \\
5x^2+x \\
\underline{-\left(5x^2+15x\right)} \\
-14x-42 \\
\underline{-(-14x-42)} \\
0
\end{array}
$$

$$\frac{x^3+8x^2+x-42}{x+3}=x^2+5x-14$$

27.

$$
\begin{array}{r}
w^2-4w-5 \\
w+4\overline{\smash{)}w^3+0w^2-21w-20} \\
\underline{-\left(w^3+4w^2\right)} \\
-4w^2-21w \\
\underline{-\left(-4w^2-16w\right)} \\
-5w-20 \\
\underline{-(-5w-20)} \\
0
\end{array}
$$

$$\frac{w^3-21w-20}{w+4}=w^2-4w-5$$

29.

$$
\begin{array}{r}
3x^2-14x-5 \\
2x+5\overline{\smash{)}6x^3-13x^2-80x-25} \\
\underline{-\left(6x^3+15x^2\right)} \\
-28x^2-80x \\
\underline{-\left(-28x^2-70x\right)} \\
-10x-25 \\
\underline{-(-10x-25)} \\
0
\end{array}
$$

$$\frac{6x^3-13x^2-80x-25}{2x+5}=3x^2-14x-5$$

31.

$$
\begin{array}{r}
x-7 \\
x^2+3\overline{\smash{)}x^3-7x^2+3x-21} \\
\underline{-\left(x^3\qquad+3x\right)} \\
-7x^2\qquad-21 \\
\underline{-\left(-7x^2\qquad-21\right)} \\
0
\end{array}
$$

$$\frac{x^3-7x^2+3x-21}{x^2+3}=x-7$$

33.

$$
\begin{array}{r}
z+7 \\
3z^2+1\overline{\smash{)}3z^3+21z^2+5z+2} \\
\underline{-\left(3z^3\qquad+z\right)} \\
21z^2+4z+2 \\
\underline{-\left(21z^2\qquad+7\right)} \\
4z-5
\end{array}
$$

$$\frac{3z^3+21z^2+5z+2}{3z^2+1}=z+7+\frac{4z-5}{3z^2+1}$$

35.

$$x^2+2x+5 \overline{\smash{\big)}\, 2x^4-11x^3+8x^2-22x+144} \quad \underset{2x^2-15x+28}{}$$

$$\underline{-\left(2x^4+4x^3+10x^2\right)}$$

$$-15x^3-2x^2-22x$$

$$\underline{-\left(-15x^3-30x^2-75x\right)}$$

$$28x^2+53x+144$$

$$\underline{-\left(28x^2+56x+140\right)}$$

$$-3x+4$$

$$\frac{2x^4-11x^3+8x^2-22x+144}{x^2+2x+5}=2x^2-15x+28+\frac{-3x+4}{x^2+2x+5}$$

37. The divisor is $x-5$ so $c=5$.

$$5\overline{)\begin{array}{ccc} 1 & -3 & -10 \\ & 5 & 10 \\ \hline 1 & 2 & 0 \end{array}}$$

$$\frac{x^2-3x-10}{x-5}=x+2$$

39. The divisor is $x+4$ so $c=-4$.

$$-4\overline{)\begin{array}{ccc} 2 & 11 & 12 \\ & -8 & -12 \\ \hline 2 & 3 & 0 \end{array}}$$

$$\frac{2x^2+11x+12}{x+4}=2x+3$$

41. The divisor is $x-6$ so $c=6$.

$$6\overline{)\begin{array}{ccc} 1 & -3 & -14 \\ & 6 & 18 \\ \hline 1 & 3 & 4 \end{array}}$$

$$\frac{x^2-3x-14}{x-6}=x+3+\frac{4}{x-6}$$

43. The divisor is $x-5$ so $c=5$.

$$5\overline{)\begin{array}{cccc} 1 & 0 & -19 & -15 \\ & 5 & 25 & 30 \\ \hline 1 & 5 & 6 & 15 \end{array}}$$

$$\frac{x^3-19x-15}{x-5}=x^2+5x+6+\frac{15}{x-5}$$

45. The divisor is $x-3$ so $c=3$.

$$3\overline{)\begin{array}{ccccc} 3 & -5 & -21 & 17 & 25 \\ & 9 & 12 & -27 & -30 \\ \hline 3 & 4 & -9 & -10 & -5 \end{array}}$$

$$\frac{3x^4-5x^3-21x^2+17x+25}{x-3}=3x^3+4x^2-9x-10-\frac{5}{x-3}$$

47. The divisor is $x+6$ so $c=-6$.

$$-6\overline{)\begin{array}{ccccc} 1 & 0 & -40 & 0 & 109 \\ & -6 & 36 & 24 & -144 \\ \hline 1 & -6 & -4 & 24 & -35 \end{array}}$$

$$\frac{x^4-40x^2+109}{x+6}=x^3-6x^2-4x+24-\frac{35}{x+6}$$

49. The divisor is $x-\dfrac{5}{2}$ so $c=\dfrac{5}{2}$.

$$\tfrac{5}{2}\overline{)\begin{array}{cccc} 2 & 3 & -14 & -15 \\ & 5 & 20 & 15 \\ \hline 2 & 8 & 6 & 0 \end{array}}$$

$$\frac{2x^3+3x^2-14x-15}{x-\dfrac{5}{2}}=2x^2+8x+6$$

51. a. $\left(\dfrac{f}{g}\right)(x) = \dfrac{4x^3 - 8x^2 + 12x}{4x}$

$$= \dfrac{4x^3}{4x} - \dfrac{8x^2}{4x} + \dfrac{12x}{4x}$$

$$= \dfrac{4}{4}x^{3-1} - \dfrac{8}{4}x^{2-1} + \dfrac{12}{4}x^{1-1}$$

$$= x^2 - 2x + 3$$

b. Using the result from part **a**, we have:

$$\left(\dfrac{f}{g}\right)(2) = (2)^2 - 2(2) + 3$$

$$= 4 - 4 + 3$$

$$= 3$$

53. a. $\left(\dfrac{f}{g}\right)(x) = \dfrac{x^2 - x - 12}{x - 4}$

The divisor is $x - 4$ so $c = 4$.

$$\begin{array}{r} 4\overline{)1 \quad -1 \quad -12} \\ \underline{\quad 4 \quad 12} \\ 1 \quad 3 \quad 0 \end{array}$$

$$\left(\dfrac{f}{g}\right)(x) = x + 3$$

b. $\left(\dfrac{f}{g}\right)(2) = 2 + 3 = 5$

55. a. $\left(\dfrac{f}{g}\right)(x) = \dfrac{2x^2 + 5x - 1}{x + 3}$

The divisor is $x + 3$ so $c = -3$.

$$\begin{array}{r} -3\overline{)2 \quad 5 \quad -1} \\ \underline{\quad -6 \quad 3} \\ 2 \quad -1 \quad 2 \end{array}$$

$$\left(\dfrac{f}{g}\right)(x) = 2x - 1 + \dfrac{2}{x + 3}$$

b. $\left(\dfrac{f}{g}\right)(2) = 2(2) - 1 + \dfrac{2}{2 + 3}$

$$= 4 - 1 + \dfrac{2}{5}$$

$$= \dfrac{17}{5}$$

57. a. $\left(\dfrac{f}{g}\right)(x) = \dfrac{2x^3 + 9x^2 + x - 12}{2x + 3}$

$$\begin{array}{r} x^2 + 3x - 4 \\ 2x + 3\overline{)2x^3 + 9x^2 + x - 12} \\ \underline{-\left(2x^3 + 3x^2\right)} \\ 6x^2 + x \\ \underline{-\left(6x^2 + 9x\right)} \\ -8x - 12 \\ \underline{-(-8x - 12)} \\ 0 \end{array}$$

$$\dfrac{2x^3 + 9x^2 + x - 12}{2x + 3} = x^2 + 3x - 4$$

b. $\left(\dfrac{f}{g}\right)(2) = (2)^2 + 3(2) - 4$

$$= 4 + 6 - 4$$

$$= 6$$

59. a. $\left(\dfrac{f}{g}\right)(x) = \dfrac{x^3 - 13x - 12}{x^2 - 9}$

$$\begin{array}{r} x \\ x^2 - 9\overline{)x^3 + 0x^2 - 13x - 12} \\ \underline{-\left(x^3 \qquad - 9x\right)} \\ -4x - 12 \end{array}$$

$$\dfrac{x^3 - 13x - 12}{x^2 - 9} = x - \dfrac{4x + 12}{x^2 - 9}$$

b. $\left(\dfrac{f}{g}\right)(2) = 2 - \dfrac{4(2) + 12}{(2)^2 - 9}$

$$= 2 - \dfrac{8 + 12}{4 - 9}$$

$$= 2 - \dfrac{20}{-5}$$

$$= 2 + 4$$

$$= 6$$

61. The divisor is $x - 2$ so $c = 2$.

$$f(2) = (2)^2 - 5(2) + 1$$

$$= 4 - 10 + 1$$

$$= -5$$

The remainder is -5.

63. The divisor is $x+4$ so $c=-4$.

$$f(-4)=(-4)^3-2(-4)^2+5(-4)-3$$
$$=-64-2(16)-20-3$$
$$=-64-32-20-3$$
$$=-119$$

The remainder is -119.

65. The divisor is $x-5$ so $c=5$.

$$f(5)=2(5)^3-4(5)+1$$
$$=2(125)-20+1$$
$$=250-20+1$$
$$=231$$

The remainder is 231.

67. The divisor is $x-1$ so $c=1$.

$$f(1)=(1)^4+1$$
$$=1+1$$
$$=2$$

The remainder is 2.

69. $c=2$

$$f(2)=(2)^2-3(2)+2$$
$$=4-6+2$$
$$=0$$

Since the remainder is 0, $x-2$ is a factor.

$$\begin{array}{r|rrr} 2 & 1 & -3 & 2 \\ & & 2 & -2 \\ \hline & 1 & -1 & 0 \end{array}$$

$$f(x)=(x-2)(x-1)$$

71. $c=-2$

$$f(-2)=2(-2)^2+5(-2)+2$$
$$=2(4)-10+2$$
$$=8-10+2$$
$$=0$$

Since the remainder is 0, $x+2$ is a factor.

$$\begin{array}{r|rrr} -2 & 2 & 5 & 2 \\ & & -4 & -2 \\ \hline & 2 & 1 & 0 \end{array}$$

$$f(x)=(x+2)(2x+1)$$

73. $c=3$

$$f(3)=4(3)^3-9(3)^2-49(3)-30$$
$$=4(27)-9(9)-147-30$$
$$=108-81-147-30$$
$$=-150$$

Since the remainder is not 0, $x-3$ is not a factor of $f(x)$.

75. $c=-1$

$$f(-1)=4(-1)^3-7(-1)^2-5(-1)+6$$
$$=-4-7+5+6$$
$$=0$$

Since the remainder is 0, $x+1$ is a factor.

$$\begin{array}{r|rrrr} -1 & 4 & -7 & -5 & 6 \\ & & -4 & 11 & -6 \\ \hline & 4 & -11 & 6 & 0 \end{array}$$

$$f(x)=(x+1)(4x^2-11x+6)$$

77.

$$\frac{3a^3b^2-9a^2b+18ab}{3ab}$$

$$=\frac{3a^3b^2}{3ab}-\frac{9a^2b}{3ab}+\frac{18ab}{3ab}$$

$$=\frac{3}{3}a^{3-1}b^{2-1}-\frac{9}{3}a^{2-1}b^{1-1}+\frac{18}{3}a^{1-1}b^{1-1}$$

$$=a^2b-3ab^0+6a^0b^0$$

$$=a^2b-3a+6$$

79.

$$\begin{array}{r} y+3 \\ 3y+2 \overline{\smash{\big)}\,3y^2+11y+6} \\ \underline{-(3y^2+2y)} \\ 9y+6 \\ \underline{-(9y+6)} \\ 0 \end{array}$$

$$\frac{3y^2+11y+6}{3y+2}=y+3$$

81.

$$x^2+5 \overline{)x^3+6x^2+8x+32} \quad \frac{x+6}{}$$

$$\underline{-\left(x^3 \qquad +5x\right)}$$

$$6x^2+3x+32$$

$$\underline{-\left(6x^2 \qquad +30\right)}$$

$$3x+2$$

$$\frac{x^3+6x^2+8x+32}{x^2+5}=x+6+\frac{3x+2}{x^2+5}$$

83.

$$\frac{8x^3+6x}{12x^2}=\frac{8x^3}{12x^2}+\frac{6x}{12x^2}=\frac{2x^{3-2}}{3}+\frac{1}{2x^{2-1}}$$

$$=\frac{2}{3}x+\frac{1}{2x}$$

85. The divisor is $x+4$ so $c=-4$.

$$-4 \overline{)\begin{array}{cccc} 1 & 7 & 2 & -46 \end{array}}$$

$$\begin{array}{cccc} & -4 & -12 & 40 \end{array}$$

$$\begin{array}{cccc} 1 & 3 & -10 & -6 \end{array}$$

$$\frac{x^3+7x^2+2x-46}{x+4}=x^2+3x-10-\frac{6}{x+4}$$

87.

$$3x+5 \overline{)3x^3+5x^2-24x-40} \quad \frac{x^2-8}{}$$

$$\underline{-\left(3x^3+5x^2\right)}$$

$$0-24x-40$$

$$\underline{-\left(-24x-40\right)}$$

$$0$$

$$\frac{3x^3+5x^2-24x-40}{3x+5}=x^2-8$$

89.

$$2x-3 \overline{)8x^3+0x^2+0x-27} \quad \frac{4x^2+6x+9}{}$$

$$\underline{-\left(8x^3-12x^2\right)}$$

$$12x^2 \qquad -27$$

$$\underline{-\left(12x^2-18x\right)}$$

$$18x-27$$

$$\underline{-\left(18x-27\right)}$$

$$0$$

$$\frac{8x^3-27}{2x-3}=4x^2+6x+9$$

91. Since the area of a rectangle is the product of the length and width, we can find the length by dividing the area by the width.

$$3x-1 \overline{)15x^2+x-2} \quad \frac{5x+2}{}$$

$$\underline{-\left(15x^2-5x\right)}$$

$$6x-2$$

$$\underline{-\left(6x-2\right)}$$

$$0$$

The area of the rectangle is given by

$$A=15x^2+x-2=\left(3x-1\right)\left(5x+2\right).$$

The length of the rectangle is $5x+2$ feet.

93. The volume of a rectangular box is the product of the length, width, and height. The product of the width and height is given by

$$\left(x+5\right)\left(x-3\right)=x^2-3x+5x-15$$

$$=x^2+2x-15$$

To find the length, we need to divide the volume by this quantity.

$$x^2+2x-15 \overline{)2x^3+9x^2-20x-75} \quad \frac{2x+5}{}$$

$$\underline{-\left(2x^3+4x^2-30x\right)}$$

$$5x^2+10x-75$$

$$\underline{-\left(5x^2+10x-75\right)}$$

$$0$$

The volume of the box is given by

$$V=2x^3+9x^2-20x-75=\left(2x+5\right)\left(x+5\right)\left(x-3\right)$$

The length of the box is $2x+5$ centimeters.

95. a. $\overline{C}(x) = \dfrac{0.01x^3 - 0.4x^2 + 13x + 400}{x}$

$= \dfrac{0.01x^3}{x} - \dfrac{0.4x^2}{x} + \dfrac{13x}{x} + \dfrac{400}{x}$

$= 0.01x^2 - 0.4x + 13 + \dfrac{400}{x}$

b. $\overline{C}(50) = 0.01(50)^2 - 0.4(50) + 13 + \dfrac{400}{50}$

$= 25 - 20 + 13 + 8$

$= 26$

The average cost of manufacturing $x = 50$ wristwatches in a day is 26.

97. $\dfrac{f(x)}{x-5} = 3x + 5$

$f(x) = (x-5)(3x+5)$

$= x \cdot 3x + x \cdot 5 - 5 \cdot 3x - 5 \cdot 5$

$= 3x^2 + 5x - 15x - 25$

$= 3x^2 - 10x - 25$

99. $\dfrac{f(x)}{x-3} = x + 8 + \dfrac{4}{x-3}$

$f(x) = (x-3)\left(x + 8 + \dfrac{4}{x-3}\right)$

$= x(x-3) + 8(x-3) + \dfrac{4}{x-3}(x-3)$

$= x^2 - 3x + 8x - 24 + 4$

$= x^2 + 5x - 20$

101. $\dfrac{2x^3 - 3x^2 - 26x - 37}{x+2} = ax^2 + bx + c + \dfrac{d}{x+2}$

Since the divisor is linear, we can use synthetic division.

$$
\begin{array}{r|rrrr}
-2 & 2 & -3 & -26 & -37 \\
   &   & -4 & 14 & 24 \\
\hline
   & 2 & -7 & -12 & -13
\end{array}
$$

$\dfrac{2x^3 - 3x^2 - 26x - 37}{x+2} = 2x^2 - 7x - 12 + \dfrac{-13}{x+2}$.

This gives us $a = 2$, $b = -7$, $c = -12$, and $d = -13$.

Thus,

$a + b + c + d = 2 + (-7) + (-12) + (-13) = -30$

Putting the Concepts Together (Sections 5.1-5.3)

1. $5m^4 - 2m^3 + 3m + 8$

Degree: 4

2. $\left(7a^2 - 4a^3 + 7a - 1\right) + \left(2a^2 - 6a - 7\right)$

$= 7a^2 - 4a^3 + 7a - 1 + 2a^2 - 6a - 7$

$= -4a^3 + 7a^2 + 2a^2 + 7a - 6a - 1 - 7$

$= -4a^3 + (7+2)a^2 + (7-6)a + (-1-7)$

$= -4a^3 + 9a^2 + a - 8$

3. $\left(\frac{1}{5}y^2 + 2y - 6\right) - \left(4y^2 - y + 2\right)$

$= \frac{1}{5}y^2 + 2y - 6 - 4y^2 + y - 2$

$= \frac{1}{5}y^2 - 4y^2 + 2y + y - 6 - 2$

$= -\frac{19}{5}y^2 + 3y - 8$

4. $f(x) = 2x^3 - x^2 + 4x + 9$

$f(2) = 2(2)^3 - (2)^2 + 4(2) + 9$

$= 2(8) - 4 + 8 + 9$

$= 16 - 4 + 8 + 9$

$= 29$

5. $(f+g)(x) = (6x+5) + \left(-x^2 + 2x + 3\right)$

$= 6x + 5 - x^2 + 2x + 3$

$= -x^2 + 8x + 8$

$(f+g)(-3) = -(-3)^2 + 8(-3) + 8$

$= -9 - 24 + 8$

$= -25$

6. $(f-g)(x) = \left(2x^2 + 7\right) - \left(x^2 - 4x - 3\right)$

$= 2x^2 + 7 - x^2 + 4x + 3$

$= 2x^2 - x^2 + 4x + 7 + 3$

$= x^2 + 4x + 10$

7. $2mn^3\left(m^2n - 4mn + 6\right)$

$= 2mn^3 \cdot m^2n - 2mn^3 \cdot 4mn + 2mn^3 \cdot 6$

$= 2m^{1+2}n^{3+1} - 8m^{1+1}n^{3+1} + 12mn^3$

$= 2m^3n^4 - 8m^2n^4 + 12mn^3$

8. $(3a-5b)^2 = (3a)^2 - 2(3a)(5b) + (5b)^2$

$= 9a^2 - 30ab + 25b^2$

9. $(7n^2+3)(7n^2-3) = (7n^2)^2 - (3)^2$

$= 49n^4 - 9$

10. $(3a+2b)(6a^2-2ab+b^2)$

$= 3a \cdot 6a^2 - 3a \cdot 2ab + 3a \cdot b^2 + 2b \cdot 6a^2$

$\qquad - 2b \cdot 2ab + 2b \cdot b^2$

$= 18a^3 - 6a^2b + 3ab^2 + 12a^2b - 4ab^2 + 2b^3$

$= 18a^3 + 6a^2b - ab^2 + 2b^3$

11. $(f \cdot g)(x) = (x+2)(x^2 - 4x + 11)$

$= x \cdot x^2 - x \cdot 4x + x \cdot 11 + 2 \cdot x^2$

$\qquad - 2 \cdot 4x + 2 \cdot 11$

$= x^3 - 4x^2 + 11x + 2x^2 - 8x + 22$

$= x^3 - 2x^2 + 3x + 22$

12.

$$
\begin{array}{r}
5z^2 + 3z - 7 \\
2z+7 \overline{)10z^3 + 41z^2 + 7z - 49} \\
\underline{-(10z^3 + 35z^2)} \\
6z^2 + 7z \\
\underline{-(6z^2 + 21z)} \\
-14z - 49 \\
\underline{-(-14z - 49)} \\
0
\end{array}
$$

$\dfrac{10z^3 + 41z^2 + 7z - 49}{2z + 7} = 5z^2 + 3z - 7$

13. The divisor is $x+9$ so $c = -9$.

$$
\begin{array}{r|rrrr}
-9 & 2 & 25 & 62 & -6 \\
   &   & -18 & -63 & 9 \\
\hline
   & 2 & 7 & -1 & 3
\end{array}
$$

$\dfrac{2x^3 + 25x^2 + 62x - 6}{x + 9} = 2x^2 + 7x - 1 + \dfrac{3}{x+9}$

14. $\left(\dfrac{f}{g}\right)(x) = \dfrac{x^3 + 2x^2 - 4x + 5}{x - 1}$

The divisor is $x - 1$ so $c = 1$.

$$
\begin{array}{r|rrrr}
1 & 1 & 2 & -4 & 5 \\
  &   & 1 & 3 & -1 \\
\hline
  & 1 & 3 & -1 & 4
\end{array}
$$

$\left(\dfrac{f}{g}\right)(x) = x^2 + 3x - 1 + \dfrac{4}{x-1}$

15. The divisor is $x+5$ so $c = -5$.

$f(x) = 3x^3 + 8x^2 - 23x + 60$

$f(-5) = 3(-5)^3 + 8(-5)^2 - 23(-5) + 60$

$\qquad = 3(-125) + 8(25) + 115 + 60$

$\qquad = -375 + 200 + 115 + 60$

$\qquad = 0$

Since $f(-5) = 0$, the remainder is 0 and $x+5$ is a factor of $f(x)$.

$$
\begin{array}{r|rrrr}
-5 & 3 & 8 & -23 & 60 \\
   &   & -15 & 35 & -60 \\
\hline
   & 3 & -7 & 12 & 0
\end{array}
$$

$f(x) = (x+5)(3x^2 - 7x + 12)$

5.4 Preparing for Greatest Common Factor; Factoring by Grouping

1. $24 = 8 \cdot 3$

$= 4 \cdot 2 \cdot 3$

$= 2 \cdot 2 \cdot 2 \cdot 3$

2. $4(3x-5) = 4 \cdot 3x - 4 \cdot 5$

$= 4 \cdot 3 \cdot x - 4 \cdot 5$

$= 12x - 20$

5.4 Exercises

1. factors

3. greatest common factor

5. False; Both terms in the polynomial have a common factor of 3.

7. Answers will vary. Find the largest numeric factor that evenly divides all the coefficients. Next find the variables that are common to all terms. The exponent on a variable should be the largest number of times it occurs in all the terms. Multiply the greatest common numeric factor by the greatest common variable factor of each variable.

9. $4x^2 = 2 \cdot 2 \cdot x \cdot x$
$10x = 2 \cdot 5 \cdot x$
$12x^3 = 2 \cdot 2 \cdot 3 \cdot x \cdot x \cdot x$
GCF: $2x$

11. $5a + 35$
GCF: 5
$5a + 35 = 5 \cdot a + 5 \cdot 7$
$\qquad = 5(a + 7)$

13. $-3y + 21$
GCF: -3
$-3y + 21 = -3 \cdot y + (-3) \cdot (-7)$
$\qquad = -3(y - 7)$

15. $14x^2 - 21x$
GCF: $7x$
$14x^2 - 21x = 7x \cdot 2x - 7x \cdot 3$
$\qquad = 7x(2x - 3)$

17. $3z^3 - 6z^2 + 18z$
GCF: $3z$
$3z^3 - 6z^2 + 18z = 3z \cdot z^2 - (3z) \cdot 2z + 3z \cdot 6$
$\qquad = 3z(z^2 - 2z + 6)$

19. $-5p^4 + 10p^3 - 25p^2$
GCF: $-5p^2$
$-5p^4 + 10p^3 - 25p^2$
$= -5p^2 \cdot p^2 + (-5p^2) \cdot (-2p) + (-5p^2) \cdot 5$
$= -5p^2(p^2 - 2p + 5)$

21. $49m^3n + 84mn^3 - 35m^4n^2$
GCF: $7mn$
$49m^3n + 84mn^3 - 35m^4n^2$
$= 7mn \cdot 7m^2 + 7mn \cdot 12n^2 + 7mn \cdot (-5m^3n)$
$= 7mn(7m^2 + 12n^2 - 5m^3n)$

23. $-18z^3 + 14z^2 + 4z$
GCF: $-2z$
$-18z^3 + 14z^2 + 4z$
$= -2z \cdot 9z^2 + (-2z)(-7z) + (-2z)(-2)$
$= -2z(9z^2 - 7z - 2)$

25. $5c(3c - 2) - 3(3c - 2)$
GCF: $3c - 2$
$5c(3c - 2) - 3(3c - 2) = (3c - 2) \cdot 5c + (3c - 2) \cdot (-3)$
$\qquad = (3c - 2)(5c - 3)$

27. $(4a + 3)(a - 3) + (2a - 7)(a - 3)$
GCF: $a - 3$
$(4a + 3)(a - 3) + (2a - 7)(a - 3)$
$= (a - 3) \cdot (4a + 3) + (a - 3)(2a - 7)$
$= (a - 3)(4a + 3 + 2a - 7)$
$= (a - 3)(6a - 4)$
The binomial $6a - 4$ has a greatest common factor of 2. We can write the result as
$(a - 3)(2 \cdot 3a - 2 \cdot 2) = (a - 3) \cdot 2(3a - 2)$
Thus,
$(4a + 3)(a - 3) + (2a - 7)(a - 3) = 2(a - 3)(3a - 2)$

29. $5x + 5y + ax + ay = (5x + 5y) + (ax + ay)$
$\qquad = 5(x + y) + a(x + y)$
$\qquad = (x + y)(5 + a)$

31. $2z^3 + 10z^2 - 5z - 25 = (2z^3 + 10z^2) + (-5z - 25)$
$\qquad = 2z^2(z + 5) + (-5)(z + 5)$
$\qquad = (z + 5)(2z^2 - 5)$

33. $w^2 - 5w + 3w - 15 = (w^2 - 5w) + (3w - 15)$
$\qquad = w(w - 5) + 3(w - 5)$
$\qquad = (w - 5)(w + 3)$

35. Pull out the GCF first, then factor by grouping.

$$2x^2 - 8x - 4x + 16 = 2\left(x^2 - 4x - 2x + 8\right)$$
$$= 2\left[\left(x^2 - 4x\right) + \left(-2x + 8\right)\right]$$
$$= 2\left[x(x-4) + (-2)(x-4)\right]$$
$$= 2(x-4)(x-2)$$

37. Pull out the GCF first, then factor by grouping.

$$3x^3 + 15x^2 - 12x^2 - 60x$$
$$= 3x\left(x^2 + 5x - 4x - 20\right)$$
$$= 3x\left[\left(x^2 + 5x\right) + \left(-4x - 20\right)\right]$$
$$= 3x\left[x(x+5) + (-4)(x+5)\right]$$
$$= 3x(x+5)(x-4)$$

39. $2ax - 2ay - bx + by = (2ax - 2ay) + (-bx + by)$
$$= 2a(x-y) + (-b)(x-y)$$
$$= (x-y)(2a-b)$$

41. $(w+3)(w-3) - (w-2)(w-3)$

GCF: $(w-3)$

$$(w+3)(w-3) - (w-2)(w-3)$$
$$= (w-3)\cdot(w+3) - (w-3)\cdot(w-2)$$
$$= (w-3)(w+3-w+2)$$
$$= (w-3)(5)$$
$$= 5(w-3)$$

43. $2y^2 + 5y - 4y - 10 = \left(2y^2 + 5y\right) + (-4y - 10)$
$$= y(2y+5) + (-2)(2y+5)$$
$$= (2y+5)(y-2)$$

45. $6x^3y^3 + 9x^2y - 21x^3y^2$

GCF: $3x^2y$

$$6x^3y^3 + 9x^2y - 21x^3y^2$$
$$= 3x^2y\cdot 2xy^2 + 3x^2y\cdot 3 + 3x^2y\cdot(-7xy)$$
$$= 3x^2y\left(2xy^2 + 3 - 7xy\right)$$
$$= 3x^2y\left(2xy^2 - 7xy + 3\right)$$

47. $x^3 + x^2 + 3x + 3 = \left(x^3 + x^2\right) + (3x+3)$
$$= x^2(x+1) + 3(x+1)$$
$$= (x+1)\left(x^2 + 3\right)$$

49. $x(x-2) + 3(x-2)^2$

GCF: $(x-2)$

$$x(x-2) + 3(x-2)(x-2)$$
$$= (x-2)\cdot x + (x-2)(3)(x-2)$$
$$= (x-2)(x+3(x-2))$$
$$= (x-2)(x+3x-6)$$
$$= (x-2)(4x-6)$$
$$= (x-2)(2\cdot 2x - 2\cdot 3)$$
$$= 2(x-2)(2x-3)$$

51. The shaded area is the difference between the area of the square and the area of the circle. The radius of the circle is x, and this is also half the length of one side of the square. Thus, we have

$$A = A_{\text{square}} - A_{\text{circle}}$$
$$= (2x)^2 - \pi x^2$$
$$= 4x^2 - \pi x^2$$
$$= x^2(4-\pi)$$

The area of the shaded region is $x^2(4-\pi)$ square units.

53. $S = 2\pi r^2 + 8\pi r$
$$= 2\pi r\cdot r + 2\pi r\cdot 4$$
$$= 2\pi r(r+4)$$

The surface area is $2\pi r(r+4)$ square inches.

55. a. The selling price of the shirt is the supplier's cost plus the markup. That is,
$$x + 0.4x = 1.4x$$

b. The discount is 40% of the selling price. We obtain the sale price by subtracting this amount from the original price. That is,
$$1.4x - 0.4(1.4x)$$

c. $1.4x - 0.4(1.4x) = 1.4x(1-0.4)$
$$= 0.6(1.4x)$$
$$= 0.84x$$

d. No, the sale price is less than the amount that the store paid for the shirt. The 40% increase is on a smaller amount than the 40% decrease. Therefore, the decrease will be larger in magnitude than the increase.

57. a. The stock price is the original price plus the increase. That is,
$$x + 0.15x = 1.15x$$

b. The second year increase is based on the ending price for the first year. That is,
$$(1.15x) + 0.1(1.15x)$$

c.
$$(1.15x) + 0.1(1.15x) = (1.15x)(1 + 0.1)$$
$$= 1.1(1.15x)$$
$$= 1.265x$$

d. $x = 20$
$$1.265(20) = 25.30$$
After two years, the value of the stock will be $25.30.

59. $\dfrac{1}{4}x - \dfrac{7}{4} = \dfrac{1}{4}\cdot x - \dfrac{1}{4}\cdot 7$
$$= \frac{1}{4}(x - 7)$$

61. $\dfrac{1}{5}b^3 + \dfrac{8}{25}b = \dfrac{5}{25}b^3 + \dfrac{8}{25}b$
$$= \frac{1}{25}b\cdot 5b^2 + \frac{1}{25}b\cdot 8$$
$$= \frac{1}{25}b\left(5b^2 + 8\right)$$

5.5 Preparing for Factoring Trinomials

1.

factors	1, 18	2, 9	3, 6
sum	19	11	9

9 and 2 are the factors of 18 that sum to 11.

2.

factors	1, −24	2, −12	3, −8	4, −6
sum	−23	−10	−5	−2

−6 and 4 are the factors of −24 that sum to −2. (note: since the sum is negative, we restrict our choice of factors so that the larger factor (in absolute value) is negative.

3. $4x^2 - 9x + 2$
The coefficients are the numeric factors of the terms. The coefficients are 4, −9, and 2.

5.5 Exercises

1. $m\cdot n$; $m + n$

3. True

5. The Trial and Error method would be better when $a\cdot c$ gets large and there are lots of factors of the product whose sums must be determined.

7. The problem was not completely factored. The first binomial has a common factor of 3 than can be pulled out.
$$3p^2 - 9p - 30 = 3\left(p^2 - 3p - 10\right)$$
$$= 3(p + 2)(p - 5)$$

9. $x^2 + 8x + 15$
We are looking for two factors of $c = 15$ whose sum is $b = 8$. Since both c and b are positive, the two factors must be positive.

Factors	1, 15	3, 5
Sum	16	8

$$x^2 + 8x + 15 = (x + 3)(x + 5)$$

11. $p^2 + 3p - 18$

We are looking for two factors of $c = -18$ whose sum is $b = 3$. Since c is negative the two factors have opposite signs, and since b is positive the factor with the larger absolute value must be positive.

Factors	−1,18	−2,9	−3,6
Sum	17	7	3

$p^2 + 3p - 18 = (p+6)(p-3)$

13. $r^2 + 10r + 25$

We are looking for two factors of $c = 25$ whose sum is $b = 10$. Since both c and b are positive, the two factors must be positive.

Factors	1, 25	5, 5
Sum	26	10

$r^2 + 10r + 25 = (r+5)(r+5) = (r+5)^2$

15. $s^2 + 7s - 60$

We are looking for two factors of $c = -60$ whose sum is $b = 7$. Since c is negative the two factors have opposite signs, and since b is positive the factor with the larger absolute value must be positive.

Factors	−1,60	−2,30	−3,20	−4,15	−5,12	−6,10
Sum	59	28	17	11	7	4

$s^2 + 7s - 60 = (s+12)(s-5)$

17. $x^2 - 15x + 56$

We are looking for two factors of $c = 56$ whose sum is $b = -15$. Since c is positive the two factors have the same sign, and since b is negative the factors are both negative.

Factors	−1,−56	−2,−28	−4,−14	−7,−8
Sum	−57	−30	−18	−15

$x^2 - 15x + 56 = (x-7)(x-8)$

19. $-w^2 - 2w + 24$

Start by factoring out a -1.

$-1(w^2 + 2w - 24)$

We are looking for two factors of $c = -24$ whose sum is $b = 2$. Since c is negative the two factors have opposite signs, and since b is positive the factor with the larger absolute value must be positive.

Factors	−1,24	−2,12	−3,8	−4,6
Sum	23	10	5	2

$-w^2 - 2w + 24 = -(w-4)(w+6)$

21. $x^2 + 7xy + 12y^2$

We are looking for two factors of $c = 12$ that sum to $b = 7$. Since both c and b are positive, the two factors are both positive.

Factors	1,12	2,6	3,4
Sum	13	8	7

$x^2 + 7xy + 12y^2 = (x+3y)(x+4y)$

23. $p^2 + 2pq - 24q^2$

We are looking for two factors of $c = -24$ whose sum is $b = 2$. Since c is negative the two factors have opposite signs. Since b is positive the factor with the larger absolute value must be positive.

Factors	−1,24	−2,12	−3,8	−4,6
Sum	23	10	5	2

$p^2 + 2pq - 24q^2 = (p-4q)(p+6q)$

25. $2x^2 + 12x - 54$

Start by factoring out the GCF.

$2(x^2 + 6x - 27)$

We are looking for two factors of $c = -27$ whose sum is $b = 6$. Since c is negative the two factors have opposite signs, and since b is positive the factor with the larger absolute value must be positive.

Factors	−1,27	−3,9
Sum	26	6

$2x^2 + 12x - 54 = 2(x-3)(x+9)$

27. $-3r^2 + 39r - 120$

Start by factoring out the GCF.

$-3\left(r^2 - 13r + 40\right)$

We are looking for two factors of $c = 40$ whose sum is $b = -13$. Since c is positive the two factors must have the same sign, and since b is negative the two factors must be negative.

Factors	$-1,-40$	$-2,-20$	$-4,-10$	$-5,-8$
Sum	-41	-22	-14	-13

$-3r^2 + 39r - 120 = -3(r-5)(r-8)$

29. *ac* Method:

$a \cdot c = 2 \cdot -8 = -16$

We are looking for two factors of -16 whose sum is -15. Since the product is negative, the factors will have opposite signs. The sum is negative so the factor with the largest absolute value will be negative.

factor 1	factor 2	sum
1	-16	$-15 \leftarrow$ okay
2	-8	-6
4	-4	0

$2p^2 - 15p - 8 = 2p^2 + p - 16p - 8$
$$= p(2p+1) - 8(2p+1)$$
$$= (2p+1)(p-8)$$

Trial and Error Method:

First note that there are no common factors and that $a = 2$, $b = -15$, and $c = -8$. Since c is negative, the signs in our factors will be opposites. We will consider factorizations with this form:

$(\underline{\quad} p + \underline{\quad})(\underline{\quad} p - \underline{\quad})$

If our choice results in a middle term with the wrong sign, we simply switch the signs of the factors.

Since $a = 2$ can be factored as $2 \cdot 1$, we have the following form:

$(2p + \underline{\quad})(p - \underline{\quad})$

$|c| = |-8| = 8$ can be factored as $1 \cdot 8$ and $2 \cdot 4$.

Since the original expression had no common factors, the binomials we select cannot have a common factor.

$(2p+1)(p-8) \rightarrow 2p^2 - 15p - 8$

The correct factorization is

$2p^2 - 15p - 8 = (2p+1)(p-8)$

31. *ac* Method:

$a \cdot c = 4 \cdot 6 = 24$

We are looking for two factors of 24 whose sum is -11. Since the product is positive, the factors will have the same sign. The sum is negative so the factors will be negative.

factor 1	factor 2	sum
-1	-24	-25
-2	-12	-14
-3	-8	$-11 \leftarrow$ okay
-4	-6	-10

$4y^2 - 11y + 6 = 4y^2 - 8y - 3y + 6$
$$= 4y(y-2) - 3(y-2)$$
$$= (y-2)(4y-3)$$

Trial and Error Method:

First note that there are no common factors and that $a = 4$, $b = -11$, and $c = 6$. Since c is positive the signs of our factors will be the same. Since b is negative, the signs in our factors will be negative. We will consider factorizations with this form:

$(\underline{\quad} y - \underline{\quad})(\underline{\quad} y - \underline{\quad})$

Since $a = 4$ can be factored as $1 \cdot 4$ or $2 \cdot 2$, we have the following forms:

$(y - \underline{\quad})(4y - \underline{\quad})$

$(2y - \underline{\quad})(2y - \underline{\quad})$

$|c| = |6| = 6$ can be factored as $1 \cdot 6$ and $2 \cdot 3$.

Since the original expression had no common factors, the binomials we select cannot have a common factor.

$(y-6)(4y-1) \rightarrow 4y^2 - 25y + 6$

$(y-2)(4y-3) \rightarrow 4y^2 - 11y + 6$

The correct factorization is

$4y^2 - 11y + 6 = (y-2)(4y-3)$

33. *ac* Method:

$a \cdot c = 8 \cdot -3 = -24$

We are looking for two factors of -24 whose sum is 2. Since the product is negative, the factors will have opposite signs. The sum is positive so the factor with the larger absolute value will be positive.

factor 1	factor 2	sum
-1	24	23
-2	12	10
-3	8	5
-4	6	2 $\leftarrow$ okay

$$8s^2 + 2s - 3 = 8s^2 - 4s + 6s - 3$$
$$= 4s(2s-1) + 3(2s-1)$$
$$= (2s-1)(4s+3)$$

<u>Trial and Error Method:</u>
First note that there are no common factors and that $a = 8$, $b = 2$, and $c = -3$. Since c is negative, the signs in our factors will be opposites. We will consider factorizations with this form:

$$(\underline{}\, s + \underline{})(\underline{}\, s - \underline{})$$

If our choice results in a middle term with the wrong sign, we simply switch the signs of the factors.
Since $a = 8$ can be factored as $1 \cdot 8$ and $2 \cdot 4$, we have the following forms:

$$(s + \underline{})(8s - \underline{})$$
$$(2s + \underline{})(4s - \underline{})$$

$|c| = |-3| = 3$ can be factored as $1 \cdot 3$. Since the original expression had no common factors, the binomials we select cannot have a common factor.

$$(s+1)(8s-3) \rightarrow 8s^2 + 5s - 3$$
$$(s+3)(8s-1) \rightarrow 8s^2 + 23s - 3$$
$$(2s+1)(4s-3) \rightarrow 8s^2 - 2s - 3$$
$$(2s+3)(4s-1) \rightarrow 8s^2 + 10s - 3$$

Notice that our third choice is correct except that the sign of the middle term is wrong. Therefore, we simply need to switch the signs of the factors. The correct factorization is

$$8s^2 + 2s - 3 = (2s-1)(4s+3)$$

35. *ac* Method:
$$a \cdot c = 16 \cdot -15 = -240$$
We are looking for two factors of -240 whose sum is 8. Since the product is negative, the factors will have opposite signs. The sum is positive so the factor with the largest absolute value will be positive.

factor 1	factor 2	sum
-8	30	22 too large
-10	24	14 too large
-12	20	8 ← okay

$$16z^2 + 8z - 15 = 16z^2 - 12z + 20z - 15$$
$$= 4z(4z-3) + 5(4z-3)$$
$$= (4z-3)(4z+5)$$

<u>Trial and Error Method:</u>
First note that there are no common factors and that $a = 16$, $b = 8$, and $c = -15$. Since c is negative, the signs in our factors will be opposites. We will consider factorizations with this form:

$$(\underline{}\, z + \underline{})(\underline{}\, z - \underline{})$$

If our choice results in a middle term with the wrong sign, we simply switch the signs of the factors.
Since $a = 16$ can be factored as $1 \cdot 16$, $2 \cdot 8$, and $4 \cdot 4$, we have the following forms:

$$(z + \underline{})(16z - \underline{})$$
$$(2z + \underline{})(8z - \underline{})$$
$$(4z + \underline{})(4z - \underline{})$$

$|c| = |-15| = 15$ can be factored as $1 \cdot 15$ and $3 \cdot 5$. Since the original expression had no common factors, the binomials we select cannot have a common factor.

$$(z+1)(16z-15) \rightarrow 16z^2 + z - 15$$
$$(z+15)(16z-1) \rightarrow 16z^2 + 239z - 15$$
$$(z+3)(16z-5) \rightarrow 16z^2 + 43z - 15$$
$$(z+5)(16z-3) \rightarrow 16z^2 + 77z - 15$$
$$(2z+1)(8z-15) \rightarrow 16z^2 - 22z - 15$$
$$(2z+15)(8z-1) \rightarrow 16z^2 + 118z - 15$$
$$(2z+3)(8z-5) \rightarrow 16z^2 + 14z - 15$$
$$(2z+5)(8z-3) \rightarrow 16z^2 + 34z - 15$$
$$(4z+1)(4z-15) \rightarrow 16z^2 - 56z - 15$$
$$(4z+3)(4z-5) \rightarrow 16z^2 - 8z - 15$$

Notice that our last choice is correct except for the sign on the middle term. Therefore, we simply need to switch the signs of our factors. The correct factorization is

$$16z^2 + 8z - 15 = (4z-3)(4z+5)$$

37. <u>*ac* Method:</u>

$a \cdot c = 18 \cdot 4 = 72$

We are looking for two factors of 72 whose sum is 17. Since the product is positive, the factors will have the same sign. The sum is positive so the factors will both be positive. Since we are adding two positive numbers to get 17, neither factor can exceed 17.

factor 1	factor 2	sum
6	12	18
8	9	17 ← okay

$$18y^2 + 17y + 4 = 18y^2 + 9y + 8y + 4$$
$$= 9y(2y+1) + 4(2y+1)$$
$$= (2y+1)(9y+4)$$

<u>Trial and Error Method:</u>

First note that there are no common factors and that $a = 18$, $b = 17$, and $c = 4$. Since c is positive, the signs in our factors will be the same. Since b is also positive, the signs of our factors will be positive. We will consider factorizations with this form:

$$(\underline{}y + \underline{})(\underline{}y + \underline{})$$

Since $a = 18$ can be factored as $1 \cdot 18$, $2 \cdot 9$, and $3 \cdot 6$, we have the following forms:

$$(y + \underline{})(18y + \underline{})$$
$$(2y + \underline{})(9y + \underline{})$$
$$(3y + \underline{})(6y + \underline{})$$

$|c| = |4| = 4$ can be factored as $1 \cdot 4$ and $2 \cdot 2$. Since the original expression had no common factors, the binomials we select cannot have a common factor.

$$(y+4)(18y+1) \rightarrow 18y^2 + 73y + 4$$
$$(2y+1)(9y+4) \rightarrow 18y^2 + 17y + 4$$
$$(3y+4)(6y+1) \rightarrow 18y^2 + 27y + 4$$

The correct factorization is

$$18y^2 + 17y + 4 = (2y+1)(9y+4)$$

39. <u>*ac* Method:</u>

Start by factoring out the GCF.

$$-16m^2 + 12m + 70 = -2(8m^2 - 6m - 35)$$

Now focus on the reduced trinomial.

$a \cdot c = 8 \cdot -35 = -280$

We are looking for two factors of -280 whose sum is -6. Since the product is negative, the factors will have opposite signs. The sum is negative so the factor with the larger absolute

value will be negative. Since the sum is not very large, we want factors whose absolute values are near each other.

factor 1	factor 2	sum
8	−35	−27 too small
10	−28	−18 too small
14	−20	−6 ← okay

$$-16m^2 + 12m + 70 = -2(8m^2 - 6m - 35)$$
$$= -2(8m^2 - 20m + 14m - 35)$$
$$= -2(4m(2m-5) + 7(2m-5))$$
$$= -2(2m-5)(4m+7)$$

<u>Trial and Error Method:</u>

Start by factoring out the GCF.

$$-16m^2 + 12m + 70 = -2(8m^2 - 6m - 35)$$

Now focus on the reduced trinomial.

$a = 8$, $b = -6$, and $c = -35$. Since c is negative, the signs in our factors will be opposites. We will consider factorizations with this form:

$$(\underline{}m + \underline{})(\underline{}m - \underline{})$$

If our choice results in a middle term with the wrong sign, we simply switch the signs of the factors.

Since $a = 8$ can be factored as $1 \cdot 8$ and $2 \cdot 4$, we have the following forms:

$$(m + \underline{})(8m - \underline{})$$
$$(2m + \underline{})(4m - \underline{})$$

$|c| = |-35| = 35$ can be factored as $1 \cdot 35$ and $5 \cdot 7$. Since the original expression had no common factors, the binomials we select cannot have a common factor.

$$(m+1)(8m-35) \rightarrow 8m^2 - 27m - 35$$
$$(m+35)(8m-1) \rightarrow 8m^2 + 279m - 35$$
$$(m+5)(8m-7) \rightarrow 8m^2 + 33m - 35$$
$$(m+7)(8m-5) \rightarrow 8m^2 + 51m - 35$$
$$(2m+1)(4m-35) \rightarrow 8m^2 - 66m - 35$$
$$(2m+35)(4m-1) \rightarrow 8m^2 + 138m - 35$$
$$(2m+5)(4m-7) \rightarrow 8m^2 + 6m - 35$$
$$(2m+7)(4m-5) \rightarrow 8m^2 + 18m - 35$$

Notice that our seventh choice is correct except for the sign on the middle term. Therefore, we simply need to switch the signs of the factors. The correct factorization is

$$-16m^2 + 12m + 70 = -2(2m-5)(4m+7)$$

41. *ac* Method:

Start by factoring out the GCF.

$$48z^2 + 124z + 28 = 4\left(12z^2 + 31z + 7\right)$$

Now focus on the reduced trinomial.

$a \cdot c = 12 \cdot 7 = 84$

We are looking for two factors of 84 whose sum is 31. Since the product is positive, the factors will have the same sign. The sum is also positive so the factors will both be positive. Since we are adding two positive numbers to get 31, both factors need to be less than 31.

factor 1	factor 2	sum
7	12	19 too small
4	21	25 too small
3	28	31 ← okay

$$48z^2 + 124z + 28 = 4\left(12z^2 + 31z + 7\right)$$
$$= 4\left(12z^2 + 3z + 28z + 7\right)$$
$$= 4\left(3z(4z+1) + 7(4z+1)\right)$$
$$= 4(4z+1)(3z+7)$$

Trial and Error Method:

Start by factoring out the GCF.

$$48z^2 + 124z + 28 = 4\left(12z^2 + 31z + 7\right)$$

Now focus on the reduced trinomial.

$a = 12$, $b = 31$, and $c = 7$. Since c is positive, the signs in our factors will be the same. Since b is also positive, the two factors will be positive. We will consider factorizations with this form:

$$(\underline{\quad}z + \underline{\quad})(\underline{\quad}z + \underline{\quad})$$

Since $a = 12$ can be factored as $1 \cdot 12$, $2 \cdot 6$, and $3 \cdot 4$, we have the following forms:

$$(z + \underline{\quad})(12z + \underline{\quad})$$
$$(2z + \underline{\quad})(6z + \underline{\quad})$$
$$(3z + \underline{\quad})(4z + \underline{\quad})$$

$|c| = |7| = 7$ can be factored as $1 \cdot 7$. Since the original expression had no common factors, the binomials we select cannot have a common factor.

$$(z+1)(12z+7) \to 12z^2 + 19z + 7$$
$$(z+7)(12z+1) \to 12z^2 + 85z + 7$$
$$(2z+1)(6z+7) \to 12z^2 + 20z + 7$$
$$(2z+7)(6z+1) \to 12z^2 + 44z + 7$$
$$(3z+1)(4z+7) \to 12z^2 + 25z + 7$$
$$(3z+7)(4z+1) \to 12z^2 + 31z + 7$$

The correct factorization is

$$48z^2 + 124z + 28 = 4\left(12z^2 + 31z + 7\right)$$
$$= 4(3z+7)(4z+1)$$

43. *ac* Method:

$a \cdot c = 2 \cdot -21 = -42$

We are looking for two factors of -42 whose sum is 11. Since the product is negative, the factors will have opposite signs. The sum is positive so the factor with the larger absolute value will be positive. Since the sum is not too large, we want factors whose absolute values are near each other.

factor 1	factor 2	sum
21	-2	19 too large
7	-6	1 too small
14	-3	11 ← okay

$$2x^2 + 11xy - 21y^2 = 2x^2 + 14xy - 3xy - 21y^2$$
$$= 2x(x+7y) - 3y(x+7y)$$
$$= (x+7y)(2x-3y)$$

Trial and Error Method:

$a = 2$, $b = 11$, and $c = -21$. Since c is negative, the signs in our factors will be opposites. We will consider factorizations with this form:

$$(\underline{\quad}x + \underline{\quad}y)(\underline{\quad}x - \underline{\quad}y)$$

If our choice results in a middle term with the wrong sign, we simply switch the signs of the factors.

Since $a = 2$ can be factored as $1 \cdot 2$, we have the following form:

$$(x + \underline{\quad}y)(2x - \underline{\quad}y)$$

$|c| = |-21| = 21$ can be factored as $1 \cdot 21$ and $3 \cdot 7$. Since the original expression had no common factors, the binomials we select cannot have a common factor.

$$(x+y)(2x-21y) \to 2x^2 - 19xy - 21y^2$$
$$(x+21y)(2x-y) \to 2x^2 + 41xy - 21y^2$$
$$(x+3y)(2x-7y) \to 2x^2 - xy - 21y^2$$
$$(x+7y)(2x-3y) \to 2x^2 + 11xy - 21y^2$$

The correct factorization is

$$2x^2 + 11xy - 21y^2 = (x+7y)(2x-3y)$$

45. *ac* Method:

$a \cdot c = 4 \cdot 15 = 60$

We are looking for two factors of 60 whose sum is -23. Since the product is positive, the factors will have the same sign. The sum is negative so the factors will be negative. Since we are adding two negatives to get -23, neither factor can be less than -23.

factor 1	factor 2	sum
-10	-6	-16 too large
-15	-4	-19 too large
-20	-3	$-23 \leftarrow$ okay

$$4r^2 - 23rs + 15s^2 = 4r^2 - 20rs - 3rs + 15s^2$$
$$= 4r(r - 5s) - 3s(r - 5s)$$
$$= (r - 5s)(4r - 3s)$$

Trial and Error Method:

$a = 4$, $b = -23$, and $c = 15$. Since c is positive, the signs in our factors will be the same. Since b is negative, the two factors will be negative. We will consider factorizations with this form:

$$(\_\_r - \_\_s)(\_\_r - \_\_s)$$

Since $a = 4$ can be factored as $1 \cdot 4$ and $2 \cdot 2$, we have the following forms:

$$(r - \_\_s)(4r - \_\_s)$$
$$(2r - \_\_s)(2r - \_\_s)$$

$|c| = |15| = 15$ can be factored as $1 \cdot 15$ and $3 \cdot 5$.

Since the original expression had no common factors, the binomials we select cannot have a common factor.

$$(r - s)(4r - 15s) \rightarrow 4r^2 - 19rs + 15s^2$$
$$(r - 15s)(4r - s) \rightarrow 4r^2 - 61rs + 15s^2$$
$$(r - 3s)(4r - 5s) \rightarrow 4r^2 - 17rs + 15s^2$$
$$(r - 5s)(4r - 3s) \rightarrow 4r^2 - 23rs + 15s^2$$
$$(2r - s)(2r - 15s) \rightarrow 4r^2 - 32rs + 15s^2$$
$$(2r - 3s)(2r - 5s) \rightarrow 4r^2 - 16rs + 15s^2$$

The correct factorization is

$$4r^2 - 23rs + 15s^2 = (r - 5s)(4r - 3s)$$

47. *ac* Method:

First note that there are no common factors and that $a = 24$, $b = 23$, and $c = -12$.

$a \cdot c = 24 \cdot -12 = -288$. We want to determine two factors whose product is -288 and whose sum is 23. Since the product is negative we know the two factors have opposite signs. Since the sum is positive we know that the factor with

the larger absolute value must be positive. Since 23 is not very large, we want to keep the absolute value of the factors somewhat close to each other.

factor 1	factor 2	sum
-16	18	2 too small
-12	24	12 too small
-9	32	$23 \leftarrow$ okay

$$24r^2 + 23rs - 12s^2 = 24r^2 + 32rs - 9rs - 12s^2$$
$$= 8r(3r + 4s) - 3s(3r + 4s)$$
$$= (3r + 4s)(8r - 3s)$$

Trial and Error Method:

First note that there are no common factors and that $a = 24$, $b = 23$, and $c = -12$.

Since c is negative the signs in our factors will be opposite. We will consider factorizations with this form:

$$(\_\_r + \_\_s)(\_\_r - \_\_s).$$

If our choice results in a middle term with the wrong sign, we simply switch the signs of the factors.

Since $a = 24$ can be factored as $1 \cdot 24$, $2 \cdot 12$, $3 \cdot 8$, and $4 \cdot 6$, we have the following forms:

$$(r + \_\_s)(24r - \_\_s)$$
$$(2r + \_\_s)(12r - \_\_s)$$
$$(3r + \_\_s)(8r - \_\_s)$$
$$(4r + \_\_s)(6r - \_\_s)$$

$|c| = |-12| = 12$ can be factored as $1 \cdot 12$, $2 \cdot 6$, and $3 \cdot 4$. Since the original expression had no common factors, the binomials we select cannot have a common factor.

$$(r + 12s)(24r - s) \rightarrow 24r^2 + 287rs - 12s^2$$
$$(3r + 4s)(8r - 3s) \rightarrow 24r^2 + 23rs - 12s^2$$

The correct factorization is

$$24r^2 + 23rs - 12s^2 = (3r + 4s)(8r - 3s)$$

49. Start by factoring out the GCF.

$$3x^3 - 6x^2 - 240x = 3x\left(x^2 - 2x - 80\right)$$

Now we focus on the reduced trinomial. We need two factors of -80 whose sum is -2. Since the product is negative, the factors will have opposite signs. Since the sum is also negative, the factor with the larger absolute value will be negative.

Factors	$1,-80$	$2,-40$	$4,-20$	$5,-16$	$8,-10$
Sum	-79	-38	-16	-11	-2

$$3x^3 - 6x^2 - 240x = 3x\left(x^2 - 2x - 80\right)$$
$$= 3x(x-10)(x+8)$$

51. Start by factoring out the GCF.

$$8x^3y^2 - 76x^2y^2 + 140xy^2$$
$$= 4xy^2\left(2x^2 - 19x + 35\right)$$

Now we focus on the reduced trinomial.
$a \cdot c = 2 \cdot 35 = 70$
We need two factors of 70 whose sum is -19. Since the product is positive, the two factors will have the same sign. Since the sum is negative, the two factors will be negative.

factor 1	factor 2	sum
-1	-70	-71
-2	-35	-37
-5	-14	$-19 \leftarrow$ okay
-7	-10	-17

$$8x^3y^2 - 76x^2y^2 + 140xy^2 = 4xy^2\left(2x^2 - 19x + 35\right)$$
$$= 4xy^2\left(2x^2 - 14x - 5x + 35\right)$$
$$= 4xy^2\left(2x(x-7) - 5(x-7)\right)$$
$$= 4xy^2(x-7)(2x-5)$$

53. Start by factoring out the GCF.

$$70r^4s - 36r^3s - 16r^2s = 2r^2s\left(35r^2 - 18r - 8\right)$$

Now we focus on the reduced trinomial.
$a \cdot c = 35 \cdot (-8) = -280$
We need two factors of -280 whose sum is -18. Since the product is negative, the two factors will have opposite signs. Since the sum is negative, the factor with the larger absolute value will be negative.

factor 1	factor 2	sum
4	-70	-66
5	-56	-51
7	-40	-33
10	-28	$-18 \leftarrow$ okay

$$70r^4s - 36r^3s - 16r^2s$$
$$= 2r^2s\left(35r^2 - 18r - 8\right)$$
$$= 2r^2s\left(35r^2 - 28r + 10r - 8\right)$$
$$= 2r^2s\left(7r(5r-4) + 2(5r-4)\right)$$
$$= 2r^2s(5r-4)(7r+2)$$

55. $x^4 - 3x^2 + 2$

Let $u = x^2$. This gives us $u^2 - 3u + 2$.
We need two factors of 2 whose sum is -3. Since the product is positive, the two factors will have the same sign. Since the sum is negative, the signs will both be negative. The only possibility is:

$$u^2 - 3u + 2 = (u-1)(u-2)$$

Now get back in terms of x.

$$x^4 - 3x^2 + 2 = \left(x^2 - 1\right)\left(x^2 - 2\right)$$
$$= (x-1)(x+1)\left(x^2 - 2\right)$$

57. $m^2n^2 + 5mn - 14$

Let $u = mn$. This gives us $u^2 + 5u - 14$.
We need two factors of -14 whose sum is 5. Since the product is negative, the factors will have opposite signs. Since the sum is positive, the factor with the larger absolute value will be positive.

$$u^2 + 5u - 14 = (u+7)(u-2)$$

Now get back in terms of m and n.

$$m^2n^2 + 5mn - 14 = (mn+7)(mn-2)$$

59. $(x+1)^2 - 6(x+1) - 16$

Let $u = x+1$. This gives us $u^2 - 6u - 16$.
We need two factors of -16 whose sum is -6.
Since the product is negative, the factors will
have opposite signs. Since the sum is negative,
the factor with the largest absolute value will be
negative.
$u^2 - 6u - 16 = (u-8)(u+2)$
Now get back in terms of x.
$(x+1)^2 - 6(x+1) - 16 = (x+1-8)(x+1+2)$
$$= (x-7)(x+3)$$

61. $(3r-1)^2 - 9(3r-1) + 20$

Let $u = 3r-1$. This gives us $u^2 - 9u + 20$.
We need two factors of 20 whose sum is -9.
Since the product is positive, the factors will
have the same sign. Since the sum is negative,
the two factors will be negative.
$u^2 - 9u + 20 = (u-5)(u-4)$
Now get back in terms of r.
$(3r-1)^2 - 9(3r-1) + 20 = (3r-1-5)(3r-1-4)$
$$= (3r-6)(3r-5)$$
$$= 3(r-2)(3r-5)$$

63. $2(y-3)^2 + 13(y-3) + 15$

Let $u = y-3$. This gives us $2u^2 + 13u + 15$.
$a \cdot c = 2 \cdot 15 = 30$
We need two factors of 30 whose sum is 13.
Since the product is positive and the sum is
positive, both factors will be positive.

factor 1	factor 2	sum
1	30	31
2	15	17
3	10	13 ← okay
5	6	11

$2u^2 + 13u + 15 = 2u^2 + 10u + 3u + 15$
$$= 2u(u+5) + 3(u+5)$$
$$= (u+5)(2u+3)$$
Now get back in terms of y.
$2(y-3)^2 + 13(y-3) + 15$
$= (y-3+5)(2(y-3)+3)$
$= (y+2)(2y-6+3)$
$= (y+2)(2y-3)$

65. <u>*ac* Method:</u>
$a \cdot c = 10 \cdot 21 = 210$
We are looking for two factors of 210 whose
sum is 41. Since the product is positive, the
factors will have the same sign. The sum is
positive so the factors will both be positive.

factor 1	factor 2	sum
1	210	211
2	105	107
3	70	73
5	42	47
6	35	41 ← okay

$10w^2 + 41w + 21 = 10w^2 + 6w + 35w + 21$
$$= 2w(5w+3) + 7(5w+3)$$
$$= (5w+3)(2w+7)$$

<u>Trial and Error Method:</u>
First note that there are no common factors and
that $a = 10$, $b = 41$, and $c = 21$. Since c is
positive, the signs in our factors will be the
same. Since b is also positive, the signs of our
factors will be positive. We will consider
factorizations with this form:
$(\_\_w + \_\_)(\_\_w + \_\_)$
Since $a = 10$ can be factored as $1 \cdot 10$ and $2 \cdot 5$,
we have the following forms:
$(w + \_\_)(10w + \_\_)$
$(2w + \_\_)(5w + \_\_)$
$|c| = |21| = 21$ can be factored as $1 \cdot 21$ or $3 \cdot 7$.
Since the original expression had no common
factors, the binomials we select cannot have a
common factor.
$(w+1)(10w+21) \rightarrow 10w^2 + 31w + 21$
$(w+21)(10w+1) \rightarrow 10w^2 + 211w + 21$
$(2w+1)(5w+21) \rightarrow 10w^2 + 47w + 21$
$(2w+21)(5w+1) \rightarrow 10w^2 + 107w + 21$
$(w+3)(10w+7) \rightarrow 10w^2 + 37w + 21$
$(w+7)(10w+3) \rightarrow 10w^2 + 73w + 21$
$(2w+3)(5w+7) \rightarrow 10w^2 + 29w + 21$
$(2w+7)(5w+3) \rightarrow 10w^2 + 41w + 21$
The correct factorization is
$10w^2 + 41w + 21 = (5w+3)(2w+7)$

67. $4(2y+1)^2 - 3(2y+1) - 1$

Let $u = 2y+1$. This gives us $4u^2 - 3u - 1$.

$a \cdot c = 4 \cdot -1 = -4$

We need two factors of -4 whose sum is -3. Since the product is negative, the factors will have opposite signs. Since the sum is also negative, the factor with the larger absolute value will be negative.

factor 1	factor 2	sum
1	-4	-3 ← okay
2	-2	0

$4u^2 - 3u - 1 = 4u^2 - 4u + u - 1$
$\qquad = 4u(u-1) + (u-1)$
$\qquad = (u-1)(4u+1)$

Now get back in terms of y.

$4(2y+1)^2 - 3(2y+1) - 1$
$= (2y+1-1)(4(2y+1)+1)$
$= (2y)(8y+4+1) = 2y(8y+5)$

69. <u>ac Method:</u>

First note that there are no common factors and that $a = 12$, $b = 23$, and $c = 10$.

$a \cdot c = 12 \cdot 10 = 120$. We want to determine two factors whose product is 120 and whose sum is 23. Since the product is positive we know the two integers have the same sign. Since the sum is positive we know that they must both be positive and neither factor can be larger than 23.

factor 1	factor 2	sum
10	12	22 too small
20	6	26 too large
15	8	23 ← okay

$12x^2 + 23xy + 10y^2 = 12x^2 + 8xy + 15xy + 10y^2$
$\qquad = 4x(3x+2y) + 5y(3x+2y)$
$\qquad = (3x+2y)(4x+5y)$

<u>Trial and Error Method:</u>

First note that there are no common factors and that $a = 12$, $b = 23$, and $c = 10$.

Since c is positive the signs in our factors will be the same, and since b is positive we know that the signs will both be positive. We will consider factorizations with this form:

$(\underline{}x + \underline{}y)(\underline{}x + \underline{}y)$.

Since $a = 12$ can be factored as $1 \cdot 12$, $2 \cdot 6$, and $3 \cdot 4$, we have the following forms:

$(1x + \underline{}y)(12x + \underline{}y)$
$(2x + \underline{}y)(6x + \underline{}y)$
$(3x + \underline{}y)(4x + \underline{}y)$

$|c| = |10| = 10$ can be factored as $1 \cdot 10$ or $2 \cdot 5$.

Since the original expression had no common factors, the binomials we select cannot have a common factor.

$(x+10y)(12x+y) \rightarrow 12x^2 + 121xy + 10y^2$
$(3x+10y)(4x+y) \rightarrow 12x^2 + 43xy + 10y^2$
$(x+2y)(12x+5y) \rightarrow 12x^2 + 29xy + 10y^2$
$(3x+2y)(4x+5y) \rightarrow 12x^2 + 23xy + 10y^2$

The correct factorization is
$12x^2 + 23xy + 10y^2 = (3x+2y)(4x+5y)$

71. $y^2 + 2y - 27$

We are looking for two factors of $c = -27$ whose sum is $b = 2$. Since c is negative the two factors have opposite signs, and since b is positive the factor with the larger absolute value must be positive.

Factors	$-1, 27$	$-3, 9$
Sum	26	6

Since none of the possibilities work,
$y^2 + 2y - 27$ is prime.

73. $x^4 + 6x^2 + 8$

Let $u = x^2$. This gives us $u^2 + 6u + 8$.

We need two factors of $c = 8$ whose sum is $b = 6$. Since the product is positive, the two factors will have the same sign. Since the sum is also positive, the factors will both be positive.

$u^2 + 6u + 8 = (u+4)(u+2)$

Now get back in terms of x.

$x^4 + 6x^2 + 8 = (x^2+4)(x^2+2)$

75. $z^6 + 9z^3 + 20$

Let $u = z^3$. This gives us $u^2 + 9u + 20$.
We need two factors of 20 whose sum is 9. Since the product is positive, the two factors will have the same sign. Since the sum is also positive, the factors will both be positive.
$$u^2 + 9u + 20 = (u+5)(u+4)$$
Now get back in terms of z.
$$z^6 + 5z^3 + 4 = (z^3 + 5)(z^3 + 4)$$

77. $r^2 - 12rs + 32s^2$

We are looking for two factors of $c = 32$ whose sum is $b = -12$. Since c is positive the two factors must have the same sign, and since b is negative the factors must both be negative.

Factors	$-1,-32$	$-2,-16$	$-4,-8$
Sum	-33	-18	-12

$$r^2 - 12rs + 32s^2 = (r-4s)(r-8s)$$

79. $8(z+1)^2 + 2(z+1) - 1$

Let $u = z+1$. This gives us $8u^2 + 2u - 1$.
$a \cdot c = 8 \cdot -1 = -8$
We need two factors of -8 whose sum is 2. Since the product is negative, the factors will have opposite signs. Since the sum is positive, the factor with the larger absolute value will be positive.

factor 1	factor 2	sum
-1	8	7
-2	4	2 ← okay

$$8u^2 + 2u - 1 = 8u^2 + 4u - 2u - 1$$
$$= 4u(2u+1) - 1(2u+1)$$
$$= (2u+1)(4u-1)$$
Now get back in terms of z.
$$8(z+1)^2 + 2(z+1) - 1$$
$$= (2(z+1)+1)(4(z+1)-1)$$
$$= (2z+2+1)(4z+4-1)$$
$$= (2z+3)(4z+3)$$

81. $3x^2 - 7x - 12$

We need two factors of $c = -12$ whose sum is $b = -7$. Since c is negative, the two factors will have opposite signs. Since b is also negative, the factor with the larger absolute value will be negative.

Factors	1, -12	2, -6	3, -4
Sum	-11	-4	-1

Since none of the possibilities work,
$3x^2 - 7x - 12$ is prime.

83. a. $V(3) = 4(3)^3 - 108(3)^2 + 720(3)$
$$= 4(27) - 108(9) + 720(3)$$
$$= 108 - 972 + 2160$$
$$= 1296$$
When 3-inch square corners are cut from the piece of cardboard, the resulting box will have a volume of 1296 cubic inches.

b. $V(x) = 4x^3 - 108x^2 + 720x$
$$= 4x(x^2 - 27x + 180)$$
$$= 4x(x-15)(x-12)$$

c. $V(3) = 4(3)(3-15)(3-12)$
$$= 12(-12)(-9)$$
$$= -144(-9)$$
$$= 1296$$
The volume is 1296 cubic inches.

d. Answers may vary. Often it will be easier in factored form.

85. If we know one factor, we can find the other by dividing the polynomial by the known factor.

$$\begin{array}{r} 2x - 5 \\ 3x+2\overline{)6x^2 - 11x - 10} \\ \underline{-(6x^2 + 4x)} \\ -15x - 10 \\ \underline{-(-15x - 10)} \\ 0 \end{array}$$

The other factor is $2x - 5$.
$$6x^2 - 11x - 10 = (3x+2)(2x-5).$$

87. $\dfrac{1}{2}x^2 + 3x + 4 = \dfrac{1}{2}x^2 + \dfrac{6}{2}x + \dfrac{8}{2}$

$\qquad\qquad\qquad = \dfrac{1}{2}\left(x^2 + 6x + 8\right)$

$\qquad\qquad\qquad = \dfrac{1}{2}(x+4)(x+2)$

89. $\dfrac{1}{3}p^2 - \dfrac{2}{3}p - 1 = \dfrac{1}{3}p^2 - \dfrac{2}{3}p - \dfrac{3}{3}$

$\qquad\qquad\qquad = \dfrac{1}{3}\left(p^2 - 2p - 3\right)$

$\qquad\qquad\qquad = \dfrac{1}{3}(p-3)(p+1)$

91. $\dfrac{4}{3}a^2 - \dfrac{8}{3}a - 32 = \dfrac{4}{3}a^2 - \dfrac{8}{3}a - \dfrac{96}{3}$

$\qquad\qquad\qquad = \dfrac{4}{3}a^2 - \dfrac{4}{3}\cdot 2a - \dfrac{4}{3}\cdot 24$

$\qquad\qquad\qquad = \dfrac{4}{3}\left(a^2 - 2a - 24\right)$

$\qquad\qquad\qquad = \dfrac{4}{3}(a-6)(a+4)$

5.6 Preparing for Factoring Special Products

1. $1^2 = 1\cdot 1 = 1;\quad 2^2 = 2\cdot 2 = 4;$
$3^2 = 3\cdot 3 = 9;\quad 4^2 = 4\cdot 4 = 16;$
$5^2 = 5\cdot 5 = 25$

2. $\left(-\dfrac{3}{2}\right)^2 = \left(-\dfrac{3}{2}\right)\left(-\dfrac{3}{2}\right) = \dfrac{9}{4}$

5.6 Exercises

1. perfect square trinomial

3. False. $4x^2 + 12x + 9$ would be a perfect square trinomial since it could be written as $(2x)^2 + 2\cdot 2x\cdot 3 + 3^2$.

5. Answers will vary. The binomial $x^2 + 4$ is the sum of two squares. Since the sum of two squares does not factor over the integers, $x^2 + 4$ is prime.

7. $x^2 + 4x + 4 = x^2 + 2\cdot x\cdot 2 + 2^2$

$\qquad\qquad\quad = (x+2)^2$

9. $36 + 12w + w^2 = 6^2 + 2\cdot 6\cdot w + w^2$

$\qquad\qquad\qquad = (6+w)^2 \quad \text{or} \quad (w+6)^2$

11. $4x^2 + 4x + 1 = (2x)^2 + 2\cdot 2x\cdot 1 + 1^2$

$\qquad\qquad\qquad = (2x+1)^2$

13. $9p^2 - 30p + 25 = (3p)^2 - 2\cdot 3p\cdot 5 + 5^2$

$\qquad\qquad\qquad = (3p-5)^2$

15. $25a^2 + 90a + 81 = (5a)^2 + 2\cdot 5a\cdot 9 + 9^2$

$\qquad\qquad\qquad = (5a+9)^2$

17. $9x^2 + 24xy + 16y^2 = (3x)^2 + 2(3x)(4y) + (4y)^2$

$\qquad\qquad\qquad\qquad = (3x+4y)^2$

19. $3w^2 - 30w + 75 = 3\left(w^2 - 10w + 25\right)$

$\qquad\qquad\qquad = 3\left(w^2 - 2\cdot w\cdot 5 + 5^2\right)$

$\qquad\qquad\qquad = 3(w-5)^2$

21. $-5t^2 - 70t - 245 = -5\left(t^2 + 14t + 49\right)$

$\qquad\qquad\qquad = -5\left(t^2 + 2\cdot t\cdot 7 + 7^2\right)$

$\qquad\qquad\qquad = -5(t+7)^2$

23. $32a^2 - 80ab + 50b^2 = 2\left(16a^2 - 40ab + 25b^2\right)$

$\qquad\qquad\qquad = 2\left((4a)^2 - 2\cdot 4a\cdot 5b + (5b)^2\right)$

$\qquad\qquad\qquad = 2(4a-5b)^2$

25. $z^4 - 6z^2 + 9 = \left(z^2\right)^2 - 2\cdot z^2\cdot 3 + 3^2$

$\qquad\qquad\qquad = \left(z^2 - 3\right)^2$

27. $x^2 - 9 = x^2 - 3^2$

$\qquad\qquad = (x-3)(x+3)$

29. $4 - y^2 = 2^2 - y^2$
$$= (2 - y)(2 + y)$$

31. $4z^2 - 9 = (2z)^2 - 3^2$
$$= (2z - 3)(2z + 3)$$

33. $100m^2 - 81n^2 = (10m)^2 - (9n)^2$
$$= (10m - 9n)(10m + 9n)$$

35. $m^4 - 36n^2 = \left(m^2\right)^2 - (6n)^2$
$$= \left(m^2 - 6n\right)\left(m^2 + 6n\right)$$

37. $8p^2 - 18q^2 = 2\left(4p^2 - 9q^2\right)$
$$= 2\left((2p)^2 - (3q)^2\right)$$
$$= 2(2p - 3q)(2p + 3q)$$

39. $80p^2r - 245b^2r = 5r\left(16p^2 - 49b^2\right)$
$$= 5r\left((4p)^2 - (7b)^2\right)$$
$$= 5r(4p - 7b)(4p + 7b)$$

41. $(x + y)^2 - 9 = (x + y)^2 - 3^2$
$$= (x + y - 3)(x + y + 3)$$

43. $x^3 - 8 = x^3 - 2^3$
$$= (x - 2)\left(x^2 + x(2) + 2^2\right)$$
$$= (x - 2)\left(x^2 + 2x + 4\right)$$

45. $125 + m^3 = 5^3 + m^3$
$$= (5 + m)\left(5^2 - 5m + m^2\right)$$
$$= (5 + m)\left(25 - 5m + m^2\right)$$
$$= (m + 5)\left(m^2 - 5m + 25\right)$$

47. $x^6 - 64y^3 = \left(x^2\right)^3 - (4y)^3$
$$= \left(x^2 - 4y\right)\left(\left(x^2\right)^2 + x^2 \cdot 4y + (4y)^2\right)$$
$$= \left(x^2 - 4y\right)\left(x^4 + 4x^2y + 16y^2\right)$$

49. $24x^3 - 375y^3$
$$= 3\left(8x^3 - 125y^3\right)$$
$$= 3\left((2x)^3 - (5y)^3\right)$$
$$= 3(2x - 5y)\left((2x)^2 + 2x \cdot 5y + (5y)^2\right)$$
$$= 3(2x - 5y)\left(4x^2 + 10xy + 25y^2\right)$$

51. $(p + 1)^3 - 27$
$$= (p + 1)^3 - 3^3$$
$$= (p + 1 - 3)\left((p + 1)^2 + (p + 1) \cdot 3 + 3^2\right)$$
$$= (p - 2)\left(p^2 + 2p + 1 + 3p + 3 + 9\right)$$
$$= (p - 2)\left(p^2 + 5p + 13\right)$$

53. $(3y + 1)^3 + 8y^3$
$$= (3y + 1)^3 + (2y)^3$$
$$= (3y + 1 + 2y)\left((3y + 1)^2 - (3y + 1) \cdot 2y + (2y)^2\right)$$
$$= (5y + 1)\left(9y^2 + 6y + 1 - 6y^2 - 2y + 4y^2\right)$$
$$= (5y + 1)\left(7y^2 + 4y + 1\right)$$

55. $(x + 3)^3 - (x - 3)^3$
$$= (x + 3 - x + 3)\left[(x + 3)^2 + (x + 3)(x - 3) + (x - 3)^2\right]$$
$$= 6\left(x^2 + 6x + 9 + x^2 - 9 + x^2 - 6x + 9\right)$$
$$= 6\left(3x^2 + 9\right)$$
$$= 6 \cdot 3\left(x^2 + 3\right)$$
$$= 18\left(x^2 + 3\right)$$

57. $y^6 + z^9 = \left(y^2\right)^3 + \left(z^3\right)^3$
$$= \left(y^2 + z^3\right)\left(\left(y^2\right)^2 - y^2z^3 + \left(z^3\right)^2\right)$$
$$= \left(y^2 + z^3\right)\left(y^4 - y^2z^3 + z^6\right)$$

59. $y^9 - 1 = \left(y^3\right)^3 - 1^3$

$\quad = \left(y^3 - 1\right)\left(\left(y^3\right)^2 + y^3 \cdot 1 + 1^2\right)$

$\quad = \left(y^3 - 1\right)\left(y^6 + y^3 + 1\right)$

$\quad = \left(y^3 - 1^3\right)\left(y^6 + y^3 + 1\right)$

$\quad = (y-1)\left(y^2 + y + 1\right)\left(y^6 + y^3 + 1\right)$

61. $25x^2 - y^2 = (5x)^2 - y^2$

$\quad = (5x - y)(5x + y)$

63. $8x^3 + 27 = (2x)^3 + 3^3$

$\quad = (2x+3)\left((2x)^2 - 2x \cdot 3 + 3^2\right)$

$\quad = (2x+3)\left(4x^2 - 6x + 9\right)$

65. $z^2 - 8z + 16 = z^2 - 2 \cdot z \cdot 4 + 4^2$

$\quad = (z-4)^2$

67. $5x^4 - 40xy^3 = 5x\left(x^3 - 8y^3\right)$

$\quad = 5x\left(x^3 - (2y)^3\right)$

$\quad = 5x(x - 2y)\left(x^2 + x \cdot 2y + (2y)^2\right)$

$\quad = 5x(x - 2y)\left(x^2 + 2xy + 4y^2\right)$

69. $49m^2 - 42mn + 9n^2 = (7m)^2 - 2(7m)(3n) + (3n)^2$

$\quad = (7m - 3n)^2$

71. $y^4 - 8y^2 + 16 = \left(y^2\right)^2 - 2 \cdot y^2 \cdot 4 + 4^2$

$\quad = \left(y^2 - 4\right)^2$

$\quad = \left[y^2 - 2^2\right]^2$

$\quad = \left[(y-2)(y+2)\right]^2$

$\quad = (y-2)^2 (y+2)^2$

73. $4a^2b^2 + 12ab + 9 = (2ab)^2 + 2 \cdot 2ab \cdot 3 + 3^2$

$\quad = (2ab + 3)^2$

75. $x^2 - 4x + 4 - y^2 = \left(x^2 - 4x + 4\right) - y^2$

$\quad = \left(x^2 - 2 \cdot x \cdot 2 + 2^2\right) - y^2$

$\quad = (x-2)^2 - y^2$

$\quad = (x - 2 - y)(x - 2 + y)$

$\quad = (x - y - 2)(x + y - 2)$

77. $2n^2 - 2m^2 + 40m - 200$

$\quad = 2\left(n^2 - m^2 + 20m - 100\right)$

$\quad = 2\left(n^2 - \left(m^2 - 20m + 100\right)\right)$

$\quad = 2\left(n^2 - \left(m^2 - 2 \cdot m \cdot 10 + 10^2\right)\right)$

$\quad = 2\left(n^2 - (m - 10)^2\right)$

$\quad = 2\left[(n - (m-10))(n + (m-10))\right]$

$\quad = 2(n - m + 10)(n + m - 10)$

79. $3y^3 - 24 = 3\left(y^3 - 8\right)$

$\quad = 3\left(y^3 - 2^3\right)$

$\quad = 3(y-2)\left(y^2 + 2y + 4\right)$

81. $16x^2 + 24xy + 9y^2 - 100$

$\quad = \left(16x^2 + 24xy + 9y^2\right) - 100$

$\quad = \left((4x)^2 + 2 \cdot 4x \cdot 3y + (3y)^2\right) - 10^2$

$\quad = (4x + 3y)^2 - 10^2$

$\quad = (4x + 3y - 10)(4x + 3y + 10)$

83. The area of the shaded region is the area of the larger square minus the area of the smaller square.

$x^2 - 3^2 = (x - 3)(x + 3)$

The area of the shaded region is $(x-3)(x+3)$ square units.

85. The area of the shaded region is the area of the large square minus the total area of the four square corners.

$$x^2 - 4\left(2^2\right) = x^2 - 16$$
$$= x^2 - 4^2$$
$$= (x-4)(x+4)$$

The area of the shaded region is $(x-4)(x+4)$ square units.

87. The area of the shaded region is the area of the larger circle minus the area of the smaller circle.

$$\pi R^2 - \pi r^2 = \pi\left(R^2 - r^2\right)$$
$$= \pi(R-r)(R+r)$$

The area of the shaded region is $\pi(R-r)(R+r)$ square units.

89. The volume of the shaded region is the volume of the whole solid minus the volume of the rectangular solid in the middle.

$$V = a \cdot 2a \cdot 5a - b \cdot 2b \cdot 5a$$
$$= 10a^3 - 10ab^2$$
$$= 10a\left(a^2 - b^2\right)$$
$$= 10a(a-b)(a+b)$$

The volume of the shaded region is $10a(a-b)(a+b)$ cubic units.

91. $A = a \cdot a + a \cdot b + a \cdot b + b \cdot b$
$$= a^2 + ab + ab + b^2$$
$$= a^2 + 2ab + b^2$$
$$= (a+b)^2$$

93. $4x^2 + bx + 81$

To be a perfect square trinomial, the middle term must equal $\pm$ twice the product of the quantities that are squared to get the first and last terms.

$$4x^2 = (2x)^2$$

$$81 = 9^2$$

Thus, the middle term must equal $\pm$ twice the product of $2x$ and 9.

$$bx = \pm 2 \cdot 2x \cdot 9$$

$$bx = \pm 36x$$

Therefore, $b = \pm 36$.

95. $x^2 + 18x$

To be a perfect square trinomial, we need to have the form $a^2 + 2ab + b^2$. Here we know that $a = x$ and we want $2ab = 18x$.

$$2ab = 18x$$
$$2(x)b = 18x$$
$$2bx = 18x$$
$$2b = 18$$
$$b = 9$$

Since $b = 9$, we need to add $9^2 = 81$ to make a perfect square trinomial.

$$x^2 + 18x + 81 = (x+9)^2$$

97. $b^2 - 0.4b + 0.04 = b^2 - 2 \cdot b \cdot (0.2) + (0.2)^2$
$$= (b-0.2)^2$$

99. $9b^2 - \dfrac{1}{25} = (3b)^2 - \left(\dfrac{1}{5}\right)^2$
$$= \left(3b - \dfrac{1}{5}\right)\left(3b + \dfrac{1}{5}\right)$$

101. $\dfrac{x^2}{9} - \dfrac{y^2}{25} = \left(\dfrac{x}{3}\right)^2 - \left(\dfrac{y}{5}\right)^2$
$$= \left(\dfrac{x}{3} - \dfrac{y}{5}\right)\left(\dfrac{x}{3} + \dfrac{y}{5}\right)$$

103. $\dfrac{x^3}{8} - \dfrac{y^3}{27} = \left(\dfrac{x}{2}\right)^3 - \left(\dfrac{y}{3}\right)^3$
$$= \left(\dfrac{x}{2} - \dfrac{y}{3}\right)\left(\left(\dfrac{x}{2}\right)^2 + \dfrac{x}{2} \cdot \dfrac{y}{3} + \left(\dfrac{y}{3}\right)^2\right)$$
$$= \left(\dfrac{x}{2} - \dfrac{y}{3}\right)\left(\dfrac{x^2}{4} + \dfrac{xy}{6} + \dfrac{y^2}{9}\right)$$

5.7 Exercises

1. Answers will vary.
   1) Factor out the GCF
   2) Count the number of terms
      a) Check for special two-term cases.
      b) Check for special three-term cases.
      c) Try to factor by grouping with four terms.
      d) Trial and error

3. $2x^2 - 12x - 144 = 2(x^2 - 6x - 72)$
   $$= 2(x-12)(x+6)$$

5. $-3y^2 + 27 = -3(y^2 - 9)$
   $$= -3(y^2 - 3^2)$$
   $$= -3(y-3)(y+3)$$

7. $4b^2 + 20b + 25 = (2b)^2 + 2 \cdot 2b \cdot 5 + 5^2$
   $$= (2b+5)^2$$

9. $16w^3 + 2y^6$
   $$= 2(8w^3 + y^6)$$
   $$= 2((2w)^3 + (y^2)^3)$$
   $$= 2(2w + y^2)((2w)^2 - 2w \cdot y^2 + (y^2)^2)$$
   $$= 2(2w + y^2)(4w^2 - 2wy^2 + y^4)$$

11. $-3z^2 + 12z - 18 = -3(z^2 - 4z + 6)$

13. $a \cdot c = 20 \cdot -18 = -360$
    We need two factors of -360 that add to get -9. Since the product is negative, they must have different signs, and since the sum is negative, the factor with the larger absolute value must be negative. The sum is also not too far from 0 so we want the factors to be near each other in magnitude.

factor 1	factor 2	sum	
12	−30	−18	too small
18	−20	−2	too large
15	−24	−9	okay

    $20y^2 - 9y - 18 = 20y^2 + 15y - 24y - 18$
    $$= 5y(4y+3) - 6(4y+3)$$
    $$= (4y+3)(5y-6)$$

15. $x^3 - 4x^2 + 5x - 20 = (x^3 - 4x^2) + (5x - 20)$
    $$= x^2(x-4) + 5(x-4)$$
    $$= (x-4)(x^2+5)$$

17. $200x^2 + 18y^2 = 2(100x^2 + 9y^2)$

19. $x^4 - 81 = (x^2)^2 - (9)^2$
    $$= (x^2 - 9)(x^2 + 9)$$
    $$= (x^2 - 3^2)(x^2 + 9)$$
    $$= (x-3)(x+3)(x^2+9)$$

21. $a \cdot c = 3 \cdot -16 = -48$
    We need two factors of -48 that add to get -7. Since the product is negative, they must have different signs, and since the sum is negative, the factor with the larger absolute value must be negative. The sum is also not too far from 0 so we want the factors to be near each other in magnitude.

factor 1	factor 2	sum
1	−48	−47
2	−24	−22
3	−16	−13
4	−12	−8
6	−8	−2

    None of the possibilities work. The expression is prime.

23. $36q^3 + 24q^2 + 4q = 4q(9q^2 + 6q + 1)$
    $$= 4q((3q)^2 + 2 \cdot 3q \cdot 1 + 1^2)$$
    $$= 4q(3q+1)^2$$

25. $24m^3n - 66m^2n - 63mn = 3mn\left(8m^2 - 22m - 21\right)$

Focusing on the reduced trinomial we get:

$a \cdot c = 8 \cdot -21 = -168$

We need two factors of -168 that add to get -22. Since the product is negative, they must have different signs, and since the sum is negative, the factor with the larger absolute value must be negative.

factor 1	factor 2	sum
8	−21	−13 too large
4	−42	−38 too small
6	−28	−22 okay

$3mn\left(8m^2 - 22m - 21\right)$

$= 3mn\left(8m^2 + 6m - 28m - 21\right)$

$= 3mn\left(2m(4m+3) - 7(4m+3)\right)$

$= 3mn(4m+3)(2m-7)$

27. $3r^5 - 24r^2s^3 = 3r^2\left(r^3 - 8s^3\right)$

$= 3r^2\left(r^3 - (2s)^3\right)$

$= 3r^2(r-2s)\left(r^2 + r \cdot 2s + (2s)^2\right)$

$= 3r^2(r-2s)\left(r^2 + 2rs + 4s^2\right)$

29. $2x^3 + 8x^2 - 18x - 72$

$= 2\left(x^3 + 4x^2 - 9x - 36\right)$

$= 2\left(\left(x^3 + 4x^2\right) + (-9x - 36)\right)$

$= 2\left(x^2(x+4) - 9(x+4)\right)$

$= 2(x+4)\left(x^2 - 9\right)$

$= 2(x+4)\left(x^2 - 3^2\right)$

$= 2(x+4)(x-3)(x+3)$

31. $9x^4 - 1 = \left(3x^2\right)^2 - 1^2$

$= \left(3x^2 - 1\right)\left(3x^2 + 1\right)$

33. Let $u = w^2$. This gives

$3u^2 + 4u - 15$

$a \cdot c = 3 \cdot -15 = -45$

We need factors of -45 that add to get 4. Since the product is negative, they must have different signs, and since the sum is positive, the factor

with the larger absolute value must be positive.

factor 1	factor 2	sum
15	−3	12 too large
9	−5	4 okay

$3u^2 + 4u - 15 = 3u^2 + 9u - 5u - 15$

$= 3u(u+3) - 5(u+3)$

$= (u+3)(3u-5)$

Now get back in terms of w.

$3w^4 + 4w^2 - 15 = \left(w^2 + 3\right)\left(3w^2 - 5\right)$

35. $(2y+3)^2 - 5(2y+3) + 6$

Let $u = 2y+3$. This gives

$u^2 - 5u + 6 = (u-3)(u-2)$

Now get back in terms of y.

$(2y+3)^2 - 5(2y+3) + 6 = (2y+3-3)(2y+3-2)$

$= 2y(2y+1)$

37. $p^2 - 10p + 25 - 36q^2 = \left(p^2 - 10p + 25\right) - 36q^2$

$= \left(p^2 - 2 \cdot p \cdot 5 + 5^2\right) - 36q^2$

$= (p-5)^2 - 36q^2$

$= (p-5)^2 - (6q)^2$

$= (p-5-6q)(p-5+6q)$

$= (p-6q-5)(p+6q-5)$

39. $y^6 + 6y^3 - 16$

Let $u = y^3$. This gives

$u^2 + 6u - 16 = (u+8)(u-2)$

Now get back in terms of y.

$y^6 + 6y^3 - 16 = \left(y^3 + 8\right)\left(y^3 - 2\right)$

$= \left(y^3 + 2^3\right)\left(y^3 - 2\right)$

$= (y+2)\left(y^2 - 2 \cdot y + 2^2\right)\left(y^3 - 2\right)$

$= (y+2)\left(y^2 - 2y + 4\right)\left(y^3 - 2\right)$

41. $p^6 - 1 = \left(p^3\right)^2 - 1^2$

$= \left(p^3 - 1\right)\left(p^3 + 1\right)$

$= (p-1)\left(p^2 + p + 1\right)(p+1)\left(p^2 - p + 1\right)$

$= (p-1)(p+1)\left(p^2 + p + 1\right)\left(p^2 - p + 1\right)$

43. $-3x^3 - 15x^2 + 27x + 135$

$= -3(x^3 + 5x^2 - 9x - 45)$

$= -3\left[(x^3 + 5x^2) + (-9x - 45)\right]$

$= -3\left[x^2(x + 5) - 9(x + 5)\right]$

$= -3(x + 5)(x^2 - 9)$

$= -3(x + 5)(x - 3)(x + 3)$

45. $3a - 27a^3 = 3a(1 - 9a^2)$

$= 3a\left(1^2 - (3a)^2\right)$

$= 3a(1 - 3a)(1 + 3a)$

47. $8t^5 + 14t^3 - 72t = 2t(4t^4 + 7t^2 - 36)$

Focusing on the reduced trinomial we get:

$a \cdot c = 4 \cdot -36 = -144$

We need two factors of -144 that add to get 7. Since the product is negative, they must have different signs, and since the sum is positive, the factor with the larger absolute value must be positive.

factor 1	factor 2	sum	
-6	24	18	too large
-12	12	0	too small
-9	16	7	okay

$2t(4t^4 + 7t^2 - 36)$

$= 2t(4t^4 + 16t^2 - 9t^2 - 36)$

$= 2t\left(4t^2(t^2 + 4) - 9(t^2 + 4)\right)$

$= 2t(t^2 + 4)(4t^2 - 9)$

$= 2t(t^2 + 4)\left((2t)^2 - 3^2\right)$

$= 2t(t^2 + 4)(2t - 3)(2t + 3)$

49. $2x^4 y + 10x^3 y - 18x^2 y - 90xy$

$= 2xy(x^3 + 5x^2 - 9x - 45)$

$= 2xy\left(x^2(x + 5) - 9(x + 5)\right)$

$= 2xy(x + 5)(x^2 - 9)$

$= 2xy(x + 5)(x^2 - 3^2)$

$= 2xy(x + 5)(x - 3)(x + 3)$

51. The area of the shaded region is the area of the large square minus the area of the small square.

$(2x + 5)^2 - (x + 2)^2$

$= \left[(2x + 5) - (x + 2)\right]\left[(2x + 5) + (x + 2)\right]$

$= (2x + 5 - x - 2)(2x + 5 + x + 2)$

$= (x + 3)(3x + 7)$

The area of the shaded region is $(x + 3)(3x + 7)$ square units.

53. The area of the shaded region is the area of the large rectangle minus the area of the unshaded rectangle.

$x(x + y) - y(x + y) = (x + y)(x - y)$

The area of the shaded region is $(x + y)(x - y)$ square units.

55. $(3x)^3 - (4)^3 = (3x - 4)\left((3x)^2 + 3x \cdot 4 + (4)^2\right)$

$= (3x - 4)(9x^2 + 12x + 16)$

The volumes of the boxes differ by $(3x - 4)(9x^2 + 12x + 16)$ cubic units.

57. Answers will vary. The binomial $x^2 + 9$ is the sum of two squares. Since the sum of two squares does not factor over the integers (or the real numbers), $x^2 + 9$ is prime.

59. $x^{5/2} - 9x^{1/2} = x^{1/2}(x^2 - 9)$

$= x^{1/2}(x^2 - 3^2)$

$= x^{1/2}(x - 3)(x + 3)$

61. $1 + 6x^{-1} + 8x^{-2} = x^{-2}(x^2 + 6x + 8)$

$= x^{-2}(x + 4)(x + 2)$

5.8 Preparing for Polynomial Equations

1. $x + 4 = 0$

$x + 4 - 4 = 0 - 4$

$x = -4$

Solution set: $\{-4\}$

2. $3(x - 2) - 12 = 0$

$3x - 6 - 12 = 0$

$3x - 18 = 0$

$3x - 18 + 18 = 0 + 18$

$3x = 18$

$\dfrac{3x}{3} = \dfrac{18}{3}$

$x = 6$

Solution set: $\{6\}$

3. $2x^2 + 3x + 1$

a.   When $x = 2$, we get

$2x^2 + 3x + 1 = 2(2)^2 + 3(2) + 1$

$= 2(4) + 3(2) + 1$

$= 8 + 6 + 1$

$= 15$

b.   When $x = -1$, we get

$2x^2 + 3x + 1 = 2(-1)^2 + 3(-1) + 1$

$= 2(1) + 3(-1) + 1$

$= 2 - 3 + 1$

$= 0$

4. $f(x) = 4x + 3$

$11 = 4x + 3$

$11 - 3 = 4x + 3 - 3$

$8 = 4x$

$\dfrac{8}{4} = \dfrac{4x}{4}$

$2 = x$

Solution set: $\{2\}$

The point $(2, 11)$ is on the graph of f.

5. $f(x) = -2x + 8$

$f(4) = -2(4) + 8$

$= -8 + 8$

$= 0$

The point $(4, 0)$ is on the graph of f.

5.8 Exercises

1. polynomial equation

3. third

5. False. The Zero-Product Property states that if $a \cdot b = 0$ then $a = 0$ **or** $b = 0$ **or** both a and b are equal to 0.

7. Answers will vary. The degree of a polynomial equation is the degree of the polynomial expression in the equation.

9. $(x - 3)(x + 1) = 0$

$x - 3 = 0$ or $x + 1 = 0$

$x = 3$ or $x = -1$

The solution set is $\{-1, 3\}$.

11. $2x(3x + 4) = 0$

$2x = 0$ or $3x + 4 = 0$

$x = 0$ $3x = -4$

$x = -\dfrac{4}{3}$

The solution set is $\left\{ -\dfrac{4}{3}, 0 \right\}$.

13. $y(y - 5)(y + 3) = 0$

$y = 0$ or $y - 5 = 0$ or $y + 3 = 0$

$y = 5$ $y = -3$

The solution set is $\{-3, 0, 5\}$.

15. $3p^2 - 12p = 0$

$3p(p - 4) = 0$

$3p = 0$ or $p - 4 = 0$

$p = 0$ $p = 4$

The solution set is $\{0, 4\}$.

17.
$$2w^2 = 16w$$
$$2w^2 - 16w = 0$$
$$2w(w-8) = 0$$
$$2w = 0 \quad \text{or} \quad w - 8 = 0$$
$$w = 0 \qquad\qquad w = 8$$
The solution set is $\{0, 8\}$.

19. $\quad m^2 + 2m - 15 = 0$
$$(m+5)(m-3) = 0$$
$$m + 5 = 0 \quad \text{or} \quad m - 3 = 0$$
$$m = -5 \qquad\qquad m = 3$$
The solution set is $\{-5, 3\}$.

21.
$$w^2 - 13w = -36$$
$$w^2 - 13w + 36 = 0$$
$$(w-9)(w-4) = 0$$
$$w - 9 = 0 \quad \text{or} \quad w - 4 = 0$$
$$w = 9 \qquad\qquad w = 4$$
The solution set is $\{4, 9\}$.

23. $\quad p^2 - 6p + 9 = 0$
$$(p-3)^2 = 0$$
$$p - 3 = 0$$
$$p = 3$$
The solution set is $\{3\}$.

25.
$$5x^2 = 2x + 3$$
$$5x^2 - 2x - 3 = 0$$
$$(5x+3)(x-1) = 0$$
$$5x + 3 = 0 \quad \text{or} \quad x - 1 = 0$$
$$5x = -3 \qquad\qquad x = 1$$
$$x = -\frac{3}{5}$$
The solution set is $\left\{-\dfrac{3}{5}, 1\right\}$.

27.
$$6m^2 = 23m - 15$$
$$6m^2 - 23m + 15 = 0$$
$$(m-3)(6m-5) = 0$$
$$m - 3 = 0 \quad \text{or} \quad 6m - 5 = 0$$
$$m = 3 \qquad\qquad 6m = 5$$
$$m = \frac{5}{6}$$
The solution set is $\left\{\dfrac{5}{6}, 3\right\}$.

29. $\quad 3p^2 + 9p - 120 = 0$
$$3(p^2 + 3p - 40) = 0$$
$$3(p+8)(p-5) = 0$$
$$p + 8 = 0 \quad \text{or} \quad p - 5 = 0$$
$$p = -8 \qquad\qquad p = 5$$
The solution set is $\{-8, 5\}$.

31. $\quad -4b^2 - 14b + 60 = 0$
$$-2(2b^2 + 7b - 30) = 0$$
$$-2(2b-5)(b+6) = 0$$
$$2b - 5 = 0 \quad \text{or} \quad b + 6 = 0$$
$$2b = 5 \qquad\qquad b = -6$$
$$b = \frac{5}{2}$$
The solution set is $\left\{-6, \dfrac{5}{2}\right\}$.

33. $\quad \dfrac{1}{2}x^2 + 2x - 6 = 0$
$$2\left(\frac{1}{2}x^2 + 2x - 6\right) = 2 \cdot 0$$
$$x^2 + 4x - 12 = 0$$
$$(x+6)(x-2) = 0$$
$$x + 6 = 0 \quad \text{or} \quad x - 2 = 0$$
$$x = -6 \qquad\qquad x = 2$$
The solution set is $\{-6, 2\}$.

35. $\dfrac{2}{3}x^2 + x = \dfrac{14}{3}$

$3\left(\dfrac{2}{3}x^2 + x\right) = 3 \cdot \dfrac{14}{3}$

$2x^2 + 3x = 14$

$2x^2 + 3x - 14 = 0$

$(2x+7)(x-2) = 0$

$2x+7 = 0$ or $x-2 = 0$

$2x = -7$ $x = 2$

$x = -\dfrac{7}{2}$

The solution set is $\left\{-\dfrac{7}{2}, 2\right\}$.

37. $x(x+8) = 33$

$x^2 + 8x = 33$

$x^2 + 8x - 33 = 0$

$(x+11)(x-3) = 0$

$x+11 = 0$ or $x-3 = 0$

$x = -11$ $x = 3$

The solution set is $\{-11, 3\}$.

39. $(x-2)(x+1)(x+5) = 0$

$x-2 = 0$ or $x+1 = 0$ or $x+5 = 0$

$x = 2$ $x = -1$ $x = -5$

The solution set is $\{-5, -1, 2\}$.

41. $2z^3 - 5z^2 = 3z$

$2z^3 - 5z^2 - 3z = 0$

$z\left(2z^2 - 5z - 3\right) = 0$

$z(2z+1)(z-3) = 0$

$z = 0$ or $2z+1 = 0$ or $z-3 = 0$

$2z = -1$ $z = 3$

$z = -\dfrac{1}{2}$

The solution set is $\left\{-\dfrac{1}{2}, 0, 3\right\}$.

43. $2p^3 + 5p^2 - 8p - 20 = 0$

$p^2(2p+5) - 4(2p+5) = 0$

$(2p+5)(p^2 - 4) = 0$

$(2p+5)(p-2)(p+2) = 0$

$2p+5 = 0$ or $p-2 = 0$ or $p+2 = 0$

$2p = -5$ $p = 2$ $p = -2$

$p = -\dfrac{5}{2}$

The solution set is $\left\{-\dfrac{5}{2}, -2, 2\right\}$.

45. $-30b^3 - 38b^2 = 12b$

$-30b^3 - 38b^2 - 12b = 0$

$-2b\left(15b^2 + 19b + 6\right) = 0$

$-2b(5b+3)(3b+2) = 0$

$-2b = 0$ or $5b+3 = 0$ or $3b+2 = 0$

$b = 0$ $5b = -3$ $3b = -2$

$b = -\dfrac{3}{5}$ $b = -\dfrac{2}{3}$

The solution set is $\left\{-\dfrac{2}{3}, -\dfrac{3}{5}, 0\right\}$.

47. $(x-2)^3 = x^3 - 2x$

$(x-2)(x-2)(x-2) = x^3 - 2x$

$\left(x^2 - 4x + 4\right)(x-2) = x^3 - 2x$

$x^3 - 4x^2 + 4x - 2x^2 + 8x - 8 = x^3 - 2x$

$x^3 - 6x^2 + 12x - 8 = x^3 - 2x$

$-6x^2 + 14x - 8 = 0$

$-2\left(3x^2 - 7x + 4\right) = 0$

$-2(3x-4)(x-1) = 0$

$3x-4 = 0$ or $x-1 = 0$

$3x = 4$ $x = 1$

$x = \dfrac{4}{3}$

The solution set is $\left\{1, \dfrac{4}{3}\right\}$.

49. a.
$$f(x) = 2$$
$$x^2 + 7x + 12 = 2$$
$$x^2 + 7x + 10 = 0$$
$$(x + 5)(x + 2) = 0$$
$$x + 5 = 0 \quad \text{or} \quad x + 2 = 0$$
$$x = -5 \qquad x = -2$$
The solution set is $\{-5, -2\}$.

b.
$$f(x) = 20$$
$$x^2 + 7x + 12 = 20$$
$$x^2 + 7x - 8 = 0$$
$$(x + 8)(x - 1) = 0$$
$$x + 8 = 0 \quad \text{or} \quad x - 1 = 0$$
$$x = -8 \qquad x = 1$$
The solution set is $\{-8, 1\}$.

The points $(-5, 2)$, $(-2, 2)$, $(-8, 20)$, and $(1, 20)$ are on the graph of f.

51. a.
$$g(x) = 3$$
$$2x^2 - 6x - 5 = 3$$
$$2x^2 - 6x - 8 = 0$$
$$2(x^2 - 3x - 4) = 0$$
$$2(x - 4)(x + 1) = 0$$
$$x - 4 = 0 \quad \text{or} \quad x + 1 = 0$$
$$x = 4 \qquad x = -1$$
The solution set is $\{-1, 4\}$.

b.
$$g(x) = 15$$
$$2x^2 - 6x - 5 = 15$$
$$2x^2 - 6x - 20 = 0$$
$$2(x^2 - 3x - 10) = 0$$
$$2(x - 5)(x + 2) = 0$$
$$x - 5 = 0 \quad \text{or} \quad x + 2 = 0$$
$$x = 5 \qquad x = -2$$
The solution set is $\{-2, 5\}$.

The points $(-1, 3)$, $(4, 3)$, $(-2, 15)$, and $(5, 15)$ are on the graph of g.

53. a.
$$F(x) = 5$$
$$-3x^2 + 12x + 5 = 5$$
$$-3x^2 + 12x = 0$$
$$-3x(x - 4) = 0$$
$$-3x = 0 \quad \text{or} \quad x - 4 = 0$$
$$x = 0 \qquad x = 4$$
The solution set is $\{0, 4\}$.

b.
$$F(x) = -10$$
$$-3x^2 + 12x + 5 = -10$$
$$-3x^2 + 12x + 15 = 0$$
$$-3(x^2 - 4x - 5) = 0$$
$$-3(x - 5)(x + 1) = 0$$
$$x - 5 = 0 \quad \text{or} \quad x + 1 = 0$$
$$x = 5 \qquad x = -1$$
The solution set is $\{-1, 5\}$.

The points $(0, 5)$, $(4, 5)$, $(-1, -10)$, and $(5, -10)$ are on the graph of F.

55.
$$f(x) = x^2 + 9x + 14$$
$$0 = x^2 + 9x + 14$$
$$0 = (x + 7)(x + 2)$$
$$x + 7 = 0 \quad \text{or} \quad x + 2 = 0$$
$$x = -7 \qquad x = -2$$
The zeros of $f(x)$ are -7 and -2.
The x-intercepts are -7 and -2.

57.
$$g(t) = 6t^2 - 25t - 9$$
$$0 = 6t^2 - 25t - 9$$
$$0 = (3t + 1)(2t - 9)$$
$$3t + 1 = 0 \quad \text{or} \quad 2t - 9 = 0$$
$$3t = -1 \qquad 2t = 9$$
$$t = -\frac{1}{3} \qquad t = \frac{9}{2}$$
The zeros of $g(t)$ are $-\dfrac{1}{3}$ and $\dfrac{9}{2}$.

The x-intercepts are $-\dfrac{1}{3}$ and $\dfrac{9}{2}$.

59. $s(d) = 2d^3 + 2d^2 - 40d$

$0 = 2d^3 + 2d^2 - 40d$

$0 = 2d(d^2 + d - 20)$

$0 = 2d(d+5)(d-4)$

$2d = 0$ or $d+5 = 0$ or $d-4 = 0$

$d = 0$ $\qquad d = -5$ $\qquad d = 4$

The zeros of $s(d)$ are -5, 0, and 4.

The x-intercepts are -5, 0, and 4.

61. $(x+3)(x-5) = 9$

$x^2 + 3x - 5x - 15 = 9$

$x^2 - 2x - 15 = 9$

$x^2 - 2x - 24 = 0$

$(x-6)(x+4) = 0$

$x - 6 = 0$ or $x + 4 = 0$

$x = 6$ $\qquad x = -4$

The solution set is $\{-4, 6\}$.

63. $2q^2 + 3q - 14 = 0$

$(2q+7)(q-2) = 0$

$2q + 7 = 0$ or $q - 2 = 0$

$2q = -7$ $\qquad q = 2$

$q = -\dfrac{7}{2}$

The solution set is $\left\{-\dfrac{7}{2}, 2\right\}$.

65. $-3b^2 + 21b = 0$

$-3b(b-7) = 0$

$-3b = 0$ or $b - 7 = 0$

$b = 0$ $\qquad b = 7$

The solution set is $\{0, 7\}$.

67. $(x+2)(x+3) = 0$

$x + 2 = 0$ or $x + 3 = 0$

$x = -2$ $\qquad x = -3$

The solution set is $\{-3, -2\}$.

69. $x^3 + 5x^2 - 4x - 20 = 0$

$x^2(x+5) - 4(x+5) = 0$

$(x+5)(x^2 - 4) = 0$

$(x+5)(x-2)(x+2) = 0$

$x + 5 = 0$ or $x - 2 = 0$ or $x + 2 = 0$

$x = -5$ $\qquad x = 2$ $\qquad x = -2$

The solution set is $\{-5, -2, 2\}$.

71. Let $x = $ width, then $x - 8 = $ length.

$A = $ width $\cdot$ length

$A = x(x-8)$

$x(x-8) = 128$

$x^2 - 8x = 128$

$x^2 - 8x - 128 = 0$

$(x-16)(x+8) = 0$

$x - 16 = 0$ or $x + 8 = 0$

$x = 16$ $\qquad \cancel{x = -8}$

The width of the rectangle is 16 centimeters and the length is 8 centimeters.

73. Let $x = $ base, then $x + 12 = $ height.

$A = \dfrac{1}{2} \cdot$ base $\cdot$ height

$= \dfrac{1}{2}x(x+12)$

$\dfrac{1}{2}x(x+12) = 110$

$\dfrac{1}{2}x^2 + 6x = 110$

$x^2 + 12x = 220$

$x^2 + 12x - 220 = 0$

$(x+22)(x-10) = 0$

$x + 22 = 0$ or $x - 10 = 0$

$\cancel{x = -22}$ $\qquad x = 10$

The base of the triangle is 10 feet and the height is 22 feet.

75.
$$D = \frac{n(n-3)}{2}$$
$$20 = \frac{n(n-3)}{2}$$
$$40 = n(n-3)$$
$$40 = n^2 - 3n$$
$$n^2 - 3n - 40 = 0$$
$$(n-8)(n+5) = 0$$
$$n-8 = 0 \quad \text{or} \quad n+5 = 0$$
$$n = 8 \qquad \cancel{n = -5}$$

A convex polygon with 20 diagonals has 8 sides (octagon).

77. Let $x =$ length of plot bordering river . The width must be $\frac{100-x}{2}$.

$$A = \text{length} \cdot \text{width}$$
$$= x \cdot \frac{(100-x)}{2}$$
$$= \frac{x(100-x)}{2}$$
$$800 = \frac{x(100-x)}{2}$$
$$1600 = x(100-x)$$
$$1600 = 100x - x^2$$
$$x^2 - 100x + 1600 = 0$$
$$(x-80)(x-20) = 0$$
$$x - 80 = 0 \quad \text{or} \quad x - 20 = 0$$
$$x = 80 \qquad\qquad x = 20$$
$$\frac{100-80}{2} = 10 \qquad \frac{100-20}{2} = 40$$

The dimensions of the plot are 40 meters by 20 meters (along the river) or 10 meters by 80 meters (along the river).

79. Let $x =$ width of walkway .
$$(8+2x)(12+2x) = 252$$
$$96 + 24x + 16x + 4x^2 = 252$$
$$4x^2 + 40x - 156 = 0$$
$$4(x^2 + 10x - 39) = 0$$
$$4(x+13)(x-3) = 0$$
$$x + 13 = 0 \quad \text{or} \quad x - 3 = 0$$
$$\cancel{x = -13} \qquad\qquad x = 3$$

The walkway is 3 feet wide.

81. Let $x =$ width of the piece of cardboard , then $x + 5 =$ length .

To obtain the length and width of the box, we subtract 4 from both the length and width of the cardboard because a corner is cut from each end.
$$V = \text{length} \cdot \text{width} \cdot \text{height}$$
$$168 = (x+5-4)(x-4)(2)$$
$$168 = 2(x+1)(x-4)$$
$$84 = (x+1)(x-4)$$
$$84 = x^2 + x - 4x - 4$$
$$0 = x^2 - 3x - 88$$
$$0 = (x-11)(x+8)$$
$$x - 11 = 0 \quad \text{or} \quad x + 8 = 0$$
$$x = 11 \qquad\qquad \cancel{x = -8}$$

The width of the piece of cardboard is 11 inches and the length is 16 inches.

83. a. $C(x) = x^2 - 40x + 600$
$$C(30) = (30)^2 - 40(30) + 600$$
$$= 900 - 1200 + 600$$
$$= 300$$

The marginal cost for producing the 30th bicycle is $300.

b. $x^2 - 40x + 600 = 200$
$$x^2 - 40x + 400 = 0$$
$$(x-20)^2 = 0$$
$$x - 20 = 0$$
$$x = 20$$

20 bicycles must be manufactured to have a marginal cost of $200.

c. $x^2 - 40x + 600 = 225$

$x^2 - 40x + 375 = 0$

$(x - 25)(x - 15) = 0$

$x - 25 = 0$ or $x - 15 = 0$

$x = 25$ $\qquad$ $x = 15$

Since production would continue until marginal revenue equals marginal cost, the company should manufacture 15 bicycles.

85. a. $\qquad s(t) = -16t^2 + 120t$

$\qquad 200 = -16t^2 + 120t$

$16t^2 - 120t + 200 = 0$

$8(2t^2 - 15t + 25) = 0$

$8(t - 5)(2t - 5) = 0$

$t - 5 = 0$ or $2t - 5 = 0$

$t = 5$ $\qquad$ $2t = 5$

$\qquad\qquad t = \dfrac{5}{2}$

The ball will be at a height of 200 feet after 2.5 seconds (on the way up), and again after 5 seconds (on the way down).

b. The ball will hit the ground when $s(t) = 0$.

$-16t^2 + 120t = 0$

$-8t(2t - 15) = 0$

$-8t = 0$ or $2t - 15 = 0$

$t = 0$ $\qquad$ $2t = 15$

$\qquad\qquad t = \dfrac{15}{2}$

The ball will hit the ground after 7.5 seconds.

87. $\qquad 4x^4 - 17x^2 + 4 = 0$

$(4x^2 - 1)(x^2 - 4) = 0$

$\left((2x)^2 - 1^2\right)(x^2 - 2^2) = 0$

$(2x - 1)(2x + 1)(x - 2)(x + 2) = 0$

$2x - 1 = 0$ or $2x + 1 = 0$ or $x - 2 = 0$ or $x + 2 = 0$

$2x = 1$ $\qquad$ $2x = -1$ $\qquad$ $x = 2$ $\qquad$ $x = -2$

$x = \dfrac{1}{2}$ $\qquad$ $x = -\dfrac{1}{2}$

The solution set is $\left\{-2, -\dfrac{1}{2}, \dfrac{1}{2}, 2\right\}$.

89. $(a + 3)^2 - 5(a + 3) = -6$

Let $u = a + 3$.

$u^2 - 5u = -6$

$u^2 - 5u + 6 = 0$

$(u - 3)(u - 2) = 0$

$u - 3 = 0$ or $u - 2 = 0$

$u = 3$ $\qquad$ $u = 2$

Now get back in terms of a.

$a + 3 = 3$ or $a + 3 = 2$

$a = 0$ $\qquad$ $a = -1$

The solution set is $\{-1, 0\}$.

91. $f(x) = \dfrac{5}{x^2 - 4}$

The domain is all real numbers except where the denominator equals 0.

$x^2 - 4 = 0$

$(x - 2)(x + 2) = 0$

$x - 2 = 0$ or $x + 2 = 0$

$x = 2$ $\qquad$ $x = -2$

The domain is all real numbers except ± 2. That is, $\{x \mid x \neq \pm 2\}$.

93. $g(x) = \dfrac{4x + 3}{2x^2 - 3x + 1}$

The domain is all real numbers except where the denominator equals 0.

$2x^2 - 3x + 1 = 0$

$(2x - 1)(x - 1) = 0$

$2x - 1 = 0$ or $x - 1 = 0$

$2x = 1$ $\qquad$ $x = 1$

$x = \dfrac{1}{2}$

The domain is all real numbers except $\dfrac{1}{2}$ and 1.

That is $\left\{x \mid x \neq \dfrac{1}{2}, 1\right\}$.

95. $2x^2 - 7x - 5 = 0$

The solution set is $\{-0.61, 4.11\}$.

97. $0.2x^2 - 5.1x + 3 = 0$

The solution set is $\{0.60, 24.90\}$.

99. $-x^2 + 0.6x = -2$ or $-x^2 + 0.6x + 2 = 0$

The solution set is $\{-1.15, 1.75\}$.

Chapter 5 Review

1. Coefficient: -7

Degree: 4

2. Coefficient: $\dfrac{1}{9}$

Degree: 3

3. $7x^3 - 2x^2 + x - 8$

Degree: 3

4. $y^4 - 3y^2 + 2y + 3$

Degree: 4

5. $\left(x^2 + 2x - 7\right) + \left(3x^2 - x - 4\right)$

$= x^2 + 2x - 7 + 3x^2 - x - 4$

$= x^2 + 3x^2 + 2x - x - 7 - 4$

$= (1+3)x^2 + (2-1)x + (-7-4)$

$= 4x^2 + x - 11$

6. $\left(4x^3 - 3x^2 + x - 5\right) - \left(x^4 + 2x^2 - 7x + 1\right)$

$= 4x^3 - 3x^2 + x - 5 - x^4 - 2x^2 + 7x - 1$

$= -x^4 + 4x^3 - 3x^2 - 2x^2 + x + 7x - 5 - 1$

$= -x^4 + 4x^3 + (-3-2)x^2 + (1+7)x + (-5-1)$

$= -x^4 + 4x^3 - 5x^2 + 8x - 6$

7. $\left(\dfrac{1}{4}x^2 - \dfrac{1}{2}x\right) - \left(4x - \dfrac{1}{6}\right)$

$= \dfrac{1}{4}x^2 - \dfrac{1}{2}x - 4x + \dfrac{1}{6}$

$= \dfrac{1}{4}x^2 + \left(-\dfrac{1}{2} - 4\right)x + \dfrac{1}{6}$

$= \dfrac{1}{4}x^2 - \dfrac{9}{2}x + \dfrac{1}{6}$

8. $\left(\dfrac{1}{2}x^2 - x + \dfrac{1}{4}\right) + \left(\dfrac{1}{3}x^2 + \dfrac{2}{5}\right)$

$= \dfrac{1}{2}x^2 - x + \dfrac{1}{4} + \dfrac{1}{3}x^2 + \dfrac{2}{5}$

$= \dfrac{1}{2}x^2 + \dfrac{1}{3}x^2 - x + \dfrac{1}{4} + \dfrac{2}{5}$

$= \left(\dfrac{1}{2} + \dfrac{1}{3}\right)x^2 - x + \left(\dfrac{1}{4} + \dfrac{2}{5}\right)$

$= \dfrac{5}{6}x^2 - x + \dfrac{13}{20}$

9. $\left(x^3y^2 + 6x^2y^2 - xy\right) + \left(-x^3y^2 + 4x^2y^2 + xy\right)$

$= x^3y^2 + 6x^2y^2 - xy - x^3y^2 + 4x^2y^2 + xy$

$= x^3y^2 - x^3y^2 + 6x^2y^2 + 4x^2y^2 - xy + xy$

$= (1-1)x^3y^2 + (6+4)x^2y^2 + (-1+1)xy$

$= 10x^2y^2$

10. $\left(a^2b - 4ab^2 + 3\right) - \left(2a^2b + 2ab^2 + 7\right)$

$= a^2b - 4ab^2 + 3 - 2a^2b - 2ab^2 - 7$

$= a^2b - 2a^2b - 4ab^2 - 2ab^2 + 3 - 7$

$= (1-2)a^2b + (-4-2)ab^2 + (3-7)$

$= -a^2b - 6ab^2 - 4$

11. a. $f(x) = -3x^2 + 2x - 8$

$f(-2) = -3(-2)^2 + 2(-2) - 8$

$\qquad = -3(4) - 4 - 8$

$\qquad = -12 - 4 - 8$

$\qquad = -24$

b. $f(x) = -3x^2 + 2x - 8$

$f(0) = -3(0)^2 + 2(0) - 8$

$\qquad = 0 + 0 - 8$

$\qquad = -8$

c. $f(x) = -3x^2 + 2x - 8$

$f(3) = -3(3)^2 + 2(3) - 8$

$\qquad = -3(9) + 6 - 8$

$\qquad = -27 + 6 - 8$

$\qquad = -29$

12. a. $f(x) = x^3 - 5x^2 + 3x - 1$

$f(-3) = (-3)^3 - 5(-3)^2 + 3(-3) - 1$

$\qquad = -27 - 5(9) - 9 - 1$

$\qquad = -27 - 45 - 9 - 1$

$\qquad = -82$

b. $f(x) = x^3 - 5x^2 + 3x - 1$

$f(0) = (0)^3 - 5(0)^2 + 3(0) - 1$

$\qquad = 0 - 0 + 0 - 1$

$\qquad = -1$

c. $f(x) = x^3 - 5x^2 + 3x - 1$

$f(2) = (2)^3 - 5(2)^2 + 3(2) - 1$

$\qquad = 8 - 5(4) + 6 - 1$

$\qquad = 8 - 20 + 6 - 1$

$\qquad = -7$

13. a. $(f+g)(x) = (4x-3) + \left(x^2 + 3x + 2\right)$

$\qquad = 4x - 3 + x^2 + 3x + 2$

$\qquad = x^2 + 4x + 3x - 3 + 2$

$\qquad = x^2 + 7x - 1$

b. Since $(f+g)(x) = x^2 + 7x - 1$, we have

$(f+g)(3) = (3)^2 + 7(3) - 1$

$\qquad = 9 + 21 - 1$

$\qquad = 29$

14. a. $(f-g)(x) = \left(2x^3 + x^2 - 7\right) - \left(3x^2 - x + 5\right)$

$\qquad = 2x^3 + x^2 - 7 - 3x^2 + x - 5$

$\qquad = 2x^3 + x^2 - 3x^2 + x - 7 - 5$

$\qquad = 2x^3 - 2x^2 + x - 12$

b. Since $(f-g)(x) = 2x^3 - 2x^2 + x - 12$, we have

$(f-g)(2) = 2(2)^3 - 2(2)^2 + (2) - 12$

$\qquad = 2(8) - 2(4) + 2 - 12$

$\qquad = 16 - 8 + 2 - 12$

$\qquad = -2$

15. a. Profit is the difference between revenue and costs. Thus,

$P(x) = R(x) - C(x)$

$\qquad = \left(-1.5x^2 + 180x\right) - \left(x^2 - 100x + 3290\right)$

$\qquad = -1.5x^2 + 180x - x^2 + 100x - 3290$

$\qquad = -1.5x^2 - x^2 + 180x + 100x - 3290$

$\qquad = -2.5x^2 + 280x - 3290$

The profit function is:

$P(x) = -2.5x^2 + 280x - 3290$

b. $P(25) = -2.5(25)^2 + 280(25) - 3290$

$\qquad = -2.5(625) + 7000 - 3290$

$\qquad = -1562.5 + 7000 - 3290$

$\qquad = 2147.5$

If 25 graphing calculators are sold, there would be a profit of $2147.50.

16. a. If the point is $(2,1)$, then $x = 2$.

$$A(x) = -x^2 + 5x$$
$$A(2) = -(2)^2 + 5(2)$$
$$= -4 + 10$$
$$= 6$$

The area of the region would be 6 square units.

b. If the point is $(1,3)$, then $x = 1$.

$$A(x) = -x^2 + 5x$$
$$A(1) = -(1)^2 + 5(1)$$
$$= -1 + 5$$
$$= 4$$

The area of the region would be 4 square units.

17. $\left(-3x^3 y\right)\left(4xy^2\right) = (-3 \cdot 4)\left(x^3 \cdot x\right)\left(y \cdot y^2\right)$
$$= -12x^{3+1} y^{1+2}$$
$$= -12x^4 y^3$$

18. $\left(\frac{1}{3} mn^4\right)\left(18m^3 n^3\right) = \left(\frac{1}{3} \cdot 18\right)\left(m \cdot m^3\right)\left(n^4 \cdot n^3\right)$
$$= \frac{18}{3} m^{1+3} n^{4+3}$$
$$= 6m^4 n^7$$

19. $5ab\left(-2a^2 b + ab^2 - 3ab\right)$
$$= -5ab \cdot 2a^2 b + 5ab \cdot ab^2 - 5ab \cdot 3ab$$
$$= -10a^3 b^2 + 5a^2 b^3 - 15a^2 b^2$$

20. $0.5c\left(1.7c^2 + 4.3c + 8.9\right)$
$$= 0.5c \cdot 1.7c^2 + 0.5c \cdot 4.3c + 0.5c \cdot 8.9$$
$$= 0.85c^3 + 2.15c^2 + 4.45c$$

21. $(x+2)(x-9) = x \cdot x - x \cdot 9 + 2 \cdot x - 2 \cdot 9$
$$= x^2 - 9x + 2x - 18$$
$$= x^2 - 7x - 18$$

22. $(-3x+1)(2x-8)$
$$= -3x \cdot 2x - 3x \cdot (-8) + 1 \cdot 2x - 1 \cdot 8$$
$$= -6x^2 + 24x + 2x - 8$$
$$= -6x^2 + 26x - 8$$

23. $(m-4n)(2m+n)$
$$= m \cdot 2m + m \cdot n - 4n \cdot 2m - 4n \cdot n$$
$$= 2m^2 + mn - 8mn - 4n^2$$
$$= 2m^2 - 7mn - 4n^2$$

24. $(2a+15)(-a+3)$
$$= 2a \cdot (-a) + 2a \cdot 3 + 15 \cdot (-a) + 15 \cdot 3$$
$$= -2a^2 + 6a - 15a + 45$$
$$= -2a^2 - 9a + 45$$

25. $(x+2)\left(3x^2 - 5x + 1\right)$
$$= x \cdot 3x^2 - x \cdot 5x + x \cdot 1 + 2 \cdot 3x^2 - 2 \cdot 5x + 2 \cdot 1$$
$$= 3x^3 - 5x^2 + x + 6x^2 - 10x + 2$$
$$= 3x^3 + x^2 - 9x + 2$$

26. $(w-4)\left(w^2 + w - 8\right)$
$$= w \cdot w^2 + w \cdot w - w \cdot 8 - 4 \cdot w^2 - 4 \cdot w - 4 \cdot (-8)$$
$$= w^3 + w^2 - 8w - 4w^2 - 4w + 32$$
$$= w^3 - 3w^2 - 12w + 32$$

27. $\left(m^2 - 2m + 3\right)\left(2m^2 + 5m - 7\right)$
$$= m^2 \cdot 2m^2 + m^2 \cdot 5m - m^2 \cdot 7 - 2m \cdot 2m^2 - 2m \cdot 5m$$
$$\qquad - 2m \cdot (-7) + 3 \cdot 2m^2 + 3 \cdot 5m - 3 \cdot 7$$
$$= 2m^4 + 5m^3 - 7m^2 - 4m^3 - 10m^2 + 14m$$
$$\qquad + 6m^2 + 15m - 21$$
$$= 2m^4 + m^3 - 11m^2 + 29m - 21$$

28. $(2p-3q)\left(p^2 + 7pq - 4q^2\right)$
$$= 2p \cdot p^2 + 2p \cdot 7pq - 2p \cdot 4q^2 - 3q \cdot p^2$$
$$\qquad - 3q \cdot 7pq - 3q \cdot \left(-4q^2\right)$$
$$= 2p^3 + 14p^2 q - 8pq^2 - 3p^2 q - 21pq^2 + 12q^3$$
$$= 2p^3 + 11p^2 q - 29pq^2 + 12q^3$$

29. $(3w+1)(3w-1) = (3w)^2 - (1)^2$
$$= 9w^2 - 1$$

30. $(2x-5y)(2x+5y) = (2x)^2 - (5y)^2$
$$= 4x^2 - 25y^2$$

31. $(6k-5)^2 = (6k)^2 - 2(6k)(5) + (5)^2$
$$= 36k^2 - 60k + 25$$

32. $(3a+2b)^2 = (3a)^2 + 2(3a)(2b) + (2b)^2$
$$= 9a^2 + 12ab + 4b^2$$

33. $(x+2)(x^2 - 2x + 4)$
$$= x \cdot x^2 - x \cdot 2x + x \cdot 4 + 2 \cdot x^2 - 2 \cdot 2x + 2 \cdot 4$$
$$= x^3 - 2x^2 + 4x + 2x^2 - 4x + 8$$
$$= x^3 + 8$$

34. $(2x-3)(4x^2 + 6x + 9)$
$$= 2x \cdot 4x^2 + 2x \cdot 6x + 2x \cdot 9 - 3 \cdot 4x^2 - 3 \cdot 6x - 3 \cdot 9$$
$$= 8x^3 + 12x^2 + 18x - 12x^2 - 18x - 27$$
$$= 8x^3 - 27$$

35. a. $(f \cdot g)(x) = f(x) \cdot g(x)$
$$= (3x-7)(6x+5)$$
$$= 3x \cdot 6x + 3x \cdot 5 - 7 \cdot 6x - 7 \cdot 5$$
$$= 18x^2 + 15x - 42x - 35$$
$$= 18x^2 - 27x - 35$$

   b. Since $(f \cdot g)(x) = 18x^2 - 27x - 35$, we have
$$(f \cdot g)(-2) = 18(-2)^2 - 27(-2) - 35$$
$$= 18(4) + 54 - 35$$
$$= 72 + 54 - 35$$
$$= 91$$

36. a. $(f \cdot g)(x) = f(x) \cdot g(x)$
$$= (x+2)(3x^2 - x + 1)$$
$$= x \cdot 3x^2 - x \cdot x + x \cdot 1 + 2 \cdot 3x^2$$
$$\quad - 2 \cdot x + 2 \cdot 1$$
$$= 3x^3 - x^2 + x + 6x^2 - 2x + 2$$
$$= 3x^3 + 5x^2 - x + 2$$

   b. Since $(f \cdot g)(x) = 3x^3 + 5x^2 - x + 2$, we have
$$(f \cdot g)(4) = 3(4)^3 + 5(4)^2 - (4) + 2$$
$$= 3(64) + 5(16) - 4 + 2$$
$$= 192 + 80 - 4 + 2$$
$$= 270$$

37. $f(x) = 5x^2 + 8$
$$f(x-3) = 5(x-3)^2 + 8$$
$$= 5(x^2 - 2 \cdot x \cdot 3 + 3^2) + 8$$
$$= 5(x^2 - 6x + 9) + 8$$
$$= 5x^2 - 30x + 45 + 8$$
$$= 5x^2 - 30x + 53$$

38. $f(x+h) - f(x) = \left[-(x+h)^2 + 3(x+h) - 5 \right]$
$$\qquad - \left[-x^2 + 3x - 5 \right]$$
$$= \left[-x^2 - 2xh - h^2 + 3x + 3h - 5 \right]$$
$$\qquad - \left[-x^2 + 3x - 5 \right]$$
$$= -x^2 - 2xh - h^2 + 3x + 3h - 5$$
$$\qquad + x^2 - 3x + 5$$
$$= -2xh + 3h - h^2$$

39. $\dfrac{12x^3 - 6x^2}{3x} = \dfrac{12x^3}{3x} - \dfrac{6x^2}{3x}$
$$= \frac{12}{3} x^{3-1} - \frac{6}{3} x^{2-1}$$
$$= 4x^2 - 2x$$

40. $\dfrac{15w^5 - 5w^3 + 25w^2 + 10w}{5w}$
$$= \frac{15w^5}{5w} - \frac{5w^3}{5w} + \frac{25w^2}{5w} + \frac{10w}{5w}$$
$$= \frac{15}{5} w^{5-1} - \frac{5}{5} w^{3-1} + \frac{25}{5} w^{2-1} + \frac{10}{5} w^{1-1}$$
$$= 3w^4 - w^2 + 5w + 2$$

41. $\dfrac{7y^3 + 12y^2 - 6y}{2y} = \dfrac{7y^3}{2y} + \dfrac{12y^2}{2y} - \dfrac{6y}{2y}$
$$= \frac{7}{2} y^{3-1} + \frac{12}{2} y^{2-1} - \frac{6}{2} y^{1-1}$$
$$= \frac{7}{2} y^2 + 6y - 3$$

42. $\dfrac{2m^3n^2 + 8m^2n^2 - 14mn^3}{4m^2n^3}$

$= \dfrac{2m^3n^2}{4m^2n^3} + \dfrac{8m^2n^2}{4m^2n^3} - \dfrac{14mn^3}{4m^2n^3}$

$= \dfrac{2}{4}m^{3-2}n^{2-3} + \dfrac{8}{4}m^{2-2}n^{2-3} - \dfrac{14}{4}m^{1-2}n^{3-3}$

$= \dfrac{1}{2}mn^{-1} + 2n^{-1} - \dfrac{7}{2}m^{-1}$

$= \dfrac{m}{2n} + \dfrac{2}{n} - \dfrac{7}{2m}$

43.
$$\begin{array}{r} 3x+4 \\ x-2\overline{)3x^2-2x-8} \\ \underline{-(3x^2-6x)} \\ 4x-8 \\ \underline{-(4x-8)} \\ 0 \end{array}$$

$\dfrac{3x^2-2x-8}{x-2} = 3x+4$

44.
$$\begin{array}{r} -2x+7 \\ x+5\overline{)-2x^2-3x+40} \\ \underline{-(-2x^2-10x)} \\ 7x+40 \\ \underline{-(7x+35)} \\ 5 \end{array}$$

$\dfrac{-2x^2-3x+40}{x+5} = -2x+7+\dfrac{5}{x+5}$

45.
$$\begin{array}{r} 3z^2+2 \\ 2z+3\overline{)6z^3+9z^2+4z-6} \\ \underline{-(6z^3+9z^2)} \\ 4z-6 \\ \underline{-(4z+6)} \\ -12 \end{array}$$

$\dfrac{6z^3+9z^2+4z-6}{2z+3} = 3z^2+2-\dfrac{12}{2z+3}$

46.
$$\begin{array}{r} 4k^2+k-2 \\ 3k-8\overline{)12k^3-29k^2-14k+16} \\ \underline{-(12k^3-32k^2)} \\ 3k^2-14k \\ \underline{-(3k^2-8k)} \\ -6k+16 \\ \underline{-(-6k+16)} \\ 0 \end{array}$$

$\dfrac{12k^3-29k^2-14k+16}{3k-8} = 4k^2+k-2$

47.
$$\begin{array}{r} 8x^3+12x^2+18x+27 \\ 2x-3\overline{)16x^4+0x^3+0x^2+0x-81} \\ \underline{-(16x^4-24x^3)} \\ 24x^3+0x^2 \\ \underline{-(24x^3-36x^2)} \\ 36x^2+0x \\ \underline{-(36x^2-54x)} \\ 54x-81 \\ \underline{-(54x-81)} \\ 0 \end{array}$$

$\dfrac{16x^4-81}{2x-3} = 8x^3+12x^2+18x+27$

48.
$$\begin{array}{r} 2x^2-5x+12 \\ x^2-3x+4\overline{)2x^4-11x^3+35x^2-54x+55} \\ \underline{-(2x^4-6x^3+8x^2)} \\ -5x^3+27x^2-54x \\ \underline{-(-5x^3+15x^2-20x)} \\ 12x^2-34x+55 \\ \underline{-(12x^2-36x+48)} \\ 2x+7 \end{array}$$

$\dfrac{2x^4-11x^3+35x^2-54x+55}{x^2-3x+4}$

$= 2x^2-5x+12+\dfrac{2x+7}{x^2-3x+4}$

49. The divisor is $x+2$ so $c=-2$.

$$-2\overline{)\begin{array}{ccc} 5 & 11 & 8 \end{array}}$$
$$\begin{array}{ccc} & -10 & -2 \\ \hline 5 & 1 & 6 \end{array}$$

$$\frac{5x^2+11x+8}{x+2}=5x+1+\frac{6}{x+2}$$

50. The divisor is $a-2$ so $c=2$.

$$2\overline{)\begin{array}{ccc} 9 & -14 & -8 \end{array}}$$
$$\begin{array}{ccc} & 18 & 8 \\ \hline 9 & 4 & 0 \end{array}$$

$$\frac{9a^2-14a-8}{a-2}=9a+4$$

51. The divisor is $m+3$ so $c=-3$.

$$-3\overline{)\begin{array}{cccc} 3 & 11 & -5 & -33 \end{array}}$$
$$\begin{array}{cccc} & -9 & -6 & 33 \\ \hline 3 & 2 & -11 & 0 \end{array}$$

$$\frac{3m^3+11m^2-5m-33}{m+3}=3m^2+2m-11$$

52. The divisor is $n-4$ so $c=4$.

$$4\overline{)\begin{array}{cccc} 1 & 2 & -39 & 67 \end{array}}$$
$$\begin{array}{cccc} & 4 & 24 & -60 \\ \hline 1 & 6 & -15 & 7 \end{array}$$

$$\frac{n^3+2n^2-39n+67}{n-4}=n^2+6n-15+\frac{7}{n-4}$$

53. The divisor is $x+1$ so $c=-1$.

$$-1\overline{)\begin{array}{ccccc} 1 & 0 & 6 & 0 & -7 \end{array}}$$
$$\begin{array}{ccccc} & -1 & 1 & -7 & 7 \\ \hline 1 & -1 & 7 & -7 & 0 \end{array}$$

$$\frac{x^4+6x^2-7}{x+1}=x^3-x^2+7x-7$$

54. The divisor is $x+2$ so $c=-2$.

$$-2\overline{)\begin{array}{cccc} 2 & 0 & 5 & -8 \end{array}}$$
$$\begin{array}{cccc} & -4 & 8 & -26 \\ \hline 2 & -4 & 13 & -34 \end{array}$$

$$\frac{2x^3+5x-8}{x+2}=2x^2-4x+13-\frac{34}{x+2}$$

55. a.

$$\left(\frac{f}{g}\right)(x)=\frac{5x^3+25x^2-15x}{5x}$$
$$=\frac{5x^3}{5x}+\frac{25x^2}{5x}-\frac{15x}{5x}$$
$$=\frac{5}{5}x^{3-1}+\frac{25}{5}x^{2-1}-\frac{15}{5}x^{1-1}$$
$$=x^2+5x-3$$

$$\left(\frac{f}{g}\right)(x)=x^2+5x-3$$

b. Since $\left(\frac{f}{g}\right)(x)=x^2+5x-3$, we have

$$\left(\frac{f}{g}\right)(2)=(2)^2+5(2)-3$$
$$=4+10-3$$
$$=11$$

56. a.

$$\left(\frac{f}{g}\right)(x)=\frac{9x^2+54x-31}{3x-2}$$

$$\begin{array}{r} 3x+20 \\ 3x-2\overline{)9x^2+54x-31} \\ \underline{-\left(9x^2-6x\right)} \\ 60x-31 \\ \underline{-\left(60x-40\right)} \\ 9 \end{array}$$

$$\left(\frac{f}{g}\right)(x)=3x+20+\frac{9}{3x-2}$$

b. Since $\left(\frac{f}{g}\right)(x)=3x+20+\frac{9}{3x-2}$, we have

$$\left(\frac{f}{g}\right)(-3)=3(-3)+20+\frac{9}{3(-3)-2}$$
$$=-9+20+\frac{9}{-11}$$
$$=11-\frac{9}{11}$$
$$=\frac{112}{11}$$

57. a. $\left(\dfrac{f}{g}\right)(x) = \dfrac{2x^3 + 12x^2 + 9x - 28}{x+4}$

The divisor is $x+4$ so $c=-4$.

$$
\begin{array}{r|rrrr}
-4 & 2 & 12 & 9 & -28 \\
   &   & -8 & -16 & 28 \\
\hline
   & 2 & 4 & -7 & 0
\end{array}
$$

$\left(\dfrac{f}{g}\right)(x) = 2x^2 + 4x - 7$

b. Since $\left(\dfrac{f}{g}\right)(x) = 2x^2 + 4x - 7$, we have

$\left(\dfrac{f}{g}\right)(-2) = 2(-2)^2 + 4(-2) - 7$

$= 2(4) - 8 - 7$

$= 8 - 8 - 7$

$= -7$

58. a. $\left(\dfrac{f}{g}\right)(x) = \dfrac{3x^4 - 14x^3 + 31x^2 - 58x + 22}{x^2 - x + 5}$

$$
\require{enclose}
\begin{array}{r}
3x^2 - 11x + 5 \\
x^2 - x + 5 \enclose{longdiv}{3x^4 - 14x^3 + 31x^2 - 58x + 22}
\end{array}
$$

$\underline{-\left(3x^4 - 3x^3 + 15x^2\right)}$

$-11x^3 + 16x^2 - 58x$

$\underline{-\left(-11x^3 + 11x^2 - 55x\right)}$

$5x^2 - 3x + 22$

$\underline{-\left(5x^2 - 5x + 25\right)}$

$2x - 3$

$\left(\dfrac{f}{g}\right)(x) = 3x^2 - 11x + 5 + \dfrac{2x-3}{x^2 - x + 5}$

b. Since $\left(\dfrac{f}{g}\right)(x) = 3x^2 - 11x + 5 + \dfrac{2x-3}{x^2-x+5}$,

we have

$\left(\dfrac{f}{g}\right)(4) = 3(4)^2 - 11(4) + 5 + \dfrac{2(4)-3}{(4)^2 - (4) + 5}$

$= 3(16) - 44 + 5 + \dfrac{8-3}{16-4+5}$

$= 48 - 44 + 5 + \dfrac{5}{17}$

$= 9 + \dfrac{5}{17}$

$= \dfrac{158}{17}$

59. The divisor is $x-4$ so $c=4$

$f(4) = 4(4)^2 - 7(4) + 23$

$= 4(16) - 28 + 23$

$= 64 - 28 + 23$

$= 59$

The remainder is 59.

60. The divisor is $x+2$ so $c=-2$

$f(-2) = (-2)^3 - 2(-2)^2 + 12(-2) - 5$

$= -8 - 2(4) - 24 - 5$

$= -8 - 8 - 24 - 5 = -45$

The remainder is -45.

61. $c=2$

$f(2) = 3(2)^2 + (2) - 14$

$= 3(4) + 2 - 14$

$= 12 + 2 - 14$

$= 0$

Since the remainder is 0, $x-2$ is a factor.

$$
\begin{array}{r|rrr}
2 & 3 & 1 & -14 \\
  &   & 6 & 14 \\
\hline
  & 3 & 7 & 0
\end{array}
$$

$f(x) = (x-2)(3x+7)$

62. $c=-4$

$f(-4) = 2(-4)^2 + 13(-4) + 22$

$= 2(16) - 52 + 22$

$= 32 - 52 + 22 = 2$

Since the remainder is not 0, $x+4$ is not a factor of $f(x)$.

63. Since $A = L \cdot W$ we get $L = \dfrac{A}{W}$

$$
\begin{array}{r}
5x+1 \\
4x-3{\overline{\smash{\big)}\,20x^2-11x-3}} \\
\underline{-\left(20x^2-15x\right)} \\
4x-3 \\
\underline{-\left(4x-3\right)} \\
0
\end{array}
$$

The length of the rectangle is $5x+1$ meters.

64. We have $V = L \cdot W \cdot H$ and the area of the top of the box is $L \cdot W$. We can rewrite to get

$$L \cdot W = \frac{V}{H}$$

$$
\begin{array}{r}
2\,)\overline{\,2 \quad 1 \quad -7 \quad -6} \\
4 \quad 10 \quad 6 \\
\hline
2 \quad 5 \quad 3 \quad 0
\end{array}
$$

The area of the top of the box is $2x^2 + 5x + 3$ square centimeters.

65. $4z + 24$
GCF: 4
$4z + 24 = 4 \cdot z + 4 \cdot 6$
$\qquad = 4(z+6)$

66. $-7y^2 + 91y$
GCF: $-7y$

$-7y^2 + 91y = -7y \cdot y - 7y \cdot (-13)$
$\qquad\qquad = -7y(y-13)$

67. $14x^3 y^2 + 2xy^2 - 8x^2 y$
GCF: $2xy$

$14x^3 y^2 + 2xy^2 - 8x^2 y$
$= 2xy \cdot 7x^2 y + 2xy \cdot y + 2xy \cdot (-4x)$
$= 2xy\left(7x^2 y + y - 4x\right)$
$= 2xy\left(7x^2 y - 4x + y\right)$

68. $30a^4 b^3 + 15a^3 b - 25a^2 b^2$
GCF: $5a^2 b$
$30a^4 b^3 + 15a^3 b - 25a^2 b^2$
$= 5a^2 b \cdot 6a^2 b^2 + 5a^2 b \cdot 3a + 5a^2 b \cdot (-5b)$
$= 5a^2 b\left(6a^2 b^2 + 3a - 5b\right)$

69. $3x(x+5) - 4(x+5)$
GCF: $x+5$
$3x(x+5) - 4(x+5) = 3x \cdot (x+5) - 4 \cdot (x+5)$
$\qquad\qquad = (x+5)(3x-4)$

70. $-4c(2c+9) + 3(2c+9)$
GCF: $2c+9$
$-4c(2c+9) + 3(2c+9)$
$= -4c \cdot (2c+9) + 3 \cdot (2c+9)$
$= (2c+9)(-4c+3)$
$= (2c+9)(3-4c)$

71. $(5x+3)(x-5y) + (x+2)(x-5y)$
GCF: $x-5y$
$(5x+3)(x-5y) + (x+2)(x-5y)$
$= (x-5y)\big((5x+3)+(x+2)\big)$
$= (x-5y)(5x+3+x+2)$
$= (x-5y)(6x+5)$

72. $(3a-b)(a+7) - (a+1)(a+7)$
GCF: $a+7$
$(3a-b)(a+7) - (a+1)(a+7)$
$= (a+7)\big((3a-b)-(a+1)\big)$
$= (a+7)(3a-b-a-1)$
$= (a+7)(2a-b-1)$

73. $x^2 + 6x - 3x - 18 = \left(x^2+6x\right) + \left(-3x-18\right)$
$\qquad\qquad = x(x+6) - 3(x+6)$
$\qquad\qquad = (x+6)(x-3)$

74. $c^2 + 2c - 5c - 10 = \left(c^2+2c\right) + \left(-5c-10\right)$
$\qquad\qquad = c(c+2) - 5(c+2)$
$\qquad\qquad = (c+2)(c-5)$

75. $14z^2 + 16z - 21z - 24$

$= \left(14z^2 + 16z\right) + \left(-21z - 24\right)$

$= 2z(7z + 8) - 3(7z + 8)$

$= (7z + 8)(2z - 3)$

76. $21w^2 - 28w + 6w - 8 = \left(21w^2 - 28w\right) + \left(6w - 8\right)$

$= 7w(3w - 4) + 2(3w - 4)$

$= (3w - 4)(7w + 2)$

77. Pull out the GCF first and then factor by grouping.

$2x^3 + 2x^2 - 18x^2 - 18x$

$= 2x\left(x^2 + x - 9x - 9\right)$

$= 2x\left(\left(x^2 + x\right) + \left(-9x - 9\right)\right)$

$= 2x\left(x(x + 1) - 9(x + 1)\right)$

$= 2x(x + 1)(x - 9)$

78. Pull out the GCF first and then factor by grouping.

$10a^4 + 15a^3 + 70a^3 + 105a^2$

$= 5a^2\left(2a^2 + 3a + 14a + 21\right)$

$= 5a^2\left(\left(2a^2 + 3a\right) + \left(14a + 21\right)\right)$

$= 5a^2\left(a(2a + 3) + 7(2a + 3)\right)$

$= 5a^2(2a + 3)(a + 7)$

79. a. $\dfrac{1}{2}n^2 + \dfrac{1}{2}n = \dfrac{1}{2}n \cdot n + \dfrac{1}{2}n \cdot 1$

$= \dfrac{1}{2}n(n + 1)$

b. $n = 32$

$\dfrac{1}{2}(32)(32 + 1) = 16(33) = 528$

80. $R(x) = 5200x - 2x^3$

$= 2x \cdot 2600 - 2x \cdot x^2$

$= 2x\left(2600 - x^2\right)$

The revenue function is $R(x) = 2x\left(2600 - x^2\right)$.

81. $w^2 - 11w - 26$

We are looking for two factors of $c = -26$ whose sum is $b = -11$. Since c is negative, the factors will have opposite signs, and since b is negative the factor with the larger absolute value must be negative.

Factors	1, −26	2, −13
Sum	−25	−11

$w^2 - 11w - 26 = (w + 2)(w - 13)$

82. $x^2 - 9x + 15$

We are looking for two factors of $c = 15$ whose sum is $b = -9$. Since c is positive the two factors have the same sign, and since b is negative the factors are both negative.

Factors	−1, −15	−3, −5
Sum	−16	−8

Since none of the possibilities work, $x^2 - 9x + 15$ is prime.

83. $-t^2 + 6t + 72$

Start by factoring out -1.

$-t^2 + 6t + 72 = -1\left(t^2 - 6t - 72\right)$

We are looking for two factors of $c = -72$ whose sum is $b = -6$. Since c is negative, the two factors will have opposite signs. Since b is negative the factor with the larger absolute value will be negative.

Factors	1, −72	2, −36	3, −24	4, −18	6, −12	8, −9
Sum	−71	−34	−21	−14	−6	−1

$-t^2 + 6t + 72 = -1\left(t^2 - 6t - 72\right)$

$= -1(t - 12)(t + 6)$

84. $m^2 + 10m + 21$

We are looking for two factors of $c = 21$ whose sum is $b = 10$. Since both c and b are positive, the two factors must be positive.

Factors	1, 21	3, 7
Sum	22	10

$m^2 + 10m + 21 = (m + 3)(m + 7)$

85. $x^2 + 4xy - 320y^2$

We are looking for two factors of $c = -320$ whose sum is $b = 4$. Since c is negative, the two factors have opposite signs, and since b is positive the factor with the larger absolute value must be positive.

Factors	$-1,320$	$-2,160$	$-4,80$	$-5,64$
Sum	319	158	76	59

Factors	$-8,40$	$-10,32$	$-16,20$
Sum	32	22	4

$x^2 + 4xy - 320y^2 = (x + 20y)(x - 16y)$

86. $r^2 - 5rs + 6s^2$

We are looking for two factors of $c = 6$ whose sum is $b = -5$. Since c is positive, the factors will have the same sign, and since b is negative the factors will both be negative.

Factors	$-1,-6$	$-2,-3$
Sum	-7	-5

$r^2 - 5rs + 6s^2 = (r - 2s)(r - 3s)$

87. *ac* Method:

$a \cdot c = 5 \cdot -6 = -30$

We are looking for two factors of -30 whose sum is 13. Since the product is negative, the factors will have opposite signs. The sum is positive so the factor with the larger absolute value will be positive.

factor 1	factor 2	sum	
-1	30	29	
-2	15	13	← okay
-3	10	7	
-5	6	1	

$5x^2 + 13x - 6 = 5x^2 - 2x + 15x - 6$
$\qquad = x(5x - 2) + 3(5x - 2)$
$\qquad = (x + 3)(5x - 2)$

Trial and Error Method:

First note that there are no common factors and that $a = 5$, $b = 13$, and $c = -6$. Since c is negative, the signs in our factors will be opposites. We will consider factorizations with this form:

$(\_\_x + \_\_)(\_\_x - \_\_)$

If our choice results in a middle term with the wrong sign, we simply switch the signs of the factors.

Since $a = 5$ can be factored as $1 \cdot 5$, we have the following form:

$(x + \_\_)(5x - \_\_)$

$|c| = |-6| = 6$ can be factored as $1 \cdot 6$ or $2 \cdot 3$.

$(x + 1)(5x - 6) \rightarrow 5x^2 - x - 6$

$(x + 6)(5x - 1) \rightarrow 5x^2 + 29x - 6$

$(x + 2)(5x - 3) \rightarrow 5x^2 + 7x - 6$

$(x + 3)(5x - 2) \rightarrow 5x^2 + 13x - 6$

The correct factorization is
$5x^2 + 13x - 6 = (x + 3)(5x - 2)$

88. *ac* Method:

$a \cdot c = 6 \cdot 44 = 264$

We are looking for two factors of 264 whose sum is 41. Since the product is positive, the factors will have the same sign. The sum is positive so the factors will both be positive, and both must be less than 41.

factor 1	factor 2	sum	
8	33	41	← okay
11	24	35	
12	22	34	

$6m^2 + 41m + 44 = 6m^2 + 8m + 33m + 44$
$\qquad = 2m(3m + 4) + 11(3m + 4)$
$\qquad = (2m + 11)(3m + 4)$

Trial and Error Method:

First note that there are no common factors and that $a = 6$, $b = 41$, and $c = 44$. Since c is positive, the signs in our factors will be the same. Since b is positive, both factors will be positive. We will consider factorizations with this form:

$(\_\_m + \_\_)(\_\_m + \_\_)$

Since $a = 6$ can be factored as $1 \cdot 6$ or $2 \cdot 3$, we have the following forms:

$(m + \_\_)(6m + \_\_)$

$(2m + \_\_)(3m + \_\_)$

$c = 44$ can be factored as $1 \cdot 44$, $2 \cdot 22$, or $4 \cdot 11$. Since the original expression had no common factors, the binomials we select cannot have a common factor.

$(m + 44)(6m + 1) \rightarrow 6m^2 + 265m + 44$

$$(2m+11)(3m+4) \rightarrow 6m^2 + 41m + 44$$

$$(2m+1)(3m+44) \rightarrow 6m^2 + 91m + 44$$

$$(m+4)(6m+11) \rightarrow 6m^2 + 35m + 44$$

The correct factorization is

$$6m^2 + 41m + 44 = (2m+11)(3m+4)$$

89. *ac* Method:

$a \cdot c = 4 \cdot 7 = 28$

We are looking for two factors of 28 whose sum is -5. Since the product is positive, the factors will have the same sign. The sum is negative so the factors will both be negative.

factor 1	factor 2	sum
-1	-28	-29
-2	-14	-16
-4	-7	-11

Since none of the possibilities work, the expression is prime.

Trial and Error Method:

First note that there are no common factors and that $a = 4$, $b = -5$, and $c = 7$. Since c is positive, the signs in our factors will be the same. Since b is negative, the signs will both be negative. We will consider factorizations with this form:

$$(\_\_ y - \_\_)(\_\_ y - \_\_)$$

Since $a = 4$ can be factored as $1 \cdot 4$ or $2 \cdot 2$, we have the following forms:

$$(y - \_\_)(4y - \_\_)$$

$$(2y - \_\_)(2y - \_\_)$$

$c = 7$ can be factored as $1 \cdot 7$.

$$(y-1)(4y-7) \rightarrow 4y^2 - 11y + 7$$

$$(y-7)(4y-1) \rightarrow 4y^2 - 29y + 7$$

$$(2y-1)(2y-7) \rightarrow 4y^2 - 16y + 7$$

None of the possibilities yield the given expression. Therefore, the expression is prime.

90. *ac* Method:

Start by factoring out the GCF.

$$8t^2 + 22t - 6 = 2(4t^2 + 11t - 3)$$

Now focus on the reduced trinomial.

$a \cdot c = 4 \cdot -3 = -12$

We are looking for two factors of -12 whose sum is 11. Since the product is negative, the two factors will have opposite signs. The sum is positive so the factor with the larger absolute value will be positive.

factor 1	factor 2	sum
-1	12	11 ← okay
-2	6	4
-3	4	1

$$8t^2 + 22t - 6 = 2(4t^2 + 11t - 3)$$

$$= 2(4t^2 + 12t - t - 3)$$

$$= 2(4t(t+3) - 1(t+3))$$

$$= 2(t+3)(4t-1)$$

Trial and Error Method:

Start by factoring out the GCF.

$$8t^2 + 22t - 6 = 2(4t^2 + 11t - 3)$$

Now focus on the reduced trinomial with $a = 4$, $b = 11$, and $c = -3$. Since c is negative, our factors will have opposite signs. We will consider factorizations of this form:

$$(\_\_ t + \_\_)(\_\_ t - \_\_)$$

If our choice results in a middle term with the wrong sign, we simply switch the signs in our factors to obtain the correct result.

Since $a = 4$ can be factored as $1 \cdot 4$ or $2 \cdot 2$, we have the following forms:

$$(t + \_\_)(4t - \_\_)$$

$$(2t + \_\_)(2t - \_\_)$$

$|c| = |-3| = 3$ can be factored as $1 \cdot 3$.

$$(t+1)(4t-3) \rightarrow 4t^2 + t - 3$$

$$(t+3)(4t-1) \rightarrow 4t^2 + 11t - 3$$

$$(2t+1)(2t-3) \rightarrow 4t^2 - 4t - 3$$

The correct factorization is

$$8t^2 + 22t - 6 = 2(t+3)(4t-1)$$

91. *ac* Method:

$a \cdot c = 6 \cdot 5 = 30$

We are looking for two factors of 30 whose sum is -13. Since the product is positive, the factors will have the same sign. The sum is negative so the factors will both be negative.

factor 1	factor 2	sum
-1	-30	-31
-2	-15	-17
-3	-10	-13 ← okay
-5	-6	-11

$$6x^2 - 13x + 5 = 6x^2 - 3x - 10x + 5$$
$$= 3x(2x - 1) - 5(2x - 1)$$
$$= (2x - 1)(3x - 5)$$

Trial and Error Method:
First note that there are no common factors and that $a = 6$, $b = -13$, and $c = 5$. Since c is positive, the signs in our factors will be the same. Since b is negative, the signs will both be negative. We will consider factorizations with this form:
$$(\_\,x - \_)(\_\,x - \_)$$
Since $a = 6$ can be factored as $1 \cdot 6$ or $2 \cdot 3$, we have the following forms:
$$(x - \_)(6x - \_)$$
$$(2x - \_)(3x - \_)$$
$c = 5$ can be factored as $1 \cdot 5$.
$$(x - 1)(6x - 5) \rightarrow 6x^2 - 11x + 5$$
$$(x - 5)(6x - 1) \rightarrow 6x^2 - 31x + 5$$
$$(2x - 1)(3x - 5) \rightarrow 6x^2 - 13x + 5$$
$$(2x - 5)(3x - 1) \rightarrow 6x^2 - 17x + 5$$
The correct factorization is
$$6x^2 - 13x + 5 = (2x - 1)(3x - 5)$$

92. *ac* Method:
$a \cdot c = 21 \cdot -2 = -42$
We are looking for two factors of -42 whose sum is -1. Since the product is negative, the two factors will have opposite signs. Since the sum is negative, the factor with the larger absolute value will be negative.

factor 1	factor 2	sum
1	-42	-41
2	-21	-19
3	-14	-11
6	-7	-1 ← okay

$$21r^2 - rs - 2s^2 = 21r^2 + 6rs - 7rs - 2s^2$$
$$= 3r(7r + 2s) - s(7r + 2s)$$
$$= (7r + 2s)(3r - s)$$

Trial and Error Method:
First note that there are no common factors and that $a = 21$, $b = -1$, and $c = -2$. Since c is negative, the factors will have opposite signs. We will consider factorizations with this form:

$$(\_\,r + \_\,s)(\_\,r - \_\,s)$$
If our choice results in a middle term with the wrong sign, we simply switch the signs in our factors to obtain the correct result.
Since $a = 21$ can be factored as $1 \cdot 21$ or $3 \cdot 7$, we have the following forms:
$$(r + \_\,s)(21r - \_\,s)$$
$$(3r + \_\,s)(7r - \_\,s)$$
$|c| = |-2| = 2$ can be factored as $1 \cdot 2$.
$$(r + s)(21r - 2s) \rightarrow 21r^2 + 19rs - 2s^2$$
$$(r + 2s)(21r - s) \rightarrow 21r^2 + 41rs - 2s^2$$
$$(3r + s)(7r - 2s) \rightarrow 21r^2 + rs - 2s^2$$
$$(3r + 2s)(7r - s) \rightarrow 21r^2 + 11rs - 2s^2$$
The third result is almost what we need, except the sign on the middle term is wrong. We simply change the signs of the factors to get the correct result.
$$(3r - s)(7r + 2s) \rightarrow 21r^2 - rs - 2s^2$$
The correct factorization is
$$21r^2 - rs - 2s^2 = (3r - s)(7r + 2s)$$

93. *ac* Method:
$a \cdot c = 20 \cdot 27 = 540$
We are looking for two factors of 540 whose sum is -57. Since the product is positive, the two factors will have the same sign. Since the sum is negative, the factors will both be negative. We are adding two negative numbers to get -57 so neither can be less than -57.

factor 1	factor 2	sum
-10	-54	-64 too small
-15	-36	-51 too large
-12	-45	-57 ← okay

$$20x^2 - 57xy + 27y^2 = 20x^2 - 12xy - 45xy + 27y^2$$
$$= 4x(5x - 3y) - 9y(5x - 3y)$$
$$= (5x - 3y)(4x - 9y)$$

Trial and Error Method
First note that there are no common factors and that $a = 20$, $b = -57$, and $c = 27$. Since c is positive, the signs in our factors will be the same. Since b is negative, the signs will both be negative. We will consider factorizations with this form:
$$(\_\,x - \_\,y)(\_\,x - \_\,y)$$

Since $a = 20$ can be factored as $1 \cdot 20$, $2 \cdot 10$, or $4 \cdot 5$, we have the following forms:

$\left(x - \underline{} y \right)\left(20x - \underline{} y \right)$

$\left(2x - \underline{} y \right)\left(10x - \underline{} y \right)$

$\left(4x - \underline{} y \right)\left(5x - \underline{} y \right)$

$c = 27$ can be factored as $1 \cdot 27$ or $3 \cdot 9$.

$\left(x - y \right)\left(20x - 27y \right) \rightarrow 20x^2 - 47xy + 27y^2$

$\left(x - 27y \right)\left(20x - y \right) \rightarrow 20x^2 - 541xy + 27y^2$

$\left(2x - y \right)\left(10x - 27y \right) \rightarrow 20x^2 - 64xy + 27y^2$

$\left(2x - 27y \right)\left(10x - y \right) \rightarrow 20x^2 - 272xy + 27y^2$

$\left(4x - y \right)\left(5x - 27y \right) \rightarrow 20x^2 - 113xy + 27y^2$

$\left(4x - 27y \right)\left(5x - y \right) \rightarrow 20x^2 - 139xy + 27y^2$

$\left(x - 3y \right)\left(20x - 9y \right) \rightarrow 20x^2 - 69xy + 27y^2$

$\left(x - 9y \right)\left(20x - 3y \right) \rightarrow 20x^2 - 183xy + 27y^2$

$\left(2x - 3y \right)\left(10x - 9y \right) \rightarrow 20x^2 - 48xy + 27y^2$

$\left(2x - 9y \right)\left(10x - 3y \right) \rightarrow 20x^2 - 96xy + 27y^2$

$\left(4x - 3y \right)\left(5x - 9y \right) \rightarrow 20x^2 - 51xy + 27y^2$

$\left(4x - 9y \right)\left(5x - 3y \right) \rightarrow 20x^2 - 57xy + 27y^2$

The correct factorization is

$20x^2 - 57xy + 27y^2 = \left(4x - 9y \right)\left(5x - 3y \right)$

94. Begin by factoring out the GCF.

$-2s^2 + 12s + 14 = -2\left(s^2 - 6s - 7 \right)$

Now focus on the reduced trinomial.
We are looking for two factors of -7 whose sum is -6. Since the product is negative, the factors have opposite signs. Since the sum is negative, the factor with the larger absolute value must be negative.

$-2s^2 + 12s + 14 = -2\left(s^2 - 6s - 7 \right)$

$\qquad\qquad\qquad\quad = -2\left(s - 7 \right)\left(s + 1 \right)$

95. $x^4 - 10x^2 - 11$

Let $u = x^2$. This gives $u^2 - 10u - 11$.
We need two factors of -11 whose sum is -10. Since the product is negative, the two factors will have opposite signs. Since the sum is negative, the factor with the larger absolute value will be negative.

$u^2 - 10u - 11 = \left(u + 1 \right)\left(u - 11 \right)$

Now get back in terms of x.

$x^4 - 10x^2 - 11 = \left(x^2 + 1 \right)\left(x^2 - 11 \right)$

96. $10x^2 y^2 + 41xy + 4$

Let $u = xy$. This gives $10u^2 + 41u + 4$.

$a \cdot c = 10 \cdot 4 = 40$

We need two factors of 40 whose sum is 41.
Since the product is positive, the two factors will have the same sign. Since the sum is also positive, the two factors are both positive.

factor 1	factor 2	sum
1	40	41 ← okay
2	20	22
4	10	14
5	8	13

$10u^2 + 41u + 4 = 10u^2 + 40u + u + 4$

$\qquad\qquad\qquad\quad = 10u\left(u + 4 \right) + 1\left(u + 4 \right)$

$\qquad\qquad\qquad\quad = \left(u + 4 \right)\left(10u + 1 \right)$

Now get back in terms of x and y.

$10x^2 y^2 + 41xy + 4 = \left(xy + 4 \right)\left(10xy + 1 \right)$

97. $\left(a + 4 \right)^2 - 9\left(a + 4 \right) - 36$

Let $u = a + 4$. This gives $u^2 - 9u - 36$.
We need two factors of -36 whose sum is -9. Since the product is negative, the two factors will have opposite signs. Since the sum is negative, the factor with the larger absolute value will be negative.

factor 1	factor 2	sum
1	−36	−35
2	−18	−16
3	−12	−9 ← okay
4	−9	−5
6	−6	0

$u^2 - 9u - 36 = \left(u + 3 \right)\left(u - 12 \right)$

Now get back in terms of a.

$\left(a + 4 \right)^2 - 9\left(a + 4 \right) - 36 = \left(a + 4 + 3 \right)\left(a + 4 - 12 \right)$

$\qquad\qquad\qquad\qquad\qquad\qquad = \left(a + 7 \right)\left(a - 8 \right)$

98. $2(w-1)^2 + 11(w-1) + 9$

Let $u = w - 1$. This gives $2u^2 + 11u + 9$.
$a \cdot c = 2 \cdot 9 = 18$
We are looking for two factors of 18 whose sum is 11. Since the product is positive, the factors will have the same sign. Since the sum is also positive, the two factors will both be positive.

factor 1	factor 2	sum
1	18	19
2	9	11 ← okay
3	6	9

$2u^2 + 11u + 9 = 2u^2 + 2u + 9u + 9$
$\qquad = 2u(u+1) + 9(u+1)$
$\qquad = (u+1)(2u+9)$

Now go back in terms of w.
$2(w-1)^2 + 11(w-1) + 9$
$= (w-1+1)(2(w-1)+9)$
$= w(2w-2+9)$
$= w(2w+7)$

99. $x^2 + 22x + 121 = x^2 + 2 \cdot 11 \cdot x + 11^2$
$\qquad = (x+11)^2$

100. $w^2 - 34w + 289 = w^2 - 2 \cdot 17 \cdot w + 17^2$
$\qquad = (w-17)^2$

101. $144 - 24c + c^2 = 12^2 - 2 \cdot 12 \cdot c + c^2$
$\qquad = (12-c)^2$

102. $x^2 - 8x + 16 = x^2 - 2 \cdot (4) \cdot x + (4)^2$
$\qquad = (x-4)^2$

103. $64y^2 + 80y + 25 = (8y)^2 + 2 \cdot (8y) \cdot 5 + 5^2$
$\qquad = (8y+5)^2$

104. $12z^2 + 48z + 48 = 12(z^2 + 4z + 4)$
$\qquad = 12(z^2 + 2 \cdot 2 \cdot z + 2^2)$
$\qquad = 12(z+2)^2$

105. $x^2 - 196 = x^2 - 14^2$
$\qquad = (x-14)(x+14)$

106. $49 - y^2 = 7^2 - y^2$
$\qquad = (7-y)(7+y)$

107. $t^2 - 225 = t^2 - (15)^2$
$\qquad = (t-15)(t+15)$

108. $4w^2 - 81 = (2w)^2 - 9^2$
$\qquad = (2w-9)(2w+9)$

109. $36x^4 - 25y^2 = (6x^2)^2 - (5y)^2$
$\qquad = (6x^2 - 5y)(6x^2 + 5y)$

110. $80mn^2 - 20m = 20m(4n^2 - 1)$
$\qquad = 20m((2n)^2 - 1^2)$
$\qquad = 20m(2n-1)(2n+1)$

111. $x^3 - 343 = x^3 - 7^3$
$\qquad = (x-7)(x^2 + (7)x + 7^2)$
$\qquad = (x-7)(x^2 + 7x + 49)$

112. $729 - y^3 = 9^3 - y^3$
$\qquad = (9-y)(9^2 + 9(y) + y^2)$
$\qquad = (9-y)(81 + 9y + y^2)$
$\qquad = (9-y)(y^2 + 9y + 81)$

113. $27x^3 - 125y^3$
$= (3x)^3 - (5y)^3$
$= (3x-5y)((3x)^2 + (3x)(5y) + (5y)^2)$
$= (3x-5y)(9x^2 + 15xy + 25y^2)$

114. $8m^6 + 27n^3$

$= \left(2m^2\right)^3 + \left(3n\right)^3$

$= \left(2m^2 + 3n\right)\left(\left(2m^2\right)^2 - \left(2m^2\right)(3n) + \left(3n\right)^2\right)$

$= \left(2m^2 + 3n\right)\left(4m^4 - 6m^2n + 9n^2\right)$

115. $2a^6 - 2b^6$

$= 2\left(a^6 - b^6\right)$

$= 2\left(\left(a^3\right)^2 - \left(b^3\right)^2\right)$

$= 2\left(a^3 - b^3\right)\left(a^3 + b^3\right)$

$= 2(a-b)\left(a^2 + ab + b^2\right)(a+b)\left(a^2 - ab + b^2\right)$

$= 2(a-b)(a+b)\left(a^2 + ab + b^2\right)\left(a^2 - ab + b^2\right)$

116. $(y-1)^3 + 64$

$= (y-1)^3 + 4^3$

$= (y-1+4)\left((y-1)^2 - (y-1)(4) + 4^2\right)$

$= (y+3)\left(y^2 - 2y + 1 - 4y + 4 + 16\right)$

$= (y+3)\left(y^2 - 6y + 21\right)$

117. $x^2 + 7x + 6 = (x+1)(x+6)$

118. $c^2 - 24c + 144 = c^2 - 2(12)c + (12)^2$

$= (c-12)^2$

119. $z^2 - 9z - 112$

We need two factors of -112 whose sum is -9. Since the product is negative, the factors will have opposite signs. Since the sum is negative, the factor with the larger absolute value will be negative.

factor 1	factor 2	sum	
2	−56	−54	too small
8	−14	−6	too big
7	−16	−9	← okay

$z^2 - 9z - 112 = (z+7)(z-16)$

120. $-8x^2y^3 + 12xy^3 = -4xy^3(2x - 3)$

121. $7x^3 - 28x^2 + 63x = 7x\left(x^2 - 4x + 9\right)$

122. $3x^2 - 3x - 18 = 3\left(x^2 - x - 6\right)$

$= 3(x-3)(x+2)$

123. $4z^2 - 60z + 225 = (2z)^2 - 2(2z)(15) + 15^2$

$= (2z - 15)^2$

124. $12x^2 + 7x - 49$

$a \cdot c = 12 \cdot -49 = -588$

We are looking for two factors of -588 whose sum is 7. Since the product is negative, the factors will have opposite signs. Since the sum is positive, the factor with the larger absolute value will be positive. The difference is relatively small, so we should select factors whose absolute values are close to each other.

factor 1	factor 2	sum	
−14	42	28	
−21	28	7	← okay

$12x^2 + 7x - 49 = 12x^2 - 21x + 28x - 49$

$= 3x(4x - 7) + 7(4x - 7)$

$= (3x + 7)(4x - 7)$

125. $45 + 6x - 3x^2 = -3\left(x^2 - 2x - 15\right)$

$= -3(x - 5)(x + 3)$

126. $10n^2 - 33n - 7$

$a \cdot c = 10 \cdot -7 = -70$

We are looking for two factors of -70 whose sum is -33. Since the product is negative, the factors will have opposite signs. Since the sum is also negative, the factor with the larger absolute value will be negative.

factor 1	factor 2	sum	
1	−70	−69	
2	−35	−33	← okay

$10n^2 - 33n - 7 = 10n^2 + 2n - 35n - 7$

$= 2n(5n + 1) - 7(5n + 1)$

$= (2n - 7)(5n + 1)$

127. $8 - 2y - y^2 = -\left(y^2 + 2y - 8\right)$

$= -(y - 2)(y + 4)$

128. $2x^3 - 10x^2 + 6x - 30 = 2\left(x^3 - 5x^2 + 3x - 15\right)$
$$= 2\left(x^2(x-5) + 3(x-5)\right)$$
$$= 2(x-5)\left(x^2 + 3\right)$$

129. $(w - 3z)^2 - (z+2)^2$
$$= \left((w-3z) - (z+2)\right)\left((w-3z) + (z+2)\right)$$
$$= (w - 3z - z - 2)(w - 3z + z + 2)$$
$$= (w - 4z - 2)(w - 2z + 2)$$

130. $(3h+2)^3 + 64$
$$= (3h+2)^3 + 4^3$$
$$= (3h + 2 + 4)\left((3h+2)^2 - (3h+2)(4) + 4^2\right)$$
$$= (3h+6)\left((3h)^2 + 2(3h)(2) + 2^2 - 12h - 8 + 16\right)$$
$$= 3(h+2)\left(9h^2 + 12h + 4 - 12h + 8\right)$$
$$= 3(h+2)\left(9h^2 + 12\right)$$
$$= 3(h+2) \cdot 3\left(3h^2 + 4\right)$$
$$= 9(h+2)\left(3h^2 + 4\right)$$

131. $5p^3q^2 - 80p = 5p\left(p^2q^2 - 16\right)$
$$= 5p\left((pq)^2 - 4^2\right)$$
$$= 5p(pq - 4)(pq + 4)$$

132. $36a^2 - 20a - 27a + 15 = 4a(9a - 5) - 3(9a - 5)$
$$= (4a - 3)(9a - 5)$$

133. $m^4 - 5m^2 + 4 = \left(m^2\right)^2 - 5\left(m^2\right) + 4$

Let $u = m^2$. This gives $u^2 - 5u + 4$.
$$u^2 - 5u + 4 = (u - 1)(u - 4)$$
Now go back in terms of m.
$$m^4 - 5m^2 + 4 = \left(m^2 - 1\right)\left(m^2 - 4\right)$$
$$= (m - 1)(m + 1)(m - 2)(m + 2)$$

134. $686 - 16m^6$
$$= -2\left(8m^6 - 343\right)$$
$$= -2\left(\left(2m^2\right)^3 - 7^3\right)$$
$$= -2\left(2m^2 - 7\right)\left(\left(2m^2\right)^2 + \left(2m^2\right)(7) + 7^2\right)$$
$$= -2\left(2m^2 - 7\right)\left(4m^4 + 14m^2 + 49\right)$$

135. $h^3 + 2h^2 - h - 2 = h^2(h+2) - 1(h+2)$
$$= \left(h^2 - 1\right)(h+2)$$
$$= (h-1)(h+1)(h+2)$$

136. $108x^3 + 4y^3 = 4\left(27x^3 + y^3\right)$
$$= 4\left((3x)^3 + y^3\right)$$
$$= 4(3x + y)\left((3x)^2 - (3x)(y) + y^2\right)$$
$$= 4(3x + y)\left(9x^2 - 3xy + y^2\right)$$

137. The area of the larger square is $x \cdot x = x^2$ and the area of the smaller square is $5 \cdot 5 = 25$. The shaded area is the difference of the areas of the two squares.
$$x^2 - 25 = x^2 - 5^2$$
$$= (x-5)(x+5)$$
The area of the shaded region is $(x-5)(x+5)$ square units.

138. The area of the shaded region is the difference between the area of the square and the area of the circle. The length of each side of the square is twice the radius of the circle, or $2x$. Thus, the area of the square is $(2x)^2 = 4x^2$ and the area of the circle is πx^2. The difference is
$$4x^2 - \pi x^2 = (4 - \pi)x^2.$$
The area of the shaded region is $(4 - \pi)x^2$ square units.

139. $(w+5)(w-13) = 0$
$$w + 5 = 0 \text{ or } w - 13 = 0$$
$$w = -5 \text{ or } w = 13$$
The solution set is $\{-5, 13\}$.

140. $x(2x+1)(3x-5)=0$

$x=0$ or $2x+1=0$ or $3x-5=0$

$x=0$ or $2x=-1$ or $3x=5$

$x=0$ or $x=-\dfrac{1}{2}$ or $x=\dfrac{5}{3}$

The solution set is $\left\{-\frac{1}{2},0,\frac{5}{3}\right\}$.

141. $5a^2=-20a$

$5a^2+20a=0$

$5a(a+4)=0$

$5a=0$ or $a+4=0$

$a=0$ or $a=-4$

The solution set is $\{-4,0\}$.

142. $y^2+2y=15$

$y^2+2y-15=0$

$(y+5)(y-3)=0$

$y+5=0$ or $y-3=0$

$y=-5$ or $y=3$

The solution set is $\{-5,3\}$.

143. $x^2+21x+54=0$

$(x+18)(x+3)=0$

$x+18=0$ or $x+3=0$

$x=-18$ or $x=-3$

The solution set is $\{-18,-3\}$.

144. $15x^2+29x-14=0$

$(5x-2)(3x+7)=0$

$5x-2=0$ or $3x+7=0$

$5x=2$ or $3x=-7$

$x=\dfrac{2}{5}$ or $x=-\dfrac{7}{3}$

The solution set is $\left\{-\frac{7}{3},\frac{2}{5}\right\}$.

145. $x(x+1)=110$

$x^2+x=110$

$x^2+x-110=0$

$(x+11)(x-10)=0$

$x+11=0$ or $x-10=0$

$x=-11$ or $x=10$

The solution set is $\{-11,10\}$.

146. $\dfrac{1}{2}x^2+5x+12=0$

$2\left(\frac{1}{2}x^2+5x+12\right)=2\cdot 0$

$x^2+10x+24=0$

$(x+6)(x+4)=0$

$x+6=0$ or $x+4=0$

$x=-6$ or $x=-4$

The solution set is $\{-6,-4\}$.

147. $(b+1)(b-3)=5$

$b^2+b-3b-3=5$

$b^2-2b-3=5$

$b^2-2b-8=0$

$(b-4)(b+2)=0$

$b-4=0$ or $b+2=0$

$b=4$ or $b=-2$

The solution set is $\{-2,4\}$.

148. $(x+7)^3=x^3+133$

$(x+7)(x+7)^2=x^3+133$

$(x+7)(x^2+14x+49)=x^3+133$

$x^3+14x^2+49x+7x^2+98x+343=x^3+133$

$x^3+21x^2+147x+343=x^3+133$

$21x^2+147x+210=0$

$21(x^2+7x+10)=0$

$x^2+7x+10=0$

$(x+5)(x+2)=0$

$x+5=0$ or $x+2=0$

$x=-5$ or $x=-2$

The solution set is $\{-5,-2\}$.

149. a. $f(x)=x^2+5x-18$

$6=x^2+5x-18$

$0=x^2+5x-24$

$0=(x+8)(x-3)$

$x+8=0$ or $x-3=0$

$x=-8$ or $x=3$

The solution set is $\{-8,3\}$.

b. $f(x) = x^2 + 5x - 18$

$-4 = x^2 + 5x - 18$

$0 = x^2 + 5x - 14$

$0 = (x+7)(x-2)$

$x + 7 = 0$ or $x - 2 = 0$

$x = -7$ or $x = 2$

The solution set is $\{-7, 2\}$.

The points $(-8, 6)$, $(3, 6)$, $(-7, -4)$, and $(2, -4)$ are on the graph.

150. a. $f(x) = 5x^2 - 4x + 3$

$3 = 5x^2 - 4x + 3$

$0 = 5x^2 - 4x$

$0 = x(5x - 4)$

$x = 0$ or $5x - 4 = 0$

$x = 0$ or $x = \dfrac{4}{5}$

The solution set is $\left\{0, \dfrac{4}{5}\right\}$.

b. $f(x) = 5x^2 - 4x + 3$

$4 = 5x^2 - 4x + 3$

$0 = 5x^2 - 4x - 1$

$0 = (5x + 1)(x - 1)$

$5x + 1 = 0$ or $x - 1 = 0$

$x = -\dfrac{1}{5}$ or $x = 1$

The solution set is $\left\{-\dfrac{1}{5}, 1\right\}$.

The points $(0, 3)$, $\left(\dfrac{4}{5}, 3\right)$, $\left(-\dfrac{1}{5}, 4\right)$, and $(1, 4)$ are on the graph of f.

151. $f(x) = 3x^3 + 18x^2 + 24x$

$0 = 3x(x^2 + 6x + 8)$

$0 = 3x(x + 4)(x + 2)$

$3x = 0$ or $x + 4 = 0$ or $x + 2 = 0$

$x = 0$ or $x = -4$ or $x = -2$

The zeros of $f(x)$ are -4, -2, and 0. The x-intercepts are also -4, -2, and 0.

152. $f(x) = -4x^2 + 22x + 42$

$0 = -4x^2 + 22x + 42$

$0 = 2x^2 - 11x - 21$

$0 = (2x + 3)(x - 7)$

$2x + 3 = 0$ or $x - 7 = 0$

$x = -\dfrac{3}{2}$ or $x = 7$

The zeros of $f(x)$ are $-\dfrac{3}{2}$ and 7. The x-intercepts are also $-\dfrac{3}{2}$ and 7.

153. $s(t) = -16t^2 + 2064$

$1280 = -16t^2 + 2064$

$0 = -16t^2 + 784$

$0 = t^2 - 49$

$0 = (t - 7)(t + 7)$

$t - 7 = 0$ or $t + 7 = 0$

$t = 7$ or $t = -7$

The object will be 1280 feet above the ground after 7 seconds.

154. a. $R = 1 - (1 - r)^2$

$0.96 = 1 - (1 - r)^2$

$0 = (1 - r)^2 - 0.04$

$0 = \big((1 - r) - 0.2\big)\big((1 - r) + 0.2\big)$

$0 = (0.8 - r)(1.2 - r)$

$0.8 - r = 0$ or $1.2 - r = 0$

$r = 0.8$ or $r = 1.2$

The component reliability is 0.80. (Reliability cannot exceed 1)

b. $R = 1 - (1 - r)^2$

$0.99 = 1 - (1 - r)^2$

$0 = (1 - r)^2 - 0.01$

$0 = \big((1 - r) - 0.1\big)\big((1 - r) + 0.1\big)$

$0 = (0.9 - r)(1.1 - r)$

$0.9 - r = 0$ or $1.1 - r = 0$

$r = 0.9$ or $r = 1.1$

The component reliability is 0.90. (Reliability cannot exceed 1)

Chapter 5 Test

1. $-5x^7 + x^4 + 7x^2 - x + 1$
   Degree: 7

2. $\left(-2a^3b^2 + 5a^2b + ab + 1\right) + \left(\frac{1}{3}a^3b^2 + 4a^2b - 6ab - 5\right)$
   $= -2a^3b^2 + 5a^2b + ab + 1 + \frac{1}{3}a^3b^2 + 4a^2b - 6ab - 5$
   $= -2a^3b^2 + \frac{1}{3}a^3b^2 + 5a^2b + 4a^2b + ab - 6ab + 1 - 5$
   $= -\frac{5}{3}a^3b^2 + 9a^2b - 5ab - 4$

3. $f(x) = x^3 + 3x^2 - x + 1$
   $f(-2) = (-2)^3 + 3(-2)^2 - (-2) + 1$
   $\quad = -8 + 3(4) + 2 + 1$
   $\quad = -8 + 12 + 2 + 1$
   $\quad = 7$

4. $(f-g)(x) = \left(7x^3 - 1\right) - \left(4x^2 + 3x - 2\right)$
   $\quad = 7x^3 - 1 - 4x^2 - 3x + 2$
   $\quad = 7x^3 - 4x^2 - 3x + 1$

5. $\frac{1}{2}a^2b\left(4ab^2 - 6ab + 8\right)$
   $= \frac{1}{2}a^2b \cdot 4ab^2 - \frac{1}{2}a^2b \cdot 6ab + \frac{1}{2}a^2b \cdot 8$
   $= 2a^{2+1}b^{1+2} - 3a^{2+1}b^{1+1} + 4a^2b$
   $= 2a^3b^3 - 3a^3b^2 + 4a^2b$

6. $(3x-1)(4x+17) = 3x \cdot 4x + 3x \cdot 17 - 1 \cdot 4x - 1 \cdot 17$
   $\quad = 12x^2 + 51x - 4x - 17$
   $\quad = 12x^2 + 47x - 17$

7. $(2m-n)^2 = (2m)^2 - 2(2m)(n) + n^2$
   $\quad = 4m^2 - 4mn + n^2$

8. $2z^2 + 1 \overline{\smash{)}\,6z^3 - 14z^2 + z + 4}$ quotient $3z - 7$
   $\underline{-\left(6z^3 \qquad + 3z\right)}$
   $\qquad -14z^2 - 2z + 4$
   $\qquad \underline{-\left(-14z^2 \qquad - 7\right)}$
   $\qquad\qquad -2z + 11$
   $\dfrac{6z^3 - 14z^2 + z + 4}{2z^2 + 1} = 3z - 7 + \dfrac{-2z + 11}{2z^2 + 1}$

9. $6 \overline{\smash{)}\,5 \quad -27 \quad -18}$
   $\qquad \underline{\;30 \qquad 18\;}$
   $\qquad 5 \quad\; 3 \qquad 0$
   $\dfrac{5x^2 - 27x - 18}{x - 6} = 5x + 3$

10. $2x + 3 \overline{\smash{)}\,6x^2 + x - 12}$ quotient $3x - 4$
    $\underline{-\left(6x^2 + 9x\right)}$
    $\qquad -8x - 12$
    $\qquad \underline{-\left(-8x - 12\right)}$
    $\qquad\qquad 0$
    $\left(\frac{f}{g}\right)(x) = 3x - 4$
    $\left(\frac{f}{g}\right)(2) = 3(2) - 4 = 6 - 4 = 2$

11. The divisor is $x - 3$ so $c = 3$.
    $f(3) = 2(3)^3 - 3(3)^2 - 4(3) + 7$
    $\quad = 2(27) - 3(9) - 12 + 7$
    $\quad = 54 - 27 - 12 + 7$
    $\quad = 22$

12. GCF: $4ab^2$
    $12a^3b^2 + 8a^2b^2 - 16ab^3$
    $= 4ab^2 \cdot 3a^2 + 4ab^2 \cdot 2a - 4ab^2 \cdot 4b$
    $= 4ab^2\left(3a^2 + 2a - 4b\right)$

13. $6c^2 + 21c - 4c - 14 = 3c(2c + 7) - 2(2c + 7)$
    $\qquad\qquad\qquad\qquad = (2c + 7)(3c - 2)$

14. $x^2 - 13x - 48$
    We need two factors of -48 whose sum is -13. Since the product is negative, the factors will have opposite signs. Since the sum is also negative, the factor with the larger absolute value will be negative.

Factors	$1, -48$	$2, -24$	$3, -16$	$4, -12$	$6, -8$
Sum	-47	-22	-13	-8	-2

$x^2 - 13x - 48 = (x - 16)(x + 3)$

15. $-14p^2 - 17p + 6$

$a \cdot c = -14 \cdot 6 = -84$

We need two factors of -84 whose sum is -17. The product is negative, so the two factors will have opposite signs. Since the sum is also negative, the factor with the larger absolute value will be negative.

factor 1	factor 2	sum
3	−28	−25 ← too small
6	−14	−8 ← too large
4	−21	−17 ← okay

$-14p^2 - 17p + 6 = -14p^2 - 21p + 4p + 6$

$\qquad = -7p(2p + 3) + 2(2p + 3)$

$\qquad = (2p + 3)(-7p + 2)$

$\qquad$ or

$\qquad = (2p + 3)(2 - 7p)$

16. $5(z-1)^2 + 17(z-1) - 12$

Let $u = z - 1$. This gives $5u^2 + 17u - 12$.

$a \cdot c = 5 \cdot -12 = -60$

We need two factors of -60 whose sum is 17. The product is negative, so the two factors will have opposite signs. Since the sum is positive, the factor with the larger absolute value will be positive.

factor 1	factor 2	sum
15	−4	11 ← too small
30	−2	28 ← too large
20	−3	17 ← okay

$5u^2 + 17u - 12 = 5u^2 + 20u - 3u - 12$

$\qquad = 5u(u + 4) - 3(u + 4)$

$\qquad = (u + 4)(5u - 3)$

Now go back in terms of z.

$5(z-1)^2 + 17(z-1) - 12$

$= (z - 1 + 4)(5(z - 1) - 3)$

$= (z + 3)(5z - 5 - 3)$

$= (z + 3)(5z - 8)$

17. $-98x^2 + 112x - 32 = -2(49x^2 - 56x + 16)$

$\qquad = -2\left((7x)^2 - 2(7x)(4) + 4^2\right)$

$\qquad = -2(7x - 4)^2$

18. $16x^2 - 196 = 4(4x^2 - 49)$

$\qquad = 4\left((2x)^2 - 7^2\right)$

$\qquad = 4(2x - 7)(2x + 7)$

19. $\qquad 3m^2 - 5m = 5m - 7$

$3m^2 - 5m - 5m + 7 = 0$

$\qquad 3m^2 - 10m + 7 = 0$

$\qquad (3m - 7)(m - 1) = 0$

$\qquad 3m - 7 = 0 \ \text{ or } \ m - 1 = 0$

$\qquad m = \dfrac{7}{3} \ \text{ or } \ m = 1$

The solution set is $\left\{1, \dfrac{7}{3}\right\}$.

20. Let $x =$ the width (shorter side). Then $x + 3$ is the length (longer side).

From the formula for the area of a rectangle, we have:

$A = (\text{length})(\text{width})$

$\quad = (x + 3)(x)$

$\quad = x^2 + 3x$

We know the area is 108 square meters, so we have:

$108 = x^2 + 3x$

$0 = x^2 + 3x - 108$

$0 = (x - 9)(x + 12)$

$x - 9 = 0 \ \text{ or } \ x + 12 = 0$

$\quad x = 9 \ \text{ or } \ \cancel{x = -12}$

The patio is 9 meters wide and $9 + 3 = 12$ meters long.

Cumulative Review Chapters R-5

1. $(-3)^2 + 4 - 16 \div 2 = 9 + 4 - 8 = 13 - 8 = 5$

2. $\left|2 - 3^2\right| + 7 = |2 - 9| + 7$

$\qquad = |-7| + 7$

$\qquad = 7 + 7 = 14$

3. $2(5x + 1) - 4(x - 3) = 10x + 2 - 4x + 12$

$\qquad = 10x - 4x + 2 + 12$

$\qquad = 6x + 14$

4. $3(x+2)-10=4x$

$3x+6-10=4x$

$3x-4=4x$

$-4=x$

The solution set is $\{-4\}$.

5. $2|x-5|+3=5$

$2|x-5|=2$

$|x-5|=1$

$x-5=1$ or $x-5=-1$

$x=6$ or $x=4$

The solution set is $\{4,6\}$.

6. $4x-5y=30$

$-5y=-4x+30$

$\dfrac{-5y}{-5}=\dfrac{-4x+30}{-5}$

$y=\dfrac{4}{5}x-6$

7. $4x-3(x+1)\geq 7-4x$

$4x-3x-3\geq 7-4x$

$x-3\geq 7-4x$

$5x-3\geq 7$

$5x\geq 10$

$\dfrac{5x}{5}\geq \dfrac{10}{5}$

$x\geq 2$

Solution set: $\{x\,|\,x\geq 2\}$

Interval: $[2,\infty)$

8. Let x = liters of 70% sulfuric acid solution. There will be $x+12$ liters in the final solution.

total acid = acid in 30% sol. + acid added

(%)(liters) = (%)(liters) + (%)(liters)

$0.40(x+12)=0.30(12)+0.70(x)$

$0.4x+4.8=3.6+0.7x$

$4.8=3.6+0.3x$

$1.2=0.3x$

$4=x$

4 liters of the 70% solution should be added to obtain a 40% sulfuric acid solution.

9. To find x-intercepts, we locate the points where the graph crosses the x-axis. From the graph, we see that the x-intercepts are $x=-1$ and $x=2$. To find the y-intercept, we locate the points where the graph crosses the y-axis. From the graph, we see that the y-intercept is $y=-2$.

The intercepts are $(-1,0),(2,0)$, and $(0,-2)$.

10. $y=2x^2+4x-1$

x	$y=2x^2+4x-1$	Point
-3	$y=2(-3)^2+4(-3)-1=5$	$(-3,5)$
-2	$y=2(-2)^2+4(-2)-1=-1$	$(-2,-1)$
-1	$y=2(-1)^2+4(-1)-1=-3$	$(-1,-3)$
0	$y=2(0)^2+4(0)-1=-1$	$(0,-1)$
1	$y=2(1)^2+4(1)-1=5$	$(1,5)$

Domain: $\{x\,|\,x \text{ is any real number}\}$ or $(-\infty,\infty)$

Range: $\{y\,|\,y\geq -3\}$ or $[-3,\infty)$

11, a. Function. For each value of the independent variable (input) there is exactly one corresponding value for the dependent variable (output).

Domain: $\{-2,3,5,7,10\}$

Range: $\{-3,1,4,13\}$

b. Not a function. The graph fails the vertical line test. For a given input, it is possible to have more than one corresponding output.

Domain: $\{x\,|\,x\geq 2\}$ or $[2,\infty)$

Range: $\{y\,|\,y \text{ is any real number}\}$ or $(-\infty,\infty)$

12. Let $x = -4, -2, 0,$ and 2.

$$x = -4: \quad 3(-4) - 2y = 6$$
$$-12 - 2y = 6$$
$$-2y = 18$$
$$y = -9$$

$$x = -2: \quad 3(-2) - 2y = 6$$
$$-6 - 2y = 6$$
$$-2y = 12$$
$$y = -6$$

$$x = 0: \quad 3(0) - 2y = 6$$
$$0 - 2y = 6$$
$$-2y = 6$$
$$y = -3$$

$$x = 2: \quad 3(2) - 2y = 6$$
$$6 - 2y = 6$$
$$-2y = 0$$
$$y = 0$$

So the points $(-4, -9)$, $(-2, -6)$, $(0, -3)$, and $(2, 0)$ are on the graph.

13. $m = \frac{2}{5}$, $(x_1, y_1) = (10, -4)$

$$y - y_1 = m(x - x_1)$$
$$y - (-4) = \frac{2}{5}(x - 10)$$
$$y + 4 = \frac{2}{5}x - 4$$
$$y = \frac{2}{5}x - 8 \quad \text{or} \quad 2x - 5y = 40$$

14. a. For roughly the first four months shown, the average price per gallon steadily decreased. Beginning in mid-December, the price began to steadily increase for the last two months.

b. During this time period it appears, according to the graph, that gas was cheapest around December 14th.

c. According to the graph, on January 1, 2004 the average price per gallon was roughly $1.49.

15. Replace the inequality symbol with an equal sign to obtain $4x - 2y = 5$. Because the inequality is strict, graph $4x - 2y = 5$ $\left(y = 2x - \frac{5}{2} \right)$ using a dashed line.

Test Point: $(0, 0)$: $\quad 4(0) - 2(0) \overset{?}{<} 5$

$$0 \overset{?}{<} 5 \quad \text{True}$$

Therefore, $(0, 0)$ is a solution to $4x - 2y < 5$.

Shade the half-plane that contains $(0, 0)$.

16. $\begin{cases} y = x - 3 & (1) \\ 3x - 2y = 4 & (2) \end{cases}$

Since equation (1) is already solved for y, we will use substitution to solve the system. Substituting $x - 3$ for y in equation (2), we obtain

$$3x - 2(x - 3) = 4$$
$$3x - 2x + 6 = 4$$
$$x + 6 = 4$$
$$x = -2$$

Substituting -2 for x in equation (1), we obtain

$$y = (-2) - 3 = -5$$

The solution is the ordered pair $(-2, -5)$.

17. $\begin{cases} 6x + 2y = 2 \\ 3x - y = 11 \end{cases}$

Each equation is in standard form so we can write the augmented matrix:

$$\begin{bmatrix} 6 & 2 & | & 2 \\ 3 & -1 & | & 11 \end{bmatrix}$$

Now we need to put this matrix into row echelon form.

$$\begin{bmatrix} 6 & 2 & | & 2 \\ 3 & -1 & | & 11 \end{bmatrix} R_1 = \frac{1}{6}r_1$$

$$\begin{bmatrix} 1 & \frac{1}{3} & | & \frac{1}{3} \\ 3 & -1 & | & 11 \end{bmatrix} R_2 = -3r_1 + r_2$$

$$\begin{bmatrix} 1 & \frac{1}{3} & | & \frac{1}{3} \\ 0 & -2 & | & 10 \end{bmatrix} R_2 = -\frac{1}{2}r_2$$

$$\begin{bmatrix} 1 & \frac{1}{3} & | & \frac{1}{3} \\ 0 & 1 & | & -5 \end{bmatrix}$$

Write the system that corresponds to the row echelon matrix.

$$x + \frac{1}{3}y = \frac{1}{3}$$
$$y = -5$$

The system is consistent and independent.
Substitute -5 for y in the first equation to get

$$x + \frac{1}{3}(-5) = \frac{1}{3}$$
$$x - \frac{5}{3} = \frac{1}{3}$$
$$x = \frac{6}{3}$$
$$x = 2$$

The solution is the ordered pair $(2, -5)$.

18. From the problem statement, we can write two ordered pairs, (x, y), where x is the year and y is the average cost of a 30 second ad (in millions) during the Super Bowl. The ordered pairs are: $(1994, 0.9)$ and $(2004, 2.3)$.

The average rate of change is the slope of the line connecting these ordered pairs.

$$m = \frac{2.3 - 0.9}{2004 - 1994}$$
$$= \frac{1.4}{10}$$
$$= 0.14$$

The average rate of change in Super Bowl ad price is $140,000$ per year.

19. Define the following:

x = price of a cheese pizza

y = price of a sausage pizza

z = price of a pepperoni pizza

From the problem statement we need to write three equations, one for each seller.

Brandon: $4x + 5y + 2z = 77.50$

Matt: $8x + 3y + 5z = 110.50$

Ethan: $1x + 4y + 7z = 92.00$

We can solve the system using matrices. Begin with the augmented matrix.

$$\begin{bmatrix} 4 & 5 & 2 & | & 77.50 \\ 8 & 3 & 5 & | & 110.50 \\ 1 & 4 & 7 & | & 92.00 \end{bmatrix}$$

Now get the matrix in row echelon form.

$$\begin{bmatrix} 4 & 5 & 2 & | & 77.50 \\ 8 & 3 & 5 & | & 110.50 \\ 1 & 4 & 7 & | & 92.00 \end{bmatrix} \text{Switch rows 1 and 3}$$

$$\begin{bmatrix} 1 & 4 & 7 & | & 92.00 \\ 8 & 3 & 5 & | & 110.50 \\ 4 & 5 & 2 & | & 77.50 \end{bmatrix} \begin{matrix} \\ R_2 = -8r_1 + r_2 \\ R_3 = -4r_1 + r_3 \end{matrix}$$

$$\begin{bmatrix} 1 & 4 & 7 & | & 92.00 \\ 0 & -29 & -51 & | & -625.50 \\ 0 & -11 & -26 & | & -290.50 \end{bmatrix} R_2 = r_2 \div -29$$

$$\begin{bmatrix} 1 & 4 & 7 & | & 92.00 \\ 0 & 1 & \frac{51}{29} & | & \frac{625.50}{29} \\ 0 & -11 & -26 & | & -290.50 \end{bmatrix} R_3 = 11r_2 + r_3$$

$$\begin{bmatrix} 1 & 4 & 7 & | & 92.00 \\ 0 & 1 & \frac{51}{29} & | & \frac{625.50}{29} \\ 0 & 0 & -\frac{193}{29} & | & -\frac{1544}{29} \end{bmatrix} R_3 = -\frac{29}{193}r_3$$

$$\begin{bmatrix} 1 & 4 & 7 & | & 92.00 \\ 0 & 1 & \frac{51}{29} & | & \frac{625.50}{29} \\ 0 & 0 & 1 & | & 8 \end{bmatrix}$$

Write the system that corresponds to the row echelon matrix.

$$x + 4y + 7z = 92.00$$
$$y + \frac{51}{29}z = \frac{625.50}{29}$$
$$z = 8$$

The system is consistent and independent.
Substitute 8 for z in the second equation to get

$$y + \frac{51}{29}(8) = \frac{625.50}{29}$$
$$y + \frac{408}{29} = \frac{625.50}{29}$$
$$y = 7.50$$

Substitute 8 for z and 7.5 for y in the first equation to get

$$x + 4(7.5) + 7(8) = 92.00$$
$$x + 30 + 56 = 92$$
$$x + 86 = 92$$
$$x = 6$$

Therefore, the cheese pizzas cost 6, the sausage pizzas cost 7.50, and the pepperoni pizzas cost 8.

20. a. Cost: $C(x) = 0.22x + 50$

Revenue: $R(x) = 0.75x$

b. To make a profit, revenue must exceed costs. That is, we need

$$R(x) > C(x)$$
$$0.75x > 0.22x + 50$$
$$0.75x - 0.22x > 0.22x + 50 - 0.22x$$
$$0.53x > 50$$
$$\frac{0.53x}{0.53} > \frac{50}{0.53}$$
$$x > 94.34$$

The band must sell at least 95 candy bars to make a profit.

c. To purchase the saxophone, the band needs to profit at least \$1396. The profit function is

$$P(x) = R(x) - C(x)$$
$$= 0.75x - (0.22x + 50)$$
$$= 0.75x - 0.22x - 50$$
$$= 0.53x - 50$$

Therefore, the band needs

$$P(x) \geq 1396$$
$$0.53x - 50 \geq 1396$$
$$0.53x - 50 + 50 \geq 1396 + 50$$
$$0.53x \geq 1446$$
$$\frac{0.53x}{0.53} \geq \frac{1446}{0.53}$$
$$x \geq 2728.30$$

To purchase the saxophone, the band needs to sell at least 2729 candy bars.

21. $\left(12x^3 + 5x^2 - 3x + 1\right) - \left(2x^3 - 4x + 8\right)$

$$= 12x^3 + 5x^2 - 3x + 1 - 2x^3 + 4x - 8$$
$$= 10x^3 + 5x^2 + x - 7$$

22. $(2x+1)\left(x^2 - 3x + 5\right)$

$$= 2x\left(x^2 - 3x + 5\right) + 1\left(x^2 - 3x + 5\right)$$
$$= 2x^3 - 6x^2 + 10x + x^2 - 3x + 5$$
$$= 2x^3 - 5x^2 + 7x + 5$$

23. The divisor is $x + 5$ so $c = -5$.

$$-5\,\overline{)\begin{array}{ccccc} 3 & 10 & -23 & 1 \\ & -15 & 25 & -10 \\ \hline 3 & -5 & 2 & -9 \end{array}}$$

$$\frac{3x^3 + 10x^2 - 23x + 1}{x + 5} = 3x^2 - 5x + 2 - \frac{9}{x+5}$$

24. a. $\frac{1}{3}x^2 + 2x + 3 = \frac{1}{3}\left(x^2 + 6x + 9\right)$

$$= \frac{1}{3}\left(x^2 + 2(3)x + 3^2\right)$$
$$= \frac{1}{3}(x+3)^2$$

b. $w^2 - 7w - 60 = (w - 12)(w + 5)$

c. $32a^4 - 128a^2 = 32a^2\left(a^2 - 4\right)$

$$= 32a^2(a - 2)(a + 2)$$

25. $f(x) = 4x^2 - 2x - 30$

$$0 = 4x^2 - 2x - 30$$
$$0 = 2x^2 - x - 15$$
$$0 = (2x + 5)(x - 3)$$
$$2x + 5 = 0 \text{ or } x - 3 = 0$$
$$x = -\frac{5}{2} \text{ or } x = 3$$

The zeros of $f(x)$ are $-\frac{5}{2}$ and 3.

Getting Ready for Chapter 6

1. lowest terms

3. Answers may vary.
Completely factor the numerator and denominator. Cancel any common factors in the numerator and denominator.

5. Answers may vary.
Find the least common denominator. Rewrite each rational number with the common denominator. Add the numerators and keep the LCD as the denominator. Reduce if necessary.

7. $\dfrac{4}{12} = \dfrac{\cancel{2} \cdot \cancel{2}}{\cancel{2} \cdot \cancel{2} \cdot 3} = \dfrac{1}{3}$

9. $\dfrac{-15}{35} = \dfrac{-1 \cdot 3 \cdot \cancel{5}}{\cancel{5} \cdot 7} = \dfrac{-3}{7} = -\dfrac{3}{7}$

11. $\dfrac{-50}{-10} = \dfrac{\cancel{1} \cdot 5 \cdot \cancel{5} \cdot \cancel{2}}{\cancel{1} \cdot \cancel{5} \cdot \cancel{2}} = \dfrac{5}{1} = 5$

13. $\dfrac{3}{4} \cdot \dfrac{20}{9} = \dfrac{\cancel{3}}{\cancel{2} \cdot \cancel{2}} \cdot \dfrac{\cancel{2} \cdot \cancel{2} \cdot 5}{\cancel{3} \cdot 3} = \dfrac{5}{3}$

15. $-\dfrac{5}{6} \cdot \dfrac{18}{5} = \dfrac{-1 \cdot \cancel{5}}{\cancel{2} \cdot \cancel{3}} \cdot \dfrac{\cancel{2} \cdot \cancel{3} \cdot 3}{\cancel{5}} = \dfrac{-3}{1} = -3$

17. $\dfrac{5}{8} \cdot \dfrac{2}{15} = \dfrac{\cancel{5}}{\cancel{2} \cdot 2 \cdot 2} \cdot \dfrac{\cancel{2}}{3 \cdot \cancel{5}} = \dfrac{1}{12}$

19. $\dfrac{5}{2} \div \dfrac{25}{4} = \dfrac{5}{2} \cdot \dfrac{4}{25} = \dfrac{\cancel{5}}{\cancel{2}} \cdot \dfrac{\cancel{2} \cdot 2}{\cancel{5} \cdot 5} = \dfrac{2}{5}$

21. $\dfrac{\dfrac{-6}{5}}{\dfrac{8}{15}} = \dfrac{-6}{5} \cdot \dfrac{15}{8} = \dfrac{-1 \cdot \cancel{2} \cdot 3}{\cancel{5}} \cdot \dfrac{3 \cdot \cancel{5}}{\cancel{2} \cdot 2 \cdot 2} = \dfrac{-9}{4} = -\dfrac{9}{4}$

23. $\dfrac{\dfrac{9}{2}}{\dfrac{-3}{4}} = -\dfrac{9}{2} \cdot \dfrac{4}{-3} = \dfrac{\cancel{1} \cdot \cancel{3} \cdot 3}{\cancel{2}} \cdot \dfrac{\cancel{2} \cdot 2}{\cancel{1} \cdot \cancel{3}} = \dfrac{6}{1} = 6$

25. $\dfrac{5}{3} + \dfrac{1}{3} = \dfrac{5+1}{3} = \dfrac{6}{3} = \dfrac{2 \cdot \cancel{3}}{\cancel{3}} = \dfrac{2}{1} = 2$

27. $\dfrac{11}{6} - \dfrac{1}{6} = \dfrac{11-1}{6} = \dfrac{10}{6} = \dfrac{\cancel{2} \cdot 5}{\cancel{2} \cdot 3} = \dfrac{5}{3}$

29. $4 = 2 \cdot 2$
5 is prime
The LCD $= 2 \cdot 2 \cdot 5 = 20$
$\dfrac{3}{4} + \dfrac{1}{5} = \dfrac{3}{4} \cdot \dfrac{5}{5} + \dfrac{1}{5} \cdot \dfrac{4}{4} = \dfrac{15}{20} + \dfrac{4}{20} = \dfrac{15+4}{20} = \dfrac{19}{20}$

31. $4 = 2 \cdot 2$
$6 = \quad 2 \cdot 3$
LCD $= 2 \cdot 2 \cdot 3 = 12$
$\dfrac{1}{4} + \dfrac{5}{6} = \dfrac{1}{4} \cdot \dfrac{3}{3} + \dfrac{5}{6} \cdot \dfrac{2}{2} = \dfrac{3}{12} + \dfrac{10}{12} = \dfrac{3+10}{12} = \dfrac{13}{12}$

33. $10 = 2 \cdot 5$
$15 = \quad 5 \cdot 3$
LCD $= 2 \cdot 5 \cdot 3 = 30$
$-\dfrac{3}{10} - \dfrac{7}{15} = -\dfrac{3}{10} \cdot \dfrac{3}{3} - \dfrac{7}{15} \cdot \dfrac{2}{2}$
$= -\dfrac{9}{30} - \dfrac{14}{30}$
$= \dfrac{-9-14}{30}$
$= -\dfrac{23}{30}$

35. $18 = 2 \cdot 3 \cdot 3$
$15 = \quad 3 \cdot 5$
LCD $= 2 \cdot 3 \cdot 3 \cdot 5 = 90$
$\dfrac{5}{18} - \dfrac{11}{15} = \dfrac{5}{18} \cdot \dfrac{5}{5} - \dfrac{11}{15} \cdot \dfrac{6}{6}$
$= \dfrac{25}{90} - \dfrac{66}{90}$
$= \dfrac{25-66}{90}$
$= -\dfrac{41}{90}$

37. $8 = 2 \cdot 2 \cdot 2$

$10 = \quad 2 \cdot 5$

$LCD = 2 \cdot 2 \cdot 2 \cdot 5 = 40$

$$-\frac{7}{8} + \frac{3}{10} = -\frac{7}{8} \cdot \frac{5}{5} + \frac{3}{10} \cdot \frac{4}{4}$$

$$= -\frac{35}{40} + \frac{12}{40}$$

$$= \frac{-35 + 12}{40}$$

$$= -\frac{23}{40}$$

39. $24 = 3 \cdot 2 \cdot 2 \cdot 2$

$20 = \quad 2 \cdot 2 \cdot 5$

$LCD = 3 \cdot 2 \cdot 2 \cdot 2 \cdot 5 = 120$

$$\frac{7}{24} - \frac{3}{20} = \frac{7}{24} \cdot \frac{5}{5} - \frac{3}{20} \cdot \frac{6}{6}$$

$$= \frac{35}{120} - \frac{18}{120}$$

$$= \frac{35 - 18}{120}$$

$$= \frac{17}{120}$$

41. $9 = 3 \cdot 3$

$15 = \quad 3 \cdot 5$

$LCD = 3 \cdot 3 \cdot 5 = 45$

$$-\frac{7}{9} - \frac{2}{15} = -\frac{7}{9} \cdot \frac{5}{5} - \frac{2}{15} \cdot \frac{3}{3}$$

$$= \frac{-35}{45} - \frac{6}{45}$$

$$= \frac{-35 - 6}{45}$$

$$= -\frac{41}{45}$$

43. $25 = 5 \cdot 5$

$30 = \quad 5 \cdot 2 \cdot 3$

$LCD = 5 \cdot 5 \cdot 2 \cdot 3 = 150$

$$\frac{-4}{25} - \frac{7}{30} = \frac{-4}{25} \cdot \frac{6}{6} - \frac{7}{30} \cdot \frac{5}{5}$$

$$= \frac{-24}{150} - \frac{35}{150}$$

$$= \frac{-24 - 35}{150}$$

$$= -\frac{59}{150}$$

Chapter 6

6.1 Preparing for Multiplying and Dividing Rational Expressions

1. $a \cdot c = 2(-21) = -42$

   The factors of -42 that add to -11 (the linear coefficient) are -14 and 3. Thus,
   $$2x^2 - 11x - 21 = 2x^2 - 14x + 3x - 21$$
   $$= 2x(x-7) + 3(x-7)$$
   $$= (2x+3)(x-7)$$

2. $\quad q^2 - 16 = 0$
   $$(q+4)(q-4) = 0$$
   $$q + 4 = 0 \quad \text{or} \quad q - 4 = 0$$
   $$q = -4 \quad \text{or} \quad q = 4$$
   The solution set is $\{-4, \ 4\}$.

3. The reciprocal of $\dfrac{5}{2}$ is $\dfrac{2}{5}$ because $\dfrac{5}{2} \cdot \dfrac{2}{5} = 1$.

4. The domain is the set of all inputs for which the relation (or function) is defined.

6.1 Exercises

1. rational expression

3. TRUE

5. Answers will vary. One possibility follows: A rational expression is the quotient of two polynomials. A rational number is a number that can be written as the quotient of two integers.

7. Answers will vary. One possibility follows: Dividing out common factors in the numerator and denominator of a rational expression will result in an equivalent expression. Dividing out common terms will not generally result in an equivalent expression. For example, is the following statement true:
   $$\frac{7}{3} = \frac{5+2}{1+2} = \frac{5+\cancel{2}}{1+\cancel{2}} = \frac{5}{1} = 5? \ \text{NO!} \ \frac{7}{3} \neq 5.$$
   Canceling the terms does not result in an equivalent value.

9. We need to find all values of x that cause the denominator $x+5$ to equal 0.
   $$x + 5 = 0$$
   $$x = -5$$
   Thus, the domain of $\dfrac{3}{x+5}$ is $\{x \mid x \neq -5\}$.

11. We need to find all values of x that cause the denominator $x^2 - 6x - 16$ to equal 0.
   $$x^2 - 6x - 16 = 0$$
   $$(x+2)(x-8) = 0$$
   $$x + 2 = 0 \quad \text{or} \quad x - 8 = 0$$
   $$x = -2 \quad \text{or} \quad x = 8$$
   Thus, the domain of $\dfrac{x-1}{x^2 - 6x - 16}$ is
   $\{x \mid x \neq -2, x \neq 8\}$.

13. We need to find all values of p that cause the denominator $2p^2 + p - 10$ to equal 0.
   $$2p^2 + p - 10 = 0$$
   $$(2p+5)(p-2) = 0$$
   $$2p + 5 = 0 \quad \text{or} \quad p - 2 = 0$$
   $$p = -\frac{5}{2} \quad \text{or} \quad p = 2$$
   Thus, the domain of $\dfrac{p^2 - 4}{2p^2 + p - 10}$ is
   $\left\{ p \ \middle| \ p \neq -\dfrac{5}{2}, p \neq 2 \right\}$.

15. We need to find all values of x that cause the denominator $x^2 + 1$ to equal 0. However, if x is a real number, then $x^2 + 1$ can never equal 0.
   Thus, the domain of $\dfrac{x+1}{x^2+1}$ is
   $\{x \mid x \text{ is any real number}\}$.

17. We need to find all values of x that cause the denominator $(x-1)^2$ to equal 0.
   $$(x-1)^2 = 0$$
   $$x - 1 = 0$$
   $$x = 1$$
   Thus, the domain of $\dfrac{3x-2}{(x-1)^2}$ is $\{x \mid x \neq 1\}$.

SSM – 301

19. $\dfrac{2x+8}{x^2-16} = \dfrac{2\cancel{(x+4)}}{\cancel{(x+4)}(x-4)} = \dfrac{2}{x-4}$

21. $\dfrac{p^2+4p+3}{p+1} = \dfrac{\cancel{(p+1)}(p+3)}{\cancel{p+1}} = \dfrac{p+3}{1} = p+3$

23. $\dfrac{5x+25}{x^3+5x^2} = \dfrac{5\cancel{(x+5)}}{x^2\cancel{(x+5)}} = \dfrac{5}{x^2}$

25. $\dfrac{q^2-3q-18}{q^2-8q+12} = \dfrac{(q+3)\cancel{(q-6)}}{(q-2)\cancel{(q-6)}} = \dfrac{q+3}{q-2}$

27. $\dfrac{2y^2-3y-20}{2y^2+15y+25} = \dfrac{\cancel{(2y+5)}(y-4)}{\cancel{(2y+5)}(y+5)} = \dfrac{y-4}{y+5}$

29. $\dfrac{9-x^2}{x^2+2x-15} = \dfrac{-1\cancel{(x-3)}(x+3)}{\cancel{(x-3)}(x+5)}$

$\qquad = \dfrac{-1(x+3)}{x+5} = -\dfrac{x+3}{x+5}$

31. $\dfrac{x^3+2x^2-8x}{2x^4-32x^2} = \dfrac{\cancel{x}(x-2)\cancel{(x+4)}}{\underset{2x}{\cancel{2x^2}}(x-4)\cancel{(x+4)}} = \dfrac{x-2}{2x(x-4)}$

33. $\dfrac{x^2-xy-6y^2}{x^2-4y^2} = \dfrac{(x-3y)\cancel{(x+2y)}}{(x-2y)\cancel{(x+2y)}} = \dfrac{x-3y}{x-2y}$

35. $\dfrac{x^3-5x^2+3x-15}{x^2-10x+25} = \dfrac{\cancel{(x-5)}(x^2+3)}{\cancel{(x-5)}(x-5)} = \dfrac{x^2+3}{x-5}$

37. $\dfrac{x^3+8}{x^2-5x-14} = \dfrac{\cancel{(x+2)}(x^2-2x+4)}{\cancel{(x+2)}(x-7)} = \dfrac{x^2-2x+4}{x-7}$

39. $\dfrac{3x}{x^2-x-12}\cdot\dfrac{x-4}{12x^2} = \dfrac{3x}{(x-4)(x+3)}\cdot\dfrac{x-4}{3x\cdot4x}$

$\qquad = \dfrac{3x}{\cancel{(x-4)}(x+3)}\cdot\dfrac{\cancel{x-4}}{3x\cdot4x}$

$\qquad = \dfrac{1}{4x(x+3)}$

41. $\dfrac{2x^2-x-6}{x^2+3x-4}\cdot\dfrac{x^2-x-20}{2x^2-7x-15}$

$\qquad = \dfrac{(2x+3)(x-2)}{(x-1)(x+4)}\cdot\dfrac{(x-5)(x+4)}{(2x+3)(x-5)}$

$\qquad = \dfrac{\cancel{(2x+3)}(x-2)}{(x-1)\cancel{(x+4)}}\cdot\dfrac{\cancel{(x-5)}\cancel{(x+4)}}{\cancel{(2x+3)}\cancel{(x-5)}} = \dfrac{x-2}{x-1}$

43. $\dfrac{x^2-9}{x^2-25}\cdot\dfrac{x^2-2x-15}{x^2+4x-21}$

$\qquad = \dfrac{(x-3)(x+3)}{(x+5)(x-5)}\cdot\dfrac{(x-5)(x+3)}{(x-3)(x+7)}$

$\qquad = \dfrac{\cancel{(x-3)}(x+3)}{(x+5)\cancel{(x-5)}}\cdot\dfrac{\cancel{(x-5)}(x+3)}{\cancel{(x-3)}(x+7)} = \dfrac{(x+3)^2}{(x+5)(x+7)}$

45. $\dfrac{2q^2-5q-3}{3q^2+19q+6}\cdot\dfrac{3q^2+7q+2}{3-q}$

$\qquad = \dfrac{(2q+1)(q-3)}{(3q+1)(q+6)}\cdot\dfrac{(3q+1)(q+2)}{-1(q-3)}$

$\qquad = \dfrac{(2q+1)\cancel{(q-3)}}{\cancel{(3q+1)}(q+6)}\cdot\dfrac{\cancel{(3q+1)}(q+2)}{-1\cancel{(q-3)}}$

$\qquad = \dfrac{(2q+1)(q+2)}{-1(q+6)}$ or $-\dfrac{(2q+1)(q+2)}{q+6}$

47. $\dfrac{x^2-5x+6}{x^2+2x-8}\cdot(x+4) = \dfrac{(x-2)(x-3)}{(x-2)(x+4)}\cdot(x+4)$

$\qquad = \dfrac{\cancel{(x-2)}(x-3)}{\cancel{(x-2)}\cancel{(x+4)}}\cdot\cancel{(x+4)}$

$\qquad = x-3$

49. $\dfrac{m^2-n^2}{5m-5n}\cdot\dfrac{10m+5n}{2m^2+3mn+n^2}$

$\qquad = \dfrac{(m-n)(m+n)}{5(m-n)}\cdot\dfrac{5(2m+n)}{(2m+n)(m+n)}$

$\qquad = \dfrac{\cancel{(m-n)}\cancel{(m+n)}}{\cancel{5}\cancel{(m-n)}}\cdot\dfrac{\cancel{5}\cancel{(2m+n)}}{\cancel{(2m+n)}\cancel{(m+n)}} = 1$

51. $\dfrac{\dfrac{x+3}{2x-8}}{\dfrac{4x}{9}} = \dfrac{x+3}{2x-8}\cdot\dfrac{9}{4x} = \dfrac{x+3}{2(x-4)}\cdot\dfrac{9}{4x} = \dfrac{9(x+3)}{8x(x-4)}$

53. $\dfrac{\dfrac{4a}{b^2}}{\dfrac{2a^2}{b}} = \dfrac{4a}{b^2} \cdot \dfrac{b}{2a^2} = \dfrac{\overset{2}{\cancel{4}} \cdot a}{\cancel{b} \cdot b} \cdot \dfrac{\cancel{b}}{\cancel{2} \cdot a \cdot a} = \dfrac{2}{ab}$

55. $\dfrac{\dfrac{p^2-4p-5}{2p^2-3p-2}}{\dfrac{p^2+p}{p^2+p-6}} = \dfrac{p^2-4p-5}{2p^2-3p-2} \cdot \dfrac{p^2+p-6}{p^2+p}$

$= \dfrac{(p-5)(p+1)}{(2p+1)(p-2)} \cdot \dfrac{(p-2)(p+3)}{p(p+1)}$

$= \dfrac{(p-5)\cancel{(p+1)}}{(2p+1)\cancel{(p-2)}} \cdot \dfrac{\cancel{(p-2)}(p+3)}{p\cancel{(p+1)}}$

$= \dfrac{(p-5)(p+3)}{p(2p+1)}$

57. $\dfrac{\dfrac{x^3-1}{x^2-1}}{\dfrac{3x^2+3x+3}{x^2+3x+1}} = \dfrac{x^3-1}{x^2-1} \cdot \dfrac{x^2+3x+1}{3x^2+3x+3}$

$= \dfrac{(x-1)(x^2+x+1)}{(x-1)(x+1)} \cdot \dfrac{x^2+3x+1}{3(x^2+x+1)}$

$= \dfrac{\cancel{(x-1)}\cancel{(x^2+x+1)}}{\cancel{(x-1)}(x+1)} \cdot \dfrac{x^2+3x+1}{3\cancel{(x^2+x+1)}}$

$= \dfrac{x^2+3x+1}{3(x+1)}$

59. We need to find all values of x that cause the denominator $x-1$ to equal 0.

$x-1=0$

$x=1$

Thus, the domain of $R(x)=\dfrac{2}{x-1}$ is $\{x \mid x \neq 1\}$.

61. We need to find all values of x that cause the denominator $(2x+1)(x-4)$ to equal 0.

$(2x+1)(x-4)=0$

$2x+1=0 \quad$ or $x-4=0$

$x=-\dfrac{1}{2} \,$ or $\qquad x=4$

Thus, the domain of $R(x)=\dfrac{x-2}{(2x+1)(x-4)}$ is

$\left\{x \mid x \neq -\dfrac{1}{2}, x \neq 4\right\}$.

63. We need to find all values of x that cause the denominator x^2+6x+5 to equal 0.

$x^2+6x+5=0$

$(x+1)(x+5)=0$

$x+1=0 \quad$ or $x+5=0$

$x=-1 \,$ or $\qquad x=-5$

Thus, the domain of $R(x)=\dfrac{x+9}{x^2+6x+5}$ is

$\{x \mid x \neq -5, x \neq -1\}$.

65. We need to find all values of x that cause the denominator $2x^2-9x+10$ to equal 0.

$2x^2-9x+10=0$

$(2x-5)(x-2)=0$

$2x-5=0 \quad$ or $x-2=0$

$x=\dfrac{5}{2} \,$ or $\qquad x=2$

Thus, the domain of $R(x)=\dfrac{x-2}{2x^2-9x+10}$ is

$\left\{x \mid x \neq 2, x \neq \dfrac{5}{2}\right\}$.

67. We need to find all values of x that cause the denominator x^2+1 to equal 0. However, x^2+1 cannot equal 0 if x is a real number, so the domain of $R(x)=\dfrac{x-1}{x^2+1}$ is $\{x \mid x$ is any real number$\}$.

69. a. $R(x)=f(x) \cdot g(x)$

$= \dfrac{x^2-2x-15}{x+6} \cdot \dfrac{x^2+5x-6}{2x^2-7x-15}$

$= \dfrac{(x-5)(x+3)}{x+6} \cdot \dfrac{(x-1)(x+6)}{(2x+3)(x-5)}$

$= \dfrac{\cancel{(x-5)}(x+3)}{\cancel{x+6}} \cdot \dfrac{(x-1)\cancel{(x+6)}}{(2x+3)\cancel{(x-5)}}$

$= \dfrac{(x+3)(x-1)}{2x+3}$

The domain of $f(x)$ is $\{x \mid x \neq -6\}$. The

domain of $g(x)$ is $\left\{x \mid x \neq -\dfrac{3}{2}, x \neq 5\right\}$.

Therefore, the domain of $R(x)$ is

$\left\{x \mid x \neq -6, x \neq -\dfrac{3}{2}, x \neq 5\right\}$.

b. $R(x) = \dfrac{f(x)}{h(x)} = \dfrac{\dfrac{x^2 - 2x - 15}{x + 6}}{\dfrac{x + 3}{3x^2 + 17x - 6}}$

$= \dfrac{x^2 - 2x - 15}{x + 6} \cdot \dfrac{3x^2 + 17x - 6}{x + 3}$

$= \dfrac{(x - 5)(x + 3)}{x + 6} \cdot \dfrac{(3x - 1)(x + 6)}{x + 3}$

$= \dfrac{(x - 5)\cancel{(x + 3)}}{\cancel{x + 6}} \cdot \dfrac{(3x - 1)\cancel{(x + 6)}}{\cancel{x + 3}}$

$= (x - 5)(3x - 1)$

The domain of $f(x)$ is $\{x \mid x \neq -6\}$. The

domain of $h(x)$ is $\left\{x \mid x \neq -6, x \neq \dfrac{1}{3}\right\}$.

Because the denominator of $R(x)$ cannot equal 0, we must exclude those values of x such that the numerator of $h(x)$ is 0. That is, we must exclude the values of x such that $x + 3 = 0$. The only such value is $x = -3$. Therefore, the domain of $R(x)$ is

$\left\{x \mid x \neq -6, x \neq -3, x \neq \dfrac{1}{3}\right\}$.

71. a. $R(x) = (f \cdot g)(x)$

$= \dfrac{3x^2 - x - 10}{x^3 - 1} \cdot \dfrac{x^2 + 5x - 6}{2x^2 + 3x - 14}$

$= \dfrac{(3x + 5)(x - 2)}{(x - 1)(x^2 + x + 1)} \cdot \dfrac{(x - 1)(x + 6)}{(2x + 7)(x - 2)}$

$= \dfrac{(3x + 5)\cancel{(x - 2)}}{\cancel{(x - 1)}(x^2 + x + 1)} \cdot \dfrac{\cancel{(x - 1)}(x + 6)}{(2x + 7)\cancel{(x - 2)}}$

$= \dfrac{(3x + 5)(x + 6)}{(x^2 + x + 1)(2x + 7)}$

The domain of $f(x)$ is $\{x \mid x \neq 1\}$. (Note that $x^2 + x + 1 = 0$ has no real solution.) The

domain of $g(x)$ is $\left\{x \mid x \neq -\dfrac{7}{2}, x \neq 2\right\}$.

Therefore, the domain of $R(x)$ is

$\left\{x \mid x \neq -\dfrac{7}{2}, x \neq 1, x \neq 2\right\}$.

b. $R(x) = \left(\dfrac{f}{h}\right)(x) = \dfrac{\dfrac{3x^2 - x - 10}{x^3 - 1}}{\dfrac{3x^2 + 8x + 5}{x^2 - 1}}$

$= \dfrac{3x^2 - x - 10}{x^3 - 1} \cdot \dfrac{x^2 - 1}{3x^2 + 8x + 5}$

$= \dfrac{(3x + 5)(x - 2)}{(x - 1)(x^2 + x + 1)} \cdot \dfrac{(x - 1)(x + 1)}{(3x + 5)(x + 1)}$

$= \dfrac{\cancel{(3x + 5)}(x - 2)}{\cancel{(x - 1)}(x^2 + x + 1)} \cdot \dfrac{\cancel{(x - 1)}\cancel{(x + 1)}}{\cancel{(3x + 5)}\cancel{(x + 1)}}$

$= \dfrac{x - 2}{x^2 + x + 1}$

The domain of $f(x)$ is $\{x \mid x \neq 1\}$. (Note that $x^2 + x + 1 = 0$ has no real solution.) The domain of $h(x)$ is $\{x \mid x \neq -1, x \neq 1\}$.

Because the denominator of $R(x)$ cannot equal 0, we must exclude those values of x such that the numerator of $h(x)$ is 0. That is, we must exclude the values of x such that $3x^2 + 8x + 5 = 0$. These values are $x = -\dfrac{5}{3}$

and $x = -1$. Therefore, the domain of

$R(x)$ is $\left\{x \mid x \neq -\dfrac{5}{3}, x \neq -1, x \neq 1\right\}$.

73. $\dfrac{z^3 + 8}{z^2 - 3z - 10} \cdot \dfrac{z^2 - 2z - 15}{2z^2 - 4z + 8}$

$= \dfrac{(z + 2)(z^2 - 2z + 4)}{(z - 5)(z + 2)} \cdot \dfrac{(z - 5)(z + 3)}{2(z^2 - 2z + 4)}$

$= \dfrac{\cancel{(z + 2)}\cancel{(z^2 - 2z + 4)}}{\cancel{(z - 5)}\cancel{(z + 2)}} \cdot \dfrac{\cancel{(z - 5)}(z + 3)}{2\cancel{(z^2 - 2z + 4)}}$

$= \dfrac{z + 3}{2}$

75. $\dfrac{\dfrac{m^2-4n^2}{m^3-n^3}}{\dfrac{2m+4n}{m^2+mn+n^2}} = \dfrac{m^2-4n^2}{m^3-n^3} \cdot \dfrac{m^2+mn+n^2}{2m+4n}$

$= \dfrac{(m-2n)(m+2n)}{(m-n)(m^2+mn+n^2)} \cdot \dfrac{m^2+mn+n^2}{2(m+2n)}$

$= \dfrac{(m-2n)\cancel{(m+2n)}}{(m-n)\cancel{(m^2+mn+n^2)}} \cdot \dfrac{\cancel{m^2+mn+n^2}}{2\cancel{(m+2n)}}$

$= \dfrac{m-2n}{2(m-n)}$

77. $\dfrac{4w+8}{w^2-4w} \cdot \dfrac{w^2-3w-4}{w^2+3w+2}$

$= \dfrac{4(w+2)}{w(w-4)} \cdot \dfrac{(w-4)(w+1)}{(w+1)(w+2)}$

$= \dfrac{4\cancel{(w+2)}}{w\cancel{(w-4)}} \cdot \dfrac{\cancel{(w-4)}\cancel{(w+1)}}{\cancel{(w+1)}\cancel{(w+2)}}$

$= \dfrac{4}{w}$

79. $\dfrac{\dfrac{2x-6}{x^2+x}}{\dfrac{x^2-4x+3}{x^2}} = \dfrac{2x-6}{x^2+x} \cdot \dfrac{x^2}{x^2-4x+3}$

$= \dfrac{2(x-3)}{x(x+1)} \cdot \dfrac{x \cdot x}{(x-1)(x-3)}$

$= \dfrac{2\cancel{(x-3)}}{\cancel{x}(x+1)} \cdot \dfrac{\cancel{x} \cdot x}{(x-1)\cancel{(x-3)}}$

$= \dfrac{2x}{(x+1)(x-1)}$

81. Answers will vary. Any rational expression with $x-3$ as a factor of the denominator, but not the numerator, will be undefined at $x=3$. One possible expression is $\dfrac{x}{x-3}$.

83. Answers will vary. Any rational expression with both $x+4$ and $x-5$ as factors of the denominator, but not the numerator, will be undefined at $x=-4$ and $x=5$. One possible rational expression $\dfrac{7}{(x+4)(x-5)} = \dfrac{7}{x^2-x-20}$.

85. The rational function will have both $x+2$ and $x-1$ as factors of the denominator. Consider the function $R(x) = \dfrac{k}{(x+2)(x-1)} = \dfrac{k}{x^2+x-2}$, where k is a real number. To determine the value of k, we solve the following for k:

$R(-3) = 1$

$\dfrac{k}{(-3)^2+(-3)-2} = 1$

$\dfrac{k}{4} = 1$

$k = 4$

Thus, a rational function R that is undefined at $x=-2$ and $x=1$ such that $R(-3)=1$ will be

$R(x) = \dfrac{4}{x^2+x-2}$.

87. a. $g(0) = \dfrac{3.99 \times 10^{14}}{\left(6.374 \times 10^6 + 0\right)^2} \approx 9.8208$ m/sec^2

b. $g(1600) = \dfrac{3.99 \times 10^{14}}{\left(6.374 \times 10^6 + 1600\right)^2}$

≈ 9.8159 m/sec^2

c. $g(8848) = \dfrac{3.99 \times 10^{14}}{\left(6.374 \times 10^6 + 8848\right)^2}$

≈ 9.7936 m/sec^2

89. a. We need to find all values of x that cause the denominator $x-2$ to equal 0:

$x-2 = 0$

$x = 2$

The domain of $f(x) = \dfrac{1}{x-2}$ is $\{x \mid x \neq 2\}$.

b. $f(x) = \dfrac{1}{x-2}$

x	3	2.5	2.1	2.01	2.001	2.0001
$f(x)$	1	2	10	100	1000	10,000

As x approaches 2, but remains greater than 2, f gets larger in the positive direction (i.e. f approaches ∞).

c.

x	1	1.5	1.9	1.99	1.999	1.9999
$f(x)$	−1	−2	−10	−100	−1000	−10,000

As x approaches 2, but remains less than 2, f gets larger in the negative direction (i.e. f approaches $-\infty$).

d. As x approaches 2, but remains greater than 2, f gets larger in the positive direction (i.e. f approaches ∞). As x approaches 2, but remains less than 2, f gets larger in the negative direction (i.e. f approaches $-\infty$). These results are the same as those in parts (b) and (c).

91. a. $R(x) = \dfrac{x^2 - 2x - 35}{x^2 - x - 42}$

$= \dfrac{(x+5)(x-7)}{(x+6)(x-7)}$

$= \dfrac{x+5}{x+6}$

b. $R(x) = 0$

$\dfrac{x^2 - 2x - 35}{x^2 - x - 42} = 0$

$\dfrac{x+5}{x+6} = 0$

$x + 5 = 0$

$x = -5$

The x-intercept of the graph of R is -5 .

93. $\dfrac{x^{-1}}{x+1} = \dfrac{\frac{1}{x}}{x+1} = \dfrac{1}{x} \cdot \dfrac{1}{x+1} = \dfrac{1}{x(x+1)}$ or $\dfrac{1}{x^2 + x}$

95. For $f(x) = 2x - 3$, the slope is 2 and the y-intercept is -3 . Begin at $(0,-3)$ and move to the right 1 unit and up 2 units to find the point $(1,-1)$.

97. For $F(x) = -4x + 8$, the slope is -4 and the y-intercept is 8. Begin at $(0,8)$ and move to the right 1 unit and down 4 units to find the point $(1,4)$.

99. $h(x) = x^2 - 4$

Let $x = -3, \ -2, \ -1, \ 0, \ 1, \ 2,$ and 3 .

$h(-3) = (-3)^2 - 4 = 9 - 4 = 5$

$h(-2) = (-2)^2 - 4 = 4 - 4 = 0$

$h(-1) = (-1)^2 - 4 = 1 - 4 = -3$

$h(0) = 0^2 - 4 = 0 - 4 = -4$

$h(1) = 1^2 - 4 = 1 - 4 = -3$

$h(2) = 2^2 - 4 = 4 - 4 = 0$

$h(3) = 3^2 - 4 = 9 - 4 = 5$

Thus, the points $(-3,5)$, $(-2,0)$, $(-1,-3)$, $(0,-4)$, $(1,-3)$, $(2,0)$, and $(3,5)$ are on the graph. We plot these points and connect them with a smooth curve.

101. Answers will vary.

6.2 Preparing for Adding and Subtracting Rational Expressions

1. $\dfrac{1}{6} - \dfrac{5}{8} = \dfrac{4}{24} - \dfrac{15}{24} = \dfrac{4-15}{24} = -\dfrac{11}{24}$

2. a. The additive inverse of 5 is -5 because $5 + (-5) = 0$.

b. The additive inverse of $x - 2$ is $-(x-2) = -x + 2 = 2 - x$ because $(x-2) + (2-x) = 0$.

6.2 Exercises

1. least common denominator

3. TRUE

5. Answers may vary. One possibility follows: To find the least common denominator, first factor each denominator completely. Second, list the factors that are common to all denominators. Finally, list the factors that are not common.

7. $\dfrac{3x}{x+1} + \dfrac{5}{x+1} = \dfrac{3x+5}{x+1}$

9. $\dfrac{2x}{2x+5} - \dfrac{1}{2x+5} = \dfrac{2x-1}{2x+5}$

11. $\dfrac{2x}{2x^2-7x-15} + \dfrac{3}{2x^2-7x-15}$
$= \dfrac{2x+3}{2x^2-7x-15} = \dfrac{2x+3}{(2x+3)(x-5)} = \dfrac{1}{x-5}$

13. $\dfrac{2x^2-5x+7}{x^2-2x-15} - \dfrac{x^2+3x-8}{x^2-2x-15}$
$= \dfrac{2x^2-5x+7-\left(x^2+3x-8\right)}{x^2-2x-15}$
$= \dfrac{2x^2-5x+7-x^2-3x+8}{x^2-2x-15}$
$= \dfrac{x^2-8x+15}{x^2-2x-15} = \dfrac{(x-5)(x-3)}{(x-5)(x+3)} = \dfrac{x-3}{x+3}$

15. $\dfrac{3x}{x-5} + \dfrac{1}{5-x} = \dfrac{3x}{x-5} + \dfrac{1}{-1(x-5)}$
$= \dfrac{3x}{x-5} + \dfrac{-1}{x-5} = \dfrac{3x-1}{x-5}$

17. $\dfrac{2x^2-4x-1}{x-3} - \dfrac{x^2-3x+4}{3-x}$
$= \dfrac{2x^2-4x-1}{x-3} - \dfrac{x^2-3x+4}{-1(x-3)}$
$= \dfrac{2x^2-4x-1}{x-3} + \dfrac{x^2-3x+4}{x-3}$
$= \dfrac{2x^2-4x-1+x^2-3x+4}{x-3} = \dfrac{3x^2-7x+3}{x-3}$

19. $4x^3 = 2^2 \cdot x^3$
$8x = 2^3 \cdot x$
$\text{LCD} = 2^3 \cdot x^3 = 8x^3$

21. $15xy^2 = 3 \cdot 5 \cdot x \cdot y^2$
$18x^3 y = 2 \cdot 3^2 \cdot x^3 \cdot y$
$\text{LCD} = 3^2 \cdot x^3 \cdot y^2 \cdot 2 \cdot 5 = 90x^3 y^2$

23. $x-4$
$x+2$
$\text{LCD} = (x-4)(x+2)$

25. $x^2 - x - 12 = (x-4)(x+3)$
$x^2 - 9x + 20 = (x-5)(x-4)$
$\text{LCD} = (x-4)(x+3)(x-5)$

27. $2p^2 + 3p - 2 = (2p-1)(p+2)$
$p^3 + 2p^2 = p^2(p+2)$
$\text{LCD} = p^2(p+2)(2p-1)$

29. $4x^2 = 2^2 \cdot x^2$
$8x = 2^3 \cdot x$
$\text{LCD} = 2^3 \cdot x^2 = 8x^2$
$\dfrac{3}{4x^2} + \dfrac{5}{8x} = \dfrac{3}{4x^2} \cdot \dfrac{2}{2} + \dfrac{5}{8x} \cdot \dfrac{x}{x}$
$\qquad = \dfrac{6}{8x^2} + \dfrac{5x}{8x^2} = \dfrac{6+5x}{8x^2}$ or $\dfrac{5x+6}{8x^2}$

31. $12a^2 b = 2^2 \cdot 3 \cdot a^2 \cdot b$
$15ab^2 = 3 \cdot 5 \cdot a \cdot b^2$
$\text{LCD} = 3 \cdot a^2 \cdot b^2 \cdot 2^2 \cdot 5 = 60a^2 b^2$
$\dfrac{5}{12a^2 b} - \dfrac{4}{15ab^2} = \dfrac{5}{12a^2 b} \cdot \dfrac{5b}{5b} - \dfrac{4}{15ab^2} \cdot \dfrac{4a}{4a}$
$\qquad = \dfrac{25b}{60a^2 b^2} - \dfrac{16a}{60a^2 b^2} = \dfrac{25b-16a}{60a^2 b^2}$

33. $y-5$
$y+3$
$\text{LCD} = (y-5)(y+3)$
$\dfrac{y+2}{y-5} - \dfrac{y-4}{y+3} = \dfrac{y+2}{y-5} \cdot \dfrac{y+3}{y+3} - \dfrac{y-4}{y+3} \cdot \dfrac{y-5}{y-5}$
$\qquad = \dfrac{y^2+5y+6}{(y-5)(y+3)} - \dfrac{y^2-9y+20}{(y-5)(y+3)}$
$\qquad = \dfrac{y^2+5y+6-\left(y^2-9y+20\right)}{(y-5)(y+3)}$
$\qquad = \dfrac{y^2+5y+6-y^2+9y-20}{(y-5)(y+3)}$
$\qquad = \dfrac{14y-14}{(y-5)(y+3)}$ or $\dfrac{14(y-1)}{(y-5)(y+3)}$

SSM – 307

35. $a-2$

$a^2-4=(a-2)(a+2)$

$\text{LCD}=(a-2)(a+2)$

$\dfrac{a+5}{a-2}-\dfrac{5a+18}{a^2-4}=\dfrac{a+5}{a-2}\cdot\dfrac{a+2}{a+2}-\dfrac{5a+18}{(a-2)(a+2)}$

$=\dfrac{a^2+7a+10}{(a-2)(a+2)}-\dfrac{5a+18}{(a-2)(a+2)}$

$=\dfrac{a^2+7a+10-(5a+18)}{(a-2)(a+2)}$

$=\dfrac{a^2+7a+10-5a-18}{(a-2)(a+2)}$

$=\dfrac{a^2+2a-8}{(a-2)(a+2)}$

$=\dfrac{(a-2)(a+4)}{(a-2)(a+2)}=\dfrac{a+4}{a+2}$

37. $(x-2)(x+3)$

$(x+3)(x+4)$

$\text{LCD}=(x+3)(x-2)(x+4)$

$\dfrac{3}{(x-2)(x+3)}-\dfrac{5}{(x+3)(x+4)}$

$=\dfrac{3}{(x-2)(x+3)}\cdot\dfrac{x+4}{x+4}-\dfrac{5}{(x+3)(x+4)}\cdot\dfrac{x-2}{x-2}$

$=\dfrac{3x+12}{(x+3)(x-2)(x+4)}-\dfrac{5x-10}{(x+3)(x-2)(x+4)}$

$=\dfrac{3x+12-(5x-10)}{(x+3)(x-2)(x+4)}$

$=\dfrac{3x+12-5x+10}{(x+3)(x-2)(x+4)}$

$=\dfrac{-2x+22}{(x+3)(x-2)(x+4)}$ or $\dfrac{-2(x-11)}{(x+3)(x-2)(x+4)}$

39. $x^2+3x+2=(x+1)(x+2)$

$x^2-4=(x-2)(x+2)$

$\text{LCD}=(x+2)(x+1)(x-2)$

$\dfrac{x-3}{x^2+3x+2}+\dfrac{x-1}{x^2-4}$

$=\dfrac{x-3}{(x+1)(x+2)}\cdot\dfrac{x-2}{x-2}+\dfrac{x-1}{(x-2)(x+2)}\cdot\dfrac{x+1}{x+1}$

$=\dfrac{x^2-5x+6}{(x+2)(x+1)(x-2)}+\dfrac{x^2-1}{(x+2)(x+1)(x-2)}$

$=\dfrac{x^2-5x+6+x^2-1}{(x+2)(x+1)(x-2)}=\dfrac{2x^2-5x+5}{(x+2)(x+1)(x-2)}$

41. $2w^2+3w+1=(2w+1)(w+1)$

$2w^2-5w-3=(2w+1)(w-3)$

$\text{LCD}=(2w+1)(w+1)(w-3)$

$\dfrac{w-4}{2w^2+3w+1}-\dfrac{w+3}{2w^2-5w-3}$

$=\dfrac{w-4}{(2w+1)(w+1)}\cdot\dfrac{w-3}{w-3}-\dfrac{w+3}{(2w+1)(w-3)}\cdot\dfrac{w+1}{w+1}$

$=\dfrac{w^2-7w+12}{(2w+1)(w+1)(w-3)}-\dfrac{w^2+4w+3}{(2w+1)(w+1)(w-3)}$

$=\dfrac{w^2-7w+12-(w^2+4w+3)}{(2w+1)(w+1)(w-3)}$

$=\dfrac{w^2-7w+12-w^2-4w-3}{(2w+1)(w+1)(w-3)}$

$=\dfrac{-11w+9}{(2w+1)(w+1)(w-3)}$

43. $x^2-6xy+9y^2=(x-3y)^2$

$x^2-2xy-3y^2=(x+y)(x-3y)$

$\text{LCD}=(x-3y)^2(x+y)$

$\dfrac{x+y}{x^2-6xy+9y^2}+\dfrac{x+2y}{x^2-2xy-3y^2}$

$=\dfrac{x+y}{(x-3y)^2}\cdot\dfrac{x+y}{x+y}+\dfrac{x+2y}{(x+y)(x-3y)}\cdot\dfrac{x-3y}{x-3y}$

$=\dfrac{x^2+2xy+y^2}{(x-3y)^2(x+y)}+\dfrac{x^2-xy-6y^2}{(x-3y)^2(x+y)}$

$=\dfrac{x^2+2xy+y^2+x^2-xy-6y^2}{(x-3y)^2(x+y)}$

$=\dfrac{2x^2+xy-5y^2}{(x-3y)^2(x+y)}$

45. $x^2-4x-5=(x-5)(x+1)$

$x^2-6x+5=(x-5)(x-1)$

$\text{LCD}=(x-5)(x+1)(x-1)$

$\dfrac{3}{x^2-4x-5}-\dfrac{2}{x^2-6x+5}$

$=\dfrac{3}{(x-5)(x+1)}\cdot\dfrac{x-1}{x-1}-\dfrac{2}{(x-5)(x-1)}\cdot\dfrac{x+1}{x+1}$

$=\dfrac{3x-3}{(x-5)(x+1)(x-1)}-\dfrac{2x+2}{(x-5)(x+1)(x-1)}$

$=\dfrac{3x-3-(2x+2)}{(x-5)(x+1)(x-1)}=\dfrac{3x-3-2x-2}{(x-5)(x+1)(x-1)}$

$=\dfrac{x-5}{(x-5)(x+1)(x-1)}=\dfrac{1}{(x+1)(x-1)}$

47. $p^2 - 16 = (p-4)(p+4)$

$16 - p^2 = -1(p-4)(p+4)$

$\text{LCD} = (p-4)(p+4)$

$\dfrac{p^2 - 3p - 10}{p^2 - 16} + \dfrac{p^2 - 3p - 10}{16 - p^2}$

$= \dfrac{p^2 - 3p - 10}{(p-4)(p+4)} + \dfrac{p^2 - 3p - 10}{-1(p-4)(p+4)} \cdot \dfrac{-1}{-1}$

$= \dfrac{p^2 - 3p - 10}{(p-4)(p+4)} + \dfrac{-p^2 + 3p + 10}{(p-4)(p+4)}$

$= \dfrac{p^2 - 3p - 10 - p^2 + 3p + 10}{(p-4)(p+4)}$

$= \dfrac{0}{(p-4)(p+4)} = 0$

49. $w + 2$

w

$w^2 - 4 = (w-2)(w+2)$

$\text{LCD} = w(w-2)(w+2)$

$\dfrac{2}{w+2} - \dfrac{3}{w} + \dfrac{w+10}{w^2 - 4}$

$= \dfrac{2}{w+2} \cdot \dfrac{w(w-2)}{w(w-2)} - \dfrac{3}{w} \cdot \dfrac{(w-2)(w+2)}{(w-2)(w+2)} +$

$\qquad \dfrac{w+10}{(w-2)(w+2)} \cdot \dfrac{w}{w}$

$= \dfrac{2w^2 - 4w}{w(w-2)(w+2)} - \dfrac{3w^2 - 12}{w(w-2)(w+2)} +$

$\qquad \dfrac{w^2 + 10w}{w(w-2)(w+2)}$

$= \dfrac{2w^2 - 4w - (3w^2 - 12) + w^2 + 10w}{w(w-2)(w+2)}$

$= \dfrac{2w^2 - 4w - 3w^2 + 12 + w^2 + 10w}{w(w-2)(w+2)}$

$= \dfrac{6w + 12}{w(w-2)(w+2)}$

$= \dfrac{6(w+2)}{w(w-2)(w+2)}$

$= \dfrac{6}{w(w-2)}$

51. $p^2 + 6p + 9 = (p+3)^2$

$p + 3$

$2p^2 + p - 15 = (2p-5)(p+3)$

$\text{LCD} = (p+3)^2(2p-5)$

$\dfrac{p-2}{p^2 + 6p + 9} + \dfrac{1}{p+3} - \dfrac{2p+1}{2p^2 + p - 15}$

$= \dfrac{p-2}{(p+3)^2} \cdot \dfrac{2p-5}{2p-5} + \dfrac{1}{p+3} \cdot \dfrac{(p+3)(2p-5)}{(p+3)(2p-5)} -$

$\qquad \dfrac{2p+1}{(2p-5)(p+3)} \cdot \dfrac{p+3}{p+3}$

$= \dfrac{2p^2 - 9p + 10}{(p+3)^2(2p-5)} + \dfrac{2p^2 + p - 15}{(p+3)^2(2p-5)} -$

$\qquad \dfrac{2p^2 + 7p + 3}{(p+3)^2(2p-5)}$

$= \dfrac{2p^2 - 9p + 10 + 2p^2 + p - 15 - (2p^2 + 7p + 3)}{(p+3)^2(2p-5)}$

$= \dfrac{2p^2 - 9p + 10 + 2p^2 + p - 15 - 2p^2 - 7p - 3}{(p+3)^2(2p-5)}$

$= \dfrac{2p^2 - 15p - 8}{(p+3)^2(2p-5)}$ or $\dfrac{(2p+1)(p-8)}{(p+3)^2(2p-5)}$

53. x

$x - 1$

$(x-1)^2$

$\text{LCD} = x(x-1)^2$

$\dfrac{2}{x} - \dfrac{2}{x-1} + \dfrac{3}{(x-1)^2}$

$= \dfrac{2}{x} \cdot \dfrac{(x-1)^2}{(x-1)^2} - \dfrac{2}{x-1} \cdot \dfrac{x(x-1)}{x(x-1)} + \dfrac{3}{(x-1)^2} \cdot \dfrac{x}{x}$

$= \dfrac{2x^2 - 4x + 2}{x(x-1)^2} - \dfrac{2x^2 - 2x}{x(x-1)^2} + \dfrac{3x}{x(x-1)^2}$

$= \dfrac{2x^2 - 4x + 2 - (2x^2 - 2x) + 3x}{x(x-1)^2}$

$= \dfrac{2x^2 - 4x + 2 - 2x^2 + 2x + 3x}{x(x-1)^2}$

$= \dfrac{x+2}{x(x-1)^2}$

55. a. $x-2$

$x+1$

$\text{LCD} = (x-2)(x+1)$

$R(x) = f(x) + g(x) = \dfrac{3}{x-2} + \dfrac{2}{x+1}$

$= \dfrac{3}{x-2} \cdot \dfrac{x+1}{x+1} + \dfrac{2}{x+1} \cdot \dfrac{x-2}{x-2}$

$= \dfrac{3x+3}{(x-2)(x+1)} + \dfrac{2x-4}{(x-2)(x+1)}$

$= \dfrac{3x+3+2x-4}{(x-2)(x+1)}$

$= \dfrac{5x-1}{(x-2)(x+1)}$

b. Since R is the sum of f and g, the restrictions for the domain of R will consist of all the restrictions for the domains of both f and g. Since 2 is restricted from the domain of f and since -1 is restricted from the domain of g, both 2 and -1 are restricted from the domain of R. That is, the domain of $R(x)$ is $\{x \mid x \ne -1, x \ne 2\}$.

57. $x^2 - 3x - 4 = (x-4)(x+1)$

$x^2 - x - 12 = (x-4)(x+3)$

$\text{LCD} = (x-4)(x+1)(x+3)$

a. $R(x) = f(x) + g(x)$

$= \dfrac{x+1}{x^2-3x-4} + \dfrac{x+4}{x^2-x-12}$

$= \dfrac{x+1}{(x-4)(x+1)} \cdot \dfrac{x+3}{x+3} + \dfrac{x+4}{(x-4)(x+3)} \cdot \dfrac{x+1}{x+1}$

$= \dfrac{x^2+4x+3}{(x-4)(x+1)(x+3)} + \dfrac{x^2+5x+4}{(x-4)(x+1)(x+3)}$

$= \dfrac{x^2+4x+3+x^2+5x+4}{(x-4)(x+1)(x+3)}$

$= \dfrac{2x^2+9x+7}{(x-4)(x+1)(x+3)}$

$= \dfrac{(2x+7)(x+1)}{(x-4)(x+1)(x+3)} = \dfrac{2x+7}{(x-4)(x+3)}$

b. Since R is the sum of f and g, the restrictions for the domain of R will consist of all the restrictions for the domains of both f and g. Since 4 and -1 are restricted from the domain of f and since 4 and -3 are restricted from the domain of g, then 4, -1, and -3 are restricted from the domain of R. That is, the domain of $R(x)$ is $\{x \mid x \ne -3, x \ne -1, x \ne 4\}$.

c. $H(x) = f(x) - g(x)$

$= \dfrac{x+1}{x^2-3x-4} - \dfrac{x+4}{x^2-x-12}$

$= \dfrac{x+1}{(x-4)(x+1)} \cdot \dfrac{x+3}{x+3} - \dfrac{x+4}{(x-4)(x+3)} \cdot \dfrac{x+1}{x+1}$

$= \dfrac{x^2+4x+3}{(x-4)(x+1)(x+3)} - \dfrac{x^2+5x+4}{(x-4)(x+1)(x+3)}$

$= \dfrac{x^2+4x+3-\left(x^2+5x+4\right)}{(x-4)(x+1)(x+3)}$

$= \dfrac{x^2+4x+3-x^2-5x-4}{(x-4)(x+1)(x+3)}$

$= \dfrac{-x-1}{(x-4)(x+1)(x+3)}$

$= \dfrac{-1(x+1)}{(x-4)(x+1)(x+3)} = \dfrac{-1}{(x-4)(x+3)}$

d. Since H is the difference of f and g, the restrictions for the domain of H will consist of all the restrictions for the domains of both f and g. Since 4 and -1 are restricted from the domain of f and since 4 and -3 are restricted from the domain of g, then 4, -1, and -3 are restricted from the domain of H. That is, the domain of $H(x)$ is $\{x \mid x \ne -3, x \ne -1, x \ne 4\}$.

59. $x-3$

$x^3 - 27 = (x-3)\left(x^2+3x+9\right)$

$\text{LCD} = (x-3)\left(x^2+3x+9\right)$

$\dfrac{1}{x-3} - \dfrac{x^2+18}{x^3-27}$

$= \dfrac{1}{x-3} \cdot \dfrac{x^2+3x+9}{x^2+3x+9} - \dfrac{x^2+18}{(x-3)\left(x^2+3x+9\right)}$

$= \dfrac{x^2+3x+9}{(x-3)\left(x^2+3x+9\right)} - \dfrac{x^2+18}{(x-3)\left(x^2+3x+9\right)}$

$= \dfrac{x^2+3x+9-\left(x^2+18\right)}{(x-3)\left(x^2+3x+9\right)}$

$= \dfrac{x^2+3x+9-x^2-18}{(x-3)\left(x^2+3x+9\right)}$

$= \dfrac{3x-9}{(x-3)\left(x^2+3x+9\right)}$

$= \dfrac{3(x-3)}{(x-3)\left(x^2+3x+9\right)} = \dfrac{3}{x^2+3x+9}$

61. $\dfrac{2x^2 - x}{x+3} + \dfrac{3x}{x+3} - \dfrac{x^2+3}{x+3}$

$= \dfrac{2x^2 - x + 3x - \left(x^2 + 3\right)}{x+3}$

$= \dfrac{2x^2 - x + 3x - x^2 - 3}{x+3}$

$= \dfrac{x^2 + 2x - 3}{x+3} = \dfrac{(x-1)(x+3)}{x+3} = x - 1$

63. 1

$x + 3$

$\text{LCD} = x + 3$

$6 + \dfrac{x-3}{x+3} = \dfrac{6}{1} \cdot \dfrac{x+3}{x+3} + \dfrac{x-3}{x+3}$

$= \dfrac{6x+18}{x+3} + \dfrac{x-3}{x+3}$

$= \dfrac{6x + 18 + x - 3}{x+3} = \dfrac{7x + 15}{x+3}$

65. $b^2 + 2b - 8 = (b-2)(b+4)$

$b^2 - 4 = (b-2)(b+2)$

$\text{LCD} = (b-2)(b+2)(b+4)$

$\dfrac{b+3}{b^2 + 2b - 8} - \dfrac{b+2}{b^2 - 4}$

$= \dfrac{b+3}{(b-2)(b+4)} \cdot \dfrac{b+2}{b+2} - \dfrac{b+2}{(b-2)(b+2)} \cdot \dfrac{b+4}{b+4}$

$= \dfrac{b^2 + 5b + 6}{(b-2)(b+2)(b+4)} - \dfrac{b^2 + 6b + 8}{(b-2)(b+2)(b+4)}$

$= \dfrac{b^2 + 5b + 6 - \left(b^2 + 6b + 8\right)}{(b-2)(b+2)(b+4)}$

$= \dfrac{b^2 + 5b + 6 - b^2 - 6b - 8}{(b-2)(b+2)(b+4)}$

$= \dfrac{-b - 2}{(b-2)(b+2)(b+4)}$

$= \dfrac{-(b+2)}{(b-2)(b+2)(b+4)} = \dfrac{-1}{(b-2)(b+4)}$

67. $y + 4$

$y + 3$

$y^2 + 7y + 12 = (y+3)(y+4)$

$\text{LCD} = (y+3)(y+4)$

$\dfrac{y-1}{y+4} + \dfrac{y-2}{y+3} - \dfrac{y^2 + 3y + 1}{y^2 + 7y + 12}$

$= \dfrac{y-1}{y+4} \cdot \dfrac{y+3}{y+3} + \dfrac{y-2}{y+3} \cdot \dfrac{y+4}{y+4} - \dfrac{y^2 + 3y + 1}{(y+3)(y+4)}$

$= \dfrac{y^2 + 2y - 3}{(y+3)(y+4)} + \dfrac{y^2 + 2y - 8}{(y+3)(y+4)} - \dfrac{y^2 + 3y + 1}{(y+3)(y+4)}$

$= \dfrac{y^2 + 2y - 3 + \left(y^2 + 2y - 8\right) - \left(y^2 + 3y + 1\right)}{(y+3)(y+4)}$

$= \dfrac{y^2 + 2y - 3 + y^2 + 2y - 8 - y^2 - 3y - 1}{(y+3)(y+4)}$

$= \dfrac{y^2 + y - 12}{(y+3)(y+4)} = \dfrac{(y-3)(y+4)}{(y+3)(y+4)} = \dfrac{y-3}{y+3}$

69. $x^2 - 5x + 6 = (x-2)(x-3)$

$x^2 - 2x - 3 = (x-3)(x+1)$

$x^2 - x - 2 = (x+1)(x-2)$

$\text{LCD} = (x-2)(x-3)(x+1)$

$\dfrac{x+4}{x^2 - 5x + 6} + \dfrac{x-1}{x^2 - 2x - 3} - \dfrac{2x+1}{x^2 - x - 2}$

$= \dfrac{x+4}{(x-2)(x-3)} \cdot \dfrac{x+1}{x+1} + \dfrac{x-1}{(x-3)(x+1)} \cdot \dfrac{x-2}{x-2}$

$\quad - \dfrac{2x+1}{(x+1)(x-2)} \cdot \dfrac{x-3}{x-3}$

$= \dfrac{x^2 + 5x + 4}{(x-2)(x-3)(x+1)} + \dfrac{x^2 - 3x + 2}{(x-2)(x-3)(x+1)}$

$\quad - \dfrac{2x^2 - 5x - 3}{(x-2)(x-3)(x+1)}$

$= \dfrac{x^2 + 5x + 4 + \left(x^2 - 3x + 2\right) - \left(2x^2 - 5x - 3\right)}{(x-2)(x-3)(x+1)}$

$= \dfrac{x^2 + 5x + 4 + x^2 - 3x + 2 - 2x^2 + 5x + 3}{(x-2)(x-3)(x+1)}$

$= \dfrac{7x + 9}{(x-2)(x-3)(x+1)}$

71. a. $S(x) = 2x^2 + \dfrac{8000}{x}$ (Note: $\text{LCD} = x$)

$= \dfrac{2x^2}{1} \cdot \dfrac{x}{x} + \dfrac{8000}{x}$

$= \dfrac{2x^3}{x} + \dfrac{8000}{x}$

$= \dfrac{2x^3 + 8000}{x}$

b. $S(10) = \dfrac{2(10)^3 + 8000}{10} = \dfrac{10,000}{10} = 1000$

For the square-based, closed box with volume 2000 cubic inches, if the length of the base is 10 inches, then the surface area of the box will be 1000 square inches.

73. a. s

$s + 10$

$LCD = s(s + 10)$

$T(s) = \dfrac{50}{s} + \dfrac{150}{s + 10}$

$= \dfrac{50}{s} \cdot \dfrac{s + 10}{s + 10} + \dfrac{150}{s + 10} \cdot \dfrac{s}{s}$

$= \dfrac{50s + 500}{s(s + 10)} + \dfrac{150s}{s(s + 10)}$

$= \dfrac{200s + 500}{s(s + 10)}$ or $\dfrac{100(2s + 5)}{s(s + 10)}$

b. $T(50) = \dfrac{200(50) + 500}{50(50 + 10)} = \dfrac{10,500}{3000} = 3.5$

If the average speed for the first 50 miles of the trip is 50 miles per hour, then it will take a total time of 3.5 hours to get to the neighboring university.

75. $x^{-1} + y^{-1} = \dfrac{1}{x} + \dfrac{1}{y}$ (Note: $LCD = xy$)

$= \dfrac{1}{x} \cdot \dfrac{y}{y} + \dfrac{1}{y} \cdot \dfrac{x}{x}$

$= \dfrac{y}{xy} + \dfrac{x}{xy}$

$= \dfrac{y + x}{xy}$ or $\dfrac{x + y}{xy}$

77. $4a(a - 3) = 4a \cdot a - 4a \cdot 3 = 4a^2 - 12a$

79. $(p - 3)(p + 3) = p^2 + 3p - 3p - 9 = p^2 - 9$

81. $(w - 2)(w^2 + 2w + 4)$

$= w^3 + 2w^2 + 4w - 2w^2 - 4w - 8$

$= w^3 - 8$

6.3 Preparing for Complex Rational Expressions

1. $a \cdot c = 6(-6) = -36$

The factors of -36 that add to -5 (the linear coefficient) are -9 and 4. Thus,

$6y^2 - 5y - 6 = 6y^2 - 9y + 4y - 6$

$= 3y(2y - 3) + 2(2y - 3)$

$= (3y + 2)(2y - 3)$

2. $\left(\dfrac{3ab^2}{2a^{-1}b^5}\right)^{-2} = \left(\dfrac{2a^{-1}b^5}{3ab^2}\right)^2 = \left(\dfrac{2b^{5-2}}{3a^{1+1}}\right)^2$

$= \left(\dfrac{2b^3}{3a^2}\right)^2 = \dfrac{2^2 b^{3 \cdot 2}}{3^2 a^{2 \cdot 2}} = \dfrac{4b^6}{9a^4}$

6.3 Exercises

1. complex rational expression

3. Answers will vary. One possibility follows: A complex rational expression is a rational expression in which the numerator and/or denominator contain rational expressions.

5. Method 1: Write the numerator of the complex rational expression as a single rational expression. Note that the LCD of the rational expressions in the numerator is x.

$1 + \dfrac{1}{x} = \dfrac{1}{x} \cdot \dfrac{x}{x} + \dfrac{1}{x} = \dfrac{x}{x} + \dfrac{1}{x} = \dfrac{x + 1}{x}$

Write the denominator of the complex rational expression as a single rational expression. Note that the LCD of the rational expressions in the denominator is x.

$1 - \dfrac{1}{x} = \dfrac{1}{x} \cdot \dfrac{x}{x} - \dfrac{1}{x} = \dfrac{x}{x} - \dfrac{1}{x} = \dfrac{x - 1}{x}$

Rewrite the complex rational expression using the single rational expressions and simplify.

$\dfrac{1 + \dfrac{1}{x}}{1 - \dfrac{1}{x}} = \dfrac{\dfrac{x + 1}{x}}{\dfrac{x - 1}{x}} = \dfrac{x + 1}{x} \cdot \dfrac{x}{x - 1} = \dfrac{x + 1}{\cancel{x}} \cdot \dfrac{\cancel{x}}{x - 1} = \dfrac{x + 1}{x - 1}$

Method 2: The LCD of all the denominators in the complex rational expression is x.

$\dfrac{1 + \dfrac{1}{x}}{1 - \dfrac{1}{x}} = \dfrac{1 + \dfrac{1}{x}}{1 - \dfrac{1}{x}} \cdot \dfrac{x}{x} = \dfrac{1 \cdot x + \dfrac{1}{x} \cdot x}{1 \cdot x - \dfrac{1}{x} \cdot x} = \dfrac{x + 1}{x - 1}$

7. Method 1: Write the numerator of the complex rational expression as a single rational expression. Note that the LCD of the rational expressions in the numerator is w.

$$w - \frac{1}{w} = \frac{w}{1} \cdot \frac{w}{w} - \frac{1}{w} = \frac{w^2}{w} - \frac{1}{w} = \frac{w^2 - 1}{w}$$

Write the denominator of the complex rational expression as a single rational expression. Note that the LCD of the rational expressions in the denominator is w.

$$w + \frac{1}{w} = \frac{w}{1} \cdot \frac{w}{w} + \frac{1}{w} = \frac{w^2}{w} + \frac{1}{w} = \frac{w^2 + 1}{w}$$

Rewrite the complex rational expression using the single rational expressions and simplify.

$$\frac{w - \dfrac{1}{w}}{w + \dfrac{1}{w}} = \frac{\dfrac{w^2 - 1}{w}}{\dfrac{w^2 + 1}{w}} = \frac{w^2 - 1}{w} \cdot \frac{w}{w^2 + 1}$$

$$= \frac{w^2 - 1}{\cancel{w}} \cdot \frac{\cancel{w}}{w^2 + 1}$$

$$= \frac{w^2 - 1}{w^2 + 1} \quad \text{or} \quad \frac{(w-1)(w+1)}{w^2 + 1}$$

Method 2: The LCD of all the denominators in the complex rational expression is w.

$$\frac{w - \dfrac{1}{w}}{w + \dfrac{1}{w}} = \frac{w - \dfrac{1}{w}}{w + \dfrac{1}{w}} \cdot \frac{w}{w} = \frac{w \cdot w - \dfrac{1}{w} \cdot w}{w \cdot w + \dfrac{1}{w} \cdot w}$$

$$= \frac{w^2 - 1}{w^2 + 1} \quad \text{or} \quad \frac{(w-1)(w+1)}{w^2 + 1}$$

9. Method 1: Write the numerator of the complex rational expression as a single rational expression. Note that the LCD of the rational expressions in the numerator is $a - 2$.

$$1 - \frac{a}{a-2} = \frac{1}{1} \cdot \frac{a-2}{a-2} - \frac{a}{a-2}$$

$$= \frac{a-2}{a-2} - \frac{a}{a-2} = \frac{a-2-a}{a-2} = \frac{-2}{a-2}$$

Write the denominator of the complex rational expression as a single rational expression. Note that the LCD of the rational expressions in the denominator is a.

$$2 - \frac{a+2}{a} = \frac{2}{1} \cdot \frac{a}{a} - \frac{a+2}{a} = \frac{2a}{a} - \frac{a+2}{a}$$

$$= \frac{2a - (a+2)}{a} = \frac{2a - a - 2}{a} = \frac{a-2}{a}$$

Rewrite the complex rational expression using the single rational expressions and simplify.

$$\frac{1 - \dfrac{a}{a-2}}{2 - \dfrac{a+2}{a}} = \frac{\dfrac{-2}{a-2}}{\dfrac{a-2}{a}} = \frac{-2}{a-2} \cdot \frac{a}{a-2} = \frac{-2a}{(a-2)^2}$$

Method 2: The LCD of all the denominators in the complex rational expression is $a(a-2)$.

$$\frac{1 - \dfrac{a}{a-2}}{2 - \dfrac{a+2}{a}} = \frac{1 - \dfrac{a}{a-2}}{2 - \dfrac{a+2}{a}} \cdot \frac{a(a-2)}{a(a-2)}$$

$$= \frac{1 \cdot a(a-2) - \dfrac{a}{a-2} \cdot a(a-2)}{2 \cdot a(a-2) - \dfrac{a+2}{a} \cdot a(a-2)}$$

$$= \frac{1 \cdot a(a-2) - \dfrac{a}{\cancel{a-2}} \cdot a(\cancel{a-2})}{2 \cdot a(a-2) - \dfrac{a+2}{\cancel{a}} \cdot \cancel{a}(a-2)}$$

$$= \frac{a^2 - 2a - a^2}{2a^2 - 4a - (a^2 - 4)}$$

$$= \frac{a^2 - 2a - a^2}{2a^2 - 4a - a^2 + 4}$$

$$= \frac{-2a}{a^2 - 4a + 4} \quad \text{or} \quad \frac{-2a}{(a-2)^2}$$

11. Method 1: Write the numerator of the complex rational expression as a single rational expression. Note that the LCD of the rational expressions in the numerator is $(x-1)(x+3)$.

$$\frac{x+2}{x-1} - \frac{x+5}{x+3} = \frac{x+2}{x-1} \cdot \frac{x+3}{x+3} - \frac{x+5}{x+3} \cdot \frac{x-1}{x-1}$$

$$= \frac{x^2 + 5x + 6}{(x-1)(x+3)} - \frac{x^2 + 4x - 5}{(x-1)(x+3)}$$

$$= \frac{x^2 + 5x + 6 - (x^2 + 4x - 5)}{(x-1)(x+3)}$$

$$= \frac{x^2 + 5x + 6 - x^2 - 4x + 5}{(x-1)(x+3)}$$

$$= \frac{x + 11}{(x-1)(x+3)}$$

The denominator is already a single rational expression: $\dfrac{x+11}{1}$.

Rewrite the complex rational expression using the single rational expressions and simplify.

SSM – 313

$$\frac{\dfrac{x+2}{x-1}-\dfrac{x+5}{x+3}}{x+11}=\frac{x+11}{(x-1)(x+3)}\cdot\frac{1}{x+11}$$

$$=\frac{\cancel{x+11}}{(x-1)(x+3)}\cdot\frac{1}{\cancel{x+11}}$$

$$=\frac{1}{(x-1)(x+3)}$$

Method 2: The LCD of all the denominators in the complex rational expression is $(x-1)(x+3)$.

$$\frac{\dfrac{x+2}{x-1}-\dfrac{x+5}{x+3}}{x+11}=\frac{\dfrac{x+2}{x-1}-\dfrac{x+5}{x+3}}{x+11}\cdot\frac{(x-1)(x+3)}{(x-1)(x+3)}$$

$$=\frac{\dfrac{x+2}{x-1}\cdot(x-1)(x+3)-\dfrac{x+5}{x+3}\cdot(x-1)(x+3)}{(x+11)\cdot(x-1)(x+3)}$$

$$=\frac{\dfrac{x+2}{\cancel{x-1}}\cdot\cancel{(x-1)}(x+3)-\dfrac{x+5}{\cancel{x+3}}\cdot(x-1)\cancel{(x+3)}}{(x+11)\cdot(x-1)(x+3)}$$

$$=\frac{(x+2)(x+3)-(x+5)(x-1)}{(x+11)(x-1)(x+3)}$$

$$=\frac{x^2+5x+6-\left(x^2+4x-5\right)}{(x+11)(x-1)(x+3)}$$

$$=\frac{x^2+5x+6-x^2-4x+5}{(x+11)(x-1)(x+3)}$$

$$=\frac{x+11}{(x+11)(x-1)(x+3)}=\frac{1}{(x-1)(x+3)}$$

13. Method 1: Write the numerator of the complex rational expression as a single rational expression. Note that the LCD of the rational expressions in the numerator is $(x-4)(x-2)$.

$$\frac{x-1}{x-4}-\frac{x}{x-2}=\frac{x-1}{x-4}\cdot\frac{x-2}{x-2}-\frac{x}{x-2}\cdot\frac{x-4}{x-4}$$

$$=\frac{x^2-3x+2}{(x-4)(x-2)}-\frac{x^2-4x}{(x-4)(x-2)}$$

$$=\frac{x^2-3x+2-\left(x^2-4x\right)}{(x-4)(x-2)}$$

$$=\frac{x^2-3x+2-x^2+4x}{(x-4)(x-2)}$$

$$=\frac{x+2}{(x-4)(x-2)}$$

Write the denominator of the complex rational expression as a single rational expression. Note that the LCD of the rational expressions in the

denominator is $x-4$.

$$1-\frac{3}{x-4}=\frac{1}{1}\cdot\frac{x-4}{x-4}-\frac{3}{x-4}$$

$$=\frac{x-4}{x-4}-\frac{3}{x-4}=\frac{x-4-3}{x-4}=\frac{x-7}{x-4}$$

Rewrite the complex rational expression using the single rational expressions and simplify.

$$\frac{\dfrac{x-1}{x-4}-\dfrac{x}{x-2}}{1-\dfrac{3}{x-4}}=\frac{\dfrac{x+2}{(x-4)(x-2)}}{\dfrac{x-7}{x-4}}$$

$$=\frac{x+2}{(x-4)(x-2)}\cdot\frac{x-4}{x-7}$$

$$=\frac{x+2}{(x-4)(x-2)}\cdot\frac{\cancel{x-4}}{x-7}$$

$$=\frac{x+2}{(x-2)(x-7)}$$

Method 2: The LCD of all the denominators in the complex rational expression is $(x-4)(x-2)$.

$$\frac{\dfrac{x-1}{x-4}-\dfrac{x}{x-2}}{1-\dfrac{3}{x-4}}=\frac{\dfrac{x-1}{x-4}-\dfrac{x}{x-2}}{1-\dfrac{3}{x-4}}\cdot\frac{(x-4)(x-2)}{(x-4)(x-2)}$$

$$=\frac{\dfrac{x-1}{x-4}\cdot(x-4)(x-2)-\dfrac{x}{x-2}\cdot(x-4)(x-2)}{1\cdot(x-4)(x-2)-\dfrac{3}{x-4}\cdot(x-4)(x-2)}$$

$$=\frac{\dfrac{x-1}{\cancel{x-4}}\cdot\cancel{(x-4)}(x-2)-\dfrac{x}{\cancel{x-2}}\cdot(x-4)\cancel{(x-2)}}{1\cdot(x-4)(x-2)-\dfrac{3}{\cancel{x-4}}\cdot\cancel{(x-4)}(x-2)}$$

$$=\frac{(x-1)(x-2)-x(x-4)}{(x-4)(x-2)-3(x-2)}$$

$$=\frac{x^2-3x+2-x^2+4x}{(x-2)\left[(x-4)-3\right]}=\frac{x+2}{(x-2)(x-7)}$$

15. Using Method 2, the LCD of all the denominators in the complex rational expression is y.

$$\frac{\dfrac{3}{y}-1}{\dfrac{9}{y}-y}=\frac{\dfrac{3}{y}-1}{\dfrac{9}{y}-y}\cdot\frac{y}{y}=\frac{\dfrac{3}{y}\cdot y-1\cdot y}{\dfrac{9}{y}\cdot y-y\cdot y}=\frac{3-y}{9-y^2}$$

$$=\frac{3-y}{(3-y)(3+y)}=\frac{1}{3+y}\text{ or }\frac{1}{y+3}$$

17. Using Method 2, the LCD of all the denominators in the complex rational expression is mn.

$$\frac{\dfrac{4n}{m}-\dfrac{4m}{n}}{\dfrac{2}{m}+\dfrac{2}{n}}=\frac{\dfrac{4n}{m}-\dfrac{4m}{n}}{\dfrac{2}{m}+\dfrac{2}{n}}\cdot\frac{mn}{mn}=\frac{\dfrac{4n}{m}\cdot mn-\dfrac{4m}{n}\cdot mn}{\dfrac{2}{m}\cdot mn+\dfrac{2}{n}\cdot mn}$$

$$=\frac{\dfrac{4n}{\cancel{m}}\cdot \cancel{m}n-\dfrac{4m}{\cancel{n}}\cdot m\cancel{n}}{\dfrac{2}{\cancel{m}}\cdot \cancel{m}n+\dfrac{2}{\cancel{n}}\cdot m\cancel{n}}$$

$$=\frac{4n^2-4m^2}{2n+2m}$$

$$=\frac{4\left(n^2-m^2\right)}{2(n+m)}$$

$$=\frac{2\cdot2(n-m)(n+m)}{2(n+m)}$$

$$=\frac{\cancel{2}\cdot2(n-m)\cancel{(n+m)}}{\cancel{2}\cancel{(n+m)}}$$

$$=2(n-m)$$

19. Using Method 1, write the numerator of the complex rational expression as a single rational expression. Note that the LCD of the rational expressions in the numerator is x.

$$2+\frac{3}{x}=\frac{2}{1}\cdot\frac{x}{x}+\frac{3}{x}=\frac{2x}{x}+\frac{3}{x}=\frac{2x+3}{x}$$

Write the denominator of the complex rational expression as a single rational expression. Note that the LCD of the rational expressions in the denominator is $x+3$.

$$\frac{2x^2}{x+3}-3=\frac{2x^2}{x+3}-\frac{3}{1}\cdot\frac{x+3}{x+3}$$

$$=\frac{2x^2}{x+3}-\frac{3x+9}{x+3}=\frac{2x^2-(3x+9)}{x+3}$$

$$=\frac{2x^2-3x-9}{x+3}=\frac{(2x+3)(x-3)}{x+3}$$

Rewrite the complex rational expression using the single rational expressions and simplify.

$$\frac{2+\dfrac{3}{x}}{\dfrac{2x^2}{x+3}-3}=\frac{\dfrac{2x+3}{x}}{\dfrac{(2x+3)(x-3)}{x+3}}$$

$$=\frac{2x+3}{x}\cdot\frac{x+3}{(2x+3)(x-3)}$$

$$=\frac{\cancel{2x+3}}{x}\cdot\frac{x+3}{\cancel{(2x+3)}(x-3)}=\frac{x+3}{x(x-3)}$$

21. Using Method 2, the LCD of all the denominators in the complex rational expression is $3x^2$.

$$\frac{\dfrac{x}{3}-\dfrac{3}{x}}{\dfrac{3}{x^2}-\dfrac{1}{3}}=\frac{\dfrac{x}{3}-\dfrac{3}{x}}{\dfrac{3}{x^2}-\dfrac{1}{3}}\cdot\frac{3x^2}{3x^2}$$

$$=\frac{\dfrac{x}{3}\cdot3x^2-\dfrac{3}{x}\cdot3x^2}{\dfrac{3}{x^2}\cdot3x^2-\dfrac{1}{3}\cdot3x^2}$$

$$=\frac{\dfrac{x}{\cancel{3}}\cdot\cancel{3}x^2-\dfrac{3}{\cancel{x}}\cdot3x^{\cancel{2}}}{\dfrac{3}{\cancel{x^2}}\cdot3\cancel{x^2}-\dfrac{1}{\cancel{3}}\cdot\cancel{3}x^2}$$

$$=\frac{x^3-9x}{9-x^2}$$

$$=\frac{-x(3-x)(3+x)}{(3-x)(3+x)}$$

$$=\frac{-x\cancel{(3-x)}\cancel{(3+x)}}{\cancel{(3-x)}\cancel{(3+x)}}=-x$$

23. Using Method 1, write the numerator of the complex rational expression as a single rational expression. Note that the LCD of the rational expressions in the numerator is $(x-1)(x-3)$.

$$\frac{2x+1}{x-1}-\frac{x-1}{x-3}=\frac{2x+1}{x-1}\cdot\frac{x-3}{x-3}-\frac{x-1}{x-3}\cdot\frac{x-1}{x-1}$$

$$=\frac{2x^2-5x-3}{(x-1)(x-3)}-\frac{x^2-2x+1}{(x-1)(x-3)}$$

$$=\frac{2x^2-5x-3-\left(x^2-2x+1\right)}{(x-1)(x-3)}$$

$$=\frac{2x^2-5x-3-x^2+2x-1}{(x-1)(x-3)}$$

$$=\frac{x^2-3x-4}{(x-1)(x-3)}$$

$$=\frac{(x-4)(x+1)}{(x-1)(x-3)}$$

The denominator is already a single rational expression: $x^2-3x-4=(x-4)(x+1)$.

Rewrite the complex rational expression using the single rational expressions and simplify.

$$\frac{\dfrac{2x+1}{x-1}-\dfrac{x-1}{x-3}}{x^2-3x-4}=\frac{\dfrac{(x-4)(x+1)}{(x-1)(x-3)}}{\dfrac{(x-4)(x+1)}{1}}$$

$$=\frac{(x-4)(x+1)}{(x-1)(x-3)}\cdot\frac{1}{(x-4)(x+1)}$$

$$=\frac{\cancel{(x-4)}\,\cancel{(x+1)}}{(x-1)(x-3)}\cdot\frac{1}{\cancel{(x-4)}\,\cancel{(x+1)}}$$

$$=\frac{1}{(x-1)(x-3)}$$

25. Using Method 2, the LCD of all the denominators in the complex rational expression is $(x-2)(x+4)$.

$$\frac{\dfrac{x-4}{x+4}+\dfrac{x-4}{x-2}}{1-\dfrac{2}{x-2}}=\frac{\left(\dfrac{x-4}{x+4}+\dfrac{x-4}{x-2}\right)}{\left(1-\dfrac{2}{x-2}\right)}\cdot\frac{(x-2)(x+4)}{(x-2)(x+4)}$$

$$=\frac{\dfrac{x-4}{x+4}\cdot(x-2)(x+4)+\dfrac{x-4}{x-2}\cdot(x-2)(x+4)}{1\cdot(x-2)(x+4)-\dfrac{2}{x-2}\cdot(x-2)(x+4)}$$

$$=\frac{\dfrac{x-4}{\cancel{x+4}}\cdot(x-2)\cancel{(x+4)}+\dfrac{x-4}{\cancel{x-2}}\cdot\cancel{(x-2)}(x+4)}{1\cdot(x-2)(x+4)-\dfrac{2}{\cancel{x-2}}\cdot\cancel{(x-2)}(x+4)}$$

$$=\frac{(x-4)(x-2)+(x-4)(x+4)}{(x-2)(x+4)-2(x+4)}$$

$$=\frac{(x-4)\big[(x-2)+(x+4)\big]}{(x+4)\big[(x-2)-2\big]}$$

$$=\frac{(x-4)\big[2x+2\big]}{(x+4)\big[x-4\big]}$$

$$=\frac{2(x-4)(x+1)}{(x+4)(x-4)}$$

$$=\frac{2(x+1)}{x+4}$$

27. Using Method 1, write the numerator of the complex rational expression as a single rational expression. Note that the LCD of the rational expressions in the numerator is $(z-2)(z+2)$.

$$\frac{z+2}{z-2}+\frac{z-2}{z+2}=\frac{z+2}{z-2}\cdot\frac{z+2}{z+2}+\frac{z-2}{z+2}\cdot\frac{z-2}{z-2}$$

$$=\frac{z^2+4z+4}{(z-2)(z+2)}+\frac{z^2-4z+4}{(z-2)(z+2)}$$

$$=\frac{z^2+4z+4+z^2-4z+4}{(z-2)(z+2)}$$

$$=\frac{2z^2+8}{(z-2)(z+2)}$$

$$=\frac{2\left(z^2+4\right)}{(z-2)(z+2)}$$

Write the denominator of the complex rational expression as a single rational expression. Note that the LCD of the rational expressions in the denominator is $(z-2)(z+2)$.

$$\frac{z+2}{z-2}-\frac{z-2}{z+2}=\frac{z+2}{z-2}\cdot\frac{z+2}{z+2}-\frac{z-2}{z+2}\cdot\frac{z-2}{z-2}$$

$$=\frac{z^2+4z+4}{(z-2)(z+2)}-\frac{z^2-4z+4}{(z-2)(z+2)}$$

$$=\frac{z^2+4z+4-\left(z^2-4z+4\right)}{(z-2)(z+2)}$$

$$=\frac{z^2+4z+4-z^2+4z-4}{(z-2)(z+2)}$$

$$=\frac{8z}{(z-2)(z+2)}$$

Rewrite the complex rational expression using the single rational expressions and simplify.

$$\frac{\dfrac{z+2}{z-2}+\dfrac{z-2}{z+2}}{\dfrac{z+2}{z-2}-\dfrac{z-2}{z+2}}=\frac{\dfrac{2\left(z^2+4\right)}{(z-2)(z+2)}}{\dfrac{8z}{(z-2)(z+2)}}$$

$$=\frac{2\left(z^2+4\right)}{(z-2)(z+2)}\cdot\frac{(z-2)(z+2)}{8z}$$

$$=\frac{\cancel{2}\left(z^2+4\right)}{\cancel{(z-2)}\,\cancel{(z+2)}}\cdot\frac{\cancel{(z-2)}\,\cancel{(z+2)}}{\cancel{2}\cdot4z}$$

$$=\frac{z^2+4}{4z}$$

29. Using Method 1, write the numerator of the complex rational expression as a single rational expression. Note that the LCD of the rational expressions in the numerator is $(b-5)(b+5)$.

$$\frac{b^2}{b^2-25}-\frac{b}{b+5}=\frac{b^2}{(b-5)(b+5)}-\frac{b}{b+5}\cdot\frac{b-5}{b-5}$$

$$=\frac{b^2}{(b-5)(b+5)}-\frac{b^2-5b}{(b-5)(b+5)}$$

$$=\frac{b^2-(b^2-5b)}{(b-5)(b+5)}$$

$$=\frac{b^2-b^2+5b}{(b-5)(b+5)}$$

$$=\frac{5b}{(b-5)(b+5)}$$

Write the denominator of the complex rational expression as a single rational expression. Note that the LCD of the rational expressions in the denominator is $(b-5)(b+5)$.

$$\frac{b}{b^2-25}-\frac{1}{b-5}=\frac{b}{(b-5)(b+5)}-\frac{1}{b-5}\cdot\frac{b+5}{b+5}$$

$$=\frac{b}{(b-5)(b+5)}-\frac{b+5}{(b-5)(b+5)}$$

$$=\frac{b-(b+5)}{(b-5)(b+5)}$$

$$=\frac{b-b-5}{(b-5)(b+5)}$$

$$=\frac{-5}{(b-5)(b+5)}$$

Rewrite the complex rational expression using the single rational expressions and simplify.

$$\frac{\dfrac{b^2}{b^2-25}-\dfrac{b}{b+5}}{\dfrac{b}{b^2-25}-\dfrac{1}{b-5}}=\frac{\dfrac{5b}{(b-5)(b+5)}}{\dfrac{-5}{(b-5)(b+5)}}$$

$$=\frac{5b}{(b-5)(b+5)}\cdot\frac{(b-5)(b+5)}{-5}$$

$$=\frac{\cancel{5}b}{\cancel{(b-5)}\cancel{(b+5)}}\cdot\frac{\cancel{(b-5)}\cancel{(b+5)}}{-1\cdot\cancel{5}}$$

$$=\frac{b}{-1}=-b$$

31. Rewrite the expression so that it does not contain any negative exponents.

$$\frac{3x^{-1}+3y^{-1}}{x^{-2}-y^{-2}}=\frac{\dfrac{3}{x}+\dfrac{3}{y}}{\dfrac{1}{x^2}-\dfrac{1}{y^2}}$$

Using Method 2, the LCD of all the denominators in the complex rational expression is x^2y^2.

$$\frac{3x^{-1}+3y^{-1}}{x^{-2}-y^{-2}}=\frac{\dfrac{3}{x}+\dfrac{3}{y}}{\dfrac{1}{x^2}-\dfrac{1}{y^2}}=\frac{\dfrac{3}{x}+\dfrac{3}{y}}{\dfrac{1}{x^2}-\dfrac{1}{y^2}}\cdot\frac{x^2y^2}{x^2y^2}$$

$$=\frac{\dfrac{3}{x}\cdot x^2y^2+\dfrac{3}{y}\cdot x^2y^2}{\dfrac{1}{x^2}\cdot x^2y^2-\dfrac{1}{y^2}\cdot x^2y^2}$$

$$=\frac{3xy^2+3x^2y}{y^2-x^2}$$

$$=\frac{3xy(y+x)}{(y-x)(y+x)}=\frac{3xy}{y-x}$$

33. Rewrite the expression so that it does not contain any negative exponents.

$$\frac{(m+n)^{-1}}{m^{-1}+n^{-1}}=\frac{\dfrac{1}{m+n}}{\dfrac{1}{m}+\dfrac{1}{n}}$$

Using Method 1, note the numerator of the complex rational expression is already a single rational expression.

Write the denominator of the complex rational expression as a single rational expression. Note that the LCD of the rational expressions in the denominator is mn.

$$\frac{1}{m}+\frac{1}{n}=\frac{1}{m}\cdot\frac{n}{n}+\frac{1}{n}\cdot\frac{m}{m}$$

$$=\frac{n}{mn}+\frac{m}{mn}=\frac{n+m}{mn}=\frac{m+n}{mn}$$

Rewrite the complex rational expression using the single rational expressions and simplify.

$$\frac{(m+n)^{-1}}{m^{-1}+n^{-1}}=\frac{\dfrac{1}{m+n}}{\dfrac{1}{m}+\dfrac{1}{n}}=\frac{\dfrac{1}{m+n}}{\dfrac{m+n}{mn}}$$

$$=\frac{1}{m+n}\cdot\frac{mn}{m+n}=\frac{mn}{(m+n)^2}$$

35. Rewrite the expression so that it does not contain any negative exponents.

$$\frac{a^{-2}b^{-1}-a^{-1}b^{-2}}{4a^{-2}-4b^{-2}}=\frac{\dfrac{1}{a^2b}-\dfrac{1}{ab^2}}{\dfrac{4}{a^2}-\dfrac{4}{b^2}}$$

Using Method 2, the LCD of all the denominators in the complex rational expression is a^2b^2.

$$\frac{a^{-2}b^{-1}-a^{-1}b^{-2}}{4a^{-2}-4b^{-2}}=\frac{\dfrac{1}{a^2b}-\dfrac{1}{ab^2}}{\dfrac{4}{a^2}-\dfrac{4}{b^2}}$$

$$=\frac{\dfrac{1}{a^2b}-\dfrac{1}{ab^2}}{\dfrac{4}{a^2}-\dfrac{4}{b^2}}\cdot\frac{a^2b^2}{a^2b^2}$$

$$=\frac{\dfrac{1}{a^2b}\cdot a^2b^2-\dfrac{1}{ab^2}\cdot a^2b^2}{\dfrac{4}{a^2}\cdot a^2b^2-\dfrac{4}{b^2}\cdot a^2b^2}$$

$$=\frac{b-a}{4b^2-4a^2}$$

$$=\frac{b-a}{4(b-a)(b+a)}$$

$$=\frac{1}{4(b+a)}$$

37. a. Using Method 2, the LCD of all the denominators in the complex rational expression is R_1R_2.

$$R=\frac{1}{\dfrac{1}{R_1}+\dfrac{1}{R_2}}=\frac{1}{\dfrac{1}{R_1}+\dfrac{1}{R_2}}\cdot\frac{R_1R_2}{R_1R_2}$$

$$=\frac{1\cdot R_1R_2}{\dfrac{1}{R_1}\cdot R_1R_2+\dfrac{1}{R_2}\cdot R_1R_2}$$

$$=\frac{1\cdot R_1R_2}{\dfrac{1}{R_1}\cdot R_1R_2+\dfrac{1}{R_2}\cdot R_1R_2}$$

$$=\frac{R_1R_2}{R_2+R_1}\text{ or }\frac{R_1R_2}{R_1+R_2}$$

b. For $R_1=4$ ohms and $R_2=10$ ohms,

$$R=\frac{R_1R_2}{R_1+R_2}=\frac{4\cdot10}{4+10}=\frac{40}{14}=\frac{20}{7}\approx2.857$$

ohms.

39. a. Using Method 2, the LCD of all the denominators in the complex rational expression is $(1+i)^5$.

$$V=\frac{Pi}{1-\dfrac{1}{(1+i)^5}}=\frac{Pi}{1-\dfrac{1}{(1+i)^5}}\cdot\frac{(1+i)^5}{(1+i)^5}$$

$$=\frac{Pi\cdot(1+i)^5}{1\cdot(1+i)^5-\dfrac{1}{(1+i)^5}\cdot(1+i)^5}$$

$$=\frac{Pi\cdot(1+i)^5}{1\cdot(1+i)^5-\dfrac{1}{(1+i)^5}\cdot(1+i)^5}$$

$$=\frac{Pi\cdot(1+i)^5}{(1+i)^5-1}$$

b. For $i=5\%=0.05$ and $P=\$1000$,

$$A=\frac{1000\cdot0.05\cdot(1+.05)^5}{(1+0.05)^5-1}$$

$$=\frac{1000\cdot0.05\cdot1.05^5}{1.05^5-1}\approx\$230.97$$

41. a. $H=\dfrac{2}{\dfrac{1}{48}+\dfrac{1}{52}}=49.92$ miles per hour

b. $H=\dfrac{4}{\dfrac{1}{4.3}+\dfrac{1}{4.1}+\dfrac{1}{3.8}+\dfrac{1}{4.3}}\approx4.1145$ Kb/sec

43. $4x+3=15$

$4x=12$

$x=3$

The solution set is $\{3\}$.

45. $\dfrac{1}{2}w+3=5$

$\dfrac{1}{2}w=2$

$2\left(\dfrac{1}{2}w\right)=2(2)$

$w=4$

The solution set is $\{4\}$.

47.
$$y^2 - 5y = 50$$
$$y^2 - 5y - 50 = 0$$
$$(y - 10)(y + 5) = 0$$
$$y - 10 = 0 \quad \text{or} \quad y + 5 = 0$$
$$y = 10 \quad \text{or} \quad y = -5$$
The solution set is $\{-5, 10\}$.

Putting the Concepts Together (Sections 6.1 – 6.3)

1. We need to find all values of x that cause the denominator $3x^2 - 17x - 6$ to equal 0.

$$3x^2 - 17x - 6 = 0$$
$$(3x + 1)(x - 6) = 0$$

$$3x + 1 = 0 \quad \text{or} \quad x - 6 = 0$$
$$3x = -1 \quad \text{or} \quad x = 6$$
$$x = -\frac{1}{3}$$

Thus, the domain of $g(x) = \dfrac{3x + 1}{3x^2 - 17x - 6}$ is

$$\left\{ x \middle| x \neq -\frac{1}{3},\ x \neq 6 \right\}.$$

2.
$$\frac{24n - 4n^2}{2n^2 - 9n - 18} = \frac{-4n(n - 6)}{(2n + 3)(n - 6)}$$
$$= \frac{-4n\cancel{(n - 6)}}{(2n + 3)\cancel{(n - 6)}}$$
$$= \frac{-4n}{2n + 3}$$

3.
$$\frac{2p^2 - pq - 10q^2}{3p^2 + 2pq - 8q^2} = \frac{(2p - 5q)(p + 2q)}{(3p - 4q)(p + 2q)}$$
$$= \frac{(2p - 5q)\cancel{(p + 2q)}}{(3p - 4q)\cancel{(p + 2q)}}$$
$$= \frac{2p - 5q}{3p - 4q}$$

4.
$$\frac{a^2 - 16}{12a^2 + 48a} \cdot \frac{6a^3 - 30a^2}{a^2 + 2a - 24}$$
$$= \frac{(a - 4)(a + 4)}{12a(a + 4)} \cdot \frac{6a^2(a - 5)}{(a - 4)(a + 6)}$$
$$= \frac{\cancel{(a - 4)}\cancel{(a + 4)}}{2 \cdot \cancel{6a}\cancel{(a + 4)}} \cdot \frac{\cancel{6a} \cdot a(a - 5)}{\cancel{(a - 4)}(a + 6)} = \frac{a(a - 5)}{2(a + 6)}$$

5.
$$\frac{\dfrac{x^2 + x - 2}{3x^2 - 5x - 2}}{\dfrac{x^2 - 9x + 14}{3x^2 - 2x - 1}} = \frac{x^2 + x - 2}{3x^2 - 5x - 2} \cdot \frac{x^2 - 9x + 14}{3x^2 - 2x - 1}$$

$$= \frac{(x - 1)(x + 2)}{(3x + 1)(x - 2)} \cdot \frac{(x - 2)(x - 7)}{(3x + 1)(x - 1)}$$

$$= \frac{\cancel{(x - 1)}(x + 2)}{(3x + 1)\cancel{(x - 2)}} \cdot \frac{\cancel{(x - 2)}(x - 7)}{(3x + 1)\cancel{(x - 1)}}$$

$$= \frac{(x + 2)(x - 7)}{(3x + 1)^2}$$

6.
$$\frac{x^2 - 10}{x^2 - 4} - \frac{3x}{x^2 - 4} = \frac{x^2 - 10 - 3x}{x^2 - 4} = \frac{x^2 - 3x - 10}{x^2 - 4}$$

$$= \frac{(x - 5)(x + 2)}{(x - 2)(x + 2)} = \frac{(x - 5)\cancel{(x + 2)}}{(x - 2)\cancel{(x + 2)}} = \frac{x - 5}{x - 2}$$

7.
$$n^2 - 7n + 10 = (n - 2)(n - 5)$$
$$n^2 - 8n + 15 = (n - 3)(n - 5)$$
$$\text{LCD} = (n - 2)(n - 3)(n - 5)$$

$$\frac{3n}{n^2 - 7n + 10} - \frac{2n}{n^2 - 8n + 15}$$

$$= \frac{3n}{(n - 2)(n - 5)} - \frac{2n}{(n - 3)(n - 5)}$$

$$= \frac{3n}{(n - 2)(n - 5)} \cdot \frac{n - 3}{n - 3} - \frac{2n}{(n - 2)(n - 3)(n - 5)} \cdot \frac{n - 2}{n - 2}$$

$$= \frac{3n^2 - 9n}{(n - 2)(n - 3)(n - 5)} - \frac{2n^2 - 4n}{(n - 2)(n - 3)(n - 5)}$$

$$= \frac{3n^2 - 9n - (2n^2 - 4n)}{(n - 2)(n - 3)(n - 5)} = \frac{3n^2 - 9n - 2n^2 + 4n}{(n - 2)(n - 3)(n - 5)}$$

$$= \frac{n^2 - 5n}{(n - 2)(n - 3)(n - 5)} = \frac{n(n - 5)}{(n - 2)(n - 3)(n - 5)}$$

$$= \frac{n}{(n - 2)(n - 3)}$$

8. $y^2 + 5y - 24 = (y-3)(y+8)$

$y^2 + 4y - 32 = (y-4)(y+8)$

$LCD = (y-3)(y-4)(y+8)$

$\dfrac{3y+2}{y^2+5y-24} + \dfrac{7}{y^2+4y-32}$

$= \dfrac{3y+2}{(y-3)(y+8)} \cdot \dfrac{y-4}{y-4} + \dfrac{7}{(y-4)(y+8)} \cdot \dfrac{y-3}{y-3}$

$= \dfrac{3y^2-10y-8}{(y-3)(y-4)(y+8)} + \dfrac{7y-21}{(y-3)(y-4)(y+8)}$

$= \dfrac{3y^2-10y-8+7y-21}{(y-3)(y-4)(y+8)}$

$= \dfrac{3y^2-3y-29}{(y-3)(y-4)(y+8)}$

9. $P(x) = f(x) \cdot g(x)$

$= \dfrac{2x+1}{x^2-11x+28} \cdot \dfrac{3x-12}{4x^2+4x+1}$

$= \dfrac{2x+1}{(x-4)(x-7)} \cdot \dfrac{3(x-4)}{(2x+1)(2x+1)}$

$= \dfrac{2x+1}{(x-4)(x-7)} \cdot \dfrac{3(x-4)}{(2x+1)(2x+1)}$

$= \dfrac{3}{(x-7)(2x+1)}$

10. $x - 7 = x - 7$

$x^2 - 11x + 28 = (x-4)(x-7)$

$LCD = (x-4)(x-7)$

$D(x) = h(x) - f(x)$

$= \dfrac{3x}{x-7} - \dfrac{2x+1}{x^2-11x+28}$

$= \dfrac{3x}{x-7} - \dfrac{2x+1}{(x-4)(x-7)}$

$= \dfrac{3x}{x-7} \cdot \dfrac{x-4}{x-4} - \dfrac{2x+1}{(x-4)(x-7)}$

$= \dfrac{3x^2-12x}{(x-4)(x-7)} - \dfrac{2x+1}{(x-4)(x-7)}$

$= \dfrac{3x^2-12x-(2x+1)}{(x-4)(x-7)}$

$= \dfrac{3x^2-12x-2x-1}{(x-4)(x-7)}$

$= \dfrac{3x^2-14x-1}{(x-4)(x-7)}$

11. Using Method 2, the LCD of all the denominators in the complex rational expression is $m^2 n^2$.

$\dfrac{\dfrac{1}{m^2}-\dfrac{1}{n^2}}{\dfrac{1}{m}-\dfrac{1}{n}} = \dfrac{\dfrac{1}{m^2}-\dfrac{1}{n^2}}{\dfrac{1}{m}-\dfrac{1}{n}} \cdot \dfrac{m^2 n^2}{m^2 n^2}$

$= \dfrac{\dfrac{1}{m^2} \cdot m^2 n^2 - \dfrac{1}{n^2} \cdot m^2 n^2}{\dfrac{1}{m} \cdot m^2 n^2 - \dfrac{1}{n} \cdot m^2 n^2}$

$= \dfrac{n^2 - m^2}{mn^2 - m^2 n}$

$= \dfrac{(n-m)(n+m)}{mn(n-m)}$

$= \dfrac{n+m}{mn}$

12. Using Method 2, the LCD of all the denominators in the complex rational expression is $(z-2)(z+2)$.

$\dfrac{\dfrac{z^2-2}{z^2-4}+\dfrac{7}{z-2}}{\dfrac{z^2+z-24}{z^2-4}-\dfrac{2}{z+2}} = \dfrac{\dfrac{z^2-2}{(z-2)(z+2)}+\dfrac{7}{z-2}}{\dfrac{z^2+z-24}{(z-2)(z+2)}-\dfrac{2}{z+2}}$

$= \dfrac{\dfrac{z^2-2}{(z-2)(z+2)}+\dfrac{7}{z-2}}{\dfrac{z^2+z-24}{(z-2)(z+2)}-\dfrac{2}{z+2}} \cdot \dfrac{(z-2)(z+2)}{(z-2)(z+2)}$

$= \dfrac{\dfrac{z^2-2}{(z-2)(z+2)} \cdot (z-2)(z+2)+\dfrac{7}{z-2} \cdot (z-2)(z+2)}{\dfrac{z^2+z-24}{(z-2)(z+2)} \cdot (z-2)(z+2)-\dfrac{2}{z+2} \cdot (z-2)(z+2)}$

$= \dfrac{z^2-2+7(z+2)}{z^2+z-24-2(z-2)}$

$= \dfrac{z^2-2+7z+14}{z^2+z-24-2z+4}$

$= \dfrac{z^2+7z+12}{z^2-z-20}$

$= \dfrac{(z+3)(z+4)}{(z+4)(z-5)} = \dfrac{z+3}{z-5}$

6.4 Preparing for Rational Equations

1.
$$\frac{2}{3}x + \frac{1}{2} = \frac{3}{4}$$
$$12\left(\frac{2}{3}x + \frac{1}{2}\right) = 12\left(\frac{3}{4}\right)$$
$$8x + 6 = 9$$
$$8x = 3$$
$$x = \frac{3}{8}$$

The solution set is $\left\{\frac{3}{8}\right\}$.

2. $a \cdot c = 3(-4) = -12$

The factors of -12 that add to 11 (the linear coefficient) are -1 and 12. Thus,

$$3z^2 + 11z - 4 = 3z^2 + 12z - z - 4$$
$$= 3z(z + 4) - 1(z + 4)$$
$$= (3z - 1)(z + 4)$$

3.
$$6y^2 - y - 12 = 0$$
$$(3y + 4)(2y - 3) = 0$$
$$3y + 4 = 0 \quad \text{or} \quad 2y - 3 = 0$$
$$3y = -4 \quad \text{or} \quad 2y = 3$$
$$y = -\frac{4}{3} \quad \text{or} \quad y = \frac{3}{2}$$

The solution set is $\left\{-\frac{4}{3}, \frac{3}{2}\right\}$.

4. a. If $x = -4$, then

$$\frac{x+4}{x^2 - 5x - 24} = \frac{-4+4}{(-4)^2 - 5(-4) - 24}$$
$$= \frac{-4+4}{16 + 20 - 24} = \frac{0}{12} = 0$$

Since $\frac{x+4}{x^2 - 5x - 24}$ is defined for $x = -4$, -4 is in the domain.

b. If $x = 8$, then

$$\frac{x+4}{x^2 - 5x - 24} = \frac{8+4}{8^2 - 5(8) - 24}$$
$$= \frac{8+4}{64 - 40 - 24} = \frac{12}{0} = \text{undefined}$$

Since $\frac{x+4}{x^2 - 5x - 24}$ is not defined for $x = 8$, 8 is not in the domain.

5.
$$f(x) = 3$$
$$x^2 - 3x - 15 = 3$$
$$x^2 - 3x - 18 = 0$$
$$(x + 3)(x - 6) = 0$$
$$x + 3 = 0 \quad \text{or} \quad x - 6 = 0$$
$$x = -3 \quad \text{or} \qquad x = 6$$

The solution set is $\{-3, 6\}$.

6. If $g(4) = 3$, means that $y = 3$ when $x = 4$. Thus, the point $(4, 3)$ is on the graph of g.

6.4 Exercises

1. Extraneous solutions

3. TRUE.

5. Answers will vary. One possibility follows: The solution(s) of the rational equation must be within the domain of the variable of the equation. As we work through the algebraic process of solving the equation, if we find a "solution" that is not in the domain of the variable, then that "solution" is not really a solution at all. It is an extraneous solution.

7.
$$\frac{3}{z} - \frac{1}{2z} = -\frac{5}{8}$$
$$8z\left(\frac{3}{z} - \frac{1}{2z}\right) = 8z\left(-\frac{5}{8}\right)$$
$$8(3) - 4(1) = z(-5)$$
$$24 - 4 = -5z$$
$$20 = -5z$$
$$-4 = z$$

Check:
$$\frac{3}{-4} - \frac{1}{2(-4)} \overset{?}{=} -\frac{5}{8}$$
$$-\frac{3}{4} - \left(-\frac{1}{8}\right) \overset{?}{=} -\frac{5}{8}$$
$$-\frac{6}{8} + \frac{1}{8} \overset{?}{=} -\frac{5}{8}$$
$$-\frac{5}{8} = -\frac{5}{8}$$
$$\uparrow$$
True

The solution checks, so the solution set is $\{-4\}$.

9.
$$\frac{4}{x+2} = \frac{7}{x+4}$$
$$(x+2)(x+4)\left(\frac{4}{x+2}\right) = (x+2)(x+4)\left(\frac{7}{x+4}\right)$$
$$4(x+4) = 7(x+2)$$
$$4x+16 = 7x+14$$
$$-3x = -2$$
$$x = \frac{2}{3}$$

Check:
$$\frac{4}{\frac{2}{3}+2} \overset{?}{=} \frac{7}{\frac{2}{3}+4}$$
$$\frac{4}{\frac{2}{3}+2} \cdot \frac{3}{3} \overset{?}{=} \frac{7}{\frac{2}{3}+4} \cdot \frac{3}{3}$$
$$\frac{12}{2+6} \overset{?}{=} \frac{21}{2+12}$$
$$\frac{12}{8} \overset{?}{=} \frac{21}{14}$$
$$\frac{3}{2} = \frac{3}{2} \leftarrow \text{True}$$

The solution checks, so the solution set is $\left\{\frac{2}{3}\right\}$.

11.
$$\frac{y+2}{y-5} = \frac{y+6}{y+1}$$
$$(y-5)(y+1)\left(\frac{y+2}{y-5}\right) = (y-5)(y+1)\left(\frac{y+6}{y+1}\right)$$
$$(y+1)(y+2) = (y-5)(y+6)$$
$$y^2+3y+2 = y^2+y-30$$
$$2y = -32$$
$$y = -16$$

Check:
$$\frac{-16+2}{-16-5} \overset{?}{=} \frac{-16+6}{-16+1}$$
$$\frac{-14}{-21} \overset{?}{=} \frac{-10}{-15}$$
$$\frac{2}{3} = \frac{2}{3} \leftarrow \text{True}$$

The solution checks, so the solution set is $\{-16\}$.

13.
$$\frac{x+8}{x+4} = \frac{x+2}{x-2}$$
$$(x+4)(x-2)\left(\frac{x+8}{x+4}\right) = (x+4)(x-2)\left(\frac{x+2}{x-2}\right)$$
$$(x-2)(x+8) = (x+4)(x+2)$$
$$x^2+6x-16 = x^2+6x+8$$
$$-16 = 8$$

The final statement is a contradiction, so the solution set is { } or $\varnothing$.

15.
$$a-\frac{5}{a} = 4$$
$$a\left(a-\frac{5}{a}\right) = a\cdot 4$$
$$a^2-5 = 4a$$
$$a^2-4a-5 = 0$$
$$(a-5)(a+1) = 0$$
$$a-5 = 0 \text{ or } a+1 = 0$$
$$a = 5 \text{ or } a = -1$$

Check:
$$5-\frac{5}{5} \overset{?}{=} 4$$
$$5-1 \overset{?}{=} 4$$
$$4 = 4 \leftarrow \text{True}$$

Check:
$$-1-\frac{5}{(-1)} \overset{?}{=} 4$$
$$-1+5 \overset{?}{=} 4$$
$$4 = 4 \leftarrow \text{True}$$

Both solutions check, so the solution set is $\{-1,5\}$.

17.
$$6p-\frac{3}{p} = 7$$
$$p\left(6p-\frac{3}{p}\right) = p\cdot 7$$
$$6p^2-3 = 7p$$
$$6p^2-7p-3 = 0$$
$$(3p+1)(2p-3) = 0$$
$$3p+1 = 0 \quad \text{or} \quad 2p-3 = 0$$
$$3p = -1 \quad \text{or} \quad 2p = 3$$
$$p = -\frac{1}{3} \quad \text{or} \quad p = \frac{3}{2}$$

Check:
$$6\left(-\frac{1}{3}\right)-\frac{3}{\left(-\frac{1}{3}\right)} \overset{?}{=} 7$$
$$-2+9 \overset{?}{=} 7$$
$$7 = 7$$
$$\uparrow$$
$$\text{True}$$

Check:
$$6\left(\frac{3}{2}\right)-\frac{3}{\left(\frac{3}{2}\right)} \overset{?}{=} 7$$
$$9-2 \overset{?}{=} 7$$
$$7 = 7$$
$$\uparrow$$
$$\text{True}$$

Both solutions check, so the solution set is $\left\{-\frac{1}{3}, \frac{3}{2}\right\}$.

19.

$$1 + \frac{10}{w-3} = \frac{2}{w}$$

$$w(w-3)\left(1 + \frac{10}{w-3}\right) = w(w-3)\left(\frac{2}{w}\right)$$

$$w(w-3) + 10w = 2(w-3)$$

$$w^2 - 3w + 10w = 2w - 6$$

$$w^2 + 5w + 6 = 0$$

$$(w+2)(w+3) = 0$$

$$w + 2 = 0 \text{ or } w + 3 = 0$$

$$w = -2 \text{ or } w = -3$$

Check:

$$1 + \frac{10}{-2-3} \overset{?}{=} \frac{2}{-2}$$

$$1 + \frac{10}{-5} \overset{?}{=} -1$$

$$1 - 2 \overset{?}{=} -1$$

$$-1 = -1 \leftarrow \text{True}$$

Check:

$$1 + \frac{10}{-3-3} \overset{?}{=} \frac{2}{-3}$$

$$1 + \frac{10}{-6} \overset{?}{=} -\frac{2}{3}$$

$$\frac{3}{3} - \frac{5}{3} \overset{?}{=} \frac{2}{3}$$

$$-\frac{2}{3} = -\frac{2}{3} \leftarrow \text{True}$$

Both solutions check, so the solution set is $\{-3, -2\}$.

21.

$$\frac{5-p}{p-5} + 2 = \frac{1}{p}$$

$$p(p-5)\left(\frac{5-p}{p-5} + 2\right) = p(p-5)\left(\frac{1}{p}\right)$$

$$p(5-p) + 2p(p-5) = p - 5$$

$$5p - p^2 + 2p^2 - 10p = p - 5$$

$$p^2 - 6p + 5 = 0$$

$$(p-5)(p-1) = 0$$

$$p - 5 = 0 \text{ or } p - 1 = 0$$

$$p = 5 \text{ or } p = 1$$

Since $p = 5$ is not in the domain of the variable, it is an extraneous solution.

Check $p = 1$:

$$\frac{5-1}{1-5} + 2 \overset{?}{=} \frac{1}{1}$$

$$\frac{4}{-4} + 2 \overset{?}{=} 1$$

$$-1 + 2 \overset{?}{=} 1$$

$$1 = 1 \leftarrow \text{True}$$

The solution set is $\{1\}$.

23.

$$\frac{3}{2} + \frac{5}{x-3} = \frac{x+9}{2x-6}$$

$$\frac{3}{2} + \frac{5}{x-3} = \frac{x+9}{2(x-3)}$$

$$2(x-3)\left(\frac{3}{2} + \frac{5}{x-3}\right) = 2(x-3)\left(\frac{x+9}{2(x-3)}\right)$$

$$3(x-3) + 2(5) = x + 9$$

$$3x - 9 + 10 = x + 9$$

$$2x = 8$$

$$x = 4$$

Check: $\dfrac{3}{2} + \dfrac{5}{4-3} \overset{?}{=} \dfrac{4+9}{2 \cdot 4 - 6}$

$$\frac{3}{2} + \frac{5}{1} \overset{?}{=} \frac{13}{8-6}$$

$$\frac{3}{2} + \frac{10}{2} \overset{?}{=} \frac{13}{2}$$

$$\frac{13}{2} = \frac{13}{2} \leftarrow \text{True}$$

The solution set is $\{4\}$.

25.

$$1 + \frac{3}{x+3} = \frac{4}{x-3}$$

$$(x-3)(x+3)\left(1 + \frac{3}{x+3}\right) = (x-3)(x+3)\left(\frac{4}{x-3}\right)$$

$$(x-3)(x+3) + 3(x-3) = 4(x+3)$$

$$x^2 + 3x - 3x - 9 + 3x - 9 = 4x + 12$$

$$x^2 + 3x - 18 = 4x + 12$$

$$x^2 - x - 30 = 0$$

$$(x-6)(x+5) = 0$$

$$x - 6 = 0 \text{ or } x + 5 = 0$$

$$x = 6 \text{ or } \quad x = -5$$

Check:

$$1 + \frac{3}{6+3} \overset{?}{=} \frac{4}{6-3}$$

$$1 + \frac{3}{9} \overset{?}{=} \frac{4}{3}$$

$$1 + \frac{1}{3} \overset{?}{=} \frac{4}{3}$$

$$\frac{4}{3} = \frac{4}{3} \leftarrow \text{True}$$

Check:

$$1 + \frac{3}{-5+3} \overset{?}{=} \frac{4}{-5-3}$$

$$1 + \frac{3}{-2} \overset{?}{=} \frac{4}{-8}$$

$$1 - \frac{3}{2} \overset{?}{=} -\frac{1}{2}$$

$$-\frac{1}{2} = -\frac{1}{2} \leftarrow \text{True}$$

Both solutions check, so the solution set is $\{-5, 6\}$.

27.

$$\frac{4}{x-5}+\frac{3}{x-2}=\frac{x+1}{x^2-7x+10}$$

$$\frac{4}{x-5}+\frac{3}{x-2}=\frac{x+1}{(x-5)(x-2)}$$

$$(x-5)(x-2)\left(\frac{4}{x-5}+\frac{3}{x-2}\right)=$$

$$(x-5)(x-2)\left(\frac{x+1}{(x-5)(x-2)}\right)$$

$$4(x-2)+3(x-5)=x+1$$

$$7x-23=x+1$$

$$6x=24$$

$$x=4$$

Check:

$$\frac{4}{4-5}+\frac{3}{4-2}\overset{?}{=}\frac{4+1}{4^2-7(4)+10}$$

$$\frac{4}{-1}+\frac{3}{2}\overset{?}{=}\frac{5}{16-28+10}$$

$$-\frac{8}{2}+\frac{3}{2}\overset{?}{=}\frac{5}{-2}$$

$$-\frac{5}{2}=-\frac{5}{2}\leftarrow\text{True}$$

The solution checks, so the solution set is $\{4\}$.

29.

$$\frac{2}{x+5}=\frac{2x}{x^2-25}-\frac{3}{x-5}$$

$$\frac{2}{x+5}=\frac{2x}{(x-5)(x+5)}-\frac{3}{x-5}$$

$$(x-5)(x+5)\left(\frac{2}{x+5}\right)=$$

$$(x-5)(x+5)\left(\frac{2x}{(x-5)(x+5)}-\frac{3}{x-5}\right)$$

$$2(x-5)=2x-3(x+5)$$

$$2x-10=2x-3x-15$$

$$3x=-5$$

$$x=-\frac{5}{3}$$

Check:

$$\frac{2}{\left(-\frac{5}{3}\right)+5}\overset{?}{=}\frac{2\left(-\frac{5}{3}\right)}{\left(-\frac{5}{3}\right)^2-25}-\frac{3}{\left(-\frac{5}{3}\right)-5}$$

$$\frac{2}{\left(-\frac{5}{3}\right)+5}\overset{?}{=}\frac{-\frac{10}{3}}{\frac{25}{9}-25}-\frac{3}{\left(-\frac{5}{3}\right)-5}$$

$$\frac{2}{\left(-\frac{5}{3}\right)+5}\cdot\frac{3}{3}\overset{?}{=}\frac{-\frac{10}{3}}{\frac{25}{9}-25}\cdot\frac{9}{9}-\frac{3}{\left(-\frac{5}{3}\right)-5}\cdot\frac{3}{3}$$

$$\frac{6}{-5+15}\overset{?}{=}\frac{-30}{25-225}-\frac{9}{-5-15}$$

$$\frac{3}{5}\overset{?}{=}\frac{-30}{-200}-\frac{9}{-20}$$

$$\frac{3}{5}\overset{?}{=}\frac{3}{20}+\frac{9}{20}$$

$$\frac{3}{5}\overset{?}{=}\frac{12}{20}$$

$$\frac{3}{5}=\frac{3}{5}\leftarrow\text{True}$$

The solution checks, so the solution set is $\left\{-\frac{5}{3}\right\}$.

31.

$$\frac{3}{x-1}-\frac{2}{x+4}=\frac{x^2+8x+6}{x^2+3x-4}$$

$$\frac{3}{x-1}-\frac{2}{x+4}=\frac{x^2+8x+6}{(x-1)(x+4)}$$

$$(x-1)(x+4)\left(\frac{3}{x-1}-\frac{2}{x+4}\right)=$$

$$(x-1)(x+4)\left(\frac{x^2+8x+6}{(x-1)(x+4)}\right)$$

$$3(x+4)-2(x-1)=x^2+8x+6$$

$$3x+12-2x+2=x^2+8x+6$$

$$x+14=x^2+8x+6$$

$$0=x^2+7x-8$$

$$0=(x-1)(x+8)$$

$$x-1=0\ \text{ or }\ x+8=0$$

$$x=1\ \text{ or }\ x=-8$$

Since $x=1$ is not in the domain of the variable, it is an extraneous solution.

Check $x=-8$:

$$\frac{3}{(-8)-1}-\frac{2}{(-8)+4}\overset{?}{=}\frac{(-8)^2+8(-8)+6}{(-8)^2+3(-8)-4}$$

$$\frac{3}{-9}-\frac{2}{-4}\overset{?}{=}\frac{64-64+6}{64-24-4}$$

$$-\frac{12}{36}+\frac{18}{36}\overset{?}{=}\frac{6}{36}$$

$$\frac{6}{36}=\frac{6}{36}\leftarrow\text{True}$$

The solution set is $\{-8\}$.

33.
$$\frac{7}{y^2+y-12}-\frac{4y}{y^2+7y+12}=\frac{6}{y^2-9}$$

$$\frac{7}{(y-3)(y+4)}-\frac{4y}{(y+3)(y+4)}=\frac{6}{(y-3)(y+3)}$$

$$(y-3)(y+3)(y+4)\left(\frac{7}{(y-3)(y+4)}-\frac{4y}{(y+3)(y+4)}\right)=$$

$$(y-3)(y+3)(y+4)\left(\frac{6}{(y-3)(y+3)}\right)$$

$$7(y+3)-4y(y-3)=6(y+4)$$
$$7y+21-4y^2+12y=6y+24$$
$$-4y^2+19y+21=6y+24$$
$$0=4y^2-13y+3$$
$$0=(4y-1)(y-3)$$
$$4y-1=0 \quad \text{or} \quad y-3=0$$
$$y=\frac{1}{4} \quad \text{or} \quad y=3$$

Since $y=3$ is not in the domain of the variable, it is an extraneous solution.

Check $y=\dfrac{1}{4}$:

$$\frac{7}{\left(\frac{1}{4}\right)^2+\left(\frac{1}{4}\right)-12}-\frac{4\left(\frac{1}{4}\right)}{\left(\frac{1}{4}\right)^2+7\left(\frac{1}{4}\right)+12}\overset{?}{=}\frac{6}{\left(\frac{1}{4}\right)^2-9}$$

$$\frac{7}{\frac{1}{16}+\frac{1}{4}-12}-\frac{1}{\frac{1}{16}+\frac{7}{4}+12}\overset{?}{=}\frac{6}{\frac{1}{16}-9}$$

$$\frac{7}{\frac{1}{16}+\frac{1}{4}-12}\cdot\frac{16}{16}-\frac{1}{\frac{1}{16}+\frac{7}{4}+12}\cdot\frac{16}{16}\overset{?}{=}\frac{6}{\frac{1}{16}-9}\cdot\frac{16}{16}$$

$$\frac{112}{1+4-192}-\frac{16}{1+28+192}\overset{?}{=}\frac{96}{1-144}$$

$$\frac{112}{-187}-\frac{16}{221}\overset{?}{=}\frac{96}{-143}$$

$$\frac{1456}{2431}-\frac{176}{2431}\overset{?}{=}\frac{96}{143}$$

$$\frac{1632}{2431}\overset{?}{=}-\frac{96}{143}$$

$$-\frac{96}{143}=-\frac{96}{143}\leftarrow\text{True}$$

The solution set is $\left\{\dfrac{1}{4}\right\}$.

35.
$$\frac{2x+3}{x-3}+\frac{x+6}{x-4}=\frac{x+6}{x-3}$$

$$(x-3)(x-4)\left(\frac{2x+3}{x-3}+\frac{x+6}{x-4}\right)=(x-3)(x-4)\left(\frac{x+6}{x-3}\right)$$

$$(x-4)(2x+3)+(x-3)(x+6)=(x-4)(x+6)$$
$$2x^2-5x-12+x^2+3x-18=x^2+2x-24$$
$$3x^2-2x-30=x^2+2x-24$$
$$2x^2-4x-6=0$$
$$2(x-3)(x+1)=0$$
$$x-3=0 \quad \text{or} \quad x+1=0$$
$$x=3 \quad \text{or} \quad x=-1$$

Since $x=3$ is not in the domain of the variable, it is an extraneous solution.

Check $x=-1$:
$$\frac{2(-1)+3}{(-1)-3}+\frac{(-1)+6}{(-1)-4}\overset{?}{=}\frac{(-1)+6}{(-1)-3}$$

$$\frac{-2+3}{-4}+\frac{5}{-5}\overset{?}{=}\frac{5}{-4}$$

$$-\frac{1}{4}-1\overset{?}{=}-\frac{5}{4}$$

$$-\frac{5}{4}=-\frac{5}{4}\leftarrow\text{True}$$

The solution set is $\{-1\}$.

37.
$$f(x)=10$$
$$x+\frac{9}{x}=10$$
$$x\left(x+\frac{9}{x}\right)=x\cdot 10$$
$$x^2+9=10x$$
$$x^2-10x+9=0$$
$$(x-9)(x-1)=0$$
$$x-9=0 \quad \text{or} \quad x-1=0$$
$$x=9 \quad \text{or} \quad x=1$$

Thus, $f(1)=10$ and $f(9)=10$, so the points $(1,10)$ and $(9,10)$ are on the graph of f.

39.
$$f(x) = -9$$
$$2x + \frac{4}{x} = -9$$
$$x\left(2x + \frac{4}{x}\right) = x \cdot (-9)$$
$$2x^2 + 4 = -9x$$
$$2x^2 + 9x + 4 = 0$$
$$(2x+1)(x+4) = 0$$
$$2x + 1 = 0 \text{ or } x + 4 = 0$$
$$x = -\frac{1}{2} \text{ or } x = -4$$

Thus, $f\left(-\frac{1}{2}\right) = -9$ and $f(-4) = -9$, so the points $\left(-\frac{1}{2}, -9\right)$ and $(-4, -9)$ are on the graph of f.

41.
$$f(x) = \frac{9}{2}$$
$$\frac{x+3}{x-4} = \frac{9}{2}$$
$$2(x-4)\left(\frac{x+3}{x-4}\right) = 2(x-4) \cdot \left(\frac{9}{2}\right)$$
$$2(x+3) = 9(x-4)$$
$$2x + 6 = 9x - 36$$
$$42 = 7x$$
$$6 = x$$

Thus, $f(6) = \frac{9}{2}$, so the point $\left(6, \frac{9}{2}\right)$ is on the graph of f.

43.
$$f(x) = g(x)$$
$$\frac{x+2}{2x+9} = \frac{x-1}{x+3}$$
$$(2x+9)(x+3)\left(\frac{x+2}{2x+9}\right) = (2x+9)(x+3)\left(\frac{x-1}{x+3}\right)$$
$$(x+3)(x+2) = (2x+9)(x-1)$$
$$x^2 + 5x + 6 = 2x^2 + 7x - 9$$
$$0 = x^2 + 2x - 15$$
$$0 = (x+5)(x-3)$$
$$x + 5 = 0 \text{ or } x - 3 = 0$$
$$x = -5 \text{ or } x = 3$$

Now, $f(-5) = \frac{-5+2}{2(-5)+9} = \frac{-3}{-10+9} = \frac{-3}{-1} = 3$,

$g(-5) = \frac{-5-1}{-5+3} = \frac{-6}{-2} = 3$, $f(3) = \frac{3+2}{2(3)+9} = \frac{5}{15} = \frac{1}{3}$,

and $g(3) = \frac{3-1}{3+3} = \frac{2}{6} = \frac{1}{3}$, so the intersection points

of f and g are $(-5, 3)$ and $\left(3, \frac{1}{3}\right)$.

45.
$$\frac{4}{z+4} - \frac{3}{4} = \frac{5z+2}{4z+16}$$
$$\frac{4}{z+4} - \frac{3}{4} = \frac{5z+2}{4(z+4)}$$
$$4(z+4)\left(\frac{4}{z+4} - \frac{3}{4}\right) = 4(z+4)\left(\frac{5z+2}{4(z+4)}\right)$$
$$4(4) - 3(z+4) = 5z + 2$$
$$16 - 3z - 12 = 5z + 2$$
$$-3z + 4 = 5z + 2$$
$$-8z = -2$$
$$z = \frac{-2}{-8} = \frac{1}{4}$$

Check:
$$\frac{4}{\frac{1}{4}+4} - \frac{3}{4} \overset{?}{=} \frac{5\left(\frac{1}{4}\right)+2}{4\left(\frac{1}{4}\right)+16}$$
$$\frac{4}{\frac{1}{4}+4} - \frac{3}{4} \overset{?}{=} \frac{\frac{5}{4}+2}{1+16}$$
$$\frac{4}{\frac{1}{4}+4} \cdot \frac{4}{4} - \frac{3}{4} \overset{?}{=} \frac{\frac{5}{4}+2}{1+16} \cdot \frac{4}{4}$$
$$\frac{16}{1+16} - \frac{3}{4} \overset{?}{=} \frac{5+8}{4+64}$$
$$\frac{16}{17} - \frac{3}{4} \overset{?}{=} \frac{13}{68}$$
$$\frac{64}{68} - \frac{51}{68} \overset{?}{=} \frac{13}{68}$$
$$\frac{13}{68} = \frac{13}{68} \leftarrow \text{True}$$

The solution checks, so the solution set is $\left\{\frac{1}{4}\right\}$.

47.

$$x + \frac{9}{x} = 6$$

$$x\left(x + \frac{9}{x}\right) = x \cdot 6$$

$$x^2 + 9 = 6x$$

$$x^2 - 6x + 9 = 0$$

$$(x-3)(x-3) = 0$$

$$x - 3 = 0$$

$$x = 3$$

Check:

$$3 + \frac{9}{3} \overset{?}{=} 6$$

$$3 + 3 \overset{?}{=} 6$$

$$6 = 6 \leftarrow \text{True}$$

The solution checks, so the solution set is $\{3\}$.

49.

$$\frac{2}{z^2 + 2z - 3} + \frac{3}{z^2 + 4z + 3} = \frac{6}{z^2 - 1}$$

$$\frac{2}{(z-1)(z+3)} + \frac{3}{(z+1)(z+3)} = \frac{6}{(z-1)(z+1)}$$

$$(z-1)(z+1)(z+3)\left(\frac{2}{(z-1)(z+3)} + \frac{3}{(z+1)(z+3)}\right) =$$

$$(z-1)(z+1)(z+3)\left(\frac{6}{(z-1)(z+1)}\right)$$

$$2(z+1) + 3(z-1) = 6(z+3)$$

$$2z + 2 + 3z - 3 = 6z + 18$$

$$5z - 1 = 6z + 18$$

$$-19 = z$$

Check:

$$\frac{2}{(-19)^2 + 2(-19) - 3} +$$

$$\frac{3}{(-19)^2 + 4(-19) + 3} \overset{?}{=} \frac{6}{(-19)^2 - 1}$$

$$\frac{2}{361 - 38 - 3} + \frac{3}{361 - 76 + 3} \overset{?}{=} \frac{6}{361 - 1}$$

$$\frac{2}{320} + \frac{3}{288} \overset{?}{=} \frac{6}{360}$$

$$\frac{18}{2880} + \frac{30}{2880} \overset{?}{=} \frac{48}{2880}$$

$$\frac{48}{2880} = \frac{48}{2880} \leftarrow \text{True}$$

The solution set is $\{-19\}$.

51.

$$\frac{4}{x} - \frac{5}{2x} = \frac{3}{4}$$

$$4x\left(\frac{4}{x} - \frac{5}{2x}\right) = 4x \cdot \frac{3}{4}$$

$$16 - 10 = 3x$$

$$6 = 3x$$

$$2 = x$$

Check:

$$\frac{4}{2} - \frac{5}{2(2)} \overset{?}{=} \frac{3}{4}$$

$$2 - \frac{5}{4} \overset{?}{=} \frac{3}{4}$$

$$\frac{3}{4} = \frac{3}{4} \leftarrow \text{True}$$

The solution checks, so the solution set is 2.

53.

$$\frac{3y+1}{y-1} + 3 = \frac{y+2}{y+1}$$

$$(y-1)(y+1)\left(\frac{3y+1}{y-1} + 3\right) = (y-1)(y+1)\left(\frac{y+2}{y+1}\right)$$

$$(y+1)(3y+1) + 3(y-1)(y+1) = (y-1)(y+2)$$

$$3y^2 + 4y + 1 + 3y^2 - 3 = y^2 + y - 2$$

$$6y^2 + 4y - 2 = y^2 + y - 2$$

$$5y^2 + 3y = 0$$

$$y(5y+3) = 0$$

$$y = 0 \ \text{ or } \ 5y + 3 = 0$$

$$5y = -3$$

$$y = -\frac{3}{5}$$

Check: $y = 0$

$$\frac{3(0)+1}{0-1} + 3 \overset{?}{=} \frac{0+2}{0+1}$$

$$\frac{1}{-1} + 3 \overset{?}{=} \frac{2}{1}$$

$$-1 + 3 \overset{?}{=} 2$$

$$2 = 2 \leftarrow \text{True}$$

Check: $y = -\frac{3}{5}$

$$\frac{3\left(-\frac{3}{5}\right)+1}{\left(-\frac{3}{5}\right)-1} + 3 \overset{?}{=} \frac{\left(-\frac{3}{5}\right)+2}{\left(-\frac{3}{5}\right)+1}$$

$$\frac{-\frac{9}{5}+1}{-\frac{8}{5}} + 3 \overset{?}{=} \frac{\frac{7}{5}}{\frac{2}{5}}$$

$$\frac{-\frac{4}{5}}{-\frac{8}{5}} + 3 \overset{?}{=} \frac{\frac{7}{5}}{\frac{2}{5}}$$

$$-\frac{4}{5}\left(-\frac{5}{8}\right) + 3 \overset{?}{=} \frac{7}{5}\left(\frac{5}{2}\right)$$

$$\frac{1}{2} + 3 \overset{?}{=} \frac{7}{2}$$

$$\frac{7}{2} = \frac{7}{2} \leftarrow \text{True}$$

Both check, so the solution set is $\left\{-\frac{3}{5}, 0\right\}$.

55.
$$\overline{C}(x) = 225$$
$$\frac{x^2 + 75x + 5000}{x} = 225$$
$$x\left(\frac{x^2 + 75x + 5000}{x}\right) = x \cdot 225$$
$$x^2 + 75x + 5000 = 225x$$
$$x^2 - 150x + 5000 = 0$$
$$(x - 100)(x - 50) = 0$$
$$x - 100 = 0 \text{ or } x - 50 = 0$$
$$x = 100 \text{ or } x = 50$$

The average daily cost will be $225 when either 50 or 100 bicycles are manufactured.

57. a.
$$C(x) = 100$$
$$\frac{25x}{100 - x} = 100$$
$$(100 - x)\left(\frac{25x}{100 - x}\right) = (100 - x) \cdot 100$$
$$25x = 10,000 - 100x$$
$$125x = 10,000$$
$$x = 80$$

Thus, 80% of the pollutants can be removed with a budget of $100 million.

b.
$$C(x) = 225$$
$$\frac{25x}{100 - x} = 225$$
$$(100 - x)\left(\frac{25x}{100 - x}\right) = (100 - x) \cdot 225$$
$$25x = 22,500 - 225x$$
$$250x = 22,500$$
$$x = 90$$

Thus, 90% of the pollutants can be removed with a budget of $225 million.

59. Substitute $R = 750$, $h = 1400$, $t = 2250$, and $b = 5500$ into the given formula and solve for w:
$$R = \frac{(h + w)t}{b + w}$$
$$750 = \frac{(1400 + w)2250}{5500 + w}$$
$$750 = \frac{3,150,000 + 2250w}{5500 + w}$$
$$(5500 + w)750 = (5500 + w)\left(\frac{3,150,000 + 2250w}{5500 + w}\right)$$
$$4,125,000 + 750w = 3,150,000 + 2250w$$
$$975,000 = 1500w$$
$$650 = w$$

We predict that the Athletics had 650 walks.

61. Answers will vary. One possibility follows:

The equation $\dfrac{2}{x - 1} = \dfrac{3}{x + 1}$ has one real solution, namely $\{5\}$.

63.
$$\left(\frac{4}{x + 3}\right)^2 - 5\left(\frac{4}{x + 3}\right) + 6 = 0$$
$$\frac{16}{(x + 3)^2} - \frac{20}{x + 3} + 6 = 0$$
$$(x + 3)^2\left(\frac{16}{(x + 3)^2} - \frac{20}{x + 3} + 6\right) = 0(x + 3)^2$$
$$16 - 20(x + 3) + 6(x + 3)^2 = 0$$
$$16 - 20(x + 3) + 6(x^2 + 6x + 9) = 0$$
$$16 - 20x - 60 + 6x^2 + 36x + 54 = 0$$
$$6x^2 + 16x + 10 = 0$$
$$3x^2 + 8x + 5 = 0$$
$$(3x + 5)(x + 1) = 0$$
$$3x + 5 = 0 \text{ or } x + 1 = 0$$
$$x = -\frac{5}{3} \text{ or } x = -1$$

Both solutions check. The solution set is $\left\{-\dfrac{5}{3}, -1\right\}$.

65.
$$\frac{2a^6}{\left(a^3\right)^2} - \frac{5a^2}{a^3} = 3\frac{a}{a^3}$$
$$\frac{2a^6}{a^6} - \frac{5a^2}{a^3} = \frac{3a}{a^3}$$
$$2 - \frac{5}{a} = \frac{3}{a^2}$$
$$a^2\left(2 - \frac{5}{a}\right) = a^2\left(\frac{3}{a^2}\right)$$
$$2a^2 - 5a = 3$$
$$2a^2 - 5a - 3 = 0$$
$$(2a + 1)(a - 3) = 0$$
$$2a + 1 = 0 \text{ or } a - 3 = 0$$
$$a = -\frac{1}{2} \text{ or } a = 3$$

Both solutions check. The solution set is $\left\{-\dfrac{1}{2}, 3\right\}$.

67. $\dfrac{3}{x-2} - \dfrac{2x+1}{x+1} = \dfrac{3}{x-2} \cdot \dfrac{x+1}{x+1} - \dfrac{2x+1}{x+1} \cdot \dfrac{x-2}{x-2}$

$$= \dfrac{3(x+1)}{(x-2)(x+1)} - \dfrac{(2x+1)(x-2)}{(x-2)(x+1)}$$

$$= \dfrac{3(x+1)-(2x+1)(x-2)}{(x-2)(x+1)}$$

$$= \dfrac{3x+3-\left(2x^2-4x+x-2\right)}{(x-2)(x+1)}$$

$$= \dfrac{3x+3-2x^2+4x-x+2}{(x-2)(x+1)}$$

$$= \dfrac{-2x^2+6x+5}{(x-2)(x+1)}$$

69. $\dfrac{x+1}{2x+3} - \dfrac{3}{x-4} = \dfrac{-3}{2x^2-5x-12}$

$\dfrac{x+1}{2x+3} - \dfrac{3}{x-4} = \dfrac{-3}{(2x+3)(x-4)}$

$(2x+3)(x-4)\left(\dfrac{x+1}{2x+3} - \dfrac{3}{x-4}\right) =$

$$(2x+3)(x-4)\left(\dfrac{-3}{(2x+3)(x-4)}\right)$$

$(x-4)(x+1)-3(2x+3) = -3$

$x^2+x-4x-4-6x-9 = -3$

$x^2-9x-13 = -3$

$x^2-9x-10 = 0$

$(x-10)(x+1) = 0$

$x-10 = 0$ or $x+1 = 0$

$x = 10$ or $x = -1$

Both solutions check. The solution set is $\{-1,\ 10\}$.

71. $\dfrac{x-4}{x+4} = \dfrac{1}{2}$

The solution set is $\{12\}$.

73. $\dfrac{3}{5} + \dfrac{4}{x+6} = \dfrac{x+12}{5x+30}$

The solution set is $\{-13\}$.

75. $\dfrac{2x^2+11x+12}{x+4} = -5$

The apparent solution is $x = -4$. However, notice that -4 is not in the domain of the left side of the equation. Thus, the equation has no solution. The solution set is $\varnothing$ or { }.

6.5 Preparing for Rational Inequalities

1. The inequality $-1 < x \le 8$ in interval notation is $(-1,\ 8]$.

2. $2x+3 > 4x-9$

$-4x+2x+3 > -4x+4x-9$

$-2x+3 > -9$

$-2x+3-3 > -9-3$

$-2x > -12$

$\dfrac{-2x}{-2} < \dfrac{-12}{-2}$

$x < 6$

The solution set is $\{x \mid x < 6\}$ or, using interval notation, $(-\infty,\ 6)$.

6.5 Exercises

1. rational

3. The statement $(-1,4)$ indicates that neither endpoint is included in the solution set. The statement $\{x \mid -1 \le x \le 4\}$ indicates that both endpoints are included in the solution set. In fact, the solution of the inequality $\dfrac{x-4}{x+1} \le 0$ should include the endpoint 4, but it should not include the endpoint -1. Therefore, the statement of the solution set should be $\{x \mid -1 < x \le 4\}$ using set-builder notation or $(-1, 4]$ using interval notation.

5. $\dfrac{x-4}{x+1} > 0$

The rational expression will equal 0 when $x = 4$. It is undefined when $x = -1$.
Determine where the numerator and denominator are positive and negative and where the quotient is positive and negative.

Interval	$(-\infty, -1)$	-1	$(-1, 4)$	4	$(4, \infty)$
$x-4$	$----$	$-$	$----$	0	$++++$
$x+1$	$----$	0	$++++$	$+$	$++++$
$\frac{x-4}{x+1}$	$++++$	$\varnothing$	$----$	0	$++++$

The rational function is undefined at $x = -1$, so -1 is not part of the solution. The inequality is strict, so 4 is not part of the solution. Now, $\dfrac{x-4}{x+1}$ is greater than zero where the quotient is positive. The solution is $\{x \mid x < -1 \text{ or } x > 4\}$ in set-builder notation; the solution is $(-\infty, -1) \cup (4, \infty)$ in interval notation.

7. $\dfrac{x+9}{x-3} < 0$

The rational expression will equal 0 when $x = -9$. It is undefined when $x = 3$.
Determine where the numerator and denominator are positive and negative and where the quotient is positive and negative.

Interval	$(-\infty, -9)$	-9	$(-9, 3)$	3	$(3, \infty)$
$x+9$	$----$	0	$++++$	$+$	$++++$
$x-3$	$----$	$-$	$----$	0	$++++$
$\frac{x+9}{x-3}$	$++++$	0	$----$	$\varnothing$	$++++$

The rational function is undefined at $x = 3$, so 3 is not part of the solution. The inequality is strict, so -9 is not part of the solution. Now, $\dfrac{x+9}{x-3}$ is less than zero where the quotient is negative. The solution is $\{x \mid -9 < x < 3\}$ in set-builder notation; the solution is $(-9, 3)$ in interval notation.

9. $\dfrac{x+10}{x-4} \ge 0$

The rational expression will equal 0 when $x = -10$. It is undefined when $x = 4$.
Determine where the numerator and denominator are positive and negative and where the quotient is positive and negative.

Interval	$(-\infty, -10)$	-10	$(-10, 4)$	4	$(4, \infty)$
$x+10$	$----$	0	$++++$	$+$	$++++$
$x-4$	$----$	$-$	$----$	0	$++++$
$\frac{x+10}{x-4}$	$++++$	0	$----$	$\varnothing$	$++++$

The rational function is undefined at $x = 4$, so 4 is not part of the solution. The inequality is non-strict, so -10 is part of the solution. Now, $\dfrac{x+10}{x-4}$ is greater than zero where the quotient is positive. The solution is $\{x \mid x \le -10 \text{ or } x > 4\}$ in set-builder notation; the solution is $(-\infty, -10] \cup (4, \infty)$ in interval notation.

11. $\dfrac{x+7}{x-8} \le 0$

The rational expression will equal 0 when $x = -7$. It is undefined when $x = 8$. Determine where the numerator and denominator are positive and negative and where the quotient is positive and negative.

Interval	$(-\infty, -7)$	-7	$(-7, 8)$	8	$(8, \infty)$
$x + 7$	$----$	0	$++++$ $+$		$++++$
$x - 8$	$----$	$-$	$----$	0	$++++$
$\frac{x+7}{x-8}$	$++++$	0	$----$	$\varnothing$	$++++$

The rational function is undefined at $x = 8$, so 8 is not part of the solution. The inequality is non-strict, so -7 is part of the solution. Now, $\dfrac{x+7}{x-8}$ is less than zero where the quotient is negative. The solution is $\{x \mid -7 \le x < 8\}$ in set-builder notation; the solution is $[-7, 8)$ in interval notation.

13. $\dfrac{(2x-1)(x+3)}{x-5} > 0$

The rational expression will equal 0 when $x = \dfrac{1}{2}$ and when $x = -3$. It is undefined when $x = 5$. Determine where the factors of the numerator and denominator are positive and negative and where the quotient is positive and negative.

Interval	$(-\infty, -3)$	-3	$\left(-3, \frac{1}{2}\right)$	$\frac{1}{2}$	$\left(\frac{1}{2}, 5\right)$	5	$(5, \infty)$
$2x - 1$	$---$	$-$	$---$	0	$+++$ $+$		$+++$
$x + 3$	$---$	0	$+++$ $+$		$+++$ $+$		$+++$
$x - 5$	$---$	$-$	$---$	$-$	$---$	0	$+++$
$\frac{(2x-1)(x+3)}{x-5}$	$---$	0	$+++$	0	$---$	$\varnothing$	$+++$

The rational function is undefined at $x = 5$, so 5 is not part of the solution. The inequality is strict, so -3 and $\dfrac{1}{2}$ are not part of the solution.

Now, $\dfrac{(2x-1)(x+3)}{x-5}$ is greater than zero where the quotient is positive. The solution is

$\left\{ x \,\middle|\, -3 < x < \dfrac{1}{2} \text{ or } x > 5 \right\}$ in set-builder notation;

the solution is $\left(-3, \dfrac{1}{2}\right) \cup (5, \infty)$ in interval notation.

15. $\dfrac{(3x+5)(x+8)}{x-2} \le 0$

The rational expression will equal 0 when $x = -\dfrac{5}{3}$ and when $x = -8$. It is undefined when $x = 2$. Determine where the factors of the numerator and denominator are positive and negative and where the quotient is positive and negative.

Interval	$(-\infty, -8)$	-8	$\left(-8, -\frac{5}{3}\right)$	$-\frac{5}{3}$	$\left(-\frac{5}{3}, 2\right)$	2	$(2, \infty)$
$3x + 5$	$---$ $-$		$---$	0	$+++$ $+$		$+++$
$x + 8$	$---$	0	$+++$ $+$		$+++$ $+$		$+++$
$x - 2$	$---$ $-$		$---$	$-$	$---$	0	$+++$
$\frac{(3x+5)(x+8)}{x-2}$	$---$	0	$+++$	0	$---$	$\varnothing$	$+++$

The rational function is undefined at $x = 2$, so 2 is not part of the solution. The inequality is non-strict, so -8 and $-\dfrac{5}{3}$ are part of the solution.

Now, $\dfrac{(3x+5)(x+8)}{x-2}$ is less than zero where the quotient is negative. The solution is

$\left\{ x \mid x \le -8 \text{ or } -\dfrac{5}{3} \le x < 2 \right\}$ in set-builder

notation; the solution is $\left(-\infty, -8\right] \cup \left[-\dfrac{5}{3}, 2\right)$ in interval notation.

17.
$$\frac{x-5}{x+1}<1$$
$$\frac{x-5}{x+1}-1<0$$
$$\frac{x-5}{x+1}-\frac{x+1}{x+1}<0$$
$$\frac{x-5-x-1}{x+1}<0$$
$$\frac{-6}{x+1}<0$$

The numerator is always negative, so the rational expression will never equal 0. However, it is undefined when $x=-1$.
Determine where the denominator is positive and negative and where the quotient is positive and negative.

Interval	$(-\infty,-1)$	-1	$(-1,\infty)$
-6	$----$	$-$	$----$
$x+1$	$----$	0	$++++$
$\frac{-6}{x+1}$	$++++$	$\varnothing$	$----$

The rational function is undefined at $x=-1$, so -1 is not part of the solution. Now, $\frac{-6}{x+1}$ is less than zero where the quotient is negative. The solution is $\{x\,|\,x>-1\}$ in set-builder notation; the solution is $(-1,\infty)$ in interval notation.

19.
$$\frac{3x-1}{x+4}\geq 2$$
$$\frac{3x-1}{x+4}-2\geq 0$$
$$\frac{3x-1}{x+4}-\frac{2(x+4)}{x+4}\geq 0$$
$$\frac{3x-1-2x-8}{x+4}\geq 0$$
$$\frac{x-9}{x+4}\geq 0$$

The rational expression will equal 0 when $x=9$. It is undefined when $x=-4$.
Determine where the numerator and denominator are positive and negative and where the quotient is positive and negative.

Interval	$(-\infty,-4)$	-4	$(-4,9)$	9	$(9,\infty)$
$x-9$	$----$	$-$	$----$	0	$++++$
$x+4$	$----$	0	$++++$	$+$	$++++$
$\frac{x-9}{x+4}$	$++++$	$\varnothing$	$----$	0	$++++$

The rational function is undefined at $x=-4$, so -4 is not part of the solution. The inequality is non-strict, so 9 is part of the solution. Now, $\frac{x-9}{x+4}$ is greater than zero where the quotient is positive. The solution is $\{x\,|\,x<-4\text{ or }x\geq 9\}$ in set-builder notation; the solution is $(-\infty,\,-4)\cup[9,\,\infty)$ in interval notation.

21.
$$\frac{2x-9}{x-3}>4$$
$$\frac{2x-9}{x-3}-4>0$$
$$\frac{2x-9}{x-3}-\frac{4(x-3)}{x-3}>0$$
$$\frac{2x-9-4x+12}{x-3}>0$$
$$\frac{-2x+3}{x-3}>0$$

The rational expression will equal 0 when $x=\frac{3}{2}$. It is undefined when $x=3$.
Determine where the numerator and denominator are positive and negative and where the quotient is positive and negative.

Interval	$\left(-\infty,\frac{3}{2}\right)$	$\frac{3}{2}$	$\left(\frac{3}{2},3\right)$	3	$(3,\infty)$
$-2x+3$	$++++$	0	$----$	$-$	$----$
$x-3$	$----$	$-$	$----$	0	$++++$
$\frac{-2x+3}{x-3}$	$----$	0	$++++$	$\varnothing$	$----$

The rational function is undefined at $x=3$, so 3 is not part of the solution. The inequality is strict, so 3 is not part of the solution. Now, $\frac{-2x+3}{x-3}$ is greater than zero where the quotient is positive. The solution is $\left\{x\,\middle|\,\frac{3}{2}<x<3\right\}$ in set-builder notation; the solution is $\left(\frac{3}{2},\,3\right)$ in interval notation.

23.

$$\frac{3}{x-4}+\frac{1}{x}\geq 0$$

$$\frac{3x}{x(x-4)}+\frac{x-4}{x(x-4)}\geq 0$$

$$\frac{3x+x-4}{x(x-4)}\geq 0$$

$$\frac{4x-4}{x(x-4)}\geq 0$$

The rational expression will equal 0 when $x=1$. It is undefined when $x=0$ and when $x=4$. Determine where the numerator and the factors of the denominator are positive and negative and where the quotient is positive and negative.

Interval	$(-\infty,0)$	0	$(0,1)$	1	$(1,4)$	4	$(4,\infty)$
$4x-4$	$---$	$-$	$---$	0	$+++$	$+$	$+++$
x	$---$	0	$+++$	$+$	$+++$	$+$	$+++$
$x-4$	$---$	$-$	$---$	$-$	$---$	0	$+++$
$\frac{4x-4}{x(x-4)}$	$---$	$\varnothing$	$+++$	0	$---$	$\varnothing$	$+++$

The rational function is undefined at $x=0$ and $x=4$, so 0 and 4 are not part of the solution. The inequality is non-strict, so 1 is part of the solution. Now, $\frac{4x-4}{x(x-4)}$ is greater than zero where the quotient is positive. The solution is $\{x\,|\,0<x\leq 1 \text{ or } x>4\}$ in set-builder notation; the solution is $(0,\,1]\cup(4,\,\infty)$ in interval notation.

![number line from -1 to 6 with open circle at 0, closed bracket at 1, open parenthesis at 4](number line)

25.

$$\frac{3}{x-2}\leq\frac{4}{x+5}$$

$$\frac{3}{x-2}-\frac{4}{x+5}\leq 0$$

$$\frac{3(x+5)}{(x+5)(x-2)}-\frac{4(x-2)}{(x+5)(x-2)}\leq 0$$

$$\frac{3(x+5)-4(x-2)}{(x+5)(x-2)}\leq 0$$

$$\frac{3x+15-4x+8}{(x+5)(x-2)}\leq 0$$

$$\frac{23-x}{(x+5)(x-2)}\leq 0$$

The rational expression will equal 0 when $x=23$. It is undefined when $x=2$ and when $x=-5$.

Determine where the numerator and the factors of the denominator are positive and negative and where the quotient is positive and negative.

Interval	$(-\infty,-5)$	-5	$(-5,2)$	2	$(2,23)$	23	$(23,\infty)$
$23-x$	$+++$	$+$	$+++$	$+$	$+++$	0	$---$
$x+5$	$---$	0	$+++$	$+$	$+++$	$+$	$+++$
$x-2$	$---$	$-$	$---$	0	$+++$	$+$	$+++$
$\frac{23-x}{(x+5)(x-2)}$	$+++$	$\varnothing$	$---$	$\varnothing$	$+++$	0	$---$

The rational function is undefined at $x=-5$ and $x=2$, so -5 and 2 are not part of the solution. The inequality is non-strict, so 23 is part of the solution. Now, $\frac{23-x}{(x+5)(x-2)}$ is less than zero where the quotient is negative. The solution is $\{x\,|-5<x<2 \text{ or } x\geq 23\}$ in set-builder notation; the solution is $(-5,2)\cup[23,\infty)$ in interval notation.

![number line from -5 to 24 with open parentheses at -5 and 2, closed bracket at 23](number line)

27. $R(x)\leq 0$

$$\frac{x-6}{x+1}\leq 0$$

The rational expression will equal 0 when $x=6$. It is undefined when $x=-1$.

Determine where the numerator and denominator are positive and negative and where the quotient is positive and negative.

Interval	$(-\infty,-1)$	-1	$(-1,6)$	6	$(6,\infty)$
$x-6$	$----$	$-$	$----$	0	$++++$
$x+1$	$----$	0	$++++$	$+$	$++++$
$\frac{x-6}{x+1}$	$++++$	$\varnothing$	$----$	0	$++++$

The rational function is undefined at $x=-1$, so -1 is not part of the solution. The inequality is non-strict, so 6 is part of the solution. Now, $\frac{x-6}{x+1}$ is less than zero where the quotient is negative. The solution is $\{x\,|-1<x\leq 6\}$ in set-builder notation; the solution is $(-1,\,6]$ in interval notation.

![number line from -4 to 10 with open parenthesis at -1 and closed bracket at 6](number line)

29. $R(x) < 0$

$$\frac{2x-5}{x+2} < 0$$

The rational expression will equal 0 when

$x = \dfrac{5}{2}$. It is undefined when $x = -2$.

Determine where the numerator and denominator are positive and negative and where the quotient is positive and negative.

Interval	$(-\infty, -2)$	-2	$\left(-2, \frac{5}{2}\right)$	$\frac{5}{2}$	$\left(\frac{5}{2}, \infty\right)$
$2x - 5$	$----$	$-$	$----$	0	$++++$
$x + 2$	$----$	0	$++++$	$+$	$++++$
$\frac{2x-5}{x+2}$	$++++$	$\varnothing$	$----$	0	$++++$

The rational function is undefined at $x = -2$, so -2 is not part of the solution. The inequality is strict, so $\dfrac{5}{2}$ is not part of the solution. Now,

$\dfrac{2x-5}{x+2}$ is less than zero where the quotient is

negative. The solution is $\left\{ x \,\middle|\, -2 < x < \dfrac{5}{2} \right\}$ in

set-builder notation; the solution is $\left(-2, \dfrac{5}{2}\right)$ in

interval notation.

31. The average cost will be no more than \$130 when $\overline{C}(x) \le 130$.

$$\frac{80x + 5000}{x} \le 130$$

$$\frac{80x + 5000}{x} - 130 \le 0$$

$$\frac{80x + 5000}{x} - \frac{130x}{x} \le 0$$

$$\frac{5000 - 50x}{x} \le 0$$

The rational expression will equal 0 when $x = 100$. It is undefined when $x = 0$.

Determine where the numerator and denominator are positive and negative and where the quotient is positive and negative.

Interval	$(-\infty, 0)$	0	$(0, 100)$	100	$(100, \infty)$
$5000 - 50x$	$++++$	$+$	$++++$	0	$----$
x	$----$	0	$++++$	$+$	$++++$
$\frac{5000-50x}{x}$	$----$	$\varnothing$	$++++$	0	$----$

The rational function is undefined at $x = 0$, so 0 is not part of the solution. The inequality is non-strict, so 100 is part of the solution. Now,

$\dfrac{5000 - 50x}{x}$ is less than zero where the quotient is

negative. The solution is $\{x \mid x < 0 \text{ or } x \ge 100\}$ in

set-builder notation; the solution is

$(-\infty, 0) \cup [100, \infty)$ in interval notation. However,

for this problem, $x < 0$ is not meaningful. Thus, the average cost will be no more than \$130 when 100 or more bicycles are produced each day.

33. Answers may vary. One possibility follows: The left endpoint of the interval is $x = 2$, so we can use $x - 2$ as a factor of the denominator of the rational function. Now, $x - 2$ will be positive for $x > 2$ and negative for $x < 2$. If we use any positive constant for the numerator of the rational function, then the quotient will be positive when $x > 2$ and negative for $x < 2$.

Thus, the rational inequality $\dfrac{10}{x-2} > 0$ will have

$(2, \infty)$ as the solution set.

NOTE: Because the solution set does not contain the endpoint 2, the inequality must be strict.

35. To find the x-intercept(s), we solve $F(x) = 0$:

$$F(x) = 0$$
$$6x - 12 = 0$$
$$6x = 12$$
$$x = 2$$

The x-intercept of F is 2.

37. To find the x-intercept(s), we solve $f(x) = 0$:

$$f(x) = 0$$
$$2x^2 + 3x - 14 = 0$$
$$(2x + 7)(x - 2) = 0$$
$$2x + 7 = 0 \quad \text{or} \quad x - 2 = 0$$
$$x = -\frac{7}{2} \quad \text{or} \quad x = 2$$

The x-intercepts of f are $-\dfrac{7}{2}$ and 2.

39. To find the x-intercept(s), we solve $R(x) = 0$:

$$R(x) = 0$$
$$\frac{3x - 2}{x + 4} = 0$$
$$(x + 4)\left(\frac{3x - 2}{x + 4}\right) = (x + 4)0$$
$$3x - 2 = 0$$
$$3x = 2$$
$$x = \frac{2}{3}$$

The x-intercept of R is $\frac{2}{3}$.

41. $\dfrac{x - 5}{x + 1} \le 3$

Let $Y_1 = \dfrac{x - 5}{x + 1}$ and $Y_2 = 3$. Graph the functions. Use the **INTERSECT** feature to find the x-coordinates of the point(s) of intersection.

The rational function is undefined at $x = -1$, so -1 is not part of the solution. The inequality is non-strict, so -4 is part of the solution. From the graph, we can see that $\dfrac{x - 5}{x + 1} \le 3$ where $x \le -4$ and where $x > -1$. Thus, the solution set is $\{x \mid x \le -4 \text{ or } x > -1\}$ in set-builder notation; the solution is $(-\infty, -4] \cup (-1, \infty)$ in interval notation.

43. $\dfrac{2x + 5}{x - 7} > 3$

Let $Y_1 = \dfrac{2x + 5}{x - 7}$ and $Y_2 = 3$. Graph the functions. Use the **INTERSECT** feature to find the x-coordinates of the point(s) of intersection.

The rational function is undefined at $x = 7$, so 7 is not part of the solution. The inequality is strict, so 26 is not part of the solution. From the

graph, we can see that $\dfrac{2x + 5}{x - 7} > 3$ for $7 < x < 26$. Thus, the solution set is $\{x \mid 7 < x < 26\}$ in set-builder notation; the solution is $(7, 26)$ in interval notation.

6.6 Preparing for Models Involving Rational Expressions

1. $4x - 2y = 10$
$$-2y = -4x + 10$$
$$y = \frac{-4x + 10}{-2}$$
$$y = 2x - 5$$

2. Since $y = 4$ when $x = 12$, then
$$y = kx$$
$$4 = k \cdot 12$$
$$k = \frac{4}{12} = \frac{1}{3}$$

So, $y = \frac{1}{3}x$.

Thus, when $x = 24$, $y = \frac{1}{3}(24) = 8$.

6.6 Exercises

1. proportion

3. TRUE

5. A variable Q varying jointly with x and y means that Q is proportional to the product of x and y. That is, it means that $Q = kxy$ for a constant k.

Combined variation means that direct and inverse variation are occurring at the same time. For example if x varies directly with y and inversely with z, then $x = \dfrac{ky}{z}$ for a constant k.

7.
$$\frac{V_1}{V_2} = \frac{P_2}{P_1}$$
$$V_2 P_1\left(\frac{V_1}{V_2}\right) = V_2 P_1\left(\frac{P_2}{P_1}\right)$$
$$P_1 V_1 = V_2 P_2$$
$$P_1 = \frac{V_2 P_2}{V_1}$$

9.
$$R = \frac{r}{1-t}$$
$$(1-t) \cdot R = (1-t)\left(\frac{r}{1-t}\right)$$
$$R - Rt = r$$
$$-Rt = r - R$$
$$t = \frac{r-R}{-R} \quad \text{or} \quad t = \frac{R-r}{R}$$

11.
$$m = \frac{y-y_1}{x-x_1}$$
$$(x-x_1) \cdot m = (x-x_1)\left(\frac{y-y_1}{x-x_1}\right)$$
$$mx - mx_1 = y - y_1$$
$$mx = y - y_1 + mx_1$$
$$x = \frac{y-y_1+mx_1}{m}$$

13.
$$\omega = \frac{rmv}{I+mr^2}$$
$$(I+mr^2) \cdot \omega = (I+mr^2)\left(\frac{rmv}{I+mr^2}\right)$$
$$\omega(I+mr^2) = rmv$$
$$\frac{\omega(I+mr^2)}{rm} = v$$

15.
$$V = \frac{mv}{M+m}$$
$$(M+m) \cdot V = (M+m)\left(\frac{mv}{M+m}\right)$$
$$MV + mV = mv$$
$$MV = mv - mV$$
$$MV = m(v-V)$$
$$\frac{MV}{v-V} = m$$

17. a.
$$y = \frac{k}{x}$$
$$2 = \frac{k}{10}$$
$$10 \cdot 2 = 10\left(\frac{k}{10}\right)$$
$$20 = k$$

b. $y = \dfrac{20}{x}$

c. When $x = 5$, $y = \dfrac{20}{5} = 4$.

19. a.
$$y = \frac{k}{x}$$
$$3 = \frac{k}{7}$$
$$7 \cdot 3 = 7\left(\frac{k}{7}\right)$$
$$21 = k$$

b. $y = \dfrac{21}{x}$

c. When $x = 28$, $y = \dfrac{21}{28} = \dfrac{3}{4}$.

21. a.
$$y = kxz$$
$$10 = k \cdot 8 \cdot 5$$
$$10 = 40k$$
$$k = \frac{10}{40} = \frac{1}{4}$$

b. $y = \dfrac{1}{4}xz$

c. When $x = 12$ and $z = 9$, $y = \dfrac{1}{4} \cdot 12 \cdot 9 = 27$.

23. a.
$$Q = \frac{kx}{y}$$
$$\frac{13}{12} = \frac{k \cdot 5}{6}$$
$$12\left(\frac{13}{12}\right) = 12\left(\frac{k \cdot 5}{6}\right)$$
$$13 = 10k$$
$$\frac{13}{10} = k$$

b. $Q = \dfrac{(13/10)x}{y} = \dfrac{13x}{10y}$

c. When $x = 9$ and $y = 4$, $Q = \dfrac{13 \cdot 9}{10 \cdot 4} = \dfrac{117}{40}$.

25.
$$\frac{AB}{AC} = \frac{DE}{DF}$$
$$\frac{x+11}{10} = \frac{8}{x}$$
$$10x\left(\frac{x+11}{10}\right) = 10x\left(\frac{8}{x}\right)$$
$$x(x+11) = 10 \cdot 8$$
$$x^2 + 11x = 80$$
$$x^2 + 11x - 80 = 0$$
$$(x-5)(x+16) = 0$$

$x - 5 = 0$ or $x + 16 = 0$

$x = 5$ or $x = -16$

Since the length of DF cannot be negative, we discard $x = -16$ and keep $x = 5$. The length of AB is $x + 11 = 5 + 11 = 16$.

In summary, $AB = 16$ and $DF = 5$.

27. Let x represent the population in the U.S. in 2000.

$$\frac{16.1}{100,000} = \frac{41,821}{x}$$

$$100,000x\left(\frac{16.1}{100,000}\right) = 100,000x\left(\frac{41,821}{x}\right)$$

$$16.1x = 4,182,100,000$$

$$x = \frac{4,182,100,000}{16.1}$$

$$x \approx 259,757,764$$

In 2000, the population in the U.S. was 259,757,764 people.

29. Let x represent the amount of money each of the four people will have to contribute for the trip. Then $4x$ will be the total cost of the trip.

Note that the trip is 105 miles each way. Thus, the entire trip consists of a distance of 210 miles.

$$\frac{12.8}{1} = \frac{210}{4x}$$

$$4x\left(\frac{12.8}{1}\right) = 4x\left(\frac{210}{4x}\right)$$

$$51.2x = 210$$

$$x = \frac{210}{51.2}$$

$$x \approx 4.10$$

Each person must contribute approximately \$4.10 for the trip.

31. Utilize Pascal's Principal.

$$\frac{F_1}{A_1} = \frac{F_2}{A_2}$$

$$\frac{30}{12} = \frac{F_2}{5}$$

$$60\left(\frac{30}{12}\right) = 60\left(\frac{F_2}{5}\right)$$

$$150 = 12F_2$$

$$12.5 = F_2$$

Thus, the force exerted by the right pipe is 12.5 pounds.

33. Let t represent the time required if Amiri and Horus deliver the papers together.

$$\begin{pmatrix} \text{Part done} \\ \text{by Amiri} \\ \text{in 1 minute} \end{pmatrix} + \begin{pmatrix} \text{Part done} \\ \text{by Horus} \\ \text{in 1 minute} \end{pmatrix} = \begin{pmatrix} \text{Part done} \\ \text{together} \\ \text{in 1 minute} \end{pmatrix}$$

$$\frac{1}{80} + \frac{1}{60} = \frac{1}{t}$$

$$240t\left(\frac{1}{80} + \frac{1}{60}\right) = 240t\left(\frac{1}{t}\right)$$

$$3t + 4t = 240$$

$$7t = 240$$

$$t = \frac{240}{7} \approx 34.3$$

Working together, it will take Amiri and Horus approximately 34.3 minutes to deliver the papers.

35. Let t represent the time required for Connor to cut the grass when working alone.

$$\begin{pmatrix} \text{Part done} \\ \text{by Avery} \\ \text{in 1 hour} \end{pmatrix} + \begin{pmatrix} \text{Part done} \\ \text{by Connor} \\ \text{in 1 hour} \end{pmatrix} = \begin{pmatrix} \text{Part done} \\ \text{together} \\ \text{in 1 hour} \end{pmatrix}$$

$$\frac{1}{3} + \frac{1}{t} = \frac{1}{2}$$

$$6t\left(\frac{1}{3} + \frac{1}{t}\right) = 6t\left(\frac{1}{2}\right)$$

$$2t + 6 = 3t$$

$$6 = t$$

Working alone, it will take Connor 6 hours to cut the grass.

37. Let t represent the time required for 10-horsepower pump to empty the pool when working alone.

Then $t + 5$ will represent the time required for the 6-horsepower pump to empty the pool when working alone.

$$\begin{pmatrix} \text{Part done by} \\ \text{10-horse pump} \\ \text{in 1 hour} \end{pmatrix} + \begin{pmatrix} \text{Part done by} \\ \text{6-horse pump} \\ \text{in 1 hour} \end{pmatrix} = \begin{pmatrix} \text{Part done} \\ \text{together} \\ \text{in 1 hour} \end{pmatrix}$$

$$\frac{1}{t} + \frac{1}{t+5} = \frac{1}{6}$$

$$6t(t+5)\left(\frac{1}{t} + \frac{1}{t+5}\right) = 6t(t+5)\left(\frac{1}{6}\right)$$

$$6(t+5) + 6t = t(t+5)$$

$$6t + 30 + 6t = t^2 + 5t$$

$$12t + 30 = t^2 + 5t$$

$$0 = t^2 - 7t - 30$$

$$0 = (t-10)(t+3)$$

$$t - 10 = 0 \quad \text{or} \quad t + 3 = 0$$
$$t = 10 \quad \text{or} \quad t = -3$$

Since time cannot be negative, we discard $t = -3$ and keep $t = 10$.

Working alone, it will take 10-horsepower pump 10 hours to empty the pool.

39. Let x represent the average speed going to work.

Then $x - 7$ will represent the average speed on the way home.

	Distance (miles)	Rate (mph)	Time (hours)
Going to work	20	x	$\dfrac{20}{x}$
Coming home	16	$x - 7$	$\dfrac{16}{x - 7}$

$$\frac{20}{x} = \frac{16}{x - 7}$$
$$x(x-7)\left(\frac{20}{x}\right) = x(x-7)\left(\frac{16}{x-7}\right)$$
$$20(x - 7) = 16x$$
$$20x - 140 = 16x$$
$$4x = 140$$
$$x = 35$$

The average speed going to work is 35 miles per hour.

41. Let x represent Hana's walking speed.

	Distance (feet)	Rate (ft/s)	Time (sec)
With moving walkway	152	$x + 2$	$\dfrac{152}{x + 2}$
Without moving walkway	72	x	$\dfrac{72}{x}$

$$\frac{152}{x + 2} = \frac{72}{x}$$
$$x(x+2)\left(\frac{152}{x+2}\right) = x(x+2)\left(\frac{72}{x}\right)$$
$$152x = 72(x + 2)$$
$$152x = 72x + 144$$
$$80x = 144$$
$$x = \frac{144}{80} = 1.8$$

Hana's walking speed is 1.8 feet per second.

43. Let x represent the distance Shockey has run when Urlacher catches him.

Then $x + 5$ will represent the distance Urlacher has run when he catches Shockey.

	Distance (yards)	Rate (yd/s)	Time (sec)
Shockey	x	$\dfrac{100}{12}$	$\dfrac{12x}{100}$
Urlacher	$x + 5$	$\dfrac{100}{9}$	$\dfrac{9(x+5)}{100}$

$$\frac{12x}{100} = \frac{9(x+5)}{100}$$
$$100\left(\frac{12x}{100}\right) = 100\left(\frac{9(x+5)}{100}\right)$$
$$12x = 9x + 45$$
$$3x = 45$$
$$x = 15$$

Shockey will have run 15 yards when Urlacher catches up to him. Thus, Shockey will be on his own 35 yard line when Urlacher catches up to him.

45. Let x represent the speed of the bicyclist going uphill. Then $x + 8$ will represent the speed downhill.

	Distance (miles)	Rate (mph)	Time (hours)
Up	12	x	$\dfrac{12}{x}$
Down	12	$x + 8$	$\dfrac{12}{x + 8}$

$$\frac{12}{x} + \frac{12}{x+8} = \frac{9}{4}$$
$$4x(x+8)\left(\frac{12}{x} + \frac{12}{x+8}\right) = 4x(x+8)\left(\frac{9}{4}\right)$$
$$4 \cdot 12(x+8) + 4 \cdot 12x = 9x(x+8)$$
$$48x + 384 + 48x = 9x^2 + 72x$$
$$96x + 384 = 9x^2 + 72x$$
$$0 = 9x^2 - 24x - 384$$
$$0 = 3(3x+16)(x-8)$$
$$3x + 16 = 0 \quad \text{or} \quad x - 8 = 0$$
$$x = -\frac{16}{3} \quad \text{or} \quad x = 8$$

Since speed cannot be negative, we discard $x = -\dfrac{16}{3}$ and keep $x = 8$.

The speed of the bicyclist going uphill is 8 miles per hour.

47. Let x represent the speed driven for the last 68 miles of the trip.

Then $x + 9$ will represent the speed driven for the first 50 miles of the trip.

	Distance (miles)	Rate (mph)	Time (hours)
First part	50	$x + 9$	$\dfrac{50}{x+9}$
Last part	68	x	$\dfrac{68}{x}$

$$\begin{pmatrix} \text{Time of} \\ \text{first part} \end{pmatrix} + \begin{pmatrix} \text{Time of} \\ \text{second part} \end{pmatrix} = \begin{pmatrix} \text{Total} \\ \text{time} \end{pmatrix}$$

$$\frac{50}{x+9} + \frac{68}{x} = 3$$

$$x(x+9)\left(\frac{50}{x+9} + \frac{68}{x}\right) = x(x+9)\cdot 3$$

$$50x + 68(x+9) = 3x(x+9)$$

$$50x + 68x + 612 = 3x^2 + 27x$$

$$118x + 612 = 3x^2 + 27x$$

$$0 = 3x^2 - 91x - 612$$

$$0 = (3x + 17)(x - 36)$$

$$3x + 17 = 0 \text{ or } x - 36 = 0$$

$$x = -\frac{17}{3} \text{ or } x = 36$$

Since speed cannot be negative, we discard $x = -\dfrac{17}{3}$ and keep $x = 36$. Thus, the speed for the last 68 miles of the trip was 36 miles per hour.

Now $x + 9 = 36 + 9 = 45$. Thus, the speed for the first 50 miles of the trip was 45 miles per hour.

49. a.
$$D = \frac{k}{p}$$

$$150 = \frac{k}{2.50}$$

$$2.50 \cdot 150 = 2.50\left(\frac{k}{2.50}\right)$$

$$375 = k$$

Thus, the demand of the candy as a function of its price is $D(p) = \dfrac{375}{p}$.

b. $D(3) = \dfrac{375}{3} = 125$

If the price of the candy is \$3.00, then 125 bags of candy will be sold.

51.
$$V = \frac{k}{P}$$

$$600 = \frac{k}{150}$$

$$150 \cdot 600 = 150\left(\frac{k}{150}\right)$$

$$90,000 = k$$

$$V(P) = \frac{90,000}{P}$$

$$V(200) = \frac{90,000}{200} = 450$$

When the pressure is 200 mm Hg, the volume of the gas will be 450 cc.

53. Let w represent the weight of an object that is a distance d from the center of the earth.

$$w = \frac{k}{d^2}$$

$$120 = \frac{k}{3960^2}$$

$$3960^2 \cdot 120 = 3960^2\left(\frac{k}{3960^2}\right)$$

$$1,881,792,000 = k$$

$$w(d) = \frac{1,881,792,000}{d^2}$$

Now, Maria is $3960 + 3.8 = 3963.8$ miles from the center of Earth.

$$w(3963.8) = \frac{1,881,792,000}{3963.8^2} \approx 119.8$$

Maria's weight at the top of Mount McKinley is 119.8 pounds.

55. Let D represent drag force, A represent surface area, and v represent velocity.

$$D = kAv^2$$

$$1152 = k \cdot 2 \cdot 40^2$$

$$1152 = 3200k$$

$$0.36 = k$$

$$D = 0.36Av^2$$

For $A = 2.5$ and $v = 50$, $D = 0.36 \cdot 2.5 \cdot 50^2 = 2250$. The drag force on a parachutist whose surface area is 2.5 square meters falling at 50 meters per second is 2250 newtons.

57.
$$F = \frac{km_1 m_2}{r^2}$$
$$2.24112 \times 10^{-8} = \frac{k \cdot 105 \cdot 80}{5^2}$$
$$2.24112 \times 10^{-8} = 336k$$
$$\frac{2.24112 \times 10^{-8}}{336} = k$$
$$6.67 \times 10^{-11} \approx k$$
$$F = \frac{\left(6.67 \times 10^{-11}\right) m_1 m_2}{r^2}$$

For $m_1 = 105$, $m_2 = 80$, and $r = 2$,
$$F = \frac{\left(6.67030 \times 10^{-11}\right) m_1 m_2}{r^2}$$
$$= \frac{\left(6.67030 \times 10^{-11}\right)(105)(80)}{2^2}$$
$$= 1.4007 \times 10^{-7}.$$

When they are 2 meters apart, the force of gravity between the couple is 1.4007×10^{-7} newtons.

59. Let s represent stress, p represent internal pressure, d represent internal diameter and x represent thickness.
$$s = \frac{kpd}{x}$$
$$100 = \frac{k \cdot 25 \cdot 5}{0.75}$$
$$0.75(100) = 0.75 \left(\frac{k \cdot 25 \cdot 5}{0.75} \right)$$
$$75 = 125k$$
$$0.6 = k$$
$$s = \frac{0.6pd}{x}$$

For $p = 50$, $d = 6$, and $x = 0.5$,
$$s = \frac{0.6 \cdot 50 \cdot 6}{0.5} = 360.$$
The stress is 360 pounds per square inch when the internal pressure is 50 pounds per square inch, the diameter is 6 inches, and the thickness is 0.5 inches.

61. a. $\omega = 2\pi \cdot 50 = 100\pi \approx 314.16$

b. $v = \omega r = 314.16 \cdot 3 = 942.48$ meters per minute.
$$v = \frac{942.48 \text{ m}}{1 \text{ min}} \cdot \frac{1 \text{ min}}{60 \text{ sec}} \approx 15.708 \text{ meters per}$$
second.

c.
$$F = \frac{kmv^2}{r}$$
$$2.3 = \frac{k \cdot 0.5 \cdot 15.708^2}{3}$$
$$2.3 = k \cdot 41.123544$$
$$\frac{2.3}{4.1123544} = k$$
$$0.056 \approx k$$

d. For spinning rate of 80 revolutions per minute, $\omega = 2\pi \cdot 80 = 160\pi \approx 502.65$.
$v = \omega r = 502.65 \cdot 4 = 2010.60$ meters per minute.
$$v = \frac{2010.60 \text{ m}}{1 \text{ min}} \cdot \frac{1 \text{ min}}{60 \text{ sec}} = 33.51 \text{ meters per}$$
second.
$$F = \frac{0.056mv^2}{r} = \frac{0.056 \cdot 0.5 \cdot 33.51^2}{4} \approx 7.86$$

The force required to keep the stone in motion is approximately 7.86 newtons.

63. $\left(a^3 \right)^5 = a^{3 \cdot 5} = a^{15}$

65. $(ab)^{-2} \cdot \left(\dfrac{a^3}{b^2} \right)^2 = \dfrac{1}{(ab)^2} \cdot \dfrac{a^6}{b^4} = \dfrac{1}{a^2 b^2} \cdot \dfrac{a^6}{b^4} = \dfrac{a^4}{b^6}$

67. $\left(\dfrac{3m^3 n^{-1}}{mn^5} \right)^{-2} = \left(\dfrac{3m^2}{n^6} \right)^{-2}$
$$= \dfrac{3^{-2} m^{-4}}{n^{-12}} = \dfrac{n^{12}}{3^2 m^4} = \dfrac{n^{12}}{9m^4}$$

Chapter 6 Review

1. We need to find all values of x that cause the denominator $3x - 2$ to equal 0.
$$3x - 2 = 0$$
$$3x = 2$$
$$x = \frac{2}{3}$$

Thus, the domain of $\dfrac{x-5}{3x-2}$ is $\left\{ x \,\middle|\, x \neq \dfrac{2}{3} \right\}$

2. We need to find all values of x that cause the denominator $a^2 - 3a - 28$ to equal 0.

$$a^2 - 3a - 28 = 0$$
$$(a+4)(a-7) = 0$$
$$a + 4 = 0 \quad \text{or} \quad a - 7 = 0$$
$$a = -4 \quad \text{or} \quad a = 7$$

Thus, the domain of $\dfrac{a^2 - 16}{a^2 - 3a - 28}$ is

$$\{a \mid a \neq -4, \ a \neq 7\}$$

3. We need to find all values of x that cause the denominator $m^2 + 9$ to equal 0. However, if x is a real number, then $m^2 + 9$ can never equal 0. The domain of $\dfrac{m-3}{m^2+9}$ is $\{m \mid m \text{ is any real number}\}$.

4. We need to find all values of p that cause the denominator $n^2 - 2n - 8$ to equal 0.

$$n^2 - 2n - 8 = 0$$
$$(n+2)(n-4) = 0$$
$$n + 2 = 0 \quad \text{or} \quad n - 4 = 0$$
$$n = -2 \quad \text{or} \quad n = 4$$

Thus, the domain of $\dfrac{n^2 + 7n + 10}{n^2 - 2n - 8}$ is

$$\{n \mid n \neq -2, \ n \neq 4\}.$$

5. $\dfrac{6x+30}{x^2-25} = \dfrac{6(x+5)}{(x+5)(x-5)} = \dfrac{6\cancel{(x+5)}}{\cancel{(x+5)}(x-5)} = \dfrac{6}{x-5}$

6. $\dfrac{4y^2 - 28y}{2y^5 - 14y^4} = \dfrac{4y(y-7)}{2y^4(y-7)}$

$$= \dfrac{2 \cdot 2y(y-7)}{2y \cdot y^3(y-7)}$$

$$= \dfrac{2 \cdot \cancel{2y}\,\cancel{(y-7)}}{\cancel{2y} \cdot y^3\,\cancel{(y-7)}} = \dfrac{2}{y^3}$$

7. $\dfrac{w^2 - 4w - 21}{w^2 + 7w + 12} = \dfrac{(w+3)(w-7)}{(w+3)(w+4)}$

$$= \dfrac{\cancel{(w+3)}(w-7)}{\cancel{(w+3)}(w+4)} = \dfrac{w-7}{w+4}$$

8. $\dfrac{6a^2 - 7ab - 3b^2}{10a^2 - 11ab - 6b^2} = \dfrac{(3a+b)(2a-3b)}{(5a+2b)(2a-3b)}$

$$= \dfrac{(3a+b)\cancel{(2a-3b)}}{(5a+2b)\cancel{(2a-3b)}}$$

$$= \dfrac{3a+b}{5a+2b}$$

9. $\dfrac{7-m}{3m^2 - 20m - 7} = \dfrac{-1(m-7)}{(3m+1)(m-7)}$

$$= \dfrac{-1\cancel{(m-7)}}{(3m+1)\cancel{(m-7)}} = \dfrac{-1}{3m+1}$$

10. $\dfrac{n^3 - 4n^2 + 3n - 12}{n^2 - 8n + 16} = \dfrac{(n-4)(n^2+3)}{(n-4)(n-4)}$

$$= \dfrac{\cancel{(n-4)}(n^2+3)}{\cancel{(n-4)}(n-4)} = \dfrac{n^2+3}{n-4}$$

11. $\dfrac{4p^2}{p^2 - 3p - 18} \cdot \dfrac{p+3}{8p} = \dfrac{4p \cdot p}{(p+3)(p-6)} \cdot \dfrac{p+3}{2 \cdot 4p}$

$$= \dfrac{\cancel{4p} \cdot p}{\cancel{(p+3)}(p-6)} \cdot \dfrac{\cancel{p+3}}{2 \cdot \cancel{4p}}$$

$$= \dfrac{p}{2(p-6)}$$

12. $\dfrac{q^2 + 6q}{6q + 12} \cdot \dfrac{4q + 8}{q^2 + q - 30} = \dfrac{q(q+6)}{6(q+2)} \cdot \dfrac{4(q+2)}{(q-5)(q+6)}$

$$= \dfrac{q\cancel{(q+6)}}{\cancel{6}(q+2)} \cdot \dfrac{\overset{2}{\cancel{4}}\cancel{(q+2)}}{(q-5)\cancel{(q+6)}}$$

$$= \dfrac{2q}{3(q-5)}$$

13. $\dfrac{x^3 - 4x^2}{x^2 - 4} \cdot \dfrac{x^2 + 4x - 12}{x^3 + 2x^2}$

$$= \dfrac{x^2(x-4)}{(x+2)(x-2)} \cdot \dfrac{(x-2)(x+6)}{x^2(x+2)}$$

$$= \dfrac{\cancel{x^2}(x-4)}{(x+2)\cancel{(x-2)}} \cdot \dfrac{\cancel{(x-2)}(x+6)}{\cancel{x^2}(x+2)} = \dfrac{(x-4)(x+6)}{(x+2)^2}$$

14. $\dfrac{y^2-3y-28}{y^3+4y^2}\cdot\dfrac{2y^2+10y}{y^2-12y+35}$

$=\dfrac{(y+4)(y-7)}{y^2(y+4)}\cdot\dfrac{2y(y+5)}{(y-5)(y-7)}$

$=\dfrac{(y+4)(y-7)}{y\cdot y\cdot(y+4)}\cdot\dfrac{2\cdot y\cdot(y+5)}{(y-5)(y-7)}$

$=\dfrac{\cancel{(y+4)}\,\cancel{(y-7)}}{\cancel{y}\cdot y\cdot\cancel{(y+4)}}\cdot\dfrac{2\cdot\cancel{y}\cdot(y+5)}{(y-5)\cancel{(y-7)}}=\dfrac{2(y+5)}{y(y-5)}$

15. $\dfrac{6a^2+ab-b^2}{3a^2+2ab-b^2}\cdot\dfrac{3a^2+4ab+b^2}{4a^2-b^2}$

$=\dfrac{(3a-b)(2a+b)}{(3a-b)(a+b)}\cdot\dfrac{(3a+b)(a+b)}{(2a+b)(2a-b)}$

$=\dfrac{\cancel{(3a-b)}\,\cancel{(2a+b)}}{\cancel{(3a-b)}\,\cancel{(a+b)}}\cdot\dfrac{(3a+b)\cancel{(a+b)}}{\cancel{(2a+b)}\,(2a-b)}$

$=\dfrac{3a+b}{2a-b}$

16. $\dfrac{m^2+m-20}{m^3-64}\cdot\dfrac{3m^2+12m+48}{m^2+3m-10}$

$=\dfrac{(m-4)(m+5)}{(m-4)(m^2+4m+16)}\cdot\dfrac{3(m^2+4m+16)}{(m-2)(m+5)}$

$=\dfrac{\cancel{(m-4)}\,\cancel{(m+5)}}{\cancel{(m-4)}\,\cancel{(m^2+4m+16)}}\cdot\dfrac{3\cancel{(m^2+4m+16)}}{(m-2)\cancel{(m+5)}}$

$=\dfrac{3}{m-2}$

17. $\dfrac{\dfrac{4c^2}{3d^4}}{\dfrac{8c}{27d}}=\dfrac{4c^2}{3d^4}\cdot\dfrac{27d}{8c}=\dfrac{\cancel{4}c\cdot c}{3d\cdot d^3}\cdot\dfrac{9\cdot3d}{2\cdot\cancel{4}c}=\dfrac{9c}{2d^3}$

18. $\dfrac{\dfrac{6z-24}{7z+21}}{\dfrac{z-4}{z^2-9}}=\dfrac{6z-24}{7z+21}\cdot\dfrac{z^2-9}{z-4}$

$=\dfrac{6(z-4)}{7(z+3)}\cdot\dfrac{(z-3)(z+3)}{z-4}$

$=\dfrac{6\cancel{(z-4)}}{7\cancel{(z+3)}}\cdot\dfrac{(z-3)\cancel{(z+3)}}{\cancel{z-4}}=\dfrac{6(z-3)}{7}$

19. $\dfrac{\dfrac{x^2-11x+30}{x^2-8x+15}}{\dfrac{x^2-5x-6}{x^2+8x+7}}=\dfrac{x^2-11x+30}{x^2-8x+15}\cdot\dfrac{x^2+8x+7}{x^2-5x-6}$

$=\dfrac{(x-5)(x-6)}{(x-3)(x-5)}\cdot\dfrac{(x+1)(x+7)}{(x+1)(x-6)}$

$=\dfrac{\cancel{(x-5)}\,\cancel{(x-6)}}{(x-3)\cancel{(x-5)}}\cdot\dfrac{\cancel{(x+1)}(x+7)}{\cancel{(x+1)}\,\cancel{(x-6)}}$

$=\dfrac{x+7}{x-3}$

20. $\dfrac{\dfrac{m^2+mn-12n^2}{m^3-27n^3}}{\dfrac{m+5n}{m^2+3mn+9n^2}}$

$=\dfrac{m^2+mn-12n^2}{m^3-27n^3}\cdot\dfrac{m^2+3mn+9n^2}{m+5n}$

$=\dfrac{(m-3n)(m+4n)}{(m-3n)(m^2+3mn+9n^2)}\cdot\dfrac{m^2+3mn+9n^2}{m+5n}$

$=\dfrac{\cancel{(m-3n)}\,(m+4n)}{\cancel{(m-3n)}\,\cancel{(m^2+3mn+9n^2)}}\cdot\dfrac{\cancel{m^2+3mn+9n^2}}{m+5n}$

$=\dfrac{m+4n}{m+5n}$

21. $\dfrac{\dfrac{4p^3-4pq^2}{p^2-5pq-24q^2}}{\dfrac{2p^3+4p^2q+2pq^2}{p^2-7pq-8q^2}}$

$=\dfrac{4p^3-4pq^2}{p^2-5pq-24q^2}\cdot\dfrac{p^2-7pq-8q^2}{2p^3+4p^2q+2pq^2}$

$=\dfrac{4p(p-q)(p+q)}{(p-8q)(p+3q)}\cdot\dfrac{(p+q)(p-8q)}{2p(p+q)(p+q)}$

$=\dfrac{2\cdot\cancel{2p}\,(p-q)\cancel{(p+q)}}{\cancel{(p-8q)}\,(p+3q)}\cdot\dfrac{\cancel{(p+q)}\,\cancel{(p-8q)}}{\cancel{2p}\,\cancel{(p+q)}\,\cancel{(p+q)}}$

$=\dfrac{2(p-q)}{p+3q}$

22.
$$\dfrac{\dfrac{15a^2+11a-14}{25a^2-49}}{\dfrac{27a^3-8}{10a^2+11a-35}}$$

$$=\dfrac{15a^2+11a-14}{25a^2-49}\cdot\dfrac{10a^2+11a-35}{27a^3-8}$$

$$=\dfrac{(3a-2)(5a+7)}{(5a-7)(5a+7)}\cdot\dfrac{(2a+5)(5a-7)}{(3a-2)(9a^2+6a+4)}$$

$$=\dfrac{(3a-2)\,(5a+7)}{(5a-7)\,(5a+7)}\cdot\dfrac{(2a+5)\,(5a-7)}{(3a-2)(9a^2+6a+4)}$$

$$=\dfrac{2a+5}{9a^2+6a+4}$$

23. $P(x)=f(x)\cdot g(x)$

$$=\dfrac{2x^2+3x-2}{x-5}\cdot\dfrac{x^2-3x-10}{2x-1}$$

$$=\dfrac{(2x-1)(x+2)}{x-5}\cdot\dfrac{(x+2)(x-5)}{2x-1}$$

$$=\dfrac{(2x-1)(x+2)}{x-5}\cdot\dfrac{(x+2)(x-5)}{2x-1}$$

$$=(x+2)^2$$

The domain of $f(x)$ is $\left\{x\mid x\neq5\right\}$. The domain

of $g(x)$ is $\left\{x\mid x\neq\dfrac{1}{2}\right\}$. Therefore, the domain

of $P(x)$ is $\left\{x\mid x\neq\dfrac{1}{2},x\neq5\right\}$.

24. $R(x)=g(x)\cdot h(x)$

$$=\dfrac{x^2-3x-10}{2x-1}\cdot\dfrac{2x-1}{x^2+9x+14}$$

$$=\dfrac{(x+2)(x-5)}{2x-1}\cdot\dfrac{2x-1}{(x+2)(x+7)}$$

$$=\dfrac{(x+2)(x-5)}{2x-1}\cdot\dfrac{2x-1}{(x+2)(x+7)}$$

$$=\dfrac{x-5}{x+7}$$

The domain of $g(x)$ is $\left\{x\mid x\neq\dfrac{1}{2}\right\}$. The domain

of $h(x)$ is $\left\{x\mid x\neq-7,x\neq-2\right\}$. Thus, the domain

of $R(x)$ is $\left\{x\mid x\neq-7,x\neq-2,x\neq\dfrac{1}{2}\right\}$.

25. $Q(x)=\dfrac{g(x)}{f(x)}=\dfrac{\dfrac{x^2-3x-10}{2x-1}}{\dfrac{2x^2+3x-2}{x-5}}$

$$=\dfrac{x^2-3x-10}{2x-1}\cdot\dfrac{x-5}{2x^2+3x-2}$$

$$=\dfrac{(x+2)(x-5)}{2x-1}\cdot\dfrac{x-5}{(2x-1)(x+2)}$$

$$=\dfrac{(x+2)(x-5)}{2x-1}\cdot\dfrac{x-5}{(2x-1)(x+2)}$$

$$=\dfrac{(x-5)^2}{(2x-1)^2}$$

The domain of $g(x)$ is $\left\{x\mid x\neq\dfrac{1}{2}\right\}$. The

domain of $f(x)$ is $\left\{x\mid x\neq5\right\}$. Because the

denominator of $Q(x)$ cannot equal 0, we

must exclude those values of x such that the

numerator of $f(x)$ is 0. That is, we must

exclude the values of x such that

$2x^2+3x-2=0$. These values are $x=-2$

and $x=\dfrac{1}{2}$. Therefore, the domain of

$Q(x)$ is $\left\{x\mid x\neq-2,x\neq\dfrac{1}{2},x\neq5\right\}$.

26. $T(x)=\dfrac{f(x)}{h(x)}=\dfrac{\dfrac{2x^2+3x-2}{x-5}}{\dfrac{2x-1}{x^2+9x+14}}$

$$=\dfrac{2x^2+3x-2}{x-5}\cdot\dfrac{x^2+9x+14}{2x-1}$$

$$=\dfrac{(2x-1)(x+2)}{x-5}\cdot\dfrac{(x+2)(x+7)}{2x-1}$$

$$=\dfrac{(2x-1)(x+2)}{x-5}\cdot\dfrac{(x+2)(x+7)}{2x-1}$$

$$=\dfrac{(x+2)^2(x+7)}{x-5}$$

The domain of $f(x)$ is $\left\{x\mid x\neq5\right\}$. The

domain of $h(x)$ is $\left\{x\mid x\neq-7,x\neq-2\right\}$.

Because the denominator of $T(x)$ cannot

equal 0, we must exclude those values of x

such that the numerator of $h(x)$ is 0. That is,

we must exclude the value of x such that $2x - 1 = 0$. This value is $x = \dfrac{1}{2}$. Therefore, the domain of $T(x)$ is

$$\left\{ x \,\middle|\, x \ne -7, x \ne -2, x \ne \frac{1}{2}, x \ne 5 \right\}.$$

27. $\dfrac{4x}{x-5} + \dfrac{3}{x-5} = \dfrac{4x+3}{x-5}$

28. $\dfrac{4y}{y-3} - \dfrac{12}{y-3} = \dfrac{4y-12}{y-3} = \dfrac{4(y-3)}{y-3} = 4$

29. $\dfrac{a^2-2a-4}{a^2-6a+8} + \dfrac{4a-20}{a^2-6a+8} = \dfrac{a^2-2a-4+4a-20}{a^2-6a+8}$

$$= \dfrac{a^2+2a-24}{a^2-6a+8}$$

$$= \dfrac{(a-4)(a+6)}{(a-4)(a-2)}$$

$$= \dfrac{a+6}{a-2}$$

30. $\dfrac{3b^2+8b-5}{2b^2-5b-12} - \dfrac{2b^2+7b+15}{2b^2-5b-12}$

$$= \dfrac{3b^2+8b-5-\left(2b^2+7b+15\right)}{2b^2-5b-12}$$

$$= \dfrac{3b^2+8b-5-2b^2-7b-15}{2b^2-5b-12}$$

$$= \dfrac{b^2+b-20}{2b^2-5b-12} = \dfrac{(b+5)(b-4)}{(2b+3)(b-4)} = \dfrac{b+5}{2b+3}$$

31. $\dfrac{5c^2-8c}{c-8} + \dfrac{2c^2+16c}{8-c} = \dfrac{5c^2-8c}{c-8} + \dfrac{2c^2+16c}{-1(c-8)}$

$$= \dfrac{5c^2-8c}{c-8} - \dfrac{2c^2+16c}{c-8}$$

$$= \dfrac{5c^2-8c-\left(2c^2+16c\right)}{c-8}$$

$$= \dfrac{5c^2-8c-2c^2-16c}{c-8}$$

$$= \dfrac{3c^2-24c}{c-8}$$

$$= \dfrac{3c(c-8)}{c-8}$$

$$= 3c$$

32. $\dfrac{2d^2+d}{d^2-1} - \dfrac{d^2+1}{d^2-1} + \dfrac{d-2}{d^2-1} = \dfrac{2d^2+d-\left(d^2+1\right)+d-2}{d^2-1}$

$$= \dfrac{2d^2+d-d^2-1+d-2}{d^2-1}$$

$$= \dfrac{d^2+2d-3}{d^2-1}$$

$$= \dfrac{(d-1)(d+3)}{(d+1)(d-1)}$$

$$= \dfrac{d+3}{d+1}$$

33. $9x^4 = 3^2 \cdot x^4$

$12x^2 = 2^2 \cdot 3 \cdot x$

$\text{LCD} = 2^2 \cdot 3^2 \cdot x^4 = 36x^4$

34. $y-9$

$y+2$

$\text{LCD} = (y+2)(y-9)$

35. $2p^2-3p-20 = (2p+5)(p-4)$

$2p^3+5p^2 = p^2(2p+5)$

$\text{LCD} = p^2(2p+5)(p-4)$

36. $q^2+4q-5 = (q-1)(q+5)$

$q^2+2q-15 = (q-3)(q+5)$

$\text{LCD} = (q+5)(q-1)(q-3)$

37. mn^4

m^3n^2

$\text{LCD} = m^3n^4$

$\dfrac{1}{mn^4} + \dfrac{4}{m^3n^2} = \dfrac{1}{mn^4} \cdot \dfrac{m^2}{m^2} + \dfrac{4}{m^3n^2} \cdot \dfrac{n^2}{n^2}$

$$= \dfrac{m^2}{m^3n^4} + \dfrac{4n^2}{m^3n^4}$$

$$= \dfrac{m^2+4n^2}{m^3n^4}$$

38. $2xy^3 = 2 \cdot x \cdot y^3$

$6x^2y = 2 \cdot 3 \cdot x^2 \cdot y$

$\text{LCD} = 2 \cdot 3 \cdot x^2 \cdot y^3 = 6x^2y^3$

$\dfrac{3}{2xy^3} - \dfrac{7}{6x^2y} = \dfrac{3}{2xy^3} \cdot \dfrac{3x}{3x} - \dfrac{7}{6x^2y} \cdot \dfrac{y^2}{y^2}$

$$= \dfrac{9x}{6x^2y^3} - \dfrac{7y^2}{6x^2y^3}$$

$$= \dfrac{9x-7y^2}{6x^2y^3}$$

39. $p-q$
$p+q$
$\text{LCD}=(p-q)(p+q)$

$$\frac{p}{p-q}-\frac{q}{p+q}=\frac{p}{p-q}\cdot\frac{p+q}{p+q}-\frac{q}{p+q}\cdot\frac{p-q}{p-q}$$
$$=\frac{p^2+pq}{(p-q)(p+q)}-\frac{pq-q^2}{(p-q)(p+q)}$$
$$=\frac{p^2+pq-(pq-q^2)}{(p-q)(p+q)}$$
$$=\frac{p^2+pq-pq+q^2}{(p-q)(p+q)}=\frac{p^2+q^2}{(p-q)(p+q)}$$

40. $x^2-10x+21=(x-3)(x-7)$
$x^2-3x-28=(x+4)(x-7)$
$\text{LCD}=(x-7)(x-3)(x+4)$

$$\frac{x+8}{x^2-10x+21}-\frac{x-5}{x^2-3x-28}$$
$$=\frac{x+8}{(x-3)(x-7)}\cdot\frac{x+4}{x+4}-\frac{x-5}{(x+4)(x-7)}\cdot\frac{x-3}{x-3}$$
$$=\frac{x^2+12x+32}{(x-7)(x-3)(x+4)}-\frac{x^2-8x+15}{(x-7)(x-3)(x+4)}$$
$$=\frac{x^2+12x+32-(x^2-8x+15)}{(x-7)(x-3)(x+4)}$$
$$=\frac{x^2+12x+32-x^2+8x-15}{(x-7)(x-3)(x+4)}$$
$$=\frac{20x+17}{(x-7)(x-3)(x+4)}$$

41. $y^2-2y+1=(y-1)^2$
$y^2+y-2=(y-1)(y+2)$
$\text{LCD}=(y-1)^2(y+2)$

$$\frac{3}{y^2-2y+1}-\frac{2}{y^2+y-2}$$
$$=\frac{3}{(y-1)^2}\cdot\frac{y+2}{y+2}-\frac{2}{(y-1)(y+2)}\cdot\frac{y-1}{y-1}$$
$$=\frac{3y+6}{(y-1)^2(y+2)}-\frac{2y-2}{(y-1)^2(y+2)}$$
$$=\frac{3y+6-(2y-2)}{(y-1)^2(y+2)}$$
$$=\frac{3y+6-2y+2}{(y-1)^2(y+2)}=\frac{y+8}{(y-1)^2(y+2)}$$

42. $4a^2-9b^2=(2a-3b)(2a+3b)$
$2a-3b$
$\text{LCD}=(2a-3b)(2a+3b)$

$$\frac{3a-5b}{4a^2-9b^2}+\frac{4}{2a-3b}$$
$$=\frac{3a-5b}{(2a-3b)(2a+3b)}+\frac{4}{2a-3b}\cdot\frac{2a+3b}{2a+3b}$$
$$=\frac{3a-5b}{(2a-3b)(2a+3b)}+\frac{8a+12b}{(2a-3b)(2a+3b)}$$
$$=\frac{3a-5b+8a+12b}{(2a-3b)(2a+3b)}=\frac{11a+7b}{(2a-3b)(2a+3b)}$$

43. $x^2-9=(x-3)(x+3)$
$9-x^2=-1(x-3)(x+3)$
$\text{LCD}=(x-3)(x+3)$

$$\frac{4x^2-10x}{x^2-9}+\frac{8x-2x^2}{9-x^2}$$
$$=\frac{4x^2-10x}{(x-3)(x+3)}+\frac{8x-2x^2}{-1(x-3)(x+3)}\cdot\frac{-1}{-1}$$
$$=\frac{4x^2-10x}{(x-3)(x+3)}+\frac{-8x+2x^2}{(x-3)(x+3)}$$
$$=\frac{4x^2-10x-8x+2x^2}{(x-3)(x+3)}$$
$$=\frac{6x^2-18x}{(x-3)(x+3)}=\frac{6x(x-3)}{(x-3)(x+3)}=\frac{6x}{x+3}$$

44. $n+5$
$n^3+125=(n+5)(n^2-5n+25)$
$\text{LCD}=(n+5)(n^2-5n+25)$

$$\frac{1}{n+5}-\frac{n^2-10n}{n^3+125}$$
$$=\frac{1}{n+5}\cdot\frac{n^2-5n+25}{n^2-5n+25}-\frac{n^2-10n}{(n+5)(n^2-5n+25)}$$
$$=\frac{n^2-5n+25}{(n+5)(n^2-5n+25)}-\frac{n^2-10n}{(n+5)(n^2-5n+25)}$$
$$=\frac{n^2-5n+25-(n^2-10n)}{(n+5)(n^2-5n+25)}$$
$$=\frac{n^2-5n+25-n^2+10n}{(n+5)(n^2-5n+25)}=\frac{5n+25}{(n+5)(n^2-5n+25)}$$
$$=\frac{5(n+5)}{(n+5)(n^2-5n+25)}=\frac{5}{n^2-5n+25}$$

45. $m+3n$

$m-7n$

$m^2 - 4mn - 21n^2 = (m+3n)(m-7n)$

$\text{LCD} = (m+3n)(m-7n)$

$$\frac{m+n}{m+3n} - \frac{m-4n}{m-7n} + \frac{7mn+n^2}{m^2-4mn-21n^2}$$

$$= \frac{m+n}{m+3n} \cdot \frac{m-7n}{m-7n} - \frac{m-4n}{m-7n} \cdot \frac{m+3n}{m+3n} +$$

$$\frac{7mn+n^2}{(m+3n)(m-7n)}$$

$$= \frac{m^2-6mn-7n^2}{(m+3n)(m-7n)} - \frac{m^2-mn-12n^2}{(m+3n)(m-7n)} +$$

$$\frac{7mn+n^2}{(m+3n)(m-7n)}$$

$$= \frac{m^2-6mn-7n^2 - (m^2-mn-12n^2) + 7mn+n^2}{(m+3n)(m-7n)}$$

$$= \frac{m^2-6mn-7n^2-m^2+mn+12n^2+7mn+n^2}{(m+3n)(m-7n)}$$

$$= \frac{2mn+6n^2}{(m+3n)(m-7n)}$$

$$= \frac{2n(m+3n)}{(m+3n)(m-7n)} = \frac{2n}{m-7n}$$

46. $z^2-9 = (z-3)(z+3)$

$z-3$

$z+3$

$\text{LCD} = (z-3)(z+3)$

$$\frac{z^2+10z+3}{z^2-9} - \frac{2z}{z-3} + \frac{z}{z+3}$$

$$= \frac{z^2+10z+3}{(z-3)(z+3)} - \frac{2z}{z-3} \cdot \frac{z+3}{z+3} + \frac{z}{z+3} \cdot \frac{z-3}{z-3}$$

$$= \frac{z^2+10z+3}{(z-3)(z+3)} - \frac{2z^2+6z}{(z-3)(z+3)} + \frac{z^2-3z}{(z-3)(z+3)}$$

$$= \frac{z^2+10z+3 - (2z^2+6z) + z^2-3z}{(z-3)(z+3)}$$

$$= \frac{z^2+10z+3-2z^2-6z+z^2-3z}{(z-3)(z+3)}$$

$$= \frac{z+3}{(z-3)(z+3)}$$

$$= \frac{1}{z-3}$$

47. $y-2$

$y+2$

$y^2-4 = (y-2)(y+2)$

$\text{LCD} = (y-2)(y+2)$

$$\frac{y-1}{y-2} - \frac{y+1}{y+2} + \frac{y-6}{y^2-4}$$

$$= \frac{y-1}{y-2} \cdot \frac{y+2}{y+2} - \frac{y+1}{y+2} \cdot \frac{y-2}{y-2} + \frac{y-6}{(y-2)(y+2)}$$

$$= \frac{y^2+y-2}{(y-2)(y+2)} - \frac{y^2-y-2}{(y-2)(y+2)} + \frac{y-6}{(y-2)(y+2)}$$

$$= \frac{y^2+y-2 - (y^2-y-2) + y-6}{(y-2)(y+2)}$$

$$= \frac{y^2+y-2-y^2+y+2+y-6}{(y-2)(y+2)}$$

$$= \frac{3y-6}{(y-2)(y+2)}$$

$$= \frac{3(y-2)}{(y-2)(y+2)} = \frac{3}{y+2}$$

48. $a^2-16 = (a-4)(a+4)$

$a-4$

$a^2+2a-8 = (a-2)(a+4)$

$\text{LCD} = (a-4)(a+4)(a-2)$

$$\frac{2a}{a^2-16} - \frac{1}{a-4} - \frac{1}{a^2+2a-8}$$

$$= \frac{2a}{(a-4)(a+4)} \cdot \frac{a-2}{a-2} - \frac{1}{a-4} \cdot \frac{(a+4)(a-2)}{(a+4)(a-2)} -$$

$$\frac{1}{(a+4)(a-2)} \cdot \frac{a-4}{a-4}$$

$$= \frac{2a^2-4a}{(a-4)(a+4)(a-2)} - \frac{a^2+2a-8}{(a-4)(a+4)(a-2)} -$$

$$\frac{a-4}{(a-4)(a+4)(a-2)}$$

$$= \frac{2a^2-4a - (a^2+2a-8) - (a-4)}{(a-4)(a+4)(a-2)}$$

$$= \frac{2a^2-4a-a^2-2a+8-a+4}{(a-4)(a+4)(a-2)}$$

$$= \frac{a^2-7a+12}{(a-4)(a+4)(a-2)}$$

$$= \frac{(a-3)(a-4)}{(a-4)(a+4)(a-2)} = \frac{a-3}{(a+4)(a-2)}$$

49. a. $x-4$

$x+2$

$LCD = (x-4)(x+2)$

$$S(x) = f(x) + g(x) = \frac{5}{x-4} + \frac{x}{x+2}$$

$$= \frac{5}{x-4} \cdot \frac{x+2}{x+2} + \frac{x}{x+2} \cdot \frac{x-4}{x-4}$$

$$= \frac{5x+10}{(x-4)(x+2)} + \frac{x^2-4x}{(x-4)(x+2)}$$

$$= \frac{5x+10+x^2-4x}{(x-4)(x+2)}$$

$$= \frac{x^2+x+10}{(x-4)(x+2)}$$

b. Since S is the sum of f and g, the restrictions for the domain of S will consist of all the restrictions for the domains of both f and g. Since 4 is restricted from the domain of f and since -2 is restricted from the domain of g, both 4 and -2 are restricted from the domain of S. That is, the domain of $S(x)$ is

$\{x \,|\, x \neq -2, x \neq 4\}$.

50. a. $2x^2 + x - 15 = (2x-5)(x+3)$

$4x^2 - 8x - 5 = (2x-5)(2x+1)$

$LCD = (2x-5)(2x+1)(x+3)$

$D(x) = f(x) - g(x)$

$$= \frac{x+3}{2x^2+x-15} - \frac{x-7}{4x^2-8x-5}$$

$$= \frac{x+3}{(2x-5)(x+3)} \cdot \frac{2x+1}{2x+1} - \frac{x-7}{(2x-5)(2x+1)} \cdot \frac{x+3}{x+3}$$

$$= \frac{2x^2+7x+3}{(2x-5)(2x+1)(x+3)} - \frac{x^2-4x-21}{(2x-5)(2x+1)(x+3)}$$

$$= \frac{2x^2+7x+3-(x^2-4x-21)}{(2x-5)(2x+1)(x+3)}$$

$$= \frac{2x^2+7x+3-x^2+4x+21}{(2x-5)(2x+1)(x+3)}$$

$$= \frac{x^2+11x+24}{(2x-5)(2x+1)(x+3)}$$

$$= \frac{(x+3)(x+8)}{(2x-5)(2x+1)(x+3)}$$

$$= \frac{x+8}{(2x-5)(2x+1)}$$

b. Since D is the difference of f and g, the restrictions for the domain of D will consist of all the restrictions for the domains of both f and g. Since -3 and $\frac{5}{2}$ are restricted from the domain of f and since $-\frac{1}{2}$ and $\frac{5}{2}$ are restricted from the domain of g, then -3, $-\frac{1}{2}$, and $\frac{5}{2}$ are restricted from the domain of D. That is, the domain of $D(x)$ is

$\left\{ x \,\middle|\, x \neq -3, x \neq -\frac{1}{2}, x \neq \frac{5}{2} \right\}$.

51. Write the numerator of the complex rational expression as a single rational expression. Note that the LCD of the rational expressions in the numerator is x.

$$x - \frac{1}{x} = \frac{x}{1} \cdot \frac{x}{x} - \frac{1}{x} = \frac{x^2}{x} - \frac{1}{x} = \frac{x^2-1}{x}$$

Write the denominator of the complex rational expression as a single rational expression. Note that the LCD of the rational expressions in the denominator is x.

$$1 - \frac{1}{x} = \frac{1}{1} \cdot \frac{x}{x} - \frac{1}{x} = \frac{x}{x} - \frac{1}{x} = \frac{x-1}{x}$$

Rewrite the complex rational expression using the single rational expressions and simplify.

$$\frac{x - \frac{1}{x}}{1 - \frac{1}{x}} = \frac{\frac{x^2-1}{x}}{\frac{x-1}{x}} = \frac{x^2-1}{x} \cdot \frac{x}{x-1}$$

$$= \frac{(x-1)(x+1)}{x} \cdot \frac{x}{x-1}$$

$$= \frac{\cancel{(x-1)}(x+1)}{\cancel{x}} \cdot \frac{\cancel{x}}{\cancel{x-1}}$$

$$= x+1$$

52. Write the numerator of the complex rational expression as a single rational expression. Note that the LCD of the rational expressions in the numerator is xy.

$$\frac{1}{x} - \frac{1}{y} = \frac{1}{x} \cdot \frac{y}{y} - \frac{1}{y} \cdot \frac{x}{x} = \frac{y}{xy} - \frac{x}{xy} = \frac{y-x}{xy}$$

Write the denominator of the complex rational expression as a single rational expression. Note that the LCD of the rational expressions in the denominator is $x^2 y^2$.

$$\frac{1}{x^2} - \frac{1}{y^2} = \frac{1}{x^2} \cdot \frac{y^2}{y^2} - \frac{1}{y^2} \cdot \frac{x^2}{x^2}$$

$$= \frac{y^2}{x^2 y^2} - \frac{x^2}{x^2 y^2} = \frac{y^2 - x^2}{x^2 y^2}$$

Rewrite the complex rational expression using the single rational expressions and simplify.

$$\frac{\dfrac{1}{x} - \dfrac{1}{y}}{\dfrac{1}{x^2} - \dfrac{1}{y^2}} = \frac{\dfrac{y-x}{xy}}{\dfrac{y^2-x^2}{x^2 y^2}} = \frac{y-x}{xy} \cdot \frac{x^2 y^2}{y^2 - x^2}$$

$$= \frac{y-x}{xy} \cdot \frac{x^2 y^2}{(y-x)(y+x)}$$

$$= \frac{\cancel{y-x}}{\cancel{xy}} \cdot \frac{\cancel{x} \cdot x \cdot \cancel{y} \cdot y}{(\cancel{y-x})(y+x)}$$

$$= \frac{xy}{y+x} \quad \text{or} \quad \frac{xy}{x+y}$$

53. Write the numerator of the complex rational expression as a single rational expression. Note that the LCD of the rational expressions in the numerator is $b(a+b)$.

$$\frac{a}{b} - \frac{a-b}{a+b} = \frac{a}{b} \cdot \frac{a+b}{a+b} - \frac{a-b}{a+b} \cdot \frac{b}{b}$$

$$= \frac{a^2 + ab}{b(a+b)} - \frac{ab - b^2}{b(a+b)}$$

$$= \frac{a^2 + ab - (ab - b^2)}{b(a+b)}$$

$$= \frac{a^2 + ab - ab + b^2}{b(a+b)}$$

$$= \frac{a^2 + b^2}{b(a+b)}$$

Write the denominator of the complex rational expression as a single rational expression. Note that the LCD of the rational expressions in the denominator is $b(a-b)$.

$$\frac{a}{b} + \frac{a+b}{a-b} = \frac{a}{b} \cdot \frac{a-b}{a-b} + \frac{a+b}{a-b} \cdot \frac{b}{b}$$

$$= \frac{a^2 - ab}{b(a-b)} + \frac{ab + b^2}{b(a-b)}$$

$$= \frac{a^2 + b^2}{b(a-b)}$$

Rewrite the complex rational expression using the single rational expressions and simplify.

$$\frac{\dfrac{a}{b} - \dfrac{a-b}{a+b}}{\dfrac{a}{b} + \dfrac{a+b}{a-b}} = \frac{\dfrac{a^2+b^2}{b(a+b)}}{\dfrac{a^2+b^2}{b(a-b)}} = \frac{a^2+b^2}{b(a+b)} \cdot \frac{b(a-b)}{a^2+b^2}$$

$$= \frac{\cancel{a^2+b^2}}{\cancel{b}(a+b)} \cdot \frac{\cancel{b}(a-b)}{\cancel{a^2+b^2}}$$

$$= \frac{a-b}{a+b}$$

54. Write the numerator of the complex rational expression as a single rational expression. Note that the LCD of the rational expressions in the numerator is $a+2$.

$$\frac{2}{a+2} - 1 = \frac{2}{a+2} - \frac{1}{1} \cdot \frac{a+2}{a+2} = \frac{2}{a+2} - \frac{a+2}{a+2}$$

$$= \frac{2 - (a+2)}{a+2} = \frac{2 - a - 2}{a+2} = \frac{-a}{a+2}$$

Write the denominator of the complex rational expression as a single rational expression. Note that the LCD of the rational expressions in the denominator is $a+2$.

$$\frac{1}{a+2} + 1 = \frac{1}{a+2} + \frac{1}{1} \cdot \frac{a+2}{a+2}$$

$$= \frac{1}{a+2} + \frac{a+2}{a+2} = \frac{1+a+2}{a+2} = \frac{a+3}{a+2}$$

Rewrite the complex rational expression using the single rational expressions and simplify.

$$\frac{\dfrac{2}{a+2} - 1}{\dfrac{1}{a+2} + 1} = \frac{\dfrac{-a}{a+2}}{\dfrac{a+3}{a+2}} = \frac{-a}{a+2} \cdot \frac{a+2}{a+3}$$

$$= \frac{-a}{\cancel{a+2}} \cdot \frac{\cancel{a+2}}{a+3} = \frac{-a}{a+3}$$

55. The LCD of all the denominators in the complex rational expression is t^2.

$$\frac{\dfrac{3}{t} + \dfrac{4}{t^2}}{5 + \dfrac{1}{t^2}} = \frac{\dfrac{3}{t} + \dfrac{4}{t^2}}{5 + \dfrac{1}{t^2}} \cdot \frac{t^2}{t^2} = \frac{\dfrac{3}{t} \cdot t^2 + \dfrac{4}{t^2} \cdot t^2}{5 \cdot t^2 + \dfrac{1}{t^2} \cdot t^2}$$

$$= \frac{\dfrac{3}{\cancel{t}} \cdot t^{\cancel{2}} + \dfrac{4}{\cancel{t^2}} \cdot \cancel{t^2}}{5 \cdot t^2 + \dfrac{1}{\cancel{t^2}} \cdot \cancel{t^2}} = \frac{3t + 4}{5t^2 + 1}$$

56. The LCD of all the denominators in the complex rational expression is ab.

$$\frac{\dfrac{1}{a}-\dfrac{1}{b}}{\dfrac{b}{a}-\dfrac{a}{b}}=\frac{\dfrac{1}{a}-\dfrac{1}{b}}{\dfrac{b}{a}-\dfrac{a}{b}}\cdot\frac{ab}{ab}=\frac{\dfrac{1}{a}\cdot ab-\dfrac{1}{b}\cdot ab}{\dfrac{b}{a}\cdot ab-\dfrac{a}{b}\cdot ab}$$

$$=\frac{\dfrac{1}{\cancel{a}}\cdot\cancel{a}b-\dfrac{1}{\cancel{b}}\cdot a\cancel{b}}{\dfrac{b}{\cancel{a}}\cdot\cancel{a}b-\dfrac{a}{\cancel{b}}\cdot a\cancel{b}}=\frac{b-a}{b^2-a^2}$$

$$=\frac{b-a}{(b-a)(b+a)}=\frac{\cancel{b-a}}{\cancel{(b-a)}(b+a)}$$

$$=\frac{1}{b+a}\quad\text{or}\quad\frac{1}{a+b}$$

57. The LCD of all the denominators in the complex rational expression is $z(z-1)(z+1)$.

$$\frac{\dfrac{1}{z-1}-\dfrac{1}{z}}{\dfrac{1}{z}-\dfrac{1}{z+1}}=\frac{\dfrac{1}{z-1}-\dfrac{1}{z}}{\dfrac{1}{z}-\dfrac{1}{z+1}}\cdot\frac{z(z-1)(z+1)}{z(z-1)(z+1)}$$

$$=\frac{\dfrac{1}{z-1}\cdot z(z-1)(z+1)-\dfrac{1}{z}\cdot z(z-1)(z+1)}{\dfrac{1}{z}\cdot z(z-1)(z+1)-\dfrac{1}{z+1}\cdot z(z-1)(z+1)}$$

$$=\frac{\dfrac{1}{\cancel{z-1}}\cdot z\cancel{(z-1)}(z+1)-\dfrac{1}{\cancel{z}}\cdot\cancel{z}(z-1)(z+1)}{\dfrac{1}{\cancel{z}}\cdot\cancel{z}(z-1)(z+1)-\dfrac{1}{\cancel{z+1}}\cdot z(z-1)\cancel{(z+1)}}$$

$$=\frac{z(z+1)-(z-1)(z+1)}{(z-1)(z+1)-z(z-1)}$$

$$=\frac{z^2+z-\left(z^2-1\right)}{z^2-1-z^2+z}$$

$$=\frac{z^2+z-z^2+1}{z-1}=\frac{z+1}{z-1}$$

58. The LCD of all the denominators in the complex rational expression is $(x-1)(x+1)$.

$$\frac{1+\dfrac{x}{x+1}}{\dfrac{2x+1}{x-1}}=\frac{1+\dfrac{x}{x+1}}{\dfrac{2x+1}{x-1}}\cdot\frac{(x-1)(x+1)}{(x-1)(x+1)}$$

$$=\frac{1\cdot(x-1)(x+1)+\dfrac{x}{x+1}\cdot(x-1)(x+1)}{\dfrac{2x+1}{x-1}\cdot(x-1)(x+1)}$$

$$=\frac{1\cdot(x-1)(x+1)+\dfrac{x}{\cancel{x+1}}\cdot(x-1)\cancel{(x+1)}}{\dfrac{2x+1}{\cancel{x-1}}\cdot\cancel{(x-1)}(x+1)}$$

$$=\frac{(x-1)(x+1)+x(x-1)}{(2x+1)(x+1)}$$

$$=\frac{x^2-1+x^2-x}{(2x+1)(x+1)}$$

$$=\frac{2x^2-x-1}{(2x+1)(x+1)}$$

$$=\frac{(2x+1)(x-1)}{(2x+1)(x+1)}$$

$$=\frac{\cancel{(2x+1)}(x-1)}{\cancel{(2x+1)}(x+1)}=\frac{x-1}{x+1}$$

59. Using Method 2, the LCD of all the denominators in the complex rational expression is y.

$$\frac{\dfrac{x}{y}+1}{\dfrac{x}{y}-1}=\frac{\dfrac{x}{y}+1}{\dfrac{x}{y}-1}\cdot\frac{y}{y}=\frac{\dfrac{x}{y}\cdot y+1\cdot y}{\dfrac{x}{y}\cdot y-1\cdot y}$$

$$=\frac{\dfrac{x}{\cancel{y}}\cdot\cancel{y}+1\cdot y}{\dfrac{x}{\cancel{y}}\cdot\cancel{y}-1\cdot y}=\frac{x+y}{x-y}$$

60. Using Method 2, the LCD of all the denominators in the complex rational expression is $(a-b)(a+b)$.

$$\frac{\dfrac{a}{a-b}-\dfrac{b}{a+b}}{\dfrac{b}{a-b}+\dfrac{a}{a+b}}=\frac{\dfrac{a}{a-b}-\dfrac{b}{a+b}}{\dfrac{b}{a-b}+\dfrac{a}{a+b}}\cdot\frac{(a-b)(a+b)}{(a-b)(a+b)}$$

$$=\frac{\dfrac{a}{a-b}\cdot(a-b)(a+b)-\dfrac{b}{a+b}\cdot(a-b)(a+b)}{\dfrac{b}{a-b}\cdot(a-b)(a+b)+\dfrac{a}{a+b}\cdot(a-b)(a+b)}$$

$$=\frac{\dfrac{a}{\cancel{a-b}}\cdot\cancel{(a-b)}(a+b)-\dfrac{b}{\cancel{a+b}}\cdot(a-b)\cancel{(a+b)}}{\dfrac{b}{\cancel{a-b}}\cdot\cancel{(a-b)}(a+b)+\dfrac{a}{\cancel{a+b}}\cdot(a-b)\cancel{(a+b)}}$$

$$=\frac{a(a+b)-b(a-b)}{b(a+b)+a(a-b)}$$

$$=\frac{a^2+ab-ab+b^2}{ab+b^2+a^2-ab}=\frac{a^2+b^2}{a^2+b^2}=1$$

61. Using Method 1, write the numerator of the complex rational expression as a single rational expression. Note that the LCD of the rational expressions in the numerator is $(x-2)(x+2)$.

$$\frac{1}{x-2}-\frac{x}{x^2-4}=\frac{1}{x-2}-\frac{x}{(x-2)(x+2)}$$

$$=\frac{1}{x-2}\cdot\frac{x+2}{x+2}-\frac{x}{(x-2)(x+2)}$$

$$=\frac{x+2}{(x-2)(x+2)}-\frac{x}{(x-2)(x+2)}$$

$$=\frac{x+2-x}{(x-2)(x+2)}=\frac{2}{(x-2)(x+2)}$$

Write the denominator of the complex rational expression as a single rational expression. Note that the LCD of the rational expressions in the denominator is $x+2$.

$$1-\frac{2}{x+2}=\frac{1}{1}\cdot\frac{x+2}{x+2}-\frac{2}{x+2}$$

$$=\frac{x+2}{x+2}-\frac{2}{x+2}=\frac{x+2-2}{x+2}=\frac{x}{x+2}$$

Rewrite the complex rational expression using the single rational expressions and simplify.

$$\frac{\dfrac{1}{x-2}-\dfrac{x}{x^2-4}}{1-\dfrac{2}{x+2}}=\frac{\dfrac{2}{(x-2)(x+2)}}{\dfrac{x}{x+2}}$$

$$=\frac{2}{(x-2)(x+2)}\cdot\frac{x+2}{x}$$

$$=\frac{2}{(x-2)\,\cancel{(x+2)}}\cdot\frac{\cancel{x+2}}{x}$$

$$=\frac{2}{x(x-2)}$$

62. Using Method 1, write the numerator of the complex rational expression as a single rational expression. Note that the LCD of the rational expressions in the numerator is $z+5$.

$$z-\frac{5z}{z+5}=\frac{z}{1}\cdot\frac{z+5}{z+5}-\frac{5z}{z+5}$$

$$=\frac{z^2+5z}{z+5}-\frac{5z}{z+5}$$

$$=\frac{z^2+5z-5z}{z+5}=\frac{z^2}{z+5}$$

Write the denominator of the complex rational expression as a single rational expression. Note that the LCD of the rational expressions in the denominator is $z-5$.

$$z+\frac{5z}{z-5}=\frac{z}{1}\cdot\frac{z-5}{z-5}+\frac{5z}{z-5}$$

$$=\frac{z^2-5z}{z-5}+\frac{5z}{z-5}$$

$$=\frac{z^2-5z+5z}{z-5}=\frac{z^2}{z-5}$$

Rewrite the complex rational expression using the single rational expressions and simplify.

$$\frac{z-\dfrac{5z}{z+5}}{z+\dfrac{5z}{z-5}}=\frac{\dfrac{z^2}{z+5}}{\dfrac{z^2}{z-5}}=\frac{z^2}{z+5}\cdot\frac{z-5}{z^2}=\frac{\cancel{z^2}}{z+5}\cdot\frac{z-5}{\cancel{z^2}}=\frac{z-5}{z+5}$$

63. Using Method 2, the LCD of all the denominators in the complex rational expression is $mn(m+n)$.

$$\frac{\dfrac{m-n}{m+n}+\dfrac{n}{m}}{\dfrac{m}{n}-\dfrac{m-n}{m+n}}=\frac{\dfrac{m-n}{m+n}+\dfrac{n}{m}}{\dfrac{m}{n}-\dfrac{m-n}{m+n}}\cdot\frac{mn(m+n)}{mn(m+n)}$$

$$=\frac{\dfrac{m-n}{m+n}\cdot mn(m+n)+\dfrac{n}{m}\cdot mn(m+n)}{\dfrac{m}{n}\cdot mn(m+n)-\dfrac{m-n}{m+n}\cdot mn(m+n)}$$

$$=\frac{\dfrac{m-n}{\cancel{m+n}}\cdot mn\cancel{(m+n)}+\dfrac{n}{\cancel{m}}\cdot\cancel{m}n(m+n)}{\dfrac{m}{\cancel{n}}\cdot m\cancel{n}(m+n)-\dfrac{m-n}{\cancel{m+n}}\cdot mn\cancel{(m+n)}}$$

$$=\frac{mn(m-n)+n^2(m+n)}{m^2(m+n)-mn(m-n)}$$

$$=\frac{m^2n-mn^2+mn^2+n^3}{m^3+m^2n-m^2n+mn^2}$$

$$=\frac{m^2n+n^3}{m^3+mn^2}=\frac{n(m^2+n^2)}{m(m^2+n^2)}$$

$$=\frac{n\cancel{(m^2+n^2)}}{m\cancel{(m^2+n^2)}}=\frac{n}{m}$$

64. Using Method 1, write the numerator of the complex rational expression as a single rational expression. Note that the LCD of the rational expressions in the numerator is $(x+1)(x-2)$.

$$\frac{x+4}{x-2}-\frac{x-3}{x+1}=\frac{x+4}{x-2}\cdot\frac{x+1}{x+1}-\frac{x-3}{x+1}\cdot\frac{x-2}{x-2}$$

$$=\frac{x^2+5x+4}{(x+1)(x-2)}-\frac{x^2-5x+6}{(x+1)(x-2)}$$

$$= \frac{x^2 + 5x + 4 - \left(x^2 - 5x + 6\right)}{(x+1)(x-2)}$$

$$= \frac{x^2 + 5x + 4 - x^2 + 5x - 6}{(x+1)(x-2)}$$

$$= \frac{10x - 2}{(x+1)(x-2)}$$

$$= \frac{2(5x-1)}{(x+1)(x-2)}$$

The denominator is already a single rational expression: $5x^2 + 4x - 1 = (5x-1)(x+1)$.

Rewrite the complex rational expression using the single rational expressions and simplify.

$$\frac{\dfrac{x+4}{x-2} - \dfrac{x-3}{x+1}}{5x^2 + 4x - 1} = \frac{\dfrac{2(5x-1)}{(x+1)(x-2)}}{\dfrac{(5x-1)(x+1)}{1}}$$

$$= \frac{2(5x-1)}{(x+1)(x-2)} \cdot \frac{1}{(5x-1)(x+1)}$$

$$= \frac{2\cancel{(5x-1)}}{(x+1)(x-2)} \cdot \frac{1}{\cancel{(5x-1)}(x+1)}$$

$$= \frac{2}{(x+1)^2(x-2)}$$

65. Rewrite the expression so that it does not contain any negative exponents.

$$\frac{3x^{-1} - 3y^{-1}}{(x+y)^{-1}} = \frac{\dfrac{3}{x} - \dfrac{3}{y}}{\dfrac{1}{x+y}}$$

Using Method 2, the LCD of all the denominators in the complex rational expression is $xy(x+y)$.

$$\frac{3x^{-1} - 3y^{-1}}{(x+y)^{-1}} = \frac{\dfrac{3}{x} - \dfrac{3}{y}}{\dfrac{1}{x+y}} = \frac{\dfrac{3}{x} - \dfrac{3}{y}}{\dfrac{1}{x+y}} \cdot \frac{xy(x+y)}{xy(x+y)}$$

$$= \frac{\dfrac{3}{x} \cdot xy(x+y) - \dfrac{3}{y} \cdot xy(x+y)}{\dfrac{1}{x+y} \cdot xy(x+y)}$$

$$= \frac{\dfrac{3}{\cancel{x}} \cdot \cancel{x}y(x+y) - \dfrac{3}{\cancel{y}} \cdot x\cancel{y}(x+y)}{\dfrac{1}{\cancel{x+y}} \cdot xy\cancel{(x+y)}}$$

$$= \frac{3y(x+y) - 3x(x+y)}{xy}$$

$$= \frac{3xy + 3y^2 - 3x^2 - 3xy}{xy}$$

$$= \frac{3y^2 - 3x^2}{xy} \quad \text{or} \quad \frac{3(y-x)(y+x)}{xy}$$

66. Rewrite the expression so that it does not contain any negative exponents.

$$\frac{2c^{-1} - (3d)^{-1}}{(6d)^{-1}} = \frac{\dfrac{2}{c} - \dfrac{1}{3d}}{\dfrac{1}{6d}}$$

Using Method 2, the LCD of all the denominators in the complex rational expression is $6cd$.

$$\frac{2c^{-1} - (3d)^{-1}}{(6d)^{-1}} = \frac{\dfrac{2}{c} - \dfrac{1}{3d}}{\dfrac{1}{6d}} = \frac{\dfrac{2}{c} - \dfrac{1}{3d}}{\dfrac{1}{6d}} \cdot \frac{6cd}{6cd}$$

$$= \frac{\dfrac{2}{c} \cdot 6cd - \dfrac{1}{3d} \cdot 6cd}{\dfrac{1}{6d} \cdot 6cd} = \frac{\dfrac{2}{\cancel{c}} \cdot 6\cancel{c}d - \dfrac{1}{\cancel{3}\cancel{d}} \cdot \overset{2}{\cancel{6}}c\cancel{d}}{\dfrac{1}{\cancel{6d}} \cdot \cancel{6}c\cancel{d}}$$

$$= \frac{12d - 2c}{c} \quad \text{or} \quad \frac{2(6d - c)}{c}$$

67.
$$\frac{2}{z} - \frac{1}{3z} = \frac{1}{6}$$

$$6z\left(\frac{2}{z} - \frac{1}{3z}\right) = 6z\left(\frac{1}{6}\right)$$

$$12 - 2 = z$$

$$10 = z$$

Check:
$$\frac{2}{10} - \frac{1}{3 \cdot 10} \overset{?}{=} \frac{1}{6}$$

$$\frac{6}{30} - \frac{1}{30} \overset{?}{=} \frac{1}{6}$$

$$\frac{5}{30} \overset{?}{=} \frac{1}{6}$$

$$\frac{1}{6} = \frac{1}{6} \leftarrow \text{True}$$

The solution checks, so the solution set is $\{10\}$.

68.
$$\frac{4}{m-4} = \frac{-5}{m+2}$$

$$(m-4)(m+2)\left(\frac{4}{m-4}\right) = (m-4)(m+2)\left(\frac{-5}{m+2}\right)$$

$$4(m+2) = -5(m-4)$$

$$4m + 8 = -5m + 20$$

$$9m = 12$$

$$m = \frac{12}{9} = \frac{4}{3}$$

Check:

$$\frac{4}{\frac{4}{3}-4} \overset{?}{=} \frac{-5}{\frac{4}{3}+2}$$

$$\frac{4}{\frac{4}{3}-\frac{12}{3}} \overset{?}{=} \frac{-5}{\frac{4}{3}+\frac{6}{3}}$$

$$\frac{4}{-\frac{8}{3}} \overset{?}{=} \frac{-5}{\frac{10}{3}}$$

$$4 \cdot \left(-\frac{3}{8}\right) \overset{?}{=} -5 \cdot \frac{3}{10}$$

$$-\frac{3}{2} = -\frac{3}{2} \quad \leftarrow \text{True}$$

The solution checks, so the solution set is $\left\{\frac{4}{3}\right\}$.

69.
$$m - \frac{14}{m} = 5$$

$$m\left(m - \frac{14}{m}\right) = m(5)$$

$$m^2 - 14 = 5m$$

$$m^2 - 5m - 14 = 0$$

$$(m+2)(m-7) = 0$$

$$m + 2 = 0 \quad \text{or} \quad m - 7 = 0$$

$$m = -2 \quad \text{or} \quad m = 7$$

Check:

$$-2 - \frac{14}{-2} \overset{?}{=} 5 \qquad 7 - \frac{14}{7} \overset{?}{=} 5$$

$$-2 + 7 \overset{?}{=} 5 \qquad 7 - 2 \overset{?}{=} 5$$

$$-5 = 5 \quad \leftarrow \text{True} \qquad 5 = 5 \quad \leftarrow \text{True}$$

Both solutions check, so the solution set is $\{-2,\ 7\}$.

70.
$$\frac{2}{n+3} = \frac{1}{n-3}$$

$$(n-3)(n+3)\left(\frac{2}{n+3}\right) = (n-3)(n+3)\left(\frac{1}{n-3}\right)$$

$$2(n-3) = n+3$$

$$2n - 6 = n + 3$$

$$n = 9$$

Check:
$$\frac{2}{9+3} \overset{?}{=} \frac{1}{9-3}$$

$$\frac{2}{12} \overset{?}{=} \frac{1}{6}$$

$$\frac{1}{6} = \frac{1}{6} \quad \leftarrow \text{True}$$

The solution checks, so the solution set is $\{9\}$.

71.
$$\frac{s}{s-1} = 1 + \frac{2}{s}$$

$$s(s-1)\left(\frac{s}{s-1}\right) = s(s-1)\left(1 + \frac{2}{s}\right)$$

$$s^2 = s(s-1) + 2(s-1)$$

$$s^2 = s^2 - s + 2s - 2$$

$$s^2 = s^2 + s - 2$$

$$0 = s - 2$$

$$2 = s$$

Check: $\dfrac{2}{2-1} \overset{?}{=} 1 + \dfrac{2}{2}$

$$\frac{2}{1} \overset{?}{=} 1 + 1$$

$$2 = 2 \quad \leftarrow \text{True}$$

The solution checks, so the solution set is $\{2\}$.

72.
$$\frac{3}{x^2 - 7x + 10} + 2 = \frac{x-4}{x-5}$$

$$\frac{3}{(x-2)(x-5)} + 2 = \frac{x-4}{x-5}$$

$$(x-2)(x-5)\left(\frac{3}{(x-2)(x-5)} + 2\right) =$$

$$(x-2)(x-5)\left(\frac{x-4}{x-5}\right)$$

$$3 + 2(x-2)(x-5) = (x-4)(x-2)$$

$$3 + 2x^2 - 14x + 20 = x^2 - 6x + 8$$

$$2x^2 - 14x + 23 = x^2 - 6x + 8$$

$$x^2 - 8x + 15 = 0$$

$$(x-3)(x-5) = 0$$

$$x - 3 = 0 \quad \text{or} \quad x - 5 = 0$$

$$x = 3 \quad \text{or} \quad x = 5$$

Since $x = 5$ is not in the domain of the variable, it is an extraneous solution.

Check $x = 3$: $\dfrac{3}{3^2 - 7 \cdot 3 + 10} + 2 \overset{?}{=} \dfrac{3-4}{3-5}$

$$\frac{3}{9 - 21 + 10} + 2 \overset{?}{=} \frac{-1}{-2}$$

$$\frac{3}{-2} + 2 \overset{?}{=} \frac{1}{2}$$

$$\frac{1}{2} = \frac{1}{2} \quad \leftarrow \text{True}$$

The solution set is $\{3\}$.

73.

$$\frac{1}{k-1}+\frac{1}{k+2}=\frac{3}{k^2+k-2}$$

$$\frac{1}{k-1}+\frac{1}{k+2}=\frac{3}{(k-1)(k+2)}$$

$$(k-1)(k+2)\left(\frac{1}{k-1}+\frac{1}{k+2}\right)=$$

$$(k-1)(k+2)\left(\frac{3}{(k-1)(k+2)}\right)$$

$$(k+2)+(k-1)=3$$
$$2k+1=3$$
$$2k=2$$
$$k=1$$

Since $k=1$ is not in the domain of the variable, it is an extraneous solution. The solution set is $\varnothing$ or $\{\ \}$.

74.

$$x+\frac{3x}{x-3}=\frac{9}{x-3}$$

$$(x-3)\left(x+\frac{3x}{x-3}\right)=(x-3)\left(\frac{9}{x-3}\right)$$

$$x(x-3)+3x=9$$
$$x^2-3x+3x=9$$
$$x^2=9$$
$$x^2-9=0$$
$$(x-3)(x+3)=0$$
$$x-3=0 \quad \text{or} \quad x+3=0$$
$$x=3 \quad \text{or} \quad x=-3$$

Since $x=3$ is not in the domain of the variable, it is an extraneous solution.

Check $x=-3$: $-3+\dfrac{3(-3)}{-3-3}\overset{?}{=}\dfrac{9}{-3-3}$

$$-3+\frac{-9}{-6}\overset{?}{=}\frac{9}{-6}$$

$$-3+\frac{3}{2}\overset{?}{=}-\frac{3}{2}$$

$$-\frac{3}{2}=-\frac{3}{2} \leftarrow \text{True}$$

The solution set is $\{-3\}$.

75.

$$\frac{2}{a+3}-\frac{4}{a^2-4}=\frac{a+1}{a^2+5a+6}$$

$$\frac{2}{a+3}-\frac{4}{(a-2)(a+2)}=\frac{a+1}{(a+2)(a+3)}$$

$$(a-2)(a+2)(a+3)\left(\frac{2}{a+3}-\frac{4}{(a-2)(a+2)}\right)=$$

$$(a-2)(a+2)(a+3)\left(\frac{a+1}{(a+2)(a+3)}\right)$$

$$2(a-2)(a+2)-4(a+3)=(a+1)(a-2)$$
$$2a^2-8-4a-12=a^2-a-2$$
$$2a^2-4a-20=a^2-a-2$$
$$a^2-3a-18=0$$
$$(a+3)(a-6)=0$$

$$a+3=0 \quad \text{or} \quad a-6=0$$
$$a=-3 \quad \text{or} \quad a=6$$

Since $a=-3$ is not in the domain of the variable, it is an extraneous solution.

Check $a=6$:

$$\frac{2}{6+3}-\frac{4}{6^2-4}\overset{?}{=}\frac{6+1}{6^2+5\cdot6+6}$$

$$\frac{2}{9}-\frac{4}{36-4}\overset{?}{=}\frac{7}{36+30+6}$$

$$\frac{2}{9}-\frac{4}{32}\overset{?}{=}\frac{7}{72}$$

$$\frac{64}{288}-\frac{36}{288}\overset{?}{=}\frac{7}{72}$$

$$\frac{28}{288}\overset{?}{=}\frac{7}{72}$$

$$\frac{7}{72}=\frac{7}{72} \leftarrow \text{True}$$

The solution set is $\{6\}$.

76.

$$\frac{2}{z^2+2z-8}=\frac{1}{z^2+9z+20}+\frac{4}{z^2+3z-10}$$

$$\frac{2}{(z-2)(z+4)}=\frac{1}{(z+4)(z+5)}+\frac{4}{(z-2)(z+5)}$$

$$(z-2)(z+4)(z+5)\left(\frac{2}{(z-2)(z+4)}\right)=$$

$$(z-2)(z+4)(z+5)\left(\frac{1}{(z+4)(z+5)}+\frac{4}{(z-2)(z+5)}\right)$$

$$2(z+5)=(z-2)+4(z+4)$$
$$2z+10=z-2+4z+16$$
$$2z+10=5z+14$$
$$-3z=4$$
$$z=-\frac{4}{3}$$

Check:

$$\frac{2}{\left(-\frac{4}{3}\right)^2 + 2\left(-\frac{4}{3}\right) - 8} \stackrel{?}{=}$$

$$\frac{1}{\left(-\frac{4}{3}\right)^2 + 9\left(-\frac{4}{3}\right) + 20} + \frac{4}{\left(-\frac{4}{3}\right)^2 + 3\left(-\frac{4}{3}\right) - 10}$$

$$\frac{2}{\frac{16}{9} - \frac{8}{3} - 8} \stackrel{?}{=} \frac{1}{\frac{16}{9} - 12 + 20} + \frac{4}{\frac{16}{9} - 4 - 10}$$

$$\frac{2}{-\frac{80}{9}} \stackrel{?}{=} \frac{1}{\frac{88}{9}} + \frac{4}{-\frac{110}{9}}$$

$$-\frac{9}{40} \stackrel{?}{=} \frac{9}{88} - \frac{18}{55}$$

$$-\frac{9}{40} \stackrel{?}{=} \frac{45}{440} - \frac{144}{440}$$

$$-\frac{9}{40} \stackrel{?}{=} -\frac{99}{440}$$

$$-\frac{9}{40} = -\frac{9}{40} \quad \leftarrow \text{True}$$

The solution set is $\left\{-\frac{4}{3}\right\}$.

77.

$$\frac{x-3}{x+4} = \frac{14}{x^2 + 6x + 8}$$

$$\frac{x-3}{x+4} = \frac{14}{(x+2)(x+4)}$$

$$(x+2)(x+4)\left(\frac{x-3}{x+4}\right) = (x+2)(x+4)\left(\frac{14}{(x+2)(x+4)}\right)$$

$$(x+2)(x-3) = 14$$

$$x^2 - x - 6 = 14$$

$$x^2 - x - 20 = 0$$

$$(x+4)(x-5) = 0$$

$$x+4 = 0 \quad \text{or} \quad x-5 = 0$$

$$x = -4 \quad \text{or} \quad x = 5$$

Since $x = -4$ is not in the domain of the variable, it is an extraneous solution.

Check $x = 5$:

$$\frac{5-3}{5+4} \stackrel{?}{=} \frac{14}{5^2 + 6 \cdot 5 + 8}$$

$$\frac{2}{9} \stackrel{?}{=} \frac{14}{25 + 30 + 8}$$

$$\frac{2}{9} \stackrel{?}{=} \frac{14}{63}$$

$$\frac{2}{9} = \frac{2}{9} \quad \leftarrow \text{True}$$

The solution set is $\{5\}$.

78.

$$\frac{5}{y-5} + 4 = \frac{3y-10}{y-5}$$

$$(y-5)\left(\frac{5}{y-5} + 4\right) = (y-5)\left(\frac{3y-10}{y-5}\right)$$

$$5 + 4(y-5) = 3y - 10$$

$$5 + 4y - 20 = 3y - 10$$

$$4y - 15 = 3y - 10$$

$$y = 5$$

Since $y = 5$ is not in the domain of the variable, it is an extraneous solution. The solution set is $\varnothing$ or $\{\ \}$.

79.

$$f(x) = 2$$

$$\frac{6}{x-2} = 2$$

$$(x-2)\left(\frac{6}{x-2}\right) = (x-2) \cdot 2$$

$$6 = 2x - 4$$

$$10 = 2x$$

$$5 = x$$

Thus, $f(5) = 2$, so the point $(5, 2)$ is on the graph of f.

80.

$$g(x) = 4$$

$$x - \frac{21}{x} = 4$$

$$x\left(x - \frac{21}{x}\right) = x \cdot 4$$

$$x^2 - 21 = 4x$$

$$x^2 - 4x - 21 = 0$$

$$(x+3)(x-7) = 0$$

$$x+3 = 0 \quad \text{or} \quad x-7 = 0$$

$$x = -3 \quad \text{or} \quad x = 7$$

Thus, $g(-3) = 4$ and $g(7) = 4$, so the points $(-3, 4)$ and $(7, 4)$ are on the graph of f.

81.

$$\frac{x-4}{x+2} \geq 0$$

The rational expression will equal 0 when $x = 4$.
It is undefined when $x = -2$.
Determine where the numerator and denominator are positive and negative and where the quotient is positive and negative.

Interval	$(-\infty, -2)$	-2	$(-2, 4)$	4	$(4, \infty)$
$x-4$	$----$	$-$	$----$	0	$++++$
$x+2$	$----$	0	$++++$	$+$	$++++$
$\dfrac{x-4}{x+2}$	$++++$	$\varnothing$	$----$	0	$++++$

The rational function is undefined at $x = -2$, so -2 is not part of the solution. The inequality is non-strict, so 4 is part of the solution. Now, $\dfrac{x-4}{x+2}$ is greater than zero where the quotient is positive. The solution is $\{x \mid x < -2 \text{ or } x \geq 4\}$ in set-builder notation; the solution is $(-\infty,\ -2) \cup [4,\ \infty)$ in interval notation.

82. $\dfrac{y-5}{y+4} < 0$

The rational expression will equal 0 when $y = 5$. It is undefined when $y = -4$.

Determine where the numerator and denominator are positive and negative and where the quotient is positive and negative.

Interval	$(-\infty, -4)$	-4	$(-4, 5)$	5	$(5, \infty)$
$y - 5$	$----$	$-$	$----$	0	$++++$
$y + 4$	$----$	0	$++++$	$+$	$++++$
$\dfrac{y-5}{y+4}$	$++++$	$\varnothing$	$----$	0	$++++$

The rational function is undefined at $y = -4$, so -4 is not part of the solution. The inequality is strict, so 5 is not part of the solution. Now, $\dfrac{y-5}{y+4}$ is less than zero where the quotient is negative. The solution is $\{y \mid -4 < y < 5\}$ in set-builder notation; the solution is $(-4,\ 5)$ in interval notation.

83. $\dfrac{4}{z^2 - 9} \leq 0$

$\dfrac{4}{(z-3)(z+3)} \leq 0$

Because the numerator is a constant, this rational expression cannot equal 0. However, it is undefined when $z = 3$ and when $z = -3$. Determine where the factors of the denominator are positive and negative and where the quotient is positive and negative.

Interval	$(-\infty, -3)$	-3	$(-3, 3)$	3	$(3, \infty)$
4	$++++$	$+$	$++++$	$+$	$++++$
$z - 3$	$----$	$-$	$----$	0	$++++$
$z + 3$	$----$	0	$++++$	$+$	$++++$
$\dfrac{4}{(z-3)(z+3)}$	$++++$	$\varnothing$	$----$	$\varnothing$	$++++$

The rational function is undefined at $z = -3$ and $z = 3$, so -3 and 3 are not part of the solution. Now, $\dfrac{4}{(z-3)(z+3)}$ is less than zero where the quotient is negative. The solution is $\{z \mid -3 < z < 3\}$ in set-builder notation; the solution is $(-3,\ 3)$ in interval notation.

84. $\dfrac{w^2 + 5w - 14}{w - 4} < 0$

$\dfrac{(w-2)(w+7)}{w-4} < 0$

The rational expression will equal 0 when $w = 2$ and when $w = -7$. It is undefined when $w = 4$. Determine where the factors of the numerator and the denominator are positive and negative and where the quotient is positive and negative.

Interval	$(-\infty, -7)$	-7	$(-7, 2)$	2	$(2, 4)$	4	$(4, \infty)$
$w - 2$	$---$	$-$	$---$	0	$+++$	$+$	$+++$
$w + 7$	$---$	0	$+++$	$+$	$+++$	$+$	$+++$
$w - 4$	$---$	$-$	$---$	$-$	$---$	0	$+++$
$\dfrac{(w-2)(w+7)}{w-4}$	$---$	0	$+++$	0	$---$	$\varnothing$	$+++$

The rational function is undefined at $w = 4$, so 4 is not part of the solution. The inequality is strict, so -7 and 2 are not part of the solution. Now, $\dfrac{(w-2)(w+7)}{w-4}$ is less than zero where the quotient is negative. The solution is $\{w \mid w < -7 \text{ or } 2 < w < 4\}$ in set-builder notation; the solution is $(-\infty, -7) \cup (2,\ 4)$ in interval notation.

85.
$$\frac{m-5}{m^2+3m-10} \geq 0$$

$$\frac{m-5}{(m-2)(m+5)} \geq 0$$

The rational expression will equal 0 when $m = 5$. It is undefined when $m = 2$ and when $m = -5$.

Determine where the numerator and the factors of the denominator are positive and negative and where the quotient is positive and negative.

Interval	$(-\infty, -5)$	-5	$(-5, 2)$	2	$(2, 5)$	5	$(5, \infty)$
$m - 5$	$---$	$-$	$---$	$-$	$---$	0	$+++$
$m - 2$	$---$	$-$	$---$	0	$+++$	$+$	$+++$
$m + 5$	$---$	0	$+++$	$+$	$+++$	$+$	$+++$
$\frac{m-5}{(m-2)(m+5)}$	$---$	$\varnothing$	$+++$	$\varnothing$	$---$	0	$+++$

The rational function is undefined at $m = -5$ and when $m = 2$, so -5 and 2 are not part of the solution. The inequality is non-strict, so 5 is part of the solution. Now, $\frac{m-5}{(m-2)(m+5)}$ is greater than zero where the quotient is positive. The solution is $\{m \mid -5 < m < 2 \text{ or } m \geq 5\}$ in set-builder notation; the solution is $(-5, 2) \cup [5, \infty)$ in interval notation.

86.
$$\frac{4}{n-2} \leq -2$$

$$\frac{4}{n-2} + 2 \leq 0$$

$$\frac{4}{n-2} + \frac{2(n-2)}{n-2} \leq 0$$

$$\frac{4+2n-4}{n-2} \leq 0$$

$$\frac{2n}{n-2} \leq 0$$

The rational expression will equal 0 when $n = 0$. It is undefined when $n = 2$.

Determine where the numerator and denominator are positive and negative and where the quotient is positive and negative.

Interval	$(-\infty, 0)$	0	$(0, 2)$	2	$(2, \infty)$
$2n$	$----$	0	$++++$	$+$	$++++$
$n - 2$	$----$	$-$	$----$	0	$++++$
$\frac{2n}{n-2}$	$++++$	0	$----$	$\varnothing$	$++++$

The rational function is undefined at $n = 2$, so 2 is not part of the solution. The inequality is non-strict, so 0 is part of the solution. Now, $\frac{2n}{n-2}$ is less than zero where the quotient is negative. The solution is $\{n \mid 0 \leq n < 2\}$ in set-builder notation; the solution is $[0, 2)$ in interval notation.

87.
$$\frac{a+1}{a-2} > 3$$

$$\frac{a+1}{a-2} - 3 > 0$$

$$\frac{a+1}{a-2} - \frac{3(a-2)}{a-2} > 0$$

$$\frac{a+1-3a+6}{a-2} > 0$$

$$\frac{-2a+7}{a-2} > 0$$

The rational expression will equal 0 when $a = \frac{7}{2}$. It is undefined when $a = 2$.

Determine where the numerator and denominator are positive and negative and where the quotient is positive and negative.

Interval	$(-\infty, 2)$	2	$\left(2, \frac{7}{2}\right)$	$\frac{7}{2}$	$\left(\frac{7}{2}, \infty\right)$
$-2a + 7$	$++++$	$+$	$++++$	0	$----$
$a - 2$	$----$	0	$++++$	$+$	$++++$
$\frac{-2a+7}{a-2}$	$----$	$\varnothing$	$++++$	0	$----$

The rational function is undefined at $a = 2$, so 2 is not part of the solution. The inequality is strict, so $\frac{7}{2}$ is not part of the solution. Now, $\frac{-2a+7}{a-2}$ is greater than zero where the quotient is positive. The solution is $\left\{a \mid 2 < a < \frac{7}{2}\right\}$ in set-builder notation; the solution is $\left(2, \dfrac{7}{2}\right)$ in interval notation.

88.
$$\dfrac{4}{c-2} - \dfrac{3}{c} < 0$$

$$\dfrac{4c}{c(c-2)} - \dfrac{3(c-2)}{c(c-2)} < 0$$

$$\dfrac{4c - 3c + 6}{c(c-2)} < 0$$

$$\dfrac{c+6}{c(c-2)} < 0$$

The rational expression will equal 0 when $c = -6$. It is undefined when $c = 0$ and when $c = 2$.

Determine where the numerator and the factors of the denominator are positive and negative and where the quotient is positive and negative.

Interval	$(-\infty, -6)$	-6	$(-6, 0)$	0	$(0, 2)$	2	$(2, \infty)$
$c + 6$	$-\,-\,-$	0	$+\,+\,+$	$+$	$+\,+\,+$	$+$	$+\,+\,+$
c	$-\,-\,-$	$-$	$-\,-\,-$	0	$+\,+\,+$	$+$	$+\,+\,+$
$c - 2$	$-\,-\,-$	$-$	$-\,-\,-$	$-$	$-\,-\,-$	0	$+\,+\,+$
$\dfrac{c+6}{c(c-2)}$	$-\,-\,-$	0	$+\,+\,+$	$\varnothing$	$-\,-\,-$	$\varnothing$	$+\,+\,+$

The rational function is undefined at $c = 0$ and $c = 2$, so 0 and 2 are not part of the solution. The inequality is strict, so -6 is not part of the solution. Now, $\dfrac{c+6}{c(c-2)}$ is less than zero where the quotient is negative. The solution is $\{c \mid c < -6 \text{ or } 0 < c < 2\}$ in set-builder notation; the solution is $(-\infty, -6) \cup (0, 2)$ in interval notation.

89. $Q(x) < 0$

$$\dfrac{2x+3}{x-4} < 0$$

The rational expression will equal 0 when $x = -\dfrac{3}{2}$. It is undefined when $x = 4$.

Determine where the numerator and denominator are positive and negative and where the quotient is positive and negative.

Interval	$\left(-\infty, -\tfrac{3}{2}\right)$	$-\tfrac{3}{2}$	$\left(-\tfrac{3}{2}, 4\right)$	4	$(4, \infty)$
$2x + 3$	$-\,-\,-\,-$	0	$+\,+\,+\,+$	$+$	$+\,+\,+\,+$
$x - 4$	$-\,-\,-\,-$	$-$	$-\,-\,-\,-$	0	$+\,+\,+\,+$
$\dfrac{2x+3}{x-4}$	$+\,+\,+\,+$	0	$-\,-\,-\,-$	$\varnothing$	$+\,+\,+\,+$

The rational function is undefined at $x = 4$, so 4 is not part of the solution. The inequality is strict, so $-\dfrac{3}{2}$ is not part of the solution. Now, $\dfrac{2x+3}{x-4}$ is less than zero where the quotient is negative. The solution is $\left\{x \mid -\dfrac{3}{2} < x < 4\right\}$ in set-builder notation; the solution is $\left(-\dfrac{3}{2}, 4\right)$ in interval notation.

90. $R(x) \geq 0$

$$\dfrac{x+5}{x+1} \geq 0$$

The rational expression will equal 0 when $x = -5$. It is undefined when $x = -1$.
Determine where the numerator and the denominator are positive and negative and where the quotient is positive and negative.

Interval	$(-\infty, -5)$	-5	$(-5, -1)$	-1	$(-1, \infty)$
$x + 5$	$-\,-\,-\,-$	0	$+\,+\,+\,+$	$+$	$+\,+\,+\,+$
$x + 1$	$-\,-\,-\,-$	$-$	$-\,-\,-\,-$	0	$+\,+\,+\,+$
$\dfrac{x+5}{x+1}$	$+\,+\,+\,+$	0	$-\,-\,-\,-$	$\varnothing$	$+\,+\,+\,+$

The rational function is undefined at $x = -1$, so -1 is not part of the solution. The inequality is non-strict, so -5 is part of the solution. Now, $\dfrac{x+5}{x+1}$ is greater than zero where the quotient is positive. The solution is $\{x \mid x \le -5 \text{ or } x > -1\}$ in set-builder notation; the solution is $(-\infty, -5] \cup (-1, \infty)$ in interval notation.

91.

$$\frac{1}{C_1} + \frac{1}{C_2} = \frac{1}{C}$$

$$CC_1C_2\left(\frac{1}{C_1} + \frac{1}{C_2}\right) = CC_1C_2\left(\frac{1}{C}\right)$$

$$CC_2 + CC_1 = C_1C_2$$

$$C(C_2 + C_1) = C_1C_2$$

$$C = \frac{C_1C_2}{C_2 + C_1}$$

92.

$$\frac{P_1V_1}{T_1} = \frac{P_2V_2}{T_2}$$

$$T_1T_2\left(\frac{P_1V_1}{T_1}\right) = T_1T_2\left(\frac{P_2V_2}{T_2}\right)$$

$$T_2P_1V_1 = T_1P_2V_2$$

$$T_2 = \frac{T_1P_2V_2}{P_1V_1}$$

93.

$$T = \frac{4\pi^2 a^2}{MG}$$

$$MG \cdot T = MG\left(\frac{4\pi^2 a^2}{MG}\right)$$

$$MGT = 4\pi^2 a^2$$

$$G = \frac{4\pi^2 a^2}{MT}$$

94.

$$z = \frac{x - \mu}{\sigma}$$

$$z \cdot \sigma = \left(\frac{x - \mu}{\sigma}\right)\sigma$$

$$z \cdot \sigma = x - \mu$$

$$z \cdot \sigma + \mu = x$$

95.

$$\frac{AB}{AC} = \frac{DE}{DF}$$

$$\frac{3x - 6}{16} = \frac{15}{x}$$

$$16x\left(\frac{3x - 6}{16}\right) = 16x\left(\frac{15}{x}\right)$$

$$x(3x - 6) = 16 \cdot 15$$

$$3x^2 - 6x = 240$$

$$3x^2 - 6x - 240 = 0$$

$$3(x^2 - 2x - 80) = 0$$

$$3(x + 8)(x - 10) = 0$$

$$x + 8 = 0 \quad \text{or} \quad x - 10 = 0$$

$$x = -8 \quad \text{or} \quad x = 10$$

Since the length of DF cannot be negative, we discard $x = -8$ and keep $x = 10$. The length of AB is $3x - 6 = 3 \cdot 10 - 6 = 30 - 6 = 24$.

In summary, $AB = 24$ and $DF = 10$.

96. Let x represent the height of the tree.

$$\frac{\text{tree's height}}{\text{tree's shadow length}} = \frac{\text{post's height}}{\text{post's shadow length}}$$

$$\frac{x}{30} = \frac{5}{8}$$

$$120\left(\frac{x}{30}\right) = 120\left(\frac{5}{8}\right)$$

$$4x = 75$$

$$x = \frac{75}{4} = 18.75$$

The height of the pine tree is 18.75 feet.

97. Let x represent the number of grams of total carbohydrates in the 3-cup bowl.

$$\frac{\frac{3}{4}}{26} = \frac{3}{x}$$

$$26x\left(\frac{\frac{3}{4}}{26}\right) = 26x\left(\frac{3}{x}\right)$$

$$\frac{3}{4}x = 78$$

$$\frac{4}{3}\left(\frac{3}{4}x\right) = \frac{4}{3}(78)$$

$$x = 104$$

Three bowls of Honey Nut Chex® will contain 104 grams of total carbohydrates.

98. Let x represent the amount Jeri will earn working an 8-hour day.

$$\frac{48.75}{5} = \frac{x}{8}$$

$$40\left(\frac{48.75}{5}\right) = 40\left(\frac{x}{8}\right)$$

$$8(48.75) = 5x$$

$$390 = 5x$$

$$78 = x$$

Jeri will earn $78.00 for working an 8-hour day.

99. Let t represent the time required to fill the tank if both pipes are used.

NOTE: 1 hour and 12 minutes = 72 minutes

$$\begin{pmatrix} \text{Part filled by} \\ \text{first pipe} \\ \text{in 1 minute} \end{pmatrix} + \begin{pmatrix} \text{Part filled by} \\ \text{second pipe} \\ \text{in 1 minute} \end{pmatrix} = \begin{pmatrix} \text{Part filled} \\ \text{together} \\ \text{in 1 minute} \end{pmatrix}$$

$$\frac{1}{48} \quad + \quad \frac{1}{72} \quad = \quad \frac{1}{t}$$

$$144t\left(\frac{1}{48} + \frac{1}{72}\right) = 144t\left(\frac{1}{t}\right)$$

$$3t + 2t = 144$$

$$5t = 144$$

$$t = \frac{144}{5} = 28.8$$

If both pipes are used, it will take 28.8 minutes (or 28 minutes and 48 seconds) to fill the tank.

100. Let t represent the time required for Craig to mow the lawn when working alone.

NOTE: 1 hour and 10 minutes = $\frac{7}{6}$ hours

$$\begin{pmatrix} \text{Part done} \\ \text{by Diane} \\ \text{in 1 hour} \end{pmatrix} + \begin{pmatrix} \text{Part done} \\ \text{by Craig} \\ \text{in 1 hour} \end{pmatrix} = \begin{pmatrix} \text{Part done} \\ \text{together} \\ \text{in 1 hour} \end{pmatrix}$$

$$\frac{1}{2} \quad + \quad \frac{1}{t} \quad = \quad \frac{1}{\frac{7}{6}}$$

$$\frac{1}{2} + \frac{1}{t} = \frac{6}{7}$$

$$14t\left(\frac{1}{2} + \frac{1}{t}\right) = 14t\left(\frac{6}{7}\right)$$

$$7t + 14 = 12t$$

$$14 = 5t$$

$$t = \frac{14}{5} = 2.8$$

Working alone, it will take Craig 2.8 hours (or 2 hours and 48 minutes) to mow the lawn.

101. Let t represent the time required for John to carpet the room when working alone.

Then $t - 7$ will represent the time required for Rick to carpet the room when working alone.

$$\begin{pmatrix} \text{Part done} \\ \text{by John} \\ \text{in 1 hour} \end{pmatrix} + \begin{pmatrix} \text{Part done} \\ \text{by Rick} \\ \text{in 1 hour} \end{pmatrix} = \begin{pmatrix} \text{Part done} \\ \text{together} \\ \text{in 1 hour} \end{pmatrix}$$

$$\frac{1}{t} \quad + \quad \frac{1}{t-7} \quad = \quad \frac{1}{12}$$

$$12t(t-7)\left(\frac{1}{t} + \frac{1}{t-7}\right) = 12t(t-7)\left(\frac{1}{12}\right)$$

$$12(t-7) + 12t = t(t-7)$$

$$12t - 84 + 12t = t^2 - 7t$$

$$24t - 84 = t^2 - 7t$$

$$0 = t^2 - 31t + 84$$

$$0 = (t-3)(t-28)$$

$$t - 3 = 0 \quad \text{or} \quad t - 28 = 0$$

$$t = 3 \quad \text{or} \qquad t = 28$$

If John's time is $t = 3$, then Rick's time will be $t - 7 = 3 - 7 = -4$. Since time cannot be negative, we discard $t = 3$ and keep $t = 28$.

Working alone, it would take John 28 hours to carpet the room. It would take Rick $28 - 7 = 21$ hours to carpet the room alone.

102. Let t represent the time required for the drain to empty a full sink.

NOTE: 1 minute 30 seconds = 1.5 minutes.

$$\begin{pmatrix} \text{Part filled in} \\ \text{1 minute if} \\ \text{the drain is} \\ \text{plugged} \end{pmatrix} - \begin{pmatrix} \text{Part emptied} \\ \text{in 1 minute} \\ \text{if the drain} \\ \text{is unplugged} \end{pmatrix} = \begin{pmatrix} \text{Part filled in} \\ \text{1 minute if} \\ \text{the drain is} \\ \text{unplugged} \end{pmatrix}$$

$$\frac{1}{1} \quad - \quad \frac{1}{t} \quad = \quad \frac{1}{1.5}$$

$$3t\left(1 - \frac{1}{t}\right) = 3t\left(\frac{1}{1.5}\right)$$

$$3t - 3 = 2t$$

$$t = 3$$

It will take 3 minutes for the drain to empty a full sink.

103. Let x represent the speed of the wind.

NOTE: 1 hour and 15 minutes $= \dfrac{5}{4}$ hours.

	Distance (miles)	Rate (mph)	Time (hours)
With the wind	100	$180 + x$	$\dfrac{100}{180 + x}$
Against the wind	100	$180 - x$	$\dfrac{100}{180 - x}$
Total	200		$\dfrac{5}{4}$

$$\frac{100}{180 + x} + \frac{100}{180 - x} = \frac{5}{4}$$

$$4(180 + x)(180 - x)\left(\frac{100}{180 + x} + \frac{100}{180 - x}\right) =$$

$$4(180 + x)(180 - x)\left(\frac{5}{4}\right)$$

$$400(180 - x) + 400(180 + x) = 5(180 + x)(180 - x)$$

$$72{,}000 - 400x + 72{,}000 + 400x = 162{,}000 - 5x^2$$

$$144{,}000 = 162{,}000 - 5x^2$$

$$\frac{144{,}000}{5} = \frac{162{,}000 - 5x^2}{5}$$

$$28{,}800 = 32{,}400 - x^2$$

$$x^2 - 3600 = 0$$

$$(x - 60)(x + 60) = 0$$

$$x - 60 = 0 \quad \text{or} \quad x + 60 = 0$$

$$x = 60 \quad \text{or} \quad x = -60$$

Because the rate cannot be negative, we discard $x = -60$ and keep $x = 60$. The speed of the wind was 60 miles per hour.

104. Let x represent the speed of Jesse's boat in still water. Then $x + 5$ will represent the speed of his boat downstream and $x - 5$ will be the speed of his boat up stream.

	Distance (miles)	Rate (mph)	Time (hours)
Down	20	$x + 5$	$\dfrac{20}{x + 5}$
Up	10	$x - 5$	$\dfrac{10}{x - 5}$

$$\frac{20}{x + 5} = \frac{10}{x - 5}$$

$$(x + 5)(x - 5)\left(\frac{20}{x + 5}\right) = (x + 5)(x - 5)\left(\frac{10}{x - 5}\right)$$

$$20(x - 5) = 10(x + 5)$$

$$20x - 100 = 10x + 50$$

$$10x = 150$$

$$x = 15$$

Jesse's boat can travel 15 miles per hour in still water.

105. Let x represent the average speed at which Todd walks. Then $4x$ will represent the average speed at which he runs.

NOTE: 35 minutes $= \dfrac{7}{12}$ hours.

	Distance (miles)	Rate (mph)	Time (hours)
Walking	1	x	$\dfrac{1}{x}$
Running	3	$4x$	$\dfrac{3}{4x}$

$$\frac{1}{x} + \frac{3}{4x} = \frac{7}{12}$$

$$12x\left(\frac{1}{x} + \frac{3}{4x}\right) = 12x\left(\frac{7}{12}\right)$$

$$12 + 9 = 7x$$

$$21 = 7x$$

$$3 = x$$

Todd's average walking speed is 3 miles per hour. His average running speed is $4(3) = 12$ miles per hour.

106. Let x represent the average speed for the last 80 miles of the trip.

	Distance (miles)	Rate (mph)	Time (hours)
First 20 miles	20	30	$\dfrac{20}{30} = \dfrac{2}{3}$
Last 80 miles	80	x	$\dfrac{80}{x}$
Whole trip	100	50	$\dfrac{100}{50} = 2$

$$\frac{2}{3} + \frac{80}{x} = 2$$
$$3x\left(\frac{2}{3} + \frac{80}{x}\right) = 3x \cdot 2$$
$$2x + 240 = 6x$$
$$240 = 4x$$
$$60 = x$$

Danielle's average speed for the last 80 miles of her trip was 60 miles per hour.

107. a.
$$y = \frac{k}{x}$$
$$15 = \frac{k}{4}$$
$$60 = k$$

b.
$$y = \frac{60}{x}$$

c. If $x = 5$, then $y = \dfrac{60}{5} = 12$.

108. a.
$$y = kxz$$
$$45 = k \cdot 6 \cdot 10$$
$$45 = 60k$$
$$k = \frac{45}{60} = \frac{3}{4}$$

b.
$$y = \frac{3}{4}xz$$

c. If $x = 8$ and $z = 7$, then $y = \dfrac{3}{4} \cdot 8 \cdot 7 = 42$.

109. a.
$$s = \frac{k}{t^2}$$
$$18 = \frac{k}{2^2}$$
$$18 = \frac{k}{4}$$
$$72 = k$$

b. $s = \dfrac{72}{t^2}$

c. If $t = 3$, then $s = \dfrac{72}{3^2} = \dfrac{72}{9} = 8$.

110. a.
$$w = k \cdot \frac{x}{z}$$
$$\frac{4}{3} = k \cdot \frac{10}{12}$$
$$k = \frac{4}{3} \cdot \frac{12}{10} = \frac{8}{5}$$

b. $w = \dfrac{8}{5} \cdot \dfrac{x}{z}$ or $w = \dfrac{8x}{5z}$

c. If $x = 9$ and $z = 16$, then $w = \dfrac{8 \cdot 9}{5 \cdot 16} = \dfrac{9}{10}$.

111. Let f represent the frequency of a radio signal with wavelength l.
$$f = \frac{k}{l}$$
$$800 = \frac{k}{375}$$
$$375 \cdot 800 = 375\left(\frac{k}{375}\right)$$
$$300,000 = k$$
$$f(l) = \frac{300,000}{l}$$
$$f(250) = \frac{300,000}{250} = 1200$$

When the wavelength is 250 meters, the frequency is 1200 kilohertz.

112. Let C represent the electrical current when the resistance is R.
$$C = \frac{k}{R}$$
$$8 = \frac{k}{15}$$
$$15 \cdot 8 = 15\left(\frac{k}{15}\right)$$
$$120 = k$$
$$C(R) = \frac{120}{R}$$
$$C(10) = \frac{120}{10} = 12$$

If the electrical current is 10 amperes, then the resistance is 12 ohms.

113.
$$V = khd^2$$
$$231 = k \cdot 6 \cdot 7^2$$
$$231 = 294k$$
$$k = \frac{231}{294} = \frac{11}{14}$$
$$V = \frac{11}{14}hd^2$$

For $h = 14$ and $d = 8$, $V = \frac{11}{14}(14)(8)^2 = 704$.

If the diameter is 8 centimeters and the height is 14 centimeters, then the volume of the cylinder is 704 cubic centimeters.

114.
$$V = kBh$$
$$270 = k(81)(10)$$
$$270 = 810k$$
$$k = \frac{270}{810} = \frac{1}{3}$$
$$V = \frac{1}{3}Bh$$

For $B = 125$ and $h = 9$, $V = \frac{1}{3}(125)(9) = 375$.

When the area of the base is 125 square inches and the height is 9 inches, the volume of the pyramid is 375 cubic inches.

Chapter 6 Test

1. We need to find all values of x that cause the denominator $2x^2 - 13x - 7$ to equal 0.
$$2x^2 - 13x - 7 = 0$$
$$(2x+1)(x-7) = 0$$
$$2x + 1 = 0 \quad \text{or} \quad x - 7 = 0$$
$$2x = -1 \quad \text{or} \quad x = 7$$
$$x = -\frac{1}{2}$$

Thus, the domain of $f(x) = \dfrac{2x+1}{2x^2 - 13x - 7}$ is

$$\left\{ x \,\middle|\, x \neq -\frac{1}{2},\ x \neq 7 \right\}.$$

2.
$$\frac{2m^2 + 5m - 12}{3m^2 + 11m - 4} = \frac{(2m-3)(m+4)}{(3m-1)(m+4)}$$
$$= \frac{(2m-3)\cancel{(m+4)}}{(3m-1)\cancel{(m+4)}}$$
$$= \frac{2m-3}{3m-1}$$

3.
$$\frac{2b - 3a}{3a^2 + 10ab - 8b^2} = \frac{-1(3a - 2b)}{(3a - 2b)(a + 4b)}$$
$$= \frac{-1\cancel{(3a-2b)}}{\cancel{(3a-2b)}(a+4b)}$$
$$= \frac{-1}{a + 4b}$$

4.
$$\frac{4x^2 - 12x}{x^2 - 9} \cdot \frac{2x^2 + 11x + 15}{8x^3 - 32x^2}$$
$$= \frac{4x(x-3)}{(x+3)(x-3)} \cdot \frac{(2x+5)(x+3)}{8x^2(x-4)}$$
$$= \frac{\cancel{4x}\cancel{(x-3)}}{\cancel{(x+3)}\cancel{(x-3)}} \cdot \frac{(2x+5)\cancel{(x+3)}}{2x \cdot \cancel{4x}(x-4)}$$
$$= \frac{2x+5}{2x(x-4)}$$

5.
$$\frac{\dfrac{y^2 + 2y - 8}{4y^2 - 5y - 6}}{\dfrac{3y^2 - 14y - 5}{4y^2 - 17y - 15}}$$
$$= \frac{y^2 + 2y - 8}{4y^2 - 5y - 6} \cdot \frac{4y^2 - 17y - 15}{3y^2 - 14y - 5}$$
$$= \frac{(y-2)(y+4)}{(4y+3)(y-2)} \cdot \frac{(4y+3)(y-5)}{(3y+1)(y-5)}$$
$$= \frac{\cancel{(y-2)}(y+4)}{\cancel{(4y+3)}\cancel{(y-2)}} \cdot \frac{\cancel{(4y+3)}\cancel{(y-5)}}{(3y+1)\cancel{(y-5)}}$$
$$= \frac{y+4}{3y+1}$$

6. $p^2 - q^2 = (p-q)(p+q)$

$p - q$

$\text{LCD} = (p-q)(p+q)$

$$\frac{3p^2 + 3pq}{p^2 - q^2} - \frac{3p - 2q}{p - q}$$

$$= \frac{3p^2 + 3pq}{(p-q)(p+q)} - \frac{3p - 2q}{p-q} \cdot \frac{p+q}{p+q}$$

$$= \frac{3p^2 + 3pq}{(p-q)(p+q)} - \frac{3p^2 + pq - 2q^2}{(p-q)(p+q)}$$

$$= \frac{3p^2 + 3pq - \left(3p^2 + pq - 2q^2\right)}{(p-q)(p+q)}$$

$$= \frac{3p^2 + 3pq - 3p^2 - pq + 2q^2}{(p-q)(p+q)}$$

$$= \frac{2pq + 2q^2}{(p-q)(p+q)}$$

$$= \frac{2q(p+q)}{(p-q)(p+q)}$$

$$= \frac{2q}{p-q}$$

7. $3c^2 - 2c - 8 = (3c+4)(c-2)$

$3c^2 + c - 4 = (3c+4)(c-1)$

$\text{LCD} = (3c+4)(c-2)(c-1)$

$$\frac{9c+2}{3c^2 - 2c - 8} + \frac{7}{3c^2 + c - 4}$$

$$= \frac{9c+2}{(3c+4)(c-2)} \cdot \frac{c-1}{c-1} + \frac{7}{(3c+4)(c-1)} \cdot \frac{c-2}{c-2}$$

$$= \frac{9c^2 - 7c - 2}{(3c+4)(c-2)(c-1)} + \frac{7c - 14}{(3c+4)(c-2)(c-1)}$$

$$= \frac{9c^2 - 7c - 2 + 7c - 14}{(3c+4)(c-2)(c-1)}$$

$$= \frac{9c^2 - 16}{(3c+4)(c-2)(c-1)}$$

$$= \frac{(3c+4)(3c-4)}{(3c+4)(c-2)(c-1)}$$

$$= \frac{3c-4}{(c-2)(c-1)}$$

8. $Q(x) = \dfrac{f(x)}{h(x)} = \dfrac{\dfrac{3x}{x^2 - 4}}{\dfrac{9x^2 - 45x}{x^2 - 2x - 8}}$

$$= \frac{3x}{x^2 - 4} \cdot \frac{x^2 - 2x - 8}{9x^2 - 45x}$$

$$= \frac{3x}{(x+2)(x-2)} \cdot \frac{(x-4)(x+2)}{9x(x-5)}$$

$$= \frac{3x}{(x+2)(x-2)} \cdot \frac{(x-4)(x+2)}{3 \cdot 3x(x-5)}$$

$$= \frac{x-4}{3(x-2)(x-5)}$$

The domain of $f(x)$ is $\{x \mid x \neq -2, x \neq 2\}$. The domain of $h(x)$ is $\{x \mid x \neq -2, x \neq 4\}$. Because the denominator of $Q(x)$ cannot equal 0, we must exclude those values of x such that the numerator of $h(x)$ is 0. That is, we must exclude the values of x such that $9x^2 - 45x$. These values are $x = 0$ and $x = 5$. Therefore, the domain of $Q(x)$ is $\{x \mid x \neq -2, x \neq 0, x \neq 2, x \neq 4, x \neq 5\}$.

9. $x^2 - 4 = (x+2)(x-2)$

$x^2 + 2x = x(x+2)$

$\text{LCD} = x(x+2)(x-2)$

$S(x) = f(x) + g(x)$

$$= \frac{3x}{x^2 - 4} + \frac{6}{x^2 + 2x}$$

$$= \frac{3x}{(x+2)(x-2)} \cdot \frac{x}{x} + \frac{6}{x(x+2)} \cdot \frac{x-2}{x-2}$$

$$= \frac{3x^2}{x(x+2)(x-2)} + \frac{6x - 12}{x(x+2)(x-2)}$$

$$= \frac{3x^2 + 6x - 12}{x(x+2)(x-2)} \text{ or } \frac{3\left(x^2 + 2x - 4\right)}{x(x+2)(x-2)}$$

The domain of $f(x)$ is $\{x \mid x \neq -2, x \neq 2\}$. The domain of $g(x)$ is $\{x \mid x \neq -2, x \neq 0\}$. Therefore, the domain of $S(x)$ is $\{x \mid x \neq -2, x \neq 0, x \neq 2\}$.

10. Using Method 2, the LCD of all the denominators in the complex rational expression is a^2.

$$\frac{1-\dfrac{1}{a}}{1-\dfrac{1}{a^2}} = \frac{1-\dfrac{1}{a}}{1-\dfrac{1}{a^2}} \cdot \frac{a^2}{a^2} = \frac{1 \cdot a^2 - \dfrac{1}{a} \cdot a^2}{1 \cdot a^2 - \dfrac{1}{a^2} \cdot a^2}$$

$$= \frac{a^2 - a}{a^2 - 1} = \frac{a(a-1)}{(a+1)(a-1)} = \frac{a}{a+1}$$

11. Using Method 2, the LCD of all the denominators in the complex rational expression is $(d+2)(d-2)$.

$$\frac{\dfrac{5}{d+2} - \dfrac{1}{d-2}}{\dfrac{3}{d+2} - \dfrac{6}{d-2}} = \frac{\dfrac{5}{d+2} - \dfrac{1}{d-2}}{\dfrac{3}{d+2} - \dfrac{6}{d-2}} \cdot \frac{(d+2)(d-2)}{(d+2)(d-2)}$$

$$= \frac{\dfrac{5}{d+2} \cdot (d+2)(d-2) - \dfrac{1}{d-2} \cdot (d+2)(d-2)}{\dfrac{3}{d+2} \cdot (d+2)(d-2) - \dfrac{6}{d-2} \cdot (d+2)(d-2)}$$

$$= \frac{5(d-2) - (d+2)}{3(d-2) - 6(d+2)}$$

$$= \frac{5d-10-d-2}{3d-6-6d-12} = \frac{4d-12}{-3d-18} \text{ or } \frac{4(d-3)}{-3(d+6)}$$

12.
$$\frac{1}{6x} - \frac{1}{3} = \frac{5}{4x} + \frac{3}{4}$$
$$12x\left(\frac{1}{6x} - \frac{1}{3}\right) = 12x\left(\frac{5}{4x} + \frac{3}{4}\right)$$
$$12x\left(\frac{1}{6x}\right) - 12x\left(\frac{1}{3}\right) = 12x\left(\frac{5}{4x}\right) + 12x\left(\frac{3}{4}\right)$$
$$2 - 4x = 15 + 9x$$
$$-13x = 13$$
$$x = -1$$

Check:
$$\frac{1}{6(-1)} - \frac{1}{3} \overset{?}{=} \frac{5}{4(-1)} + \frac{3}{4}$$
$$\frac{1}{-6} - \frac{1}{3} \overset{?}{=} \frac{5}{-4} + \frac{3}{4}$$
$$\frac{1}{6} - \frac{2}{6} \overset{?}{=} -\frac{5}{4} + \frac{3}{4}$$
$$\frac{-3}{6} \overset{?}{=} \frac{-2}{4}$$
$$-\frac{1}{2} = -\frac{1}{2} \quad \leftarrow \text{True}$$

The solution checks, so the solution set is $\{-1\}$.

13.
$$\frac{7n}{n+3} + \frac{21}{n-3} = \frac{126}{n^2-9}$$
$$\frac{7n}{n+3} + \frac{21}{n-3} = \frac{126}{(n+3)(n-3)}$$
$$(n+3)(n-3)\left(\frac{7n}{n+3} + \frac{21}{n-3}\right) =$$
$$(n+3)(n-3)\left(\frac{126}{(n+3)(n-3)}\right)$$
$$7n(n-3) + 21(n+3) = 126$$
$$7n^2 - 21n + 21n + 63 = 126$$
$$7n^2 + 63 = 126$$
$$7n^2 - 63 = 0$$
$$\frac{7n^2 - 63}{7} = \frac{0}{7}$$
$$n^2 - 9 = 0$$
$$(n+3)(n-3) = 0$$
$$n+3 = 0 \quad \text{or} \quad n-3 = 0$$
$$n = -3 \quad \text{or} \quad n = 3$$

Since $n = -3$ and $n = 3$ are neither in the domain of the variable, they are both extraneous solutions. The solution set is $\varnothing$ or $\{\ \}$.

14.
$$\frac{x+5}{x-2} \geq 3$$
$$\frac{x+5}{x-2} - 3 \geq 0$$
$$\frac{x+5}{x-2} - \frac{3(x-2)}{x-2} \geq 0$$
$$\frac{x+5-3x+6}{x-2} \geq 0$$
$$\frac{-2x+11}{x-2} \geq 0$$

The rational expression will equal 0 when $x = \dfrac{11}{2}$.

It is undefined when $x = 2$.

Determine where the numerator and denominator are positive and negative and where the quotient is positive and negative.

Interval	$(-\infty, 2)$	2	$\left(2, \frac{11}{2}\right)$	$\frac{11}{2}$	$\left(\frac{11}{2}, \infty\right)$
$-2x+11$	$++++$	$+$	$++++$	0	$----$
$x-2$	$----$	0	$++++$	$+$	$++++$
$\dfrac{-2x+11}{x-2}$	$----$	$\varnothing$	$++++$	0	$----$

The rational function is undefined at $x = 2$, so 2 is not part of the solution. The inequality is non-strict, so $\dfrac{11}{2}$ is part of the solution. Now,

$\dfrac{-2x+11}{x-2}$ is greater than zero where the quotient

is positive. The solution is $\left\{ x \middle| 2 < x \le \dfrac{11}{2} \right\}$ in

set-builder notation; the solution is $\left(2, \dfrac{11}{2} \right]$ in

interval notation.

15.
$$\frac{1}{F} = \frac{D^2}{kq_1q_2}$$
$$Fkq_1q_2\left(\frac{1}{F}\right) = Fkq_1q_2\left(\frac{D^2}{kq_1q_2}\right)$$
$$kq_1q_2 = FD^2$$
$$k = \frac{FD^2}{q_1q_2}$$

16. Let t represent the time to print out the 48-page document.

$$\frac{\text{Number of pages}}{\text{time to print document}} = \frac{\text{Number of pages}}{\text{time to print document}}$$
$$\frac{10}{25} = \frac{48}{t}$$
$$25t\left(\frac{10}{25}\right) = 25t\left(\frac{48}{t}\right)$$
$$10t = 1200$$
$$t = 120$$

The printer will take 120 seconds (or 2 minutes) to print out the 48-page document.

17. Let t represent the time required if Linnette and Darrell work together to clean their house.

$$\begin{pmatrix}\text{Part done} \\ \text{by Linnette} \\ \text{in 1 hour}\end{pmatrix} + \begin{pmatrix}\text{Part done} \\ \text{by Darrell} \\ \text{in 1 hour}\end{pmatrix} = \begin{pmatrix}\text{Part done} \\ \text{together} \\ \text{in 1 hour}\end{pmatrix}$$
$$\frac{1}{4} + \frac{1}{6} = \frac{1}{t}$$
$$24t\left(\frac{1}{4} + \frac{1}{6}\right) = 24t\left(\frac{1}{t}\right)$$
$$6t + 4t = 24$$
$$10t = 24$$
$$t = \frac{24}{10} = 2.4$$

Working together, it will take Linnette and Darrell 2.4 hours (or 2 hours and 24 minutes) to clean their house.

18. Let x represent the speed of the current.

	Distance (miles)	Rate (mph)	Time (hours)
Up	4	$7-x$	$\dfrac{4}{7-x}$
Down	10	$7+x$	$\dfrac{10}{7+x}$

$$\frac{4}{7-x} = \frac{10}{7+x}$$
$$(7-x)(7+x)\left(\frac{4}{7-x}\right) = (7-x)(7+x)\left(\frac{10}{7+x}\right)$$
$$4(7+x) = 10(7-x)$$
$$28 + 4x = 70 - 10x$$
$$14x = 42$$
$$x = 3$$
The rate of the current is 3 miles per hour.

19.
$$F = \frac{k}{l}$$
$$50 = \frac{k}{4}$$
$$200 = k$$
$$F = \frac{200}{l}$$

If $l = 10$, then $F = \dfrac{200}{10} = 20$.

If the length of the length of the force arm of the lever is 10 feet, the force required to lift the boulder will be 20 pounds.

20.
$$L = krh$$
$$528 = k(7)(12)$$
$$528 = 84k$$
$$k = \frac{528}{84} = \frac{44}{7}$$
$$L = \frac{44}{7}rh$$

For $r = 9$ and $h = 14$, $L = \dfrac{44}{7}(9)(14) = 792$.

When the radius is 9 centimeters and the height is 14 centimeters, the lateral surface area of the right circular cylinder is 792 square centimeters.

Getting Ready for Chapter 7

1. radical sign

3. $|a|$

5. True

7. Perfect squares:
$4 = 2^2$, $9 = 3^2$, $16 = 4^2$, $25 = 5^2$

9. $\sqrt{1} = \sqrt{1^2} = 1$

11. $-\sqrt{100} = -\sqrt{10^2} = -10$

13. $\sqrt{\dfrac{1}{4}} = \sqrt{\left(\dfrac{1}{2}\right)^2} = \dfrac{1}{2}$

15. $\sqrt{0.36} = \sqrt{(0.6)^2} = 0.6$

17. $\left(\sqrt{1.6}\right)^2 = 1.6$

19. $\sqrt{-14}$ is not a real number because the radicand of the square root is negative.

21. $\sqrt{64}$ is rational because 64 is a perfect square.
$\sqrt{64} = \sqrt{(8)^2} = 8$

23. $\sqrt{\dfrac{1}{16}}$ is rational because $\dfrac{1}{16}$ is a perfect square.
$\sqrt{\dfrac{1}{16}} = \sqrt{\left(\dfrac{1}{4}\right)^2} = \dfrac{1}{4}$

25. $\sqrt{44}$ is irrational because 44 is not a perfect square.
$\sqrt{44} \approx 6.63$

27. $\sqrt{50}$ is irrational because 50 is not a perfect square.
$\sqrt{50} \approx 7.07$

29. $\sqrt{-16}$ is not a real number because the radicand of the square root is negative.

31. $\sqrt{8^2} = 8$

33. $\sqrt{(-19)^2} = |-19| = 19$

35. $\sqrt{r^2} = |r|$

37. $\sqrt{(x+4)^2} = |x+4|$

39. $\sqrt{(4x-3)^2} = |4x-3|$

41. $\sqrt{4y^2 + 12y + 9} = \sqrt{(2y+3)^2} = |2y+3|$

43. $\sqrt{25 + 144} = \sqrt{169} = \sqrt{(13)^2} = 13$

45. $\sqrt{25} + \sqrt{144} = \sqrt{5^2} + \sqrt{12^2} = 5 + 12 = 17$

47. $\sqrt{-144}$ is not a real number.

49. $3\sqrt{25} = 3\sqrt{(5)^2} = 3 \cdot 5 = 15$

51. $5\sqrt{\dfrac{16}{25}} - \sqrt{144} = 5\sqrt{\left(\dfrac{4}{5}\right)^2} - \sqrt{12^2} = 5 \cdot \dfrac{4}{5} - 12$
$= 4 - 12 = -8$

53. $\sqrt{8^2 - 4 \cdot 1 \cdot 7} = \sqrt{64 - 28} = \sqrt{36} = \sqrt{6^2} = 6$

55. $\sqrt{(-5)^2 - 4 \cdot 2 \cdot 5} = \sqrt{25 - 40} = \sqrt{-15}$ is not a real number.

57. $\dfrac{-(-1) + \sqrt{(-1)^2 - 4 \cdot 6 \cdot (-2)}}{2 \cdot (-1)} = \dfrac{1 + \sqrt{1 + 48}}{-2}$
$= \dfrac{1 + \sqrt{49}}{-2} = \dfrac{1 + 7}{-2} = \dfrac{8}{-2} = -4$

59. $\sqrt{(6-1)^2 + (15-3)^2} = \sqrt{5^2 + 12^2}$
$= \sqrt{25 + 144} = \sqrt{169} = \sqrt{13^2} = 13$

61. The square roots of 36 are 6 and -6 because $(6)^2 = 36$ and $(-6)^2 = 36$.
$\sqrt{36} = 6$ (the principal square root).

63. $Z = \dfrac{X - \mu}{\dfrac{\sigma}{\sqrt{n}}} = \dfrac{120 - 100}{\dfrac{15}{\sqrt{13}}} = \dfrac{20}{\dfrac{15}{\sqrt{13}}}$
$= 20 \cdot \dfrac{\sqrt{13}}{15} = \dfrac{4\sqrt{13}}{3} \approx 4.81$

Chapter 7

7.1 Preparing for *n*th Root and Rational Exponents

1. $\left(\dfrac{x^2 y}{xy^{-2}}\right)^{-3} = \left(x^{2-1}y^{1-(-2)}\right)^{-3}$

$\quad = \left(xy^3\right)^{-3}$

$\quad = \left(\dfrac{1}{xy^3}\right)^{3}$

$\quad = \dfrac{1}{x^3 y^9}$

2. $\left(\sqrt{7}\right)^2 = 7$

3. $\sqrt{64} = 8$ since $8^2 = 64$.

7.1 Exercises

1. $\sqrt[n]{a}$

3. index

5. False; $a^{1/n}$ does not exist in the real number system for even integer values of n when $a < 0$.

7. Answers will vary.

9. $\sqrt[3]{125} = \sqrt[3]{5^3} = 5$

11. $\sqrt[3]{-27} = \sqrt[3]{(-3)^3} = -3$

13. $-\sqrt[4]{625} = -\sqrt[4]{5^4} = -5$

15. $\sqrt[3]{-\dfrac{1}{8}} = \sqrt[3]{\left(-\dfrac{1}{2}\right)^3} = -\dfrac{1}{2}$

17. $-\sqrt[5]{-243} = -\sqrt[5]{(-3)^5} = -(-3) = 3$

19. $\sqrt[3]{5^3} = 5$

21. $\sqrt[4]{m^4} = |m|$

23. $\sqrt[9]{(x-3)^9} = x-3$

25. $-\sqrt[4]{(3p+1)^4} = -|3p+1|$

27. $4^{1/2} = \sqrt{4} = \sqrt{2^2} = 2$

29. $-36^{1/2} = -\sqrt{36} = -\sqrt{6^2} = -6$

31. $8^{1/3} = \sqrt[3]{8} = \sqrt[3]{2^3} = 2$

33. $-16^{1/4} = -\sqrt[4]{16} = -\sqrt[4]{2^4} = -2$

35. $\left(\dfrac{4}{25}\right)^{1/2} = \sqrt{\dfrac{4}{25}} = \dfrac{\sqrt{4}}{\sqrt{25}} = \dfrac{\sqrt{2^2}}{\sqrt{5^2}} = \dfrac{2}{5}$

37. $(-125)^{1/3} = \sqrt[3]{-125} = \sqrt[3]{(-5)^3} = -5$

39. $(-4)^{1/2} = \sqrt{-4}$ is not a real number.

41. $4^{5/2} = \left(\sqrt{4}\right)^5 = 2^5 = 32$

43. $-16^{3/2} = -\left(\sqrt{16}\right)^3 = -4^3 = -64$

45. $8^{4/3} = \left(\sqrt[3]{8}\right)^4 = 2^4 = 16$

47. $(-64)^{2/3} = \left(\sqrt[3]{-64}\right)^2 = (-4)^2 = 16$

49. $-(-32)^{3/5} = -\left(\sqrt[5]{-32}\right)^3 = -(-2)^3 = -(-8) = 8$

51. $144^{-1/2} = \left(\sqrt{144}\right)^{-1} = (12)^{-1} = \dfrac{1}{12}$

53. $\dfrac{1}{25^{-3/2}} = 25^{3/2} = \left(\sqrt{25}\right)^3 = 5^3 = 125$

55. $\dfrac{1}{8^{-5/3}} = 8^{5/3} = \left(\sqrt[3]{8}\right)^5 = 2^5 = 32$

57. $\sqrt[3]{3x} = (3x)^{1/3}$

59. $\sqrt[4]{\dfrac{x}{3}} = \left(\dfrac{x}{3}\right)^{1/4}$

61. $\sqrt[4]{x^3} = x^{3/4}$

63. $\left(\sqrt[5]{3x}\right)^2 = (3x)^{2/5}$

65. $\sqrt{\left(\dfrac{5x}{y}\right)^3} = \left(\dfrac{5x}{y}\right)^{3/2}$

67. $\sqrt[3]{(9ab)^4} = (9ab)^{4/3}$

69. $\sqrt[3]{25} = 25\,^\wedge(1/3) \approx 2.92$

71. $\sqrt[4]{12} = 12\,^\wedge(1/4) \approx 1.86$

73. $20^{1/2} = \sqrt{20} \approx 4.47$

75. $4^{5/3} = 4\,^\wedge(5/3) \approx 10.08$

77. $10^{0.1} = 10\,^\wedge(0.1) \approx 1.26$

79. $\sqrt[3]{512} = \sqrt[3]{8^3} = 8$

81. $9^{5/2} = \left(\sqrt{9}\right)^5 = 3^5 = 243$

83. $\sqrt[4]{-16}$ is not a real number because the index is even and the radicand is negative.

85. $144^{-1/2} = \dfrac{1}{144^{1/2}} = \dfrac{1}{\sqrt{144}} = \dfrac{1}{12}$

87. $\sqrt[3]{0.008} = \sqrt[3]{(0.2)^3} = 0.2$

89. $4^{1/2} + 25^{3/2} = \sqrt{4} + \left(\sqrt{25}\right)^3 = 2 + 5^3$
$$= 2 + 125 = 127$$

91. $(-25)^{5/2} = \left(\sqrt{-25}\right)^5$ is not a real number.

93. 10 is the only cube root of 1000.
$$\sqrt[3]{1000} = \sqrt[3]{(10)^3} = 10$$

95. a. $W = 35.74 + 0.6215(30) - 35.75(10)^{0.16}$
$$+ 0.4275(30)(10)^{0.16}$$
$$\approx 21.25$$
The windchill would be about $21.25°F$.

b. $W = 35.74 + 0.6215(30) - 35.75(20)^{0.16}$
$$+ 0.4275(30)(20)^{0.16}$$
$$\approx 17.36$$
The windchill would be about $17.36°F$.

c. $W = 35.74 + 0.6215(0) - 35.75(10)^{0.16}$
$$+ 0.4275(0)(10)^{0.16}$$
$$\approx -15.93$$
The windchill would be about $-15.93°F$.

97. a. $v_t = \sqrt{\dfrac{2mg}{C\rho A}}$
$$= \sqrt{\dfrac{2 \cdot \dfrac{4}{3}\pi r^3 \rho_w \cdot g}{C\rho \cdot \pi r^2}}$$
$$= \sqrt{\dfrac{8r\rho_w g}{3C\rho}}\ \text{m/s}$$

b. The radius is $1.5\text{ mm} = 0.0015\text{ m}$. We also have $\rho_w = 1000\text{ kg/m}^3$, $g \approx 9.81\text{ m/s}^2$, $C = 0.6$, and $\rho \approx 1.2\text{ kg/m}^3$.
$$v_t = \sqrt{\dfrac{8(0.0015)(1000)(9.81)}{3(0.6)(1.2)}} \approx 7.38\text{ m/s}$$
The terminal velocity is about 7.38 meters per second.

99. $f(x) = x^{3/2}$
$$f(4) = 4^{3/2} = \left(\sqrt{4}\right)^3 = 2^3 = 8$$

101. $F(z) = z^{4/3}$
$$F(-8) = (-8)^{4/3} = \left(\sqrt[3]{-8}\right)^4 = (-2)^4 = 16$$

103. $\left(\dfrac{x^2 y}{y^{-2}}\right)^3 = \left(x^2 y^{1-(-2)}\right)^3 = \left(x^2 y^3\right)^3$
$$= \left(x^2\right)^3 \left(y^3\right)^3 = x^6 y^9$$

105. $\dfrac{(x-1)^2\left(x^2+5x+6\right)}{(x+2)\sqrt{x-1}}$

$=\dfrac{(x-1)^2(x+2)(x+3)}{(x+2)(x-1)^{1/2}}$

$=(x-1)^{2-1/2}(x+2)^{1-1}(x+3)$

$=(x-1)^{3/2}(x+3)$

107. $\dfrac{\left(4z^2-7z+3\right)+\left(-3z^2-z+9\right)}{\left(4z^2-2z-7\right)+\left(-3z^2-z+9\right)}$

$=\dfrac{4z^2-7z+3-3z^2-z+9}{4z^2-2z-7-3z^2-z+9}$

$=\dfrac{z^2-8z+12}{z^2-3z+2}=\dfrac{(z-6)(z-2)}{(z-1)(z-2)}$

$=\dfrac{z-6}{z-1}$

7.2 Preparing for Simplifying Expressions Using the Laws of Exponents

1. $z^{-3}=\dfrac{1}{z^3}$

2. $x^{-2}\cdot x^5=x^{-2+5}=x^3$

3. $\left(\dfrac{2a^2}{b^{-1}}\right)^3=\left(2a^2b\right)^3=2^3\left(a^2\right)^3 b^3=8a^6b^3$

4. $\sqrt{64}=8$ because $8^2=64$.

7.2 Exercises

1. $a^r b^r$

3. $5^{1/2}\cdot 5^{3/2}=5^{\frac{1}{2}+\frac{3}{2}}=5^{\frac{4}{2}}=5^2=25$

5. $\dfrac{8^{5/4}}{8^{1/4}}=8^{\frac{5}{4}-\frac{1}{4}}=8^{4/4}=8^1=8$

7. $2^{1/3}\cdot 2^{-3/2}=2^{\frac{1}{3}+\left(-\frac{3}{2}\right)}=2^{\frac{2}{6}-\frac{9}{6}}=2^{-7/6}=\dfrac{1}{2^{7/6}}$

9. $\dfrac{x^{1/4}}{x^{5/6}}=x^{\frac{1}{4}-\frac{5}{6}}=x^{\frac{3}{12}-\frac{10}{12}}=x^{-7/12}=\dfrac{1}{x^{7/12}}$

11. $\left(4^{4/3}\right)^{3/8}=4^{\frac{4}{3}\cdot\frac{3}{8}}=4^{1/2}=\sqrt{4}=2$

13. $\left(25^{3/4}\cdot 4^{-3/4}\right)^2=\left[\left(25\cdot 4^{-1}\right)^{3/4}\right]^2$

$=\left(\dfrac{25}{4}\right)^{\frac{3}{4}\cdot 2}=\left(\dfrac{25}{4}\right)^{3/2}$

$=\left(\sqrt{\dfrac{25}{4}}\right)^3=\left(\dfrac{5}{2}\right)^3=\dfrac{125}{8}$

15. $\left(x^{3/4}\cdot y^{1/3}\right)^{2/3}=\left(x^{3/4}\right)^{2/3}\cdot\left(y^{1/3}\right)^{2/3}$

$=x^{\frac{3}{4}\cdot\frac{2}{3}}\cdot y^{\frac{1}{3}\cdot\frac{2}{3}}$

$=x^{1/2}y^{2/9}$

17. $\left(x^{-1/3}\cdot y\right)\left(x^{1/2}\cdot y^{-4/3}\right)=x^{-\frac{1}{3}+\frac{1}{2}}\cdot y^{1+\left(-\frac{4}{3}\right)}$

$=x^{-\frac{2}{6}+\frac{3}{6}}\cdot y^{\frac{3}{3}-\frac{4}{3}}$

$=x^{1/6}\cdot y^{-1/3}$

$=\dfrac{x^{1/6}}{y^{1/3}}$

19. $\left(4a^2 b^{-3/2}\right)^{1/2}=4^{1/2}\cdot\left(a^2\right)^{1/2}\cdot\left(b^{-3/2}\right)^{1/2}$

$=2\cdot a^{2\cdot\frac{1}{2}}\cdot b^{-\frac{3}{2}\cdot\frac{1}{2}}$

$=2a^1 b^{-3/4}$

$=\dfrac{2a}{b^{3/4}}$

21. $\left(\dfrac{x^{2/3}y^{-1/3}}{8x^{1/2}y}\right)^{1/3} = \left(\dfrac{1}{8}x^{(2/3)-(1/2)}y^{(-1/3)-1}\right)^{1/3}$

$= \left(\dfrac{1}{8}x^{1/6}y^{-4/3}\right)^{1/3}$

$= \left(\dfrac{1}{8}\right)^{1/3}\left(x^{1/6}\right)^{1/3}\left(y^{-4/3}\right)^{1/3}$

$= \dfrac{1}{2}x^{1/18}y^{-4/9}$

$= \dfrac{x^{1/18}}{2y^{4/9}}$

23. $\left(\dfrac{50x^{3/4}y}{2x^{1/2}}\right)^{1/2} + \left(\dfrac{x^{1/2}y^{1/2}}{9x^{3/4}y^{3/2}}\right)^{-1/2}$

$= \left(25x^{\frac{3}{4}-\frac{1}{2}}y\right)^{1/2} + \left(\dfrac{1}{9}x^{\frac{1}{2}-\frac{3}{4}}y^{\frac{1}{2}-\frac{3}{2}}\right)^{-1/2}$

$= \left(25x^{1/4}y\right)^{1/2} + \left(\dfrac{1}{9}x^{-1/4}y^{-1}\right)^{-1/2}$

$= \left(25x^{1/4}y\right)^{1/2} + \left(\dfrac{1}{9x^{1/4}y^{1}}\right)^{-1/2}$

$= \left(25x^{1/4}y\right)^{1/2} + \left(9x^{1/4}y\right)^{1/2}$

$= 25^{1/2}\left(x^{1/4}\right)^{1/2}y^{1/2} + 9^{1/2}\left(x^{1/4}\right)^{1/2}y^{1/2}$

$= 5x^{1/8}y^{1/2} + 3x^{1/8}y^{1/2}$

$= 8x^{1/8}y^{1/2}$

25. $x^{1/2}\left(x^{3/2}-2\right) = x^{1/2}\cdot x^{3/2} - x^{1/2}\cdot 2$

$= x^{4/2} - 2x^{1/2}$

$= x^2 - 2x^{1/2}$

27. $2y^{-1/3}\left(1+3y\right) = 2y^{-1/3}\cdot 1 + 2y^{-1/3}\cdot 3y$

$= 2y^{-1/3} + 6y^{-\frac{1}{3}+1}$

$= \dfrac{2}{y^{1/3}} + 6y^{2/3}$

29. $4z^{3/2}\left(z^{3/2}-8z^{-3/2}\right) = 4z^{3/2}\cdot z^{3/2} - 4z^{3/2}\cdot 8z^{-3/2}$

$= 4z^{\frac{3}{2}+\frac{3}{2}} - 32z^{\frac{3}{2}+\left(-\frac{3}{2}\right)}$

$= 4z^{6/2} - 32z^0$

$= 4z^3 - 32$

$= 4\left(z^3-8\right)$

$= 4\left(z-2\right)\left(z^2+2z+4\right)$

31. $\sqrt{x^8} = \left(x^8\right)^{1/2} = x^{8\cdot\frac{1}{2}} = x^4$

33. $\sqrt[12]{8^4} = \left(8^4\right)^{1/12} = 8^{4\cdot\frac{1}{12}} = 8^{1/3} = \sqrt[3]{8} = 2$

35. $\sqrt[3]{8a^3b^{12}} = \left(8a^3b^{12}\right)^{1/3}$

$= 8^{1/3}\left(a^3\right)^{1/3}\left(b^{12}\right)^{1/3}$

$= 2ab^4$

37. $\dfrac{\sqrt{x}}{\sqrt[4]{x}} = \dfrac{x^{1/2}}{x^{1/4}} = x^{\frac{1}{2}-\frac{1}{4}} = x^{\frac{2}{4}-\frac{1}{4}} = x^{1/4} = \sqrt[4]{x}$

39. $\sqrt{x}\cdot\sqrt[3]{x} = x^{1/2}\cdot x^{1/3} = x^{\frac{1}{2}+\frac{1}{3}}$

$= x^{\frac{3}{6}+\frac{2}{6}} = x^{5/6}$

$= \sqrt[6]{x^5}$

41. $\sqrt{\sqrt[4]{x^3}} = \left(\left(x^3\right)^{1/4}\right)^{1/2} = \left(x^{3/4}\right)^{1/2} = x^{3/8} = \sqrt[8]{x^3}$

43. $\sqrt{3}\cdot\sqrt[3]{9} = \sqrt{3}\cdot\sqrt[3]{3^2}$

$= 3^{1/2}\cdot 3^{2/3}$

$= 3^{\frac{1}{2}+\frac{2}{3}}$

$= 3^{7/6}$

$= \sqrt[6]{3^7}$

45. $\dfrac{\sqrt{6}}{\sqrt[4]{36}} = \dfrac{\sqrt{6}}{\sqrt[4]{6^2}} = \dfrac{6^{1/2}}{6^{2/4}} = 6^{\frac{1}{2}-\frac{2}{4}} = 6^{\frac{1}{2}-\frac{1}{2}} = 6^0 = 1$

47. $2x^{3/2} + 3x^{1/2}(x+5) = 2x^{1/2} \cdot x + 3x^{1/2}(x+5)$
$$= x^{1/2}(2x + 3(x+5))$$
$$= x^{1/2}(2x + 3x + 15)$$
$$= x^{1/2}(5x + 15)$$
$$= 5x^{1/2}(x+3)$$

49. $5(x+2)^{2/3}(3x-2) + 9(x+2)^{5/3}$
$$= 5(x+2)^{2/3}(3x-2) + 9(x+2)^{2/3} \cdot (x+2)^{3/3}$$
$$= (x+2)^{2/3}(5(3x-2) + 9(x+2))$$
$$= (x+2)^{2/3}(15x - 10 + 9x + 18)$$
$$= (x+2)^{2/3}(24x + 8)$$
$$= 8(x+2)^{2/3}(3x+1)$$

51. $x^{-1/2}(2x+5) + 4x^{1/2}$
$$= x^{-1/2}(2x+5) + 4x^{-1/2} \cdot x^{2/2}$$
$$= x^{-1/2}(2x + 5 + 4x)$$
$$= x^{-1/2}(6x + 5)$$
$$= \frac{6x+5}{x^{1/2}}$$

53. $2(x-4)^{-1/3}(4x-3) + 12(x-4)^{2/3}$
$$= 2(x-4)^{-1/3}(4x-3) + 12(x-4)^{-1/3}(x-4)^{3/3}$$
$$= 2(x-4)^{-1/3}((4x-3) + 6(x-4))$$
$$= 2(x-4)^{-1/3}(4x - 3 + 6x - 24)$$
$$= 2(x-4)^{-1/3}(10x - 27)$$
$$= \frac{2(10x-27)}{(x-4)^{1/3}}$$

55. $15x(x^2+4)^{1/2} + 5(x^2+4)^{3/2}$
$$= 15x(x^2+4)^{1/2} + 5(x^2+4)^{1/2}(x^2+4)^{2/2}$$
$$= 5(x^2+4)^{1/2}(3x + x^2 + 4)$$
$$= 5(x^2+4)^{1/2}(x^2 + 3x + 4)$$

57. $\sqrt[8]{4^4} = 4^{4/8} = 4^{1/2} = (2^2)^{1/2} = 2$

59. $(-2)^{1/2} \cdot (-2)^{3/2} = (-2)^{4/2} = (-2)^2 = 4$

61. $(100^{1/3})^{3/2} = 100^{\frac{1}{3} \cdot \frac{3}{2}} = 100^{1/2} = \sqrt{100} = 10$

63. $(\sqrt[4]{25})^2 = 25^{2/4} = 25^{1/2} = \sqrt{25} = 5$

65. $\sqrt[4]{x^2} - \frac{\sqrt[4]{x^6}}{x} = x^{2/4} - \frac{x^{6/4}}{x}$
$$= x^{1/2} - x^{\frac{3}{2}-1}$$
$$= x^{1/2} - x^{1/2}$$
$$= 0$$

67. $(4 \cdot 9^{1/4})^{-2} = 4^{-2} \cdot (9^{1/4})^{-2}$
$$= \frac{1}{4^2} \cdot 9^{-1/2} = \frac{1}{16 \cdot 9^{1/2}}$$
$$= \frac{1}{16\sqrt{9}} = \frac{1}{16(3)} = \frac{1}{48}$$

69. $3^x = 25$
$$3^{x/2} = 3^{x \cdot \frac{1}{2}} = (3^x)^{1/2} = (25)^{1/2} = 5$$
Thus, $3^{x/2} = 5$.

71. $7^x = 9$
$$\sqrt{7^x} = \sqrt{9} = 3$$

73. $\sqrt[4]{\sqrt[3]{\sqrt{x}}} = (\sqrt[3]{\sqrt{x}})^{1/4}$
$$= ((\sqrt{x})^{1/3})^{1/4}$$
$$= (\sqrt{x})^{1/12}$$
$$= (x^{1/2})^{1/12}$$
$$= x^{1/24}$$
$$= \sqrt[24]{x}$$

75. $(6^{\sqrt{2}})^{\sqrt{2}} = 6^{\sqrt{2} \cdot \sqrt{2}} = 6^2 = 36$

77. $f(x) = (x+3)^{1/2}(x+1)^{-1/2} = \dfrac{\sqrt{x+3}}{\sqrt{x+1}}$

We need $x+3 \geq 0$ and $x+1 > 0$.

$x+3 \geq 0$ and $x+1 > 0$

    $x \geq -3$ $x > -1$

The domain is the set of values that satisfy both inequalities. Thus, the domain is $x > -1$.

Domain: $\{x \mid x > -1\}$ or $(-1, \infty)$

We can check this graphically:

79. $3a(a-3) + (a+3)(a-2)$

$= 3a^2 - 9a + a^2 - 2a + 3a - 6$

$= 4a^2 - 8a - 6$

$= 2(2a^2 - 4a - 3)$

81. $\dfrac{x^2 - 4}{x+2} \cdot (x+5) - (x+4)(x-1)$

$= \dfrac{(x+2)(x-2)(x+5)}{(x+2)} - (x+4)(x-1)$

$= (x-2)(x+5) - (x+4)(x-1)$

$= (x^2 + 3x - 10) - (x^2 + 3x - 4)$

$= x^2 + 3x - 10 - x^2 - 3x + 4$

$= -6$

7.3 Preparing for Simplifying Radical Expressions

1. $1^2 = 1$, $2^2 = 4$, $3^2 = 9$, $4^2 = 16$, $5^2 = 25$,
$6^2 = 36$, $7^2 = 49$, $8^2 = 64$, $9^2 = 81$,
$10^2 = 100$, $11^2 = 121$, $12^2 = 144$, $13^2 = 169$,
and $14^2 = 196$.

2. $1^3 = 1$, $2^3 = 8$, $3^3 = 27$, $4^3 = 64$, and $5^3 = 125$.

3. a. $\sqrt{16} = \sqrt{4^2} = 4$

   b. $\sqrt{p^2} = |p|$

7.3 Exercises

1. $\sqrt[n]{a} \cdot \sqrt[n]{b} = \sqrt[n]{a \cdot b}$

3. False; $\sqrt{8x} = \sqrt{4 \cdot 2x} = \sqrt{4} \cdot \sqrt{2x} = 2\sqrt{2x}$

5. $0 = 0^2$, $1 = 1^2$, $4 = 2^2$, $9 = 3^2$, $16 = 4^2$, $25 = 5^2$

7. Answers may vary. One possibility:
Factor the radicand into the product of a perfect cube and everything else. Split up the radical and simplify the portion with the perfect cube.
$\sqrt[3]{16a^5} = \sqrt[3]{8a^3 \cdot 2a^2} = \sqrt[3]{8a^3} \cdot \sqrt[3]{2a^2} = 2a\sqrt[3]{2a^2}$

9. $\sqrt{2} \cdot \sqrt{7} = \sqrt{2 \cdot 7} = \sqrt{14}$

11. $\sqrt[3]{6} \cdot \sqrt[3]{10} = \sqrt[3]{6 \cdot 10} = \sqrt[3]{60}$

13. $\sqrt{3a} \cdot \sqrt{5b} = \sqrt{3a \cdot 5b} = \sqrt{15ab}$ if $a, b \geq 0$.
(If $a, b < 0$, then the result is $-\sqrt{15ab}$. If a and b have opposite signs, the result is not a real number.)

15. $\sqrt{x-7} \cdot \sqrt{x+7} = \sqrt{(x-7)(x+7)} = \sqrt{x^2 - 49}$
if $|x| \geq 7$, otherwise the result is not a real number.

17. $\sqrt{\dfrac{5x}{3}} \cdot \sqrt{\dfrac{3}{x}} = \sqrt{\dfrac{5x}{3} \cdot \dfrac{3}{x}} = \sqrt{5}$ if $x > 0$.

19. $\sqrt{50} = \sqrt{25 \cdot 2} = \sqrt{25} \cdot \sqrt{2} = 5\sqrt{2}$

21. $\sqrt[3]{54} = \sqrt[3]{27 \cdot 2} = \sqrt[3]{27} \cdot \sqrt[3]{2} = 3\sqrt[3]{2}$

23. $\sqrt{48x^2} = \sqrt{16x^2 \cdot 3} = \sqrt{16x^2} \cdot \sqrt{3} = 4|x|\sqrt{3}$

25. $\sqrt[3]{-27x^3} = -3x$

27. $\sqrt[4]{32m^4} = \sqrt[4]{16m^4 \cdot 2} = \sqrt[4]{16m^4} \cdot \sqrt[4]{2} = 2|m|\sqrt[4]{2}$

29. $\sqrt{12p^2q} = \sqrt{4p^2 \cdot 3q} = \sqrt{4p^2} \cdot \sqrt{3q} = 2|p|\sqrt{3q}$

31. $3\sqrt{24a} = 3\sqrt{4 \cdot 6a} = 3 \cdot \sqrt{4} \cdot \sqrt{6a} = 6\sqrt{6a}$

33. $\sqrt{162m^4} = \sqrt{81m^4 \cdot 2} = \sqrt{81m^4} \cdot \sqrt{2} = 9m^2\sqrt{2}$

35. $\sqrt{y^{13}} = \sqrt{y^{12} \cdot y} = \sqrt{y^{12}} \cdot \sqrt{y} = y^6\sqrt{y}$

37. $\sqrt[3]{c^8} = \sqrt[3]{c^6 \cdot c^2} = \sqrt[3]{c^6} \cdot \sqrt[3]{c^2} = c^2\sqrt[3]{c^2}$

39. $\sqrt{m^5n^3} = \sqrt{m^4n^2 \cdot mn}$
$= \sqrt{m^4n^2} \cdot \sqrt{mn}$
$= m^2|n|\sqrt{mn}$

41. $\sqrt{125p^3q^4} = \sqrt{25p^2q^4 \cdot 5p} = \sqrt{25p^2q^4} \cdot \sqrt{5p}$
$= 5|p|q^2\sqrt{5p}$

43. $\sqrt[3]{-16x^9} = \sqrt[3]{-8x^9 \cdot 2} = \sqrt[3]{-8x^9} \cdot \sqrt[3]{2} = -2x^3\sqrt[3]{2}$

45. $\sqrt{p^3q^5r} = \sqrt{p^2q^4 \cdot pqr}$
$= \sqrt{p^2q^4} \cdot \sqrt{pqr}$
$= |p|q^2\sqrt{pqr}$

47. $\sqrt[5]{-16m^8n^2} = \sqrt[5]{-m^5 \cdot 16m^3n^2}$
$= \sqrt[5]{-m^5} \cdot \sqrt[5]{16m^3n^2}$
$= -m\sqrt[5]{16m^3n^2}$

49. $\sqrt[4]{(x-y)^5} = \sqrt[4]{(x-y)^4 \cdot (x-y)}$
$= \sqrt[4]{(x-y)^4} \cdot \sqrt[4]{x-y}$
$= (x-y)\sqrt[4]{x-y}$

51. $\sqrt[3]{8x^3 - 8y^3} = \sqrt[3]{8(x^3 - y^3)}$
$= \sqrt[3]{8} \cdot \sqrt[3]{x^3 - y^3}$
$= 2\sqrt[3]{x^3 - y^3}$

53. $\dfrac{4 + \sqrt{36}}{2} = \dfrac{4 + 6}{2} = \dfrac{10}{2} = 5$

55. $\dfrac{9 + \sqrt{18}}{3} = \dfrac{9 + \sqrt{9 \cdot 2}}{3} = \dfrac{9 + \sqrt{9} \cdot \sqrt{2}}{3}$
$= \dfrac{9 + 3\sqrt{2}}{3} = \dfrac{3(3 + \sqrt{2})}{3}$
$= 3 + \sqrt{2}$

57. $\dfrac{-4 - \sqrt{162}}{6} = \dfrac{-4 - \sqrt{81 \cdot 2}}{6}$
$= \dfrac{-4 - \sqrt{81} \cdot \sqrt{2}}{6}$
$= \dfrac{-4 - 9\sqrt{2}}{6}$

59. $\dfrac{7 - \sqrt{98}}{14} = \dfrac{7 - \sqrt{49 \cdot 2}}{14} = \dfrac{7 - \sqrt{49} \cdot \sqrt{2}}{14}$
$= \dfrac{7 - 7\sqrt{2}}{14} = \dfrac{7(1 - \sqrt{2})}{7 \cdot 2}$
$= \dfrac{1 - \sqrt{2}}{2}$

61. $\sqrt{5} \cdot \sqrt{5} = \sqrt{5 \cdot 5} = \sqrt{25} = 5$

63. $\sqrt{2} \cdot \sqrt{8} = \sqrt{2 \cdot 8} = \sqrt{16} = 4$

65. $\sqrt[3]{4} \cdot \sqrt[3]{2} = \sqrt[3]{4 \cdot 2} = \sqrt[3]{8} = 2$

67. $\sqrt{5x} \cdot \sqrt{15x} = \sqrt{5x \cdot 15x}$
$= \sqrt{75x^2}$
$= \sqrt{25x^2 \cdot 3}$
$= \sqrt{25x^2} \cdot \sqrt{3}$
$= 5x\sqrt{3}$

69. $\sqrt[3]{4b^2} \cdot \sqrt[3]{6b^2} = \sqrt[3]{4b^2 \cdot 6b^2}$
$= \sqrt[3]{24b^4}$
$= \sqrt[3]{8b^3 \cdot 3b}$
$= \sqrt[3]{8b^3} \cdot \sqrt[3]{3b}$
$= 2b\sqrt[3]{3b}$

71. $2\sqrt{6ab} \cdot 3\sqrt{15ab^3} = 6\sqrt{6ab \cdot 15ab^3}$
$$= 6\sqrt{90a^2b^4}$$
$$= 6\sqrt{9a^2b^4 \cdot 10}$$
$$= 6\sqrt{9a^2b^4} \cdot \sqrt{10}$$
$$= 18ab^2\sqrt{10}$$

73. $\sqrt[4]{27p^3q^2} \cdot \sqrt[4]{12p^2q^2} = \sqrt[4]{27p^3q^2 \cdot 12p^2q^2}$
$$= \sqrt[4]{324p^5q^4}$$
$$= \sqrt[4]{81p^4q^4 \cdot 4p}$$
$$= \sqrt[4]{81p^4q^4} \cdot \sqrt[4]{4p}$$
$$= 3pq\sqrt[4]{4p}$$

75. $\sqrt[5]{-8a^3b^4} \cdot \sqrt[5]{12a^3b} = \sqrt[5]{-8a^3b^4 \cdot 12a^3b}$
$$= \sqrt[5]{-96a^6b^5}$$
$$= \sqrt[5]{-32a^5b^5 \cdot 3a}$$
$$= \sqrt[5]{-32a^5b^5} \cdot \sqrt[5]{3a}$$
$$= -2ab\sqrt[5]{3a}$$

77. $\sqrt[4]{8(x-y)^2} \cdot \sqrt[4]{6(x-y)^3}$
$$= \sqrt[4]{8(x-y)^2 \cdot 6(x-y)^3}$$
$$= \sqrt[4]{48(x-y)^5}$$
$$= \sqrt[4]{16(x-y)^4 \cdot 3(x-y)}$$
$$= \sqrt[4]{16(x-y)^4} \cdot \sqrt[4]{3(x-y)}$$
$$= 2(x-y)\sqrt[4]{3(x-y)}$$

79. $\sqrt{\dfrac{3}{16}} = \dfrac{\sqrt{3}}{\sqrt{16}} = \dfrac{\sqrt{3}}{4}$

81. $\sqrt{\dfrac{121}{100}} = \dfrac{\sqrt{121}}{\sqrt{100}} = \dfrac{11}{10}$

83. $\sqrt[4]{\dfrac{5x^4}{16}} = \dfrac{\sqrt[4]{5x^4}}{\sqrt[4]{16}} = \dfrac{x\sqrt[4]{5}}{2}$

85. $\sqrt{\dfrac{9y^2}{25x^2}} = \dfrac{\sqrt{9y^2}}{\sqrt{25x^2}} = \dfrac{3y}{5x}$

87. $\sqrt[3]{\dfrac{-27x^9}{64y^{12}}} = \dfrac{\sqrt[3]{-27x^9}}{\sqrt[3]{64y^{12}}} = \dfrac{-3x^3}{4y^4} = -\dfrac{3x^3}{4y^4}$

89. $\dfrac{\sqrt{8}}{\sqrt{2}} = \sqrt{\dfrac{8}{2}} = \sqrt{4} = 2$

91. $\dfrac{\sqrt[3]{128}}{\sqrt[3]{2}} = \sqrt[3]{\dfrac{128}{2}} = \sqrt[3]{64} = 4$

93. $\dfrac{\sqrt{48a^3}}{\sqrt{6a}} = \sqrt{\dfrac{48a^3}{6a}} = \sqrt{8a^2} = 2a\sqrt{2}$

95. $\dfrac{\sqrt{24a^5b}}{\sqrt{3ab^3}} = \sqrt{\dfrac{24a^5b}{3ab^3}} = \sqrt{\dfrac{8a^4}{b^2}} = \dfrac{\sqrt{8a^4}}{\sqrt{b^2}} = \dfrac{2a^2\sqrt{2}}{b}$

97. $\dfrac{\sqrt{512a^7b}}{3\sqrt{2ab^3}} = \dfrac{1}{3}\sqrt{\dfrac{512a^7b}{2ab^3}} = \dfrac{1}{3}\sqrt{\dfrac{256a^6}{b^2}} = \dfrac{16a^3}{3b}$

99. $\dfrac{\sqrt[3]{104a^5}}{\sqrt[3]{4a^{-1}}} = \sqrt[3]{\dfrac{104a^5}{4a^{-1}}} = \sqrt[3]{26a^6} = a^2\sqrt[3]{26}$

101. $\dfrac{\sqrt{90x^3y^{-1}}}{\sqrt{2x^{-3}y}} = \sqrt{\dfrac{90x^3y^{-1}}{2x^{-3}y}}$
$$= \sqrt{\dfrac{45x^6}{y^2}}$$
$$= \dfrac{\sqrt{45x^6}}{\sqrt{y^2}}$$
$$= \dfrac{3x^3\sqrt{5}}{y}$$

103. $\sqrt{3} \cdot \sqrt[3]{4} = 3^{1/2} \cdot 4^{1/3}$
$$= 3^{3/6} \cdot 4^{2/6}$$
$$= \left(3^3\right)^{1/6} \cdot \left(4^2\right)^{1/6}$$
$$= \left(3^3 \cdot 4^2\right)^{1/6}$$
$$= (432)^{1/6}$$
$$= \sqrt[6]{432}$$

105. $\sqrt[3]{2} \cdot \sqrt[6]{3} = 2^{1/3} \cdot 3^{1/6}$
$= 2^{2/6} \cdot 3^{1/6}$
$= \left(2^2\right)^{1/6} \cdot (3)^{1/6}$
$= \left(2^2 \cdot 3\right)^{1/6}$
$= (12)^{1/6}$
$= \sqrt[6]{12}$

107. $\sqrt{3} \cdot \sqrt[3]{18} = 3^{1/2} \cdot 18^{1/3}$
$= 3^{3/6} \cdot 18^{2/6}$
$= \left(3^3\right)^{1/6} \cdot \left(18^2\right)^{1/6}$
$= \left(3^3 \cdot 18^2\right)^{1/6}$
$= \left(3^3 \cdot (2 \cdot 3 \cdot 3)^2\right)^{1/6}$
$= \left(3^3 \cdot 2^2 \cdot 3^2 \cdot 3^2\right)^{1/6}$
$= \left(3^7 \cdot 2^2\right)^{1/6}$
$= 3\left(3 \cdot 2^2\right)^{1/6}$
$= 3(12)^{1/6}$
$= 3\sqrt[6]{12}$

109. $\sqrt[4]{9} \cdot \sqrt[6]{12} = 9^{1/4} \cdot 12^{1/6}$
$= \left(3^2\right)^{1/4} \cdot 12^{1/6}$
$= 3^{1/2} \cdot 12^{1/6}$
$= 3^{3/6} \cdot 12^{1/6}$
$= \left(3^3\right)^{1/6} \cdot (12)^{1/6}$
$= \left(3^3 \cdot 12\right)^{1/6}$
$= \left(3^3 \cdot 3 \cdot 2^2\right)^{1/6}$
$= \left(3^4 \cdot 2^2\right)^{1/6}$
$= \left(\left(3^2 \cdot 2\right)^2\right)^{1/6}$
$= \left(3^2 \cdot 2\right)^{1/3}$
$= \sqrt[3]{18}$

111. $\sqrt[3]{\dfrac{5x}{8}} = \dfrac{\sqrt[3]{5x}}{\sqrt[3]{8}} = \dfrac{\sqrt[3]{5x}}{2}$

113. $\sqrt[3]{5a} \cdot \sqrt[3]{9a} = \sqrt[3]{5a \cdot 9a} = \sqrt[3]{45a^2}$

115. $\sqrt{72a^4} = \sqrt{36a^4 \cdot 2} = \sqrt{36a^4} \cdot \sqrt{2} = 6a^2\sqrt{2}$

117. $\sqrt[3]{6a^2b} \cdot \sqrt[3]{9ab} = \sqrt[3]{6a^2b \cdot 9ab}$
$= \sqrt[3]{54a^3b^2}$
$= \sqrt[3]{27a^3 \cdot 2b^2}$
$= \sqrt[3]{27a^3} \cdot \sqrt[3]{2b^2}$
$= 3a\sqrt[3]{2b^2}$

119. $\dfrac{\sqrt[3]{-32a}}{\sqrt[3]{2a^4}} = \sqrt[3]{\dfrac{-32a}{2a^4}} = \sqrt[3]{\dfrac{-16}{a^3}} = \dfrac{\sqrt[3]{-16}}{\sqrt[3]{a^3}} = \dfrac{-2\sqrt[3]{2}}{a}$

121. $-5\sqrt[3]{32m^3} = -5\sqrt[3]{8m^3 \cdot 4}$
$= -5 \cdot \sqrt[3]{8m^3} \cdot \sqrt[3]{4}$
$= -5 \cdot 2m \cdot \sqrt[3]{4}$
$= -10m\sqrt[3]{4}$

123. $\sqrt[3]{81a^4b^7} = \sqrt[3]{27a^3b^6 \cdot 3ab}$
$= \sqrt[3]{27a^3b^6} \cdot \sqrt[3]{3ab}$
$= 3ab^2\sqrt[3]{3ab}$

125. $\sqrt[3]{12} \cdot \sqrt[3]{18} = \sqrt[3]{12 \cdot 18}$
$= \sqrt[3]{216}$
$= 6$

127. a.

b. $\sqrt{\left(5-(-1)\right)^2 + \left(2-(-1)\right)^2}$

$= \sqrt{(5+1)^2 + (2+1)^2}$

$= \sqrt{6^2 + 3^2}$

$= \sqrt{36+9}$

$= \sqrt{45}$

$= 3\sqrt{5}$

The line segment has a length of $3\sqrt{5}$ units.

129. a. $R(8) = \sqrt[3]{\dfrac{8}{2}} = \sqrt[3]{4} \approx 1.587$

The company's annual revenue will be roughly $1,587,000 after 8 years.

b. $R(27) = \sqrt[3]{\dfrac{27}{2}} = \dfrac{\sqrt[3]{27}}{\sqrt[3]{2}} = \dfrac{3}{\sqrt[3]{2}} \approx 2.381$

The company's annual revenue will be roughly $2,381,000 after 27 years.

131. a. $(f \cdot g)(x) = f(x) \cdot g(x)$

$= \sqrt{2x} \cdot \sqrt{8x^3}$

$= \sqrt{2x \cdot 8x^3}$

$= \sqrt{16x^4}$

$= 4x^2$

b. Using the result from part (a), we get

$(f \cdot g)(3) = 4(3)^2 = 36$

133. $a = 1, b = 6, c = 3$

$x = \dfrac{-6 \pm \sqrt{6^2 - 4(1)(3)}}{2(1)}$

$= \dfrac{-6 \pm \sqrt{36-12}}{2}$

$= \dfrac{-6 \pm \sqrt{24}}{2}$

$= \dfrac{-6 \pm 2\sqrt{6}}{2}$

$= -3 \pm \sqrt{6}$

$x = -3 - \sqrt{6}$ or $x = -3 + \sqrt{6}$.

135. $a = 3, b = 4, c = -1$

$x = \dfrac{-4 \pm \sqrt{4^2 - 4(3)(-1)}}{2(3)}$

$= \dfrac{-4 \pm \sqrt{16+12}}{6}$

$= \dfrac{-4 \pm \sqrt{28}}{6}$

$= \dfrac{-4 \pm 2\sqrt{7}}{6}$

$= \dfrac{-2 \pm \sqrt{7}}{3}$

$x = \dfrac{-2 - \sqrt{7}}{3}$ or $x = \dfrac{-2 + \sqrt{7}}{3}$.

137. $2|7x-1| + 4 = 16$

$2|7x-1| = 12$

$|7x-1| = 6$

$7x - 1 = -6$ or $7x - 1 = 6$

$7x = -5$ $7x = 7$

$x = -\dfrac{5}{7}$ $x = 1$

The solution set is $\left\{-\dfrac{5}{7}, 1\right\}$.

139. $\dfrac{5}{2}|x+1| + 1 \le 11$

$\dfrac{5}{2}|x+1| \le 10$

$|x+1| \le 4$

$-4 \le x + 1 \le 4$

$-4 - 1 \le x + 1 - 1 \le 4 - 1$

$-5 \le x \le 3$

The solution set is $\{x \mid -5 \le x \le 3\}$, or in interval notation we would write $[-5, 3]$.

141. a.

The graphs of $y = \sqrt{x^2}$ and $y = x$ are not the same so the expressions cannot be equal.

The graphs of $y = \sqrt{x^2}$ and $y = |x|$ appear to be the same. $\sqrt{x^2} = |x|$

b.

The graphs of $y = \sqrt[3]{x^3}$ and $y = x$ appear to be the same. $\sqrt[3]{x^3} = x$

The graph of $y = \sqrt[3]{x^3}$ and $y = |x|$ are not the same so the expressions cannot be equal.

c.

The graphs of $y = \sqrt[4]{x^4}$ and $y = x$ are not the same so the expressions cannot be equal.

The graphs of $y = \sqrt[4]{x^4}$ and $y = |x|$ appear to be the same. $\sqrt[4]{x^4} = |x|$

d. Answers will vary.

$\sqrt[n]{x^n} = x$ if the index is odd and $\sqrt[n]{x^n} = |x|$ if the index is even.

7.4 Preparing for Adding, Subtracting, and Multiplying Radical Expressions

1. $4y^3 - 2y^2 + 8y - 1 + \left(-2y^3 + 7y^2 - 3y + 9\right)$
$= 4y^3 - 2y^3 - 2y^2 + 7y^2 + 8y - 3y - 1 + 9$
$= 2y^3 + 5y^2 + 5y + 8$

2. $5z^2 + 6 - \left(3z^2 - 8z - 3\right)$
$= 5z^2 + 6 - 3z^2 + 8z + 3$
$= 5z^2 - 3z^2 + 8z + 6 + 3$
$= 2z^2 + 8z + 9$

3. $\left(4x + 3\right)\left(x - 5\right) = 4x \cdot x - 4x \cdot 5 + 3 \cdot x - 3 \cdot 5$
$= 4x^2 - 20x + 3x - 15$
$= 4x^2 - 17x - 15$

4. $\left(2y - 3\right)\left(2y + 3\right) = \left(2y\right)^2 - 3^2$
$= 4y^2 - 9$

7.4 Exercises

1. like radicals

3. True, assuming both radicals have been simplified as much as possible.

5. Answers may vary.

7. $3\sqrt{2} + 7\sqrt{2} = \left(3 + 7\right)\sqrt{2} = 10\sqrt{2}$

9. $5\sqrt[3]{x} - 3\sqrt[3]{x} = \left(5 - 3\right)\sqrt[3]{x} = 2\sqrt[3]{x}$

11. $8\sqrt{5x} - 3\sqrt{5x} + 9\sqrt{5x} = \left(8 - 3 + 9\right)\sqrt{5x}$
$= 14\sqrt{5x}$

13. $4\sqrt[3]{5} - 3\sqrt{5} + 7\sqrt[3]{5} - 8\sqrt{5}$
$= \left(4 + 7\right)\sqrt[3]{5} + \left(-3 - 8\right)\sqrt{5}$
$= 11\sqrt[3]{5} - 11\sqrt{5}$

15. $\sqrt{8} + 6\sqrt{2} = \sqrt{4} \cdot \sqrt{2} + 6\sqrt{2}$

$\qquad = 2\sqrt{2} + 6\sqrt{2}$

$\qquad = (2+6)\sqrt{2}$

$\qquad = 8\sqrt{2}$

17. $\sqrt[3]{24} - 4\sqrt[3]{3} = \sqrt[3]{8} \cdot \sqrt[3]{3} - 4\sqrt[3]{3}$

$\qquad = 2\sqrt[3]{3} - 4\sqrt[3]{3}$

$\qquad = (2-4)\sqrt[3]{3}$

$\qquad = -2\sqrt[3]{3}$

19. $\sqrt[3]{54} - 7\sqrt[3]{128} = \sqrt[3]{27} \cdot \sqrt[3]{2} - 7 \cdot \sqrt[3]{64} \cdot \sqrt[3]{2}$

$\qquad = 3\sqrt[3]{2} - 7 \cdot 4 \cdot \sqrt[3]{2}$

$\qquad = 3\sqrt[3]{2} - 28\sqrt[3]{2}$

$\qquad = (3-28)\sqrt[3]{2}$

$\qquad = -25\sqrt[3]{2}$

21. $5\sqrt{54x} - 3\sqrt{24x}$

$\quad = 5 \cdot \sqrt{9} \cdot \sqrt{6x} - 3 \cdot \sqrt{4} \cdot \sqrt{6x}$

$\quad = 5 \cdot 3 \cdot \sqrt{6x} - 3 \cdot 2 \cdot \sqrt{6x}$

$\quad = 15\sqrt{6x} - 6\sqrt{6x}$

$\quad = (15-6)\sqrt{6x}$

$\quad = 9\sqrt{6x}$

23. $2\sqrt{8} + 3\sqrt{10} = 2\sqrt{4} \cdot \sqrt{2} + 3\sqrt{10}$

$\qquad = 2 \cdot 2\sqrt{2} + 3\sqrt{10}$

$\qquad = 4\sqrt{2} + 3\sqrt{10}$

Cannot be simplified further.

25. $\sqrt{12x^3} + 5x\sqrt{108x}$

$\quad = \sqrt{4x^2} \cdot \sqrt{3x} + 5x \cdot \sqrt{36} \cdot \sqrt{3x}$

$\quad = 2x\sqrt{3x} + 5x \cdot 6 \cdot \sqrt{3x}$

$\quad = 2x\sqrt{3x} + 30x\sqrt{3x}$

$\quad = (2x + 30x)\sqrt{3x}$

$\quad = 32x\sqrt{3x}$

27. $\sqrt{12x^2} + 3x\sqrt{2} - 2\sqrt{98x^2}$

$\quad = \sqrt{4x^2} \cdot \sqrt{3} + 3x\sqrt{2} - 2\sqrt{49x^2} \cdot \sqrt{2}$

$\quad = 2x\sqrt{3} + 3x\sqrt{2} - 2 \cdot 7x\sqrt{2}$

$\quad = 2x\sqrt{3} + 3x\sqrt{2} - 14x\sqrt{2}$

$\quad = 2x\sqrt{3} + (3-14)x\sqrt{2}$

$\quad = 2x\sqrt{3} - 11x\sqrt{2}$

29. $\sqrt[3]{-54x^3} + 3x\sqrt[3]{16} - 2\sqrt[3]{128}$

$\quad = \sqrt[3]{-27x^3} \cdot \sqrt[3]{2} + 3x\sqrt[3]{8} \cdot \sqrt[3]{2} - 2\sqrt[3]{64} \cdot \sqrt[3]{2}$

$\quad = -3x\sqrt[3]{2} + 3x \cdot 2\sqrt[3]{2} - 2 \cdot 4\sqrt[3]{2}$

$\quad = -3x\sqrt[3]{2} + 6x\sqrt[3]{2} - 8\sqrt[3]{2}$

$\quad = (-3x + 6x - 8)\sqrt[3]{2}$

$\quad = (3x-8)\sqrt[3]{2}$

31. $\sqrt{9x-9} + \sqrt{4x-4}$

$\quad = \sqrt{9(x-1)} + \sqrt{4(x-1)}$

$\quad = \sqrt{9} \cdot \sqrt{x-1} + \sqrt{4} \cdot \sqrt{x-1}$

$\quad = 3\sqrt{x-1} + 2\sqrt{x-1}$

$\quad = (3+2)\sqrt{x-1}$

$\quad = 5\sqrt{x-1}$

33. $\sqrt{16x} - \sqrt[6]{x^3} = \sqrt{16x} - x^{3/6}$

$\qquad = \sqrt{16} \cdot \sqrt{x} - x^{1/2}$

$\qquad = 4\sqrt{x} - \sqrt{x}$

$\qquad = (4-1)\sqrt{x}$

$\qquad = 3\sqrt{x}$

35. $\sqrt[3]{27x} + 2\sqrt[9]{x^3} = \sqrt[3]{27} \cdot \sqrt[3]{x} + 2 \cdot x^{3/9}$

$\qquad = 3\sqrt[3]{x} + 2x^{1/3}$

$\qquad = 3\sqrt[3]{x} + 2\sqrt[3]{x}$

$\qquad = (3+2)\sqrt[3]{x}$

$\qquad = 5\sqrt[3]{x}$

37. $\sqrt{3}\left(2 - 3\sqrt{2}\right) = \sqrt{3} \cdot 2 - \sqrt{3} \cdot 3\sqrt{2}$

$\qquad = 2\sqrt{3} - 3\sqrt{2 \cdot 3}$

$\qquad = 2\sqrt{3} - 3\sqrt{6}$

39. $\sqrt{3}\left(\sqrt{2}+\sqrt{6}\right)=\sqrt{3}\cdot\sqrt{2}+\sqrt{3}\cdot\sqrt{6}$

$\qquad=\sqrt{3\cdot2}+\sqrt{3\cdot6}$

$\qquad=\sqrt{6}+\sqrt{18}$

$\qquad=\sqrt{6}+\sqrt{9}\cdot\sqrt{2}$

$\qquad=\sqrt{6}+3\sqrt{2}$

41. $\sqrt[3]{4}\left(\sqrt[3]{3}-\sqrt[3]{6}\right)=\sqrt[3]{4}\cdot\sqrt[3]{3}-\sqrt[3]{4}\cdot\sqrt[3]{6}$

$\qquad=\sqrt[3]{4\cdot3}-\sqrt[3]{4\cdot6}$

$\qquad=\sqrt[3]{12}-\sqrt[3]{24}$

$\qquad=\sqrt[3]{12}-\sqrt[3]{8}\cdot\sqrt[3]{3}$

$\qquad=\sqrt[3]{12}-2\sqrt[3]{3}$

43. $\sqrt{2x}\left(3-\sqrt{10x}\right)=\sqrt{2x}\cdot3-\sqrt{2x}\cdot\sqrt{10x}$

$\qquad=3\sqrt{2x}-\sqrt{20x^2}$

$\qquad=3\sqrt{2x}-\sqrt{4x^2}\cdot\sqrt{5}$

$\qquad=3\sqrt{2x}-2x\sqrt{5}$

45. $\left(3+\sqrt{2}\right)\left(4+\sqrt{3}\right)$

$\qquad=3\cdot4+3\cdot\sqrt{3}+\sqrt{2}\cdot4+\sqrt{2}\cdot\sqrt{3}$

$\qquad=12+3\sqrt{3}+4\sqrt{2}+\sqrt{6}$

47. $\left(6+\sqrt{3}\right)\left(2-\sqrt{7}\right)$

$\qquad=6\cdot2-6\cdot\sqrt{7}+\sqrt{3}\cdot2-\sqrt{3}\cdot\sqrt{7}$

$\qquad=12-6\sqrt{7}+2\sqrt{3}-\sqrt{21}$

49. $\left(4-2\sqrt{7}\right)\left(3+3\sqrt{7}\right)$

$\qquad=4\cdot3+4\cdot3\sqrt{7}-2\sqrt{7}\cdot3-2\sqrt{7}\cdot3\sqrt{7}$

$\qquad=12+12\sqrt{7}-6\sqrt{7}-6\sqrt{49}$

$\qquad=12+\left(12-6\right)\sqrt{7}-6\cdot7$

$\qquad=12+6\sqrt{7}-42$

$\qquad=6\sqrt{7}-30$

51. $\left(\sqrt{2}+3\sqrt{6}\right)\left(\sqrt{3}-2\sqrt{2}\right)$

$\qquad=\sqrt{2}\cdot\sqrt{3}-\sqrt{2}\cdot2\sqrt{2}+3\sqrt{6}\cdot\sqrt{3}-3\sqrt{6}\cdot2\sqrt{2}$

$\qquad=\sqrt{6}-2\sqrt{4}+3\sqrt{18}-6\sqrt{12}$

$\qquad=\sqrt{6}-2\cdot2+3\cdot3\sqrt{2}-6\cdot2\sqrt{3}$

$\qquad=\sqrt{6}-4+9\sqrt{2}-12\sqrt{3}$

$\qquad=\sqrt{6}-12\sqrt{3}+9\sqrt{2}-4$

53. $\left(2\sqrt{5}+\sqrt{3}\right)\left(4\sqrt{5}-3\sqrt{3}\right)$

$\qquad=2\sqrt{5}\cdot4\sqrt{5}-2\sqrt{5}\cdot3\sqrt{3}+\sqrt{3}\cdot4\sqrt{5}-\sqrt{3}\cdot3\sqrt{3}$

$\qquad=8\sqrt{25}-6\sqrt{15}+4\sqrt{15}-3\sqrt{9}$

$\qquad=8\cdot5+\left(-6+4\right)\sqrt{15}-3\cdot3$

$\qquad=40-2\sqrt{15}-9$

$\qquad=31-2\sqrt{15}$

55. $\left(1+\sqrt{3}\right)^2=\left(1\right)^2+2\left(1\right)\left(\sqrt{3}\right)+\left(\sqrt{3}\right)^2$

$\qquad=1+2\sqrt{3}+\sqrt{9}$

$\qquad=1+2\sqrt{3}+3$

$\qquad=4+2\sqrt{3}$

57. $\left(\sqrt{2}-\sqrt{5}\right)^2=\left(\sqrt{2}\right)^2-2\left(\sqrt{2}\right)\left(\sqrt{5}\right)+\left(\sqrt{5}\right)^2$

$\qquad=\sqrt{4}-2\sqrt{10}+\sqrt{25}$

$\qquad=2-2\sqrt{10}+5$

$\qquad=7-2\sqrt{10}$

59. $\left(\sqrt{x}-\sqrt{2}\right)^2=\left(\sqrt{x}\right)^2-2\left(\sqrt{x}\right)\left(\sqrt{2}\right)+\left(\sqrt{2}\right)^2$

$\qquad=\sqrt{x^2}-2\sqrt{2x}+\sqrt{4}$

$\qquad=x-2\sqrt{2x}+2$

61. $\left(\sqrt{2}-1\right)\left(\sqrt{2}+1\right)=\left(\sqrt{2}\right)^2-\left(1\right)^2$

$\qquad=\sqrt{4}-1$

$\qquad=2-1$

$\qquad=1$

63. $\left(3-2\sqrt{5}\right)\left(3+2\sqrt{5}\right)=\left(3\right)^2-\left(2\sqrt{5}\right)^2$
$$=9-4\sqrt{25}$$
$$=9-4\cdot5$$
$$=9-20$$
$$=-11$$

65. $\left(\sqrt{2x}+\sqrt{3y}\right)\left(\sqrt{2x}-\sqrt{3y}\right)$
$$=\left(\sqrt{2x}\right)^2-\left(\sqrt{3y}\right)^2$$
$$=\sqrt{4x^2}-\sqrt{9y^2}$$
$$=2x-3y$$

67. $\left(\sqrt[3]{x}+4\right)\left(\sqrt[3]{x}-3\right)$
$$=\sqrt[3]{x}\cdot\sqrt[3]{x}-\sqrt[3]{x}\cdot3+4\cdot\sqrt[3]{x}-4\cdot3$$
$$=\sqrt[3]{x^2}-3\sqrt[3]{x}+4\sqrt[3]{x}-12$$
$$=\sqrt[3]{x^2}+\left(-3+4\right)\sqrt[3]{x}-12$$
$$=\sqrt[3]{x^2}+\sqrt[3]{x}-12$$

69. $\left(\sqrt[3]{2a}-5\right)\left(\sqrt[3]{2a}+5\right)=\left(\sqrt[3]{2a}\right)^2-\left(5\right)^2$
$$=\sqrt[3]{4a^2}-25$$

71. $\sqrt{5}\left(\sqrt{3}+\sqrt{10}\right)=\sqrt{5}\cdot\sqrt{3}+\sqrt{5}\cdot\sqrt{10}$
$$=\sqrt{15}+\sqrt{50}$$
$$=\sqrt{15}+\sqrt{25}\cdot\sqrt{2}$$
$$=\sqrt{15}+5\sqrt{2}$$

73. $\sqrt{28x^5}-x\sqrt{7x^3}+5\sqrt{175x^5}$
$$=\sqrt{4x^4}\cdot\sqrt{7x}-x\sqrt{x^2}\cdot\sqrt{7x}+5\sqrt{25x^4}\cdot\sqrt{7x}$$
$$=2x^2\sqrt{7x}-x^2\sqrt{7x}+25x^2\sqrt{7x}$$
$$=\left(2x^2-x^2+25x^2\right)\sqrt{7x}$$
$$=26x^2\sqrt{7x}$$

75. $\left(2\sqrt{3}+5\right)\left(2\sqrt{3}-5\right)=\left(2\sqrt{3}\right)^2-5^2$
$$=4\sqrt{9}-25$$
$$=4\cdot3-25$$
$$=12-25$$
$$=-13$$

77. $\sqrt[3]{7}\left(2+\sqrt[3]{4}\right)=\sqrt[3]{7}\cdot2+\sqrt[3]{7}\cdot\sqrt[3]{4}$
$$=2\sqrt[3]{7}+\sqrt[3]{7\cdot4}$$
$$=2\sqrt[3]{7}+\sqrt[3]{28}$$

79. $\left(2\sqrt{2}+5\right)\left(4\sqrt{2}-4\right)$
$$=2\sqrt{2}\cdot4\sqrt{2}-2\sqrt{2}\cdot4+5\cdot4\sqrt{2}-5\cdot4$$
$$=8\sqrt{4}-8\sqrt{2}+20\sqrt{2}-20$$
$$=8\cdot2+\left(-8+20\right)\sqrt{2}-20$$
$$=16+12\sqrt{2}-20$$
$$=-4+12\sqrt{2}$$

81. $4\sqrt{18}+2\sqrt{32}=4\cdot\sqrt{9}\cdot\sqrt{2}+2\cdot\sqrt{16}\cdot\sqrt{2}$
$$=4\cdot3\cdot\sqrt{2}+2\cdot4\cdot\sqrt{2}$$
$$=12\sqrt{2}+8\sqrt{2}$$
$$=\left(12+8\right)\sqrt{2}$$
$$=20\sqrt{2}$$

83. $\left(\sqrt{5}-\sqrt{3}\right)^2=\left(\sqrt{5}\right)^2-2\left(\sqrt{5}\right)\left(\sqrt{3}\right)+\left(\sqrt{3}\right)^2$
$$=\sqrt{25}-2\sqrt{15}+\sqrt{9}$$
$$=5-2\sqrt{15}+3$$
$$=8-2\sqrt{15}$$

85. $3\sqrt[3]{5x^3y}+\sqrt[3]{40y}$
$$=3\cdot\sqrt[3]{x^3}\cdot\sqrt[3]{5y}+\sqrt[3]{8}\cdot\sqrt[3]{5y}$$
$$=3x\cdot\sqrt[3]{5y}+2\cdot\sqrt[3]{5y}$$
$$=\left(3x+2\right)\sqrt[3]{5y}$$

87. $\left(\sqrt{2x}-\sqrt{7y}\right)\left(\sqrt{2x}+\sqrt{7y}\right)=\left(\sqrt{2x}\right)^2-\left(\sqrt{7y}\right)^2$
$$=\sqrt{4x^2}-\sqrt{49y^2}$$
$$=2x-7y$$

89. $-\dfrac{3}{5} \cdot \left(-\dfrac{\sqrt{5}}{5}\right) - \dfrac{4}{5} \cdot \left(-\dfrac{2\sqrt{5}}{5}\right)$

$= \dfrac{3\sqrt{5}}{25} + \dfrac{8\sqrt{5}}{25}$

$= \dfrac{3\sqrt{5} + 8\sqrt{5}}{25}$

$= \dfrac{(3+8)\sqrt{5}}{25}$

$= \dfrac{11\sqrt{5}}{25}$

91. $A = l \cdot w$

$= \sqrt{162} \cdot \sqrt{72}$

$= \sqrt{81} \cdot \sqrt{2} \cdot \sqrt{36} \cdot \sqrt{2}$

$= 9\sqrt{2} \cdot 6\sqrt{2}$

$= 54\sqrt{4}$

$= 54 \cdot 2$

$= 108$

The area is 108 square units.

$P = 2l + 2w$

$= 2\left(\sqrt{162}\right) + 2\left(\sqrt{72}\right)$

$= 2\sqrt{81} \cdot \sqrt{2} + 2\sqrt{36} \cdot \sqrt{2}$

$= 18\sqrt{2} + 12\sqrt{2}$

$= (18 + 12)\sqrt{2}$

$= 30\sqrt{2}$

The perimeter is $30\sqrt{2}$ units.

93. Area of larger triangle:

$s = \dfrac{1}{2}(14 + 10 + 8) = \dfrac{1}{2}(32) = 16$

$A = \sqrt{16(16-14)(16-10)(16-8)}$

$= \sqrt{16(2)(6)(8)} = \sqrt{16 \cdot 16 \cdot 6}$

$= \sqrt{16} \cdot \sqrt{16} \cdot \sqrt{6} = 4 \cdot 4 \cdot \sqrt{6}$

$= 16\sqrt{6}$

Area of smaller triangle:

$s = \dfrac{1}{2}(7 + 5 + 4) = \dfrac{1}{2}(16) = 8$

$A = \sqrt{8(8-7)(8-5)(8-4)}$

$= \sqrt{8(1)(3)(4)} = \sqrt{96} = \sqrt{16} \cdot \sqrt{6}$

$= 4\sqrt{6}$

Area of shaded region:

area of larger $-$ area of smaller

$= 16\sqrt{6} - 4\sqrt{6} = (16-4)\sqrt{6} = 12\sqrt{6}$

The area of the shaded region is $12\sqrt{6}$ square units.

95. a. $(f+g)(x) = \sqrt{3x} + \sqrt{12x}$

$= \sqrt{3x} + \sqrt{4} \cdot \sqrt{3x}$

$= \sqrt{3x} + 2\sqrt{3x}$

$= (1+2)\sqrt{3x}$

$= 3\sqrt{3x}$

b. Use the result from part (a).

$(f+g)(4) = 3\sqrt{3(4)}$

$= 3\sqrt{12}$

$= 3\sqrt{4} \cdot \sqrt{3}$

$= 3 \cdot 2\sqrt{3}$

$= 6\sqrt{3}$

c. $(f \cdot g)(x) = \sqrt{3x} \cdot \sqrt{12x}$

$= \sqrt{36x^2}$

$= 6x$

97. Check $x = -2 + \sqrt{5}$:

$0 \overset{?}{=} x^2 + 4x - 1$

$0 \overset{?}{=} \left(-2+\sqrt{5}\right)^2 + 4\left(-2+\sqrt{5}\right) - 1$

$0 \overset{?}{=} (-2)^2 + 2(-2)\left(\sqrt{5}\right) + \left(\sqrt{5}\right)^2 - 8 + 4\sqrt{5} - 1$

$0 \overset{?}{=} 4 - 4\sqrt{5} + \sqrt{25} - 8 + 4\sqrt{5} - 1$

$0 \overset{?}{=} 9 - 9$

$0 = 0$ true

Substituting $-2 + \sqrt{5}$ for x yields a true statement, therefore the value is a solution.

Check $x = -2 - \sqrt{5}$:

$$0 \stackrel{?}{=} x^2 + 4x - 1$$

$$0 \stackrel{?}{=} \left(-2 - \sqrt{5}\right)^2 + 4\left(-2 - \sqrt{5}\right) - 1$$

$$0 \stackrel{?}{=} (-2)^2 - 2(-2)\left(\sqrt{5}\right) + \left(\sqrt{5}\right)^2 - 8 - 4\sqrt{5} - 1$$

$$0 \stackrel{?}{=} 4 + 4\sqrt{5} + \sqrt{25} - 8 - 4\sqrt{5} - 1$$

$$0 \stackrel{?}{=} 9 - 9$$

$$0 = 0 \text{ true}$$

Substituting $-2 - \sqrt{5}$ for x yields a true statement, therefore the value is a solution.

99. $(3p - 1)(2p + 3) = 3p(2p + 3) - 1(2p + 3)$
$$= 6p^2 + 9p - 2p - 3$$
$$= 6p^2 + 7p - 3$$

101. $(m - 4)(m + 4) = m^2 - 4^2 = m^2 - 16$

103. $\left(\sqrt{x} + 2\right)\left(\sqrt{x} - 2\right) = \left(\sqrt{x}\right)^2 - 2^2 = x - 4$

7.5 Preparing for Rationalizing Radical Expressions

1. Start by finding the prime factors of 12.
$12 = 3 \cdot 4 = 3 \cdot 2 \cdot 2$
To make a perfect square, we need to have each unique prime factor occur an even number of times. To make the smallest perfect square, we want to use the smallest even number possible for each factor. In this case, the factor 2 occurs twice so no additional factors of 2 are needed. However, the factor 3 only occurs once. Therefore, we need to multiply by one more factor of 3.
The smallest perfect square that is a multiple of 12 is $12 \cdot 3 = 36$.

2. $\sqrt{25x^2} = \sqrt{(5x)^2} = 5x$

(since $x > 0$, we do not need $|x|$)

7.5 Exercises

1. rationalizing the denominator

3. False; we would multiply the numerator and denominator by $-2 - \sqrt{7}$.

5. $\dfrac{1}{\sqrt{2}} = \dfrac{1}{\sqrt{2}} \cdot \dfrac{\sqrt{2}}{\sqrt{2}} = \dfrac{\sqrt{2}}{\sqrt{4}} = \dfrac{\sqrt{2}}{2}$

7. $-\dfrac{6}{5\sqrt{3}} = -\dfrac{6}{5\sqrt{3}} \cdot \dfrac{\sqrt{3}}{\sqrt{3}}$
$$= -\dfrac{6\sqrt{3}}{5\sqrt{9}}$$
$$= -\dfrac{6\sqrt{3}}{5 \cdot 3}$$
$$= -\dfrac{2\sqrt{3}}{5}$$

9. $\dfrac{3}{\sqrt{12}} = \dfrac{3}{2\sqrt{3}} = \dfrac{3}{2\sqrt{3}} \cdot \dfrac{\sqrt{3}}{\sqrt{3}}$
$$= \dfrac{3\sqrt{3}}{2\sqrt{9}}$$
$$= \dfrac{3\sqrt{3}}{2 \cdot 3}$$
$$= \dfrac{\sqrt{3}}{2}$$

11. $\dfrac{\sqrt{2}}{\sqrt{6}} = \dfrac{\sqrt{2}}{\sqrt{6}} \cdot \dfrac{\sqrt{6}}{\sqrt{6}} = \dfrac{\sqrt{12}}{\sqrt{36}} = \dfrac{2\sqrt{3}}{6} = \dfrac{\sqrt{3}}{3}$

13. $\sqrt{\dfrac{2}{p}} = \dfrac{\sqrt{2}}{\sqrt{p}} = \dfrac{\sqrt{2}}{\sqrt{p}} \cdot \dfrac{\sqrt{p}}{\sqrt{p}} = \dfrac{\sqrt{2p}}{\sqrt{p^2}} = \dfrac{\sqrt{2p}}{p}$

15. $\dfrac{\sqrt{8}}{\sqrt{y^3}} = \dfrac{2\sqrt{2}}{y\sqrt{y}} = \dfrac{2\sqrt{2}}{y\sqrt{y}} \cdot \dfrac{\sqrt{y}}{\sqrt{y}}$
$$= \dfrac{2\sqrt{2y}}{y\sqrt{y^2}} = \dfrac{2\sqrt{2y}}{y \cdot y}$$
$$= \dfrac{2\sqrt{2y}}{y^2}$$

17. $\dfrac{2}{\sqrt[3]{2}} = \dfrac{2}{\sqrt[3]{2}} \cdot \dfrac{\sqrt[3]{4}}{\sqrt[3]{4}} = \dfrac{2\sqrt[3]{4}}{\sqrt[3]{8}} = \dfrac{2\sqrt[3]{4}}{2} = \sqrt[3]{4}$

19. $\sqrt[3]{\dfrac{7}{q}} = \dfrac{\sqrt[3]{7}}{\sqrt[3]{q}} = \dfrac{\sqrt[3]{7}}{\sqrt[3]{q}} \cdot \dfrac{\sqrt[3]{q^2}}{\sqrt[3]{q^2}}$

$\qquad = \dfrac{\sqrt[3]{7q^2}}{\sqrt[3]{q^3}}$

$\qquad = \dfrac{\sqrt[3]{7q^2}}{q}$

21. $\sqrt[3]{\dfrac{-3}{50}} = \dfrac{\sqrt[3]{-3}}{\sqrt[3]{50}} = \dfrac{\sqrt[3]{-3}}{\sqrt[3]{50}} \cdot \dfrac{\sqrt[3]{20}}{\sqrt[3]{20}}$

$\qquad = \dfrac{\sqrt[3]{-60}}{\sqrt[3]{1000}}$

$\qquad = -\dfrac{\sqrt[3]{60}}{10}$

23. $\dfrac{2}{\sqrt[3]{20y}} = \dfrac{2}{\sqrt[3]{20y}} \cdot \dfrac{\sqrt[3]{50y^2}}{\sqrt[3]{50y^2}}$

$\qquad = \dfrac{2\sqrt[3]{50y^2}}{\sqrt[3]{1000y^3}} = \dfrac{2\sqrt[3]{50y^2}}{10y}$

$\qquad = \dfrac{\sqrt[3]{50y^2}}{5y}$

25. $\dfrac{-4}{\sqrt[4]{3x^3}} = \dfrac{-4}{\sqrt[4]{3x^3}} \cdot \dfrac{\sqrt[4]{27x}}{\sqrt[4]{27x}}$

$\qquad = \dfrac{-4\sqrt[4]{27x}}{\sqrt[4]{81x^4}}$

$\qquad = -\dfrac{4\sqrt[4]{27x}}{3x}$

27. $\dfrac{12}{\sqrt[5]{m^3n^2}} = \dfrac{12}{\sqrt[5]{m^3n^2}} \cdot \dfrac{\sqrt[5]{m^2n^3}}{\sqrt[5]{m^2n^3}}$

$\qquad = \dfrac{12\sqrt[5]{m^2n^3}}{\sqrt[5]{m^5n^5}}$

$\qquad = \dfrac{12\sqrt[5]{m^2n^3}}{mn}$

29. $\dfrac{4}{\sqrt{6}-2} = \dfrac{4}{\sqrt{6}-2} \cdot \dfrac{\sqrt{6}+2}{\sqrt{6}+2} = \dfrac{4\left(\sqrt{6}+2\right)}{\left(\sqrt{6}\right)^2 - 2^2}$

$\qquad = \dfrac{4\left(\sqrt{6}+2\right)}{6-4} = \dfrac{4\left(\sqrt{6}+2\right)}{2}$

$\qquad = 2\left(\sqrt{6}+2\right)$

31. $\dfrac{5}{\sqrt{5}+2} = \dfrac{5}{\sqrt{5}+2} \cdot \dfrac{\sqrt{5}-2}{\sqrt{5}-2}$

$\qquad = \dfrac{5\left(\sqrt{5}-2\right)}{\left(\sqrt{5}\right)^2 - 2^2} = \dfrac{5\left(\sqrt{5}-2\right)}{5-4}$

$\qquad = 5\left(\sqrt{5}-2\right)$

33. $\dfrac{8}{\sqrt{7}-\sqrt{3}} = \dfrac{8}{\sqrt{7}-\sqrt{3}} \cdot \dfrac{\sqrt{7}+\sqrt{3}}{\sqrt{7}+\sqrt{3}}$

$\qquad = \dfrac{8\left(\sqrt{7}+\sqrt{3}\right)}{\left(\sqrt{7}\right)^2 - \left(\sqrt{3}\right)^2}$

$\qquad = \dfrac{8\left(\sqrt{7}+\sqrt{3}\right)}{7-3}$

$\qquad = \dfrac{8\left(\sqrt{7}+\sqrt{3}\right)}{4}$

$\qquad = 2\left(\sqrt{7}+\sqrt{3}\right)$

35. $\dfrac{\sqrt{2}}{\sqrt{10}-\sqrt{6}} = \dfrac{\sqrt{2}}{\sqrt{2}\sqrt{5}-\sqrt{2}\sqrt{3}}$

$\qquad = \dfrac{1}{\sqrt{5}-\sqrt{3}}$

$\qquad = \dfrac{1}{\sqrt{5}-\sqrt{3}} \cdot \dfrac{\sqrt{5}+\sqrt{3}}{\sqrt{5}+\sqrt{3}}$

$\qquad = \dfrac{\sqrt{5}+\sqrt{3}}{\left(\sqrt{5}\right)^2 - \left(\sqrt{3}\right)^2}$

$\qquad = \dfrac{\sqrt{5}+\sqrt{3}}{5-3}$

$\qquad = \dfrac{\sqrt{5}+\sqrt{3}}{2}$

37. $\dfrac{\sqrt{p}}{\sqrt{p}+\sqrt{q}} = \dfrac{\sqrt{p}}{\sqrt{p}+\sqrt{q}} \cdot \dfrac{\sqrt{p}-\sqrt{q}}{\sqrt{p}-\sqrt{q}}$

$\qquad = \dfrac{\sqrt{p}\left(\sqrt{p}-\sqrt{q}\right)}{\left(\sqrt{p}\right)^2-\left(\sqrt{q}\right)^2}$

$\qquad = \dfrac{\sqrt{p^2}-\sqrt{pq}}{p-q}$

$\qquad = \dfrac{p-\sqrt{pq}}{p-q}$

39. $\dfrac{18}{2\sqrt{3}+3\sqrt{2}} = \dfrac{18}{2\sqrt{3}+3\sqrt{2}} \cdot \dfrac{2\sqrt{3}-3\sqrt{2}}{2\sqrt{3}-3\sqrt{2}}$

$\qquad = \dfrac{18\left(2\sqrt{3}-3\sqrt{2}\right)}{\left(2\sqrt{3}\right)^2-\left(3\sqrt{2}\right)^2}$

$\qquad = \dfrac{18\left(2\sqrt{3}-3\sqrt{2}\right)}{12-18}$

$\qquad = \dfrac{18\left(2\sqrt{3}-3\sqrt{2}\right)}{-6}$

$\qquad = -3\left(2\sqrt{3}-3\sqrt{2}\right)$ or $3\left(3\sqrt{2}-2\sqrt{3}\right)$

41. $\dfrac{\sqrt{7}+3}{\sqrt{7}-3} = \dfrac{\sqrt{7}+3}{\sqrt{7}-3} \cdot \dfrac{\sqrt{7}+3}{\sqrt{7}+3}$

$\qquad = \dfrac{\left(\sqrt{7}+3\right)\left(\sqrt{7}+3\right)}{\left(\sqrt{7}-3\right)\left(\sqrt{7}+3\right)}$

$\qquad = \dfrac{\left(\sqrt{7}\right)^2+2\left(\sqrt{7}\right)(3)+(3)^2}{\left(\sqrt{7}\right)^2-(3)^2}$

$\qquad = \dfrac{7+6\sqrt{7}+9}{7-9}$

$\qquad = \dfrac{16+6\sqrt{7}}{-2}$

$\qquad = -8-3\sqrt{7}$ or $-3\sqrt{7}-8$

43. $\dfrac{\sqrt{3}-4\sqrt{2}}{2\sqrt{3}+5\sqrt{2}} = \dfrac{\sqrt{3}-4\sqrt{2}}{2\sqrt{3}+5\sqrt{2}} \cdot \dfrac{2\sqrt{3}-5\sqrt{2}}{2\sqrt{3}-5\sqrt{2}}$

$\qquad = \dfrac{\left(\sqrt{3}-4\sqrt{2}\right)\left(2\sqrt{3}-5\sqrt{2}\right)}{\left(2\sqrt{3}+5\sqrt{2}\right)\left(2\sqrt{3}-5\sqrt{2}\right)}$

$\qquad = \dfrac{2\sqrt{9}-5\sqrt{6}-8\sqrt{6}+20\sqrt{4}}{\left(2\sqrt{3}\right)^2-\left(5\sqrt{2}\right)^2}$

$\qquad = \dfrac{6-13\sqrt{6}+40}{12-50}$

$\qquad = \dfrac{46-13\sqrt{6}}{-38}$

$\qquad = \dfrac{13\sqrt{6}-46}{38}$

45. $\dfrac{\sqrt{p}+2}{\sqrt{p}-2} = \dfrac{\sqrt{p}+2}{\sqrt{p}-2} \cdot \dfrac{\sqrt{p}+2}{\sqrt{p}+2}$

$\qquad = \dfrac{\left(\sqrt{p}+2\right)\left(\sqrt{p}+2\right)}{\left(\sqrt{p}-2\right)\left(\sqrt{p}+2\right)}$

$\qquad = \dfrac{\left(\sqrt{p}\right)^2+2\left(\sqrt{p}\right)(2)+2^2}{\left(\sqrt{p}\right)^2-2^2}$

$\qquad = \dfrac{p+4\sqrt{p}+4}{p-4}$

47. $\dfrac{\sqrt{2}-3}{\sqrt{8}-\sqrt{2}} = \dfrac{\sqrt{2}-3}{2\sqrt{2}-\sqrt{2}}$

$\qquad = \dfrac{\sqrt{2}-3}{\sqrt{2}}$

$\qquad = \dfrac{\sqrt{2}-3}{\sqrt{2}} \cdot \dfrac{\sqrt{2}}{\sqrt{2}}$

$\qquad = \dfrac{\sqrt{4}-3\sqrt{2}}{\sqrt{4}}$

$\qquad = \dfrac{2-3\sqrt{2}}{2}$

49. $\sqrt{3}+\dfrac{1}{\sqrt{3}} = \sqrt{3}+\dfrac{1}{\sqrt{3}} \cdot \dfrac{\sqrt{3}}{\sqrt{3}} = \sqrt{3}+\dfrac{\sqrt{3}}{3}$

$\qquad = \dfrac{3\sqrt{3}}{3}+\dfrac{\sqrt{3}}{3} = \dfrac{3\sqrt{3}+\sqrt{3}}{3}$

$\qquad = \dfrac{4\sqrt{3}}{3}$

51. $\dfrac{\sqrt{10}}{2} - \dfrac{1}{\sqrt{2}} = \dfrac{\sqrt{10}}{2} - \dfrac{1}{\sqrt{2}} \cdot \dfrac{\sqrt{2}}{\sqrt{2}}$

$\qquad = \dfrac{\sqrt{10}}{2} - \dfrac{\sqrt{2}}{2}$

$\qquad = \dfrac{\sqrt{10} - \sqrt{2}}{2}$

53. $\sqrt{\dfrac{1}{3}} + \sqrt{12} + \sqrt{75} = \dfrac{\sqrt{1}}{\sqrt{3}} + 2\sqrt{3} + 5\sqrt{3}$

$\qquad = \dfrac{1}{\sqrt{3}} + 7\sqrt{3}$

$\qquad = \dfrac{1}{\sqrt{3}} \cdot \dfrac{\sqrt{3}}{\sqrt{3}} + 7\sqrt{3}$

$\qquad = \dfrac{\sqrt{3}}{3} + 7\sqrt{3}$

$\qquad = \dfrac{\sqrt{3}}{3} + \dfrac{21\sqrt{3}}{3}$

$\qquad = \dfrac{\sqrt{3} + 21\sqrt{3}}{3}$

$\qquad = \dfrac{22\sqrt{3}}{3}$

55. $\dfrac{3}{\sqrt{18}} - \sqrt{\dfrac{1}{2}} = \dfrac{3}{3\sqrt{2}} - \dfrac{\sqrt{1}}{\sqrt{2}}$

$\qquad = \dfrac{1}{\sqrt{2}} - \dfrac{1}{\sqrt{2}}$

$\qquad = 0$

57. $\dfrac{\sqrt{3}}{\sqrt{12}} = \dfrac{\sqrt{3}}{2\sqrt{3}} = \dfrac{1}{2}$

59. $\dfrac{3}{\sqrt{72}} = \dfrac{3}{6\sqrt{2}} = \dfrac{1}{2\sqrt{2}}$

$\qquad = \dfrac{1}{2\sqrt{2}} \cdot \dfrac{\sqrt{2}}{\sqrt{2}} = \dfrac{\sqrt{2}}{2 \cdot 2}$

$\qquad = \dfrac{\sqrt{2}}{4}$

61. $\sqrt{\dfrac{4}{3}} = \dfrac{\sqrt{4}}{\sqrt{3}} = \dfrac{2}{\sqrt{3}} = \dfrac{2}{\sqrt{3}} \cdot \dfrac{\sqrt{3}}{\sqrt{3}} = \dfrac{2\sqrt{3}}{3}$

63. $\dfrac{\sqrt{3}-3}{\sqrt{3}+3} = \dfrac{\sqrt{3}-3}{\sqrt{3}+3} \cdot \dfrac{\sqrt{3}-3}{\sqrt{3}-3}$

$\qquad = \dfrac{\left(\sqrt{3}\right)^2 - 2\left(\sqrt{3}\right)(3) + 3^2}{\left(\sqrt{3}\right)^2 - 3^2}$

$\qquad = \dfrac{3 - 6\sqrt{3} + 9}{3 - 9} = \dfrac{12 - 6\sqrt{3}}{-6}$

$\qquad = \sqrt{3} - 2$

65. $\dfrac{2}{\sqrt{5}+2} = \dfrac{2}{\sqrt{5}+2} \cdot \dfrac{\sqrt{5}-2}{\sqrt{5}-2}$

$\qquad = \dfrac{2\left(\sqrt{5}-2\right)}{\left(\sqrt{5}\right)^2 - 2^2} = \dfrac{2\left(\sqrt{5}-2\right)}{5-4}$

$\qquad = 2\left(\sqrt{5}-2\right)$

67. $\dfrac{\sqrt{8}}{\sqrt{2}} = \dfrac{2\sqrt{2}}{\sqrt{2}} = 2$

69. $\dfrac{1}{\sqrt{3}} = \dfrac{1}{\sqrt{3}} \cdot \dfrac{\sqrt{3}}{\sqrt{3}} = \dfrac{\sqrt{3}}{3}$

71. $\dfrac{1}{\sqrt[3]{12}} = \dfrac{1}{\sqrt[3]{12}} \cdot \dfrac{\sqrt[3]{18}}{\sqrt[3]{18}} = \dfrac{\sqrt[3]{18}}{\sqrt[3]{216}} = \dfrac{\sqrt[3]{18}}{6}$

(Since $12 = 2^2 \cdot 3$, we need to multiply by $2 \cdot 3^2$ to get powers of 3 on the factors.)

73. $\dfrac{1}{\sqrt{3}+5} = \dfrac{1}{\sqrt{3}+5} \cdot \dfrac{\sqrt{3}-5}{\sqrt{3}-5}$

$\qquad = \dfrac{\sqrt{3}-5}{\left(\sqrt{3}+5\right)\left(\sqrt{3}-5\right)}$

$\qquad = \dfrac{\sqrt{3}-5}{\left(\sqrt{3}\right)^2 - 5^2}$

$\qquad = \dfrac{\sqrt{3}-5}{3-25}$

$\qquad = \dfrac{\sqrt{3}-5}{-22}$

$\qquad = \dfrac{5-\sqrt{3}}{22}$

75. $\dfrac{1}{\sqrt{2}} \cdot \dfrac{\sqrt{3}}{2} - \dfrac{1}{\sqrt{2}} \cdot \dfrac{1}{2} = \dfrac{\sqrt{3}}{2\sqrt{2}} - \dfrac{1}{2\sqrt{2}}$

$$= \dfrac{\sqrt{3} - 1}{2\sqrt{2}}$$

$$= \dfrac{\sqrt{3} - 1}{2\sqrt{2}} \cdot \dfrac{\sqrt{2}}{\sqrt{2}}$$

$$= \dfrac{\sqrt{6} - \sqrt{2}}{4}$$

77. $\dfrac{\sqrt{2} + 1}{3} = \dfrac{\sqrt{2} + 1}{3} \cdot \dfrac{\sqrt{2} - 1}{\sqrt{2} - 1}$

$$= \dfrac{\left(\sqrt{2} + 1\right)\left(\sqrt{2} - 1\right)}{3\left(\sqrt{2} - 1\right)}$$

$$= \dfrac{\left(\sqrt{2}\right)^2 - 1^2}{3\sqrt{2} - 3}$$

$$= \dfrac{2 - 1}{3\sqrt{2} - 3}$$

$$= \dfrac{1}{3\sqrt{2} - 3} = \dfrac{1}{3\left(\sqrt{2} - 1\right)}$$

79. $\dfrac{\sqrt{x} - \sqrt{h}}{\sqrt{x}} = \dfrac{\sqrt{x} - \sqrt{h}}{\sqrt{x}} \cdot \dfrac{\sqrt{x} + \sqrt{h}}{\sqrt{x} + \sqrt{h}}$

$$= \dfrac{\left(\sqrt{x} - \sqrt{h}\right)\left(\sqrt{x} + \sqrt{h}\right)}{\sqrt{x}\left(\sqrt{x} + \sqrt{h}\right)}$$

$$= \dfrac{\left(\sqrt{x}\right)^2 - \left(\sqrt{h}\right)^2}{\sqrt{x^2} + \sqrt{xh}}$$

$$= \dfrac{x - h}{x + \sqrt{xh}}$$

81. $\left(\dfrac{\sqrt{6} + \sqrt{2}}{4}\right)^2 \overset{?}{=} \left(\dfrac{\sqrt{2} + \sqrt{3}}{2}\right)^2$

$$\dfrac{\left(\sqrt{6}\right)^2 + 2 \cdot \sqrt{6} \cdot \sqrt{2} + \left(\sqrt{2}\right)^2}{4^2} \overset{?}{=} \dfrac{2 + \sqrt{3}}{4}$$

$$\dfrac{6 + 2\sqrt{12} + 2}{16} \overset{?}{=} \dfrac{2 + \sqrt{3}}{4}$$

$$\dfrac{8 + 2 \cdot 2\sqrt{3}}{16} \overset{?}{=} \dfrac{2 + \sqrt{3}}{4}$$

$$\dfrac{8 + 4\sqrt{3}}{16} \overset{?}{=} \dfrac{2 + \sqrt{3}}{4}$$

$$\dfrac{2 + \sqrt{3}}{4} = \dfrac{2 + \sqrt{3}}{4}$$

83. $f(x) = 5x - 3$

x	$y = 5x - 3$	(x, y)
0	$y = 5(0) - 3 = -3$	$(0, -3)$
1	$y = 5(1) - 3 = 2$	$(1, 2)$
2	$y = 5(2) - 3 = 7$	$(2, 7)$

85. $G(x) = x^2$

x	$y = x^2$	(x, y)
-2	$y = (-2)^2 = 4$	$(-2, 4)$
-1	$y = (-1)^2 = 1$	$(-1, 1)$
0	$y = (0)^2 = 0$	$(0, 0)$
1	$y = (1)^2 = 1$	$(1, 1)$
2	$y = (2)^2 = 4$	$(2, 4)$

Putting the Concepts Together (Sections 7.1-7.5)

1. $-25^{1/2} = -\sqrt{25} = -5$

2. $(-64)^{-2/3} = \dfrac{1}{(-64)^{2/3}} = \dfrac{1}{\left(\sqrt[3]{-64}\right)^2} = \dfrac{1}{(-4)^2} = \dfrac{1}{16}$

3. $\sqrt[4]{3x^3} = \left(3x^3\right)^{1/4}$

4. $7z^{4/5} = 7\left(z^4\right)^{1/5} = 7\sqrt[5]{z^4}$

5. $\sqrt[3]{\sqrt{64x^3}} = \left(\left(64x^3\right)^{1/2}\right)^{1/3}$
   $= \left(64x^3\right)^{1/6}$
   $= \left(2^6 x^3\right)^{1/6}$
   $= 2^{6/6} x^{3/6}$
   $= 2x^{1/2}$ or $2\sqrt{x}$

6. $c^{1/2}\left(c^{3/2} + c^{5/2}\right) = c^{1/2} \cdot c^{3/2} + c^{1/2} \cdot c^{5/2}$
   $= c^{\frac{1}{2}+\frac{3}{2}} + c^{\frac{1}{2}+\frac{5}{2}}$
   $= c^{\frac{4}{2}} + c^{\frac{6}{2}}$
   $= c^2 + c^3$

7. $\left(a^{2/3}b^{-1/3}\right)\left(a^{4/3}b^{-5/3}\right) = a^{\frac{2}{3}+\frac{4}{3}} b^{-\frac{1}{3}+\left(-\frac{5}{3}\right)}$
   $= a^{6/3}b^{-6/3}$
   $= a^2 b^{-2}$
   $= \dfrac{a^2}{b^2}$

8. $\dfrac{x^{3/4}}{x^{1/8}} = x^{\frac{3}{4}-\frac{1}{8}} = x^{\frac{6}{8}-\frac{1}{8}} = x^{5/8}$ or $\sqrt[8]{x^5}$

9. $\left(x^{3/4}y^{-1/8}\right)^8 = \left(x^{3/4}\right)^8\left(y^{-1/8}\right)^8$
   $= x^{\frac{3}{4}\cdot 8} y^{-\frac{1}{8}\cdot 8}$
   $= x^6 y^{-1}$
   $= \dfrac{x^6}{y}$

10. $\sqrt{15a} \cdot \sqrt{2b} = \sqrt{15a \cdot 2b} = \sqrt{30ab}$

11. $\sqrt{10m^3 n^2} \cdot \sqrt{20mn} = \sqrt{10m^3 n^2 \cdot 20mn}$
    $= \sqrt{200m^4 n^3}$
    $= \sqrt{100m^4 n^2 \cdot 2n}$
    $= \sqrt{100m^4 n^2} \cdot \sqrt{2n}$
    $= 10m^2 n\sqrt{2n}$

12. $\sqrt[3]{\dfrac{-32xy^4}{4x^{-2}y}} = \sqrt[3]{-8x^3 y^3} = \sqrt[3]{(-2)^3 x^3 y^3} = -2xy$

13. $2\sqrt{108} - 3\sqrt{75} + \sqrt{48}$
    $= 2 \cdot \sqrt{36 \cdot 3} - 3\sqrt{25 \cdot 3} + \sqrt{16 \cdot 3}$
    $= 2\sqrt{36} \cdot \sqrt{3} - 3\sqrt{25} \cdot \sqrt{3} + \sqrt{16} \cdot \sqrt{3}$
    $= 2 \cdot 6\sqrt{3} - 3 \cdot 5\sqrt{3} + 4\sqrt{3}$
    $= 12\sqrt{3} - 15\sqrt{3} + 4\sqrt{3}$
    $= (12 - 15 + 4)\sqrt{3}$
    $= \sqrt{3}$

14. $-5b\sqrt{8b} + 7\sqrt{18b^3} = -5b\sqrt{4 \cdot 2b} + 7\sqrt{9b^2 \cdot 2b}$
    $= -5b\sqrt{4} \cdot \sqrt{2b} + 7\sqrt{9b^2} \cdot \sqrt{2b}$
    $= -5b \cdot 2\sqrt{2b} + 7 \cdot 3b\sqrt{2b}$
    $= -10b\sqrt{2b} + 21b\sqrt{2b}$
    $= (-10 + 21)b\sqrt{2b}$
    $= 11b\sqrt{2b}$

15. $\sqrt[3]{16y^4} - y\sqrt[3]{2y} = \sqrt[3]{8y^3 \cdot 2y} - y\sqrt[3]{2y}$
    $= \sqrt[3]{8y^3} \cdot \sqrt[3]{2y} - y\sqrt[3]{2y}$
    $= 2y\sqrt[3]{2y} - y\sqrt[3]{2y}$
    $= (2-1)y\sqrt[3]{2y}$
    $= y\sqrt[3]{2y}$

16. $\left(3\sqrt{x}\right)\left(4\sqrt{x}\right) = 3 \cdot 4 \cdot \sqrt{x \cdot x}$
    $= 12\sqrt{x^2}$
    $= 12x$

17. $3\sqrt{x} + 4\sqrt{x} = (3+4)\sqrt{x} = 7\sqrt{x}$

18. $\left(2-3\sqrt{2}\right)\left(10+\sqrt{2}\right)$

$= 2\cdot10 + 2\cdot\sqrt{2} - 3\sqrt{2}\cdot10 - 3\sqrt{2}\cdot\sqrt{2}$

$= 20 + 2\sqrt{2} - 30\sqrt{2} - 3\cdot2$

$= 20 - 28\sqrt{2} - 6$

$= 14 - 28\sqrt{2} = 14\left(1 - 2\sqrt{2}\right)$

19. $\left(4\sqrt{2}-3\right)^2 = \left(4\sqrt{2}\right)^2 - 2\left(4\sqrt{2}\right)(3) + (3)^2$

$= 16\cdot2 - 24\sqrt{2} + 9$

$= 32 - 24\sqrt{2} + 9$

$= 41 - 24\sqrt{2}$

20. $\dfrac{3}{2\sqrt{32}} = \dfrac{3}{2\cdot4\sqrt{2}} = \dfrac{3}{8\sqrt{2}}$

$= \dfrac{3}{8\sqrt{2}}\cdot\dfrac{\sqrt{2}}{\sqrt{2}} = \dfrac{3\sqrt{2}}{8\cdot2}$

$= \dfrac{3\sqrt{2}}{16}$

21. $\dfrac{4}{\sqrt{3}-8} = \dfrac{4}{\sqrt{3}-8}\cdot\dfrac{\sqrt{3}+8}{\sqrt{3}+8}$

$= \dfrac{4\left(\sqrt{3}+8\right)}{\left(\sqrt{3}-8\right)\left(\sqrt{3}+8\right)}$

$= \dfrac{4\left(\sqrt{3}+8\right)}{\left(\sqrt{3}\right)^2 - 8^2}$

$= \dfrac{4\sqrt{3}+32}{3-64}$

$= \dfrac{4\sqrt{3}+32}{-61}$

$= -\dfrac{4\sqrt{3}+32}{61} = -\dfrac{4\left(\sqrt{3}+8\right)}{61}$

7.6 Preparing for Functions Involving Radicals

1. $\sqrt{121} = \sqrt{11^2} = 11$

2. $\sqrt{p^2} = |p|$

3. $f(x) = x^2 - 4$

$f(3) = (3)^2 - 4 = 9 - 4 = 5$

4. $-2x + 3 \geq 0$

$-2x + 3 - 3 \geq 0 - 3$

$-2x \geq -3$

$\dfrac{-2x}{-2} \leq \dfrac{-3}{-2}$

$x \leq \dfrac{3}{2}$

The solution set is $\left\{x \mid x \leq \dfrac{3}{2}\right\}$, or $\left(-\infty, \dfrac{3}{2}\right]$ in interval notation.

5. $f(x) = x^2 + 1$

x	$y = x^2 + 1$	(x, y)
-2	$y = (-2)^2 + 1 = 5$	$(-2, 5)$
-1	$y = (-1)^2 + 1 = 2$	$(-1, 2)$
0	$y = (0)^2 + 1 = 1$	$(0, 1)$
1	$y = (1)^2 + 1 = 2$	$(1, 2)$
2	$y = (2)^2 + 1 = 5$	$(2, 5)$

7.6 Exercises

1. even

3. True

5. $f(x) = \sqrt{x+6}$

a. $f(3) = \sqrt{3+6} = \sqrt{9} = 3$

b. $f(8) = \sqrt{8+6} = \sqrt{14}$

c. $f(-2) = \sqrt{-2+6} = \sqrt{4} = 2$

7. $g(x) = -\sqrt{2x+3}$

    a. $g(11) = -\sqrt{2(11)+3}$

           $= -\sqrt{25}$

           $= -5$

    b. $g(-1) = -\sqrt{2(-1)+3}$

           $= -\sqrt{1}$

           $= -1$

    c. $g\left(\dfrac{1}{8}\right) = -\sqrt{2\left(\dfrac{1}{8}\right)+3}$

           $= -\sqrt{\dfrac{13}{4}}$

           $= -\dfrac{\sqrt{13}}{\sqrt{4}}$

           $= -\dfrac{\sqrt{13}}{2}$

9. $G(m) = 2\sqrt{5m-1}$

    a. $G(1) = 2\sqrt{5(1)-1}$

           $= 2\sqrt{4}$

           $= 2 \cdot 2$

           $= 4$

    b. $G(5) = 2\sqrt{5(5)-1}$

           $= 2\sqrt{24}$

           $= 4\sqrt{6}$

    c. $G\left(\dfrac{1}{2}\right) = 2\sqrt{5\left(\dfrac{1}{2}\right)-1}$

           $= 2\sqrt{\dfrac{3}{2}}$

           $= \dfrac{2\sqrt{3}}{\sqrt{2}} \cdot \dfrac{\sqrt{2}}{\sqrt{2}}$

           $= \dfrac{2\sqrt{6}}{2}$

           $= \sqrt{6}$

11. $H(z) = \sqrt[3]{z+4}$

    a. $H(4) = \sqrt[3]{4+4} = \sqrt[3]{8} = 2$

    b. $H(-12) = \sqrt[3]{-12+4} = \sqrt[3]{-8} = -2$

    c. $H(-20) = \sqrt[3]{-20+4}$

           $= \sqrt[3]{-16}$

           $= \sqrt[3]{-8} \cdot \sqrt[3]{2}$

           $= -2\sqrt[3]{2}$

13. $f(x) = \sqrt{\dfrac{x-2}{x+2}}$

    a. $f(7) = \sqrt{\dfrac{7-2}{7+2}} = \sqrt{\dfrac{5}{9}} = \dfrac{\sqrt{5}}{\sqrt{9}} = \dfrac{\sqrt{5}}{3}$

    b. $f(6) = \sqrt{\dfrac{6-2}{6+2}}$

           $= \sqrt{\dfrac{1}{2}}$

           $= \dfrac{1}{\sqrt{2}} \cdot \dfrac{\sqrt{2}}{\sqrt{2}}$

           $= \dfrac{\sqrt{2}}{2}$

    c. $f(10) = \sqrt{\dfrac{10-2}{10+2}} = \sqrt{\dfrac{2}{3}}$

           $= \dfrac{\sqrt{2}}{\sqrt{3}} \cdot \dfrac{\sqrt{3}}{\sqrt{3}}$

           $= \dfrac{\sqrt{6}}{3}$

15. $g(z) = \sqrt[3]{\dfrac{2z}{z-4}}$

    a. $g(-4) = \sqrt[3]{\dfrac{2(-4)}{-4-4}} = \sqrt[3]{\dfrac{-8}{-8}} = \sqrt[3]{1} = 1$

    b. $g(8) = \sqrt[3]{\dfrac{2(8)}{8-4}} = \sqrt[3]{\dfrac{16}{4}} = \sqrt[3]{4}$

    c. $g(12) = \sqrt[3]{\dfrac{2(12)}{12-4}} = \sqrt[3]{\dfrac{24}{8}} = \sqrt[3]{3}$

SSM – 389

17. $f(x) = \sqrt{x-7}$

$x - 7 \geq 0$

$x \geq 7$

The domain of the function is $\{x \mid x \geq 7\}$ or the interval $[7, \infty)$.

19. $g(x) = \sqrt{2x+7}$

$2x + 7 \geq 0$

$2x \geq -7$

$x \geq -\dfrac{7}{2}$

The domain of the function is $\left\{x \mid x \geq -\dfrac{7}{2}\right\}$ or the interval $\left[-\dfrac{7}{2}, \infty\right)$.

21. $F(x) = \sqrt{4-3x}$

$4 - 3x \geq 0$

$-3x \geq -4$

$x \leq \dfrac{4}{3}$

The domain of the function is $\left\{x \mid x \leq \dfrac{4}{3}\right\}$ or the interval $\left(-\infty, \dfrac{4}{3}\right]$.

23. $H(z) = \sqrt[3]{2z+1}$

Since the index is odd, the domain of the function is all real numbers.

$\{z \mid z \text{ is any real number}\}$ or $(-\infty, \infty)$.

25. $W(p) = \sqrt[4]{7p-2}$

$7p - 2 \geq 0$

$7p \geq 2$

$p \geq \dfrac{2}{7}$

The domain of the function is $\left\{p \mid p \geq \dfrac{2}{7}\right\}$ or the interval $\left[\dfrac{2}{7}, \infty\right)$.

27. $g(x) = \sqrt[5]{x-3}$

Since the index is odd, the domain of the function is all real numbers.

$\{x \mid x \text{ is any real number}\}$ or $(-\infty, \infty)$.

29. $f(x) = \sqrt{\dfrac{3}{x+5}}$

The index is even so we need the radicand to be nonnegative. The numerator is positive which means we need the denominator to be positive as well.

$x + 5 > 0$

$x > -5$

The domain of the function is $\{x \mid x > -5\}$ or the interval $(-5, \infty)$.

31. $H(x) = \sqrt{\dfrac{x+3}{x-3}}$

The index is even so we need the radicand to be nonnegative. That is, we need to solve

$\dfrac{x+3}{x-3} \geq 0$

The radicand equals 0 when $x = -3$ and it is undefined when $x = 3$. We can use these two values to split up the real number line into subintervals.

		-3		3	

Interval	$(-\infty, -3)$	$(-3, 3)$	$(3, \infty)$
Num. chosen	-4	0	4
Value of radicand	$\dfrac{1}{7}$	-1	7
Conclusion	positive	negative	positive

Since we need the radicand to be positive or 0, the domain is $\{x \mid x \leq -3 \text{ or } x > 3\}$ or the interval $(-\infty, -3] \cup (3, \infty)$.

33. $f(x) = \sqrt{x-4}$

a. $x - 4 \geq 0$

$x \geq 4$

The domain is $\{x \mid x \geq 4\}$ or the interval $[4, \infty)$.

b.

x	$f(x)=\sqrt{x-4}$	(x,y)
4	$f(4)=\sqrt{4-4}=0$	$(4,0)$
5	$f(5)=1$	$(5,1)$
8	$f(8)=2$	$(8,2)$
13	$f(13)=3$	$(13,3)$
20	$f(20)=4$	$(20,4)$

c. Based on the graph, the range is $[0,\infty)$.

35. $g(x)=\sqrt{x+2}$

  a. $x+2\geq 0$

     $x\geq -2$

  The domain is $\{x\,|\,x\geq -2\}$ or the interval $[-2,\infty)$.

b.

x	$g(x)=\sqrt{x+2}$	(x,y)
-2	$g(-2)=\sqrt{-2+2}=0$	$(-2,0)$
-1	$g(-1)=1$	$(-1,1)$
2	$g(2)=2$	$(2,2)$
7	$g(7)=3$	$(7,3)$
14	$g(14)=4$	$(14,4)$

  c. Based on the graph, the range is $[0,\infty)$.

37. $G(x)=\sqrt{2-x}$

  a. $2-x\geq 0$

    $-x\geq -2$

    $x\leq 2$

  The domain is $\{x\,|\,x\leq 2\}$ or the interval $(-\infty,2]$.

b.

x	$G(x)=\sqrt{2-x}$	(x,y)
-14	$G(-14)=\sqrt{2+14}=4$	$(-14,4)$
-7	$G(-7)=3$	$(-7,3)$
-2	$G(-2)=2$	$(-2,2)$
1	$G(1)=1$	$(1,1)$
2	$G(2)=0$	$(2,0)$

  c. Based on the graph, the range is $[0,\infty)$.

39. $f(x)=\sqrt{x}+3$

  a. The domain is $\{x\,|\,x\geq 0\}$ or the interval $[0,\infty)$.

b.

x	$f(x)=\sqrt{x}+3$	(x,y)
0	$f(0)=\sqrt{0}+3=3$	$(0,3)$
1	$f(1)=4$	$(1,4)$
4	$f(4)=5$	$(4,5)$
9	$f(9)=6$	$(9,6)$
16	$f(16)=7$	$(16,7)$

  c. Based on the graph, the range is $[3,\infty)$.

41. $g(x) = \sqrt{x} - 4$

  a. The domain is $\{x \mid x \geq 0\}$ or the interval $[0, \infty)$.

  b.

x	$g(x) = \sqrt{x} - 4$	(x, y)
0	$g(0) = \sqrt{0} - 4 = -4$	$(0, -4)$
1	$g(1) = -3$	$(1, -3)$
4	$g(4) = -2$	$(4, -2)$
9	$g(9) = -1$	$(9, -1)$
16	$g(16) = 0$	$(16, 0)$

  c. Based on the graph, the range is $[-4, \infty)$.

43. $H(x) = 2\sqrt{x}$

  a. The domain is $\{x \mid x \geq 0\}$ or the interval $[0, \infty)$.

  b.

x	$H(x) = 2\sqrt{x}$	(x, y)
0	$H(0) = 2\sqrt{0} = 0$	$(0, 0)$
1	$H(1) = 2$	$(1, 2)$
4	$H(4) = 4$	$(4, 4)$
9	$H(9) = 6$	$(9, 6)$
16	$H(16) = 8$	$(16, 8)$

  c. Based on the graph, the range is $[0, \infty)$.

45. $f(x) = \dfrac{1}{2}\sqrt{x}$

  a. The domain is $\{x \mid x \geq 0\}$ or the interval $[0, \infty)$.

  b.

x	$f(x) = \dfrac{1}{2}\sqrt{x}$	(x, y)
0	$f(0) = \dfrac{1}{2}\sqrt{0} = 0$	$(0, 0)$
1	$f(1) = \dfrac{1}{2}$	$\left(1, \dfrac{1}{2}\right)$
4	$f(4) = 1$	$(4, 1)$
9	$f(9) = \dfrac{3}{2}$	$\left(9, \dfrac{3}{2}\right)$
16	$f(16) = 2$	$(16, 2)$

  c. Based on the graph, the range is $[0, \infty)$.

47. $G(x) = -\sqrt{x}$

  a. The domain is $\{x \mid x \geq 0\}$ or the interval $[0, \infty)$.

  b.

x	$G(x) = -\sqrt{x}$	(x, y)
0	$G(0) = -\sqrt{0} = 0$	$(0, 0)$
1	$G(1) = -1$	$(1, -1)$
4	$G(4) = -2$	$(4, -2)$
9	$G(9) = -3$	$(9, -3)$
16	$G(16) = -4$	$(16, -4)$

  c. Based on the graph, the range is $(-\infty, 0]$.

49. $h(x) = \sqrt[3]{x+2}$

    a. The index is odd so the domain is all real numbers, $\{x \mid x \text{ is any real number}\}$ or $(-\infty, \infty)$.

    b.

x	$h(x) = \sqrt[3]{x+2}$	(x,y)
-10	$h(-10) = \sqrt[3]{-10+2} = -2$	$(-10,-2)$
-3	$h(-3) = -1$	$(-3,-1)$
-2	$h(-2) = 0$	$(-2,0)$
-1	$h(-1) = 1$	$(-1,1)$
6	$h(6) = 2$	$(6,2)$

    c. Based on the graph, the range is $(-\infty, \infty)$.

51. $f(x) = \sqrt[3]{x} - 3$

    a. The index is odd so the domain is all real numbers, $\{x \mid x \text{ is any real number}\}$ or $(-\infty, \infty)$.

    b.

x	$f(x) = \sqrt[3]{x} - 3$	(x,y)
-8	$f(-8) = \sqrt[3]{-8} - 3 = -5$	$(-8,-5)$
-1	$f(-1) = -4$	$(-1,-4)$
0	$f(0) = -3$	$(0,-3)$
1	$f(1) = -2$	$(1,-2)$
8	$f(8) = -1$	$(8,-1)$

    c. Based on the graph, the range is $(-\infty, \infty)$.

53. $G(x) = 2\sqrt[3]{x}$

    a. The index is odd so the domain is all real numbers, $\{x \mid x \text{ is any real number}\}$ or $(-\infty, \infty)$.

    b.

x	$G(x) = 2\sqrt[3]{x}$	(x,y)
-8	$G(-8) = 2\sqrt[3]{-8} = -4$	$(-8,-4)$
-1	$G(-1) = -2$	$(-1,-2)$
0	$G(0) = 0$	$(0,0)$
1	$G(1) = 2$	$(1,2)$
8	$G(8) = 4$	$(8,4)$

    c. Based on the graph, the range is $(-\infty, \infty)$.

55. a. $d(0) = \sqrt{0^4 - 9(0)^2 + 25} = \sqrt{25} = 5$
       The distance is 5 units.

    b. $d(1) = \sqrt{1^4 - 9(1)^2 + 25} = \sqrt{17}$
       The distance is $\sqrt{17} \approx 4.123$ units.

    c. $d(5) = \sqrt{5^4 - 9(5)^2 + 25} = \sqrt{425} = 5\sqrt{17}$
       The distance is $5\sqrt{17} \approx 20.616$ units.

57. a. $x = 1$
       $A(1) = 2(1) \cdot \sqrt{9-1^2} = 2\sqrt{8} = 4\sqrt{2}$
       The area is $4\sqrt{2} \approx 5.657$ square units.

    b. $x = 2$
       $A(2) = 2(2) \cdot \sqrt{9-2^2} = 4\sqrt{5}$
       The area is $4\sqrt{5} \approx 8.944$ square units.

    c. $x = \sqrt{2}$
       $A(\sqrt{2}) = 2(\sqrt{2}) \cdot \sqrt{9 - (\sqrt{2})^2}$
       $= 2\sqrt{2} \cdot \sqrt{7} = 2\sqrt{14}$
       The area is $2\sqrt{14} \approx 7.483$ square units.

59. The graph of $g(x) = \sqrt{x+c}$ can be obtained from the graph of $f(x) = \sqrt{x}$ by shifting the graph of $f(x)$ c units to the right (if $c < 0$) or left (if $c > 0$).

61. $\dfrac{1}{3} + \dfrac{1}{2} = \dfrac{2}{6} + \dfrac{3}{6} = \dfrac{2+3}{6} = \dfrac{5}{6}$

63. $\dfrac{1}{x} + \dfrac{3}{x+1} = \dfrac{1}{x} \cdot \dfrac{(x+1)}{(x+1)} + \dfrac{3}{x+1} \cdot \dfrac{x}{x}$

$\qquad = \dfrac{x+1}{x(x+1)} + \dfrac{3x}{x(x+1)}$

$\qquad = \dfrac{x+1+3x}{x(x+1)}$

$\qquad = \dfrac{4x+1}{x(x+1)}$

65. $\dfrac{4}{x-1} + \dfrac{3}{x+1} = \dfrac{4}{x-1} \cdot \dfrac{x+1}{x+1} + \dfrac{3}{x+1} \cdot \dfrac{x-1}{x-1}$

$\qquad = \dfrac{4(x+1)+3(x-1)}{(x-1)(x+1)}$

$\qquad = \dfrac{4x+4+3x-3}{(x-1)(x+1)}$

$\qquad = \dfrac{7x+1}{(x-1)(x+1)} \quad \text{or} \quad \dfrac{7x+1}{x^2-1}$

67. $f(x) = \sqrt{x-4}$

69. $g(x) = \sqrt{x+2}$

71. $G(x) = \sqrt{2-x}$

73. $f(x) = \sqrt{x} + 3$

75. $g(x) = \sqrt{x} - 4$

77. $H(x) = 2\sqrt{x}$

79. $f(x) = \dfrac{1}{2}\sqrt{x}$

81. $G(x) = -\sqrt{x}$

83. $h(x) = \sqrt[3]{x+2}$

85. $f(x) = \sqrt[3]{x} - 3$

87. $G(x) = 2\sqrt[3]{x}$

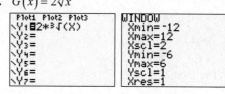

7.7 Preparing for Radical Equations and Their Applications

1. $3x - 5 = 0$

$3x = 5$

$x = \dfrac{5}{3}$

The solution set is $\left\{\dfrac{5}{3}\right\}$.

2. $2p^2 + 4p - 6 = 0$

$p^2 + 2p - 3 = 0$

$(p+3)(p-1) = 0$

$p + 3 = 0 \quad \text{or} \quad p - 1 = 0$

$p = -3 \qquad\qquad p = 1$

The solution set is $\{-3, 1\}$.

3. $\left(\sqrt[3]{x-5}\right)^3 = x - 5$

7.7 Exercises

1. radical equation

3. False; the first step would be to isolate the radical by subtracting x from both sides.

5. Answers will vary. It is necessary to check solutions to radical equations because manipulations of the equation may have introduced extraneous solutions.

7. $\sqrt{x} = 4$

$\left(\sqrt{x}\right)^2 = 4^2$

$x = 16$

Check: $\sqrt{16} = 4$?

$4 = 4$ ✓

The solution set is $\{16\}$.

9. $\sqrt{x-3} = 2$

$\left(\sqrt{x-3}\right)^2 = 2^2$

$x - 3 = 4$

$x = 7$

Check: $\sqrt{7-3} = 2$?

$\sqrt{4} = 2$?

$2 = 2$ ✓

The solution set is $\{7\}$.

11. $\sqrt{2t+3} = 5$

$\left(\sqrt{2t+3}\right)^2 = 5^2$

$2t + 3 = 25$

$2t = 22$

$t = 11$

Check: $\sqrt{2(11)+3} = 5$?

$\sqrt{25} = 5$?

$5 = 5$ ✓

The solution set is $\{11\}$.

13. $\sqrt{4x+3} = -2$

Since the principal square root is never negative, this equation has no real solution. Solving this equation by squaring both sides will yield an extraneous solution.

$\sqrt{4x+3} = -2$

$\left(\sqrt{4x+3}\right)^2 = (-2)^2$

$4x + 3 = 4$

$4x = 1$

$x = \dfrac{1}{4}$

Check: $\sqrt{4\left(\dfrac{1}{4}\right)+3} = -2$?

$\sqrt{4} = -2$?

$2 = -2$ False

The solution does not check so the problem has no real solution.

15. $\sqrt[3]{4t} = 2$

$\left(\sqrt[3]{4t}\right)^3 = 2^3$

$4t = 8$

$t = 2$

Check: $\sqrt[3]{4(2)} = 2$?

$\sqrt[3]{8} = 2$?

$2 = 2$ ✓

The solution set is $\{2\}$.

17. $\sqrt[3]{5q+4} = 4$

$\left(\sqrt[3]{5q+4}\right)^3 = 4^3$

$5q + 4 = 64$

$5q = 60$

$q = 12$

Check: $\sqrt[3]{5(12)+4} = 4$?

$\sqrt[3]{64} = 4$?

$4 = 4$ ✓

The solution set is $\{12\}$.

19. $\sqrt{y} + 3 = 8$

$\sqrt{y} = 5$

$\left(\sqrt{y}\right)^2 = 5^2$

$y = 25$

Check: $\sqrt{25} + 3 = 8$?

$5 + 3 = 8$?

$8 = 8$ ✓

The solution set is $\{25\}$.

21. $\sqrt{x+5} - 3 = 1$

$\sqrt{x+5} = 4$

$\left(\sqrt{x+5}\right)^2 = 4^2$

$x + 5 = 16$

$x = 11$

Check: $\sqrt{11+5} - 3 = 1$?

$\sqrt{16} - 3 = 1$?

$4 - 3 = 1$?

$1 = 1$ ✓

The solution set is $\{11\}$.

23. $\sqrt{2x-1} + 5 = 8$

$\sqrt{2x-1} = 3$

$\left(\sqrt{2x-1}\right)^2 = 3^2$

$2x - 1 = 9$

$2x = 10$

$x = 5$

Check: $\sqrt{2(5)-1} + 5 = 8$?

$\sqrt{9} + 5 = 8$?

$3 + 5 = 8$?

$8 = 8$ ✓

The solution set is $\{5\}$.

25. $3\sqrt{x} + 5 = 8$

$3\sqrt{x} = 3$

$\sqrt{x} = 1$

$\left(\sqrt{x}\right)^2 = 1^2$

$x = 1$

Check: $3\sqrt{1} + 5 = 8$?

$3 + 5 = 8$?

$8 = 8$ ✓

The solution set is $\{1\}$.

27. $\sqrt{4-x} - 3 = 0$

$\sqrt{4-x} = 3$

$\left(\sqrt{4-x}\right)^2 = 3^2$

$4 - x = 9$

$-x = 5$

$x = -5$

Check: $\sqrt{4-(-5)} - 3 = 0$?

$\sqrt{9} - 3 = 0$?

$3 - 3 = 0$?

$0 = 0$ ✓

The solution set is $\{-5\}$.

29. $\sqrt{p} = 2p$

$\left(\sqrt{p}\right)^2 = (2p)^2$

$p = 4p^2$

$0 = 4p^2 - p$

$0 = p(4p-1)$

$p = 0$ or $4p - 1 = 0$

$p = 0$ or $p = \dfrac{1}{4}$

Check:

$\sqrt{0} = 2(0)$?

$0 = 0$ ✓

$\sqrt{\dfrac{1}{4}} = 2\left(\dfrac{1}{4}\right)$?

$\dfrac{1}{2} = \dfrac{1}{2}$ ✓

The solution set is $\left\{0, \dfrac{1}{4}\right\}$.

31.
$$\sqrt{x+6} = x$$
$$\left(\sqrt{x+6}\right)^2 = x^2$$
$$x+6 = x^2$$
$$0 = x^2 - x - 6$$
$$0 = (x-3)(x+2)$$
$$x-3 = 0 \text{ or } x+2 = 0$$
$$x = 3 \text{ or } x = -2$$

Check:
$$\sqrt{3+6} = 3 \text{ ?}$$
$$\sqrt{9} = 3 \text{ ?}$$
$$3 = 3 \checkmark$$

$$\sqrt{-2+6} = -2 \text{ ?}$$
$$\sqrt{4} = -2 \text{ ?}$$
$$2 = -2 \text{ False}$$
The second solution does not check. It is extraneous. The solution set is $\{3\}$.

33.
$$\sqrt{w} = w - 6$$
$$\left(\sqrt{w}\right)^2 = (w-6)^2$$
$$w = w^2 - 12w + 36$$
$$0 = w^2 - 13w + 36$$
$$0 = (w-9)(w-4)$$
$$w - 9 = 0 \text{ or } w - 4 = 0$$
$$w = 9 \text{ or } w = 4$$

Check:
$$\sqrt{9} = 9 - 6 \text{ ?}$$
$$3 = 3 \checkmark$$

$$\sqrt{4} = 4 - 6 \text{ ?}$$
$$2 = -2 \text{ False}$$
The second solution is extraneous. The solution set is $\{9\}$.

35.
$$\sqrt{17-2x} + 1 = x$$
$$\sqrt{17-2x} = x - 1$$
$$\left(\sqrt{17-2x}\right)^2 = (x-1)^2$$
$$17 - 2x = x^2 - 2x + 1$$
$$0 = x^2 - 16$$
$$0 = (x-4)(x+4)$$
$$x - 4 = 0 \text{ or } x + 4 = 0$$
$$x = 4 \text{ or } x = -4$$

Check:
$$\sqrt{17-2(4)} + 1 = 4 \text{ ?}$$
$$\sqrt{9} + 1 = 4 \text{ ?}$$
$$3 + 1 = 4 \text{ ?}$$
$$4 = 4 \checkmark$$

$$\sqrt{17-2(-4)} + 1 = -4 \text{ ?}$$
$$\sqrt{17+8} + 1 = -4 \text{ ?}$$
$$\sqrt{25} + 1 = -4 \text{ ?}$$
$$5 + 1 = -4 \text{ ?}$$
$$6 = -4 \text{ False}$$
The second solution is extraneous, so the solution set is $\{4\}$.

37.
$$\sqrt{w^2 - 11} + 5 = w + 4$$
$$\sqrt{w^2 - 11} = w - 1$$
$$\left(\sqrt{w^2 - 11}\right)^2 = (w-1)^2$$
$$w^2 - 11 = w^2 - 2w + 1$$
$$0 = -2w + 12$$
$$2w = 12$$
$$w = 6$$

Check: $\sqrt{6^2 - 11} + 5 = 6 + 4$?
$$\sqrt{36-11} + 5 = 10 \text{ ?}$$
$$\sqrt{25} + 5 = 10 \text{ ?}$$
$$5 + 5 = 10 \text{ ?}$$
$$10 = 10 \checkmark$$
The solution set is $\{6\}$.

39.

$$\sqrt{x+9} = \sqrt{2x+5}$$
$$\left(\sqrt{x+9}\right)^2 = \left(\sqrt{2x+5}\right)^2$$
$$x+9 = 2x+5$$
$$-x = -4$$
$$x = 4$$

Check: $\sqrt{4+9} = \sqrt{2(4)+5}$?
$$\sqrt{13} = \sqrt{8+5} \text{ ?}$$
$$\sqrt{13} = \sqrt{13} \checkmark$$

The solution set is $\{4\}$.

41.

$$\sqrt[3]{4x-3} = \sqrt[3]{2x-9}$$
$$\left(\sqrt[3]{4x-3}\right)^3 = \left(\sqrt[3]{2x-9}\right)^3$$
$$4x-3 = 2x-9$$
$$2x = -6$$
$$x = -3$$

Check: $\sqrt[3]{4(-3)-3} = \sqrt[3]{2(-3)-9}$?
$$\sqrt[3]{-12-3} = \sqrt[3]{-6-9} \text{ ?}$$
$$\sqrt[3]{-15} = \sqrt[3]{-15} \checkmark$$

The solution set is $\{-3\}$.

43.

$$\sqrt{2w^2-3w-4} = \sqrt{w^2+6w+6}$$
$$\left(\sqrt{2w^2-3w-4}\right)^2 = \left(\sqrt{w^2+6w+6}\right)^2$$
$$2w^2-3w-4 = w^2+6w+6$$
$$w^2-9w-10 = 0$$
$$(w-10)(w+1) = 0$$
$$w-10 = 0 \text{ or } w+1 = 0$$
$$w = 10 \text{ or } w = -1$$

Check:
$$\sqrt{2(10)^2-3(10)-4} = \sqrt{10^2+6(10)+6} \text{ ?}$$
$$\sqrt{200-30-4} = \sqrt{100+60+6} \text{ ?}$$
$$\sqrt{166} = \sqrt{166} \checkmark$$

$$\sqrt{2(-1)^2-3(-1)-4} = \sqrt{(-1)^2+6(-1)+6} \text{ ?}$$
$$\sqrt{2+3-4} = \sqrt{1-6+6} \text{ ?}$$
$$\sqrt{1} = \sqrt{1}$$
$$1 = 1 \checkmark$$

The solution set is $\{-1, 10\}$.

45.

$$\sqrt{3w+4} = 2+\sqrt{w}$$
$$\left(\sqrt{3w+4}\right)^2 = \left(2+\sqrt{w}\right)^2$$
$$3w+4 = 2^2 + 2\cdot 2\sqrt{w} + \left(\sqrt{w}\right)^2$$
$$3w+4 = 4+4\sqrt{w}+w$$
$$2w = 4\sqrt{w}$$
$$w = 2\sqrt{w}$$
$$w^2 = \left(2\sqrt{w}\right)^2$$
$$w^2 = 4w$$
$$w^2-4w = 0$$
$$w(w-4) = 0$$
$$w = 0 \text{ or } w-4 = 0$$
$$w = 0 \text{ or } w = 4$$

Check:
$$\sqrt{3(0)+4} = 2+\sqrt{0} \text{ ?}$$
$$\sqrt{4} = 2 \text{ ?}$$
$$2 = 2 \checkmark$$

$$\sqrt{3(4)+4} = 2+\sqrt{4} \text{ ?}$$
$$\sqrt{16} = 2+2 \text{ ?}$$
$$4 = 4 \checkmark$$

The solution set is $\{0, 4\}$.

47.

$$\sqrt{x+1} - \sqrt{x-2} = 1$$
$$\sqrt{x+1} = \sqrt{x-2}+1$$
$$\left(\sqrt{x+1}\right)^2 = \left(\sqrt{x-2}+1\right)^2$$
$$x+1 = (x-2)+2\sqrt{x-2}+1$$
$$x+1 = x-1+2\sqrt{x-2}$$
$$2 = 2\sqrt{x-2}$$
$$1 = \sqrt{x-2}$$
$$1^2 = \left(\sqrt{x-2}\right)^2$$
$$1 = x-2$$
$$3 = x$$

Check: $\sqrt{3+1} - \sqrt{3-2} = 1$?
$$\sqrt{4} - \sqrt{1} = 1 \text{ ?}$$
$$2-1 = 1 \text{ ?}$$
$$1 = 1 \checkmark$$

The solution set is $\{3\}$.

49. $\sqrt{2x+6} - \sqrt{x-1} = 2$

$\qquad \sqrt{2x+6} = \sqrt{x-1} + 2$

$\qquad \left(\sqrt{2x+6}\right)^2 = \left(\sqrt{x-1}+2\right)^2$

$\qquad 2x+6 = (x-1) + 2 \cdot 2\sqrt{x-1} + 2^2$

$\qquad 2x+6 = x-1 + 4\sqrt{x-1} + 4$

$\qquad x+3 = 4\sqrt{x-1}$

$\qquad (x+3)^2 = \left(4\sqrt{x-1}\right)^2$

$\qquad x^2+6x+9 = 16(x-1)$

$\qquad x^2+6x+9 = 16x-16$

$\qquad x^2-10x+25 = 0$

$\qquad (x-5)^2 = 0$

$\qquad x-5 = 0$

$\qquad x = 5$

Check: $\sqrt{2(5)+6} - \sqrt{5-1} = 2$?

$\qquad \sqrt{16} - \sqrt{4} = 2$?

$\qquad 4-2 = 2$?

$\qquad 2 = 2$ ✓

The solution set is $\{5\}$.

51. $\sqrt{2x+5} - \sqrt{x-1} = 2$

$\qquad \sqrt{2x+5} = \sqrt{x-1} + 2$

$\qquad \left(\sqrt{2x+5}\right)^2 = \left(\sqrt{x-1}+2\right)^2$

$\qquad 2x+5 = (x-1) + 2 \cdot 2\sqrt{x-1} + 2^2$

$\qquad 2x+5 = x-1 + 4\sqrt{x-1} + 4$

$\qquad x+2 = 4\sqrt{x-1}$

$\qquad (x+2)^2 = \left(4\sqrt{x-1}\right)^2$

$\qquad x^2+4x+4 = 16(x-1)$

$\qquad x^2+4x+4 = 16x-16$

$\qquad x^2-12x+20 = 0$

$\qquad (x-10)(x-2) = 0$

$\qquad x-10 = 0 \text{ or } x-2 = 0$

$\qquad x = 10 \text{ or } x = 2$

Check:

$\sqrt{2(10)+5} - \sqrt{10-1} = 2$?

$\qquad \sqrt{25} - \sqrt{9} = 2$?

$\qquad 5-3 = 2$?

$\qquad 2 = 2$ ✓

$\sqrt{2(2)+5} - \sqrt{2-1} = 2$?

$\qquad \sqrt{9} - \sqrt{1} = 2$?

$\qquad 3-1 = 2$?

$\qquad 2 = 2$ ✓

The solution set is $\{2, 10\}$.

53. $\qquad (2x+3)^{1/2} = 3$

$\qquad \left((2x+3)^{1/2}\right)^2 = 3^2$

$\qquad 2x+3 = 9$

$\qquad 2x = 6$

$\qquad x = 3$

Check: $(2(3)+3)^{1/2} = 3$?

$\qquad (9)^{1/2} = 3$?

$\qquad 3 = 3$ ✓

The solution set is $\{3\}$.

55. $\qquad (6x-1)^{1/4} = (2x+15)^{1/4}$

$\qquad \left((6x-1)^{1/4}\right)^4 = \left((2x+15)^{1/4}\right)^4$

$\qquad 6x-1 = 2x+15$

$\qquad 4x = 16$

$\qquad x = 4$

Check: $(6(4)-1)^{1/4} = (2(4)+15)^{1/4}$?

$\qquad (23)^{1/4} = (23)^{1/4}$ ✓

The solution set is $\{4\}$.

57. $(x+3)^{1/2} - (x-5)^{1/2} = 2$

$(x+3)^{1/2} = (x-5)^{1/2} + 2$

$\left((x+3)^{1/2}\right)^2 = \left((x-5)^{1/2} + 2\right)^2$

$x+3 = (x-5) + 2 \cdot 2(x-5)^{1/2} + 2^2$

$x+3 = x-5 + 4(x-5)^{1/2} + 4$

$4 = 4(x-5)^{1/2}$

$1 = (x-5)^{1/2}$

$1^2 = \left((x-5)^{1/2}\right)^2$

$1 = x-5$

$6 = x$

Check: $(6+3)^{1/2} - (6-5)^{1/2} = 2$?

$\qquad\qquad 9^{1/2} - 1^{1/2} = 2$?

$\qquad\qquad\qquad 3 - 1 = 2$?

$\qquad\qquad\qquad\quad 2 = 2$ ✓

The solution set is $\{6\}$.

59. $A = P\sqrt{1+r}$

$\dfrac{A}{P} = \sqrt{1+r}$

$\left(\dfrac{A}{P}\right)^2 = \left(\sqrt{1+r}\right)^2$

$\dfrac{A^2}{P^2} = 1 + r$

$\dfrac{A^2}{P^2} - 1 = r$ or $r = \dfrac{A^2}{P^2} - 1 = \dfrac{A^2 - P^2}{P^2}$

61. $r = \sqrt[3]{\dfrac{3V}{4\pi}}$

$r^3 = \left(\sqrt[3]{\dfrac{3V}{4\pi}}\right)^3$

$r^3 = \dfrac{3V}{4\pi}$

$4\pi r^3 = 3V$

$\dfrac{4\pi r^3}{3} = V$ or $V = \dfrac{4}{3}\pi r^3$

63. $r = \sqrt{\dfrac{4F\pi\varepsilon_0}{q_1 q_2}}$

$r^2 = \left(\sqrt{\dfrac{4F\pi\varepsilon_0}{q_1 q_2}}\right)^2$

$r^2 = \dfrac{4F\pi\varepsilon_0}{q_1 q_2}$

$q_1 q_2 r^2 = 4F\pi\varepsilon_0$

$\dfrac{q_1 q_2 r^2}{4\pi\varepsilon_0} = F$ or $F = \dfrac{q_1 q_2 r^2}{4\pi\varepsilon_0}$

65. $\sqrt{5p-3} + 7 = 3$

$\sqrt{5p-3} = -4$

At this point we see that there is no real solution. Since the principal square root is never negative, $\sqrt{5p-3} = -4$ has no real solution. Solving the usual way yields the same result.

$\left(\sqrt{5p-3}\right)^2 = (-4)^2$

$5p - 3 = 16$

$5p = 19$

$p = \dfrac{19}{5}$

Check: $\sqrt{5\left(\dfrac{19}{5}\right) - 3} + 7 = 3$?

$\qquad\qquad \sqrt{19 - 3} + 7 = 3$?

$\qquad\qquad\quad \sqrt{16} + 7 = 3$?

$\qquad\qquad\qquad\quad 4 + 7 = 3$?

$\qquad\qquad\qquad\qquad 11 = 3$ False

The solution does not check, so the equation has no real solutions.

67. $\sqrt{x+12} = x$

$$\left(\sqrt{x+12}\right)^2 = x^2$$

$$x + 12 = x^2$$

$$0 = x^2 - x - 12$$

$$0 = (x-4)(x+3)$$

$$x - 4 = 0 \quad \text{or} \quad x + 3 = 0$$

$$x = 4 \qquad\qquad x = -3$$

Check:

$$\sqrt{4+12} = 4 \ ? \qquad \sqrt{-3+12} = -3 \ ?$$

$$\sqrt{16} = 4 \ ? \qquad\quad \sqrt{9} = -3 \ ?$$

$$4 = 4 \ \checkmark \qquad\qquad 3 = -3 \ \text{False}$$

The second solution does not check. The solution set is $\{4\}$.

69. $\sqrt{2p+12} = 4$

$$\left(\sqrt{2p+12}\right)^2 = 4^2$$

$$2p + 12 = 16$$

$$2p = 4$$

$$p = 2$$

Check: $\sqrt{2(2)+12} = 4 \ ?$

$$\sqrt{16} = 4 \ ?$$

$$4 = 4 \ \checkmark$$

The solution set is $\{2\}$.

71. $\sqrt[4]{x+7} = 2$

$$\left(\sqrt[4]{x+7}\right)^4 = 2^4$$

$$x + 7 = 16$$

$$x = 9$$

Check: $\sqrt[4]{9+7} = 2 \ ?$

$$\sqrt[4]{16} = 2 \ ?$$

$$2 = 2 \ \checkmark$$

The solution set is $\{9\}$.

73. $(3x+1)^{1/3} + 2 = 0$

$$(3x+1)^{1/3} = -2$$

$$\left((3x+1)^{1/3}\right)^3 = (-2)^3$$

$$3x + 1 = -8$$

$$3x = -9$$

$$x = -3$$

Check: $(3(-3)+1)^{1/3} + 2 = 0 \ ?$

$$(-8)^{1/3} + 2 = 0 \ ?$$

$$-2 + 2 = 0 \ ?$$

$$0 = 0 \ \checkmark$$

The solution set is $\{-3\}$.

75. $\sqrt{x} + 5 = 7$

$$\sqrt{x} = 2$$

$$\left(\sqrt{x}\right)^2 = 2^2$$

$$x = 4$$

Check: $\sqrt{4} + 5 = 7 \ ?$

$$2 + 5 = 7 \ ?$$

$$7 = 7 \ \checkmark$$

The solution set is $\{4\}$.

77. $\sqrt{2x+5} = \sqrt{3x-4}$

$$\left(\sqrt{2x+5}\right)^2 = \left(\sqrt{3x-4}\right)^2$$

$$2x + 5 = 3x - 4$$

$$-x + 5 = -4$$

$$-x = -9$$

$$x = 9$$

Check: $\sqrt{2(9)+5} = \sqrt{3(9)-4} \ ?$

$$\sqrt{23} = \sqrt{23} \ \checkmark$$

The solution set is $\{9\}$.

79. $\sqrt{x-1}+\sqrt{x+4}=5$

$$\sqrt{x-1}=5-\sqrt{x+4}$$

$$\left(\sqrt{x-1}\right)^2=\left(5-\sqrt{x+4}\right)^2$$

$$x-1=5^2-2\cdot5\sqrt{x+4}+(x+4)$$

$$x-1=25-10\sqrt{x+4}+x+4$$

$$-30=-10\sqrt{x+4}$$

$$3=\sqrt{x+4}$$

$$3^2=\left(\sqrt{x+4}\right)^2$$

$$9=x+4$$

$$5=x$$

Check: $\sqrt{5-1}+\sqrt{5+4}=5$?

$$\sqrt{4}+\sqrt{9}=5 \ ?$$

$$2+3=5 \ ?$$

$$5=5 \ ✔$$

The solution set is $\{5\}$.

81. $f(x)=\sqrt{x-2}$

a. $\qquad f(x)=0$

$$\sqrt{x-2}=0$$

$$\left(\sqrt{x-2}\right)^2=0^2$$

$$x-2=0$$

$$x=2$$

The point $(2,0)$ is on the graph of f.

b. $\qquad f(x)=1$

$$\sqrt{x-2}=1$$

$$\left(\sqrt{x-2}\right)^2=1^2$$

$$x-2=1$$

$$x=3$$

The point $(3,1)$ is on the graph of f.

c. $\qquad f(x)=2$

$$\sqrt{x-2}=2$$

$$\left(\sqrt{x-2}\right)^2=2^2$$

$$x-2=4$$

$$x=6$$

The point $(6,2)$ is on the graph of f.

d. The points $(2,0)$, $(3,1)$, and $(6,2)$ are on the graph.

e. The equation $f(x)=-1$ has no solution because the graph of the function does not go below the x-axis. Therefore, the value of the function will never be negative.

83. a. $\qquad \sqrt{4^2+(y-2)^2}=5$

$$\left(\sqrt{4^2+(y-2)^2}\right)^2=5^2$$

$$4^2+(y-2)^2=5^2$$

$$16+(y-2)^2=25$$

$$(y-2)^2=9$$

$$\sqrt{(y-2)^2}=\sqrt{9}$$

$$|y-2|=3$$

$$y-2=3 \text{ or } y-2=-3$$

$$y=5 \text{ or } y=-1$$

b. The points are $(3,2)$, $(-1,-1)$, and $(-1,5)$.

The figure is an isosceles triangle whose common side has a length of 5 units. The base has a length of 6 units. If the triangle were bisected from the vertex to the base, two 3-4-5 right triangles would be formed.

85. a.

$$\sqrt[3]{\frac{t}{2}} = 1$$

$$\left(\sqrt[3]{\frac{t}{2}}\right)^3 = 1^3$$

$$\frac{t}{2} = 1$$

$$t = 2$$

Annual revenue will be $1 million after 2 years.

b.

$$\sqrt[3]{\frac{t}{2}} = 2$$

$$\left(\sqrt[3]{\frac{t}{2}}\right)^3 = 2^3$$

$$\frac{t}{2} = 8$$

$$t = 16$$

Annual revenue will be $2 million after 16 years.

87. $R(t) = 26 \cdot \sqrt[10]{t}$

a. $26 \cdot \sqrt[10]{t} = 39$

$$\sqrt[10]{t} = \frac{39}{26}$$

$$\left(\sqrt[10]{t}\right)^{10} = \left(\frac{39}{26}\right)^{10}$$

$$t \approx 57.67$$

The plural birth rate is predicted to be 39 in the year 2053.

b. $26 \cdot \sqrt[10]{t} = 36$

$$\sqrt[10]{t} = \frac{18}{13}$$

$$\left(\sqrt[10]{t}\right)^{10} = \left(\frac{18}{13}\right)^{10}$$

$$t \approx 25.9$$

The plural birth rate is predicted to be 36 in the year 2021.

89.

$$\sqrt{3\sqrt{x+1}} = \sqrt{2x+3}$$

$$\left(\sqrt{3\sqrt{x+1}}\right)^2 = \left(\sqrt{2x+3}\right)^2$$

$$3\sqrt{x+1} = 2x+3$$

$$\left(3\sqrt{x+1}\right)^2 = (2x+3)^2$$

$$9(x+1) = (2x)^2 + 2\cdot 3 \cdot 2x + 3^2$$

$$9x+9 = 4x^2 +12x+9$$

$$0 = 4x^2 +3x$$

$$0 = x(4x+3)$$

$$x = 0 \ \text{ or } \ 4x+3 = 0$$

$$x = 0 \ \text{ or } \ 4x = -3$$

$$x = 0 \ \text{ or } \ x = -\frac{3}{4}$$

Check:

$$\sqrt{3\sqrt{0+1}} = \sqrt{2(0)+3} \ ?$$

$$\sqrt{3\sqrt{1}} = \sqrt{3} \ ?$$

$$\sqrt{3} = \sqrt{3} \ \checkmark$$

$$\sqrt{3\sqrt{-\frac{3}{4}+1}} = \sqrt{2\left(-\frac{3}{4}\right)+3} \ ?$$

$$\sqrt{3\cdot\frac{1}{2}} = \sqrt{-\frac{3}{2}+3} \ ?$$

$$\sqrt{\frac{3}{2}} = \sqrt{\frac{3}{2}} \ \checkmark$$

The solution set is $\left\{-\frac{3}{4}, 0\right\}$.

91. Raising both sides of the equation to an even power (e.g. squaring both sides) may yield extraneous solutions.

93. 0, -4, 12, $\frac{2}{3}$, and $1.\overline{56}$ are rational numbers.

95. 0, -4, 12, $\frac{2}{3}$, $1.\overline{56}$, $\sqrt{2^3}$, π, and $\sqrt[3]{-4}$ are real numbers (all those listed except $\sqrt{-5}$).

97.

99.

The two graphs do not intersect. Therefore, the equation has no real solution.

7.8 Preparing for The Complex Number System

1. **a.** 8 is the only natural number in the set.

   b. 8 and 0 are the whole numbers in the set.

   c. -23, $-\dfrac{12}{3}$, 0, and 8 are the integers in the set.

   d. -23, $-\dfrac{12}{3}$, $-\dfrac{1}{3}$, 0, $1.\overline{26}$, and 8 are the rational numbers in the set.

   e. $\sqrt{2}$ is the only irrational number in the set.

   f. -23, $-\dfrac{12}{3}$, $-\dfrac{1}{3}$, 0, $1.\overline{26}$, $\sqrt{2}$, and 8 are the real numbers in the set.

2. $3x(4x-3) = 3x \cdot 4x - 3x \cdot 3 = 12x^2 - 9x$

3. $(z+4)(3z-2) = z \cdot 3z + 4 \cdot 3z - 2 \cdot z - 4 \cdot 2$
$$= 3z^2 + 12z - 2z - 8$$
$$= 3z^2 + 10z - 8$$

4. $(2y+5)(2y-5) = (2y)^2 - 5^2 = 4y^2 - 25$

7.8 Exercises

1. imaginary unit

3. conjugate

5. False; to obtain the conjugate, we only change the sign on the imaginary part of the complex number. The conjugate of $-3+5i$ is $-3-5i$.

7. Answers will vary.
   The counting numbers are a subset of the whole numbers; the whole numbers are a subset of the integers; the integers are a subset of the rational numbers; rational numbers are a subset of the real numbers; and the real numbers are a subset of the complex numbers.

9. Answers will vary.
   Complex numbers, in standard form, resemble binomials in that there are two terms separated by a + or a −.

11. $\sqrt{-4} = \sqrt{-1} \cdot \sqrt{4} = i \cdot 2 = 2i$

13. $-\sqrt{-81} = -\sqrt{-1} \cdot \sqrt{81} = -i \cdot 9 = -9i$

15. $\sqrt{-45} = \sqrt{-1} \cdot \sqrt{9} \cdot \sqrt{5} = i \cdot 3 \cdot \sqrt{5} = 3\sqrt{5}\,i$

17. $\sqrt{-300} = \sqrt{-1} \cdot \sqrt{3} \cdot \sqrt{100} = i\sqrt{3} \cdot 10 = 10\sqrt{3}\,i$

19. $\sqrt{-7} = \sqrt{-1} \cdot \sqrt{7} = i\sqrt{7} = \sqrt{7}\,i$

21. $5 + \sqrt{-49} = 5 + \sqrt{-1} \cdot \sqrt{49}$
$$= 5 + i7$$
$$= 5 + 7i$$

23. $-2 - \sqrt{-28} = -2 - \sqrt{-1} \cdot \sqrt{4} \cdot \sqrt{7}$
$$= -2 - i \cdot 2\sqrt{7}$$
$$= -2 - 2\sqrt{7}\,i$$

SSM – 405

25. $\dfrac{4+\sqrt{-4}}{2} = \dfrac{4+\sqrt{-1}\cdot\sqrt{4}}{2}$

$\qquad = \dfrac{4+i\cdot 2}{2}$

$\qquad = 2+i$

27. $\dfrac{4+\sqrt{-8}}{12} = \dfrac{4+\sqrt{-1}\cdot\sqrt{4}\cdot\sqrt{2}}{12}$

$\qquad = \dfrac{4+i\cdot 2\sqrt{2}}{12}$

$\qquad = \dfrac{2+i\sqrt{2}}{6}$

$\qquad = \dfrac{1}{3}+\dfrac{\sqrt{2}}{6}i$

29. $(4+5i)+(2-7i) = 4+5i+2-7i$

$\qquad = (4+2)+(5-7)i$

$\qquad = 6-2i$

31. $(4+i)-(8-5i) = 4+i-8+5i$

$\qquad = (4-8)+(1+5)i$

$\qquad = -4+6i$

33. $\left(4-\sqrt{-4}\right)-\left(2+\sqrt{-9}\right) = (4-2i)-(2+3i)$

$\qquad = 4-2i-2-3i$

$\qquad = (4-2)+(-2-3)i$

$\qquad = 2-5i$

35. $\left(-2+\sqrt{-18}\right)+\left(5-\sqrt{-50}\right)$

$\qquad = \left(-2+3\sqrt{2}\,i\right)+\left(5-5\sqrt{2}\,i\right)$

$\qquad = -2+3\sqrt{2}\,i+5-5\sqrt{2}\,i$

$\qquad = (-2+5)+\left(3\sqrt{2}-5\sqrt{2}\right)i$

$\qquad = 3-2\sqrt{2}\,i$

37. $6i(2-4i) = 6i\cdot 2-6i\cdot 4i$

$\qquad = 12i-24i^2$

$\qquad = 12i-24(-1)$

$\qquad = 24+12i$

39. $-\dfrac{1}{2}i(4-10i) = -\dfrac{1}{2}i\cdot 4+\dfrac{1}{2}i\cdot 10i$

$\qquad = -2i+5i^2$

$\qquad = -2i+5(-1)$

$\qquad = -5-2i$

41. $(2+i)(4+3i) = 2\cdot 4+2\cdot 3i+i\cdot 4+i\cdot 3i$

$\qquad = 8+6i+4i+3i^2$

$\qquad = 8+10i-3$

$\qquad = 5+10i$

43. $(-3-5i)(2+4i) = -3\cdot 2-3\cdot 4i-5i\cdot 2-5i\cdot 4i$

$\qquad = -6-12i-10i-20i^2$

$\qquad = -6-22i-20(-1)$

$\qquad = -6-22i+20$

$\qquad = 14-22i$

45. $(-3+5i)(5-3i)$

$\qquad = -3\cdot 5-3\cdot(-3i)+5i\cdot 5+5i\cdot(-3i)$

$\qquad = -15+9i+25i-15i^2$

$\qquad = -15+34i-15(-1)$

$\qquad = 34i$

47. $\left(3-\sqrt{2}\,i\right)\left(-2+\sqrt{2}\,i\right)$

$\qquad = 3(-2)+3\left(\sqrt{2}\,i\right)-\sqrt{2}\,i(-2)-\left(\sqrt{2}\,i\right)^2$

$\qquad = -6+3\sqrt{2}\,i+2\sqrt{2}\,i-2i^2$

$\qquad = -6+5\sqrt{2}\,i-2(-1)$

$\qquad = -4+5\sqrt{2}\,i$

49. $\left(\dfrac{1}{2}-\dfrac{1}{4}i\right)\left(\dfrac{2}{3}+\dfrac{3}{4}i\right)$

$\qquad = \dfrac{1}{2}\cdot\dfrac{2}{3}+\dfrac{1}{2}\cdot\dfrac{3}{4}i-\dfrac{1}{4}i\cdot\dfrac{2}{3}-\dfrac{1}{4}i\cdot\dfrac{3}{4}i$

$\qquad = \dfrac{1}{3}+\dfrac{3}{8}i-\dfrac{1}{6}i-\dfrac{3}{16}i^2$

$\qquad = \dfrac{1}{3}+\dfrac{5}{24}i-\dfrac{3}{16}(-1)$

$\qquad = \dfrac{25}{48}+\dfrac{5}{24}i$

51. $(3+2i)^2 = 3^2 + 2(3)(2i) + (2i)^2$

$\qquad = 9 + 12i + 4i^2$

$\qquad = 9 + 12i + 4(-1)$

$\qquad = 5 + 12i$

53. $(-4-5i)^2 = (-4)^2 - 2(-4)(5i) + (5i)^2$

$\qquad = 16 + 40i + 25i^2$

$\qquad = 16 + 40i + 25(-1)$

$\qquad = -9 + 40i$

55. $\sqrt{-9} \cdot \sqrt{-4} = 3i \cdot 2i = 6i^2 = -6$

57. $\sqrt{-8} \cdot \sqrt{-10} = 2\sqrt{2}\,i \cdot \sqrt{10}\,i$

$\qquad = 2\sqrt{20}\,i^2$

$\qquad = 2 \cdot 2\sqrt{5} \cdot (-1)$

$\qquad = -4\sqrt{5}$

59. $\left(2+\sqrt{-81}\right)\left(-3-\sqrt{-100}\right)$

$= (2+9i)(-3-10i)$

$= 2(-3) - 2(10i) - 9i(3) - 9i(10i)$

$= -6 - 20i - 27i - 90i^2$

$= -6 - 47i - 90(-1)$

$= 84 - 47i$

61. a. The conjugate of $3+5i$ is $3-5i$.

$\quad$ **b.** $(3+5i)(3-5i) = 3^2 - (5i)^2$

$\qquad = 9 - 25i^2$

$\qquad = 9 - 25(-1)$

$\qquad = 9 + 25$

$\qquad = 34$

63. a. The conjugate of $2-7i$ is $2+7i$.

$\quad$ **b.** $(2-7i)(2+7i) = 2^2 - (7i)^2$

$\qquad = 4 - 49i^2$

$\qquad = 4 - 49(-1)$

$\qquad = 4 + 49$

$\qquad = 53$

65. a. The conjugate of $-7+2i$ is $-7-2i$.

$\quad$ **b.** $(-7+2i)(-7-2i) = (-7)^2 - (2i)^2$

$\qquad = 49 - 4i^2$

$\qquad = 49 - 4(-1)$

$\qquad = 49 + 4$

$\qquad = 53$

67. $\dfrac{1+i}{3i} = \dfrac{(1+i)}{3i} \cdot \dfrac{i}{i}$

$\qquad = \dfrac{i+i^2}{3i^2}$

$\qquad = \dfrac{i+(-1)}{3(-1)}$

$\qquad = \dfrac{i-1}{-3}$

$\qquad = \dfrac{-1}{-3} + \dfrac{1}{-3}i$

$\qquad = \dfrac{1}{3} - \dfrac{1}{3}i$

69. $\dfrac{-5+2i}{5i} = \dfrac{(-5+2i)}{5i} \cdot \dfrac{i}{i}$

$\qquad = \dfrac{-5i+2i^2}{5i^2}$

$\qquad = \dfrac{-5i+2(-1)}{5(-1)}$

$\qquad = \dfrac{-5i-2}{-5}$

$\qquad = \dfrac{-2}{-5} + \dfrac{-5}{-5}i$

$\qquad = \dfrac{2}{5} + i$

71. $\dfrac{3}{2+i} = \dfrac{3}{2+i} \cdot \dfrac{2-i}{2-i}$

$\qquad = \dfrac{6-3i}{2^2-i^2}$

$\qquad = \dfrac{6-3i}{4-(-1)}$

$\qquad = \dfrac{6-3i}{5}$

$\qquad = \dfrac{6}{5} - \dfrac{3}{5}i$

73. $\dfrac{-2}{-3-7i} = \dfrac{-2}{-3-7i} \cdot \dfrac{-3+7i}{-3+7i}$

$= \dfrac{6-14i}{(-3)^2 - (7i)^2}$

$= \dfrac{6-14i}{9-49i^2}$

$= \dfrac{6-14i}{9-49(-1)}$

$= \dfrac{6-14i}{58}$

$= \dfrac{6}{58} - \dfrac{14}{58}i$

$= \dfrac{3}{29} - \dfrac{7}{29}i$

75. $\dfrac{2+3i}{3-2i} = \dfrac{2+3i}{3-2i} \cdot \dfrac{3+2i}{3+2i}$

$= \dfrac{2 \cdot 3 + 2 \cdot 2i + 3i \cdot 3 + 3i \cdot 2i}{3^2 - (2i)^2}$

$= \dfrac{6+4i+9i+6i^2}{9-4i^2}$

$= \dfrac{6+13i-6}{9+4}$

$= \dfrac{13i}{13}$

$= i$

77. $\dfrac{4+2i}{1-i} = \dfrac{4+2i}{1-i} \cdot \dfrac{1+i}{1+i}$

$= \dfrac{4 \cdot 1 + 4 \cdot i + 2i \cdot 1 + 2i \cdot i}{1^2 - i^2}$

$= \dfrac{4+4i+2i+2i^2}{1+1}$

$= \dfrac{4+6i-2}{2}$

$= \dfrac{2+6i}{2}$

$= 1+3i$

79. $\dfrac{4-2i}{1+3i} = \dfrac{4-2i}{1+3i} \cdot \dfrac{1-3i}{1-3i}$

$= \dfrac{4 \cdot 1 - 4 \cdot 3i - 2i \cdot 1 + 2i \cdot 3i}{1^2 - (3i)^2}$

$= \dfrac{4-12i-2i+6i^2}{1-9i^2}$

$= \dfrac{4-14i-6}{1+9}$

$= \dfrac{-2-14i}{10}$

$= \dfrac{-2}{10} + \dfrac{-14i}{10}$

$= -\dfrac{1}{5} - \dfrac{7}{5}i$

81. $i^{53} = i^{52} \cdot i = \left(i^4\right)^{13} \cdot i = 1 \cdot i = i$

83. $i^{43} = i^{40} \cdot i^3 = \left(i^4\right)^{10} \cdot i^3 = 1 \cdot (-i) = -i$

85. $i^{153} = i^{152} \cdot i = \left(i^4\right)^{38} \cdot i = 1 \cdot i = i$

87. $i^{-45} = i^{-48} \cdot i^3 = \left(i^4\right)^{-12} \cdot i^3 = 1 \cdot i^3 = i^3 = -i$

89. $(-4-i)(4+i) = -4 \cdot 4 - 4 \cdot i - i \cdot 4 - i \cdot i$

$= -16 - 4i - 4i - i^2$

$= -16 - 8i - (-1)$

$= -15 - 8i$

91. $(3+2i)^2 = 3^2 + 2(3)(2i) + (2i)^2$

$= 9 + 12i + 4i^2$

$= 9 + 12i - 4$

$= 5 + 12i$

93. $\dfrac{-3+2i}{3i} = \dfrac{-3+2i}{3i} \cdot \dfrac{i}{i}$

$= \dfrac{-3i+2i^2}{3i^2}$

$= \dfrac{-3i-2}{-3}$

$= \dfrac{2}{3} + i$

95. $\dfrac{-4+i}{-5-3i} = \dfrac{-4+i}{-5-3i} \cdot \dfrac{-5+3i}{-5+3i}$

$= \dfrac{-4(-5) - 4 \cdot 3i - i \cdot 5 + i \cdot 3i}{(-5)^2 - (3i)^2}$

$= \dfrac{20 - 12i - 5i + 3i^2}{25 - 9i^2}$

$= \dfrac{20 - 17i - 3}{25 + 9}$

$= \dfrac{17 - 17i}{34}$

$= \dfrac{17}{34} - \dfrac{17}{34}i$

$= \dfrac{1}{2} - \dfrac{1}{2}i$

97. $(10 - 3i) + (2 + 3i) = 10 - 3i + 2 + 3i$

$= (10 + 2) + (-3 + 3)i$

$= 12 + 0i$

$= 12$

99. $5i(-4 + 3i) = 5i \cdot (-4) + 5i(3i)$

$= -20i + 15i^2$

$= -20i - 15$

$= -15 - 20i$

101. $\sqrt{-10} \cdot \sqrt{-15} = \sqrt{-1} \cdot \sqrt{10} \cdot \sqrt{-1} \cdot \sqrt{15}$

$= i \cdot \sqrt{10} \cdot i \cdot \sqrt{15}$

$= i^2 \cdot \sqrt{150}$

$= -1 \cdot \sqrt{25} \cdot \sqrt{6}$

$= -5\sqrt{6}$

103. $\dfrac{1}{5i} = \dfrac{1}{5i} \cdot \dfrac{i}{i} = \dfrac{i}{5i^2} = \dfrac{i}{-5} = -\dfrac{1}{5}i$

105. $\dfrac{1}{2-i} = \dfrac{1}{2-i} \cdot \dfrac{2+i}{2+i}$

$= \dfrac{2+i}{2^2 - i^2}$

$= \dfrac{2+i}{4 - (-1)}$

$= \dfrac{2+i}{5}$

$= \dfrac{2}{5} + \dfrac{1}{5}i$

107. $\dfrac{1}{-4+5i} = \dfrac{1}{-4+5i} \cdot \dfrac{-4-5i}{-4-5i}$

$= \dfrac{-4-5i}{(-4)^2 - (5i)^2}$

$= \dfrac{-4-5i}{16 - 25i^2}$

$= \dfrac{-4-5i}{16 + 25}$

$= \dfrac{-4-5i}{41}$

$= -\dfrac{4}{41} - \dfrac{5}{41}i$

109. $f(x) = x^2$

a. $f(i) = i^2 = -1$

b. $f(1+i) = (1+i)^2$

$= 1^2 + 2i + i^2$

$= 1 + 2i - 1$

$= 2i$

111. $f(x) = x^2 + 2x + 2$

a. $f(3i) = (3i)^2 + 2(3i) + 2$

$= 9i^2 + 6i + 2$

$= -9 + 6i + 2$

$= -7 + 6i$

b. $f(1-i) = (1-i)^2 + 2(1-i) + 2$

$= 1^2 - 2i + i^2 + 2 - 2i + 2$

$= 1 - 2i - 1 + 2 - 2i + 2$

$= 4 - 4i$

113. a. To find the total impedance, we add the individual impedances.

$(7 + 3i) + (3 - 4i) = 7 + 3i + 3 - 4i$

$= (7 + 3) + (3 - 4)i$

$= 10 - i$

The total impedance is $10 - i$ ohms.

b. The total resistance is the real part of the impedance. Thus, the total resistance is 10 ohms.

c. The total reactance is the imaginary part of the impedance. Thus, the total reactance is -1 ohm. (Since the reactance is negative, this would be called *capacitive reactance*.)

115. $f(x) = x^2 + 4x + 5$

   a. $f(-2+i) = (-2+i)^2 + 4(-2+i) + 5$

$$= (-2)^2 + 2(-2)i + i^2 - 8 + 4i + 5$$
$$= 4 - 4i - 1 - 8 + 4i + 5$$
$$= 0$$

   b. $f(-2-i) = (-2-i)^2 + 4(-2-i) + 5$

$$= (-2)^2 - 2(-2)i + i^2 - 8 - 4i + 5$$
$$= 4 + 4i - 1 - 8 - 4i + 5$$
$$= 0$$

117. $f(x) = x^3 + 1$

   a. $f(-1) = (-1)^3 + 1 = -1 + 1 = 0$

   b. $f\left(\dfrac{1}{2} + \dfrac{\sqrt{3}}{2}i\right) = \left(\dfrac{1}{2} + \dfrac{\sqrt{3}}{2}i\right)^3 + 1$

$$= \left(\dfrac{1}{2} + \dfrac{\sqrt{3}}{2}i\right)\left(\dfrac{1}{2} + \dfrac{\sqrt{3}}{2}i\right)^2 + 1$$

$$= \left(\dfrac{1}{2} + \dfrac{\sqrt{3}}{2}i\right)\left(\dfrac{1}{4} + \dfrac{\sqrt{3}}{2}i + \dfrac{3}{4}i^2\right) + 1$$

$$= \left(\dfrac{1}{2} + \dfrac{\sqrt{3}}{2}i\right)\left(\dfrac{1}{4} + \dfrac{\sqrt{3}}{2}i - \dfrac{3}{4}\right) + 1$$

$$= \left(\dfrac{1}{2} + \dfrac{\sqrt{3}}{2}i\right)\left(-\dfrac{1}{2} + \dfrac{\sqrt{3}}{2}i\right) + 1$$

$$= \left(\dfrac{\sqrt{3}}{2}i\right)^2 - \left(\dfrac{1}{2}\right)^2 + 1$$

$$= \dfrac{3}{4}i^2 - \dfrac{1}{4} + 1$$

$$= -\dfrac{3}{4} + \dfrac{3}{4}$$

$$= 0$$

   c. $f\left(\dfrac{1}{2} - \dfrac{\sqrt{3}}{2}i\right) = \left(\dfrac{1}{2} - \dfrac{\sqrt{3}}{2}i\right)^3 + 1$

$$= \left(\dfrac{1}{2} - \dfrac{\sqrt{3}}{2}i\right)\left(\dfrac{1}{2} - \dfrac{\sqrt{3}}{2}i\right)^2 + 1$$

$$= \left(\dfrac{1}{2} - \dfrac{\sqrt{3}}{2}i\right)\left(\dfrac{1}{4} - \dfrac{\sqrt{3}}{2}i + \dfrac{3}{4}i^2\right) + 1$$

$$= \left(\dfrac{1}{2} - \dfrac{\sqrt{3}}{2}i\right)\left(\dfrac{1}{4} - \dfrac{\sqrt{3}}{2}i - \dfrac{3}{4}\right) + 1$$

$$= \left(\dfrac{1}{2} - \dfrac{\sqrt{3}}{2}i\right)\left(-\dfrac{1}{2} - \dfrac{\sqrt{3}}{2}i\right) + 1$$

$$= \left(-\dfrac{\sqrt{3}}{2}i\right)^2 - \left(\dfrac{1}{2}\right)^2 + 1$$

$$= \dfrac{3}{4}i^2 - \dfrac{1}{4} + 1$$

$$= -\dfrac{3}{4} + \dfrac{3}{4}$$

$$= 0$$

119. For a polynomial with real coefficients, the zeros will be real numbers or will occur in conjugate pairs. If the complex number $a + bi$ is a complex zero of the polynomial, then its conjugate $a - bi$ is also a complex conjugate.

121. $(y-4)^2 = y^2 - 2 \cdot y \cdot 4 + 4^2$
$$= y^2 - 8y + 16$$

123. $(4-3i)^2 = 4^2 - 2 \cdot 4 \cdot 3i + (3i)^2$
$$= 16 - 24i + 9i^2$$
$$= 16 - 24i + 9(-1)$$
$$= 7 - 24i$$

125.
```
(1.3-4.3i)+(-5.3
+0.7i)
            -4-3.6i
```

127.
```
(0.3-5.2i)(1.2+3
.9i)
         20.64-5.07i
```

129.

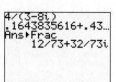

131.

Chapter 7 Review

1. $\sqrt[3]{343} = \sqrt[3]{7^3} = 7$

2. $\sqrt[3]{-125} = \sqrt[3]{(-5)^3} = -5$

3. $\sqrt[3]{\dfrac{8}{27}} = \sqrt[3]{\left(\dfrac{2}{3}\right)^3} = \dfrac{2}{3}$

4. $\sqrt[4]{81} = \sqrt[4]{3^4} = 3$

5. $-\sqrt[5]{-243} = -\sqrt[5]{(-3)^5} = -(-3) = 3$

6. $\sqrt[3]{10^3} = 10$

7. $\sqrt[5]{z^5} = z$

8. $\sqrt[4]{(5p-3)^4} = |5p-3|$

9. $81^{1/2} = \sqrt{81} = \sqrt{9^2} = 9$

10. $(-256)^{1/4} = \sqrt[4]{-256}$ is not a real number.

11. $-4^{1/2} = -\sqrt{4} = -\sqrt{2^2} = -2$

12. $729^{1/3} = \sqrt[3]{729} = \sqrt[3]{9^3} = 9$

13. $16^{7/4} = \left(\sqrt[4]{16}\right)^7 = \left(\sqrt[4]{2^4}\right)^7 = 2^7 = 128$

14. $-(-27)^{2/3} = -\left(\sqrt[3]{-27}\right)^2$
$= -\left(\sqrt[3]{(-3)^3}\right)^2$
$= -(-3)^2$
$= -9$

15. $-121^{3/2} = -\left(\sqrt{121}\right)^3$
$= -\left(\sqrt{11^2}\right)^3$
$= -(11)^3$
$= -1331$

16. $\dfrac{1}{36^{-1/2}} = 36^{1/2} = \sqrt{36} = \sqrt{6^2} = 6$

17. $(-65)^{1/3} \approx -4.02$

18. $4^{3/5} \approx 2.30$

19. $\sqrt[3]{100} \approx 4.64$

20. $\sqrt[4]{10} \approx 1.78$

21. $\sqrt[3]{5a} = (5a)^{1/3}$

22. $\sqrt[5]{p^7} = p^{7/5}$

23. $\left(\sqrt[4]{10z}\right)^3 = (10z)^{3/4}$

24. $\sqrt[6]{(2ab)^5} = (2ab)^{5/6}$

25. $4^{2/3} \cdot 4^{7/3} = 4^{\frac{2}{3}+\frac{7}{3}} = 4^{\frac{9}{3}} = 4^3 = 64$

26. $\dfrac{k^{1/2}}{k^{3/4}} = k^{\frac{1}{2}-\frac{3}{4}} = k^{\frac{2}{4}-\frac{3}{4}} = k^{-1/4} = \dfrac{1}{k^{1/4}}$

27. $\left(p^{4/3} \cdot q^4\right)^{3/2} = \left(p^{4/3}\right)^{3/2} \cdot \left(q^4\right)^{3/2}$
$= p^{\frac{4}{3}\cdot\frac{3}{2}} \cdot q^{4\cdot\frac{3}{2}}$
$= p^2 \cdot q^6$ or $\left(p \cdot q^3\right)^2$

28. $\left(32a^{-3/2} \cdot b^{1/4}\right)^{1/5} = (32)^{1/5} \cdot \left(a^{-3/2}\right)^{1/5} \cdot \left(b^{1/4}\right)^{1/5}$

$\qquad = 2 \cdot a^{-3/10} \cdot b^{1/20}$

$\qquad = \dfrac{2b^{1/20}}{a^{3/10}}$ or $2\left(\dfrac{b}{a^6}\right)^{1/20}$

29. $5m^{-2/3}\left(2m + m^{-1/3}\right)$

$\qquad = 5m^{-2/3} \cdot 2m + 5m^{-2/3} \cdot m^{-1/3}$

$\qquad = 10m^{-2/3} \cdot m^{3/3} + 5m^{-3/3}$

$\qquad = 10m^{1/3} + 5m^{-1}$

$\qquad = 10m^{1/3} + \dfrac{5}{m}$

30. $\left(\dfrac{16x^{1/3}}{x^{-1/3}}\right)^{-1/2} + \left(\dfrac{x^{-3/2}}{64x^{-1/2}}\right)^{1/3}$

$\qquad = \left(16x^{\frac{1}{3}-\left(-\frac{1}{3}\right)}\right)^{-1/2} + \left(64^{-1}x^{-\frac{3}{2}-\left(-\frac{1}{2}\right)}\right)^{1/3}$

$\qquad = \left(16x^{2/3}\right)^{-1/2} + \left(\dfrac{1}{64}x^{-1}\right)^{1/3}$

$\qquad = \left(\dfrac{1}{16}x^{-2/3}\right)^{1/2} + \left(\dfrac{1}{64}x^{-1}\right)^{1/3}$

$\qquad = \left(\dfrac{1}{16}\right)^{1/2}\left(x^{-2/3}\right)^{1/2} + \left(\dfrac{1}{64}\right)^{1/3}\left(x^{-1}\right)^{1/3}$

$\qquad = \dfrac{1}{4}x^{-1/3} + \dfrac{1}{4}x^{-1/3}$

$\qquad = \dfrac{1}{2}x^{-1/3}$

$\qquad = \dfrac{1}{2x^{1/3}}$

31. $\sqrt[8]{x^6} = x^{6/8} = x^{3/4} = \sqrt[4]{x^3}$

32. $\sqrt{121x^4 y^{10}} = \left(121x^4 y^{10}\right)^{1/2}$

$\qquad = 121^{1/2}\left(x^4\right)^{1/2}\left(y^{10}\right)^{1/2}$

$\qquad = 11x^{4/2}y^{10/2}$

$\qquad = 11x^2 y^5$

33. $\sqrt[3]{m^2} \cdot \sqrt{m^3} = m^{2/3} \cdot m^{3/2}$

$\qquad = m^{\frac{2}{3}+\frac{3}{2}}$

$\qquad = m^{\frac{4}{6}+\frac{9}{6}}$

$\qquad = m^{13/6}$

$\qquad = \sqrt[6]{m^{13}}$

$\qquad = m^2 \sqrt[6]{m}$

34. $\dfrac{\sqrt[3]{c}}{\sqrt[6]{c^4}} = \dfrac{c^{1/3}}{c^{4/6}} = \dfrac{c^{1/3}}{c^{2/3}} = c^{\frac{1}{3}-\frac{2}{3}} = c^{-1/3} = \dfrac{1}{c^{1/3}} = \dfrac{1}{\sqrt[3]{c}}$

35. $2(3m-1)^{1/4} + (m-7)(3m-1)^{5/4}$

$\qquad = 2 \cdot (3m-1)^{1/4} + (m-7)(3m-1)^{1/4} \cdot (3m-1)$

$\qquad = (3m-1)^{1/4}\left(2 + (m-7)(3m-1)\right)$

$\qquad = (3m-1)^{1/4}\left(2 + 3m^2 - 21m - m + 7\right)$

$\qquad = (3m-1)^{1/4}\left(3m^2 - 22m + 9\right)$

36. $3\left(x^2-5\right)^{1/3} - 4x\left(x^2-5\right)^{-2/3}$

$\qquad = 3\left(x^2-5\right)^{-2/3} \cdot \left(x^2-5\right) - 4x\left(x^2-5\right)^{-2/3}$

$\qquad = \left(x^2-5\right)^{-2/3}\left(3\left(x^2-5\right) - 4x\right)$

$\qquad = \left(x^2-5\right)^{-2/3}\left(3x^2 - 15 - 4x\right)$

$\qquad = \left(x^2-5\right)^{-2/3}\left(3x^2 - 4x - 15\right)$

$\qquad = \dfrac{3x^2 - 4x - 15}{\left(x^2-5\right)^{2/3}} = \dfrac{(3x+5)(x-3)}{\left(x^2-5\right)^{2/3}}$

37. $\sqrt{15} \cdot \sqrt{7} = \sqrt{15 \cdot 7} = \sqrt{105}$

38. $\sqrt[4]{2ab^2} \cdot \sqrt[4]{6a^2 b} = \sqrt[4]{2ab^2 \cdot 6a^2 b} = \sqrt[4]{12a^3 b^3}$

39. $\sqrt{80} = \sqrt{16 \cdot 5} = \sqrt{16} \cdot \sqrt{5} = 4\sqrt{5}$

40. $\sqrt[3]{-500} = \sqrt[3]{-125 \cdot 4} = \sqrt[3]{-125} \cdot \sqrt[3]{4} = -5\sqrt[3]{4}$

41. $\sqrt[3]{162m^6 n^4} = \sqrt[3]{27m^6 n^3 \cdot 6n}$

$\qquad = \sqrt[3]{27m^6 n^3} \cdot \sqrt[3]{6n}$

$\qquad = 3m^2 n \sqrt[3]{6n}$

42. $\sqrt[4]{50p^8q^4} = \sqrt[4]{p^8q^4 \cdot 50}$

$\qquad = \sqrt[4]{p^8q^4} \cdot \sqrt[4]{50}$

$\qquad = p^2|q|\sqrt[4]{50}$

43. $2\sqrt{16x^6y} = 2\sqrt{16x^6 \cdot y}$

$\qquad = 2\sqrt{16x^6} \cdot \sqrt{y}$

$\qquad = 2 \cdot 4|x^3|\sqrt{y}$

$\qquad = 8|x^3|\sqrt{y}$

as long as $y \ge 0$. Otherwise the result is not a real number.

44. $\sqrt{(2x+1)^3} = \sqrt{(2x+1)^2 \cdot (2x+1)}$

$\qquad = \sqrt{(2x+1)^2} \cdot \sqrt{2x+1}$

$\qquad = (2x+1)\sqrt{2x+1}$

as long as $2x+1 \ge 0$. Otherwise the result is not a real number.

45. $\sqrt{w^3z^2} = \sqrt{w^2z^2 \cdot w} = \sqrt{w^2z^2} \cdot \sqrt{w} = wz\sqrt{w}$

46. $\sqrt{45x^4yz^3} = \sqrt{9x^4z^2 \cdot 5yz}$

$\qquad = \sqrt{9x^4z^2} \cdot \sqrt{5yz}$

$\qquad = 3x^2z\sqrt{5yz}$

47. $\sqrt[3]{16a^{12}b^5} = \sqrt[3]{8a^{12}b^3 \cdot 2b^2}$

$\qquad = \sqrt[3]{8a^{12}b^3} \cdot \sqrt[3]{2b^2}$

$\qquad = 2a^4b\sqrt[3]{2b^2}$

48. $\sqrt{4x^2+8x+4} = \sqrt{4(x^2+2x+1)}$

$\qquad = \sqrt{4(x+1)^2}$

$\qquad = 2(x+1)$

49. $\sqrt{15} \cdot \sqrt{18} = \sqrt{15 \cdot 18}$

$\qquad = \sqrt{270}$

$\qquad = \sqrt{9 \cdot 30}$

$\qquad = \sqrt{9} \cdot \sqrt{30}$

$\qquad = 3\sqrt{30}$

50. $\sqrt[3]{20} \cdot \sqrt[3]{30} = \sqrt[3]{20 \cdot 30}$

$\qquad = \sqrt[3]{600}$

$\qquad = \sqrt[3]{8 \cdot 75}$

$\qquad = \sqrt[3]{8} \cdot \sqrt[3]{75}$

$\qquad = 2\sqrt[3]{75}$

51. $\sqrt[3]{-3x^4y^7} \cdot \sqrt[3]{24x^3y^2} = \sqrt[3]{-3x^4y^7 \cdot 24x^3y^2}$

$\qquad = \sqrt[3]{-72x^7y^9}$

$\qquad = \sqrt[3]{-8x^6y^9 \cdot 9x}$

$\qquad = \sqrt[3]{-8x^6y^9} \cdot \sqrt[3]{9x}$

$\qquad = -2x^2y^3\sqrt[3]{9x}$

52. $3\sqrt{4xy^2} \cdot 5\sqrt{3x^2y} = 15\sqrt{4xy^2 \cdot 3x^2y}$

$\qquad = 15\sqrt{12x^3y^3}$

$\qquad = 15\sqrt{4x^2y^2 \cdot 3xy}$

$\qquad = 15\sqrt{4x^2y^2} \cdot \sqrt{3xy}$

$\qquad = 15 \cdot 2xy\sqrt{3xy}$

$\qquad = 30xy\sqrt{3xy}$

53. $\sqrt{\dfrac{121}{25}} = \dfrac{\sqrt{121}}{\sqrt{25}} = \dfrac{11}{5}$

54. $\sqrt{\dfrac{5a^4}{64b^2}} = \dfrac{\sqrt{5a^4}}{\sqrt{64b^2}} = \dfrac{a^2\sqrt{5}}{8b}$

55. $\sqrt[3]{\dfrac{54k^2}{9k^5}} = \sqrt[3]{\dfrac{6}{k^3}} = \dfrac{\sqrt[3]{6}}{\sqrt[3]{k^3}} = \dfrac{\sqrt[3]{6}}{k}$

56. $\sqrt[3]{\dfrac{-160w^{11}}{343w^{-4}}} = \sqrt[3]{\dfrac{-160w^{15}}{343}}$

$\qquad = \dfrac{\sqrt[3]{-160w^{15}}}{\sqrt[3]{343}}$

$\qquad = \dfrac{\sqrt[3]{-8w^{15} \cdot 20}}{\sqrt[3]{7^3}}$

$\qquad = \dfrac{-2w^5\sqrt[3]{20}}{7}$

57. $\dfrac{\sqrt{12h^3}}{\sqrt{3h}} = \sqrt{\dfrac{12h^3}{3h}} = \sqrt{4h^2} = 2h$

58. $\dfrac{\sqrt{50a^3b^3}}{\sqrt{8a^5b^{-3}}} = \sqrt{\dfrac{50a^3b^3}{8a^5b^{-3}}} = \sqrt{\dfrac{25b^6}{4a^2}} = \dfrac{\sqrt{25b^6}}{\sqrt{4a^2}} = \dfrac{5b^3}{2a}$

59. $\dfrac{\sqrt[3]{-8x^7y}}{\sqrt[3]{27xy^4}} = \sqrt[3]{\dfrac{-8x^7y}{27xy^4}} = \sqrt[3]{\dfrac{-8x^6}{27y^3}} = \dfrac{\sqrt[3]{-8x^6}}{\sqrt[3]{27y^3}} = \dfrac{-2x^2}{3y}$

60. $\dfrac{\sqrt[4]{48m^2n^7}}{\sqrt[4]{3m^6n}} = \sqrt[4]{\dfrac{48m^2n^7}{3m^6n}}$

$= \sqrt[4]{\dfrac{16n^6}{m^4}}$

$= \dfrac{\sqrt[4]{16n^6}}{\sqrt[4]{m^4}}$

$= \dfrac{2n\sqrt[4]{n^2}}{m}$

$= \dfrac{2n\sqrt{n}}{m}$

61. $\sqrt{5} \cdot \sqrt[3]{2} = 5^{1/2} \cdot 2^{1/3}$

$= 5^{3/6} \cdot 2^{2/6}$

$= \left(5^3\right)^{1/6} \cdot \left(2^2\right)^{1/6}$

$= \left(5^3 \cdot 2^2\right)^{1/6}$

$= (125 \cdot 4)^{1/6}$

$= 500^{1/6}$

$= \sqrt[6]{500}$

62. $\sqrt[4]{8} \cdot \sqrt[6]{4} = 8^{1/4} \cdot 4^{1/6}$

$= \left(2^3\right)^{1/4} \cdot \left(2^2\right)^{1/6}$

$= 2^{3/4} \cdot 2^{1/3} = 2^{\frac{3}{4}+\frac{1}{3}}$

$= 2^{13/12} = 2^{\frac{12}{12}} \cdot 2^{\frac{1}{12}}$

$= 2\sqrt[12]{2}$

63. $2\sqrt[4]{x} + 6\sqrt[4]{x} = (2+6)\sqrt[4]{x} = 8\sqrt[4]{x}$

64. $7\sqrt[3]{4y} + 2\sqrt[3]{4y} - 3\sqrt[3]{4y} = (7+2-3)\sqrt[3]{4y}$

$= 6\sqrt[3]{4y}$

65. $5\sqrt{2} - 2\sqrt{12} = 5\sqrt{2} - 2 \cdot \sqrt{4} \cdot \sqrt{3}$

$= 5\sqrt{2} - 2 \cdot 2 \cdot \sqrt{3}$

$= 5\sqrt{2} - 4\sqrt{3}$

Cannot be simplified further.

66. $\sqrt{18} + 2\sqrt{50} = \sqrt{9} \cdot \sqrt{2} + 2\sqrt{25} \cdot \sqrt{2}$

$= 3 \cdot \sqrt{2} + 2 \cdot 5 \cdot \sqrt{2}$

$= 3\sqrt{2} + 10\sqrt{2}$

$= (3+10)\sqrt{2}$

$= 13\sqrt{2}$

67. $\sqrt[3]{-16z} + \sqrt[3]{54z} = \sqrt[3]{-8} \cdot \sqrt[3]{2z} + \sqrt[3]{27} \cdot \sqrt[3]{2z}$

$= -2\sqrt[3]{2z} + 3\sqrt[3]{2z}$

$= (-2+3)\sqrt[3]{2z}$

$= \sqrt[3]{2z}$

68. $7\sqrt[3]{8x^2} - \sqrt[3]{-27x^2} = 7 \cdot \sqrt[3]{8} \cdot \sqrt[3]{x^2} - \sqrt[3]{-27} \cdot \sqrt[3]{x^2}$

$= 7 \cdot 2 \cdot \sqrt[3]{x^2} - (-3) \cdot \sqrt[3]{x^2}$

$= 14\sqrt[3]{x^2} + 3\sqrt[3]{x^2}$

$= (14+3)\sqrt[3]{x^2}$

$= 17\sqrt[3]{x^2}$

69. $\sqrt{16a} + \sqrt[6]{729a^3} = \sqrt{16} \cdot \sqrt{a} + \sqrt[6]{729} \cdot \sqrt[6]{a^3}$

$= \sqrt{16} \cdot \sqrt{a} + \sqrt[6]{729} \cdot a^{3/6}$

$= 4\sqrt{a} + 3 \cdot a^{1/2}$

$= 4\sqrt{a} + 3\sqrt{a}$

$= (4+3)\sqrt{a}$

$= 7\sqrt{a}$

70. $\sqrt{27x^2} - x\sqrt{48} + 2\sqrt{75x^2}$

$= \sqrt{9x^2} \cdot \sqrt{3} - x \cdot \sqrt{16} \cdot \sqrt{3} + 2 \cdot \sqrt{25x^2} \cdot \sqrt{3}$

$= 3x\sqrt{3} - 4x\sqrt{3} + 10x\sqrt{3}$

$= (3+10-4)x\sqrt{3}$

$= 9x\sqrt{3}$

71. $5\sqrt[3]{4m^5y^2} - \sqrt[6]{16m^{10}y^4}$

$= 5\cdot\sqrt[3]{m^3}\cdot\sqrt[3]{4m^2y^2} - \sqrt[6]{m^6}\cdot\sqrt[6]{16m^4y^4}$

$= 5m\sqrt[3]{4m^2y^2} - m\cdot\sqrt[6]{\left(4m^2y^2\right)^2}$

$= 5m\sqrt[3]{4m^2y^2} - m\cdot\left(4m^2y^2\right)^{2/6}$

$= 5m\sqrt[3]{4m^2y^2} - m\cdot\left(4m^2y^2\right)^{1/3}$

$= 5m\sqrt[3]{4m^2y^2} - m\sqrt[3]{4m^2y^2}$

$= (5-1)m\sqrt[3]{4m^2y^2}$

$= 4m\sqrt[3]{4m^2y^2}$

72. $\sqrt{y^3-4y^2} - 2\sqrt{y-4} + \sqrt[4]{y^2-8y+16}$

$= \sqrt{y^2}\cdot\sqrt{(y-4)} - 2\sqrt{y-4} + \sqrt[4]{(y-4)^2}$

$= y\sqrt{y-4} - 2\sqrt{y-4} + (y-4)^{2/4}$

$= y\sqrt{y-4} - 2\sqrt{y-4} + (y-4)^{1/2}$

$= y\sqrt{y-4} - 2\sqrt{y-4} + \sqrt{y-4}$

$= (y-2+1)\sqrt{y-4}$

$= (y-1)\sqrt{y-4}$

73. $\sqrt{3}\left(\sqrt{5}-\sqrt{15}\right) = \sqrt{3}\cdot\sqrt{5} - \sqrt{3}\cdot\sqrt{15}$

$= \sqrt{3}\cdot\sqrt{5} - \sqrt{3\cdot15}$

$= \sqrt{3}\cdot\sqrt{5} - \sqrt{45}$

$= \sqrt{3}\cdot\sqrt{5} - \sqrt{9}\cdot\sqrt{5}$

$= \sqrt{3}\cdot\sqrt{5} - 3\cdot\sqrt{5}$

$= \sqrt{15} - 3\sqrt{5}$

74. $\sqrt[3]{5}\left(3+\sqrt[3]{4}\right) = \sqrt[3]{5}\cdot3 + \sqrt[3]{5}\cdot\sqrt[3]{4} = 3\sqrt[3]{5} + \sqrt[3]{20}$

75. $\left(3+\sqrt{5}\right)\left(4-\sqrt{5}\right) = 3\cdot4 - 3\cdot\sqrt{5} + 4\cdot\sqrt{5} - \sqrt{5}\cdot\sqrt{5}$

$= 12 - 3\sqrt{5} + 4\sqrt{5} - \sqrt{25}$

$= 12 + \sqrt{5} - 5$

$= 7 + \sqrt{5}$

76. $\left(7+\sqrt{3}\right)\left(6+\sqrt{2}\right)$

$= 7\cdot6 + 7\cdot\sqrt{2} + \sqrt{3}\cdot6 + \sqrt{3}\cdot\sqrt{2}$

$= 42 + 7\sqrt{2} + 6\sqrt{3} + \sqrt{6}$

77. $\left(1-3\sqrt{5}\right)\left(1+3\sqrt{5}\right) = (1)^2 - \left(3\sqrt{5}\right)^2$

$= 1 - 9\sqrt{25}$

$= 1 - 9\cdot5$

$= 1 - 45$

$= -44$

78. $\left(\sqrt[3]{x}+1\right)\left(9\sqrt[3]{x}-4\right)$

$= \sqrt[3]{x}\cdot9\sqrt[3]{x} + \sqrt[3]{x}\cdot(-4) + 1\cdot9\sqrt[3]{x} + 1\cdot(-4)$

$= 9\sqrt[3]{x^2} - 4\sqrt[3]{x} + 9\sqrt[3]{x} - 4$

$= 9\sqrt[3]{x^2} + 5\sqrt[3]{x} - 4$

79. $\left(\sqrt{x}-\sqrt{5}\right)^2 = \left(\sqrt{x}\right)^2 - 2\left(\sqrt{x}\right)\left(\sqrt{5}\right) + \left(\sqrt{5}\right)^2$

$= \sqrt{x^2} - 2\sqrt{5x} + \sqrt{25}$

$= x - 2\sqrt{5x} + 5$

80. $\left(11\sqrt{2}+\sqrt{5}\right)^2$

$= \left(11\sqrt{2}\right)^2 + 2\left(11\sqrt{2}\right)\left(\sqrt{5}\right) + \left(\sqrt{5}\right)^2$

$= 121\sqrt{4} + 22\sqrt{10} + \sqrt{25}$

$= 121\cdot2 + 22\sqrt{10} + 5$

$= 242 + 22\sqrt{10} + 5$

$= 247 + 22\sqrt{10}$

81. $\left(\sqrt{2a}-b\right)\left(\sqrt{2a}+b\right) = \left(\sqrt{2a}\right)^2 - (b)^2$

$= \sqrt{4a^2} - b^2$

$= 2a - b^2$

82. $\left(\sqrt[3]{6s}+2\right)\left(\sqrt[3]{6s}-7\right)$

$= \sqrt[3]{6s}\cdot\sqrt[3]{6s} + \sqrt[3]{6s}\cdot(-7) + 2\cdot\sqrt[3]{6s} + 2\cdot(-7)$

$= \sqrt[3]{36s^2} - 7\sqrt[3]{6s} + 2\sqrt[3]{6s} - 14$

$= \sqrt[3]{36s^2} - 5\sqrt[3]{6s} - 14$

83. $\dfrac{2}{\sqrt{6}} = \dfrac{2}{\sqrt{6}}\cdot\dfrac{\sqrt{6}}{\sqrt{6}} = \dfrac{2\sqrt{6}}{\sqrt{36}} = \dfrac{2\sqrt{6}}{6} = \dfrac{\sqrt{6}}{3}$

84. $\dfrac{6}{\sqrt{3}} = \dfrac{6}{\sqrt{3}}\cdot\dfrac{\sqrt{3}}{\sqrt{3}} = \dfrac{6\sqrt{3}}{\sqrt{9}} = \dfrac{6\sqrt{3}}{3} = 2\sqrt{3}$

85. $\dfrac{\sqrt{48}}{\sqrt{p^3}} = \dfrac{4\sqrt{3}}{p\sqrt{p}} = \dfrac{4\sqrt{3}}{p\sqrt{p}} \cdot \dfrac{\sqrt{p}}{\sqrt{p}}$

$\qquad = \dfrac{4\sqrt{3p}}{p\sqrt{p^2}} = \dfrac{4\sqrt{3p}}{p \cdot p}$

$\qquad = \dfrac{4\sqrt{3p}}{p^2}$

86. $\dfrac{5}{\sqrt{2a}} = \dfrac{5}{\sqrt{2a}} \cdot \dfrac{\sqrt{2a}}{\sqrt{2a}} = \dfrac{5\sqrt{2a}}{\sqrt{4a^2}} = \dfrac{5\sqrt{2a}}{2a}$

87. $\dfrac{-2}{\sqrt{6y^3}} = \dfrac{-2}{y\sqrt{6y}} = \dfrac{-2}{y\sqrt{6y}} \cdot \dfrac{\sqrt{6y}}{\sqrt{6y}}$

$\qquad = \dfrac{-2\sqrt{6y}}{y\sqrt{36y^2}} = \dfrac{-2\sqrt{6y}}{y \cdot 6y}$

$\qquad = \dfrac{-2\sqrt{6y}}{6y^2}$

$\qquad = -\dfrac{\sqrt{6y}}{3y^2}$

88. $\dfrac{3}{\sqrt[3]{5}} = \dfrac{3}{\sqrt[3]{5}} \cdot \dfrac{\sqrt[3]{25}}{\sqrt[3]{25}} = \dfrac{3\sqrt[3]{25}}{\sqrt[3]{125}} = \dfrac{3\sqrt[3]{25}}{5}$

89. $\sqrt[3]{\dfrac{-4}{45}} = \dfrac{\sqrt[3]{-4}}{\sqrt[3]{45}} = \dfrac{\sqrt[3]{-4}}{\sqrt[3]{45}} \cdot \dfrac{\sqrt[3]{75}}{\sqrt[3]{75}} = \dfrac{\sqrt[3]{-300}}{\sqrt[3]{3375}} = -\dfrac{\sqrt[3]{300}}{15}$

90. $\dfrac{27}{\sqrt[5]{8p^3q^4}} = \dfrac{27}{\sqrt[5]{8p^3q^4}} \cdot \dfrac{\sqrt[5]{4p^2q}}{\sqrt[5]{4p^2q}}$

$\qquad = \dfrac{27\sqrt[5]{4p^2q}}{\sqrt[5]{32p^5q^5}}$

$\qquad = \dfrac{27\sqrt[5]{4p^2q}}{2pq}$

91. $\dfrac{6}{7-\sqrt{6}} = \dfrac{6}{7-\sqrt{6}} \cdot \dfrac{7+\sqrt{6}}{7+\sqrt{6}}$

$\qquad = \dfrac{6\left(7+\sqrt{6}\right)}{7^2 - \left(\sqrt{6}\right)^2}$

$\qquad = \dfrac{42+6\sqrt{6}}{49-6}$

$\qquad = \dfrac{42+6\sqrt{6}}{43}$

92. $\dfrac{3}{\sqrt{3}-9} = \dfrac{3}{\sqrt{3}-9} \cdot \dfrac{\sqrt{3}+9}{\sqrt{3}+9}$

$\qquad = \dfrac{3\left(\sqrt{3}+9\right)}{\left(\sqrt{3}\right)^2 - 9^2}$

$\qquad = \dfrac{3\sqrt{3}+27}{3-81}$

$\qquad = \dfrac{3\sqrt{3}+27}{-78}$

$\qquad = -\dfrac{3\sqrt{3}+27}{78}$

$\qquad = -\dfrac{\sqrt{3}+9}{26}$

93. $\dfrac{\sqrt{3}}{3+\sqrt{2}} = \dfrac{\sqrt{3}}{3+\sqrt{2}} \cdot \dfrac{3-\sqrt{2}}{3-\sqrt{2}}$

$\qquad = \dfrac{\sqrt{3}\left(3-\sqrt{2}\right)}{3^2 - \left(\sqrt{2}\right)^2}$

$\qquad = \dfrac{\sqrt{3}\left(3-\sqrt{2}\right)}{9-2}$

$\qquad = \dfrac{\sqrt{3}\left(3-\sqrt{2}\right)}{7}$ or $\dfrac{3\sqrt{3}-\sqrt{6}}{7}$

94. $\dfrac{\sqrt{k}}{\sqrt{k}-\sqrt{m}} = \dfrac{\sqrt{k}}{\sqrt{k}-\sqrt{m}} \cdot \dfrac{\sqrt{k}+\sqrt{m}}{\sqrt{k}+\sqrt{m}}$

$\qquad = \dfrac{\sqrt{k}\left(\sqrt{k}+\sqrt{m}\right)}{\left(\sqrt{k}\right)^2 - \left(\sqrt{m}\right)^2}$

$\qquad = \dfrac{k+\sqrt{km}}{k-m}$

95. $\dfrac{\sqrt{10}+2}{\sqrt{10}-2} = \dfrac{\sqrt{10}+2}{\sqrt{10}-2} \cdot \dfrac{\sqrt{10}+2}{\sqrt{10}+2}$

$\qquad = \dfrac{\left(\sqrt{10}\right)^2 + 2 \cdot \sqrt{10} \cdot 2 + 2^2}{\left(\sqrt{10}\right)^2 - 2^2}$

$\qquad = \dfrac{10+4\sqrt{10}+4}{10-4} = \dfrac{14+4\sqrt{10}}{6}$

$\qquad = \dfrac{2\left(7+2\sqrt{10}\right)}{2(3)} = \dfrac{7+2\sqrt{10}}{3}$

96. $\dfrac{3-\sqrt{y}}{3+\sqrt{y}} = \dfrac{3-\sqrt{y}}{3+\sqrt{y}} \cdot \dfrac{3-\sqrt{y}}{3-\sqrt{y}}$

$= \dfrac{3^2 - 2\cdot 3 \cdot \sqrt{y} + \left(\sqrt{y}\right)^2}{3^2 - \left(\sqrt{y}\right)^2}$

$= \dfrac{9 - 6\sqrt{y} + y}{9 - y} \quad \text{or} \quad \dfrac{y - 6\sqrt{y} + 9}{9 - y}$

97. $\dfrac{4}{2\sqrt{3}+5\sqrt{2}} = \dfrac{4}{2\sqrt{3}+5\sqrt{2}} \cdot \dfrac{2\sqrt{3}-5\sqrt{2}}{2\sqrt{3}-5\sqrt{2}}$

$= \dfrac{4\left(2\sqrt{3}-5\sqrt{2}\right)}{\left(2\sqrt{3}\right)^2 - \left(5\sqrt{2}\right)^2}$

$= \dfrac{8\sqrt{3}-20\sqrt{2}}{4\cdot 3 - 25\cdot 2}$

$= \dfrac{8\sqrt{3}-20\sqrt{2}}{12-50}$

$= \dfrac{8\sqrt{3}-20\sqrt{2}}{-38}$

$= \dfrac{-2\left(-4\sqrt{3}+10\sqrt{2}\right)}{-2(19)}$

$= \dfrac{10\sqrt{2}-4\sqrt{3}}{19}$

98. $\dfrac{\sqrt{5}-\sqrt{6}}{\sqrt{10}+\sqrt{3}} = \dfrac{\sqrt{5}-\sqrt{6}}{\sqrt{10}+\sqrt{3}} \cdot \dfrac{\sqrt{10}-\sqrt{3}}{\sqrt{10}-\sqrt{3}}$

$= \dfrac{\left(\sqrt{5}-\sqrt{6}\right)\left(\sqrt{10}-\sqrt{3}\right)}{\left(\sqrt{10}+\sqrt{3}\right)\left(\sqrt{10}-\sqrt{3}\right)}$

$= \dfrac{\sqrt{50}-\sqrt{15}-\sqrt{60}+\sqrt{18}}{\left(\sqrt{10}\right)^2 - \left(\sqrt{3}\right)^2}$

$= \dfrac{5\sqrt{2}-\sqrt{15}-2\sqrt{15}+3\sqrt{2}}{10-3}$

$= \dfrac{8\sqrt{2}-3\sqrt{15}}{7}$

99. $\dfrac{\sqrt{7}}{3} + \dfrac{6}{\sqrt{7}} = \dfrac{\sqrt{7}}{3} \cdot \dfrac{\sqrt{7}}{\sqrt{7}} + \dfrac{6}{\sqrt{7}} \cdot \dfrac{3}{3}$

$= \dfrac{7}{3\sqrt{7}} + \dfrac{18}{3\sqrt{7}}$

$= \dfrac{25}{3\sqrt{7}}$

$= \dfrac{25}{3\sqrt{7}} \cdot \dfrac{\sqrt{7}}{\sqrt{7}}$

$= \dfrac{25\sqrt{7}}{3\cdot 7}$

$= \dfrac{25\sqrt{7}}{21}$

100. $\left(4-\sqrt{7}\right)^{-1} = \dfrac{1}{4-\sqrt{7}}$

$= \dfrac{1}{4-\sqrt{7}} \cdot \dfrac{4+\sqrt{7}}{4+\sqrt{7}}$

$= \dfrac{4+\sqrt{7}}{4^2 - \left(\sqrt{7}\right)^2}$

$= \dfrac{4+\sqrt{7}}{16-7}$

$= \dfrac{4+\sqrt{7}}{9}$

101. $f(x) = \sqrt{x+4}$

   a. $f(-3) = \sqrt{-3+4} = \sqrt{1} = 1$

   b. $f(0) = \sqrt{0+4} = \sqrt{4} = 2$

   c. $f(5) = \sqrt{5+4} = \sqrt{9} = 3$

102. $g(x) = \sqrt{3x-2}$

   a. $g\left(\dfrac{2}{3}\right) = \sqrt{3\left(\dfrac{2}{3}\right)-2} = \sqrt{2-2} = \sqrt{0} = 0$

   b. $g(2) = \sqrt{3(2)-2} = \sqrt{6-2} = \sqrt{4} = 2$

   c. $g(6) = \sqrt{3(6)-2} = \sqrt{18-2} = \sqrt{16} = 4$

103. $H(t) = \sqrt[3]{t+3}$

   a. $H(-2) = \sqrt[3]{-2+3} = \sqrt[3]{1} = 1$

   b. $H(-4) = \sqrt[3]{-4+3} = \sqrt[3]{-1} = -1$

   c. $H(5) = \sqrt[3]{5+3} = \sqrt[3]{8} = 2$

104. $G(z) = \sqrt{\dfrac{z-1}{z+2}}$

    a. $G(1) = \sqrt{\dfrac{1-1}{1+2}} = \sqrt{\dfrac{0}{3}} = \sqrt{0} = 0$

    b. $G(-3) = \sqrt{\dfrac{-3-1}{-3+2}} = \sqrt{\dfrac{-4}{-1}} = \sqrt{4} = 2$

    c. $G(2) = \sqrt{\dfrac{2-1}{2+2}} = \sqrt{\dfrac{1}{4}} = \dfrac{1}{2}$

105. $f(x) = \sqrt{3x-5}$

$3x - 5 \geq 0$

$3x \geq 5$

$x \geq \dfrac{5}{3}$

The domain of the function is $\left\{ x \mid x \geq \dfrac{5}{3} \right\}$ or the interval $\left[\dfrac{5}{3}, \infty \right)$.

106. $g(x) = \sqrt[3]{2x-7}$

Since the index is odd, the domain of the function is all real numbers, $\{x \mid x \text{ is any real number}\}$ or the interval $(-\infty, \infty)$.

107. $h(x) = \sqrt[4]{6x+1}$

$6x + 1 \geq 0$

$6x \geq -1$

$x \geq -\dfrac{1}{6}$

The domain of the function is $\left\{ x \mid x \geq -\dfrac{1}{6} \right\}$ or the interval $\left[-\dfrac{1}{6}, \infty \right)$.

108. $F(x) = \sqrt[5]{2x-9}$

Since the index is odd, the domain of the function is all real numbers, $\{x \mid x \text{ is any real number}\}$, or the interval $(-\infty, \infty)$.

109. $G(x) = \sqrt{\dfrac{4}{x-2}}$

The index is even so we need the radicand to be nonnegative. The numerator is positive, so we need the denominator to be positive as well.

$x - 2 > 0$

$x > 2$

The domain of the function is $\{x \mid x > 2\}$ or the interval $(2, \infty)$.

110. $H(x) = \sqrt{\dfrac{x-3}{x}}$

The index is even so we need the radicand to be nonnegative. The radicand will equal zero when the numerator equals zero. The radicand will be positive when the numerator and denominator have the same sign.

$x - 3 = 0$

$x = 3$

$x - 3 > 0$ and $x > 0$

$\quad x > 3$ and $x > 0 \quad \rightarrow \quad x > 3$

$x - 3 < 0$ and $x < 0$

$\quad x < 3$ and $x < 0 \quad \rightarrow \quad x < 0$

The domain of the function is $\{x \mid x < 0 \text{ or } x \geq 3\}$ or the interval $(-\infty, 0) \cup [3, \infty)$.

111. $f(x) = \frac{1}{2}\sqrt{1-x}$

   a. $1-x \geq 0$

       $x \leq 1$

   The domain of the function is $\{x \mid x \leq 1\}$ or the interval $(-\infty, 1]$.

   b.

x	$f(x) = \frac{1}{2}\sqrt{1-x}$	(x,y)
-15	$f(-15) = \frac{1}{2}\sqrt{1-(-15)} = 2$	$(-15, 2)$
-8	$f(-8) = \frac{3}{2}$	$\left(-8, \frac{3}{2}\right)$
-3	$f(-3) = 1$	$(-3, 1)$
0	$f(0) = \frac{1}{2}$	$\left(0, \frac{1}{2}\right)$
1	$f(1) = 0$	$(1, 0)$

   c. Based on the graph, the range is $[0, \infty)$.

112. $g(x) = \sqrt{x+1} - 2$

   a. $x+1 \geq 0$ or $x \geq -1$

   The domain of the function is $\{x \mid x \geq -1\}$ or the interval $[-1, \infty)$.

   b.

x	$g(x) = \sqrt{x+1} - 2$	(x,y)
-1	$g(-1) = \sqrt{-1+1} - 2 = -2$	$(-1, -2)$
0	$g(0) = -1$	$(0, -1)$
3	$g(3) = 0$	$(3, 0)$
8	$g(8) = 1$	$(8, 1)$
15	$g(15) = 2$	$(15, 2)$

   c. Based on the graph, the range is $[-2, \infty)$.

113. $h(x) = -\sqrt{x+3}$

   a. $x+3 \geq 0$

       $x \geq -3$

   The domain of the function is $\{x \mid x \geq -3\}$ or the interval $[-3, \infty)$.

   b.

x	$h(x) = -\sqrt{x+3}$	(x,y)
-3	$h(-3) = -\sqrt{-3+3} = 0$	$(-3, 0)$
-2	$h(-2) = -1$	$(-2, -1)$
1	$h(1) = -2$	$(1, -2)$
6	$h(6) = -3$	$(6, -3)$
13	$h(13) = -4$	$(13, -4)$

   c. Based on the graph, the range is $(-\infty, 0]$.

114. $F(x) = \sqrt[3]{x+1}$

   a. Since the index is odd, the domain of the function is all real numbers, $\{x \mid x \text{ is any real number}\}$, or the interval $(-\infty, \infty)$.

   b.

x	$F(x) = \sqrt[3]{x+1}$	(x,y)
-9	$F(-9) = \sqrt[3]{-9+1} = -2$	$(-9, -2)$
-2	$F(-2) = -1$	$(-2, -1)$
-1	$F(-1) = 0$	$(-1, 0)$
0	$F(0) = 1$	$(0, 1)$
7	$F(7) = 2$	$(7, 2)$

   c. Based on the graph, the range is $(-\infty, \infty)$.

115.
$$\sqrt{m} = 13$$
$$\left(\sqrt{m}\right)^2 = 13^2$$
$$m = 169$$

Check: $\sqrt{169} = 13$?
$$13 = 13 \checkmark$$
The solution set is $\{169\}$.

116.
$$\sqrt[3]{3t+1} = -2$$
$$\left(\sqrt[3]{3t+1}\right)^3 = (-2)^3$$
$$3t + 1 = -8$$
$$3t = -9$$
$$t = -3$$

Check: $\sqrt[3]{3(-3)+1} = -2$?
$$\sqrt[3]{-9+1} = -2 \text{ ?}$$
$$\sqrt[3]{-8} = -2 \text{ ?}$$
$$-2 = -2 \checkmark$$
The solution set is $\{-3\}$.

117.
$$\sqrt[4]{3x-8} = 3$$
$$\left(\sqrt[4]{3x-8}\right)^4 = 3^4$$
$$3x - 8 = 81$$
$$3x = 89$$
$$x = \frac{89}{3}$$

Check: $\sqrt[4]{3\left(\frac{89}{3}\right)-8} = 3$?
$$\sqrt[4]{89-8} = 3 \text{ ?}$$
$$\sqrt[4]{81} = 3 \text{ ?}$$
$$3 = 3 \checkmark$$
The solution set is $\left\{\frac{89}{3}\right\}$.

118.
$$\sqrt{2x+5} + 4 = 2$$
$$\sqrt{2x+5} = -2$$
$$\left(\sqrt{2x+5}\right)^2 = (-2)^2$$
$$2x + 5 = 4$$
$$2x = -1$$
$$x = -\frac{1}{2}$$

Check: $\sqrt{2\left(-\frac{1}{2}\right)+5} + 4 = 2$?
$$\sqrt{-1+5} + 4 = 2 \text{ ?}$$
$$\sqrt{4} + 4 = 2 \text{ ?}$$
$$2 + 4 = 2 \text{ ?}$$
$$6 = 2 \text{ False}$$
The solution does not check so the problem has no real solution.

119.
$$\sqrt{k+4} - 3 = -1$$
$$\sqrt{k+4} = 2$$
$$\left(\sqrt{k+4}\right)^2 = 2^2$$
$$k + 4 = 4$$
$$k = 0$$

Check: $\sqrt{0+4} - 3 = -1$?
$$\sqrt{4} - 3 = -1 \text{ ?}$$
$$2 - 3 = -1 \text{ ?}$$
$$-1 = -1 \checkmark$$
The solution set is $\{0\}$.

120.
$$3\sqrt{t} - 4 = 11$$
$$3\sqrt{t} = 15$$
$$\sqrt{t} = 5$$
$$\left(\sqrt{t}\right)^2 = 5^2$$
$$t = 25$$

Check: $3\sqrt{25} - 4 = 11$?
$$3 \cdot 5 - 4 = 11 \text{ ?}$$
$$15 - 4 = 11 \text{ ?}$$
$$11 = 11 \checkmark$$
The solution set is $\{25\}$.

121. $2\sqrt[3]{m}+5=-11$

$$2\sqrt[3]{m}=-16$$
$$\sqrt[3]{m}=-8$$
$$\left(\sqrt[3]{m}\right)^3=(-8)^3$$
$$m=-512$$

Check: $2\sqrt[3]{-512}+5=-11$?
$$2(-8)+5=-11 \text{ ?}$$
$$-16+5=-11 \text{ ?}$$
$$-11=-11 \checkmark$$
The solution set is $\{-512\}$.

122. $\sqrt{q+2}=q$
$$\left(\sqrt{q+2}\right)^2=q^2$$
$$q+2=q^2$$
$$q^2-q-2=0$$
$$(q-2)(q+1)=0$$
$$q-2=0 \text{ or } q+1=0$$
$$q=2 \text{ or } q=-1$$

Check: $\sqrt{2+2}=2$?
$$\sqrt{4}=2 \text{ ?}$$
$$2=2 \checkmark$$

$$\sqrt{-1+2}=-1 \text{ ?}$$
$$\sqrt{1}=-1 \text{ ?}$$
$$1=-1 \text{ False}$$
The second solution is extraneous, so the solution set is $\{2\}$.

123. $\sqrt{w+11}+3=w+2$
$$\sqrt{w+11}=w-1$$
$$\left(\sqrt{w+11}\right)^2=(w-1)^2$$
$$w+11=w^2-2w+1$$
$$w^2-3w-10=0$$
$$(w-5)(w+2)=0$$
$$w-5=0 \text{ or } w+2=0$$
$$w=5 \text{ or } w=-2$$

Check: $\sqrt{5+11}+3=5+2$?
$$\sqrt{16}+3=7 \text{ ?}$$
$$4+3=7 \text{ ?}$$
$$7=7 \checkmark$$

$$\sqrt{-2+11}+3=-2+2 \text{ ?}$$
$$\sqrt{9}+3=0 \text{ ?}$$
$$3+3=0 \text{ ?}$$
$$6=0 \text{ False}$$
The second solution is extraneous, so the solution set is $\{5\}$.

124. $\sqrt{p^2-2p+9}=p+1$
$$\left(\sqrt{p^2-2p+9}\right)^2=(p+1)^2$$
$$p^2-2p+9=p^2+2p+1$$
$$-4p+8=0$$
$$-4p=-8$$
$$p=2$$

Check: $\sqrt{2^2-2(2)+9}=2+1$?
$$\sqrt{4-4+9}=3 \text{ ?}$$
$$\sqrt{9}=3 \text{ ?}$$
$$3=3 \checkmark$$
The solution set is $\{2\}$.

125. $\sqrt{a+10}=\sqrt{2a-1}$
$$\left(\sqrt{a+10}\right)^2=\left(\sqrt{2a-1}\right)^2$$
$$a+10=2a-1$$
$$11=a$$

Check: $\sqrt{11+10}=\sqrt{2(11)-1}$?
$$\sqrt{21}=\sqrt{22-1} \text{ ?}$$
$$\sqrt{21}=\sqrt{21} \checkmark$$
The solution set is $\{11\}$.

126.
$$\sqrt{5x+9} = \sqrt{7x-3}$$
$$\left(\sqrt{5x+9}\right)^2 = \left(\sqrt{7x-3}\right)^2$$
$$5x+9 = 7x-3$$
$$12 = 2x$$
$$6 = x$$

Check: $\sqrt{5(6)+9} = \sqrt{7(6)-3}$?
$$\sqrt{30+9} = \sqrt{42-3} \ ?$$
$$\sqrt{39} = \sqrt{39} \ \checkmark$$

The solution set is $\{6\}$.

127.
$$\sqrt{c-8} + \sqrt{c} = 4$$
$$\sqrt{c-8} = 4 - \sqrt{c}$$
$$\left(\sqrt{c-8}\right)^2 = \left(4-\sqrt{c}\right)^2$$
$$c-8 = 4^2 - 2(4)\sqrt{c} + \left(\sqrt{c}\right)^2$$
$$c-8 = 16 - 8\sqrt{c} + c$$
$$8\sqrt{c} = 24$$
$$\sqrt{c} = 3$$
$$\left(\sqrt{c}\right)^2 = 3^2$$
$$c = 9$$

Check: $\sqrt{9-8} + \sqrt{9} = 4$?
$$\sqrt{1} + \sqrt{9} = 4 \ ?$$
$$1+3 = 4 \ ?$$
$$4 = 4 \ \checkmark$$

The solution set is $\{9\}$.

128.
$$\sqrt{x+2} - \sqrt{x+9} = 7$$
$$\sqrt{x+2} = \sqrt{x+9} + 7$$
$$\left(\sqrt{x+2}\right)^2 = \left(\sqrt{x+9}+7\right)^2$$
$$x+2 = \left(\sqrt{x+9}\right)^2 + 2(7)\sqrt{x+9} + 7^2$$
$$x+2 = x+9 + 14\sqrt{x+9} + 49$$
$$x+2 = x + 14\sqrt{x+9} + 58$$
$$-56 = 14\sqrt{x+9}$$
$$-4 = \sqrt{x+9}$$
$$(-4)^2 = \left(\sqrt{x+9}\right)^2$$
$$16 = x+9$$
$$7 = x$$

Check: $\sqrt{7+2} - \sqrt{7+9} = 7$?
$$\sqrt{9} - \sqrt{16} = 7 \ ?$$
$$3-4 = 7 \ ?$$
$$-1 = 7 \ \text{False}$$

The solution does not check so the equation has no real solution.

129.
$$(4x-3)^{1/3} - 3 = 0$$
$$(4x-3)^{1/3} = 3$$
$$\left((4x-3)^{1/3}\right)^3 = 3^3$$
$$4x-3 = 27$$
$$4x = 30$$
$$x = \frac{30}{4} = \frac{15}{2}$$

Check: $\left(4\left(\frac{15}{2}\right)-3\right)^{1/3} - 3 = 0$?
$$(30-3)^{1/3} - 3 = 0 \ ?$$
$$27^{1/3} - 3 = 0 \ ?$$
$$3-3 = 0 \ ?$$
$$0 = 0 \ \checkmark$$

The solution set is $\left\{\frac{15}{2}\right\}$.

130. $\left(x^2 - 9\right)^{1/4} = 2$

$$\left(\left(x^2 - 9\right)^{1/4}\right)^4 = 2^4$$

$$x^2 - 9 = 16$$

$$x^2 = 25$$

$$x = \pm 5$$

Check:

$$\left(5^2 - 9\right)^{1/4} = 2 \ ?$$

$$\left(25 - 9\right)^{1/4} = 2 \ ?$$

$$16^{1/4} = 2 \ ?$$

$$2 = 2 \ \checkmark$$

$$\left((-5)^2 - 9\right)^{1/4} = 2 \ ?$$

$$\left(25 - 9\right)^{1/4} = 2 \ ?$$

$$16^{1/4} = 2 \ ?$$

$$2 = 2 \ \checkmark$$

The solution set is $\{-5, 5\}$.

131. $r = \sqrt{\dfrac{3V}{\pi h}}$

$$\left(r\right)^2 = \left(\sqrt{\dfrac{3V}{\pi h}}\right)^2$$

$$r^2 = \dfrac{3V}{\pi h}$$

$$h \cdot r^2 = \dfrac{3V}{\pi}$$

$$h = \dfrac{3V}{\pi r^2}$$

132. $f_s = \sqrt[3]{\dfrac{30}{v}}$

$$\left(f_s\right)^3 = \left(\sqrt[3]{\dfrac{30}{v}}\right)^3$$

$$f_s^3 = \dfrac{30}{v}$$

$$v \cdot f_s^3 = 30$$

$$v = \dfrac{30}{f_s^3}$$

133. $\sqrt{-29} = \sqrt{-1} \cdot \sqrt{29} = i \cdot \sqrt{29} = \sqrt{29}\,i$

134. $\sqrt{-54} = \sqrt{-1} \cdot \sqrt{9} \cdot \sqrt{6} = i \cdot 3 \cdot \sqrt{6} = 3\sqrt{6}\,i$

135. $14 - \sqrt{-162} = 14 - \sqrt{-1} \cdot \sqrt{81} \cdot \sqrt{2}$

$$= 14 - i \cdot 9 \cdot \sqrt{2}$$

$$= 14 - 9\sqrt{2}\,i$$

136. $\dfrac{6 + \sqrt{-45}}{3} = \dfrac{6 + \sqrt{-1} \cdot \sqrt{9} \cdot \sqrt{5}}{3}$

$$= \dfrac{6 + i \cdot 3 \cdot \sqrt{5}}{3}$$

$$= \dfrac{6 + 3\sqrt{5}\,i}{3}$$

$$= \dfrac{3\left(2 + \sqrt{5}\,i\right)}{3}$$

$$= 2 + \sqrt{5}\,i$$

137. $\left(3 - 7i\right) + \left(-2 + 5i\right) = 3 - 2 - 7i + 5i$

$$= 1 - 2i$$

138. $\left(4 + 2i\right) - \left(9 - 8i\right) = 4 + 2i - 9 + 8i$

$$= 4 - 9 + 2i + 8i$$

$$= -5 + 10i$$

139. $\left(8 - \sqrt{-45}\right) - \left(3 + \sqrt{-80}\right)$

$$= \left(8 - 3\sqrt{5}\,i\right) - \left(3 + 4\sqrt{5}\,i\right)$$

$$= 8 - 3\sqrt{5}\,i - 3 - 4\sqrt{5}\,i$$

$$= 8 - 3 - 3\sqrt{5}\,i - 4\sqrt{5}\,i$$

$$= 5 - 7\sqrt{5}\,i$$

140. $\left(1 + \sqrt{-9}\right) + \left(-6 + \sqrt{-16}\right) = \left(1 + 3i\right) + \left(-6 + 4i\right)$

$$= 1 + 3i - 6 + 4i$$

$$= 1 - 6 + 3i + 4i$$

$$= -5 + 7i$$

141. $\left(4 - 5i\right)\left(3 + 7i\right) = 4 \cdot 3 + 4 \cdot 7i - 5i \cdot 3 - 5i \cdot 7i$

$$= 12 + 28i - 15i - 35i^2$$

$$= 12 + 13i - 35(-1)$$

$$= 12 + 13i + 35$$

$$= 47 + 13i$$

142. $\left(\frac{1}{2}+\frac{2}{3}i\right)(4-9i)$

$= \frac{1}{2}\cdot 4 + \frac{1}{2}(-9i) + \frac{2}{3}i\cdot 4 + \frac{2}{3}i(-9i)$

$= 2 - \frac{9}{2}i + \frac{8}{3}i - 6i^2$

$= 2 - \frac{11}{6}i - 6(-1)$

$= 2 - \frac{11}{6}i + 6$

$= 8 - \frac{11}{6}i$

143. $\sqrt{-3}\cdot\sqrt{-27} = \sqrt{3}\,i\cdot 3\sqrt{3}\,i$

$= 3\left(\sqrt{3}\right)^2\cdot i^2$

$= 3\cdot 3\cdot(-1)$

$= -9$

Note: It is necessary to write each radical in terms of i prior to performing the operation. Otherwise the sign of the answer will be wrong.

$\sqrt{(-3)(-27)} = \sqrt{81} = 9 \neq -9 = \sqrt{-3}\cdot\sqrt{-27}$

144. $\left(1+\sqrt{-36}\right)\left(-5-\sqrt{-144}\right)$

$= (1+6i)(-5-12i)$

$= 1\cdot(-5) + 1\cdot(-12i) + 6i\cdot(-5) + 6i\cdot(-12i)$

$= -5 - 12i - 30i - 72i^2$

$= -5 - 42i - 72(-1)$

$= -5 - 42i + 72$

$= 67 - 42i$

145. $(1+12i)(1-12i) = 1^2 - (12i)^2$

$= 1 - 144i^2$

$= 1 - 144(-1)$

$= 1 + 144$

$= 145$

146. $(7+2i)(5+4i) = 7\cdot 5 + 7\cdot 4i + 2i\cdot 5 + 2i\cdot 4i$

$= 35 + 28i + 10i + 8i^2$

$= 35 + 38i + 8(-1)$

$= 35 + 38i - 8$

$= 27 + 38i$

147. $\dfrac{4}{3+5i} = \dfrac{4}{3+5i}\cdot\dfrac{3-5i}{3-5i}$

$= \dfrac{4(3-5i)}{3^2 - (5i)^2}$

$= \dfrac{4(3-5i)}{9 - 25i^2}$

$= \dfrac{4(3-5i)}{9 + 25}$

$= \dfrac{4(3-5i)}{34}$

$= \dfrac{2\cdot 2(3-5i)}{2\cdot 17}$

$= \dfrac{2(3-5i)}{17}$

$= \dfrac{6-10i}{17}$

$= \dfrac{6}{17} - \dfrac{10}{17}i$

148. $\dfrac{-3}{7-2i} = \dfrac{-3}{7-2i}\cdot\dfrac{7+2i}{7+2i}$

$= \dfrac{-3(7+2i)}{7^2 - (2i)^2}$

$= \dfrac{-21-6i}{49 - 4i^2}$

$= \dfrac{-21-6i}{49 - 4(-1)}$

$= \dfrac{-21-6i}{49 + 4}$

$= \dfrac{-21-6i}{53}$

$= -\dfrac{21}{53} - \dfrac{6}{53}i$

149.
$$\frac{2-3i}{5+2i} = \frac{2-3i}{5+2i} \cdot \frac{5-2i}{5-2i}$$
$$= \frac{(2-3i)(5-2i)}{(5+2i)(5-2i)}$$
$$= \frac{10-4i-15i+6i^2}{25-4i^2}$$
$$= \frac{10-19i+6(-1)}{25-4(-1)}$$
$$= \frac{10-19i-6}{25+4}$$
$$= \frac{4-19i}{29}$$
$$= \frac{4}{29} - \frac{19}{29}i$$

150.
$$\frac{4+3i}{1-i} = \frac{4+3i}{1-i} \cdot \frac{1+i}{1+i}$$
$$= \frac{(4+3i)(1+i)}{(1-i)(1+i)}$$
$$= \frac{4+4i+3i+3i^2}{1-i^2}$$
$$= \frac{4+7i+3(-1)}{1-(-1)}$$
$$= \frac{4+7i-3}{1+1}$$
$$= \frac{1+7i}{2}$$
$$= \frac{1}{2} + \frac{7}{2}i$$

151. $i^{59} = i^{56} \cdot i^3 = \left(i^4\right)^{14} \cdot i^3 = 1 \cdot i^3 = i^2 \cdot i = -1 \cdot i = -i$

152. $i^{173} = i^{172} \cdot i = \left(i^4\right)^{43} \cdot i = 1 \cdot i = i$

Chapter 7 Test

1. $49^{-1/2} = \dfrac{1}{49^{1/2}} = \dfrac{1}{\sqrt{49}} = \dfrac{1}{7}$

2. $\sqrt[3]{8x^{1/2}y^3} \cdot \sqrt{9xy^{1/2}}$
$$= \left(8x^{1/2}y^3\right)^{1/3} \cdot \left(9xy^{1/2}\right)^{1/2}$$
$$= 8^{1/3}\left(x^{1/2}\right)^{1/3}\left(y^3\right)^{1/3} \cdot 9^{1/2}x^{1/2}\left(y^{1/2}\right)^{1/2}$$
$$= 2x^{1/6}y \cdot 3x^{1/2}y^{1/4}$$
$$= 6x^{\frac{1}{6}+\frac{1}{2}}y^{1+\frac{1}{4}}$$
$$= 6x^{2/3}y^{5/4}$$
$$= 6x^{8/12}y^{15/12}$$
$$= 6y\sqrt[12]{x^8y^3}$$

3. $\sqrt[5]{\left(2a^4b^3\right)^7} = \left(2a^4b^3\right)^{7/5} = 2^{7/5}a^{28/5}b^{21/5}$
$$= 2a^5b^4 \cdot 2^{2/5}a^{3/5}b^{1/5}$$
$$= 2a^5b^4\sqrt[5]{4a^3b}$$

4. $\sqrt{3m} \cdot \sqrt{13n} = \sqrt{3m \cdot 13n} = \sqrt{39mn}$

5. $\sqrt{32x^7y^4} = \sqrt{16x^6y^4 \cdot 2x}$
$$= \sqrt{16x^6y^4} \cdot \sqrt{2x}$$
$$= 4x^3y^2\sqrt{2x}$$

6. $\dfrac{\sqrt{9a^3b^{-3}}}{\sqrt{4ab}} = \sqrt{\dfrac{9a^3b^{-3}}{4ab}}$
$$= \sqrt{\dfrac{9a^2}{4b^4}}$$
$$= \dfrac{\sqrt{9a^2}}{\sqrt{4b^4}}$$
$$= \dfrac{3a}{2b^2}$$

7. $\sqrt{5x^3} + 2\sqrt{45x} = \sqrt{x^2 \cdot 5x} + 2\sqrt{9 \cdot 5x}$
$$= \sqrt{x^2} \cdot \sqrt{5x} + 2\sqrt{9} \cdot \sqrt{5x}$$
$$= x\sqrt{5x} + 2 \cdot 3 \cdot \sqrt{5x}$$
$$= x\sqrt{5x} + 6\sqrt{5x}$$
$$= (x+6)\sqrt{5x}$$

8. $\sqrt{9a^2b} - \sqrt[4]{16a^4b^2} = \sqrt{9a^2} \cdot \sqrt{b} - \sqrt[4]{16a^4} \cdot \sqrt[4]{b^2}$

$$= 3a\sqrt{b} - 2a \cdot b^{2/4}$$
$$= 3a\sqrt{b} - 2a \cdot b^{1/2}$$
$$= 3a\sqrt{b} - 2a\sqrt{b}$$
$$= (3-2)a\sqrt{b}$$
$$= a\sqrt{b}$$

9. $\left(11 + 2\sqrt{x}\right)\left(3 - \sqrt{x}\right)$

$$= 11 \cdot 3 + 11\left(-\sqrt{x}\right) + 2\sqrt{x} \cdot 3 + 2\sqrt{x}\left(-\sqrt{x}\right)$$
$$= 33 - 11\sqrt{x} + 6\sqrt{x} - 2\left(\sqrt{x}\right)^2$$
$$= 33 + (-11 + 6)\sqrt{x} - 2x$$
$$= 33 - 5\sqrt{x} - 2x$$

10. $\dfrac{-2}{3\sqrt{72}} = \dfrac{-2}{3 \cdot 6\sqrt{2}} = \dfrac{-2}{18\sqrt{2}}$

$$= \dfrac{-1}{9\sqrt{2}} = \dfrac{-1}{9\sqrt{2}} \cdot \dfrac{\sqrt{2}}{\sqrt{2}}$$
$$= \dfrac{-\sqrt{2}}{9 \cdot 2}$$
$$= \dfrac{-\sqrt{2}}{18}$$

11. $\dfrac{\sqrt{5}}{\sqrt{5}+2} = \dfrac{\sqrt{5}}{\sqrt{5}+2} \cdot \dfrac{\sqrt{5}-2}{\sqrt{5}-2}$

$$= \dfrac{\sqrt{5}\left(\sqrt{5}-2\right)}{\left(\sqrt{5}\right)^2 - 2^2}$$
$$= \dfrac{5 - 2\sqrt{5}}{5 - 4}$$
$$= 5 - 2\sqrt{5}$$

12. $f(x) = \sqrt{-2x + 3}$

a. $f(1) = \sqrt{-2(1)+3} = \sqrt{-2+3} = \sqrt{1} = 1$

b. $f(-3) = \sqrt{-2(-3)+3} = \sqrt{6+3} = \sqrt{9} = 3$

13. $g(x) = \sqrt{-3x + 5}$

$$-3x + 5 \geq 0$$
$$-3x \geq -5$$
$$x \leq \dfrac{5}{3}$$

The domain of the function is $\left\{x \mid x \leq \dfrac{5}{3}\right\}$ or the

interval $\left(-\infty, \dfrac{5}{3}\right]$.

14. $f(x) = \sqrt{x} - 3$

a. $x \geq 0$

The domain of the function is $\{x \mid x \geq 0\}$ or the interval $[0, \infty)$.

b.

x	$f(x) = \sqrt{x} - 3$	(x, y)
0	$f(0) = \sqrt{0} - 3 = -3$	$(0, -3)$
1	$f(1) = -2$	$(1, -2)$
4	$f(4) = -1$	$(4, -1)$
9	$f(9) = 0$	$(9, 0)$

c. Based on the graph, the range is $[-3, \infty)$.

15. $\sqrt{x+3} = 4$

$$\left(\sqrt{x+3}\right)^2 = 4^2$$
$$x + 3 = 16$$
$$x = 13$$

Check: $\sqrt{13+3} = 4$?

$$\sqrt{16} = 4 \; ?$$
$$4 = 4 \; \checkmark$$

The solution set is $\{13\}$.

16.
$$\sqrt{x+13}-4=x-3$$
$$\sqrt{x+13}=x+1$$
$$\left(\sqrt{x+13}\right)^2=(x+1)^2$$
$$x+13=x^2+2x+1$$
$$x^2+x-12=0$$
$$(x+4)(x-3)=0$$
$$x+4=0 \text{ or } x-3=0$$
$$x=-4 \text{ or } x=3$$

Check: $\sqrt{-4+13}-4=-4-3$?
$$\sqrt{9}-4=-7 \text{ ?}$$
$$3-4=-7 \text{ ?}$$
$$-1=-7 \text{ False}$$

$$\sqrt{3+13}-4=3-3 \text{ ?}$$
$$\sqrt{16}-4=0 \text{ ?}$$
$$4-4=0 \text{ ?}$$
$$0=0 \checkmark$$

The first solution is extraneous, so the solution set is $\{3\}$.

17.
$$\sqrt{x-1}+\sqrt{x+2}=3$$
$$\sqrt{x-1}=3-\sqrt{x+2}$$
$$\left(\sqrt{x-1}\right)^2=\left(3-\sqrt{x+2}\right)^2$$
$$x-1=3^2-2(3)\sqrt{x+2}+\left(\sqrt{x+2}\right)^2$$
$$x-1=9-6\sqrt{x+2}+x+2$$
$$-12=-6\sqrt{x+2}$$
$$2=\sqrt{x+2}$$
$$2^2=\left(\sqrt{x+2}\right)^2$$
$$4=x+2$$
$$2=x$$

Check: $\sqrt{2-1}+\sqrt{2+2}=3$?
$$\sqrt{1}+\sqrt{4}=3 \text{ ?}$$
$$1+2=3 \text{ ?}$$
$$3=3 \checkmark$$

The solution set is $\{2\}$.

18.
$$\begin{aligned}(13+2i)+(4-15i)&=13+2i+4-15i\\&=13+4+2i-15i\\&=17-13i\end{aligned}$$

19.
$$\begin{aligned}(4-7i)(2+3i)&=4\cdot2+4\cdot3i-7i\cdot2-7i\cdot3i\\&=8+12i-14i-21i^2\\&=8-2i-21(-1)\\&=8-2i+21\\&=29-2i\end{aligned}$$

20.
$$\frac{7-i}{12+11i}=\frac{7-i}{12+11i}\cdot\frac{12-11i}{12-11i}$$
$$=\frac{(7-i)(12-11i)}{(12+11i)(12-11i)}$$
$$=\frac{84-77i-12i+11i^2}{144-121i^2}$$
$$=\frac{84-89i+11(-1)}{144-121(-1)}$$
$$=\frac{84-89i-11}{144+121}$$
$$=\frac{73-89i}{265}$$
$$=\frac{73}{265}-\frac{89}{265}i$$

Cumulative Review Chapters R-7

1.
$$6-3^2\div(9-3)=6-3^2\div6$$
$$=6-9\div6$$
$$=6-\frac{3}{2}$$
$$=\frac{9}{2}$$

2.
$$\begin{aligned}(3x+2y)-(2x-5y+3)+9&=3x+2y-2x+5y-3+9\\&=3x-2x+2y+5y-3+9\\&=x+7y+6\end{aligned}$$

3. $(3x+5)-2 = 7x-13$

$3x+5-2 = 7x-13$

$3x+3 = 7x-13$

$3x+16 = 7x$

$16 = 4x$

$\dfrac{16}{4} = \dfrac{4x}{4}$

$4 = x$

The solution set is $\{4\}$.

4. $6x+\dfrac{1}{2}(4x-2) \le 3x+9$

$6x+2x-1 \le 3x+9$

$8x-1 \le 3x+9$

$5x-1 \le 9$

$5x \le 10$

$x \le 2$

Interval: $(-\infty, 2]$

5. $f(x) = 3x^2 - x + 5$

a. $f(-2) = 3(-2)^2 - (-2)+5$

$= 3(4)+2+5 = 12+7 = 19$

b. $f(3) = 3(3)^2 - (3)+5$

$= 3(9)-3+5 = 27+2 = 29$

6. The function g tells us to divide x^2-9 by x^2-2x-8. Since division by 0 is not defined, the denominator can never be 0.

$x^2-2x-8 = 0$

$(x-4)(x+2) = 0$

$x-4 = 0$ or $x+2 = 0$

$x = 4$ or $x = -2$

Thus, the domain of the function is $\{x \mid x \ne 4, -2\}$. In interval notation we would write $(-\infty, -2) \cup (-2, 4) \cup (4, \infty)$.

7. a. $n(50) = -50(50)+6,000$

$= -2,500+6,000$

$= 3,500$

If the price of the game were \$50, you would sell 3500 games per year.

b. We want to solve $n(p) = 0$.

$-50p+6,000 = 0$

$6,000 = 50p$

$\dfrac{6,000}{50} = \dfrac{50p}{50}$

$120 = p$

When the price of the game reaches \$120, no games will be sold.

8. First we use the two points to find the slope of the line.

$m = \dfrac{-2-6}{3-(-1)} = \dfrac{-8}{4} = -2$

Next, we use the slope and one of the points to determine the y-intercept.

$y = mx+b$

$6 = -2(-1)+b$

$6 = 2+b$

$4 = b$

The slope is $m = -2$ and the y-intercept is $b = 4$. Therefore, the equation of the line is $y = -2x+4$.

9. Start by solving the inequality for y.

$6x+3y > 24$

$3y > -6x+24$

$\dfrac{3y}{3} > \dfrac{-6x+24}{3}$

$y > -2x+8$

Since the inequality is strict, graph the line $y = -2x+8$ with a dashed line. We will use the point $(0,0)$ as our test point.

$6(0)+3(0) > 24$?

$0 > 24$ false

Since we obtained a contradiction, we shade the region that does not contain the point $(0,0)$.

$y = -2x+8$

10. $4x - y = 17$

$5x + 6y = 14$

Solve the first equation for y.

$4x - y = 17$

$-y = -4x + 17$

$y = 4x - 17$

Substitute this result for y in the second equation and solve for x.

$5x + 6(4x - 17) = 14$

$5x + 24x - 102 = 14$

$29x - 102 = 14$

$29x = 116$

$x = 4$

Use this result to solve for y.

$y = 4x - 17$

$y = 4(4) - 17$

$= 16 - 17$

$= -1$

The ordered pair solution is $(4, -1)$.

Check: $4(4) - (-1) = 17$?

$16 + 1 = 17$?

$17 = 17$ ✓

$5(4) + 6(-1) = 14$?

$20 - 6 = 14$?

$14 = 14$ ✓

11. Let $x =$ pounds of dried fruit and $y =$ pounds of nuts. Since the total pounds will be 10, we have the equation

$x + y = 10$

We want the total revenue to be the same. Thus, our second equation will be

$3.45x + 2.10y = 2.64(10)$

$3.45x + 2.10y = 26.40$

Putting the two equations together gives us the following system:

$x + y = 10$

$3.45x + 2.10y = 26.40$

We can solve this system by using substitution. Start by solving the first equation for y.

$x + y = 10$

$y = -x + 10$

Substitute this result for y in the second equation and solve for x.

$3.45x + 2.10(-x + 10) = 26.40$

$3.45x - 2.10x + 21.00 = 26.40$

$1.35x + 21.00 = 26.40$

$1.35x = 5.40$

$x = 4$

Use this result to solve for y.

$y = -x + 10$

$= -4 + 10$

$= 6$

The trail mix should contain 4 pounds of dried fruit and 6 pounds of nuts.

12. $\begin{vmatrix} 5 & -2 & 3 \\ 3 & -3 & 4 \\ -2 & 4 & 1 \end{vmatrix} = 5\begin{vmatrix} -3 & 4 \\ 4 & 1 \end{vmatrix} - (-2)\begin{vmatrix} 3 & 4 \\ -2 & 1 \end{vmatrix} + 3\begin{vmatrix} 3 & -3 \\ -2 & 4 \end{vmatrix}$

$= 5(-3 \cdot 1 - 4 \cdot 4) + 2(3 \cdot 1 - (-2)4)$

$\qquad + 3(3 \cdot 4 - (-2)(-3))$

$= 5(-3 - 16) + 2(3 + 8) + 3(12 - 6)$

$= 5(-19) + 2(11) + 3(6)$

$= -95 + 22 + 18$

$= -55$

13. $(8x^3 - 4x^2 + 5x + 3) + (2x^2 - 8x + 7)$

$= 8x^3 - 4x^2 + 5x + 3 + 2x^2 - 8x + 7$

$= 8x^3 - 4x^2 + 2x^2 + 5x - 8x + 3 + 7$

$= 8x^3 - 2x^2 - 3x + 10$

14. $(2x - 1)(4x^2 + 2x - 9)$

$= 8x^3 + 4x^2 - 18x - 4x^2 - 2x + 9$

$= 8x^3 + 4x^2 - 4x^2 - 18x - 2x + 9$

$= 8x^3 - 20x + 9$

15.

$$\begin{array}{r} 3x^2 + 2x - 6 \\ 2x^2 + 3x - 5{\overline{\smash{\big)}\,6x^4 + 13x^3 - 21x^2 - 28x + 37}} \\ -\left(6x^4 + 9x^3 - 15x^2\right) \\ \hline 4x^3 - 6x^2 - 28x \\ -\left(4x^3 + 6x^2 - 10x\right) \\ \hline -12x^2 - 18x + 37 \\ -\left(-12x^2 - 18x + 30\right) \\ \hline 7 \end{array}$$

$$\frac{6x^4 + 13x^3 - 21x^2 - 28x + 37}{2x^2 + 3x - 5}$$

$$= 3x^2 + 2x - 6 + \frac{7}{2x^2 + 3x - 5}$$

16. $8x^2 - 44x - 84$

Begin by factoring out the greatest common factor.

$$4\left(2x^2 - 11x - 21\right)$$

For the reduced polynomial, we can use the AC method.

$$AC = 2(-21) = -42$$

We need two factors of -42 whose sum is -11. Since the product is negative, the factors will have opposite signs. Since the sum is also negative, the factor with the larger absolute value will be negative.

factor 1	factor 2	sum	
2	-21	-19	too small
6	-7	-1	too large
3	-14	-11	okay

$$8x^2 - 44x - 84 = 4\left(2x^2 - 11x - 21\right)$$
$$= 4\left(2x^2 + 3x - 14x - 21\right)$$
$$= 4\left(x(2x+3) + (-7)(2x+3)\right)$$
$$= 4(2x+3)(x-7)$$

17. $\dfrac{2x}{x-3} - \dfrac{x+1}{x+2}$

To subtract, we need a common denominator. Since both denominators are prime, the LCD will be the product of the denominators.

$$LCD = (x-3)(x+2)$$

Next we write equivalent fractions using the LCD.

$$\frac{2x(x+2)}{(x-3)(x+2)} - \frac{(x+1)(x-3)}{(x-3)(x+2)}$$

Now we can combine the numerators and simplify.

$$\frac{2x(x+2) - (x+1)(x-3)}{(x-3)(x+2)}$$

$$= \frac{2x^2 + 4x - \left(x^2 - 2x - 3\right)}{(x-3)(x+2)}$$

$$= \frac{2x^2 + 4x - x^2 + 2x + 3}{(x-3)(x+2)}$$

$$= \frac{x^2 + 6x + 3}{(x-3)(x+2)}$$

18. $\dfrac{9}{k-2} = \dfrac{6}{k} + 3$

$$LCD = k(k-2)$$

The solution set cannot contain the restricted values 0 or 2 since these values will make one of the terms have a 0 in its denominator. Multiply each term by the LCD.

$$k(k-2)\left(\frac{9}{k-2}\right) = k(k-2)\frac{6}{k} + k(k-2)(3)$$

$$k\cancel{(k-2)}\left(\frac{9}{\cancel{k-2}}\right) = \cancel{k}(k-2)\frac{6}{\cancel{k}} + k(k-2)(3)$$

$$9k = 6(k-2) + 3k(k-2)$$

$$9k = 6k - 12 + 3k^2 - 6k$$

$$9k = 3k^2 - 12$$

$$0 = 3k^2 - 9k - 12$$

$$0 = k^2 - 3k - 4$$

$$0 = (k-4)(k+1)$$

$$k - 4 = 0 \ \text{ or } \ k + 1 = 0$$

$$k = 4 \ \text{ or } \ k = -1$$

Neither of these are restricted values, so the solution set is $\{-1, 4\}$.

19.
$$\frac{x+8}{x-4} \le 3$$

$$\frac{x+8}{x-4} - 3 \le 0$$

$$\frac{x+8}{x-4} - \frac{3(x-4)}{x-4} \le 0$$

$$\frac{x+8-3x+12}{x-4} \le 0$$

$$\frac{-2x+20}{x-4} \le 0$$

$$\frac{-2(x-10)}{x-4} \le 0$$

$$\frac{x-10}{x-4} \ge 0$$

The rational expression will equal 0 when $x = 10$. It is undefined when $x = 4$. Determine where the numerator and denominator are positive and negative, and where the quotient is positive and negative.

Interval	$(-\infty,4)$	4	$(4,10)$	10	$(10,\infty)$
$x-10$	$----$	$-$	$----$	0	$++++$
$x-4$	$----$	0	$++++$	$+$	$++++$
$\frac{x-10}{x-4}$	$++++$	$\varnothing$	$----$	0	$++++$

The rational function is undefined at $x = 4$, so 4 is not part of the solution. The inequality is non-strict, so $x = 10$ is part of the solution. Now, $\frac{x-10}{x-4}$ is greater than zero where the quotient is positive. The solution is $\{x \mid x < 4 \text{ or } x \ge 10\}$.

Interval: $(-\infty,4) \cup [10,\infty)$

Graph:

0   4   10

20. Let $x = $ hours needed to paint the room together.
$$\frac{1 \text{ room}}{4 \text{ hours}} + \frac{1 \text{ room}}{6 \text{ hours}} = \frac{1 \text{ room}}{x \text{ hours}}$$

$$12x\left(\frac{1}{4}\right) + 12x\left(\frac{1}{6}\right) = 12x\left(\frac{1}{x}\right)$$

$$3x + 2x = 12$$

$$5x = 12$$

$$x = \frac{12}{5} = 2.4$$

It will take Shawn and Payton 2.4 hours to paint the room together.

21. $\sqrt{\dfrac{50a^3b}{2a^{-1}b^3}} = \sqrt{\dfrac{50a^3b}{2a^{-1}b^3}} = \sqrt{\dfrac{25a^4}{b^2}} = \dfrac{\sqrt{25a^4}}{\sqrt{b^2}} = \dfrac{5a^2}{b}$

22. $f(x) = \sqrt[4]{8-3x}$

Since the index is even, we need the radicand to be greater than or equal to zero.
$$8 - 3x \ge 0$$

$$-3x \ge -8$$

$$\frac{-3x}{-3} \le \frac{-8}{-3}$$

$$x \le \frac{8}{3}$$

The domain of the function is $\left\{x \mid x \le \frac{8}{3}\right\}$ or the interval $\left(-\infty, \frac{8}{3}\right]$.

23. $\sqrt{x+7} - 8 = x-7$

$$\sqrt{x+7} = x+1$$

$$\left(\sqrt{x+7}\right)^2 = (x+1)^2$$

$$x+7 = x^2 + 2x + 1$$

$$0 = x^2 + x - 6$$

$$0 = (x+3)(x-2)$$

$$x+3 = 0 \text{ or } x-2 = 0$$

$$x = -3 \text{ or } x = 2$$

Check: $\sqrt{-3+7} - 8 = -3-7$?
$$\sqrt{4} - 8 = -10 \text{ ?}$$
$$2 - 8 = -10 \text{ ?}$$
$$-6 = -10 \text{ False}$$

$$\sqrt{2+7} - 8 = 2-7 \text{ ?}$$
$$\sqrt{9} - 8 = -5 \text{ ?}$$
$$3 - 8 = -5 \text{ ?}$$
$$-5 = -5 \text{ ✓}$$

The first solution is extraneous, so the solution set is $\{2\}$.

24.
$$\frac{3i}{1-7i} = \frac{3i}{1-7i} \cdot \frac{1+7i}{1+7i}$$
$$= \frac{3i+21i^2}{1-49i^2}$$
$$= \frac{3i+21(-1)}{1-49(-1)}$$
$$= \frac{-21+3i}{1+49}$$
$$= \frac{-21+3i}{50}$$
$$= -\frac{21}{50} + \frac{3}{50}i$$

25.
$$\frac{2}{4-\sqrt{11}} = \frac{2}{4-\sqrt{11}} \cdot \frac{4+\sqrt{11}}{4+\sqrt{11}}$$
$$= \frac{2\left(4+\sqrt{11}\right)}{4^2 - \left(\sqrt{11}\right)^2}$$
$$= \frac{8+2\sqrt{11}}{16-11}$$
$$= \frac{8+2\sqrt{11}}{5}$$

Chapter 8

8.1 Preparing for Solving Quadratic Equations by Completing the Square

1. $(2p+3)^2 = (2p)^2 + 2(2p)(3) + 3^2$
   $= 4p^2 + 12p + 9$

2. $y^2 - 8y + 16 = y^2 - 2\cdot y \cdot 4 + 4^2 = (y-4)^2$

3. $\quad x^2 + 5x - 14 = 0$
   $(x+7)(x-2) = 0$
   $x+7 = 0 \quad$ or $\quad x - 2 = 0$
   $\quad x = -7 \quad$ or $\quad\quad x = 2$
   The solution set is $\{-7,\ 2\}$.

4. $\quad\quad x^2 - 16 = 0$
   $(x+4)(x-4) = 0$
   $x + 4 = 0 \quad$ or $\quad x - 4 = 0$
   $\quad x = -4 \quad$ or $\quad\quad x = 4$
   The solution set is $\{-4,\ 4\}$.

5. **a.** $\sqrt{36} = 6$ because $6^2 = 36$.

   b. $\sqrt{45} = \sqrt{9\cdot 5} = 3\sqrt{5}$

   c. $\sqrt{-12} = \sqrt{-1\cdot 4\cdot 3} = 2\sqrt{3}\,i$

6. The complex conjugate is $-3 - 2i$.

8.1 Exercises

1. $\sqrt{p}$; $-\sqrt{p}$

3. hypotenuse; legs

5. FALSE. The coefficient of the square term can be any real value other than zero.

7. Answers will vary. One possibility follows: The expression "completing the square" means rewriting a quadratic equation so that it includes a perfect square trinomial on one side of the equation. For example, the quadratic equation $x^2 + 10x + 9 = 0$ can be written as follows:

$x^2 + 10x + 9 = 0$
$x^2 + 10x \quad\quad = -9$
$x^2 + 10x + 25 = -9 + 25$
$\quad\quad (x+5)^2 = 16$

In this example, $(x+5)^2 = 16$ is the completed-square form of $x^2 + 10x + 9 = 0$.

9. $y^2 = 100$
   $y = \pm\sqrt{100}$
   $y = \pm 10$
   The solution set is $\{-10,\ 10\}$.

11. $p^2 = 50$
    $p = \pm\sqrt{50}$
    $p = \pm 5\sqrt{2}$
    The solution set is $\left\{-5\sqrt{2},\ 5\sqrt{2}\right\}$.

13. $m^2 = -25$
    $m = \pm\sqrt{-25}$
    $m = \pm 5i$
    The solution set is $\{-5i,\ 5i\}$.

15. $w^2 = \dfrac{5}{4}$
    $w = \pm\sqrt{\dfrac{5}{4}}$
    $w = \pm\dfrac{\sqrt{5}}{2}$
    The solution set is $\left\{-\dfrac{\sqrt{5}}{2},\ \dfrac{\sqrt{5}}{2}\right\}$.

17. $x^2 + 5 = 13$
    $\quad x^2 = 8$
    $\quad\ x = \pm\sqrt{8}$
    $\quad\ x = \pm 2\sqrt{2}$
    The solution set is $\left\{-2\sqrt{2},\ 2\sqrt{2}\right\}$.

19. $3z^2 = 48$
    $\ z^2 = 16$
    $\quad z = \pm\sqrt{16}$
    $\quad z = \pm 4$
    The solution set is $\{-4,\ 4\}$.

21. $3x^2 = 8$

$x^2 = \dfrac{8}{3}$

$x = \pm\sqrt{\dfrac{8}{3}}$

$x = \pm\dfrac{\sqrt{8}}{\sqrt{3}}$

$x = \pm\dfrac{2\sqrt{2}}{\sqrt{3}} \cdot \dfrac{\sqrt{3}}{\sqrt{3}}$

$x = \pm\dfrac{2\sqrt{6}}{3}$

The solution set is $\left\{-\dfrac{2\sqrt{6}}{3},\ \dfrac{2\sqrt{6}}{3}\right\}$.

23. $2p^2 + 23 = 15$

$2p^2 = -8$

$p^2 = -4$

$p = \pm\sqrt{-4}$

$p = \pm 2i$

The solution set is $\{-2i,\ 2i\}$.

25. $(z+3)^2 = 64$

$z+3 = \pm\sqrt{64}$

$z+3 = \pm 8$

$z = -3 \pm 8$

$z = -3 - 8$ or $z = -3 + 8$

$z = -11$ or $z = 5$

The solution set is $\{-11,\ 5\}$.

27. $(d-1)^2 = -18$

$d-1 = \pm\sqrt{-18}$

$d-1 = \pm 3\sqrt{2}\ i$

$d = 1 \pm 3\sqrt{2}\ i$

The solution set is $\left\{1 - 3\sqrt{2}\ i,\ 1 + 3\sqrt{2}\ i\right\}$.

29. $3(q+5)^2 - 1 = 8$

$3(q+5)^2 = 9$

$(q+5)^2 = 3$

$q+5 = \pm\sqrt{3}$

$q = -5 \pm\sqrt{3}$

The solution set is $\left\{-5 - \sqrt{3},\ -5 + \sqrt{3}\right\}$.

31. $(3q+1)^2 = 9$

$3q+1 = \pm\sqrt{9}$

$3q+1 = \pm 3$

$3q = -1 \pm 3$

$3q = -1 - 3$ or $3q = -1 + 3$

$3q = -4$ or $3q = 2$

$q = -\dfrac{4}{3}$ or $q = \dfrac{2}{3}$

The solution set is $\left\{-\dfrac{4}{3},\ \dfrac{2}{3}\right\}$.

33. $\left(x - \dfrac{2}{3}\right)^2 = \dfrac{5}{9}$

$x - \dfrac{2}{3} = \pm\sqrt{\dfrac{5}{9}}$

$x - \dfrac{2}{3} = \pm\dfrac{\sqrt{5}}{3}$

$x = \dfrac{2}{3} \pm \dfrac{\sqrt{5}}{3}$

The solution set is $\left\{\dfrac{2}{3} - \dfrac{\sqrt{5}}{3},\ \dfrac{2}{3} + \dfrac{\sqrt{5}}{3}\right\}$.

35. $x^2 + 8x + 16 = 81$

$(x+4)^2 = 81$

$x+4 = \pm\sqrt{81}$

$x+4 = \pm 9$

$x = -4 \pm 9$

$x = -4 - 9$ or $x = -4 + 9$

$x = -13$ or $x = 5$

The solution set is $\{-13,\ 5\}$.

37. Start: $x^2 + 10x$

Add: $\left(\dfrac{1}{2} \cdot 10\right)^2 = 25$

Result: $x^2 + 10x + 25$

Factored Form: $(x+5)^2$

39. Start: $z^2 - 18z$

Add: $\left[\dfrac{1}{2} \cdot (-18)\right]^2 = 81$

Result: $z^2 - 18z + 81$

Factored Form: $(z-9)^2$

41. Start: $y^2 + 7y$

Add: $\left(\dfrac{1}{2} \cdot 7\right)^2 = \dfrac{49}{4}$

Result: $y^2 + 7y + \dfrac{49}{4}$

Factored Form: $\left(y + \dfrac{7}{2}\right)^2$

43. Start: $w^2 + \dfrac{1}{2}w$

Add: $\left(\dfrac{1}{2} \cdot \dfrac{1}{2}\right)^2 = \dfrac{1}{16}$

Result: $w^2 + \dfrac{1}{2}w + \dfrac{1}{16}$

Factored Form: $\left(w + \dfrac{1}{4}\right)^2$

45. Start: $q^2 - \dfrac{3}{5}q$

Add: $\left[\dfrac{1}{2} \cdot \left(-\dfrac{3}{5}\right)\right]^2 = \dfrac{9}{100}$

Result: $q^2 - \dfrac{3}{5}q + \dfrac{9}{100}$

Factored Form: $\left(q - \dfrac{3}{10}\right)^2$

47.
$$w^2 - 5w = 14$$
$$w^2 - 5w + \left(\dfrac{1}{2} \cdot (-5)\right)^2 = 14 + \left(\dfrac{1}{2} \cdot (-5)\right)^2$$
$$w^2 - 5w + \dfrac{25}{4} = 14 + \dfrac{25}{4}$$
$$\left(w - \dfrac{5}{2}\right)^2 = \dfrac{81}{4}$$
$$w - \dfrac{5}{2} = \pm\sqrt{\dfrac{81}{4}}$$
$$w - \dfrac{5}{2} = \pm\dfrac{9}{2}$$
$$w = \dfrac{5}{2} \pm \dfrac{9}{2}$$
$$w = -2 \ \text{ or } \ w = 7$$
The solution set is $\{-2, \ 7\}$.

49.
$$x^2 + 4x - 12 = 0$$
$$x^2 + 4x = 12$$
$$x^2 + 4x + \left(\dfrac{1}{2} \cdot 4\right)^2 = 12 + \left(\dfrac{1}{2} \cdot 4\right)^2$$
$$x^2 + 4x + 4 = 12 + 4$$
$$(x + 2)^2 = 16$$
$$x + 2 = \pm\sqrt{16}$$
$$x + 2 = \pm 4$$
$$x = -2 \pm 4$$
$$x = -6 \ \text{ or } \ x = 2$$
The solution set is $\{-6, \ 2\}$.

51.
$$x^2 - 4x + 1 = 0$$
$$x^2 - 4x = -1$$
$$x^2 - 4x + \left(\dfrac{1}{2} \cdot (-4)\right)^2 = -1 + \left(\dfrac{1}{2} \cdot (-4)\right)^2$$
$$x^2 - 4x + 4 = -1 + 4$$
$$(x - 2)^2 = 3$$
$$x - 2 = \pm\sqrt{3}$$
$$x = 2 \pm \sqrt{3}$$
The solution set is $\left\{2 - \sqrt{3}, \ 2 + \sqrt{3}\right\}$.

53.
$$z^2 + 8z + 9 = 0$$
$$z^2 + 8z = -9$$
$$z^2 + 8z + \left(\dfrac{1}{2} \cdot 8\right)^2 = -9 + \left(\dfrac{1}{2} \cdot 8\right)^2$$
$$z^2 + 8z + 16 = -9 + 16$$
$$(z + 4)^2 = 7$$
$$z + 4 = \pm\sqrt{7}$$
$$z = -4 \pm \sqrt{7}$$
The solution set is $\left\{-4 - \sqrt{7}, \ -4 + \sqrt{7}\right\}$.

55.
$$a^2 - 4a + 5 = 0$$
$$a^2 - 4a = -5$$
$$a^2 - 4a + \left(\dfrac{1}{2} \cdot (-4)\right)^2 = -5 + \left(\dfrac{1}{2} \cdot (-4)\right)^2$$
$$a^2 - 4a + 4 = -5 + 4$$
$$(a - 2)^2 = -1$$
$$a - 2 = \pm\sqrt{-1}$$
$$a - 2 = \pm i$$
$$a = 2 \pm i$$
The solution set is $\{2 - i, \ 2 + i\}$.

57.
$$b^2 + 5b - 2 = 0$$
$$b^2 + 5b \quad = 2$$
$$b^2 + 5b + \left(\frac{1}{2} \cdot 5\right)^2 = 2 + \left(\frac{1}{2} \cdot 5\right)^2$$
$$b^2 + 5b + \frac{25}{4} = 2 + \frac{25}{4}$$
$$\left(b + \frac{5}{2}\right)^2 = \frac{33}{4}$$
$$b + \frac{5}{2} = \pm\sqrt{\frac{33}{4}}$$
$$b + \frac{5}{2} = \pm\frac{\sqrt{33}}{2}$$
$$b = -\frac{5}{2} \pm \frac{\sqrt{33}}{2}$$

The solution set is $\left\{-\frac{5}{2} - \frac{\sqrt{33}}{2}, \ -\frac{5}{2} + \frac{\sqrt{33}}{2}\right\}$.

59.
$$p^2 - 3p - 2 = 0$$
$$p^2 - 3p \quad = 2$$
$$p^2 - 3p + \left(\frac{1}{2} \cdot (-3)\right)^2 = 2 + \left(\frac{1}{2} \cdot (-3)\right)^2$$
$$p^2 - 3p + \frac{9}{4} = 2 + \frac{9}{4}$$
$$\left(p - \frac{3}{2}\right)^2 = \frac{17}{4}$$
$$p - \frac{3}{2} = \pm\sqrt{\frac{17}{4}}$$
$$p - \frac{3}{2} = \pm\frac{\sqrt{17}}{2}$$
$$p = \frac{3}{2} \pm \frac{\sqrt{17}}{2}$$

The solution set is $\left\{\frac{3}{2} - \frac{\sqrt{17}}{2}, \ \frac{3}{2} + \frac{\sqrt{17}}{2}\right\}$.

61.
$$m^2 = 8m + 3$$
$$m^2 - 8m = 3$$
$$m^2 - 8m + \left(\frac{1}{2} \cdot (-8)\right)^2 = 3 + \left(\frac{1}{2} \cdot (-8)\right)^2$$
$$m^2 - 8m + 16 = 3 + 16$$
$$(m - 4)^2 = 19$$
$$m - 4 = \pm\sqrt{19}$$
$$m = 4 \pm \sqrt{19}$$

The solution set is $\left\{4 - \sqrt{19}, \ 4 + \sqrt{19}\right\}$.

63.
$$p^2 - p + 3 = 0$$
$$p^2 - p \quad = -3$$
$$p^2 - p + \left(\frac{1}{2} \cdot (-1)\right)^2 = -3 + \left(\frac{1}{2} \cdot (-1)\right)^2$$
$$p^2 - p + \frac{1}{4} = -3 + \frac{1}{4}$$
$$\left(p - \frac{1}{2}\right)^2 = -\frac{11}{4}$$
$$p - \frac{1}{2} = \pm\sqrt{-\frac{11}{4}}$$
$$p - \frac{1}{2} = \pm\frac{\sqrt{11}}{2}i$$
$$p = \frac{1}{2} \pm \frac{\sqrt{11}}{2}i$$

The solution set is $\left\{\frac{1}{2} - \frac{\sqrt{11}}{2}i, \ \frac{1}{2} + \frac{\sqrt{11}}{2}i\right\}$.

65.
$$2y^2 - 5y - 12 = 0$$
$$\frac{2y^2 - 5y - 12}{2} = \frac{0}{2}$$
$$y^2 - \frac{5}{2}y - 6 = 0$$
$$y^2 - \frac{5}{2}y \quad = 6$$
$$y^2 - \frac{5}{2}y + \left[\frac{1}{2} \cdot \left(-\frac{5}{2}\right)\right]^2 = 6 + \left[\frac{1}{2} \cdot \left(-\frac{5}{2}\right)\right]^2$$
$$y^2 - \frac{5}{2}y + \frac{25}{16} = 6 + \frac{25}{16}$$
$$\left(y - \frac{5}{4}\right)^2 = \frac{121}{16}$$
$$y - \frac{5}{4} = \pm\sqrt{\frac{121}{16}}$$
$$y - \frac{5}{4} = \pm\frac{11}{4}$$
$$y = \frac{5}{4} \pm \frac{11}{4}$$
$$y = -\frac{3}{2} \quad \text{or} \quad y = 4$$

The solution set is $\left\{-\frac{3}{2}, \ 4\right\}$.

67.

$$3y^2 - 6y + 2 = 0$$

$$\frac{3y^2 - 6y + 2}{3} = \frac{0}{3}$$

$$y^2 - 2y + \frac{2}{3} = 0$$

$$y^2 - 2y \quad = -\frac{2}{3}$$

$$y^2 - 2y + \left(\frac{1}{2} \cdot (-2)\right)^2 = -\frac{2}{3} + \left(\frac{1}{2} \cdot (-2)\right)^2$$

$$y^2 - 2y + 1 = -\frac{2}{3} + 1$$

$$(y-1)^2 = \frac{1}{3}$$

$$y - 1 = \pm\sqrt{\frac{1}{3}}$$

$$y - 1 = \pm\frac{1}{\sqrt{3}} \cdot \frac{\sqrt{3}}{\sqrt{3}}$$

$$y - 1 = \pm\frac{\sqrt{3}}{3}$$

$$y = 1 \pm \frac{\sqrt{3}}{3}$$

The solution set is $\left\{1 - \dfrac{\sqrt{3}}{3},\ 1 + \dfrac{\sqrt{3}}{3}\right\}$.

69.

$$2z^2 - 5z + 1 = 0$$

$$\frac{2z^2 - 5z + 1}{2} = \frac{0}{2}$$

$$z^2 - \frac{5}{2}z + \frac{1}{2} = 0$$

$$y^2 - \frac{5}{2}y \quad = -\frac{1}{2}$$

$$z^2 - \frac{5}{2}z + \left[\frac{1}{2}\left(-\frac{5}{2}\right)\right]^2 = -\frac{1}{2} + \left[\frac{1}{2}\left(-\frac{5}{2}\right)\right]^2$$

$$z^2 - \frac{5}{2}z + \frac{25}{16} = -\frac{1}{2} + \frac{25}{16}$$

$$\left(z - \frac{5}{4}\right)^2 = \frac{17}{16}$$

$$z - \frac{5}{4} = \pm\sqrt{\frac{17}{16}}$$

$$z - \frac{5}{4} = \pm\frac{\sqrt{17}}{4}$$

$$z = \frac{5}{4} \pm \frac{\sqrt{17}}{4}$$

The solution set is $\left\{\dfrac{5}{4} - \dfrac{\sqrt{17}}{4},\ \dfrac{5}{4} + \dfrac{\sqrt{17}}{4}\right\}$.

71.

$$2x^2 + 4x + 5 = 0$$

$$\frac{2x^2 + 4x + 5}{2} = \frac{0}{2}$$

$$x^2 + 2x + \frac{5}{2} = 0$$

$$x^2 + 2x \quad = -\frac{5}{2}$$

$$x^2 + 2x + \left(\frac{1}{2} \cdot 2\right)^2 = -\frac{5}{2} + \left(\frac{1}{2} \cdot 2\right)^2$$

$$x^2 + 2x + 1 = -\frac{5}{2} + 1$$

$$(x+1)^2 = -\frac{3}{2}$$

$$x + 1 = \pm\sqrt{-\frac{3}{2}}$$

$$x + 1 = \pm\frac{\sqrt{-3}}{\sqrt{2}} \cdot \frac{\sqrt{2}}{\sqrt{2}}$$

$$x + 1 = \pm\frac{\sqrt{-6}}{2}$$

$$x = -1 \pm \frac{\sqrt{6}}{2}i$$

The solution set is $\left\{-1 - \dfrac{\sqrt{6}}{2}i,\ -1 + \dfrac{\sqrt{6}}{2}i\right\}$.

73.

$$3b^2 + b - 5 = 0$$

$$\frac{3b^2 + b - 5}{3} = \frac{0}{3}$$

$$b^2 + \frac{1}{3}b - \frac{5}{3} = 0$$

$$b^2 + \frac{1}{3}b \quad = \frac{5}{3}$$

$$b^2 + \frac{1}{3}b + \left[\frac{1}{2}\left(\frac{1}{3}\right)\right]^2 = \frac{5}{3} + \left[\frac{1}{2}\left(\frac{1}{3}\right)\right]^2$$

$$b^2 + \frac{1}{3}b + \frac{1}{36} = \frac{5}{3} + \frac{1}{36}$$

$$\left(b + \frac{1}{6}\right)^2 = \frac{61}{36}$$

$$b + \frac{1}{6} = \pm\sqrt{\frac{61}{36}}$$

$$b + \frac{1}{6} = \pm\frac{\sqrt{61}}{6}$$

$$b = -\frac{1}{6} \pm \frac{\sqrt{61}}{6}$$

The solution set is $\left\{-\dfrac{1}{6} - \dfrac{\sqrt{61}}{6},\ -\dfrac{1}{6} + \dfrac{\sqrt{61}}{6}\right\}$.

75. $c^2 = 6^2 + 8^2$
$= 36 + 64$
$= 100$
$c = \sqrt{100} = 10$

77. $c^2 = 12^2 + 16^2$
$= 144 + 256$
$= 400$
$c = \sqrt{400} = 20$

79. $c^2 = 5^2 + 5^2$
$= 25 + 25$
$= 50$
$c = \sqrt{50} = 5\sqrt{2} \approx 7.07$

81. $c^2 = 1^2 + \left(\sqrt{3}\right)^2$
$= 1 + 3$
$= 4$
$c = \sqrt{4} = 2$

83. $c^2 = 6^2 + 10^2$
$= 36 + 100$
$= 136$
$c = \sqrt{136} = 2\sqrt{34} \approx 11.66$

85. $c^2 = a^2 + b^2$
$8^2 = 4^2 + b^2$
$64 = 16 + b^2$
$48 = b^2$
$b = \sqrt{48}$
$b = 4\sqrt{3} \approx 6.93$

87. $c^2 = a^2 + b^2$
$12^2 = a^2 + 8^2$
$144 = a^2 + 64$
$80 = a^2$
$a = \sqrt{80}$
$a = 4\sqrt{5} \approx 8.94$

89. $f(x) = 36$
$(x - 3)^2 = 36$
$x - 3 = \pm\sqrt{36}$
$x - 3 = \pm 6$
$x = 3 \pm 6$
$x = 3 - 6 \text{ or } x = 3 + 6$
$x = -3 \quad \text{ or } x = 9$
The solution set is $\{-3, 9\}$.

91. $g(x) = 18$
$(x + 2)^2 = 18$
$x + 2 = \pm\sqrt{18}$
$x + 2 = \pm 3\sqrt{2}$
$x = -2 \pm 3\sqrt{2}$
The solution set is $\left\{-2 - 3\sqrt{2}, \ -2 + 3\sqrt{2}\right\}$.

93. Let x represent the diagonal.
$x^2 = 8^2 + 4^2$
$x^2 = 64 + 16$
$x^2 = 80$
$x = \sqrt{80} = 4\sqrt{5} \approx 8.944$

95. Let x represent the distance from the ball to the center of the green.
$x^2 = 30^2 + 100^2$
$x^2 = 900 + 10,000$
$x^2 = 10,900$
$x = \sqrt{10,900} \approx 104.403$
The ball is approximately 104.403 yards from the center of the green.

97. Let x represent the length of the guy wire.
$x^2 = 10^2 + 30^2$
$x^2 = 100 + 900$
$x^2 = 1000$
$x = \sqrt{1000} \approx 31.623$
The guy wire is approximately 31.623 feet long.

99. a. Let x represent the height up the wall to which the ladder can reach.

25 feet

x

10 feet

$25^2 = 10^2 + x^2$
$625 = 100 + x^2$
$525 = x^2$
$x = \sqrt{525}$
$x \approx 22.913$
The ladder can reach approximately 22.913 feet up the wall.

b. Let x represent the distance that the base of the ladder can be from the wall.

$$25^2 = x^2 + 20^2$$
$$625 = x^2 + 400$$
$$225 = x^2$$
$$x = \sqrt{225}$$
$$x = 15$$

The base of the ladder can be at most 15 feet from the wall.

101. a. $s = 16t^2$
$$16 = 16t^2$$
$$1 = t^2$$
$$t = \sqrt{1}$$
$$t = 1$$

It takes 1 second for an object to fall 16 feet.

b. $s = 16t^2$
$$48 = 16t^2$$
$$3 = t^2$$
$$t = \sqrt{3}$$
$$t \approx 1.732$$

It takes approximately 1.732 seconds for an object to fall 48 feet.

c. $s = 16t^2$
$$64 = 16t^2$$
$$4 = t^2$$
$$t = \sqrt{4}$$
$$t = 2$$

It takes 2 seconds for an object to fall 64 feet.

103. $1200 = 1000(1+r)^2$
$$1.2 = (1+r)^2$$
$$1 + r = \sqrt{1.2}$$
$$r = -1 + \sqrt{1.2}$$
$$r \approx .0954$$

The required rate of interest is approximately 9.54%.

105. $17^2 \overset{?}{=} 8^2 + 15^2$
$$289 \overset{?}{=} 64 + 225$$
$$289 \overset{?}{=} 289 \quad \leftarrow \text{True}$$

Because $c^2 = a^2 + b^2$, the triangle is a right triangle. The hypotenuse is 17.

107. $20^2 \overset{?}{=} 14^2 + 18^2$
$$400 \overset{?}{=} 196 + 324$$
$$400 \overset{?}{=} 520 \quad \leftarrow \text{False}$$

Because $c^2 \neq a^2 + b^2$, the triangle is not a right triangle.

109. $c^2 = \left(m^2 + n^2\right)^2 = m^4 + 2m^2n^2 + n^4$
$$\begin{aligned} a^2 + b^2 &= \left(m^2 - n^2\right)^2 + \left(2mn\right)^2 \\ &= m^4 - 2m^2n^2 + n^4 + 4m^2n^2 \\ &= m^4 + 2m^2n^2 + n^4 \end{aligned}$$

Because c^2 and $a^2 + b^2$ result in the same expression, a, b, and c are the lengths of the sides of a right triangle.

111. $a^2 - 5a - 36 = 0$
$$(a-9)(a+4) = 0$$
$$a - 9 = 0 \quad \text{or} \quad a + 4 = 0$$
$$a = 9 \quad \text{or} \quad a = -4$$

The solution set is $\{-4,\ 9\}$.

113. $|4q+1| = 3$
$$4q + 1 = 3 \quad \text{or} \quad 4q + 1 = -3$$
$$4q = 2 \quad \text{or} \quad 4q = -4$$
$$4q = 2 \quad \text{or} \quad 4q = -4$$
$$q = \frac{1}{2} \quad \text{or} \quad q = -1$$

The solution set is $\left\{-1, \frac{1}{2}\right\}$.

115. In both cases, the simpler equations are linear.

8.2 Preparing for Solving Quadratic Equations by the Quadratic Formula

1. a. $\sqrt{54} = \sqrt{9 \cdot 6} = 3\sqrt{6}$

   b. $\sqrt{121} = 11$ because $11^2 = 121$.

2. a. $\sqrt{-9} = \sqrt{-1 \cdot 9} = 3i$

   b. $\sqrt{-72} = \sqrt{-1 \cdot 36 \cdot 2} = 6\sqrt{2}\,i$

3. $\dfrac{3 + \sqrt{18}}{6} = \dfrac{3 + 3\sqrt{2}}{6}$

$$= \dfrac{3\left(1 + \sqrt{2}\right)}{6}$$

$$= \dfrac{1 + \sqrt{2}}{2} \quad \text{or} \quad \dfrac{1}{2} + \dfrac{\sqrt{2}}{2}$$

8.2 Exercises

1. $\dfrac{-b \pm \sqrt{b^2 - 4ac}}{2a}$

3. negative

5. FALSE. The equation will have one repeated real solution.

7. Answers may vary. One possibility follows: If the quadratic equation is in the form $ax^2 + bx + c = 0$ (or if it can easily be put in that form) and if the left side is easy to factor, then use factoring to solve the equation. Note that the discriminant must be a perfect square.

9. The solutions to the equation $ax^2 + bx + c = 0$, $a \neq 0$, are given by

$$x = \dfrac{-b \pm \sqrt{b^2 - 4ac}}{2a}.$$

11. $x^2 - 4x - 12 = 0$

For this equation, $a = 1$, $b = -4$, and $c = -12$.

$$x = \dfrac{-(-4) \pm \sqrt{(-4)^2 - 4(1)(-12)}}{2(1)}$$

$$= \dfrac{4 \pm \sqrt{16 + 48}}{2}$$

$$= \dfrac{4 \pm \sqrt{64}}{2}$$

$$= \dfrac{4 \pm 8}{2}$$

$$x = \dfrac{4 - 8}{2} \quad \text{or} \quad x = \dfrac{4 + 8}{2}$$

$$= \dfrac{-4}{2} \quad \text{or} \quad = \dfrac{12}{2}$$

$$= -2 \quad \text{or} \quad = 6$$

The solution set is $\{-2,\ 6\}$.

13. $6y^2 - y - 15 = 0$

For this equation, $a = 6$, $b = -1$, and $c = -15$.

$$y = \dfrac{-(-1) \pm \sqrt{(-1)^2 - 4(6)(-15)}}{2(6)}$$

$$= \dfrac{1 \pm \sqrt{1 + 360}}{12}$$

$$= \dfrac{1 \pm \sqrt{361}}{12}$$

$$= \dfrac{1 \pm 19}{12}$$

$$y = \dfrac{1 - 19}{12} \quad \text{or} \quad y = \dfrac{1 + 19}{12}$$

$$= \dfrac{-18}{12} \quad \text{or} \quad = \dfrac{20}{12}$$

$$= -\dfrac{3}{2} \quad \text{or} \quad = \dfrac{5}{3}$$

The solution set is $\left\{ -\dfrac{3}{2},\ \dfrac{5}{3} \right\}$.

15. $4m^2 - 8m + 1 = 0$

For this equation, $a = 4$, $b = -8$, and $c = 1$.

$$m = \frac{-(-8) \pm \sqrt{(-8)^2 - 4(4)(1)}}{2(4)}$$

$$= \frac{8 \pm \sqrt{64 - 16}}{8}$$

$$= \frac{8 \pm \sqrt{48}}{8} = \frac{8}{8} \pm \frac{4\sqrt{3}}{8} = 1 \pm \frac{\sqrt{3}}{2}$$

The solution set is $\left\{ 1 - \frac{\sqrt{3}}{2}, 1 + \frac{\sqrt{3}}{2} \right\}$.

17. $\qquad 3w - 6 = \frac{1}{w}$

$$(3w - 6)w = \left(\frac{1}{w} \right)w$$

$$3w^2 - 6w = 1$$

$$3w^2 - 6w - 1 = 0$$

For this equation, $a = 3$, $b = -6$, and $c = -1$.

$$w = \frac{-(-6) \pm \sqrt{(-6)^2 - 4(3)(-1)}}{2(3)}$$

$$= \frac{6 \pm \sqrt{36 + 12}}{6}$$

$$= \frac{6 \pm \sqrt{48}}{6}$$

$$= \frac{6 \pm 4\sqrt{3}}{6} = \frac{6}{6} \pm \frac{4\sqrt{3}}{6} = 1 \pm \frac{2\sqrt{3}}{3}$$

The solution set is $\left\{ 1 - \frac{2\sqrt{3}}{3}, 1 + \frac{2\sqrt{3}}{3} \right\}$.

19. $\qquad 3p^2 = -2p + 4$

$$3p^2 + 2p - 4 = 0$$

For this equation, $a = 3$, $b = 2$, and $c = -4$.

$$p = \frac{-2 \pm \sqrt{2^2 - 4(3)(-4)}}{2(3)}$$

$$= \frac{-2 \pm \sqrt{4 + 48}}{6}$$

$$= \frac{-2 \pm \sqrt{52}}{6}$$

$$= \frac{-2 \pm 2\sqrt{13}}{6} = -\frac{2}{6} \pm \frac{2\sqrt{13}}{6} = -\frac{1}{3} \pm \frac{\sqrt{13}}{3}$$

The solution set is $\left\{ -\frac{1}{3} - \frac{\sqrt{13}}{3}, -\frac{1}{3} + \frac{\sqrt{13}}{3} \right\}$.

21. $x^2 - 2x + 7 = 0$

For this equation, $a = 1$, $b = -2$, and $c = 7$.

$$x = \frac{-(-2) \pm \sqrt{(-2)^2 - 4(1)(7)}}{2(1)}$$

$$= \frac{2 \pm \sqrt{4 - 28}}{2}$$

$$= \frac{2 \pm \sqrt{-24}}{2}$$

$$= \frac{2 \pm 2\sqrt{6}\,i}{2}$$

$$= \frac{2}{2} \pm \frac{2\sqrt{6}\,i}{2} = 1 \pm \sqrt{6}\,i$$

The solution set is $\left\{ 1 - \sqrt{6}\,i, 1 + \sqrt{6}\,i \right\}$.

23. $\qquad 2z^2 + 7 = 2z$

$$2z^2 - 2z + 7 = 0$$

For this equation, $a = 2$, $b = -2$, and $c = 7$.

$$z = \frac{-(-2) \pm \sqrt{(-2)^2 - 4(2)(7)}}{2(2)}$$

$$= \frac{2 \pm \sqrt{4 - 56}}{4}$$

$$= \frac{2 \pm \sqrt{-52}}{4}$$

$$= \frac{2 \pm 2\sqrt{13}\,i}{4}$$

$$= \frac{2}{4} \pm \frac{2\sqrt{13}\,i}{4} = \frac{1}{2} \pm \frac{\sqrt{13}}{2}i$$

The solution set is $\left\{ \frac{1}{2} - \frac{\sqrt{13}}{2}i, \frac{1}{2} + \frac{\sqrt{13}}{2}i \right\}$.

25. $\qquad 4x^2 = 2x + 1$

$$4x^2 - 2x - 1 = 0$$

For this equation, $a = 4$, $b = -2$, and $c = -1$.

$$x = \frac{-(-2) \pm \sqrt{(-2)^2 - 4(4)(-1)}}{2(4)}$$

$$= \frac{2 \pm \sqrt{4 + 16}}{8}$$

$$= \frac{2 \pm \sqrt{20}}{8}$$

$$= \frac{2 \pm 2\sqrt{5}}{8} = \frac{2}{8} \pm \frac{2\sqrt{5}}{8} = \frac{1}{4} \pm \frac{\sqrt{5}}{4}$$

The solution set is $\left\{ \frac{1}{4} - \frac{\sqrt{5}}{4}, \frac{1}{4} + \frac{\sqrt{5}}{4} \right\}$.

27. $1 = 3q^2 + 4q$

$0 = 3q^2 + 4q - 1$

For this equation, $a = 3$, $b = 4$, and $c = -1$.

$$q = \frac{-4 \pm \sqrt{4^2 - 4(3)(-1)}}{2(3)}$$

$$= \frac{-4 \pm \sqrt{16 + 12}}{6}$$

$$= \frac{-4 \pm \sqrt{28}}{6}$$

$$= \frac{-4 \pm 2\sqrt{7}}{6} = \frac{-4}{6} \pm \frac{2\sqrt{7}}{6} = -\frac{2}{3} \pm \frac{\sqrt{7}}{3}$$

The solution set is $\left\{ -\frac{2}{3} - \frac{\sqrt{7}}{3}, \ -\frac{2}{3} + \frac{\sqrt{7}}{3} \right\}$.

29. $x^2 - 5x + 1 = 0$

For this equation, $a = 1$, $b = -5$, and $c = 1$.

$b^2 - 4ac = (-5)^2 - 4(1)(1) = 25 - 4 = 21$

Because $b^2 - 4ac = 21$ is positive, but not a perfect square, the quadratic equation will have two irrational solutions.

31. $3z^2 + 2z + 5 = 0$

For this equation, $a = 3$, $b = 2$, and $c = 5$.

$b^2 - 4ac = 2^2 - 4(3)(5) = 4 - 60 = -56$

Because $b^2 - 4ac = -56$ is negative, the quadratic equation will have two complex solutions that are not real. The solutions will be complex conjugates of each other.

33. $9q^2 - 6q + 1 = 0$

For this equation, $a = 9$, $b = -6$, and $c = 1$.

$b^2 - 4ac = (-6)^2 - 4(9)(1) = 36 - 36 = 0$

Because $b^2 - 4ac = 0$, the quadratic equation will have one repeated real solution.

35. $3w^2 = 4w - 2$

$3w^2 - 4w + 2 = 0$

For this equation, $a = 3$, $b = -4$, and $c = 2$.

$b^2 - 4ac = (-4)^2 - 4(3)(2) = 16 - 24 = -8$

Because $b^2 - 4ac = -8$ is negative, the quadratic equation will have two complex solutions that are not real. The solutions will be complex conjugates of each other.

37. $6x = 2x^2 - 1$

$0 = 2x^2 - 6x - 1$

For this equation, $a = 2$, $b = -6$, and $c = -1$.

$b^2 - 4ac = (-6)^2 - 4(2)(-1) = 36 + 8 = 44$

Because $b^2 - 4ac = 44$ is positive, but not a perfect square, the quadratic equation will have two irrational solutions.

39. $w^2 - 5w + 5 = 0$

Because this equation does not easily factor, solve by using the quadratic formula. For this equation, $a = 1$, $b = -5$, and $c = 5$.

$$w = \frac{-(-5) \pm \sqrt{(-5)^2 - 4(1)(5)}}{2(1)}$$

$$= \frac{5 \pm \sqrt{25 - 20}}{2} = \frac{5 \pm \sqrt{5}}{2} = \frac{5}{2} \pm \frac{\sqrt{5}}{2}$$

The solution set is $\left\{ \frac{5}{2} - \frac{\sqrt{5}}{2}, \ \frac{5}{2} + \frac{\sqrt{5}}{2} \right\}$.

41. $3x^2 + 5x = 8$

$3x^2 + 5x - 8 = 0$

Because this equation factors easily, solve by factoring.

$(3x + 8)(x - 1) = 0$

$3x + 8 = 0 \quad$ or $\quad x - 1 = 0$

$3x = -8 \quad$ or $\qquad x = 1$

$x = -\frac{8}{3}$

The solution set is $\left\{ -\frac{8}{3}, 1 \right\}$.

43. $2x^2 = 3x + 35$

$2x^2 - 3x - 35 = 0$

Because this equation factors easily, solve by factoring.

$(2x + 7)(x - 5) = 0$

$2x + 7 = 0 \quad$ or $\quad x - 5 = 0$

$2x = -7 \quad$ or $\qquad x = 5$

$x = -\frac{7}{2}$

The solution set is $\left\{ -\frac{7}{2}, 5 \right\}$.

45. $q^2 + 2q + 8 = 0$

Because this equation does not easily factor, solve by using the quadratic formula. For this equation, $a = 1$, $b = 2$, and $c = 8$.

$$q = \frac{-2 \pm \sqrt{2^2 - 4(1)(8)}}{2(1)}$$

$$= \frac{-2 \pm \sqrt{4 - 32}}{2}$$

$$= \frac{-2 \pm \sqrt{-28}}{2}$$

$$= \frac{-2 \pm 2\sqrt{7}\ i}{2} = \frac{-2}{2} \pm \frac{2\sqrt{7}\ i}{2} = -1 \pm \sqrt{7}\ i$$

The solution set is $\left\{ -1 - \sqrt{7}\ i, \ -1 + \sqrt{7}\ i \right\}$.

47. $5z^2 = 2z + 3$

$5z^2 - 2z - 3 = 0$

Because this equation factors easily, solve by factoring.

$(5z + 3)(z - 1) = 0$

$5z + 3 = 0$ or $z - 1 = 0$

$5z = -3$ or $z = 1$

$z = -\dfrac{3}{5}$

The solution set is $\left\{ -\dfrac{3}{5}, 1 \right\}$.

49. $7q - 2 = \dfrac{4}{q}$

$(7q - 2)q = \left(\dfrac{4}{q} \right) q$

$7q^2 - 2q = 4$

$7q^2 - 2q - 4 = 0$

Because this equation does not easily factor, solve by using the quadratic formula. For this equation, $a = 7$, $b = -2$, and $c = -4$.

$$q = \frac{-(-2) \pm \sqrt{(-2)^2 - 4(7)(-4)}}{2(7)}$$

$$= \frac{2 \pm \sqrt{4 + 112}}{14} = \frac{2 \pm \sqrt{116}}{14}$$

$$= \frac{2 \pm 2\sqrt{29}}{14} = \frac{2}{14} \pm \frac{2\sqrt{29}}{14} = \frac{1}{7} \pm \frac{\sqrt{29}}{7}$$

The solution set is $\left\{ \dfrac{1}{7} - \dfrac{\sqrt{29}}{7}, \ \dfrac{1}{7} + \dfrac{\sqrt{29}}{7} \right\}$.

51. $5a^2 - 80 = 0$

Because this equation has no linear term, solve by using the square root method.

$5a^2 = 80$

$a^2 = 16$

$a = \pm\sqrt{16} = \pm 4$

The solution set is $\{-4, 4\}$.

53. $8n^2 + 1 = 4n$

$8n^2 - 4n + 1 = 0$

Because this equation does not easily factor, solve by using the quadratic formula. For this equation, $a = 8$, $b = -4$, and $c = 1$.

$$n = \frac{-(-4) \pm \sqrt{(-4)^2 - 4(8)(1)}}{2(8)}$$

$$= \frac{4 \pm \sqrt{16 - 32}}{16}$$

$$= \frac{4 \pm \sqrt{-16}}{16}$$

$$= \frac{4 \pm 4i}{16} = \frac{4}{16} \pm \frac{4i}{16} = \frac{1}{4} \pm \frac{1}{4}i$$

The solution set is $\left\{ \dfrac{1}{4} - \dfrac{1}{4}i, \ \dfrac{1}{4} + \dfrac{1}{4}i \right\}$.

55. $27x^2 + 36x + 12 = 0$

$\dfrac{27x^2 + 36x + 12}{3} = \dfrac{0}{3}$

$9x^2 + 12x + 4 = 0$

Because this equation factors easily, solve by factoring.

$(3x + 2)(3x + 2) = 0$

$3x + 2 = 0$ or $3x + 2 = 0$

$3x = -2$ or $3x = -2$

$x = -\dfrac{2}{3}$ or $x = -\dfrac{2}{3}$

The solution set is $\left\{ -\dfrac{2}{3} \right\}$.

57. $\dfrac{1}{3}x^2 + \dfrac{2}{9}x - 1 = 0$

$9\left(\dfrac{1}{3}x^2 + \dfrac{2}{9}x - 1\right) = 9(0)$

$3x^2 + 2x - 9 = 0$

Because this equation does not easily factor, solve by using the quadratic formula. For this equation, $a = 3$, $b = 2$, and $c = -9$.

$x = \dfrac{-2 \pm \sqrt{2^2 - 4(3)(-9)}}{2(3)}$

$= \dfrac{-2 \pm \sqrt{4 + 108}}{6}$

$= \dfrac{-2 \pm \sqrt{112}}{6}$

$= \dfrac{-2 \pm 4\sqrt{7}}{6}$

$= \dfrac{-2}{6} \pm \dfrac{4\sqrt{7}}{6} = -\dfrac{1}{3} \pm \dfrac{2\sqrt{7}}{3}$

The solution set is $\left\{-\dfrac{1}{3} - \dfrac{2\sqrt{7}}{3}, \ -\dfrac{1}{3} + \dfrac{2\sqrt{7}}{3}\right\}$.

59. $(x-5)(x+1) = 4$

$x^2 - 4x - 5 = 4$

$x^2 - 4x - 9 = 0$

Because this equation does not easily factor, solve by using the quadratic formula. For this equation, $a = 1$, $b = -4$, and $c = -9$.

$x = \dfrac{-(-4) \pm \sqrt{(-4)^2 - 4(1)(-9)}}{2(1)}$

$= \dfrac{4 \pm \sqrt{16 + 36}}{2}$

$= \dfrac{4 \pm \sqrt{52}}{2}$

$= \dfrac{4 \pm 2\sqrt{13}}{2}$

$= \dfrac{4}{2} \pm \dfrac{2\sqrt{13}}{2} = 2 \pm \sqrt{13}$

The solution set is $\left\{2 - \sqrt{13}, \ 2 + \sqrt{13}\right\}$.

61. Note: $x \neq -2$.

$\dfrac{x-2}{x+2} = x - 3$

$(x+2)\left(\dfrac{x-2}{x+2}\right) = (x+2)(x-3)$

$x - 2 = x^2 - x - 6$

$0 = x^2 - 2x - 4$

Because this equation does not easily factor, solve by using the quadratic formula. For this equation, $a = 1$, $b = -2$, and $c = -4$.

$x = \dfrac{-(-2) \pm \sqrt{(-2)^2 - 4(1)(-4)}}{2(1)}$

$= \dfrac{2 \pm \sqrt{4 + 16}}{2}$

$= \dfrac{2 \pm \sqrt{20}}{2}$

$= \dfrac{2 \pm 2\sqrt{5}}{2}$

$= \dfrac{2}{2} \pm \dfrac{2\sqrt{5}}{2} = 1 \pm \sqrt{5}$

The solution set is $\left\{1 - \sqrt{5}, \ 1 + \sqrt{5}\right\}$.

63. $\dfrac{x-4}{x^2+2} = 2$

$(x^2+2)\left(\dfrac{x-4}{x^2+2}\right) = (x^2+2)(2)$

$x - 4 = 2x^2 + 4$

$0 = 2x^2 - x + 8$

Because this equation does not easily factor, solve by using the quadratic formula. For this equation, $a = 2$, $b = -1$, and $c = 8$.

$x = \dfrac{-(-1) \pm \sqrt{(-1)^2 - 4(2)(8)}}{2(2)}$

$= \dfrac{1 \pm \sqrt{1 - 64}}{4}$

$= \dfrac{1 \pm \sqrt{-63}}{4}$

$= \dfrac{1 \pm 3\sqrt{7}\,i}{4} = \dfrac{1}{4} \pm \dfrac{3\sqrt{7}}{4}i$

The solution set is $\left\{\dfrac{1}{4} - \dfrac{3\sqrt{7}}{4}i, \ \dfrac{1}{4} + \dfrac{3\sqrt{7}}{4}i\right\}$.

65. a.
$$f(x) = 0$$
$$x^2 + 4x - 21 = 0$$
$$(x+7)(x-3) = 0$$
$$x+7 = 0 \quad \text{or} \quad x-3 = 0$$
$$x = -7 \quad \text{or} \quad x = 3$$
The solution set is $\{-7, 3\}$.

b.
$$f(x) = -21$$
$$x^2 + 4x - 21 = -21$$
$$x^2 + 4x = 0$$
$$x(x+4) = 0$$
$$x = 0 \quad \text{or} \quad x+4 = 0$$
$$x = -4$$
The solution set is $\{-4, 0\}$.

67. a.
$$H(x) = 0$$
$$-2x^2 - 4x + 1 = 0$$
$$2x^2 + 4x - 1 = 0$$
For this equation, $a = 2$, $b = 4$, and $c = -1$.
$$x = \frac{-4 \pm \sqrt{4^2 - 4(2)(-1)}}{2(2)}$$
$$= \frac{-4 \pm \sqrt{16 + 8}}{4}$$
$$= \frac{-4 \pm \sqrt{24}}{4}$$
$$= \frac{-4 \pm 2\sqrt{6}}{4} = \frac{-4}{4} \pm \frac{2\sqrt{6}}{4} = -1 \pm \frac{\sqrt{6}}{2}$$
The solution set is $\left\{ -1 - \frac{\sqrt{6}}{2}, \; -1 + \frac{\sqrt{6}}{2} \right\}$.

b.
$$H(x) = 2$$
$$-2x^2 - 4x + 1 = 2$$
$$0 = 2x^2 + 4x + 1$$
For this equation, $a = 2$, $b = 4$, and $c = 1$.
$$x = \frac{-4 \pm \sqrt{4^2 - 4(2)(1)}}{2(2)}$$
$$= \frac{-4 \pm \sqrt{16 - 8}}{4}$$
$$= \frac{-4 \pm \sqrt{8}}{4}$$
$$= \frac{-4 \pm 2\sqrt{2}}{4} = \frac{-4}{4} \pm \frac{2\sqrt{2}}{4} = -1 \pm \frac{\sqrt{2}}{2}$$
The solution set is $\left\{ -1 - \frac{\sqrt{2}}{2}, \; -1 + \frac{\sqrt{2}}{2} \right\}$.

69. a.
$$G(x) = 0$$
$$3x^2 + 2x + 2 = 0$$
For this equation, $a = 3$, $b = 2$, and $c = 2$.
$$x = \frac{-2 \pm \sqrt{2^2 - 4(3)(2)}}{2(3)}$$
$$= \frac{-2 \pm \sqrt{4 - 24}}{6}$$
$$= \frac{-2 \pm \sqrt{-20}}{6}$$
$$= \frac{-2 \pm 2\sqrt{5}\, i}{6} = -\frac{2}{6} \pm \frac{2\sqrt{5}}{6} i = -\frac{1}{3} \pm \frac{\sqrt{5}}{3} i$$
The solution set is $\left\{ -\frac{1}{3} - \frac{\sqrt{5}}{3} i, \; -\frac{1}{3} + \frac{\sqrt{5}}{3} i \right\}$.

b.
$$G(x) = 4$$
$$3x^2 + 2x + 2 = 4$$
$$3x^2 + 2x - 2 = 0$$
For this equation, $a = 3$, $b = 2$, and $c = -2$.
$$x = \frac{-2 \pm \sqrt{2^2 - 4(3)(-2)}}{2(3)}$$
$$= \frac{-2 \pm \sqrt{4 + 24}}{6}$$
$$= \frac{-2 \pm \sqrt{28}}{6}$$
$$= \frac{-2 \pm 2\sqrt{7}}{6} = -\frac{2}{6} \pm \frac{2\sqrt{7}}{6} = -\frac{1}{3} \pm \frac{\sqrt{7}}{3}$$
The solution set is $\left\{ -\frac{1}{3} - \frac{\sqrt{7}}{3}, \; -\frac{1}{3} + \frac{\sqrt{7}}{3} \right\}$.

71.
$$x^2 + (x+1)^2 = (2x-1)^2$$
$$x^2 + x^2 + 2x + 1 = 4x^2 - 4x + 1$$
$$2x^2 + 2x + 1 = 4x^2 - 4x + 1$$
$$0 = 2x^2 - 6x$$
$$0 = 2x(x-3)$$
$$2x = 0 \quad \text{or} \quad x-3 = 0$$
$$x = 0 \quad \text{or} \quad x = 3$$
Disregard $x = 0$ because x represents the length of one leg of the triangle. Thus, $x = 3$ is the only viable answer. Now, $x + 1 = 3 + 1 = 4$ and $2x - 1 = 2(3) - 1 = 5$. The three measurements are 3, 4, and 5.

73.
$$(5x-1)^2 + (x+2)^2 = (5x)^2$$
$$25x^2 - 10x + 1 + x^2 + 4x + 4 = 25x^2$$
$$26x^2 - 6x + 5 = 25x^2$$
$$x^2 - 6x + 5 = 0$$
$$(x-1)(x-5) = 0$$
$$x-1 = 0 \text{ or } x-5 = 0$$
$$x = 1 \text{ or } \quad x = 5$$

For $x = 1$, $x + 2 = 1 + 2 = 3$, $5x - 1 = 5(1) - 1 = 4$, and $5x = 5(1) = 5$.

For $x = 5$, $x + 2 = 5 + 2 = 7$, $5x - 1 = 5(5) - 1 = 24$, and $5x = 5(5) = 25$.

The three measurements can be either 3, 4, and 5, or 7, 24, and 25.

75. Let x represent the length of the rectangle. Then $x + 4$ will represent the width.
$$x(x+4) = 40$$
$$x^2 + 4x = 40$$
$$x^2 + 4x - 40 = 0$$

For this equation, $a = 1$, $b = 4$, and $c = -40$.
$$x = \frac{-4 \pm \sqrt{4^2 - 4(1)(-40)}}{2(1)}$$
$$= \frac{-4 \pm \sqrt{16 + 160}}{2} = \frac{-4 \pm \sqrt{176}}{2}$$
$$= \frac{-4 \pm 4\sqrt{11}}{2} = -\frac{4}{2} \pm \frac{4\sqrt{11}}{2} = -2 \pm 2\sqrt{11}$$

Disregard $x = -2 - 2\sqrt{11} \approx -8.633$ because x represents the length of the rectangle, which must be positive. Thus, $x = -2 + 2\sqrt{11} \approx 4.633$ is the only viable answer. Now, $x + 4 = -2 + 2\sqrt{11} + 4 = 2 + 2\sqrt{11} \approx 8.633$. Thus, the dimensions of the rectangle are $-2 + 2\sqrt{11}$ inches by $2 + 2\sqrt{11}$ inches, which is approximately 4.633 inches by 8.633 inches.

77. Let x represent the base of the triangle. Then $x - 3$ will represent the height.
$$\frac{1}{2}x(x-3) = 25$$
$$\frac{1}{2}x^2 - \frac{3}{2}x - 25 = 0$$
$$2\left(\frac{1}{2}x^2 - \frac{3}{2}x - 25\right) = 2(0)$$
$$x^2 - 3x - 50 = 0$$

For this equation, $a = 1$, $b = -3$, and $c = -50$.

$$x = \frac{-(-3) \pm \sqrt{(-3)^2 - 4(1)(-50)}}{2(1)}$$
$$= \frac{3 \pm \sqrt{9 + 200}}{2} = \frac{3 \pm \sqrt{209}}{2} = \frac{3}{2} \pm \frac{\sqrt{209}}{2}$$

Disregard $x = \frac{3}{2} - \frac{\sqrt{209}}{2} \approx -5.728$ because x represents the base of the triangle, which must be positive. Thus, $x = \frac{3}{2} + \frac{\sqrt{209}}{2} \approx 8.728$ is the only viable answer. Now,
$$x - 3 = \frac{3}{2} + \frac{\sqrt{209}}{2} - 3 = -\frac{3}{2} + \frac{\sqrt{209}}{2} \approx 5.728.$$

Thus, the base of the triangle is $\frac{3}{2} + \frac{\sqrt{209}}{2}$ inches, which is approximately 8.728 inches. The height of the triangle is $-\frac{3}{2} + \frac{\sqrt{209}}{2}$ inches, which is approximately 5.728 inches.

79. a. $R(17) = -0.1(17)^2 + 70(17) = 1161.1$
If 17 pairs of sunglasses are sold per week, then the company's revenue will be $1161.10.

$R(25) = -0.1(25)^2 + 70(25) = 1687.5$
If 25 pairs of sunglasses are sold per week, then the company's revenue will be $1687.50.

b.
$$R(x) = 10,000$$
$$-0.1x^2 + 70x = 10,000$$
$$0 = 0.1x^2 - 70x + 10,000$$
For this equation, $a = 0.1$, $b = -70$, and $c = 10,000$.

$$x = \frac{-(-70) \pm \sqrt{(-70)^2 - 4(0.1)(10,000)}}{2(0.1)}$$
$$= \frac{70 \pm \sqrt{4900 - 4000}}{0.2}$$
$$= \frac{70 \pm \sqrt{900}}{0.2} = \frac{70 \pm 30}{0.2}$$
$$x = \frac{70 - 30}{0.2} \quad \text{or} \quad x = \frac{70 + 30}{0.2}$$
$$= \frac{40}{0.2} = 200 \quad \text{or} \quad = \frac{100}{0.2} = 500$$

The revenue will be $10,000 per week if either 200 or 500 pairs of sunglasses are sold per week.

c.
$$R(x) = 12,250$$
$$-0.1x^2 + 70x = 12,250$$
$$0 = 0.1x^2 - 70x + 12,250$$

For this equation, $a = 0.1$, $b = -70$, and $c = 12,250$.

$$x = \frac{-(-70) \pm \sqrt{(-70)^2 - 4(0.1)(12,250)}}{2(0.1)}$$
$$= \frac{70 \pm \sqrt{4900 - 4900}}{0.2}$$
$$= \frac{70 \pm \sqrt{0}}{0.2}$$
$$= \frac{70 \pm 0}{0.2} = \frac{70}{0.2} = 350$$

The revenue will be $12,250 per week if 350 pairs of sunglasses are sold per week.

81. a.
$$s(t) = 40$$
$$40 = -16t^2 + 70t + 5$$
$$16t^2 - 70t + 35 = 0$$

For this equation, $a = 16$, $b = -70$, and $c = 35$.

$$x = \frac{-(-70) \pm \sqrt{(-70)^2 - 4(16)(35)}}{2(16)}$$
$$= \frac{70 \pm \sqrt{4900 - 2240}}{32}$$
$$= \frac{70 \pm \sqrt{2660}}{32}$$
$$= \frac{70 \pm 2\sqrt{665}}{32}$$
$$x = \frac{35 - \sqrt{665}}{16} \text{ or } x = \frac{35 + \sqrt{665}}{16}$$
$$\approx 0.576 \quad \text{or} \quad \approx 3.799$$

Rounding to the nearest tenth, the height of the ball will be 40 feet after approximately 0.6 seconds and after approximately 3.8 seconds.

b.
$$s(t) = 70$$
$$70 = -16t^2 + 70t + 5$$
$$16t^2 - 70t + 65 = 0$$

For this equation, $a = 16$, $b = -70$, and $c = 65$.

$$x = \frac{-(-70) \pm \sqrt{(-70)^2 - 4(16)(65)}}{2(16)}$$
$$= \frac{70 \pm \sqrt{4900 - 4160}}{32}$$
$$= \frac{70 \pm \sqrt{740}}{32}$$
$$= \frac{70 \pm 2\sqrt{185}}{32}$$
$$= \frac{35 \pm \sqrt{185}}{16}$$
$$x = \frac{35 - \sqrt{185}}{16} \text{ or } x = \frac{35 + \sqrt{185}}{16}$$
$$\approx 1.337 \qquad \text{or} \qquad \approx 3.038$$

Rounding to the nearest tenth, the height of the ball will be 70 feet after approximately 1.3 seconds and after approximately 3.0 seconds.

c.
$$s(t) = 150$$
$$150 = -16t^2 + 70t + 5$$
$$16t^2 - 70t + 145 = 0$$

For this equation, $a = 16$, $b = -70$, and $c = 145$.

$$x = \frac{-(-70) \pm \sqrt{(-70)^2 - 4(16)(145)}}{2(16)}$$
$$= \frac{70 \pm \sqrt{4900 - 9280}}{32}$$
$$= \frac{70 \pm \sqrt{-4380}}{32}$$
$$= \frac{70 \pm 2\sqrt{1095}\, i}{32}$$
$$= \frac{35 \pm \sqrt{1095}\, i}{16}$$
$$x = \frac{35}{16} - \frac{\sqrt{185}}{16} i \text{ or } x = \frac{35}{16} + \frac{\sqrt{185}}{16} i$$

The ball will never reach a height of 150 feet. This is clear because the solutions to the equation above are complex solutions that are not real.

83. Because $\triangle ABC \sim \triangle CDE$, we know $\dfrac{\overline{AB}}{\overline{BC}} = \dfrac{\overline{DE}}{\overline{EC}}$.

$\overline{BC} = 24$, $\overline{DE} = 6$, $\overline{AB} = x$, and $\overline{EC} = x$,

$$\frac{x}{24} = \frac{6}{x}$$

$$x \cdot x = 24 \cdot 6$$

$$x^2 = 144$$

$$x = \pm\sqrt{144} = \pm 12$$

Disregard $x = -12$ because x represents a length, which must be positive. Thus, $x = 12$ is the only viable answer.

85. a. $I(a) = 40,000$

$40,000 = -55a^2 + 5119a - 54,448$

$55a^2 - 5119a + 94,448 = 0$

For this equation, $a = 55$, $b = -5119$, and $c = 94,448$.

$$x = \frac{-(-5119) \pm \sqrt{(-5119)^2 - 4(55)(94,448)}}{2(55)}$$

$$= \frac{5119 \pm \sqrt{26,204,161 - 20,778,560}}{110}$$

$$= \frac{5119 \pm \sqrt{5,425,601}}{110}$$

$$x = \frac{5119 - \sqrt{5,425,601}}{110} \approx 25.361$$

or

$$x = \frac{5119 + \sqrt{5,425,601}}{110} \approx 67.712$$

Rounding to the nearest year, the average income equals $40,000 at ages 25 and 68.

b. $I(a) = 50,000$

$50,000 = -55a^2 + 5119a - 54,448$

$55a^2 - 5119a + 104,448 = 0$

For this equation, $a = 55$, $b = -5119$, and $c = 104,448$.

$$x = \frac{-(-5119) \pm \sqrt{(-5119)^2 - 4(55)(104,448)}}{2(55)}$$

$$= \frac{5119 \pm \sqrt{26,204,161 - 22,978,560}}{110}$$

$$= \frac{5119 \pm \sqrt{3,225,601}}{110}$$

$$x = \frac{5119 - \sqrt{3,225,601}}{110} \approx 30.209$$

or

$$x = \frac{5119 + \sqrt{3,225,601}}{110} \approx 62.864$$

Rounding to the nearest year, the average income equals $50,000 at ages 30 and 63.

87. Let x represent speed of the current.

	Distance	Rate	Time
Up Stream	4	$5 - x$	$\dfrac{4}{5 - x}$
Down Stream	4	$5 + x$	$\dfrac{4}{5 + x}$

$$\frac{4}{5-x} + \frac{4}{5+x} = 6$$

$$(5-x)(5+x)\left(\frac{4}{5-x} + \frac{4}{5+x}\right) = (5-x)(5+x)(6)$$

$$4(5+x) + 4(5-x) = (25 - x^2)(6)$$

$$20 + 4x + 20 - 4x = 150 - 6x^2$$

$$40 = 150 - 6x^2$$

$$6x^2 = 110$$

$$x^2 = \frac{110}{6}$$

$$x = \pm\sqrt{\frac{110}{6}}$$

$$x \approx \pm 4.282$$

The speed of the current is approximately 4.3 miles per hour.

89. Let t represent the time required for Susan to finish the route alone. Then $t - 1$ will represent the time required for Robert to finish the route alone.

$$\begin{pmatrix} \text{Part done} \\ \text{by Susan} \\ \text{in 1 hour} \end{pmatrix} + \begin{pmatrix} \text{Part done} \\ \text{by Robert} \\ \text{in 1 hour} \end{pmatrix} = \begin{pmatrix} \text{Part done} \\ \text{together} \\ \text{in 1 hour} \end{pmatrix}$$

$$\frac{1}{t} + \frac{1}{t-1} = \frac{1}{2}$$

$$2t(t-1)\left(\frac{1}{t} + \frac{1}{t-1}\right) = 2t(t-1)\left(\frac{1}{2}\right)$$

$$2(t-1) + 2t = t(t-1)$$

$$2t - 2 + 2t = t^2 - t$$

$$4t - 2 = t^2 - t$$

$$0 = t^2 - 5t + 2$$

For this equation, $a = 1$, $b = -5$, and $c = 2$.

$$t = \frac{-(-5) \pm \sqrt{(-5)^2 - 4(1)(2)}}{2(1)}$$

$$= \frac{5 \pm \sqrt{25 - 8}}{2} = \frac{5 \pm \sqrt{17}}{2}$$

$$t = \frac{5}{2} - \frac{\sqrt{17}}{2} \approx 0.438 \quad \text{or} \quad t = \frac{5}{2} + \frac{\sqrt{17}}{2} \approx 4.562$$

Disregard $t \approx 0.438$ because this value makes Robert's time negative: $t - 1 = 0.438 - 1 = -0.562$. The only viable answer is $t \approx 4.562$ hours. Working alone, it will take Susan approximately 4.6 hours to finish the route.

91. By the quadratic formula, the solutions of the equation $ax^2 + bx + c = 0$ are

$$x = \frac{-b - \sqrt{b^2 - 4ac}}{2a} \quad \text{and} \quad x = \frac{-b + \sqrt{b^2 - 4ac}}{2a}.$$

The sum of these two solutions is:

$$\frac{-b - \sqrt{b^2 - 4ac}}{2a} + \frac{-b + \sqrt{b^2 - 4ac}}{2a} = \frac{-2b}{2a} = -\frac{b}{a}.$$

93. Assume $b^2 - 4ac \geq 0$. The solutions of

$$ax^2 + bx + c = 0 \text{ are } x = \frac{-b \pm \sqrt{b^2 - 4ac}}{2a}.$$

The solutions of $ax^2 - bx + c = 0$ are

$$x = \frac{-(-b) \pm \sqrt{(-b)^2 - 4ac}}{2a} = \frac{b \pm \sqrt{b^2 - 4ac}}{2a}.$$

Now, the negatives of the solutions to $ax^2 - bx + c = 0$ are

$$-\left(\frac{b \pm \sqrt{b^2 - 4ac}}{2a} \right) = \frac{-b \mp \sqrt{b^2 - 4ac}}{2a}.$$

$$= \frac{-b \pm \sqrt{b^2 - 4ac}}{2a}$$

which are the solutions to $ax^2 + bx + c = 0$.
Thus, the real solutions of $ax^2 + bx + c = 0$ are the negatives of the real solution of $ax^2 - bx + c = 0$.

95. a. $f(x) = x^2 + 3x + 2$

Let $x = -3, -2, -1.5, -1,$ and 0.

$$f(-3) = (-3)^2 + 3(-3) + 2 = 9 - 9 + 2 = 2$$

$$f(-2) = (-2)^2 + 3(-2) + 2 = 4 - 6 + 2 = 0$$

$$f(-1.5) = (-1.5)^2 + 3(-1.5) + 2$$
$$= 2.25 - 4.5 + 2$$
$$= -0.25$$

$$f(-1) = (-1)^2 + 3(-1) + 2 = 1 - 3 + 2 = 0$$

$$f(0) = 0^2 + 3(0) + 2 = 0 + 0 + 2 = 2$$

Thus, the points $(-3, 2)$, $(-2, 0)$, $(-1.5, -0.25)$, $(-1, 0)$, and $(0, 2)$ are on the graph of f. We plot the points and connect them with a smooth curve.

b. $x^2 + 3x + 2 = 0$

$$(x + 1)(x + 2) = 0$$

$$x + 1 = 0 \quad \text{or} \quad x + 2 = 0$$

$$x = -1 \quad \text{or} \quad x = -2$$

The solution set is $\{-2, -1\}$.

c. From the graph in part (a), the x-intercepts of the function $f(x) = x^2 + 3x + 2$ are -2 and -1, which are the same as the solutions of the equation $x^2 + 3x + 2 = 0$. To find the x-intercepts of a function, set the function equal to zero and solve for x.

97. a. $g(x) = x^2 - 2x + 1$

Let $x = -1, 0, 1, 2,$ and 3.

$$f(-1) = (-1)^2 - 2(-1) + 1 = 1 + 2 + 1 = 4$$

$$f(0) = 0^2 - 2(0) + 1 = 0 - 0 + 1 = 1$$

$$f(1) = 1^2 - 2(1) + 1 = 1 - 2 + 1 = 0$$

$$f(2) = 2^2 - 2(2) + 1 = 4 - 4 + 1 = 1$$

$$f(3) = 3^2 - 2(3) + 1 = 9 - 6 + 1 = 4$$

Thus, the points $(-1, 4)$, $(0, 1)$, $(1, 0)$, $(2, 1)$, and $(3, 4)$ are on the graph of g. We plot the points and connect them with a smooth curve.

b. $x^2 - 2x + 1 = 0$

$$(x-1)^2 = 0$$

$$x - 1 = 0$$

$$x = 1$$

The solution set is $\{1\}$.

c. From the graph in part (a), the x-intercept of the function $g(x) = x^2 - 2x + 1$ is 1, which is the same as the solution of the equation $x^2 - 2x + 1 = 0$. To find the x-intercepts of a function, set the function equal to zero and solve for x.

99. $f(x) = 0$

$x^2 - 7x + 3 = 0$

For this equation, $a = 1$, $b = -7$, and $c = 3$.

$b^2 - 4ac = (-7)^2 - 4(1)(3) = 49 - 12 = 37$

Because $b^2 - 4ac = 37$ is positive, but not a perfect square, the equation has two irrational solutions. This conclusion based on the discriminant is apparent in the graph because the graph crosses the x-axis in two places. That is, the graph has two x-intercepts.

101. $f(x) = 0$

$-x^2 - 3x - 4 = 0$

For this equation, $a = -1$, $b = -3$, and $c = -4$.

$b^2 - 4ac = (-3)^2 - 4(-1)(-4) = 9 - 16 = -7$

Because $b^2 - 4ac = -7$ is negative, the equation has two complex solutions that are not real. This conclusion based on the discriminant is apparent in the graph because the graph does not cross the x-axis. That is, the graph has no x-intercept.

103. a. $x^2 - 5x - 24 = 0$

$$(x+3)(x-8) = 0$$

$x + 3 = 0$ or $x - 8 = 0$

$x = -3$ or $x = 8$

The solution set is $\{-3, 8\}$.

b. The x-intercepts are -3 and 8 (see graph).

The x-intercepts of $y = x^2 - 5x - 24$ are the same as the solutions of $x^2 - 5x - 24 = 0$.

105. a. $x^2 - 6x + 9 = 0$

$$(x-3)(x-3) = 0$$

$x - 3 = 0$ or $x - 3 = 0$

$x = 3$ or $x = 3$

The solution set is $\{3\}$.

b. The x-intercept is 3 (see graph).

The x-intercept of $y = x^2 - 6x + 9$ is the same as the solutions of $x^2 - 6x + 9 = 0$.

107. a. $x^2 + 5x + 8 = 0$

For this equation, $a = 1$, $b = 5$, and $c = 8$.

$$x = \frac{-5 \pm \sqrt{5^2 - 4(1)(8)}}{2(1)}$$

$$= \frac{-5 \pm \sqrt{25 - 32}}{2}$$

$$= \frac{-5 \pm \sqrt{-7}}{2}$$

$$= \frac{-5 \pm \sqrt{7}\,i}{2} = -\frac{5}{2} \pm \frac{\sqrt{7}}{2}i$$

The solution set is $\left\{ -\dfrac{5}{2} - \dfrac{\sqrt{7}}{2}i,\ -\dfrac{5}{2} + \dfrac{\sqrt{7}}{2}i \right\}$.

b. The graph has no x-intercepts (see graph).

$y = x^2 + 5x + 8$ has no x-intercepts, and the solutions of $x^2 + 5x + 8 = 0$ are not real.

8.3 Preparing for Solving Equations Quadratic in Form

1. $x^4 - 5x^2 - 6 = (x^2 - 6)(x^2 + 1)$

2. $2(p+3)^2 + 3(p+3) - 5$
$= [2(p+3)+5][(p+3)-1]$
$= (2p+6+5)(p+3-1)$
$= (2p+11)(p+2)$

3. **a.** $(x^2)^2 = x^{2 \cdot 2} = x^4$

   b. $(p^{-1})^2 = p^{-1 \cdot 2} = p^{-2} = \dfrac{1}{p^2}$

8.3 Exercises

1. equation quadratic in form

3. TRUE. Letting $u = \dfrac{x}{x-2}$ yields the quadratic equation $3u^2 - 5u + 3 = 0$.

5. Answers will vary. One possibility follows: First, look carefully at the equation and determine an appropriate substitution. To do this, look for expressions within the equation that can act as the linear and quadratic terms for the form $au^2 + bu + c = 0$. (For example, in Problem 3 above, the equation contained the expressions $\dfrac{x}{x-2}$ and $\left(\dfrac{x}{x-2}\right)^2$, which act as the linear and quadratic terms, respectively.) Second, solve $au^2 + bu + c = 0$ by using one of the methods we have studied. Third, solve for the variable in the original equation. Finally, check the solutions in the original equation.

7. The appropriate choice for u is $3x - 2$. That is, let $u = 3x - 2$.

9. $\quad x^4 - 5x^2 + 4 = 0$
$(x^2)^2 - 5(x^2) + 4 = 0$

Let $u = x^2$.

$u^2 - 5u + 4 = 0$
$(u-1)(u-4) = 0$
$u - 1 = 0 \qquad$ or $\quad u - 4 = 0$
$u = 1 \qquad$ or $\qquad u = 4$
$x^2 = 1 \qquad$ or $\qquad x^2 = 4$
$x = \pm\sqrt{1} \quad$ or $\qquad x = \pm\sqrt{4}$
$x = \pm 1 \qquad$ or $\qquad x = \pm 2$

Check:

$x = -1: \ (-1)^4 - 5(-1)^2 + 4 \overset{?}{=} 0$
$1 - 5 \cdot 1 + 4 \overset{?}{=} 0$
$1 - 5 + 4 \overset{?}{=} 0$
$0 = 0 \ \checkmark$

$x = 1: \ 1^4 - 5(1)^2 + 4 \overset{?}{=} 0$
$1 - 5 \cdot 1 + 4 \overset{?}{=} 0$
$1 - 5 + 4 \overset{?}{=} 0$
$0 = 0 \ \checkmark$

$x = -2: \ (-2)^4 - 5(-2)^2 + 4 \overset{?}{=} 0$
$16 - 5 \cdot 4 + 4 \overset{?}{=} 0$
$16 - 20 + 4 \overset{?}{=} 0$
$0 = 0 \ \checkmark$

$x = 2: \ 2^4 - 5(2)^2 + 4 \overset{?}{=} 0$
$16 - 5 \cdot 4 + 4 \overset{?}{=} 0$
$16 - 20 + 4 \overset{?}{=} 0$
$0 = 0 \ \checkmark$

All check; the solution set is $\{-2, \ -1, \ 1, \ 2\}$.

11. $\quad q^4 + 13q^2 + 36 = 0$
$(q^2)^2 + 13(q^2) + 36 = 0$

Let $u = q^2$.

$u^2 + 13u + 36 = 0$
$(u+4)(u+9) = 0$
$q^2 = -4 \quad$ or $\quad q^2 = -9$
$q = \pm\sqrt{-4} \quad$ or $\quad q = \pm\sqrt{-9}$
$q = \pm 2i \qquad$ or $\qquad q = \pm 3i$

Check:

$q = -3i:$ $(-3i)^4 + 13(-3i)^2 + 36 \overset{?}{=} 0$

$81i^4 + 13 \cdot 9i^2 + 36 \overset{?}{=} 0$

$81(1) + 13 \cdot 9 \cdot (-1) + 36 \overset{?}{=} 0$

$81 - 117 + 36 \overset{?}{=} 0$

$0 = 0$ ✓

$q = 3i:$ $(3i)^4 + 13(3i)^2 + 36 \overset{?}{=} 0$

$81i^4 + 13 \cdot 9i^2 + 36 \overset{?}{=} 0$

$81(1) + 13 \cdot 9 \cdot (-1) + 36 \overset{?}{=} 0$

$81 - 117 + 36 \overset{?}{=} 0$

$0 = 0$ ✓

$q = -2i:$ $(-2i)^4 + 13(-2i)^2 + 36 \overset{?}{=} 0$

$16i^4 + 13 \cdot 4i^2 + 36 \overset{?}{=} 0$

$16(1) + 13 \cdot 4 \cdot (-1) + 36 \overset{?}{=} 0$

$16 - 52 + 36 \overset{?}{=} 0$

$0 = 0$ ✓

$q = 2i:$ $(2i)^4 + 13(2i)^2 + 36 \overset{?}{=} 0$

$16i^4 + 13 \cdot 4i^2 + 36 \overset{?}{=} 0$

$16(1) + 13 \cdot 4 \cdot (-1) + 36 \overset{?}{=} 0$

$16 - 52 + 36 \overset{?}{=} 0$

$0 = 0$ ✓

All check; the solution set is $\{-3i, \ 3i, -2i, \ 2i\}$.

13. $4a^4 - 17a^2 + 4 = 0$

$4(a^2)^2 - 17(a^2) + 4 = 0$

Let $u = a^2$.

$4u^2 - 17u + 4 = 0$

$(4u - 1)(u - 4) = 0$

$4u - 1 = 0 \quad$ or $\quad u - 4 = 0$

$4u = 1 \quad$ or $\quad u = 4$

$u = \dfrac{1}{4}$

$a^2 = \dfrac{1}{4} \quad$ or $\quad a^2 = 4$

$a = \pm\sqrt{\dfrac{1}{4}} \quad$ or $\quad a = \pm\sqrt{4}$.

$a = \pm\dfrac{1}{2} \quad$ or $\quad a = \pm 2$

Check:

$a = -\dfrac{1}{2}:$ $4\left(-\dfrac{1}{2}\right)^4 - 17\left(-\dfrac{1}{2}\right)^2 + 4 \overset{?}{=} 0$

$4\left(\dfrac{1}{16}\right) - 17\left(\dfrac{1}{4}\right) + 4 \overset{?}{=} 0$

$\dfrac{1}{4} - \dfrac{17}{4} + 4 \overset{?}{=} 0$

$0 = 0$ ✓

$a = \dfrac{1}{2}:$ $4\left(\dfrac{1}{2}\right)^4 - 17\left(\dfrac{1}{2}\right)^2 + 4 \overset{?}{=} 0$

$4\left(\dfrac{1}{16}\right) - 17\left(\dfrac{1}{4}\right) + 4 \overset{?}{=} 0$

$\dfrac{1}{4} - \dfrac{17}{4} + 4 \overset{?}{=} 0$

$0 = 0$ ✓

$a = -2:$ $4(-2)^4 - 17(-2)^2 + 4 \overset{?}{=} 0$

$4 \cdot 16 - 17 \cdot 4 + 4 \overset{?}{=} 0$

$64 - 68 + 4 \overset{?}{=} 0$

$0 = 0$ ✓

$a = 2:$ $4(2)^4 - 17(2)^2 + 4 \overset{?}{=} 0$

$4 \cdot 16 - 17 \cdot 4 + 4 \overset{?}{=} 0$

$64 - 68 + 4 \overset{?}{=} 0$

$0 = 0$ ✓

All check; the solution set is $\left\{-2, -\dfrac{1}{2}, \ \dfrac{1}{2}, \ 2\right\}$.

15. $p^4 + 6 = 5p^2$

$p^4 - 5p^2 + 6 = 0$

$(p^2)^2 - 5(p^2) + 6 = 0$

Let $u = p^2$.

$u^2 - 5u + 6 = 0$

$(u - 2)(u - 3) = 0$

$u - 2 = 0$ or $u - 3 = 0$

$u = 2$ or $u = 3$

$p^2 = 2 \quad$ or $\quad p^2 = 3$

$p = \pm\sqrt{2} \quad$ or $\quad p = \pm\sqrt{3}$

Check:

$p = -\sqrt{2}:$ $\left(-\sqrt{2}\right)^4 + 6 \overset{?}{=} 5\left(-\sqrt{2}\right)^2$

$4 + 6 \overset{?}{=} 5 \cdot 2$

$10 = 10$ ✓

$p = \sqrt{2}: \left(\sqrt{2}\right)^4 + 6 \overset{?}{=} 5\left(\sqrt{2}\right)^2$

$$4 + 6 \overset{?}{=} 5 \cdot 2$$
$$10 = 10 \checkmark$$

$p = -\sqrt{3}: \left(-\sqrt{3}\right)^4 + 6 \overset{?}{=} 5\left(-\sqrt{3}\right)^2$

$$9 + 6 \overset{?}{=} 5 \cdot 3$$
$$15 = 15 \checkmark$$

$p = \sqrt{3}: \left(\sqrt{3}\right)^4 + 6 \overset{?}{=} 5\left(\sqrt{3}\right)^2$

$$9 + 6 \overset{?}{=} 5 \cdot 3$$
$$15 = 15 \checkmark$$

All check; the solution set is
$\left\{-\sqrt{3}, -\sqrt{2}, \sqrt{2}, \sqrt{3}\right\}$.

17. $(x-3)^2 - 6(x-3) - 7 = 0$

Let $u = x - 3$.

$$u^2 - 6u - 7 = 0$$
$$(u - 7)(u + 1) = 0$$
$$u - 7 = 0 \quad \text{or} \quad u + 1 = 0$$
$$u = 7 \quad \text{or} \quad u = -1$$
$$x - 3 = 7 \quad \text{or} \quad x - 3 = -1$$
$$x = 10 \quad \text{or} \quad x = 2$$

Check:

$x = 10: \ (10-3)^2 - 6(10-3) - 7 \overset{?}{=} 0$

$$7^2 - 6(7) - 7 \overset{?}{=} 0$$
$$49 - 42 - 7 \overset{?}{=} 0$$
$$0 = 0 \checkmark$$

$x = 2: \ (2-3)^2 - 6(2-3) - 7 \overset{?}{=} 0$

$$(-1)^2 - 6(-1) - 7 \overset{?}{=} 0$$
$$1 + 6 - 7 \overset{?}{=} 0$$
$$0 = 0 \checkmark$$

Both check; the solution set is $\{2, 10\}$.

19. $(x^2 - 1)^2 - 11(x^2 - 1) + 24 = 0$

Let $u = x^2 - 1$.

$$u^2 - 11u + 24 = 0$$
$$(u - 3)(u - 8) = 0$$
$$u - 3 = 0 \quad \text{or} \quad u - 8 = 0$$
$$u = 3 \quad \text{or} \quad u = 8$$
$$x^2 - 1 = 3 \quad \text{or} \quad x^2 - 1 = 8$$
$$x^2 = 4 \quad \text{or} \quad x^2 = 9$$
$$x = \pm\sqrt{4} \quad \text{or} \quad x = \pm\sqrt{9}$$
$$x = \pm 2 \quad \text{or} \quad x = \pm 3$$

Check:

$x = -2: \ \left((-2)^2 - 1\right)^2 - 11\left((-2)^2 - 1\right) + 24 \overset{?}{=} 0$

$$(4-1)^2 - 11(4-1) + 24 \overset{?}{=} 0$$
$$3^2 - 11 \cdot 3 + 24 \overset{?}{=} 0$$
$$9 - 33 + 24 \overset{?}{=} 0$$
$$0 = 0 \checkmark$$

$x = 2: \ \left(2^2 - 1\right)^2 - 11\left(2^2 - 1\right) + 24 \overset{?}{=} 0$

$$(4-1)^2 - 11(4-1) + 24 \overset{?}{=} 0$$
$$3^2 - 11 \cdot 3 + 24 \overset{?}{=} 0$$
$$9 - 33 + 24 \overset{?}{=} 0$$
$$0 = 0 \checkmark$$

$x = -3: \ \left((-3)^2 - 1\right)^2 - 11\left((-3)^2 - 1\right) + 24 \overset{?}{=} 0$

$$(9-1)^2 - 11(9-1) + 24 \overset{?}{=} 0$$
$$8^2 - 11 \cdot 8 + 24 \overset{?}{=} 0$$
$$64 - 88 + 24 \overset{?}{=} 0$$
$$0 = 0 \checkmark$$

$x = 3: \ \left(3^2 - 1\right)^2 - 11\left(3^2 - 1\right) + 24 \overset{?}{=} 0$

$$(9-1)^2 - 11(9-1) + 24 \overset{?}{=} 0$$
$$8^2 - 11 \cdot 8 + 24 \overset{?}{=} 0$$
$$64 - 88 + 24 \overset{?}{=} 0$$
$$0 = 0 \checkmark$$

All check; the solution set is $\{-3, -2, 2, 3\}$.

21. $\left(y^2+2\right)^2+7\left(y^2+2\right)+10=0$

Let $u=y^2+2$.

$u^2+7u+10=0$

$(u+2)(u+5)=0$

$u+2=0 \quad$ or $\quad u+5=0$

$\quad u=-2 \quad$ or $\quad\quad u=-5$

$y^2+2=-2 \quad$ or $\quad y^2+2=-5$

$\quad y^2=-4 \quad$ or $\quad\quad y^2=-7$

$\quad y=\pm\sqrt{-4}$ or $y=\pm\sqrt{-7}$

$\quad y=\pm 2i \quad$ or $\quad y=\pm\sqrt{7}\,i$

Check:

$y=-2i: \left(\left(-2i\right)^2+2\right)^2+7\left(\left(-2i\right)^2+2\right)+10\overset{?}{=}0$

$\left(4i^2+2\right)^2+7\left(4i^2+2\right)+10\overset{?}{=}0$

$\left(-4+2\right)^2+7\left(-4+2\right)+10\overset{?}{=}0$

$\left(-2\right)^2+7\left(-2\right)+10\overset{?}{=}0$

$4-14+10\overset{?}{=}0$

$0=0 \checkmark$

$y=2i: \left(\left(2i\right)^2+2\right)^2+7\left(\left(2i\right)^2+2\right)+10\overset{?}{=}0$

$\left(4i^2+2\right)^2+7\left(4i^2+2\right)+10\overset{?}{=}0$

$\left(-4+2\right)^2+7\left(-4+2\right)+10\overset{?}{=}0$

$\left(-2\right)^2+7\left(-2\right)+10\overset{?}{=}0$

$4-14+10\overset{?}{=}0$

$0=0 \checkmark$

$y=-\sqrt{7}i:$

$\left(\left(-\sqrt{7}i\right)^2+2\right)^2+7\left(\left(-\sqrt{7}i\right)^2+2\right)+10\overset{?}{=}0$

$\left(7i^2+2\right)^2+7\left(7i^2+2\right)+10\overset{?}{=}0$

$\left(-7+2\right)^2+7\left(-7+2\right)+10\overset{?}{=}0$

$\left(-5\right)^2+7\left(-5\right)+10\overset{?}{=}0$

$25-35+10\overset{?}{=}0$

$0=0 \checkmark$

$y=\sqrt{7}i:$

$\left(\left(\sqrt{7}i\right)^2+2\right)^2+7\left(\left(\sqrt{7}i\right)^2+2\right)+10\overset{?}{=}0$

$\left(7i^2+2\right)^2+7\left(7i^2+2\right)+10\overset{?}{=}0$

$\left(-7+2\right)^2+7\left(-7+2\right)+10\overset{?}{=}0$

$\left(-5\right)^2+7\left(-5\right)+10\overset{?}{=}0$

$25-35+10\overset{?}{=}0$

$0=0 \checkmark$

All check; the solution set is

$\left\{-\sqrt{7}\,i,\ \sqrt{7}\,i,-2i,\ 2i\right\}$.

23. $\qquad x-3\sqrt{x}-4=0$

$\left(\sqrt{x}\right)^2-3\left(\sqrt{x}\right)-4=0$

Let $u=\sqrt{x}$.

$u^2-3u-4=0$

$(u-4)(u+1)=0$

$u-4=0 \quad$ or $\quad u+1=0$

$\quad u=4 \quad$ or $\quad\quad u=-1$

$\sqrt{x}=4 \quad$ or $\quad \sqrt{x}=-1$

$\quad x=4^2 \quad$ or $\quad x=\left(-1\right)^2$

$\quad x=16 \quad$ or $\quad\quad x=1$

Check:

$x=16:\ 16-3\sqrt{16}-4\overset{?}{=}0$

$16-3\cdot 4-4\overset{?}{=}0$

$16-12-4\overset{?}{=}0$

$0=0 \checkmark$

$x=1:\ 1-3\sqrt{1}-4\overset{?}{=}0$

$1-3\cdot 1-4\overset{?}{=}0$

$1-3-4\overset{?}{=}0$

$-6\neq 0 \ \times$

$x=1$ does not check; the solution set is $\left\{16\right\}$.

25.
$$w + 5\sqrt{w} + 6 = 0$$
$$\left(\sqrt{w}\right)^2 + 5\left(\sqrt{w}\right) + 6 = 0$$
Let $u = \sqrt{w}$.
$$u^2 + 5u + 6 = 0$$
$$(u+2)(u+3) = 0$$
$$u + 2 = 0 \quad \text{or} \quad u + 3 = 0$$
$$u = -2 \quad \text{or} \quad u = -3$$
$$\sqrt{w} = -2 \quad \text{or} \quad \sqrt{w} = -3$$
$$w = (-2)^2 \quad \text{or} \quad w = (-3)^2$$
$$w = 4 \quad \text{or} \quad w = 9$$

Check:
$$w = 4: \quad 4 + 5\sqrt{4} + 6 \overset{?}{=} 0$$
$$4 + 5 \cdot 2 + 6 \overset{?}{=} 0$$
$$4 + 10 + 6 \overset{?}{=} 0$$
$$20 \neq 0 \; \boldsymbol{\times}$$
$$w = 9: \quad 9 + 5\sqrt{9} + 6 \overset{?}{=} 0$$
$$9 + 5 \cdot 3 + 6 \overset{?}{=} 0$$
$$9 + 15 + 6 \overset{?}{=} 0$$
$$30 \neq 0 \; \boldsymbol{\times}$$
Neither possibility checks; the equation has no solution. The solution set is $\{\ \}$ or $\varnothing$.

27.
$$2x + 5\sqrt{x} = 3$$
$$2x + 5\sqrt{x} - 3 = 0$$
$$2\left(\sqrt{x}\right)^2 + 5\left(\sqrt{x}\right) - 3 = 0$$
Let $u = \sqrt{x}$.
$$2u^2 + 5u - 3 = 0$$
$$(2u - 1)(u + 3) = 0$$
$$2u - 1 = 0 \quad \text{or} \quad u + 3 = 0$$
$$2u = 1 \quad \text{or} \quad u = -3$$
$$u = \frac{1}{2}$$
$$\sqrt{x} = \frac{1}{2} \quad \text{or} \quad \sqrt{x} = -3$$
$$x = \left(\frac{1}{2}\right)^2 \quad \text{or} \quad x = (-3)^2$$
$$x = \frac{1}{4} \quad \text{or} \quad x = 9$$

Check:
$$x = \frac{1}{4}: \quad 2 \cdot \frac{1}{4} + 5\sqrt{\frac{1}{4}} \overset{?}{=} 3$$
$$\frac{1}{2} + 5 \cdot \frac{1}{2} \overset{?}{=} 3$$
$$\frac{1}{2} + \frac{5}{2} \overset{?}{=} 3$$
$$3 = 3 \; \checkmark$$
$$x = 9: \quad 2 \cdot 9 + 5\sqrt{9} \overset{?}{=} 3$$
$$2 \cdot 9 + 5 \cdot 3 \overset{?}{=} 3$$
$$18 + 15 \overset{?}{=} 3$$
$$33 \neq 3 \; \boldsymbol{\times}$$
$x = 9$ does not check; the solution set is $\left\{\dfrac{1}{4}\right\}$.

29.
$$x^{-2} + 3x^{-1} = 28$$
$$x^{-2} + 3x^{-1} - 28 = 0$$
$$\left(x^{-1}\right)^2 + 3\left(x^{-1}\right) - 28 = 0$$
Let $u = x^{-1}$.
$$u^2 + 3u - 28 = 0$$
$$(u - 4)(u + 7) = 0$$
$$u - 4 = 0 \quad \text{or} \quad u + 7 = 0$$
$$u = 4 \quad \text{or} \quad u = -7$$
$$x^{-1} = 4 \quad \text{or} \quad x^{-1} = -7$$
$$\frac{1}{x} = 4 \quad \text{or} \quad \frac{1}{x} = -7$$
$$x = \frac{1}{4} \quad \text{or} \quad x = -\frac{1}{7}$$

Check:
$$x = \frac{1}{4}: \quad \left(\frac{1}{4}\right)^{-2} + 3\left(\frac{1}{4}\right)^{-1} \overset{?}{=} 28$$
$$(4)^2 + 3(4) \overset{?}{=} 28$$
$$16 + 12 \overset{?}{=} 28$$
$$28 = 28 \; \checkmark$$
$$x = -\frac{1}{7}: \quad \left(-\frac{1}{7}\right)^{-2} + 3\left(-\frac{1}{7}\right)^{-1} \overset{?}{=} 28$$
$$(-7)^2 + 3(-7) \overset{?}{=} 28$$
$$49 - 21 \overset{?}{=} 28$$
$$28 = 28 \; \checkmark$$
Both check; the solution set is $\left\{-\dfrac{1}{7}, \; \dfrac{1}{4}\right\}$.

31.
$$10z^{-2} + 11z^{-1} = 6$$
$$10z^{-2} + 11z^{-1} - 6 = 0$$
$$10\left(z^{-1}\right)^2 + 11\left(z^{-1}\right) - 6 = 0$$

Let $u = z^{-1}$.
$$10u^2 + 11u - 6 = 0$$
$$(5u - 2)(2u + 3) = 0$$

$5u - 2 = 0$ or $2u + 3 = 0$

$\quad 5u = 2$ or $\quad 2u = -3$

$\quad u = \dfrac{2}{5}$ or $\quad u = -\dfrac{3}{2}$

$z^{-1} = \dfrac{2}{5}$ or $z^{-1} = -\dfrac{3}{2}$

$\dfrac{1}{z} = \dfrac{2}{5}$ or $\dfrac{1}{z} = -\dfrac{3}{2}$

$z = \dfrac{5}{2}$ or $z = -\dfrac{2}{3}$

Check:

$z = \dfrac{5}{2}:\ 10\left(\dfrac{5}{2}\right)^{-2} + 11\left(\dfrac{5}{2}\right)^{-1} \overset{?}{=} 6$

$\qquad 10\left(\dfrac{2}{5}\right)^2 + 11\left(\dfrac{2}{5}\right) \overset{?}{=} 6$

$\qquad 10\left(\dfrac{4}{25}\right) + 11\left(\dfrac{2}{5}\right) \overset{?}{=} 6$

$\qquad \dfrac{8}{5} + \dfrac{22}{5} \overset{?}{=} 6$

$\qquad \dfrac{30}{5} \overset{?}{=} 6$

$\qquad 6 = 6 \ \checkmark$

$z = -\dfrac{2}{3}:\ 10\left(-\dfrac{2}{3}\right)^{-2} + 11\left(-\dfrac{2}{3}\right)^{-1} \overset{?}{=} 6$

$\qquad 10\left(-\dfrac{3}{2}\right)^2 + 11\left(-\dfrac{3}{2}\right) \overset{?}{=} 6$

$\qquad 10\left(\dfrac{9}{4}\right) + 11\left(-\dfrac{3}{2}\right) \overset{?}{=} 6$

$\qquad \dfrac{45}{2} - \dfrac{33}{2} \overset{?}{=} 6$

$\qquad \dfrac{12}{2} \overset{?}{=} 6$

$\qquad 6 = 6 \ \checkmark$

Both check; the solution set is $\left\{-\dfrac{2}{3},\ \dfrac{5}{2}\right\}$.

33.
$$x^{2/3} + 3x^{1/3} - 4 = 0$$
$$\left(x^{1/3}\right)^2 + 3\left(x^{1/3}\right) - 4 = 0$$

Let $u = x^{1/3}$.
$$u^2 + 3u - 4 = 0$$
$$(u - 1)(u + 4) = 0$$

$u - 1 = 0$ or $u + 4 = 0$

$\quad u = 1$ or $\quad u = -4$

$x^{1/3} = 1$ or $x^{1/3} = -4$

$\left(x^{1/3}\right)^3 = 1^3$ or $\left(x^{1/3}\right)^3 = (-4)^3$

$\quad x = 1$ or $\quad x = -64$

Check:

$x = 1:\ (1)^{2/3} + 3\cdot(1)^{1/3} - 4 \overset{?}{=} 0$

$\qquad \left(\sqrt[3]{1}\right)^2 + 3\left(\sqrt[3]{1}\right) - 4 \overset{?}{=} 0$

$\qquad (1)^2 + 3(1) - 4 \overset{?}{=} 0$

$\qquad 1 + 3 - 4 \overset{?}{=} 0$

$\qquad 0 = 0 \ \checkmark$

$x = -64:\ (-64)^{2/3} + 3\cdot(-64)^{1/3} - 4 \overset{?}{=} 0$

$\qquad \left(\sqrt[3]{-64}\right)^2 + 3\left(\sqrt[3]{-64}\right) - 4 \overset{?}{=} 0$

$\qquad (-4)^2 + 3(-4) - 4 \overset{?}{=} 0$

$\qquad 16 - 12 - 4 \overset{?}{=} 0$

$\qquad 0 = 0 \ \checkmark$

Both check; the solution set is $\{-64, 1\}$.

35.
$$z^{2/3} - z^{1/3} = 2$$
$$\left(z^{1/3}\right)^2 - \left(z^{1/3}\right) - 2 = 0$$

Let $u = z^{1/3}$.
$$u^2 - u - 2 = 0$$
$$(u - 2)(u + 1) = 0$$

$u - 2 = 0$ or $u + 1 = 0$

$\quad u = 2$ or $\quad u = -1$

$z^{1/3} = 2$ or $z^{1/3} = -1$

$z = 2^3 = 8$ or $z = (-1)^3 = -1$

Check:

$z = 8:$ $(8)^{2/3} - (8)^{1/3} \overset{?}{=} 2$

$\left(\sqrt[3]{8}\right)^2 - \left(\sqrt[3]{8}\right) \overset{?}{=} 2$

$(2)^2 - 2 \overset{?}{=} 2$

$4 - 2 \overset{?}{=} 2$

$2 = 2$ ✔

$z = -1:$ $(-1)^{2/3} - (-1)^{1/3} \overset{?}{=} 2$

$\left(\sqrt[3]{-1}\right)^2 - \left(\sqrt[3]{-1}\right) \overset{?}{=} 2$

$(-1)^2 - (-1) \overset{?}{=} 2$

$1 + 1 \overset{?}{=} 2$

$2 = 2$ ✔

Both check; the solution set is $\{-1,\ 8\}$.

37. $a + a^{1/2} = 30$

$\left(a^{1/2}\right)^2 + \left(a^{1/2}\right) - 30 = 0$

Let $u = a^{1/2}$.

$u^2 + u - 30 = 0$

$(u - 5)(u + 6) = 0$

$u - 5 = 0$ or $u + 6 = 0$

$u = 5$ or $u = -6$

$a^{1/2} = 5$ or $a^{1/2} = -6$

$\left(a^{1/2}\right)^2 = 5^2$ or $\left(a^{1/2}\right)^2 = (-6)^2$

$a = 25$ or $a = 36$

Check:

$a = 25:$ $25 + (25)^{1/2} \overset{?}{=} 30$

$25 + \sqrt{25} \overset{?}{=} 30$

$25 + 5 \overset{?}{=} 30$

$30 = 30$ ✔

$a = 36:$ $36 + (36)^{1/2} \overset{?}{=} 30$

$36 + \sqrt{36} \overset{?}{=} 30$

$36 + 6 \overset{?}{=} 30$

$42 \neq 30$ ✘

$a = 36$ does not check; the solution set is $\{25\}$.

39. $\dfrac{1}{x^2} - \dfrac{5}{x} + 6 = 0$

$\left(\dfrac{1}{x}\right)^2 - 5\left(\dfrac{1}{x}\right) + 6 = 0$

Let $u = \dfrac{1}{x}$.

$u^2 - 5u + 6 = 0$

$(u - 2)(u - 3) = 0$

$u - 2 = 0$ or $u - 3 = 0$

$u = 2$ or $u = 3$

$\dfrac{1}{x} = 2$ or $\dfrac{1}{x} = 3$

$x = \dfrac{1}{2}$ or $x = \dfrac{1}{3}$

Check:

$x = \dfrac{1}{2}:$ $\dfrac{1}{\left(\frac{1}{2}\right)^2} - \dfrac{5}{\frac{1}{2}} + 6 \overset{?}{=} 0$

$\dfrac{1}{\frac{1}{4}} - \dfrac{5}{\frac{1}{2}} + 6 \overset{?}{=} 0$

$4 - 10 + 6 \overset{?}{=} 0$

$0 = 0$ ✔

$x = \dfrac{1}{3}:$ $\dfrac{1}{\left(\frac{1}{3}\right)^2} - \dfrac{5}{\frac{1}{3}} + 6 \overset{?}{=} 0$

$\dfrac{1}{\frac{1}{9}} - \dfrac{5}{\frac{1}{3}} + 6 \overset{?}{=} 0$

$9 - 15 + 6 \overset{?}{=} 0$

$0 = 0$ ✔

Both check; the solution set is $\left\{\dfrac{1}{3},\ \dfrac{1}{2}\right\}$.

41.

$$\left(\frac{1}{x+2}\right)^2 + \frac{4}{x+2} = 5$$

$$\left(\frac{1}{x+2}\right)^2 + 4\left(\frac{1}{x+2}\right) - 5 = 0$$

Let $u = \dfrac{1}{x+2}$.

$$u^2 + 4u - 5 = 0$$
$$(u-1)(u+5) = 0$$
$$u - 1 = 0 \quad \text{or} \quad u + 5 = 0$$
$$u = 1 \quad \text{or} \quad u = -5$$
$$\frac{1}{x+2} = 1 \quad \text{or} \quad \frac{1}{x+2} = -5$$
$$x + 2 = 1 \quad \text{or} \quad x + 2 = -\frac{1}{5}$$
$$x = -1 \quad \text{or} \quad x = -\frac{11}{5}$$

Check:

$x = -1:$

$$\left(\frac{1}{-1+2}\right)^2 + \frac{4}{-1+2} \overset{?}{=} 5$$
$$\left(\frac{1}{1}\right)^2 + \frac{4}{1} \overset{?}{=} 5$$
$$(1)^2 + 4 \overset{?}{=} 5$$
$$1 + 4 \overset{?}{=} 5$$
$$5 = 5 \checkmark$$

$x = -\dfrac{11}{5}:$

$$\left(\frac{1}{-\frac{11}{5}+2}\right)^2 + \frac{4}{-\frac{11}{5}+2} \overset{?}{=} 5$$
$$\left(\frac{1}{-\frac{1}{5}}\right)^2 + \frac{4}{-\frac{1}{5}} \overset{?}{=} 5$$
$$(-5)^2 + 4(-5) \overset{?}{=} 5$$
$$25 - 20 \overset{?}{=} 5$$
$$5 = 5 \checkmark$$

Both check; the solution set is $\left\{-\dfrac{11}{5}, -1\right\}$.

43.

$$p^6 - 28p^3 + 27 = 0$$
$$\left(p^3\right)^2 - 28\left(p^3\right) + 27 = 0$$

Let $u = p^3$.

$$u^2 - 28u + 27 = 0$$
$$(u-1)(u-27) = 0$$
$$u - 1 = 0 \quad \text{or} \quad u - 27 = 0$$
$$p^3 - 1 = 0 \quad \text{or} \quad p^3 - 27 = 0$$

First consider $p^3 - 1 = 0$. Note that the expression on the left is a difference of cubes.

$$p^3 - 1 = 0$$
$$(p-1)\left(p^2 + p + 1\right) = 0$$
$$p - 1 = 0 \quad \text{or} \quad p^2 + p + 1 = 0$$
$$p = 1 \quad \text{or} \quad p = \frac{-1 \pm \sqrt{1^2 - 4(1)(1)}}{2(1)}$$
$$= \frac{-1 \pm \sqrt{-3}}{2}$$
$$= \frac{-1 \pm \sqrt{3}\,i}{2}$$
$$= -\frac{1}{2} \pm \frac{\sqrt{3}}{2}i$$

Now consider $p^3 - 27 = 0$. Note that the expression on the left is a difference of cubes.

$$p^3 - 27 = 0$$
$$(p-3)\left(p^2 + 3p + 9\right) = 0$$
$$p - 3 = 0 \quad \text{or} \quad p^2 + 3p + 9 = 0$$
$$p = 3 \quad \text{or} \quad p = \frac{-3 \pm \sqrt{3^2 - 4(1)(9)}}{2(1)}$$
$$= \frac{-3 \pm \sqrt{-27}}{2}$$
$$= \frac{-3 \pm 3\sqrt{3}\,i}{2}$$
$$= -\frac{3}{2} \pm \frac{3\sqrt{3}}{2}i$$

All will check; the solution set is

$$\left\{ 1, 3, -\frac{1}{2} - \frac{\sqrt{3}}{2}i, -\frac{1}{2} + \frac{\sqrt{3}}{2}i, -\frac{3}{2} - \frac{3\sqrt{3}}{2}i, \right.$$
$$\left. -\frac{3}{2} + \frac{3\sqrt{3}}{2}i \right\}$$

45.
$$8a^{-2} + 2a^{-1} = 1$$
$$8a^{-2} + 2a^{-1} - 1 = 0$$
$$8\left(a^{-1}\right)^2 + 2\left(a^{-1}\right) - 1 = 0$$

Let $u = a^{-1}$.
$$8u^2 + 2u - 1 = 0$$
$$(4u - 1)(2u + 1) = 0$$

$$4u - 1 = 0 \quad \text{or} \quad 2u + 1 = 0$$
$$4u = 1 \quad \text{or} \quad 2u = -1$$
$$u = \frac{1}{4} \quad \text{or} \quad u = -\frac{1}{2}$$
$$a^{-1} = \frac{1}{4} \quad \text{or} \quad a^{-1} = -\frac{1}{2}$$
$$\frac{1}{a} = \frac{1}{4} \quad \text{or} \quad \frac{1}{a} = -\frac{1}{2}$$
$$a = 4 \quad \text{or} \quad a = -2$$

Check:

$a = 4:$ $8(4)^{-2} + 2(4)^{-1} \overset{?}{=} 1$

$$8\left(\frac{1}{4}\right)^2 + 2\left(\frac{1}{4}\right) \overset{?}{=} 1$$
$$8\left(\frac{1}{16}\right) + 2\left(\frac{1}{4}\right) \overset{?}{=} 1$$
$$\frac{1}{2} + \frac{1}{2} \overset{?}{=} 1$$
$$1 = 1 \checkmark$$

$a = -2:$ $8(-2)^{-2} + 2(-2)^{-1} \overset{?}{=} 1$

$$8\left(-\frac{1}{2}\right)^2 + 2\left(-\frac{1}{2}\right) \overset{?}{=} 1$$
$$8\left(\frac{1}{4}\right) + 2\left(-\frac{1}{2}\right) \overset{?}{=} 1$$
$$2 - 1 \overset{?}{=} 1$$
$$1 = 1 \checkmark$$

Both check; the solution set is $\{-2, 4\}$.

47.
$$z^4 = 4z^2 + 32$$
$$z^4 - 4z^2 - 32 = 0$$
$$\left(z^2\right)^2 - 4\left(z^2\right) - 32 = 0$$

Let $u = z^2$.
$$u^2 - 4u - 32 = 0$$
$$(u - 8)(u + 4) = 0$$

$$u - 8 = 0 \quad \text{or} \quad u + 4 = 0$$
$$u = 8 \quad \text{or} \quad u = -4$$
$$z^2 = 8 \quad \text{or} \quad z^2 = -4$$
$$z = \pm\sqrt{8} \quad \text{or} \quad z = \pm\sqrt{-4}$$
$$z = \pm 2\sqrt{2} \quad \text{or} \quad z = \pm 2i$$

Check:

$z = -2\sqrt{2}:$ $\left(-2\sqrt{2}\right)^4 \overset{?}{=} 4\left(-2\sqrt{2}\right)^2 + 32$
$$64 \overset{?}{=} 4 \cdot 8 + 32$$
$$64 \overset{?}{=} 32 + 32$$
$$64 = 64 \checkmark$$

$z = 2\sqrt{2}:$ $\left(2\sqrt{2}\right)^4 \overset{?}{=} 4\left(2\sqrt{2}\right)^2 + 32$
$$64 \overset{?}{=} 4 \cdot 8 + 32$$
$$64 \overset{?}{=} 32 + 32$$
$$64 = 64 \checkmark$$

$z = -2i:$ $(-2i)^4 \overset{?}{=} 4(-2i)^2 + 32$
$$16i^4 \overset{?}{=} 4 \cdot 4i^2 + 32$$
$$16(1) \overset{?}{=} 4 \cdot (-4) + 32$$
$$16 \overset{?}{=} -16 + 32$$
$$16 = 16 \checkmark$$

$z = 2i:$ $(2i)^4 \overset{?}{=} 4(2i)^2 + 32$
$$16i^4 \overset{?}{=} 4 \cdot 4i^2 + 32$$
$$16(1) \overset{?}{=} 4 \cdot (-4) + 32$$
$$16 \overset{?}{=} -16 + 32$$
$$16 = 16 \checkmark$$

All check; the solution set is
$$\left\{-2\sqrt{2},\ 2\sqrt{2}, -2i,\ 2i\right\}.$$

49.
$$x^{1/2} + x^{1/4} - 6 = 0$$
$$\left(x^{1/4}\right)^2 + \left(x^{1/4}\right) - 6 = 0$$
Let $u = x^{1/4}$.
$$u^2 + u - 6 = 0$$
$$(u-2)(u+3) = 0$$
$$\begin{array}{lll} u - 2 = 0 & \text{or} & u + 3 = 0 \\ u = 2 & \text{or} & u = -3 \end{array}$$
$$\begin{array}{lll} x^{1/4} = 2 & \text{or} & x^{1/4} = -3 \end{array}$$
$$\begin{array}{lll} \left(x^{1/4}\right)^4 = 2^4 & \text{or} & \left(x^{1/4}\right)^4 = (-3)^4 \\ x = 16 & \text{or} & x = 81 \end{array}$$

Check:
$$x = 16: \ (16)^{1/2} + (16)^{1/4} - 6 \overset{?}{=} 0$$
$$\sqrt{16} + \sqrt[4]{16} - 6 \overset{?}{=} 0$$
$$4 + 2 - 6 \overset{?}{=} 0$$
$$0 = 0 \ \checkmark$$
$$x = 81: \ (81)^{1/2} + (81)^{1/4} - 6 \overset{?}{=} 0$$
$$\sqrt{81} + \sqrt[4]{81} - 6 \overset{?}{=} 0$$
$$9 + 3 - 6 \overset{?}{=} 0$$
$$6 \neq 0 \ \bm{\times}$$

$x = 81$ does not check; the solution set is $\{16\}$.

51.
$$w^4 - 5w^2 - 36 = 0$$
$$\left(w^2\right)^2 - 5\left(w^2\right) - 36 = 0$$
Let $u = w^2$.
$$u^2 - 5u - 36 = 0$$
$$(u-9)(u+4) = 0$$
$$\begin{array}{lll} u - 9 = 0 & \text{or} & u + 4 = 0 \\ u = 9 & \text{or} & u = -4 \end{array}$$
$$\begin{array}{lll} w^2 = 9 & \text{or} & w^2 = -4 \\ w = \pm\sqrt{9} & \text{or} & w = \pm\sqrt{-4} \\ w = \pm 3 & \text{or} & w = \pm 2i \end{array}$$

Check:
$$w = -3: \ (-3)^4 - 5(-3)^2 - 36 \overset{?}{=} 0$$
$$81 - 5 \cdot 9 - 36 \overset{?}{=} 0$$
$$81 - 45 - 36 \overset{?}{=} 0$$
$$0 = 0 \ \checkmark$$

$$w = 3: \ 3^4 - 5(3)^2 - 36 \overset{?}{=} 0$$
$$81 - 5 \cdot 9 - 36 \overset{?}{=} 0$$
$$81 - 45 - 36 \overset{?}{=} 0$$
$$0 = 0 \ \checkmark$$
$$w = -2i: \ (-2i)^4 - 5(-2i)^2 - 36 \overset{?}{=} 0$$
$$16i^4 - 5 \cdot 4i^2 - 36 \overset{?}{=} 0$$
$$16(1) - 5 \cdot 4(-1) - 36 \overset{?}{=} 0$$
$$16 + 20 - 36 \overset{?}{=} 0$$
$$0 = 0 \ \checkmark$$
$$w = 2i: \ (2i)^4 - 5(2i)^2 - 36 \overset{?}{=} 0$$
$$16i^4 - 5 \cdot 4i^2 - 36 \overset{?}{=} 0$$
$$16(1) - 5 \cdot 4(-1) - 36 \overset{?}{=} 0$$
$$16 + 20 - 36 \overset{?}{=} 0$$
$$0 = 0 \ \checkmark$$

All check; the solution set is $\{-3, \ 3, -2i, \ 2i\}$.

53.
$$\left(\frac{1}{x+3}\right)^2 + \frac{2}{x+3} = 3$$
$$\left(\frac{1}{x+3}\right)^2 + 2\left(\frac{1}{x+3}\right) - 3 = 0$$
Let $u = \dfrac{1}{x+3}$.
$$u^2 + 2u - 3 = 0$$
$$(u-1)(u+3) = 0$$
$$\begin{array}{lll} u - 1 = 0 & \text{or} & u + 3 = 0 \\ u = 1 & \text{or} & u = -3 \end{array}$$
$$\begin{array}{lll} \dfrac{1}{x+3} = 1 & \text{or} & \dfrac{1}{x+3} = -3 \end{array}$$
$$\begin{array}{lll} x + 3 = 1 & \text{or} & x + 3 = -\dfrac{1}{3} \\ x = -2 & \text{or} & x = -\dfrac{10}{3} \end{array}$$

Check:
$$x = -2: \ \left(\frac{1}{-2+3}\right)^2 + \frac{2}{-2+3} \overset{?}{=} 3$$
$$\left(\frac{1}{1}\right)^2 + \frac{2}{1} \overset{?}{=} 3$$
$$1 + 2 \overset{?}{=} 3$$
$$3 = 3 \ \checkmark$$

$$x = -\frac{10}{3}: \left(\frac{1}{-\frac{10}{3}+3}\right)^2 + \frac{2}{-\frac{10}{3}+3} \overset{?}{=} 3$$

$$\left(\frac{1}{-\frac{1}{3}}\right)^2 + \frac{2}{-\frac{1}{3}} \overset{?}{=} 3$$

$$(-3)^2 + 2(-3) \overset{?}{=} 3$$

$$9 - 6 \overset{?}{=} 3$$

$$3 = 3 \checkmark$$

Both check; the solution set is $\left\{-\frac{10}{3}, -2\right\}$.

55.
$$x - 7\sqrt{x} + 12 = 0$$
$$\left(\sqrt{x}\right)^2 - 7\left(\sqrt{x}\right) + 12 = 0$$

Let $u = \sqrt{x}$.
$$u^2 - 7u + 12 = 0$$
$$(u - 4)(u - 3) = 0$$
$$u - 4 = 0 \quad \text{or} \quad u - 3 = 0$$
$$u = 4 \quad \text{or} \quad u = 3$$
$$\sqrt{x} = 4 \quad \text{or} \quad \sqrt{x} = 3$$
$$x = 4^2 \quad \text{or} \quad x = 3^2$$
$$x = 16 \quad \text{or} \quad x = 9$$

Check:
$$x = 16: \quad 16 - 7\sqrt{16} + 12 \overset{?}{=} 0$$
$$16 - 7 \cdot 4 + 12 \overset{?}{=} 0$$
$$16 - 28 + 12 \overset{?}{=} 0$$
$$0 = 0 \checkmark$$

$$x = 9: \quad 9 - 7\sqrt{9} + 12 \overset{?}{=} 0$$
$$9 - 7 \cdot 3 + 12 \overset{?}{=} 0$$
$$9 - 21 + 12 \overset{?}{=} 0$$
$$0 = 0 \checkmark$$

Both check; the solution set is $\{9, 16\}$.

57.
$$2(x-1)^2 - 7(x-1) = 4$$
$$2(x-1)^2 - 7(x-1) - 4 = 0$$

Let $u = x - 1$.
$$2u^2 - 7u - 4 = 0$$
$$(2u + 1)(u - 4) = 0$$
$$2u + 1 = 0 \quad \text{or} \quad u - 4 = 0$$
$$u = -\frac{1}{2} \quad \text{or} \quad u = 4$$

$$x - 1 = -\frac{1}{2} \quad \text{or} \quad x - 1 = 4$$
$$x = \frac{1}{2} \quad \text{or} \quad x = 5$$

Check:
$$x = \frac{1}{2}: \quad 2\left(\frac{1}{2} - 1\right)^2 - 7\left(\frac{1}{2} - 1\right) \overset{?}{=} 4$$
$$2\left(-\frac{1}{2}\right)^2 - 7\left(-\frac{1}{2}\right) \overset{?}{=} 4$$
$$2\left(\frac{1}{4}\right) - 7\left(-\frac{1}{2}\right) \overset{?}{=} 4$$
$$\frac{1}{2} + \frac{7}{2} \overset{?}{=} 4$$
$$4 = 4 \checkmark$$

$$x = 5: \quad 2(5-1)^2 - 7(5-1) \overset{?}{=} 4$$
$$2(4)^2 - 7(4) \overset{?}{=} 4$$
$$2 \cdot 16 - 7 \cdot 4 \overset{?}{=} 4$$
$$32 - 28 \overset{?}{=} 4$$
$$4 = 4 \checkmark$$

Both check; the solution set is $\left\{\frac{1}{2}, 5\right\}$.

59. a.
$$f(x) = 12$$
$$x^4 + 7x^2 + 12 = 12$$
$$\left(x^2\right)^2 + 7\left(x^2\right) = 0$$

Let $u = x^2$.
$$u^2 + 7u = 0$$
$$u(u + 7) = 0$$
$$u + 7 = 0 \quad \text{or} \quad u = 0$$
$$u = -7$$
$$x^2 = -7 \quad \text{or} \quad x^2 = 0$$
$$x = \pm\sqrt{-7} \quad \text{or} \quad x = \pm\sqrt{0}$$
$$x = \pm\sqrt{7}\, i \quad \text{or} \quad x = 0$$

Check:
$$f\left(-\sqrt{7}\, i\right) = \left(-\sqrt{7}\, i\right)^4 + 7\left(-\sqrt{7}\, i\right)^2 + 12$$
$$= 49i^4 + 7 \cdot 7i^2 + 12$$
$$= 49(1) + 7 \cdot 7(-1) + 12$$
$$= 49 - 49 + 12$$
$$= 12 \checkmark$$

$$f\left(\sqrt{7}\ i\right) = \left(\sqrt{7}\ i\right)^4 + 7\left(\sqrt{7}\ i\right)^2 + 12$$
$$= 49i^4 + 7\cdot 7i^2 + 12$$
$$= 49(1) + 7\cdot 7(-1) + 12$$
$$= 49 - 49 + 12 = 12\ \checkmark$$
$$f(0) = 0^4 + 7\cdot 0^2 + 12$$
$$= 12\ \checkmark$$

All check; the values that make $f(x) = 12$ are $\left\{-\sqrt{7}\ i,\ \sqrt{7}\ i,\ 0\right\}$.

b.
$$f(x) = 6$$
$$x^4 + 7x^2 + 12 = 6$$
$$\left(x^2\right)^2 + 7\left(x^2\right) + 6 = 0$$

Let $u = x^2$.
$$u^2 + 7u + 6 = 0$$
$$(u+6)(u+1) = 0$$
$$u + 6 = 0 \quad \text{or} \quad u + 1 = 0$$
$$u = -6 \quad \text{or} \quad u = -1$$
$$x^2 = -6 \quad \text{or} \quad x^2 = -1$$
$$x = \pm\sqrt{-6} \quad \text{or} \quad x = \pm\sqrt{-1}$$
$$x = \pm\sqrt{6}\ i \quad \text{or} \quad x = \pm i$$

Check:
$$f\left(-\sqrt{6}\ i\right) = \left(-\sqrt{6}\ i\right)^4 + 7\left(-\sqrt{6}\ i\right)^2 + 12$$
$$= 36i^4 + 7\cdot 6i^2 + 12$$
$$= 36(1) + 7\cdot 6(-1) + 12$$
$$= 36 - 42 + 12$$
$$= 6\ \checkmark$$

$$f\left(\sqrt{6}\ i\right) = \left(\sqrt{6}\ i\right)^4 + 7\left(\sqrt{6}\ i\right)^2 + 12$$
$$= 36i^4 + 7\cdot 6i^2 + 12$$
$$= 36(1) + 7\cdot 6(-1) + 12$$
$$= 36 - 42 + 12$$
$$= 6\ \checkmark$$

$$f(-i) = (-i)^4 + 7(-i)^2 + 12$$
$$= i^4 + 7i^2 + 12$$
$$= 1 + 7(-1) + 12$$
$$= 1 - 7 + 12$$
$$= 6\ \checkmark$$

$$f(i) = i^4 + 7i^2 + 12$$
$$= 1 + 7(-1) + 12$$
$$= 1 - 7 + 12$$
$$= 6\ \checkmark$$

All check; the values that make $f(x) = 6$ are $\left\{-\sqrt{6}\ i,\ \sqrt{6}\ i,\ -i,\ i\right\}$.

61. a.
$$g(x) = -5$$
$$2x^4 - 6x^2 - 5 = -5$$
$$2\left(x^2\right)^2 - 6\left(x^2\right) = 0$$

Let $u = x^2$.
$$2u^2 - 6u = 0$$
$$2u(u-3) = 0$$
$$2u = 0 \quad \text{or} \quad u - 3 = 0$$
$$u = 0 \quad \text{or} \quad u = 3$$
$$x^2 = 0 \quad \text{or} \quad x^2 = 3$$
$$x = \pm\sqrt{0} \quad \text{or} \quad x = \pm\sqrt{3}$$
$$x = 0$$

Check:
$$g(0) = 2\cdot 0^4 - 6\cdot 0^2 - 5$$
$$= -5\ \checkmark$$

$$g\left(-\sqrt{3}\right) = 2\left(-\sqrt{3}\right)^4 - 6\left(-\sqrt{3}\right)^2 - 5$$
$$= 2\cdot 9 - 6\cdot 3 - 5$$
$$= 18 - 18 - 5$$
$$= -5\ \checkmark$$

$$g\left(\sqrt{3}\right) = 2\left(\sqrt{3}\right)^4 - 6\left(\sqrt{3}\right)^2 - 5$$
$$= 2\cdot 9 - 6\cdot 3 - 5$$
$$= 18 - 18 - 5$$
$$= -5\ \checkmark$$

All check; the values that make $g(x) = -5$ are $\left\{-\sqrt{3},\ 0,\ \sqrt{3}\right\}$.

b.
$$g(x) = 15$$
$$2x^4 - 6x^2 - 5 = 15$$
$$2x^4 - 6x^2 - 20 = 0$$
$$\frac{2x^4 - 6x^2 - 20}{2} = \frac{0}{2}$$
$$x^4 - 3x^2 - 10 = 0$$
$$\left(x^2\right)^2 - 3\left(x^2\right) - 10 = 0$$

Let $u = x^2$.
$$u^2 - 3u - 10 = 0$$
$$(u+2)(u-5) = 0$$

$$u + 2 = 0 \quad \text{or} \quad u - 5 = 0$$
$$u = -2 \quad \text{or} \quad u = 5$$
$$x^2 = -2 \quad \text{or} \quad x^2 = 5$$
$$x = \pm\sqrt{-2} \quad \text{or} \quad x = \pm\sqrt{5}$$
$$x = \pm\sqrt{2}\, i$$

Check:

$$g\left(-\sqrt{2}\, i\right) = 2\left(-\sqrt{2}\, i\right)^4 - 6\left(-\sqrt{2}\, i\right)^2 - 5$$
$$= 2 \cdot 4i^4 - 6 \cdot 2i^2 - 5$$
$$= 2 \cdot 4(1) - 6 \cdot 2(-1) - 5$$
$$= 8 + 12 - 5$$
$$= 15 \checkmark$$

$$g\left(\sqrt{2}\, i\right) = 2\left(\sqrt{2}\, i\right)^4 - 6\left(\sqrt{2}\, i\right)^2 - 5$$
$$= 2 \cdot 4i^4 - 6 \cdot 2i^2 - 5$$
$$= 2 \cdot 4(1) - 6 \cdot 2(-1) - 5$$
$$= 8 + 12 - 5$$
$$= 15 \checkmark$$

$$g\left(-\sqrt{5}\right) = 2\left(-\sqrt{5}\right)^4 - 6\left(-\sqrt{5}\right)^2 - 5$$
$$= 2 \cdot 25 - 6 \cdot 5 - 5$$
$$= 50 - 30 - 5$$
$$= 15 \checkmark$$

$$g\left(\sqrt{5}\right) = 2\left(\sqrt{5}\right)^4 - 6\left(\sqrt{5}\right)^2 - 5$$
$$= 2 \cdot 25 - 6 \cdot 5 - 5$$
$$= 50 - 30 - 5$$
$$= 15 \checkmark$$

All check; the values that make $g(x) = 15$
are $\left\{-\sqrt{2}\, i,\ \sqrt{2}\, i,\ -\sqrt{5},\ \sqrt{5}\right\}$.

63. a.
$$F(x) = 6$$
$$x^{-2} - 5x^{-1} = 6$$
$$\left(x^{-1}\right)^2 - 5\left(x^{-1}\right) - 6 = 0$$

Let $u = x^{-1}$.
$$u^2 - 5u - 6 = 0$$
$$(u - 6)(u + 1) = 0$$
$$u - 6 = 0 \quad \text{or} \quad u + 1 = 0$$
$$u = 6 \quad \text{or} \quad u = -1$$
$$x^{-1} = 6 \quad \text{or} \quad x^{-1} = -1$$
$$\frac{1}{x} = 6 \quad \text{or} \quad \frac{1}{x} = -1$$
$$x = \frac{1}{6} \quad \text{or} \quad x = -1$$

Check:

$$F\left(\frac{1}{6}\right) = \left(\frac{1}{6}\right)^{-2} - 5\left(\frac{1}{6}\right)^{-1}$$
$$= 6^2 - 5 \cdot 6^1$$
$$= 36 - 30$$
$$= 6 \checkmark$$

$$F(-1) = (-1)^{-2} - 5(-1)^{-1}$$
$$= (-1)^2 - 5(-1)^1$$
$$= 1 + 5$$
$$= 6 \checkmark$$

Both check; the values that make $F(x) = 6$

are $\left\{-1,\ \dfrac{1}{6}\right\}$.

b.
$$F(x) = 14$$
$$x^{-2} - 5x^{-1} = 14$$
$$\left(x^{-1}\right)^2 - 5\left(x^{-1}\right) - 14 = 0$$

Let $u = x^{-1}$.
$$u^2 - 5u - 14 = 0$$
$$(u - 7)(u + 2) = 0$$
$$u - 7 = 0 \quad \text{or} \quad u + 2 = 0$$
$$u = 7 \quad \text{or} \quad u = -2$$
$$x^{-1} = 7 \quad \text{or} \quad x^{-1} = -2$$
$$\frac{1}{x} = 7 \quad \text{or} \quad \frac{1}{x} = -2$$
$$x = \frac{1}{7} \quad \text{or} \quad x = -\frac{1}{2}$$

Check:

$$F\left(\frac{1}{7}\right) = \left(\frac{1}{7}\right)^{-2} - 5\left(\frac{1}{7}\right)^{-1}$$
$$= 7^2 - 5 \cdot 7^1$$
$$= 49 - 35$$
$$= 14 \checkmark$$

$$F\left(-\frac{1}{2}\right) = \left(-\frac{1}{2}\right)^{-2} - 5\left(-\frac{1}{2}\right)^{-1}$$
$$= (-2)^2 - 5 \cdot (-2)^1$$
$$= 4 + 10$$
$$= 14 \checkmark$$

Both check; the values that make
$F(x) = 14$ are $\left\{-\dfrac{1}{2},\ \dfrac{1}{7}\right\}$.

65.
$$x^4 + 9x^2 + 14 = 0$$
$$\left(x^2\right)^2 + 9\left(x^2\right) + 14 = 0$$

Let $u = x^2$.
$$u^2 + 9u + 14 = 0$$
$$(u+7)(u+2) = 0$$

$u + 7 = 0 \quad$ or $\quad u + 2 = 0$

$\quad u = -7 \quad$ or $\quad\quad u = -2$

$\quad x^2 = -7 \quad$ or $\quad\quad x^2 = -2$

$\quad x = \pm\sqrt{-7} \quad$ or $\quad x = \pm\sqrt{-2}$

$\quad x = \pm\sqrt{7}\, i \quad$ or $\quad x = \pm\sqrt{2}\, i$

Check:
$$f\left(-\sqrt{7}\, i\right) = \left(-\sqrt{7}\, i\right)^4 + 9\left(-\sqrt{7}\, i\right)^2 + 14$$
$$= 49i^4 + 9 \cdot 7i^2 + 14$$
$$= 49(1) + 9 \cdot 7(-1) + 14$$
$$= 49 - 63 + 14$$
$$= 0 \checkmark$$

$$f\left(\sqrt{7}\, i\right) = \left(\sqrt{7}\, i\right)^4 + 9\left(\sqrt{7}\, i\right)^2 + 14$$
$$= 49i^4 + 9 \cdot 7i^2 + 14$$
$$= 49(1) + 9 \cdot 7(-1) + 14$$
$$= 49 - 63 + 14$$
$$= 0 \checkmark$$

$$f\left(-\sqrt{2}\, i\right) = \left(-\sqrt{2}\, i\right)^4 + 9\left(-\sqrt{2}\, i\right)^2 + 14$$
$$= 4i^4 + 9 \cdot 2i^2 + 14$$
$$= 4(1) + 9 \cdot 2(-1) + 14$$
$$= 4 - 18 + 14$$
$$= 0 \checkmark$$

$$f\left(\sqrt{2}\, i\right) = \left(\sqrt{2}\, i\right)^4 + 9\left(\sqrt{2}\, i\right)^2 + 14$$
$$= 4i^4 + 9 \cdot 2i^2 + 14$$
$$= 4(1) + 9 \cdot 2(-1) + 14$$
$$= 4 - 18 + 14$$
$$= 0 \checkmark$$

All check; the zeros of f are
$$\left\{-\sqrt{7}\, i,\ \sqrt{7}\, i, -\sqrt{2}\, i,\ \sqrt{2}\, i\right\}.$$

67.
$$6t - 25\sqrt{t} - 9 = 0$$
$$6\left(\sqrt{t}\right)^2 - 25\left(\sqrt{t}\right) - 9 = 0$$

Let $u = \sqrt{t}$.
$$6u^2 - 25u - 9 = 0$$
$$(2u - 9)(3u + 1) = 0$$

$2u - 9 = 0 \quad$ or $\quad 3u + 1 = 0$

$\quad 2u = 9 \quad$ or $\quad\quad 3u = -1$

$\quad u = \dfrac{9}{2} \quad$ or $\quad\quad u = -\dfrac{1}{3}$

$\quad \sqrt{t} = \dfrac{9}{2} \quad$ or $\quad \sqrt{t} = -\dfrac{1}{3}$

$\quad t = \left(\dfrac{9}{2}\right)^2 \quad$ or $\quad t = \left(-\dfrac{1}{3}\right)^2$

$\quad t = \dfrac{81}{4} \quad$ or $\quad\quad t = \dfrac{1}{9}$

Check:
$$g\left(\frac{81}{4}\right) = 6 \cdot \frac{81}{4} - 25\sqrt{\frac{81}{4}} - 9$$
$$= 6 \cdot \frac{81}{4} - 25 \cdot \frac{9}{2} - 9$$
$$= \frac{243}{2} - \frac{225}{2} - 9$$
$$= 0 \checkmark$$

$$g\left(\frac{1}{9}\right) = 6 \cdot \frac{1}{9} - 25\sqrt{\frac{1}{9}} - 9$$
$$= 6 \cdot \frac{1}{9} - 25 \cdot \frac{1}{3} - 9$$
$$= \frac{2}{3} - \frac{25}{3} - 9$$
$$= -\frac{50}{3}$$
$$\neq 0 \; ✗$$

$t = \dfrac{1}{9}$ does not check; the zero of g is $\left\{\dfrac{81}{4}\right\}$.

69.
$$\frac{1}{(d+3)^2} - \frac{4}{d+3} + 3 = 0$$
$$\left(\frac{1}{d+3}\right)^2 - 4\left(\frac{1}{d+3}\right) + 3 = 0$$

Let $u = \dfrac{1}{d+3}$.
$$u^2 - 4u + 3 = 0$$
$$(u - 1)(u - 3) = 0$$

$u - 1 = 0 \quad$ or $\quad u - 3 = 0$

$\quad u = 1 \quad$ or $\quad\quad u = 3$

$\quad \dfrac{1}{d+3} = 1 \quad$ or $\quad \dfrac{1}{d+3} = 3$

$\quad d + 3 = 1 \quad$ or $\quad d + 3 = \dfrac{1}{3}$

$\quad d = -2 \quad$ or $\quad\quad d = -\dfrac{8}{3}$

Check:

$$s(-2) = \frac{1}{(-2+3)^2} - \frac{4}{-2+3} + 3$$

$$= \frac{1}{1^2} - \frac{4}{1} + 3$$

$$= 1 - 4 + 3$$

$$= 0 \checkmark$$

$$s\left(-\frac{8}{3}\right) = \frac{1}{\left(-\frac{8}{3}+3\right)^2} - \frac{4}{-\frac{8}{3}+3} + 3$$

$$= \frac{1}{\left(\frac{1}{3}\right)^2} - \frac{4}{\frac{1}{3}} + 3$$

$$= \frac{1}{\frac{1}{9}} - \frac{4}{\frac{1}{3}} + 3$$

$$= 9 - 12 + 3$$

$$= 0 \checkmark$$

Both check; the zeros of s are $\left\{-\frac{8}{3}, -2\right\}$.

71. a.
$$x^2 - 5x + 6 = 0$$
$$(x-2)(x-3) = 0$$
$$x - 2 = 0 \quad \text{or} \quad x - 3 = 0$$
$$x = 2 \quad \text{or} \quad x = 3$$
Both check; the solution set is $\{2, 3\}$.

b. $(x-3)^2 - 5(x-3) + 6 = 0$
Let $u = x - 3$.
$$u^2 - 5u + 6 = 0$$
$$(u-2)(u-3) = 0$$
$$u - 2 = 0 \quad \text{or} \quad u - 3 = 0$$
$$u = 2 \quad \text{or} \quad u = 3$$
$$x - 3 = 2 \quad \text{or} \quad x - 3 = 3$$
$$x = 5 \quad \text{or} \quad x = 6$$
Both check; the solution set is $\{5, 6\}$.

Comparing these solutions to those in part (a), we note that $5 = 2 + 3$ and $6 = 3 + 3$.

c. $(x+2)^2 - 5(x+2) + 6 = 0$
Let $u = x + 2$.
$$u^2 - 5u + 6 = 0$$
$$(u-2)(u-3) = 0$$
$$u - 2 = 0 \quad \text{or} \quad u - 3 = 0$$
$$u = 2 \quad \text{or} \quad u = 3$$
$$x + 2 = 2 \quad \text{or} \quad x + 2 = 3$$
$$x = 0 \quad \text{or} \quad x = 1$$
Both check; the solution set is $\{0, 1\}$.

Comparing these solutions to those in part (a), we note that $0 = 2 - 2$ and $1 = 3 - 2$.

d. $(x-5)^2 - 5(x-5) + 6 = 0$
Let $u = x - 5$.
$$u^2 - 5u + 6 = 0$$
$$(u-2)(u-3) = 0$$
$$u - 2 = 0 \quad \text{or} \quad u - 3 = 0$$
$$u = 2 \quad \text{or} \quad u = 3$$
$$x - 5 = 2 \quad \text{or} \quad x - 5 = 3$$
$$x = 7 \quad \text{or} \quad x = 8$$
Both check; the solution set is $\{7, 8\}$.

Comparing these solutions to those in part (a), we note that $7 = 2 + 5$ and $8 = 3 + 5$.

e. Conjecture: The solution set of the equation $(x-a)^2 - 5(x-a) + 6 = 0$ is $\{2+a, 3+a\}$.
NOTE: This conjecture can be shown to be true by using the techniques from parts (b) through (d).

73. a. $f(x) = 2x^2 - 3x + 1$
$$2x^2 - 3x + 1 = 0$$
$$(2x-1)(x-1) = 0$$
$$2x - 1 = 0 \quad \text{or} \quad x - 1 = 0$$
$$2x = 1 \quad \text{or} \quad x = 1$$
$$x = \frac{1}{2}$$
Both check; the zeros of $f(x)$ are $\left\{\frac{1}{2}, 1\right\}$.

b. $f(x-2) = 2(x-2)^2 - 3(x-2) + 1$
Let $u = x - 2$.
$$2u^2 - 3u + 1 = 0$$
$$(2u-1)(u-1) = 0$$
$$2u - 1 = 0 \quad \text{or} \quad u - 1 = 0$$
$$2u = 1 \quad \text{or} \quad u = 1$$
$$u = \frac{1}{2}$$
$$x - 2 = \frac{1}{2} \quad \text{or} \quad x - 2 = 1$$
$$x = \frac{5}{2} \quad \text{or} \quad x = 3$$
Both check; the zeros of $f(x-2)$ are $\left\{\frac{5}{2}, 3\right\}$.

Comparing these solutions to those in part (a), we note that $\frac{5}{2} = \frac{1}{2} + 2$ and $3 = 1 + 2$.

c. $f(x-5) = 2(x-5)^2 - 3(x-5) + 1$

Let $u = x - 5$.

$2u^2 - 3u + 1 = 0$

$(2u-1)(u-1) = 0$

$2u - 1 = 0$ or $u - 1 = 0$

$2u = 1$ or $u = 1$

$u = \dfrac{1}{2}$

$x - 5 = \dfrac{1}{2}$ or $x - 5 = 1$

$x = \dfrac{11}{2}$ or $x = 6$

Both check; the zeros of $f(x-5)$ are

$\left\{\dfrac{11}{2}, 6\right\}$. Comparing these solutions to

those in part (a), we note that $\dfrac{11}{2} = \dfrac{1}{2} + 5$

and $6 = 1 + 5$.

d. Conjecture: For $f(x) = 2x^2 - 3x + 1$, the

zeros of the $f(x-a)$ are $\left\{\dfrac{1}{2} + a, \ 1 + a\right\}$.

NOTE: This conjecture can be shown to be true by using the techniques from parts (b) and (c).

75. a. $R(1990)$

$= \dfrac{(1990-1990)^2}{2} + \dfrac{3(1990-1990)}{2} + 3000$

$= \dfrac{0^2}{2} + \dfrac{3(0)}{2} + 3000$

$= 3000$

Interpretation: The revenue in 1990 was $3,000 thousand (or $3,000,000).

b. $\dfrac{(x-1990)^2}{2} + \dfrac{3(x-1990)}{2} + 3000 = 3065$

$\dfrac{1}{2}(x-1990)^2 + \dfrac{3}{2}(x-1990) - 65 = 0$

Let $u = x - 1990$.

$\dfrac{1}{2}u^2 + \dfrac{3}{2}u - 65 = 0$

$2\left(\dfrac{1}{2}u^2 + \dfrac{3}{2}u - 65\right) = 2(0)$

$u^2 + 3u - 130 = 0$

$(u-10)(u+13) = 0$

$u - 10 = 0$ or $u + 13 = 0$

$u = 10$ or $u = -13$

$x - 1990 = 10$ or $x - 1990 = -13$

$x = 2000$ or $x = 1977$

Since 1977 is before 1990, disregard it. The solution set is $\{2000\}$.

Interpretation: In the year 2000, revenue was $3,065 thousand (or $3,065,000).

c. $\dfrac{(x-1990)^2}{2} + \dfrac{3(x-1990)}{2} + 3000 = 3350$

$\dfrac{1}{2}(x-1990)^2 + \dfrac{3}{2}(x-1990) - 350 = 0$

Let $u = x - 1990$.

$\dfrac{1}{2}u^2 + \dfrac{3}{2}u - 350 = 0$

$2\left(\dfrac{1}{2}u^2 + \dfrac{3}{2}u - 350\right) = 2(0)$

$u^2 + 3u - 700 = 0$

$(u-25)(u+28) = 0$

$u - 25 = 0$ or $u + 28 = 0$

$u = 25$ or $u = -28$

$x - 1990 = 25$ or $x - 1990 = -28$

$x = 2015$ or $x = 1962$

Since 1962 is before 1990, disregard it. The solution set is $\{2015\}$. The model predicts that revenue will be $3,350 thousand (or $3,350,000) in the year 2015.

77. $x^4 + 5x^2 + 2 = 0$

$(x^2)^2 + 5(x^2) + 2 = 0$

Let $u = x^2$.

$u^2 + 5u + 2 = 0$

For this equation, $a = 1$, $b = 5$, and $c = 2$.

$u = \dfrac{-5 \pm \sqrt{5^2 - 4(1)(2)}}{2(1)}$

$= \dfrac{-5 \pm \sqrt{25 - 8}}{2}$

$= \dfrac{-5 \pm \sqrt{17}}{2}$

$u = \dfrac{-5 - \sqrt{17}}{2}$ or $u = \dfrac{-5 + \sqrt{17}}{2}$

$x^2 = \dfrac{-5 - \sqrt{17}}{2}$ or $x^2 = \dfrac{-5 + \sqrt{17}}{2}$

$$x = \pm\sqrt{\frac{-5-\sqrt{17}}{2}} \quad \text{or} \quad x = \pm\sqrt{\frac{-5+\sqrt{17}}{2}}$$

$$x = \pm\sqrt{\frac{-1\left(5+\sqrt{17}\right)}{2}} \qquad x = \pm\sqrt{\frac{-1\left(5-\sqrt{17}\right)}{2}}$$

$$x = \pm i\sqrt{\frac{5+\sqrt{17}}{2}} \qquad x = \pm i\sqrt{\frac{5-\sqrt{17}}{2}}$$

$$x = \pm i\sqrt{\frac{5+\sqrt{17}}{2}\cdot\frac{2}{2}} \qquad x = \pm i\sqrt{\frac{5-\sqrt{17}}{2}\cdot\frac{2}{2}}$$

$$x = \pm\frac{\sqrt{10+2\sqrt{17}}}{2}\,i \qquad x = \pm\frac{\sqrt{10-2\sqrt{17}}}{2}\,i$$

All check, the solution set is $\left\{-\dfrac{\sqrt{10+2\sqrt{17}}}{2}\,i,\right.$

$\left.\dfrac{\sqrt{10+2\sqrt{17}}}{2}\,i,\ -\dfrac{\sqrt{10-2\sqrt{17}}}{2}\,i,\ \dfrac{\sqrt{10-2\sqrt{17}}}{2}\,i\right\}$.

79. $2(x-2)^2 + 8(x-2) - 1 = 0$

Let $u = x - 2$.

$2u^2 + 8u - 1 = 0$

For this equation, $a = 2$, $b = 8$, and $c = -1$.

$$u = \frac{-8 \pm \sqrt{8^2 - 4(2)(-1)}}{2(2)}$$

$$= \frac{-8 \pm \sqrt{64+8}}{4}$$

$$= \frac{-8 \pm \sqrt{72}}{4}$$

$$= \frac{-8 \pm 6\sqrt{2}}{4} = -2 \pm \frac{3\sqrt{2}}{2}$$

$$u = -2 - \frac{3\sqrt{2}}{2} \quad \text{or} \quad u = -2 + \frac{3\sqrt{2}}{2}$$

$$x - 2 = -2 - \frac{3\sqrt{2}}{2} \quad \text{or} \quad x - 2 = -2 + \frac{3\sqrt{2}}{2}$$

$$x = -\frac{3\sqrt{2}}{2} \quad \text{or} \quad x = \frac{3\sqrt{2}}{2}$$

Both check, the solution set is $\left\{-\dfrac{3\sqrt{2}}{2},\ \dfrac{3\sqrt{2}}{2}\right\}$.

81. $\left(4x^2 - 3x - 1\right) + \left(-3x^2 + x + 5\right)$

$= 4x^2 - 3x - 1 - 3x^2 + x + 5$

$= x^2 - 2x + 4$

83. $\left(3p^{-2} - 4p^{-1} + 8\right) - \left(2p^{-2} - 8p^{-1} - 1\right)$

$= 3p^{-2} - 4p^{-1} + 8 - 2p^{-2} + 8p^{-1} + 1$

$= p^{-2} + 4p^{-1} + 9$

85. $\sqrt[3]{16a} + \sqrt[3]{54a} - \sqrt[3]{128a^4}$

$= \sqrt[3]{8\cdot 2a} + \sqrt[3]{27\cdot 2a} - \sqrt[3]{64a^3 \cdot 2a}$

$= 2\sqrt[3]{2a} + 3\sqrt[3]{2a} - 4a\sqrt[3]{2a}$

$= 5\sqrt[3]{2a} - 4a\sqrt[3]{2a}$

87. Let $Y_1 = x^4 + 5x^2 - 14$.

The solution set is approximately $\{-1.41,\ 1.41\}$.

89. Let $Y_1 = 2(x-2)^2$ and $Y_2 = 5(x-2)+1$.

The solution set is approximately $\{1.81,\ 4.69\}$.

91. Let $Y_1 = x - 5\sqrt{x}$ and $Y_2 = -3$.

The solution set is approximately $\{0.49\}$.

93. For the graphs shown in parts (a) through (c) the WINDOW setting is the following:

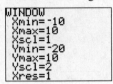

a. $Y_1 = x^2 - 5x - 6$

The x-intercepts are -1 and 6.

b. $Y_1 = (x+2)^2 - 5(x+2) - 6$

The x-intercepts are -3 and 4.

c. $Y_1 = (x+5)^2 - 5(x+5) - 6$

The x-intercepts are -6 and 1.

d. The x-intercepts of the graph of
$y = f(x) = x^2 - 5x - 6$ are -1 and 6.
The x-intercepts of the graph of
$y = f(x+a) = (x+a)^2 - 5(x+a) - 6$ are
$-1-a$ and $6-a$.

Putting the Concepts Together (8.1 – 8.3)

1. Start: $z^2 + 10z$

Add: $\left[\dfrac{1}{2} \cdot 10\right]^2 = 25$

Result: $z^2 + 10z + 25$

Factored Form: $(z+5)^2$

2. Start: $x^2 + 7x$

Add: $\left[\dfrac{1}{2} \cdot 7\right]^2 = \dfrac{49}{4}$

Result: $x^2 + 7x + \dfrac{49}{4}$

Factored Form: $\left(x + \dfrac{7}{2}\right)^2$

3. Start: $n^2 - \dfrac{1}{4}n$

Add: $\left[\dfrac{1}{2} \cdot \left(-\dfrac{1}{4}\right)\right]^2 = \dfrac{1}{64}$

Result: $n^2 - \dfrac{1}{4}n + \dfrac{1}{64}$

Factored Form: $\left(n - \dfrac{1}{8}\right)^2$

4. $(2x-3)^2 - 5 = -1$

$(2x-3)^2 = 4$

$2x - 3 = \pm\sqrt{4}$

$2x - 3 = \pm 2$

$2x = 3 \pm 2$

$2x = 1 \quad$ or $\quad 2x = 5$

$x = \dfrac{1}{2} \quad$ or $\quad x = \dfrac{5}{2}$

The solution set is $\left\{\dfrac{1}{2}, \dfrac{5}{2}\right\}$.

5. $\qquad x^2 + 8x + 4 = 0$

$\qquad x^2 + 8x \quad\;\; = -4$

$x^2 + 8x + \left(\dfrac{1}{2} \cdot 8\right)^2 = -4 + \left(\dfrac{1}{2} \cdot 8\right)^2$

$\qquad x^2 + 8x + 16 = -4 + 16$

$\qquad\quad (x+4)^2 = 12$

$\qquad\qquad x + 4 = \pm\sqrt{12}$

$\qquad\qquad x + 4 = \pm 2\sqrt{3}$

$\qquad\qquad\quad x = -4 \pm 2\sqrt{3}$

The solution set is $\left\{-4 - 2\sqrt{3}, \; -4 + 2\sqrt{3}\right\}$.

6. $x(x-6) = -7$

$x^2 - 6x + 7 = 0$

For this equation, $a = 1$, $b = -6$, and $c = 7$.

$x = \dfrac{-(-6) \pm \sqrt{(-6)^2 - 4(1)(7)}}{2(1)}$

$= \dfrac{6 \pm \sqrt{36 - 28}}{2}$

$= \dfrac{6 \pm \sqrt{8}}{2}$

$= \dfrac{6 \pm 2\sqrt{2}}{2} = \dfrac{6}{2} \pm \dfrac{2\sqrt{2}}{2} = 3 \pm \sqrt{2}$

The solution set is $\left\{ 3 - \sqrt{2},\ 3 + \sqrt{2} \right\}$.

7. $49x^2 - 80 = 0$

$49x^2 = 80$

$x^2 = \dfrac{80}{49}$

$x = \pm\sqrt{\dfrac{80}{49}} = \pm\dfrac{\sqrt{80}}{\sqrt{49}} = \pm\dfrac{4\sqrt{5}}{7}$

The solution set is $\left\{ -\dfrac{4\sqrt{5}}{7},\ \dfrac{4\sqrt{5}}{7} \right\}$.

8. $p^2 - 8p + 6 = 0$

Because this equation does not easily factor, solve by using the quadratic formula. For this equation, $a = 1$, $b = -8$, and $c = 6$.

$p = \dfrac{-(-8) \pm \sqrt{(-8)^2 - 4(1)(6)}}{2(1)}$

$= \dfrac{8 \pm \sqrt{64 - 24}}{2}$

$= \dfrac{8 \pm \sqrt{40}}{2}$

$= \dfrac{8 \pm 2\sqrt{10}}{2}$

$= \dfrac{8}{2} \pm \dfrac{2\sqrt{10}}{2} = 4 \pm \sqrt{10}$

The solution set is $\left\{ 4 - \sqrt{10},\ 4 + \sqrt{10} \right\}$.

9. $3y^2 + 6y + 4 = 0$

Because this equation does not easily factor, solve by using the quadratic formula. For this equation, $a = 3$, $b = 6$, and $c = 4$.

$y = \dfrac{-6 \pm \sqrt{6^2 - 4(3)(4)}}{2(3)}$

$= \dfrac{-6 \pm \sqrt{36 - 48}}{6}$

$= \dfrac{-6 \pm \sqrt{-12}}{6}$

$= \dfrac{-6 \pm 2\sqrt{3}\,i}{6} = \dfrac{-6}{6} \pm \dfrac{2\sqrt{3}}{6}i = -1 \pm \dfrac{\sqrt{3}}{3}i$

The solution set is $\left\{ -1 - \dfrac{\sqrt{3}}{3}i,\ -1 + \dfrac{\sqrt{3}}{3}i \right\}$.

10. $\dfrac{1}{4}n^2 + n = \dfrac{1}{6}$

$12\left(\dfrac{1}{4}n^2 + n \right) = 12\left(\dfrac{1}{6} \right)$

$3n^2 + 12n = 2$

$3n^2 + 12n - 2 = 0$

Because this equation does not easily factor, solve by using the quadratic formula. For this equation, $a = 3$, $b = 12$, and $c = -2$.

$n = \dfrac{-12 \pm \sqrt{12^2 - 4(3)(-2)}}{2(3)}$

$= \dfrac{-12 \pm \sqrt{144 + 24}}{6}$

$= \dfrac{-12 \pm \sqrt{168}}{6}$

$= \dfrac{-12 \pm 2\sqrt{42}}{6}$

$= -\dfrac{12}{6} \pm \dfrac{2\sqrt{42}}{6} = -2 \pm \dfrac{\sqrt{42}}{3}$

The solution set is $\left\{ -2 - \dfrac{\sqrt{42}}{3},\ -2 + \dfrac{\sqrt{42}}{3} \right\}$

11. $9x^2 + 12x + 4 = 0$

For this equation, $a = 9$, $b = 12$, and $c = 4$.

$b^2 - 4ac = 12^2 - 4(9)(4) = 144 - 144 = 0$

Because $b^2 - 4ac = 0$, the quadratic equation will have one repeated real solution.

12. $3x^2 + 6x - 2 = 0$

For this equation, $a = 3$, $b = 6$, and $c = -2$.

$b^2 - 4ac = 6^2 - 4(3)(-2) = 36 + 24 = 60$

Because $b^2 - 4ac = 60$ is positive, but not a perfect square, the quadratic equation will have two irrational solutions.

13. $2x^2 + 6x + 5 = 0$

For this equation, $a = 2$, $b = 6$, and $c = 5$.

$b^2 - 4ac = 6^2 - 4(2)(5) = 36 - 40 = -4$

Because $b^2 - 4ac = -4$ is negative, the quadratic equation will have two complex solutions that are not real. The solutions will be complex conjugates of each other.

14. $c^2 = 4^2 + 10^2 = 16 + 100 = 116$

$c = \sqrt{116} = 2\sqrt{29}$

15. $2m + 7\sqrt{m} - 15 = 0$

$2\left(\sqrt{m}\right)^2 + 7\left(\sqrt{m}\right) - 15 = 0$

Let $u = \sqrt{m}$.

$2u^2 + 7u - 15 = 0$

$(2u - 3)(u + 5) = 0$

$2u - 3 = 0 \quad$ or $\quad u + 5 = 0$

$2u = 3 \quad$ or $\quad u = -5$

$u = \dfrac{3}{2}$

$\sqrt{m} = \dfrac{3}{2} \quad$ or $\quad \sqrt{m} = -5$

$m = \left(\dfrac{3}{2}\right)^2 \quad$ or $\quad m = (-5)^2$

$m = \dfrac{9}{4} \quad$ or $\quad m = 25$

Check:

$m = \dfrac{9}{4}: \quad 2 \cdot \dfrac{9}{4} + 7\sqrt{\dfrac{9}{4}} - 15 \overset{?}{=} 0$

$2 \cdot \dfrac{9}{4} + 7 \cdot \dfrac{3}{2} - 15 \overset{?}{=} 0$

$\dfrac{9}{2} + \dfrac{21}{2} - 15 \overset{?}{=} 0$

$0 = 0 \checkmark$

$m = 25: \quad 2 \cdot 25 + 7\sqrt{25} - 15 \overset{?}{=} 0$

$2 \cdot 25 + 7 \cdot 5 - 15 \overset{?}{=} 0$

$50 + 35 - 15 \overset{?}{=} 0$

$70 \neq 0 \; ✗$

$m = 25$ does not check; the solution set is $\left\{\dfrac{9}{4}\right\}$.

16. $p^{-2} - 3p^{-1} - 18 = 0$

$\left(p^{-1}\right)^2 - 3\left(p^{-1}\right) - 18 = 0$

Let $u = p^{-1}$.

$u^2 - 3u - 18 = 0$

$(u + 3)(u - 6) = 0$

$u + 3 = 0 \quad$ or $\quad u - 6 = 0$

$u = -3 \quad$ or $\quad u = 6$

$p^{-1} = -3 \quad$ or $\quad p^{-1} = 6$

$\dfrac{1}{p} = -3 \quad$ or $\quad \dfrac{1}{p} = 6$

$p = -\dfrac{1}{3} \quad$ or $\quad p = \dfrac{1}{6}$

Check:

$p = -\dfrac{1}{3}: \quad \left(-\dfrac{1}{3}\right)^{-2} - 3\left(-\dfrac{1}{3}\right)^{-1} - 18 \overset{?}{=} 0$

$(-3)^2 - 3(-3) - 18 \overset{?}{=} 0$

$9 + 9 - 18 \overset{?}{=} 0$

$0 = 0 \checkmark$

$p = \dfrac{1}{6}: \quad \left(\dfrac{1}{6}\right)^{-2} - 3\left(\dfrac{1}{6}\right)^{-1} - 18 \overset{?}{=} 0$

$(6)^2 - 3(6) - 18 \overset{?}{=} 0$

$36 - 18 - 18 \overset{?}{=} 0$

$0 = 0 \checkmark$

Both check; the solution set is $\left\{\dfrac{1}{6}, \; -\dfrac{1}{3}\right\}$.

17. $12{,}000 = -0.4x^2 + 140x$

$0.4x^2 - 140x + 12{,}000 = 0$

For this equation, $a = 0.4$, $b = -140$, and $c = 12{,}000$.

$x = \dfrac{-(-140) \pm \sqrt{(-140)^2 - 4(0.4)(12{,}000)}}{2(0.4)}$

$= \dfrac{140 \pm \sqrt{400}}{0.8}$

$= \dfrac{140 \pm 20}{0.8}$

$x = \dfrac{140 + 20}{0.8} \quad$ or $\quad x = \dfrac{140 - 20}{0.8}$

$= 200 \quad$ or $\quad = 150$

Revenue will be \$12,000 when either 150 microwaves or 200 microwaves are sold.

18. Let x represent the speed of the wind.

	Distance	Rate	Time
Against Wind	300	$140 - x$	$\dfrac{300}{140 - x}$
With Wind	300	$140 + x$	$\dfrac{300}{140 + x}$

$$\frac{300}{140 - x} + \frac{300}{140 + x} = 5$$

$$(140 - x)(140 + x)\left(\frac{300}{140 - x} + \frac{300}{140 + x}\right)$$
$$= (140 - x)(140 + x)(5)$$

$$300(140 + x) + 300(140 - x) = \left(19,600 - x^2\right)(5)$$

$$42,000 + 300x + 42,000 - 300x = 98,000 - 5x^2$$

$$84,000 = 98,000 - 5x^2$$

$$-14,000 = -5x^2$$

$$2800 = x^2$$

$$x = \pm\sqrt{2800}$$

$$= \pm 20\sqrt{7}$$

$$\approx \pm 52.915$$

Because the speed should be positive, we disregard $x \approx -52.915$. Thus, the only viable answer is $x \approx 52.915$. Rounding to the nearest tenth, the speed of the wind was approximately 52.9 miles per hour.

8.4 Preparing for Graphs of Quadratic Functions Using Transfromations

1. Locate some points on the graph of $f(x) = x^2$.

x	$f(x) = x^2$	$(x, f(x))$
-3	$f(-3) = (-3)^2 = 9$	$(-3, 9)$
-2	$f(-2) = (-2)^2 = 4$	$(-2, 4)$
-1	$f(-1) = (-1)^2 = 1$	$(-1, 1)$
0	$f(0) = 0^2 = 0$	$(0, 0)$
1	$f(1) = 1^2 = 1$	$(1, 1)$
2	$f(2) = 2^2 = 4$	$(2, 4)$
3	$f(3) = 3^2 = 9$	$(3, 9)$

Plot the points and connect them with a smooth curve.

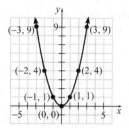

2. Locate some points on the graph of $f(x) = x^2 - 3$.

x	$f(x) = x^2 - 3$	$(x, f(x))$
-3	$f(-3) = (-3)^2 - 3 = 6$	$(-3, 6)$
-2	$f(-2) = (-2)^2 - 3 = 1$	$(-2, 1)$
-1	$f(-1) = (-1)^2 - 3 = -2$	$(-1, -2)$
0	$f(0) = 0^2 - 3 = -3$	$(0, -3)$
1	$f(1) = 1^2 - 3 = -2$	$(1, -2)$
2	$f(2) = 2^2 - 3 = 1$	$(2, 1)$
3	$f(3) = 3^2 - 3 = 6$	$(3, 6)$

Plot the points and connect them with a smooth curve.

3. For $f(x) = 2x^2 + 5x + 1$, the independent variable x can take on any value on the real number line. That is, f is defined for all real x values. Thus, the domain is the set of all real number, or $(-\infty, \infty)$.

8.4 Exercises

1. quadratic function

3. y-coordinate; a; vertically stretched; vertically compressed.

5. FALSE. To obtain the graph of $f(x) = (x + 5)^2$ we shift the graph of $y = x^2$ horizontally to the *left* 5 units.

7. The lowest or highest point on a parabola (the graph of $y = ax^2 + bx + c$) is called the *vertex*. If $a > 0$, the graph opens up and the vertex is the low point. If $a < 0$, the graph opens down and the vertex is the high point.

9. (I) The graph of $f(x) = x^2 + 3$ is the graph of $y = x^2$ shifted 3 units up. Thus, the graph of the function is graph (D).

(II) The graph of $f(x) = (x+3)^2$ is the graph of $y = x^2$ shifted 3 units to the left. Thus, the graph of the function is graph (A).

(III) The graph of $f(x) = x^2 - 3$ is the graph of $y = x^2$ shifted 3 units down. Thus, the graph of the function is graph (C).

(IV) The graph of $f(x) = (x-3)^2$ is the graph of $y = x^2$ shifted 3 units to the right. Thus, the graph of the function is graph (B).

11. To obtain the graph of $f(x) = (x+10)^2$, begin with the graph of $y = x^2$ and shift it 10 units to the left.

13. To obtain the graph of $F(x) = x^2 + 12$, begin with the graph of $y = x^2$ and shift it 12 units up.

15. To obtain the graph of $H(x) = 2(x-5)^2$, begin with the graph of $y = x^2$, shift it 5 units to the right, and vertically stretch it by a factor of 2 (multiply the y-coordinates by 2).

17. To obtain the graph of $f(x) = -3(x+5)^2 + 8$, begin with the graph of $y = x^2$, shift it 5 units to the left, multiply the y-coordinates by -3 (which means it opens down and is stretched vertically by a factor of 3), and shift the graph up 8 units.

19. Begin with the graph of $y = x^2$, then shift the graph up 1 unit to obtain the graph of $f(x) = x^2 + 1$.

21. Begin with the graph of $y = x^2$, then shift the graph up 6 units to obtain the graph of $h(x) = x^2 + 6$.

23. Begin with the graph of $y = x^2$, then shift the graph to the right 3 units to obtain the graph of $F(x) = (x-3)^2$.

25. Begin with the graph of $y = x^2$, then shift the graph 2 units to the left to obtain the graph of $h(x) = (x+2)^2$.

27. Begin with the graph of $y = x^2$, then vertically stretch the graph by a factor of 4 (multiply each y-coordinate by 4) to obtain the graph of $g(x) = 4x^2$.

29. Begin with the graph of $y = x^2$, then vertically compress the graph by a factor of $\frac{1}{3}$ (multiply each y-coordinate by $\frac{1}{3}$) to obtain the graph of

$$H(x) = \frac{1}{3}x^2.$$

31. Begin with the graph of $y = x^2$, then multiply each y-coordinate by -1 to obtain the graph of $p(x) = -x^2$.

33. Begin with the graph of $y = x^2$, then shift the graph 1 unit to the right to obtain the graph of $y = (x-1)^2$. Shift this graph down 3 units to obtain the graph of $f(x) = (x-1)^2 - 3$.

35. Begin with the graph of $y = x^2$, then shift the graph 3 units to the left to obtain the graph of $y = (x+3)^2$. Shift this graph up 1 unit to obtain the graph of $F(x) = (x+3)^2 + 1$.

37. Begin with the graph of $y = x^2$, then shift the graph 3 units to the left to obtain the graph of $y = (x+3)^2$. Multiply the y-coordinates by -1 to obtain the graph of $y = -(x+3)^2$. Lastly, shift the graph up 2 units to obtain the graph of $h(x) = -(x+3)^2 + 2$.

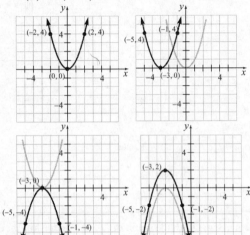

39. Begin with the graph of $y = x^2$, then shift the graph 1 unit to the left to obtain the graph of $y = (x+1)^2$. Vertically stretch this graph by a factor of 2 (multiply the y-coordinates by 2) to obtain the graph of $y = 2(x+1)^2$. Lastly, shift the graph down 2 units to obtain the graph of $G(x) = 2(x+1)^2 - 2$.

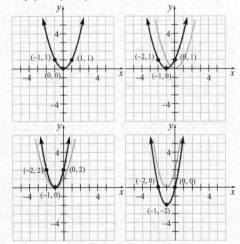

41. Begin with the graph of $y = x^2$, then shift the graph 5 units to the left to obtain the graph of $y = (x+5)^2$. Multiply the y-coordinates by $-\dfrac{1}{2}$ to obtain the graph of $y = -\dfrac{1}{2}(x+5)^2$. Lastly, shift the graph up 3 units to obtain the graph of $H(x) = -\dfrac{1}{2}(x+5)^2 + 3$.

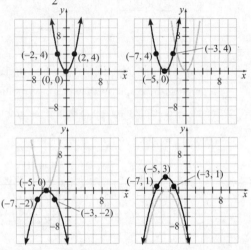

43. Use completing the square to write the function in the form $y = a(x-h)^2 + k$.

$$f(x) = x^2 + 2x - 4$$
$$= (x^2 + 2x + 1) - 4 - 1$$
$$= (x+1)^2 - 5$$

Begin with the graph of $y = x^2$, the shift the graph 1 unit to the left to obtain the graph of $y = (x+1)^2$. Shift this graph down 5 units to obtain the graph of $f(x) = (x+1)^2 - 5$.

The vertex is $(h,k)=(-1,-5)$ and the axis of symmetry is $x=-1$. The domain is the set of all real numbers or, using interval notation, $(-\infty,\infty)$. The range is $\{y \mid y \geq -5\}$ or, using interval notation, $[-5,\infty)$.

45. Use completing the square to write the function in the form $y=a(x-h)^2+k$.

$$g(x)=x^2-4x+8=\left(x^2-4x\right)+8$$
$$=\left(x^2-4x+4\right)+8-4$$
$$=(x-2)^2+4$$

Begin with the graph of $y=x^2$, then shift the graph right 2 units to obtain the graph of $y=(x-2)^2$. Shift this graph up 4 units to obtain the graph of $g(x)=(x-2)^2+4$.

The vertex is $(h,k)=(2,4)$ and the axis of symmetry is $x=2$. The domain is the set of all real numbers or, using interval notation, $(-\infty,\infty)$. The range is $\{y \mid y \geq 4\}$ or, using interval notation, $[4,\infty)$.

47. Use completing the square to write the function in the form $y=a(x-h)^2+k$.

$$f(x)=x^2+6x-16$$
$$=\left(x^2+6x\right)-16$$
$$=\left(x^2+6x+9\right)-16-9$$
$$=(x+3)^2-25$$

Begin with the graph of $y=x^2$, then shift the graph 3 units left to obtain the graph of $y=(x+3)^2$. Shift this result down 25 units to obtain the graph of $f(x)=(x+3)^2-25$.

The vertex is $(h,k)=(-3,-25)$ and the axis of symmetry is $x=-3$. The domain is the set of all real numbers or, using interval notation, $(-\infty,\infty)$. The range is $\{y \mid y \geq -25\}$ or, using interval notation, $[-25,\infty)$.

49. Use completing the square to write the function in the form $y = a(x-h)^2 + k$.

$$F(x) = x^2 + x - 12$$
$$= (x^2 + x) - 12$$
$$= \left(x^2 + x + \frac{1}{4}\right) - 12 - \frac{1}{4}$$
$$= \left(x + \frac{1}{2}\right)^2 - \frac{49}{4}$$

Begin with the graph of $y = x^2$, then shift the graph left $\frac{1}{2}$ unit to obtain the graph of $y = \left(x + \frac{1}{2}\right)^2$. Shift this graph down $\frac{49}{4}$ units to obtain the graph of $F(x) = \left(x + \frac{1}{2}\right)^2 - \frac{49}{4}$.

The vertex is $(h,k) = \left(-\frac{1}{2}, -\frac{49}{4}\right)$ and the axis of symmetry is $x = -\frac{1}{2}$. The domain is the set of all real numbers or, using interval notation, $(-\infty, \infty)$. The range is $\left\{y \mid y \geq -\frac{49}{4}\right\}$ or, using interval notation, $\left[-\frac{49}{4}, \infty\right)$.

51. Use completing the square to write the function in the form $y = a(x-h)^2 + k$.

$$H(x) = 2x^2 - 4x - 1$$
$$= (2x^2 - 4x) - 1$$
$$= 2(x^2 - 2x) - 1$$
$$= 2(x^2 - 2x + 1) - 1 - 2$$
$$= 2(x-1)^2 - 3$$

Begin with the graph of $y = x^2$, then shift the graph right 1 unit to obtain the graph of $y = (x-1)^2$. Vertically stretch this graph by a factor of 2 (multiply the y-coordinates by 2) to obtain the graph of $y = 2(x-1)^2$. Lastly, shift the graph down 3 units to obtain the graph of $H(x) = 2(x-1)^2 - 3$.

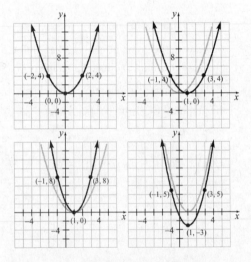

The vertex is $(h,k) = (1,-3)$ and the axis of symmetry is $x = 1$. The domain is the set of all real numbers or, using interval notation, $(-\infty, \infty)$. The range is $\{y \mid y \geq -3\}$ or, using interval notation, $[-3, \infty)$.

53. Use completing the square to write the function in the form $y = a(x-h)^2 + k$.

$$P(x) = 3x^2 + 12x + 13$$
$$= \left(3x^2 + 12x\right) + 13$$
$$= 3\left(x^2 + 4x\right) + 13$$
$$= 3\left(x^2 + 4x + 4\right) + 13 - 12$$
$$= 3(x+2)^2 + 1$$

Begin with the graph of $y = x^2$, then shift the graph left 2 units to obtain the graph of $y = (x+2)^2$. Vertically stretch this graph by a factor of 3 (multiply the y-coordinates by 3) to obtain the graph of $y = 3(x+2)^2$. Lastly, shift the graph up 1 unit to obtain the graph of $P(x) = 3(x+2)^2 + 1$.

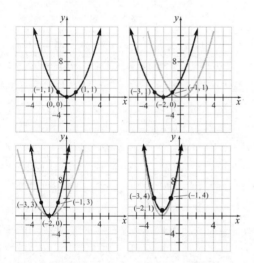

The vertex is $(h,k) = (-2,1)$ and the axis of symmetry is $x = -2$. The domain is the set of all real numbers or, using interval notation, $(-\infty, \infty)$. The range is $\{y \mid y \geq 1\}$ or, using interval notation, $[1, \infty)$.

55. Use completing the square to write the function in the form $y = a(x-h)^2 + k$.

$$F(x) = -x^2 - 10x - 21$$
$$= \left(-x^2 - 10x\right) - 21$$
$$= -\left(x^2 + 10x\right) - 21$$
$$= -\left(x^2 + 10x + 25\right) - 21 + 25$$
$$= -(x+5)^2 + 4$$

Begin with the graph of $y = x^2$, then shift the graph left 5 units to obtain the graph of $y = (x+5)^2$. Multiply the y-coordinates by -1 to obtain the graph of $y = -(x+5)^2$. Lastly, shift the graph up 4 units to obtain the graph of $F(x) = -(x+5)^2 + 4$.

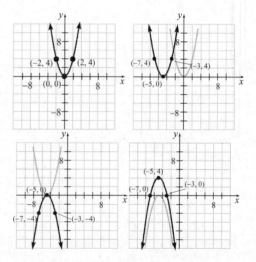

The vertex is $(h,k) = (-5,4)$ and the axis of symmetry is $x = -5$. The domain is the set of all real numbers or, using interval notation, $(-\infty, \infty)$. The range is $\{y \mid y \leq 4\}$ or, using interval notation, $(-\infty, 4]$.

57. Use completing the square to write the function in the form $y = a(x-h)^2 + k$.

$$g(x) = -x^2 + 6x - 1$$
$$= \left(-x^2 + 6x\right) - 1$$
$$= -\left(x^2 - 6x\right) - 1$$
$$= -\left(x^2 - 6x + 9\right) - 1 + 9$$
$$= -(x-3)^2 + 8$$

Begin with the graph of $y = x^2$, then shift the graph right 3 units to obtain the graph of $y = (x-3)^2$. Multiply the y-coordinates by -1 to obtain the graph of $y = -(x-3)^2$. Lastly, shift the graph up 8 units to obtain the graph of $g(x) = -(x-3)^2 + 8$.

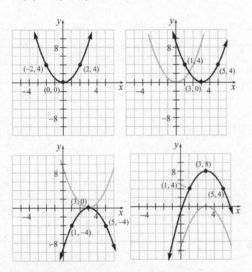

The vertex is $(h,k) = (3,8)$ and the axis of symmetry is $x = 3$. The domain is the set of all real numbers or, using interval notation, $(-\infty, \infty)$. The range is $\{y \mid y \le 8\}$ or, using interval notation, $(-\infty, 8]$.

59. Use completing the square to write the function in the form $y = a(x-h)^2 + k$.

$$H(x) = -2x^2 + 8x - 4$$
$$= \left(-2x^2 + 8x\right) - 4$$
$$= -2\left(x^2 - 4x\right) - 4$$
$$= -2\left(x^2 - 4x + 4\right) - 4 + 8$$
$$= -2(x-2)^2 + 4$$

Begin with the graph of $y = x^2$, then shift the graph right 2 units to obtain the graph of $y = (x-2)^2$. Multiply the y-coordinates by -2 to obtain the graph of $y = -2(x-2)^2$. Lastly, shift the graph up 4 units to obtain the graph of $H(x) = -2(x-2)^2 + 4$.

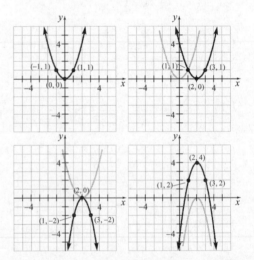

The vertex is $(h,k) = (2,4)$ and the axis of symmetry is $x = 2$. The domain is the set of all real numbers or, using interval notation, $(-\infty, \infty)$. The range is $\{y \mid y \le 4\}$ or, using interval notation, $(-\infty, 4]$.

61. Use completing the square to write the function in the form $y = a(x-h)^2 + k$.

$$f(x) = \frac{1}{3}x^2 - 2x + 4$$

$$= \left(\frac{1}{3}x^2 - 2x\right) + 4$$

$$= \frac{1}{3}\left(x^2 - 6x\right) + 4$$

$$= \frac{1}{3}\left(x^2 - 6x + 9\right) + 4 - 3$$

$$= \frac{1}{3}(x-3)^2 + 1$$

Begin with the graph of $y = x^2$, then shift the graph right 3 units to obtain the graph of $y = (x-3)^2$. Vertically compress the graph by a factor of $\frac{1}{3}$ (multiply the y-coordinates by $\frac{1}{3}$) to obtain the graph of $y = \frac{1}{3}(x-3)^2$. Lastly, shift the graph up 1 unit to obtain the graph of $f(x) = \frac{1}{3}(x-3)^2 + 1$.

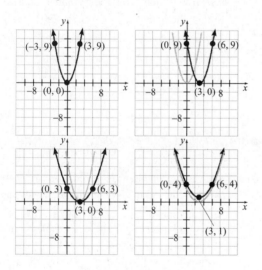

The vertex is $(h,k) = (3,1)$ and the axis of symmetry is $x = 1$. The domain is the set of all real numbers or, using interval notation, $(-\infty, \infty)$. The range is $\{y \mid y \geq 1\}$ or, using interval notation, $[1, \infty)$.

63. Use completing the square to write the function in the form $y = a(x-h)^2 + k$.

$$G(x) = -12x^2 - 12x + 1$$

$$= \left(-12x^2 - 12x\right) + 1$$

$$= -12\left(x^2 + x\right) + 1$$

$$= -12\left(x^2 + x + \frac{1}{4}\right) + 1 + 3$$

$$= -12\left(x + \frac{1}{2}\right)^2 + 4$$

Begin with the graph of $y = x^2$, then shift left $\frac{1}{2}$ unit to obtain the graph of $y = \left(x + \frac{1}{2}\right)^2$. Multiply the y-coordinates by -12 to obtain the graph of $y = -12\left(x + \frac{1}{2}\right)^2$. Lastly, shift the graph up 4 units to obtain the graph of $G(x) = -12\left(x + \frac{1}{2}\right)^2 + 4$.

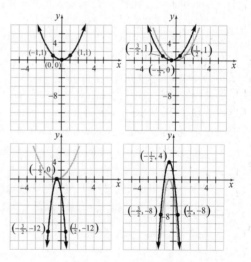

The vertex is $(h,k) = \left(-\frac{1}{2}, 4\right)$ and the axis of symmetry is $x = -\frac{1}{2}$. The domain is the set of all real numbers or, using interval notation, $(-\infty, \infty)$. The range is $\{y \mid y \leq 4\}$ or, using interval notation, $(-\infty, 4]$.

65. Answers may vary. Since the graph opens up, one possibility is to let $a = 1$. The vertex is $(3, 0)$ so we have $h = 3$ and $k = 0$. Substituting these values into the form $y = a(x - h)^2 + k$ gives $y = f(x) = (x - 3)^2$.

67. Answers may vary. Since the graph opens up, one possibility is to let $a = 1$. The vertex is $(-3, 1)$ so we have $h = -3$ and $k = 1$. Substituting these values into the form $y = a(x - h)^2 + k$ give $y = f(x) = (x + 3)^2 + 1$.

69. Answers may vary. Since the graph opens down, one possibility is to let $a = -1$. The vertex is $(5, -1)$ so we have $h = 5$ and $k = -1$. Substituting these values into the form $y = a(x - h)^2 + k$ gives $y = f(x) = -(x - 5)^2 - 1$.

71. Consider the form $y = a(x - h)^2 + k$. Since the graph opens up, we know that $a > 0$. The graph is vertically stretched by a factor of 4 so we know that $a = 4$. The vertex is $(9, -6)$ so we have $h = 9$ and $k = -6$. Substituting these values gives $y = f(x) = 4(x - 9)^2 - 6$.

73. Consider the form $y = a(x - h)^2 + k$. Since the graph opens down, we know that $a < 0$. The graph is vertically compressed by a factor of $\dfrac{1}{3}$ so we know that $a = -\dfrac{1}{3}$. The vertex is $(0, 6)$ so we have $h = 0$ and $k = 6$. Substituting these values gives $y = f(x) = -\dfrac{1}{3}x^2 + 6$.

75. Consider the form $y = a(x - h)^2 + k$. From the graph we know that the vertex is $(-1, -3)$ so we have $h = -1$ and $k = -3$. The graph also passes through the point $(x, y) = (0, -2)$. Substituting these values for x, y, h, and k, we can solve for a:

$-2 = a(0 - (-1))^2 + (-3)$

$-2 = a(1)^2 - 3$

$-2 = a - 3$

$1 = a$

The quadratic function is $f(x) = (x + 1)^2 - 3$.

77. Consider the form $y = a(x - h)^2 + k$. From the graph we know that the vertex is $(3, 7)$ so we have $h = 3$ and $k = 7$. The graph also passes through the point $(x, y) = (0, -11)$. Substituting these values for x, y, h, and k, we can solve for a:

$-11 = a(0 - 3)^2 + 7$

$-11 = a(-3)^2 + 7$

$-18 = 9a$

$-2 = a$

The quadratic function is $f(x) = -2(x - 3)^2 + 7$.

79. Consider the form $y = a(x - h)^2 + k$. From the graph we know that the vertex is $(-4, 0)$ so we have $h = -4$ and $k = 0$. The graph also passes through the point $(x, y) = (-3, 1)$. Substituting these values for x, y, h, and k, we can solve for a:

$1 = a(-3 - (-4))^2 + 0$

$1 = a(-3 + 4)^2$

$1 = a(1)^2$

$1 = a$

The quadratic function is $f(x) = (x + 4)^2$.

81. A quadratic function can never have a range of $(-\infty, \infty)$. The graph of a quadratic always has a turning point so it always has either a lowest point or a highest point. In either case, the range is limited by k, the y-coordinate of the vertex. The range will either be $(-\infty, k]$ if the graph opens down or $[k, \infty)$ if the graph opens up.

83. $12\overline{)349}$ with quotient 29: $\underline{24}$, 109, $\underline{108}$, 1. So, $\dfrac{349}{12} = 29 + \dfrac{1}{12} = 29\dfrac{1}{12}$.

85.

$$2x-1 \overline{\smash{\big)}\, 2x^4 - 11x^3 + 13x^2 - 8x}$$

$$\underline{2x^4 - x^3}$$
$$-10x^3 + 13x^2 - 8x$$
$$\underline{-10x^3 + 5x^2}$$
$$8x^2 - 8x$$
$$\underline{8x^2 - 4x}$$
$$-4x$$
$$\underline{-4x + 2}$$
$$-2$$

So,

$$\frac{2x^4 - 11x^3 + 13x^2 - 8x}{2x - 1} = x^3 - 5x^2 + 4x - 2 + \frac{-2}{2x - 1}$$

87. $f(x) = x^2 + 1.3$

Vertex: $(0, 1.3)$

Axis of symmetry: $x = 0$

Range: $\{y \mid y \geq 1.3\} = [1.3, \infty)$

89. $g(x) = (x - 2.5)^2$

Vertex: $(2.5, 0)$

Axis of symmetry: $x = 2.5$

Range: $\{y \mid y \geq 0\} = [0, \infty)$

91. $h(x) = 2.3(x - 1.4)^2 + 0.5$

Vertex: $(1.4, 0.5)$

Axis of symmetry: $x = 1.4$

Range: $\{y \mid y \geq 0.5\} = [0.5, \infty)$

93. $F(x) = -3.4(x - 2.8)^2 + 5.9$

Vertex: $(2.8, 5.9)$

Axis of symmetry: $x = 2.8$

Range: $\{y \mid y \leq 5.9\} = (-\infty, 5.9]$

8.5 Preparing for Graphing Quadratic Functions Using Properties

1. To find the *y*-intercept, let $x = 0$ and solve for *y*:
$$2(0) + 5y = 20$$
$$5y = 20$$
$$y = 4$$

To find the *x*-intercept, let $y = 0$ and solve for *x*:
$$2x + 5(0) = 20$$
$$2x = 20$$
$$x = 10$$

The intercepts are $(0, 4)$ and $(10, 0)$.

2. $2x^2 - 3x - 20 = 0$
$$(2x + 5)(x - 4) = 0$$
$$2x + 5 = 0 \quad \text{or} \quad x - 4 = 0$$
$$x = -\frac{5}{2} \quad \text{or} \quad x = 4$$

The solution set is $\left\{-\frac{5}{2}, 4\right\}$.

3. $f(x) = 0$
$$x^2 - 3x - 4 = 0$$
$$(x + 1)(x - 4) = 0$$
$$x + 1 = 0 \quad \text{or} \quad x - 4 = 0$$
$$x = -1 \quad \text{or} \quad x = 4$$

The zeros are -1 and 4.

Section 8.5

1. $x = -\dfrac{b}{2a}$

3. minimum value

5. FALSE. $f(x) = x^2 + 4x - 3$ is in standard form with $a = 1$, $b = 4$, and $c = -3$. The x-coordinate of the vertex is given by $x = -\dfrac{b}{2a} = -\dfrac{4}{2(1)} = -2$. The y-coordinate is $f(-2) = -7$, so the vertex is $(-2, -7)$.

7. Answers may vary. One possibility follows: If the discriminant $b^2 - 4ac > 0$, the graph of the quadratic function will have two different x-intercepts. If the discriminant $b^2 - 4ac = 0$, the graph will have one x-intercept. If the discriminant $b^2 - 4ac < 0$, the graph will not have any x-intercepts.

9. $f(x) = x^2 - 6x - 16$;
$a = 1, b = -6, c = -16$;
$b^2 - 4ac = (-6)^2 - 4(1)(-16) = 36 + 64 = 100$.
Because the discriminant is positive, the parabola will have two distinct x-intercepts.

The x-intercepts are:
$$f(x) = 0$$
$$x^2 - 6x - 16 = 0$$
$$(x - 8)(x + 2) = 0$$
$$x - 8 = 0 \quad \text{or} \quad x + 2 = 0$$
$$x = 8 \qquad\qquad x = -2$$

11. $G(x) = -3x^2 + x - 1$;
$a = -3, b = 1, c = -1$;
$b^2 - 4ac = 1^2 - 4(-3)(-1) = 1 - 12 = -11$.
Because the discriminant is negative, the parabola will have no x-intercepts.

13. $h(x) = 4x^2 + 4x + 1$;
$a = 4, b = 4, c = 1$;
$b^2 - 4ac = 4^2 - 4(4)(1) = 16 - 16 = 0$.
Because the discriminant is zero, the parabola will have one x-intercept.

The x-intercept is:
$$h(x) = 0$$
$$4x^2 + 4x + 1 = 0$$
$$(2x + 1)^2 = 0$$
$$2x + 1 = 0$$
$$2x = -1$$
$$x = -\dfrac{1}{2}$$

15. $F(x) = 4x^2 - x - 1$;
$a = 4, b = -1, c = -1$;
$b^2 - 4ac = (-1)^2 - 4(4)(-1) = 1 + 16 = 17$.
Because the discriminant is positive, the parabola will have two distinct x-intercepts.

The x-intercepts are:
$$F(x) = 0$$
$$4x^2 - x - 1 = 0$$
$$x = \dfrac{-(-1) \pm \sqrt{(-1)^2 - 4(4)(-1)}}{2(4)}$$
$$= \dfrac{1 \pm \sqrt{17}}{8}$$
$$x \approx -0.39 \quad \text{or} \quad x \approx 0.64$$

17. $f(x) = x^2 - 4x - 5$
$a = 1, b = -4, c = -5$
The graph opens up because $a > 0$.

vertex:
$$x = -\dfrac{b}{2a} = -\dfrac{(-4)}{2(1)} = 2$$
$$f(2) = (2)^2 - 4(2) - 5 = -9$$

The vertex is $(2, -9)$ and the axis of symmetry is $x = 2$.

y-intercept:
$$f(0) = (0)^2 - 4(0) - 5 = -5$$

x-intercepts:
$$b^2 - 4ac = (-4)^2 - 4(1)(-5) = 36 > 0$$
There are two distinct x-intercepts. We find these by solving

$$f(x) = 0$$
$$x^2 - 4x - 5 = 0$$
$$(x-5)(x+1) = 0$$
$$x - 5 = 0 \text{ or } x + 1 = 0$$
$$x = 5 \text{ or } x = -1$$

Graph:
The y-intercept point, $(0, -5)$, is two units to the left of the axis of symmetry. Therefore, if we move two units to the right of the axis of symmetry, we obtain the point $(4, -5)$ which must also be on the graph.

The domain is the set of all real numbers or, using interval notation, $(-\infty, \infty)$. The range is $\{y \mid y \geq -9\}$ or, using interval notation, $[-9, \infty)$.

19. $G(x) = x^2 + 12x + 32$
$a = 1, b = 12, c = 32$
The graph opens up because $a > 0$.

vertex:
$$x = -\frac{b}{2a} = -\frac{(12)}{2(1)} = -6$$
$$G(-6) = (-6)^2 + 12(-6) + 32 = -4$$
The vertex is $(-6, -4)$ and the axis of symmetry is $x = -6$.

y-intercept:
$$G(0) = (0)^2 + 12(0) + 32 = 32$$

x-intercepts:
$$b^2 - 4ac = (12)^2 - 4(1)(32) = 16 > 0$$
There are two distinct x-intercepts. We find these by solving

$$G(x) = 0$$
$$x^2 + 12x + 32 = 0$$
$$(x+8)(x+4) = 0$$
$$x + 8 = 0 \text{ or } x + 4 = 0$$
$$x = -8 \text{ or } x = -4$$

Graph:
The y-intercept point, $(0, 32)$, is six units to the right of the axis of symmetry. Therefore, if we move six units to the left of the axis of symmetry, we obtain the point $(-12, 32)$ which must also be on the graph.

The domain is the set of all real numbers or, using interval notation, $(-\infty, \infty)$. The range is $\{y \mid y \geq -4\}$ or, using interval notation, $[-4, \infty)$.

21. $F(x) = -x^2 + 2x + 8$
$a = -1, b = 2, c = 8$
The graph opens down because $a < 0$.

vertex:
$$x = -\frac{b}{2a} = -\frac{(2)}{2(-1)} = 1$$
$$F(1) = -(1)^2 + 2(1) + 8 = 9$$
The vertex is $(1, 9)$ and the axis of symmetry is $x = 1$.

y-intercept:
$$F(0) = -(0)^2 + 2(0) + 8 = 8$$

x-intercepts:
$$b^2 - 4ac = (2)^2 - 4(-1)(8) = 36 > 0$$
There are two distinct x-intercepts. We find these by solving

$$F(x) = 0$$
$$-x^2 + 2x + 8 = 0$$
$$x^2 - 2x - 8 = 0$$
$$(x+2)(x-4) = 0$$
$$x+2 = 0 \text{ or } x-4 = 0$$
$$x = -2 \text{ or } x = 4$$

Graph:
The *y*-intercept point, $(0, 8)$, is one unit to the left of the axis of symmetry. Therefore, if we move one unit to the right of the axis of symmetry, we obtain the point $(2, 8)$ which must also be on the graph.

The domain is the set of all real numbers or, using interval notation, $(-\infty, \infty)$. The range is $\{y \mid y \le 9\}$ or, using interval notation, $(-\infty, 9]$.

23. $H(x) = x^2 - 4x + 4$
$a = 1, b = -4, c = 4$
The graph opens up because $a > 0$.

vertex:
$$x = -\frac{b}{2a} = -\frac{(-4)}{2(1)} = 2$$
$$H(2) = (2)^2 - 4(2) + 4 = 0$$
The vertex is $(2, 0)$ and the axis of symmetry is $x = 2$.

y-intercept:
$$H(0) = (0)^2 - 4(0) + 4 = 4$$

x-intercepts:
Since the discriminant is 0, the *x*-coordinate of the vertex is the only *x*-intercept, $x = 2$.

Graph:
The *y*-intercept point, $(0, 4)$, is two units to the left of the axis of symmetry. Therefore, if we move two units to the right of the axis of symmetry, we obtain the point $(4, 4)$ which must also be on the graph.

The domain is the set of all real numbers or, using interval notation, $(-\infty, \infty)$. The range is $\{y \mid y \ge 0\}$ or, using interval notation, $[0, \infty)$.

25. $g(x) = x^2 + 2x + 5$
$a = 1, b = 2, c = 5$
The graph opens up because $a > 0$.

vertex:
$$x = -\frac{b}{2a} = -\frac{(2)}{2(1)} = -1$$
$$g(-1) = (-1)^2 + 2(-1) + 5 = 4$$
The vertex is $(-1, 4)$ and the axis of symmetry is $x = -1$.

y-intercept:
$$g(0) = (0)^2 + 2(0) + 5 = 5$$

x-intercepts:
$$b^2 - 4ac = (2)^2 - 4(1)(5) = -16 < 0$$
There are no *x*-intercepts since the discriminant is negative.

Graph:
The *y*-intercept point, $(0, 5)$, is one unit to the right of the axis of symmetry. Therefore, if we move one unit to the left of the axis of symmetry, we obtain the point $(-2, 5)$ which must also be on the graph.

The domain is the set of all real numbers, or, using interval notation, $(-\infty, \infty)$. The range is $\{y \mid y \geq 4\}$ or, using interval notation, $[4, \infty)$.

27. $h(x) = -x^2 - 10x - 25$

$a = -1, b = -10, c = -25$

The graph opens down because $a < 0$.

<u>vertex:</u>

$$x = -\frac{b}{2a} = -\frac{(-10)}{2(-1)} = -5$$

$$h(-5) = -(-5)^2 - 10(-5) - 25 = 0$$

The vertex is $(-5, 0)$ and the axis of symmetry is $x = -5$.

<u>y-intercept:</u>

$$h(0) = -(0)^2 - 10(0) - 25 = -25$$

<u>x-intercepts:</u>

$$b^2 - 4ac = (-10)^2 - 4(-1)(-25) = 100 - 100 = 0$$

Since the discriminant is 0, the x-coordinate of the vertex is the only x-intercept. $x = -5$.

<u>Graph:</u>

The y-intercept point, $(0, -25)$, is five units to the right of the axis of symmetry. Therefore, if we move five units to the left of the axis of symmetry, we obtain the point $(-10, -25)$ which must also be on the graph.

The domain is the set of all real numbers, or, using interval notation, $(-\infty, \infty)$. The range is $\{y \mid y \leq 0\}$ or, using interval notation, $(-\infty, 0]$.

29. $p(x) = -x^2 + 2x - 5$

$a = -1, b = 2, c = -5$

The graph opens down because $a < 0$.

<u>vertex:</u>

$$x = -\frac{b}{2a} = -\frac{(2)}{2(-1)} = 1$$

$$p(1) = -(1)^2 + 2(1) - 5 = -4$$

The vertex is $(1, -4)$ and the axis of symmetry is $x = 1$.

<u>y-intercept:</u>

$$p(0) = -(0)^2 + 2(0) - 5 = -5$$

<u>x-intercepts:</u>

$$b^2 - 4ac = (2)^2 - 4(-1)(-5) = -16 < 0$$

There are no x-intercepts since the discriminant is negative.

<u>Graph:</u>

The y-intercept point, $(0, -5)$, is one unit to the left of the axis of symmetry. Therefore, if we move one unit to the right of the axis of symmetry, we obtain the point $(2, -5)$ which must also be on the graph.

The domain is the set of all real numbers, or, using interval notation, $(-\infty, \infty)$. The range is $\{y \mid y \leq -4\}$ or, using interval notation, $(-\infty, -4]$.

31. $F(x) = 4x^2 - 4x - 3$

$a = 4, b = -4, c = -3$

The graph opens up because $a > 0$.

vertex:

$$x = -\frac{b}{2a} = -\frac{(-4)}{2(4)} = \frac{1}{2}$$

$$F\left(\frac{1}{2}\right) = 4\left(\frac{1}{2}\right)^2 - 4\left(\frac{1}{2}\right) - 3 = -4$$

The vertex is $\left(\frac{1}{2}, -4\right)$ and the axis of symmetry is $x = 2$.

y-intercept:

$$F(0) = 4(0)^2 - 4(0) - 3 = -3$$

x-intercepts:

$$b^2 - 4ac = (-4)^2 - 4(4)(-3) = 64 > 0$$

There are two distinct x-intercepts. We find these by solving

$$F(x) = 0$$

$$4x^2 - 4x - 3 = 0$$

$$(2x+1)(2x-3) = 0$$

$$2x + 1 = 0 \quad \text{or } 2x - 3 = 0$$

$$2x = -1 \quad \text{or } 2x = 3$$

$$x = -\frac{1}{2} \quad \text{or } x = \frac{3}{2}$$

Graph:

The y-intercept point, $(0, -3)$, is $\frac{1}{2}$ unit to the left of the axis of symmetry. Therefore, if we move $\frac{1}{2}$ unit to the right of the axis of symmetry, we obtain the point $(1, -3)$ which must also be on the graph.

The domain is the set of all real numbers or, using interval notation, $(-\infty, \infty)$. The range is $\{y \mid y \geq -4\}$ or, using interval notation, $[-4, \infty)$.

33. $G(x) = -9x^2 + 18x + 7$

$a = -9, b = 18, c = 7$

The graph opens down because $a < 0$.

vertex:

$$x = -\frac{b}{2a} = -\frac{(18)}{2(-9)} = 1$$

$$G(1) = -9(1)^2 + 18(1) + 7 = 16$$

The vertex is $(1, 16)$ and the axis of symmetry is $x = 1$.

y-intercept:

$$G(0) = -9(0)^2 + 18(0) + 7 = 7$$

x-intercepts:

$$b^2 - 4ac = (18)^2 - 4(-9)(7) = 576 > 0$$

There are two distinct x-intercepts. We find these by solving

$$G(x) = 0$$

$$-9x^2 + 18x + 7 = 0$$

$$9x^2 - 18x - 7 = 0$$

$$(3x+1)(3x-7) = 0$$

$$3x + 1 = 0 \quad \text{or } 3x - 7 = 0$$

$$3x = -1 \quad \text{or } 3x = 7$$

$$x = -\frac{1}{3} \quad \text{or } x = \frac{7}{3}$$

Graph:

The y-intercept point, $(0, 7)$, is one unit to the left of the axis of symmetry. Therefore, if we move one unit to the right of the axis of symmetry, we obtain the point $(2, 7)$ which must also be on the graph.

The domain is the set of all real numbers or, using interval notation, $(-\infty, \infty)$. The range is $\{y \mid y \leq 16\}$ or, using interval notation, $(-\infty, 16]$.

35. $H(x) = 4x^2 - 4x + 1$

$a = 4, b = -4, c = 1$

The graph opens up because $a > 0$.

vertex:

$$x = -\frac{b}{2a} = -\frac{(-4)}{2(4)} = \frac{1}{2}$$

$$H\left(\tfrac{1}{2}\right) = 4\left(\tfrac{1}{2}\right)^2 - 4\left(\tfrac{1}{2}\right) + 1 = 0$$

The vertex is $\left(\tfrac{1}{2}, 0\right)$ and the axis of symmetry is

$x = \tfrac{1}{2}$.

y-intercept:

$$H(0) = 4(0)^2 - 4(0) + 1 = 1$$

x-intercepts:

$$b^2 - 4ac = (-4)^2 - 4(4)(1) = 0$$

Since the discriminant is 0, the x-coordinate of the vertex is the only x-intercept, $x = \tfrac{1}{2}$.

Graph:

The y-intercept point, $(0, 1)$, is $\tfrac{1}{2}$ unit to the left of the axis of symmetry. If we move $\tfrac{1}{2}$ unit to the right of the axis of symmetry, we obtain the point $(1, 1)$ which must also be on the graph.

The domain is the set of all real numbers or, using interval notation, $(-\infty, \infty)$. The range is $\{y \mid y \geq 0\}$ or, using interval notation, $[0, \infty)$.

37. $f(x) = -16x^2 - 24x - 9$

$a = -16, b = -24, c = -9$

The graph opens down because $a < 0$.

vertex:

$$x = -\frac{b}{2a} = -\frac{(-24)}{2(-16)} = -\frac{3}{4}$$

$$f\left(-\tfrac{3}{4}\right) = -16\left(-\tfrac{3}{4}\right)^2 - 24\left(-\tfrac{3}{4}\right) - 9 = 0$$

The vertex is $\left(-\tfrac{3}{4}, 0\right)$ and the axis of symmetry

is $x = -\tfrac{3}{4}$.

y-intercept:

$$f(0) = -16(0)^2 - 24(0) - 9 = -9$$

x-intercepts:

$$b^2 - 4ac = (-24)^2 - 4(-16)(-9) = 0$$

Since the discriminant is 0, the only x-intercept is the x-coordinate of the vertex, $x = -\tfrac{3}{4}$.

Graph:

The y-intercept point, $(0, -9)$, is $\tfrac{3}{4}$ unit to the right of the axis of symmetry. Therefore, if we move $\tfrac{3}{4}$ unit to the left of the axis of symmetry, we obtain the point $\left(-\tfrac{3}{2}, -9\right)$ which must also be on the graph.

The domain is the set of all real numbers or, using interval notation, $(-\infty, \infty)$. The range is $\{y \mid y \leq 0\}$ or, using interval notation, $(-\infty, 0]$.

39. $f(x) = 2x^2 + 8x + 11$

$a = 2, b = 8, c = 11$

The graph opens up because $a > 0$.

vertex:

$$x = -\frac{b}{2a} = -\frac{(8)}{2(2)} = -2$$

$$f(-2) = 2(-2)^2 + 8(-2) + 11 = 3$$

The vertex is $(-2, 3)$ and the axis of symmetry is $x = -2$.

y-intercept:

$$f(0) = 2(0)^2 + 8(0) + 11 = 11$$

x-intercepts:

$$b^2 - 4ac = (8)^2 - 4(2)(11) = -24 < 0$$

There are no x-intercepts since the discriminant is negative.

Graph:

The y-intercept point, $(0, 11)$, is two units to the right of the axis of symmetry. Therefore, if we move two unit to the left of the axis of symmetry, we obtain the point $(-4, 11)$ which must also be on the graph.

The domain is the set of all real numbers or, using interval notation, $(-\infty, \infty)$. The range is $\{y \mid y \geq 3\}$ or, using interval notation, $[3, \infty)$.

41. $P(x) = -4x^2 + 6x - 3$

$a = -4, b = 6, c = -3$

The graph opens down because $a < 0$.

vertex:

$$x = -\frac{b}{2a} = -\frac{(6)}{2(-4)} = \frac{3}{4}$$

$$P\left(\tfrac{3}{4}\right) = -4\left(\tfrac{3}{4}\right)^2 + 6\left(\tfrac{3}{4}\right) - 3 = -\frac{3}{4}$$

The vertex is $\left(\tfrac{3}{4}, -\tfrac{3}{4}\right)$ and the axis of symmetry is $x = \tfrac{3}{4}$.

y-intercept:

$$P(0) = -4(0)^2 + 6(0) - 3 = -3$$

x-intercepts:

$$b^2 - 4ac = (6)^2 - 4(-4)(-3) = -12 < 0$$

There are no x-intercepts since the discriminant is negative.

Graph:

The y-intercept point, $(0, -3)$, is $\tfrac{3}{4}$ unit to the left of the axis of symmetry. Therefore, if we move $\tfrac{3}{4}$ unit to the right of the axis of symmetry, we obtain the point $\left(\tfrac{3}{2}, -3\right)$ which must also be on the graph.

The domain is the set of all real numbers or, using interval notation, $(-\infty, \infty)$. The range is $\left\{y \mid y \leq -\dfrac{3}{4}\right\}$ or, using interval notation, $\left(-\infty, -\dfrac{3}{4}\right]$.

43. $h(x) = x^2 + 5x + 3$

$a = 1, b = 5, c = 3$

The graph opens $a > 0$.

vertex:

$$x = -\frac{b}{2a} = -\frac{(5)}{2(1)} = -\frac{5}{2}$$

$$h\left(-\frac{5}{2}\right) = \left(-\frac{5}{2}\right)^2 + 5\left(-\frac{5}{2}\right) + 3 = -\frac{13}{4}$$

The vertex is $\left(-\frac{5}{2}, -\frac{13}{4}\right)$ and the axis of symmetry

is $x = -\frac{5}{2}$.

y-intercept:

$$h(0) = (0)^2 + 5(0) + 3 = 3$$

x-intercepts:

$$b^2 - 4ac = (5)^2 - 4(1)(3) = 13 > 0$$

There are two distinct x-intercepts. We find these by solving

$$h(x) = 0$$

$$x^2 + 5x + 3 = 0$$

$$x = \frac{-5 \pm \sqrt{13}}{2}$$

$$x \approx -0.70 \quad \text{or} \quad x \approx -4.30$$

Graph:

The y-intercept point, $(0, 3)$, is $\frac{5}{2}$ units to the right

of the axis of symmetry. Therefore, if we move $\frac{5}{2}$

units to the left of the axis of symmetry, we obtain

the point $(-5, 3)$ which must also be on the graph.

The domain is the set of all real numbers or, using

interval notation, $(-\infty, \infty)$. The range is

$$\left\{y \mid y \geq -\frac{13}{4}\right\} \text{ or, using interval notation,}$$

$$\left[-\frac{13}{4}, \infty\right).$$

45. $G(x) = -3x^2 + 8x + 2$

$a = -3, b = 8, c = 2$

The graph opens down because $a < 0$.

vertex:

$$x = -\frac{b}{2a} = -\frac{(8)}{2(-3)} = \frac{4}{3}$$

$$G\left(\frac{4}{3}\right) = -3\left(\frac{4}{3}\right)^2 + 8\left(\frac{4}{3}\right) + 2 = \frac{22}{3}$$

The vertex is $\left(\frac{4}{3}, \frac{22}{3}\right)$ and the axis of symmetry

is $x = \frac{4}{3}$.

y-intercept:

$$G(0) = -3(0)^2 + 8(0) + 2 = 2$$

x-intercepts:

$$b^2 - 4ac = (8)^2 - 4(-3)(2) = 88 > 0$$

There are two distinct x-intercepts. We find these by solving

$$G(x) = 0$$

$$-3x^2 + 8x + 2 = 0$$

$$x = \frac{-8 \pm \sqrt{88}}{2(-3)} = \frac{-8 \pm 2\sqrt{22}}{-6} = \frac{4 \pm \sqrt{22}}{3}$$

$$x \approx -0.23 \quad \text{or} \quad x \approx 2.90$$

Graph:

The y-intercept point, $(0, 2)$, is $\frac{4}{3}$ units to the

left of the axis of symmetry. Therefore, if we

move $\frac{4}{3}$ units to the right of the axis of

symmetry, we obtain the point $\left(\frac{8}{3}, 2\right)$ which

must also be on the graph.

The domain is the set of all real numbers or,

using interval notation, $(-\infty, \infty)$. The range is

$$\left\{y \mid y \leq \frac{22}{3}\right\} \text{ or, using interval notation,}$$

$$\left(-\infty, \frac{22}{3}\right].$$

47. $f(x) = 5x^2 - 5x + 2$

$a = 5, b = -5, c = 2$

The graph opens up because $a > 0$.

vertex:

$$x = -\frac{b}{2a} = -\frac{(-5)}{2(5)} = \frac{1}{2}$$

$$f\left(\frac{1}{2}\right) = 5\left(\frac{1}{2}\right)^2 - 5\left(\frac{1}{2}\right) + 2 = \frac{3}{4}$$

The vertex is $\left(\frac{1}{2}, \frac{3}{4}\right)$ and the axis of symmetry is

$x = \frac{1}{2}$.

y-intercept:

$$f(0) = 5(0)^2 - 5(0) + 2 = 2$$

x-intercepts:

$$b^2 - 4ac = (-5)^2 - 4(5)(2) = -15 < 0$$

There are no x-intercepts since the discriminant is negative.

Graph:

The y-intercept point, $(0, 2)$, is $\frac{1}{2}$ unit to the left of the axis of symmetry. Therefore, if we move one unit to the right of the axis of symmetry, we obtain the point $(1, 2)$ which must also be on the graph.

The domain is the set of all real numbers or, using interval notation, $(-\infty, \infty)$. The range is

$\left\{y \mid y \geq \frac{3}{4}\right\}$ or, using interval notation, $\left[\frac{3}{4}, \infty\right)$.

49. $H(x) = -3x^2 + 6x$

$a = -3, b = 6, c = 0$

The graph opens down because $a < 0$.

vertex:

$$x = -\frac{b}{2a} = -\frac{(6)}{2(-3)} = 1$$

$$H(1) = -3(1)^2 + 6(1) = 3$$

The vertex is $(1, 3)$ and the axis of symmetry is

$x = 1$.

y-intercept:

$$H(0) = -3(0)^2 + 6(0) = 0$$

x-intercepts:

$$b^2 - 4ac = (6)^2 - 4(-3)(0) = 36 > 0$$

There are two distinct x-intercepts. We find these by solving

$$H(x) = 0$$

$$-3x^2 + 6x = 0$$

$$-3x(x - 2) = 0$$

$$-3x = 0 \quad \text{or} \quad x - 2 = 0$$

$$x = 0 \quad \text{or} \quad x = 2$$

Graph:

The y-intercept point, $(0, 0)$, is one unit to the left of the axis of symmetry. Therefore, if we move one unit to the right of the axis of symmetry, we obtain the point $(2, 0)$ which must also be on the graph (these points are actually the x-intercept points).

The domain is the set of all real numbers or, using interval notation, $(-\infty, \infty)$. The range is

$\{y \mid y \leq 3\}$ or, using interval notation, $(-\infty, 3]$.

51. $f(x) = x^2 - \dfrac{5}{2}x - \dfrac{3}{2}$

$a = 1, b = -\dfrac{5}{2}, c = -\dfrac{3}{2}$

The graph opens up because $a > 0$.

vertex:

$x = -\dfrac{b}{2a} = -\dfrac{\left(-\frac{5}{2}\right)}{2(1)} = \dfrac{5}{4}$

$f\left(\dfrac{5}{4}\right) = \left(\dfrac{5}{4}\right)^2 - \dfrac{5}{2}\left(\dfrac{5}{4}\right) - \dfrac{3}{2} = -\dfrac{49}{16}$

The vertex is $\left(\dfrac{5}{4}, -\dfrac{49}{16}\right)$ and the axis of symmetry is $x = \dfrac{5}{4}$.

y-intercept:

$f(0) = (0)^2 - \dfrac{5}{2}(0) - \dfrac{3}{2} = -\dfrac{3}{2}$

x-intercepts:

$b^2 - 4ac = \left(-\dfrac{5}{2}\right)^2 - 4(1)\left(-\dfrac{3}{2}\right) = \dfrac{49}{4} > 0$

There are two distinct x-intercepts. We find these by solving

$$f(x) = 0$$
$$x^2 - \dfrac{5}{2}x - \dfrac{3}{2} = 0$$
$$2x^2 - 5x - 3 = 0$$
$$(2x+1)(x-3) = 0$$
$$2x + 1 = 0 \text{ or } x - 3 = 0$$
$$2x = -1 \text{ or } x = 3$$
$$x = -\dfrac{1}{2} \text{ or } x = 3$$

Graph:

The y-intercept point, $\left(0, -\dfrac{3}{2}\right)$, is $\dfrac{5}{4}$ units to the left of the axis of symmetry. Therefore, if we move $\dfrac{5}{4}$ units to the right of the axis of symmetry, we obtain the point $\left(\dfrac{5}{2}, -\dfrac{3}{2}\right)$ which must also be on the graph.

The domain is the set of all real numbers or, using interval notation, $(-\infty, \infty)$. The range is

$\left\{ y \mid y \geq -\dfrac{49}{16} \right\}$ or, using interval notation,

$\left[-\dfrac{49}{16}, \infty \right)$.

53. $G(x) = \dfrac{1}{2}x^2 + 2x - 6$

$a = \dfrac{1}{2}, b = 2, c = -6$

The graph opens up because $a > 0$.

vertex:

$x = -\dfrac{b}{2a} = -\dfrac{(2)}{2\left(\frac{1}{2}\right)} = -2$

$G(-2) = \dfrac{1}{2}(-2)^2 + 2(-2) - 6 = -8$

The vertex is $(-2, -8)$ and the axis of symmetry is $x = -2$.

y-intercept:

$G(0) = \dfrac{1}{2}(0)^2 + 2(0) - 6 = -6$

x-intercepts:

$b^2 - 4ac = (2)^2 - 4\left(\dfrac{1}{2}\right)(-6) = 16 > 0$

There are two distinct x-intercepts. We find these by solving

$$G(x) = 0$$
$$\dfrac{1}{2}x + 2x - 6 = 0$$
$$x^2 + 4x - 12 = 0$$
$$(x+6)(x-2) = 0$$
$$x + 6 = 0 \text{ or } x - 2 = 0$$
$$x = -6 \text{ or } x = 2$$

Graph:

The y-intercept point, $(0, -6)$, is two units to the right of the axis of symmetry. Therefore, if we move two units to the left of the axis of symmetry, we obtain the point $(-4, -6)$ which must also be on the graph.

The domain is the set of all real numbers or, using interval notation, $(-\infty, \infty)$. The range is $\{y \mid y \geq -8\}$ or, using interval notation, $[-8, \infty)$.

55. $F(x) = -\dfrac{1}{4}x^2 + x + 15$

$a = -\dfrac{1}{4}, b = 1, c = 15$

The graph opens down because $a < 0$.

vertex:

$x = -\dfrac{b}{2a} = -\dfrac{(1)}{2\left(-\frac{1}{4}\right)} = 2$

$F(2) = -\dfrac{1}{4}(2)^2 + (2) + 15 = 16$

The vertex is $(2, 16)$ and the axis of symmetry is $x = 2$.

y-intercept:

$F(0) = -\dfrac{1}{4}(0)^2 + (0) + 15 = 15$

x-intercepts:

$b^2 - 4ac = (1)^2 - 4\left(-\frac{1}{4}\right)(15) = 16 > 0$

There are two distinct x-intercepts. We find these by solving

$$F(x) = 0$$

$$-\dfrac{1}{4}x^2 + x + 15 = 0$$

$$x^2 - 4x - 60 = 0$$

$$(x - 10)(x + 6) = 0$$

$$x - 10 = 0 \text{ or } x + 6 = 0$$

$$x = 10 \text{ or } x = -6$$

Graph:

The y-intercept point, $(0, 15)$, is two units to the left of the axis of symmetry. Therefore, if we move two units to the right of the axis of

symmetry, we obtain the point $(4, 15)$ which must also be on the graph.

The domain is the set of all real numbers or, using interval notation, $(-\infty, \infty)$. The range is $\{y \mid y \leq 16\}$ or, using interval notation, $(-\infty, 16]$.

57. If we compare $f(x) = x^2 + 8x + 13$ to $f(x) = ax^2 + bx + c$, we find that $a = 1$, $b = 8$, and $c = 13$. Because $a > 0$, we know the graph will open up, so the function will have a minimum value.
The minimum value occurs at

$x = -\dfrac{b}{2a} = -\dfrac{8}{2(1)} = -4$.

The minimum value is

$f(-4) = (-4)^2 + 8(-4) + 13 = -3$.

So, the minimum value is -3 and it occurs when $x = -4$.

59. If we compare $G(x) = -x^2 - 10x + 3$ to $G(x) = ax^2 + bx + c$, we find that $a = -1$, $b = -10$, and $c = 3$. Because $a < 0$, we know the graph will open down, so the function will have a maximum value.
The maximum value occurs at

$x = -\dfrac{b}{2a} = -\dfrac{(-10)}{2(-1)} = -5$.

The maximum value is

$G(-5) = -(-5)^2 - 10(-5) + 3 = 28$.

So, the maximum value is 28 and it occurs when $x = -5$.

61. If we compare $F(x) = -2x^2 + 12x + 5$ to

$F(x) = ax^2 + bx + c$, we find that $a = -2$,

$b = 12$, and $c = 5$. Because $a < 0$, we know the graph will open down, so the function will have a maximum value.
The maximum value occurs at

$$x = -\frac{b}{2a} = -\frac{12}{2(-2)} = 3.$$

The maximum value is

$$F(3) = -2(3)^2 + 12(3) + 5 = 23.$$

So, the maximum value is 23 and it occurs when $x = 3$.

63. If we compare $h(x) = 4x^2 + 16x - 3$ to

$h(x) = ax^2 + bx + c$, we find that $a = 4$, $b = 16$,

and $c = -3$. Because $a > 0$, we know the graph will open up, so the function will have a minimum value.
The minimum value occurs at

$$x = -\frac{b}{2a} = -\frac{16}{2(4)} = -2.$$

The minimum value is

$$h(-2) = 4(-2)^2 + 16(-2) - 3 = -19.$$

So, the minimum value is -19 and it occurs when $x = -2$.

65. If we compare $f(x) = 2x^2 - 5x + 1$ to

$f(x) = ax^2 + bx + c$, we find that $a = 2$,

$b = -5$, and $c = 1$. Because $a > 0$, we know the graph will open up, so the function will have a minimum value.
The minimum value occurs at

$$x = -\frac{b}{2a} = -\frac{(-5)}{2(2)} = \frac{5}{4} \text{ or } 1.25.$$

The minimum value is

$$f\left(\tfrac{5}{4}\right) = 2\left(\tfrac{5}{4}\right)^2 - 5\left(\tfrac{5}{4}\right) + 1 = -\frac{17}{8} \text{ or } -2.125.$$

So, the minimum value is $-\frac{17}{8}$ and it occurs when $x = \frac{5}{4}$.

67. If we compare $H(x) = -3x^2 + 4x + 1$ to

$H(x) = ax^2 + bx + c$, we find that $a = -3$,

$b = 4$, and $c = 1$. Because $a < 0$, we know the graph will open down, so the function will have a maximum value.

The maximum value occurs at

$$x = -\frac{b}{2a} = -\frac{4}{2(-3)} = \frac{2}{3}.$$

The maximum value is

$$H\left(\tfrac{2}{3}\right) = -3\left(\tfrac{2}{3}\right)^2 + 4\left(\tfrac{2}{3}\right) + 1 = \tfrac{7}{3}.$$

So, the maximum value is $\frac{7}{3}$ and it occurs when $x = \frac{2}{3}$.

69. a. We first recognize that the quadratic function has the leading coefficient $a = -2.5 < 0$. This means that the graph will open down and the function indeed has a maximum value. The maximum value

occurs when $p = -\dfrac{b}{2a} = -\dfrac{600}{2(-2.5)} = 120$.

The revenue will be maximized when the DVD players are sold at a price of $120.

b. The maximum revenue is obtained by evaluating the revenue function at the price found in part (a).

$$R(120) = -2.5(120)^2 + 600(120) = 36,000$$

The maximum revenue is $36,000.

71. First we recognize that the quadratic function has the leading coefficient $a = 0.05 > 0$. This means that the graph will open up and the function will indeed have a minimum value. The minimum

value occurs when $x = -\dfrac{b}{2a} = -\dfrac{(-6)}{2(0.05)} = 60$

The marginal cost will be minimized when 60 digital cameras are produced.
To find the minimum marginal cost, we evaluate the marginal cost function for $x = 60$.

$$C(60) = 0.05(60)^2 - 6(60) + 215 = 35$$

The minimum marginal cost is $35.

73. a. First we recognize that the quadratic function has the negative leading coefficient $a = -16 < 0$. This means the graph will open down and the function will indeed have a maximum.
The maximum height will occur when

$$t = -\frac{b}{2a} = -\frac{240}{2(-16)} = 7.5.$$

The pumpkin will reach a maximum height after 7.5 seconds.

b. The maximum height can be found by evaluating $s(t)$ for the value of t found in part (a).

$$s(7.5) = -16(7.5)^2 + 240(7.5) + 10 = 910$$

The pumpkin will reach a maximum height of 910 feet.

c. When the pumpkin is on the ground, it will have a height of 0 feet. Thus, we need to solve $s(t) = 0$.

$$-16t^2 + 240t + 10 = 0$$

$$8t^2 - 120t - 5 = 0$$

$$a = 8, b = -120, c = -5$$

$$t = \frac{-(-120) \pm \sqrt{(-120)^2 - 4(8)(-5)}}{2(8)}$$

$$= \frac{120 \pm \sqrt{14560}}{16}$$

$t \approx -0.042$ or $t \approx 15.042$

Since the time of flight cannot be negative, we discard the negative solution. The pumpkin will hit the ground in about 15.042 seconds.

75. a. We first recognize that the quadratic function has the leading coefficient $a = \dfrac{-32}{335^2} < 0$. This means the graph will open down and the function will indeed have a maximum. The maximum height will occur when

$$x = -\frac{b}{2a} = -\frac{1}{2(-32/335^2)} \approx 1753.52 .$$

The pumpkin will reach a maximum height when it is about 1753.52 feet from the cannon.

b. The maximum height is obtained by evaluating $h(x)$ for the value of x found in part (a).

$$h(1753.52) = \frac{-32}{335^2}(1753.52)^2 + (1753.52) + 10$$

$$\approx 886.76$$

The pumpkin will reach a maximum height of about 886.76 feet.

c. When the pumpkin is on the ground, it will have a height of 0 feet. Thus, we need to solve $h(x) = 0$.

$$\frac{-32}{335^2}x^2 + x + 10 = 0$$

$$a = \frac{-32}{335^2}, \; b = 1, \; c = 10$$

$$x = \frac{-1 \pm \sqrt{1^2 - 4\left(\dfrac{-32}{335^2}\right)(10)}}{2\left(\dfrac{-32}{335^2}\right)}$$

$x \approx -9.97$ or $x \approx 3517.00$

Since the horizontal distance traveled cannot be negative, we discard the negative result. The pumpkin will hit the ground at a distance of about 3517 feet from the cannon.

d. The two answers are close. The difference is because the initial velocity component used in the formula for problem 73 was an approximation while the value used in the formula for this problem was exact. The exact formula for problem 73 would be

$$s(t) = -16t^2 + \frac{335}{\sqrt{2}}t + 10 .$$

If we had used this formula, the two results would be the same.

Note: The answer in part (b) of this problem is also an approximation because we approximated the time in part (a).

77. a. We first recognize that the quadratic function has the leading coefficient $a = -55 < 0$. This means the graph will open down and the function will indeed have a maximum. The maximum value occurs when

$$x = -\frac{5119}{2(-55)} = \frac{5119}{110} \approx 46.5 .$$

Average income will be maximized at an age of about 46.5 years.

b. To determine the maximum average income, we evaluate $I(a)$ for the value of a found in part (a).

$$I(46.5) = -55(46.5)^2 + 5119(46.5) - 54,448$$

$$= 64,661.75$$

The maximum average income is about $64,661.75.

79. Let x represent the first number. Then the second number must be $36 - x$. We can express the product of the two numbers as the function

$$p(x) = x(36 - x) = -x^2 + 36x$$

This is a quadratic function with $a = -1$, $b = 36$, and $c = 0$. The function is maximized when

$$x = -\frac{b}{2a} = -\frac{36}{2(-1)} = 18.$$

The maximum product can be obtained by evaluating $p(x)$ when $x = 18$.

$$p(x) = 18(36 - 18) = 18(18) = 324$$

Two numbers that sum to 36 have a maximum product of 324 when both numbers are 18.

81. Let x represent the smaller number. Then the larger number must be $x + 18$. We can express the product of the two numbers as the function

$$p(x) = x(x + 18) = x^2 + 18x.$$

This is a quadratic function with $a = 1$, $b = 18$, and $c = 0$. The product will be a minimum when

$$x = -\frac{b}{2a} = -\frac{18}{2(1)} = -9.$$

The minimum product can be found by evaluating $p(x)$ when $x = -9$.

$$p(-9) = -9(-9 + 18) = -9(9) = -81$$

Two numbers whose difference is 18 have a minimum product of -81 when the smaller number is -9 and the larger number is 9.

83. Let l = length and w = width.
The area of a rectangle is given by $A = l \cdot w$. Before we can work on maximizing area, we need to get the equation in terms of one independent variable.
The 500 yards of fencing will form the perimeter of the rectangle. That is, we have

$$2l + 2w = 500.$$

We can solve this equation for l and substitute the result in the area equation.

$$2l + 2w = 500$$

$$l + w = 250$$

$$l = 250 - w$$

Thus, the area equation becomes

$$A = l \cdot w$$

$$= (250 - w) \cdot w$$

$$= -w^2 + 250w$$

Since $a = -1 < 0$, we know the graph opens down, so there will be a maximum area. This occurs when $w = -\dfrac{b}{2a} = -\dfrac{250}{2(-1)} = 125$.

The maximum area can be found by substituting this value for w in the area equation.

$$A = 125(250 - 125) = 125(125) = 15,625$$

The rectangular field will have a maximum area of 15,625 square yards when the field measures 125 yards $\times$ 125 yards.

85. The area of a rectangular region is the product of the length and width. From the figure, we can see that the area would be

$$A = (2000 - 2x) \cdot x = -2x^2 + 2000x$$

Since $a = -2 < 0$, we know the graph opens down and there will be a maximum area. This value occurs when

$$x = -\frac{b}{2a} = -\frac{2000}{2(-2)} = 500.$$

The maximum area can be found by substituting this value for x into the area equation.

$$A = 500(2000 - 2(500)) = 500,000$$

The rectangular field will have a maximum area of 500,000 square meters when the field measures $500\text{ m} \times 1000\text{ m}$ and the long side is parallel to the river.

87. From the diagram, we can see that the cross-sectional area will be rectangular with a width of x inches and a length of $20 - 2x$ inches. The cross-sectional area is then

$$A = (20 - 2x) \cdot x = -2x^2 + 20x$$

Since $a = -2 < 0$, the graph will open down and the function will have a maximum value. This value occurs when

$$x = -\frac{b}{2a} = -\frac{20}{2(-2)} = 5$$

The maximum cross-sectional area can be found by substituting this value for x in the area equation.

$$A = (20 - 2(5)) \cdot 5 = 10 \cdot 5 = 50$$

The gutter will have a maximum cross-sectional area of 50 square inches if the gutter has a depth of 5 inches.

89. a. Since $R = x \cdot p$, we have
$$R = (-p + 110) \cdot p = -p^2 + 110p$$

b. The revenue function is quadratic with $a = -1 < 0$. This means the graph will open down and the function will have a maximum value. This value occurs when
$$p = -\frac{b}{2a} = -\frac{110}{2(-1)} = 55.$$
The maximum revenue can be found by substituting this value for p in the revenue equation.
$$R = (-(55) + 110) \cdot (55) = 55 \cdot 55 = 3025$$
There will be a maximum revenue of \$3025 if the price is set at \$55 for each pair of jeans.

c. To determine how many pairs of jeans will be sold, we substitute the maximizing price into the demand equation.
$$x = -p + 110$$
$$= -(55) + 110 = 55$$
When the price per pair is \$55, the department store will sell 55 pairs.

91. a. $a = 1$:
$$f(x) = 1(x-2)(x-6) = x^2 - 8x + 12$$
$a = 2$:
$$f(x) = 2(x-2)(x-6) = 2x^2 - 16x + 24$$
$a = -2$:
$$f(x) = -2(x-2)(x-6) = -2x^2 + 16x - 24$$

b. The value of a has no effect on the x-intercepts. These depend only on the factors and are given in the problem.
The value of a does have an effect on the y-intercept which can be expressed as
$$c = a \cdot r_1 \cdot r_2 = 12a.$$

c. The value of a has no effect on the axis of symmetry. The axis of symmetry lies halfway between the two x-intercepts which are fixed. Note that in this case we have
$$f(x) = ax^2 - 8ax + 12a$$
The axis of symmetry would be
$$x = -\frac{(-8a)}{2(a)} = \frac{8a}{2a} = 4$$
which does not depend on a.

d. Consider the general function in this case written in the form $f(x) = a(x-h)^2 + k$.
$$f(x) = ax^2 - 8ax + 12a$$
$$= a(x^2 - 8x) + 12a$$
$$= a(x^2 - 8x + 16) + 12a - 16a$$
$$= a(x-4)^2 - 4a$$
The x-coordinate of the vertex is 4, which does not depend on a. However, the y-coordinate is $-4a$ which does depend on a.

93. A revenue of \$0 when the price charged is some positive number is in an indication that the price was too high to keep any consumer demand. Regardless of the price charged, if no items are sold, then no revenue can be generated.

95. $G(x) = \frac{1}{4}x - 2$
Let $x = -4$, 0, and 4.
$$G(-4) = \frac{1}{4}(-4) - 2 = -1 - 2 = -3$$
$$G(0) = \frac{1}{4}(0) - 2 = 0 - 2 = -2$$
$$G(4) = \frac{1}{4}(4) - 2 = 1 - 2 = -1$$
Thus, the points $(-4, -3)$, $(0, -2)$, and $(4, -1)$ are on the graph.

97. $f(x) = (x+2)^2 + 4$
Let $x = -4$, -3, -2, -1, and 0.
$$f(-4) = (-4+2)^2 + 4 = (-2)^2 + 4 = 4 + 4 = 8$$
$$f(-3) = (-3+2)^2 + 4 = (-1)^2 + 4 = 1 + 4 = 5$$
$$f(-2) = (-2+2)^2 + 4 = (0)^2 + 4 = 0 + 4 = 4$$
$$f(-1) = (-1+2)^2 + 4 = (1)^2 + 4 = 1 + 4 = 5$$
$$f(0) = (0+2)^2 + 4 = (2)^2 + 4 = 4 + 4 = 8$$
Thus, the points $(-4, 8)$, $(-3, 5)$, $(-2, 4)$, $(-1, 5)$, and $(0, 8)$ are on the graph.

99. Vertex: $(3.5, -9.25)$

101. Vertex: $(3.5, 37.5)$

103. Vertex: $(-0.3, -20.45)$

105. Vertex: $(0.67, 4.78)$

107. c is the y-intercept. In terms of transformations, c is also 1 larger than the vertical shift and thus, 1 larger than the y-coordinate of the vertex. This is because we can write:

$$f(x) = x^2 + 2x + c$$
$$= (x^2 + 2x) + c$$
$$= (x^2 + 2x + 1) + c - 1$$
$$= (x+1)^2 + (c-1)$$

8.6 Preparing for Quadratic Inequalities

1. The inequality $-4 \le x < 5$ in interval notation is $[-4, 5)$.

2.
$$3x + 5 > 5x - 3$$
$$3x + 5 - 5x > 5x - 3 - 5x$$
$$-2x + 5 > -3$$
$$-2x + 5 - 5 > -3 - 5$$
$$-2x > -8$$
$$\frac{-2x}{-2} < \frac{-8}{-2}$$
$$x < 4$$

The solution set is $\{x \mid x < 4\}$ or, using interval notation, $(-\infty, 4)$.

8.6 Exercises

1. quadratic

3. FALSE. -1 is not in the interval $(-6, -2)$.

5. Answers may vary. One possibility follows:
$x^2 \ge 0$ for all real values of x, so $x^2 + 3 \ge 3$ for all real values of x. Therefore, $x^2 + 3$ can never be less than -2.

7. Answers may vary. One possibility follows:
If the quadratic inequality contains either $\le$ or $\ge$, then the solution set of that quadratic inequality will contain the endpoints. If the quadratic inequality contains either $<$ or $>$, then it will not contain the endpoints.

9. a. The graph is greater than 0 for $x < -6$ or $x > 5$. The solution is $\{x \mid x < -6 \text{ or } x > 5\}$ using set-builder notation; the solution is $(-\infty, -6) \cup (5, \infty)$ using interval notation.

b. The graph is 0 or less for $-6 \le x \le 5$. The solution is $\{x \mid -6 \le x \le 5\}$ using set-builder notation; the solution is $[-6, 5]$ using interval notation.

11. a. The graph is 0 or greater for $-6 \leq x \leq \frac{5}{2}$.

The solution is $\left\{ x \middle| -6 \leq x \leq \frac{5}{2} \right\}$ using set-

builder notation; the solution is $\left[-6, \frac{5}{2} \right]$

using interval notation.

b. The graph is less than 0 for $x < -6$ or

$x > \frac{5}{2}$. The solution is $\left\{ x \middle| x < -6 \text{ or } x > \frac{5}{2} \right\}$

using set-builder notation; the solution is

$\left(-\infty, \ -6 \right) \cup \left(\frac{5}{2}, \ \infty \right)$ using interval

notation.

13. $(x-5)(x+2) \geq 0$

Solve: $(x-5)(x+2) = 0$

$$x - 5 = 0 \quad \text{or} \quad x + 2 = 0$$
$$x = 5 \quad \text{or} \quad x = -2$$

Determine where each factor is positive and negative and where the product of these factors is positive and negative.

The inequality is non-strict, so –2 and 5 are part of the solution. Now, $(x-5)(x+2)$ is greater than zero where the product is positive. The solution is $\left\{ x \mid x \leq -2 \text{ or } x \geq 5 \right\}$ in set-builder notation; the solution is $(-\infty, \ -2] \cup [5, \ \infty)$ in interval notation.

15. $(x+3)(x+7) < 0$

Solve: $(x+3)(x+7) = 0$

$$x + 3 = 0 \quad \text{or} \quad x + 7 = 0$$
$$x = -3 \quad \text{or} \quad x = -7$$

Determine where each factor is positive and negative and where the product of these factors is positive and negative.

The inequality is strict, so –7 and –3 are not part of the solution. Now, $(x+3)(x+7)$ is less than zero where the product is negative. The solution is $\left\{ x \mid -7 < x < -3 \right\}$ in set-builder notation; the solution is $(-7, \ -3)$ in interval notation.

17. $x^2 - 2x - 35 > 0$

Solve: $x^2 - 2x - 35 = 0$

$$(x+5)(x-7) = 0$$
$$x + 5 = 0 \quad \text{or} \quad x - 7 = 0$$
$$x = -5 \quad \text{or} \quad x = 7$$

Determine where each factor is positive and negative and where the product of these factors is positive and negative.

Interval	$(-\infty, -5)$	-5	$(-5, 7)$	7	$(7, \infty)$
$x+5$	$----$	0	$++++$	$+$	$++++$
$x-7$	$----$	$-$	$----$	0	$++++$
$(x+5)(x-7)$	$++++$	0	$----$	0	$++++$

The inequality is strict, so –5 and 7 are not part of the solution. Now, $(x+5)(x-7)$ is greater than zero where the product is positive. The solution is $\left\{ x \mid x < -5 \text{ or } x > 7 \right\}$ in set-builder notation; the solution is $(-\infty, \ -5) \cup (7, \ \infty)$ in interval notation.

19. $n^2 - 6n - 8 \le 0$

Solve: $n^2 - 6n - 8 = 0$

$$n = \frac{-(-6) \pm \sqrt{(-6)^2 - 4(1)(-8)}}{2(1)}$$

$$= \frac{6 \pm \sqrt{68}}{2}$$

$$= \frac{6 \pm 2\sqrt{17}}{2}$$

$$= 3 \pm \sqrt{17}$$

$n = 3 - \sqrt{17}$ or $n = 3 + \sqrt{17}$

≈ -1.12 or ≈ 7.12

Determine where each factor is positive and negative and where the product of these factors is positive and negative.

Interval	$(-\infty, -1.12)$	$3-\sqrt{17}$ ≈ -1.12	$(-1.12, 7.12)$	$3+\sqrt{17}$ ≈ 7.12	$(7.12, \infty)$
$n - \left(3 - \sqrt{17}\right)$	$----$	0	$++++$	$+$	$++++$
$n - \left(3 + \sqrt{17}\right)$	$----$	$-$	$----$	0	$++++$
$\left[n-\left(3-\sqrt{17}\right)\right]\left[n-\left(3+\sqrt{17}\right)\right]$	$++++$	0	$----$	0	$++++$

The inequality is non-strict, so $3 - \sqrt{17}$ and $3 + \sqrt{17}$ are part of the solution. Now, $\left[n-\left(3-\sqrt{17}\right)\right]\left[n-\left(3+\sqrt{17}\right)\right]$ is less than zero where the product is negative. The solution is $\left\{n \mid 3-\sqrt{17} \le n \le 3+\sqrt{17}\right\}$ in set-builder notation; the solution is $\left[3-\sqrt{17},\ 3+\sqrt{17}\right]$ in interval notation.

21. $m^2 + 5m \ge 14$

$m^2 + 5m - 14 \ge 0$

Solve: $m^2 + 5m - 14 = 0$

$(m+7)(m-2) = 0$

$m + 7 = 0$ or $m - 2 = 0$

$m = -7$ or $m = 2$

Determine where each factor is positive and negative and where the product of these factors is positive and negative.

Interval	$(-\infty, -7)$	-7	$(-7, 2)$	2	$(2, \infty)$
$m + 7$	$----$	0	$++++$	$+$	$++++$
$m - 2$	$----$	$-$	$----$	0	$++++$
$(m+7)(m-2)$	$++++$	0	$----$	0	$++++$

The inequality is non-strict, so -7 and 2 are part of the solution. Now, $(m+7)(m-2)$ is greater than zero where the product is positive. The solution is $\{m \mid m \le -7 \text{ or } m \ge 2\}$ in set-builder notation; the solution is $(-\infty, -7] \cup [2, \infty)$ in interval notation.

23. $2q^2 \ge q + 15$

$2q^2 - q - 15 \ge 0$

Solve: $2q^2 - q - 15 = 0$

$(2q + 5)(q - 3) = 0$

$2q + 5 = 0$ or $q - 3 = 0$

$q = -\dfrac{5}{2}$ or $q = 3$

Determine where each factor is positive and negative and where the product of these factors is positive and negative.

Interval	$\left(-\infty, -\frac{5}{2}\right)$	$-\frac{5}{2}$	$\left(-\frac{5}{2}, 3\right)$	3	$(3, \infty)$
$2q + 5$	$----$	0	$++++$	$+$	$++++$
$q - 3$	$----$	$-$	$----$	0	$++++$
$(2q+5)(q-3)$	$++++$	0	$----$	0	$++++$

The inequality is non-strict, so $-\dfrac{5}{2}$ and 3 are part of the solution. Now, $(2q+5)(q-3)$ is greater than zero where the product is positive. The solution is $\left\{q \mid q \le -\dfrac{5}{2} \text{ or } q \ge 3\right\}$ in set-builder notation; the solution is $\left(-\infty,\ -\dfrac{5}{2}\right] \cup [3, \infty)$ in interval notation.

SSM – 499

25. $3x+4 \geq x^2$

$0 \geq x^2 - 3x - 4$

$x^2 - 3x - 4 \leq 0$

Solve: $x^2 - 3x - 4 = 0$

$(x+1)(x-4) = 0$

$x+1 = 0$ or $x-4 = 0$

$x = -1$ or $x = 4$

Determine where each factor is positive and negative and where the product of these factors is positive and negative.

The inequality is non-strict, so −1 and 4 are part of the solution. Now, $(x+1)(x-4)$ is less than zero where the product is negative. The solution is $\{x \mid -1 \leq x \leq 4\}$ in set-builder notation; the solution is $[-1,\ 4]$ in interval notation.

27. $-x^2 + 3x < -10$

$0 < x^2 - 3x - 10$

$x^2 - 3x - 10 > 0$

Solve: $x^2 - 3x - 10 = 0$

$(x+2)(x-5) = 0$

$x+2 = 0$ or $x-5 = 0$

$x = -2$ or $x = 5$

Determine where each factor is positive and negative and where the product of these factors is positive and negative.

Interval	$(-\infty, -2)$	-2	$(-2, 5)$	5	$(5, \infty)$
$x+2$	$----$	0	$++++$	$+$	$++++$
$x-5$	$----$	$-$	$----$	0	$++++$
$(x+2)(x-5)$	$++++$	0	$----$	0	$++++$

The inequality is strict, so −2 and 5 are not part of the solution. Now, $(x+2)(x-5)$ is greater than zero where the product is positive. The solution is $\{x \mid x < -2 \text{ or } x > 5\}$ in set-builder notation; the solution is $(-\infty, -2) \cup (5, \infty)$ in interval notation.

29. $-3x^2 \leq -10x - 8$

$0 \leq 3x^2 - 10x - 8$

$3x^2 - 10x - 8 \geq 0$

Solve: $3x^2 - 10x - 8 = 0$

$(3x+2)(x-4) = 0$

$3x+2 = 0$ or $x-4 = 0$

$x = -\dfrac{2}{3}$ or $x = 4$

Determine where each factor is positive and negative and where the product of these factors is positive and negative.

Interval	$\left(-\infty, -\frac{2}{3}\right)$	$-\frac{2}{3}$	$\left(-\frac{2}{3}, 4\right)$	4	$(4, \infty)$
$3x+2$	$----$	0	$++++$	$+$	$++++$
$x-4$	$----$	$-$	$----$	0	$++++$
$(3x+2)(x-4)$	$++++$	0	$----$	0	$++++$

The inequality is non-strict, so $-\dfrac{2}{3}$ and 4 are part of the solution. Now, $(3x+2)(x-4)$ is greater than zero where the product is positive. The solution is $\left\{ x \mid x \leq -\dfrac{2}{3} \text{ or } x \geq 4 \right\}$ in set-builder notation; the solution is $\left(-\infty, -\dfrac{2}{3}\right] \cup [4, \infty)$ in interval notation.

31. $x^2 + 4x + 1 < 0$

Solve: $x^2 + 4x + 1 = 0$

$x = \dfrac{-4 \pm \sqrt{4^2 - 4(1)(1)}}{2(1)}$

$= \dfrac{-4 \pm \sqrt{12}}{2}$

$= \dfrac{-4 \pm 2\sqrt{3}}{2}$

$= -2 \pm \sqrt{3}$

$x = -2 - \sqrt{3}$ or $x = -2 + \sqrt{3}$

≈ -3.73 or ≈ -0.27

Determine where each factor is positive and negative and where the product of these factors is positive and negative.

Interval $(-\infty, -3.73)$ | $(-3.73, -0.27)$ | $(-0.27, \infty)$

$$-2-\sqrt{3} \qquad -2+\sqrt{3}$$
$$\approx -3.73 \qquad \approx -0.27$$

$x-\left(-2-\sqrt{3}\right)$	$----$	0	$++++$	$+$	$++++$
$x-\left(-2+\sqrt{3}\right)$	$----$	$-$	$----$	0	$++++$
$\left[x-\left(-2-\sqrt{3}\right)\right]\left[x-\left(-2+\sqrt{3}\right)\right]$	$++++$	0	$----$	0	$++++$

The inequality is strict, so $-2-\sqrt{3}$ and $-2+\sqrt{3}$ are not part of the solution. Now, $\left[x-\left(-2-\sqrt{3}\right)\right]\left[x-\left(-2+\sqrt{3}\right)\right]$ is less than zero where the product is negative. The solution is $\left\{x \mid -2-\sqrt{3} < x < -2+\sqrt{3}\right\}$ in set-builder notation; the solution is $\left(-2-\sqrt{3},\ -2+\sqrt{3}\right)$ in interval notation.

$$-2-\sqrt{3} \qquad -2+\sqrt{3}$$
$$\approx -3.73 \qquad \approx -0.27$$

33. $-2a^2 + 7a \ge -4$

$0 \ge 2a^2 - 7a - 4$

$2a^2 - 7a - 4 \le 0$

Solve: $2a^2 - 7a - 4 = 0$

$\left(2a+1\right)\left(a-4\right) = 0$

$2a+1 = 0 \qquad$ or $\qquad a-4 = 0$

$a = -\dfrac{1}{2} \qquad$ or $\qquad a = 4$

Determine where each factor is positive and negative and where the product of these factors is positive and negative.

Interval $\left(-\infty, -\frac{1}{2}\right)$ $-\frac{1}{2}$ $\left(-\frac{1}{2}, 4\right)$ 4 $(4, \infty)$

$2a+1$	$----$	0	$++++$	$+$	$++++$
$a-4$	$----$	$-$	$----$	0	$++++$
$(2a+1)(a-4)$	$++++$	0	$----$	0	$++++$

The inequality is non-strict, so $-\dfrac{1}{2}$ and 4 are part of the solution. Now, $(2a+1)(a-4)$ is less than zero where the product is negative. The solution is $\left\{a \mid -\dfrac{1}{2} \le a \le 4\right\}$ in set-builder notation; the solution is $\left[-\dfrac{1}{2},\ 4\right]$ in interval notation.

35. $z^2 + 2z + 3 > 0$

Solve: $z^2 + 2z + 3 = 0$

$$z = \frac{-2 \pm \sqrt{2^2 - 4(1)(3)}}{2(1)}$$

$$= \frac{-2 \pm \sqrt{-8}}{2}$$

$$= \frac{-2 \pm 2\sqrt{2}\,i}{2} = -1 \pm \sqrt{2}\,i$$

The solutions to the equation are non-real. This means that $z^2 + 2z + 3$ will not divide the number line into positive and negative intervals. Instead, $z^2 + 2z + 3$ will either be positive on the entire number line or be negative on the entire number line. The graph below shows that $f(z) = z^2 + 2z + 3$ is always positive.

This means that $z^2 + 2z + 3$ is always greater than zero. The solution is $\{z \mid z$ is any real number$\}$; the solution is $(-\infty, \infty)$ in interval notation.

37. $2b^2 + 5b \le -6$

$2b^2 + 5b + 6 \le 0$

Solve: $2b^2 + 5b + 6 = 0$

$$b = \frac{-5 \pm \sqrt{5^2 - 4(2)(6)}}{2(1)}$$

$$= \frac{-5 \pm \sqrt{-23}}{2}$$

$$= \frac{-5 \pm \sqrt{23}\,i}{2}$$

$$= -\frac{5}{2} \pm \frac{\sqrt{23}}{2}\,i$$

The solutions to the equation are non-real. This means that $2b^2 + 5b + 6$ will not divide the number line into positive and negative intervals. Instead, $2b^2 + 5b + 6$ will either be positive on the entire number line or be negative on the entire number line. The graph below shows that $f(b) = 2b^2 + 5b + 6$ is always positive.

This means that $2b^2 + 5b + 6$ is never less than or equal to zero. The quadratic inequality has no solution: { } or $\varnothing$.

39. $x^2 + 6x + 9 \geq 0$

Solve: $x^2 + 6x + 9 = 0$

$(x+3)(x+3) = 0$

$x+3 = 0$ or $x+3 = 0$

$x = -3$ or $x = -3$

Determine where each factor is positive and negative and where the product of these factors is positive and negative.

Interval	$(-\infty, -3)$	-3	$(-3, \infty)$
$x+3$	$----$	0	$++++$
$x+3$	$----$	0	$++++$
$(x+3)(x+3)$	$++++$	0	$++++$

The inequality is non-strict, so –3 is part of the solution. Now, $(x+3)(x+3)$ is greater than zero where the product is positive. Thus, $x^2 + 6x + 9$ is always greater than or equal to zero. The solution is $\{x \mid x \text{ is any real number}\}$; the solution is $(-\infty, \infty)$ in interval notation.

41. $f(x) < 0$

$x^2 - 5x < 0$

Solve: $x^2 - 5x = 0$

$x(x-5) = 0$

$x = 0$ or $x - 5 = 0$

or $x = 5$

Determine where each factor is positive and negative and where the product of these factors is positive and negative.

Interval	$(-\infty, 0)$	0	$(0, 5)$	5	$(5, \infty)$
x	$----$	0	$++++$	$+$	$++++$
$x-5$	$----$	$-$	$----$	0	$++++$
$x(x-5)$	$++++$	0	$----$	0	$++++$

The inequality is strict, so 0 and 5 are not part of the solution. Now, $x(x-5)$ is less than zero where the product is negative. The solution is $\{x \mid 0 < x < 5\}$ in set-builder notation; the solution is $(0, 5)$ in interval notation.

43. $f(x) \geq 0$

$x^2 - 3x - 28 \geq 0$

Solve: $x^2 - 3x - 28 = 0$

$(x+4)(x-7) = 0$

$x+4 = 0$ or $x-7 = 0$

$x = -4$ or $x = 7$

Determine where each factor is positive and negative and where the product of these factors is positive and negative.

Interval	$(-\infty, -4)$	-4	$(-4, 7)$	7	$(7, \infty)$
$x+4$	$----$	0	$++++$	$+$	$++++$
$x-7$	$----$	$-$	$----$	0	$++++$
$(x+4)(x-7)$	$++++$	0	$----$	0	$++++$

The inequality is non-strict, so –4 and 7 are part of the solution. Now, $(x+4)(x-7)$ is greater than zero where the product is positive. The solution is $\{x \mid x \leq -4 \text{ or } x \geq 7\}$ in set-builder notation; the solution is $(-\infty, -4] \cup [7, \infty)$ in interval notation.

45. $g(x) > 0$

$2x^2 + x - 10 > 0$

Solve: $2x^2 + x - 10 = 0$

$(2x+5)(x-2) = 0$

$2x+5 = 0$ or $x-2 = 0$

$2x = -5$ or $x = 2$

$x = -\dfrac{5}{2}$

Determine where each factor is positive and negative and where the product of these factors is positive and negative.

Interval	$\left(-\infty, -\frac{5}{2}\right)$	$-\frac{5}{2}$	$\left(-\frac{5}{2}, 2\right)$	2	$(2, \infty)$
$2x+5$	$----$	0	$++++$	$+$	$++++$
$x-2$	$----$	$-$	$----$	0	$++++$
$(2x+5)(x-3)$	$++++$	0	$----$	0	$++++$

The inequality is strict, so $-\frac{5}{2}$ and 2 are not part of the solution. Now, $(2x+5)(x-2)$ is greater than zero where the product is positive. The solution is $\left\{ x \mid x < -\frac{5}{2} \text{ or } x > 2 \right\}$ in set-builder notation; the solution is $\left(-\infty, -\frac{5}{2}\right) \cup (2, \infty)$ in interval notation.

47. The domain of $f(x) = \sqrt{x^2 + 8x}$ will be the solution set of $x^2 + 8x \ge 0$.

Solve: $x^2 + 8x = 0$
$$x(x+8) = 0$$
$$x = 0 \quad \text{or} \quad x + 8 = 0$$
$$\text{or} \quad x = -8$$

Determine where each factor is positive and negative and where the product of these factors is positive and negative.

Interval	$(-\infty, -8)$	-8	$(-8, 0)$	0	$(0, \infty)$
x	$----$	$-$	$----$	0	$++++$
$x+8$	$----$	0	$++++$	$+$	$++++$
$x(x+8)$	$++++$	0	$----$	0	$++++$

The inequality is non-strict, so -8 and 0 are part of the solution. Now, $x(x+8)$ is greater than zero where the product is positive. Thus, the domain of f is $\left\{ x \mid x \le -8 \text{ or } x \ge 0 \right\}$ in set-builder notation; the domain is $(-\infty, -8] \cup [0, \infty)$ in interval notation.

49. The domain of $g(x) = \sqrt{x^2 - x - 30}$ will be the solution set of $x^2 - x - 30 \ge 0$.

Solve: $x^2 - x - 30 = 0$
$$(x-6)(x+5) = 0$$
$$x - 6 = 0 \quad \text{or} \quad x + 5 = 0$$
$$x = 6 \quad \text{or} \quad x = -5$$

Determine where each factor is positive and negative and where the product of these factors is positive and negative.

Interval	$(-\infty, -5)$	-5	$(-5, 6)$	6	$(6, \infty)$
$x-6$	$----$	$-$	$----$	0	$++++$
$x+5$	$----$	0	$++++$	$+$	$++++$
$(x-6)(x+5)$	$++++$	0	$----$	0	$++++$

The inequality is non-strict, so -6 and 5 are part of the solution. Now, $(x-6)(x+5)$ is greater than zero where the product is positive. Thus, the domain of g is $\left\{ x \mid x \le -5 \text{ or } x \ge 6 \right\}$ in set-builder notation; the domain is $(-\infty, -5] \cup [6, \infty)$ in interval notation.

51. The ball will be more than 596 feet above sea level when $s(t) > 596$.

$$-16t^2 + 80t + 500 > 596$$
$$0 > 16t^2 - 80t + 96$$
$$16t^2 - 80t + 96 < 0$$
$$\frac{16t^2 - 80t + 96}{16} < \frac{0}{16}$$
$$t^2 - 5t + 6 < 0$$

Solve: $t^2 - 5t + 6 = 0$
$$(t-2)(t-3) = 0$$
$$t - 2 = 0 \quad \text{or} \quad t - 3 = 0$$
$$t = 2 \quad \text{or} \quad t = 3$$

Determine where each factor is positive and negative and where the product of these factors is positive and negative.

Interval	$(-\infty, 2)$	2	$(2, 3)$	3	$(3, \infty)$
$t-2$	$----$	0	$++++$	$+$	$++++$
$t-3$	$----$	$-$	$----$	0	$++++$
$(t-2)(t-3)$	$++++$	0	$----$	0	$++++$

The inequality is strict, so 2 and 3 are not part of the solution. Now, $(t-2)(t-3)$ is less than zero where the product is negative. The solution is $\left\{ t \mid 2 < t < 3 \right\}$ in set-builder notation; the solution is $(2, 3)$ in interval notation. Thus, the ball will be more than 596 feet above sea level when the time is between 2 and 3 seconds after the ball is thrown.

53. The revenue will exceed \$35,750 when
$R(p) > 35,750$.

$$-2.5p^2 + 600p > 35,750$$
$$0 > 2.5p^2 - 600p + 35,750$$
$$2.5p^2 - 600p + 35,750 < 0$$
$$\frac{2.5p^2 - 600p + 35,750}{2.5} < \frac{0}{2.5}$$
$$p^2 - 240t + 14,300 < 0$$

Solve: $p^2 - 240t + 14,300 = 0$
$$(p - 110)(p - 130) = 0$$
$$p - 110 = 0 \quad \text{or} \quad p - 130 = 0$$
$$p = 110 \quad \text{or} \quad p = 130$$

Determine where each factor is positive and negative and where the product of these factors is positive and negative.

Interval	$(-\infty, 110)$	110	$(110, 130)$	130	$(130, \infty)$
$p - 110$	$----$	0	$++++$	$+$	$++++$
$p - 130$	$----$	$-$	$----$	0	$++++$
$(p-110)(p-130)$	$++++$	0	$----$	0	$++++$

The inequality is strict, so 110 and 130 are not part of the solution. Now, $(p-110)(p-130)$ is less than zero where the product is negative. The solution is $\{p \mid 110 < p < 130\}$ in set-builder notation; the solution is $(110, 130)$ in interval notation. Thus, the revenue will exceed \$35,750 when the DVD is sold for a price between \$110 and \$130.

55. By inspection, the only solution is $x = -3$. That is, the solution set is $\{-3\}$.

Explanation: The expression on the left side of the inequality is a perfect square. A perfect square cannot be negative (less than zero). Therefore, the only solution will be where the perfect square expression equals zero, which is -3.

57. By inspection, the solution set is the set of all real numbers.

Explanation: The expression on the left side of the inequality is a perfect square. A perfect square must always be zero or greater. Therefore, it must always be larger than -2. Thus, all values of x will make the inequality true. The solution is the set of all real numbers.

59. Answers may vary. One possibility follows:
We want $x \geq -3$ and $x \leq 2$. Now, $x \geq -3$ means $x + 3 \geq 0$ (positive), and $x \leq 2$ means $x - 2 \leq 0$ (negative). If we multiply a positive by a negative, we get a negative result. Thus, $(x+3)(x-2) \leq 0$. Multiplying out the expression on the left, we get $x^2 + x - 6 \leq 0$. The solution set of $x^2 + x - 6 \leq 0$ is $[-3, 2]$.

NOTE: Because the solution contains the endpoints -3 and 2, the inequality must be non-strict.

61. Answer will vary. One possibility follows:
The inequalities have the same solution set because they are equivalent:

$$(3x + 2)^{-2} > \frac{1}{2}$$
$$\frac{1}{(3x+2)^2} > \frac{1}{2}$$
$$2(3x+2)^2 \cdot \frac{1}{(3x+2)^2} > 2(3x+2)^2 \cdot \frac{1}{2}$$
$$2 > (3x+2)^2$$
$$(3x+2)^2 < 2$$

Note: In the third step, we multiplied both sides by $2(3x+2)^2$ which must be positive, leaving the direction of the inequality symbol unchanged.

63. $(x+3)(x-1)(x-3) < 0$

Solve: $(x+3)(x-1)(x-3) = 0$
$$x + 3 = 0 \quad \text{or} \quad x - 1 = 0 \quad \text{or} \quad x - 3 = 0$$
$$x = -3 \quad \text{or} \quad x = 1 \quad \text{or} \quad x = 3$$

Determine where each factor is positive and negative and where the product of these factors is positive and negative.

Interval	$(-\infty, -3)$	-3	$(-3, 1)$	1	$(1, 3)$	3	$(3, \infty)$
$x + 3$	$---$	0	$+++$	$+$	$+++$	$+$	$+++$
$x - 1$	$---$	$-$	$---$	0	$+++$	$+$	$+++$
$x - 3$	$---$	$-$	$---$	$-$	$---$	0	$+++$
$(x+3)(x-1)(x-3)$	$---$	0	$+++$	0	$---$	0	$+++$

The inequality is strict, so -3, 1, and 3 are not part of the solution. Now, $(x+3)(x-1)(x-3)$ is less than zero where the product is negative. The solution is $\{x \mid x < -3 \text{ or } 1 < x < 3\}$ in set-builder notation; the solution is $(-\infty, -3) \cup (1, 3)$ in interval notation.

65. $(3x+4)(x-2)(x-6) \geq 0$

Solve: $(3x+4)(x-2)(x-6) = 0$

$3x+4=0$ or $x-2=0$ or $x-6=0$

$x = -\dfrac{4}{3}$ or $x = 2$ or $x = 6$

Determine where each factor is positive and negative and where the product of these factors is positive and negative.

Interval	$\left(-\infty, -\frac{4}{3}\right)$	$-\frac{4}{3}$	$\left(-\frac{4}{3}, 2\right)$	2	$(2, 6)$	6	$(6, \infty)$
$3x+4$	$---$	0	$+++$	$+$	$+++$	$+$	$+++$
$x-2$	$---$	$-$	$---$	0	$+++$	$+$	$+++$
$x-6$	$---$	$-$	$---$	$-$	$---$	0	$+++$
$(3x+4)(x-2)(x-6)$	$---$	0	$+++$	0	$---$	0	$+++$

The inequality is non-strict, so $-\dfrac{4}{3}$, 2, and 6 are part of the solution. Now, $(3x+4)(x-2)(x-6)$ is greater than zero where the product is positive. The solution is $\left\{ x \;\middle|\; -\dfrac{4}{3} \leq x \leq 2 \text{ or } x \geq 6 \right\}$ in set-builder notation; the solution is $\left[-\dfrac{4}{3}, 2\right] \cup [6, \infty)$ in interval notation.

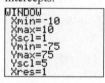

67. $\dfrac{x^2 - 3x - 10}{x+1} < 0$

$\dfrac{(x+2)(x-5)}{x+1} < 0$

The rational expression will equal 0 when $x = -2$ and when $x = 5$. It is undefined when $x = -1$. Determine where the factors of the numerator and the denominator are positive and negative and where the quotient is positive and negative.

Interval	$(-\infty, -2)$	-2	$(-2, -1)$	-1	$(-1, 5)$	5	$(5, \infty)$
$x+2$	$---$	0	$+++$	$+$	$+++$	$+$	$+++$
$x-5$	$---$	$-$	$---$	$-$	$---$	0	$+++$
$x+1$	$---$	$-$	$---$	0	$+++$	$+$	$+++$
$\frac{(x+2)(x-5)}{x+1}$	$---$	0	$+++$	$\varnothing$	$---$	0	$+++$

The inequality is strict, so -2, -1, and 5 are not part of the solution. Now, $\dfrac{(x+2)(x-5)}{x+1}$ is less

than zero where the quotient is negative. The solution is $\{x \mid x < -2 \text{ or } -1 < x < 5\}$ in set-builder notation; the solution is $(-\infty, -2) \cup (-1, 5)$ in interval notation.

69. $\left(4mn^{-3}\right)\left(-2m^4n\right) = -8m^{4+1}n^{-3+1}$

$$= -8m^5 n^{-2} = \dfrac{-8m^5}{n^2}$$

71. $\left(\dfrac{9a^{\frac{2}{3}}b^{\frac{1}{2}}}{a^{-\frac{1}{9}}b^{\frac{3}{4}}}\right)^{-1} = \left(\dfrac{a^{-\frac{1}{9}}b^{\frac{3}{4}}}{9a^{\frac{2}{3}}b^{\frac{1}{2}}}\right)^{1} = \dfrac{a^{-\frac{1}{9}}b^{\frac{3}{4}}}{9a^{\frac{2}{3}}b^{\frac{1}{2}}}$

$$= \dfrac{b^{\frac{3}{4}-\frac{1}{2}}}{9a^{\frac{2}{3}+\frac{1}{9}}} = \dfrac{b^{\frac{3}{4}-\frac{2}{4}}}{9a^{\frac{6}{9}+\frac{1}{9}}} = \dfrac{b^{\frac{1}{4}}}{9a^{\frac{7}{9}}}$$

73. $2x^2 + 7x - 49 > 0$

Let $Y_1 = 2x^2 + 7x - 49$. Graph the quadratic function. Use the **ZERO** feature to find the x-intercepts.

The inequality is strict, so -7 and 3.5 are not part of the solution. From the graph, we can see that $2x^2 + 7x - 49 > 0$ for $x < -7$ or $x > 3.5$. Thus, the solution set is $\{x \mid x < -7 \text{ or } x > 3.5\}$ in set-builder notation; the solution is $(-\infty, -7) \cup (3.5, \infty)$ in interval notation.

75. $6x^2 + x \le 40$

$6x^2 + x - 40 \le 0$

Let $Y_1 = 6x^2 + x - 40$. Graph the quadratic function. Use the ZERO feature to find the x-intercepts.

The inequality is non-strict, so $-2.\overline{6} = -\dfrac{8}{3}$ and

$2.5 = \dfrac{5}{2}$ are part of the solution. From the

graph, we can see that $6x^2 + x - 40 \le 0$ for

$-\dfrac{8}{3} \le x \le \dfrac{5}{2}$. Thus, the solution set is

$\left\{ x \middle| \ -\dfrac{8}{3} \le x \le \dfrac{5}{2} \right\}$ in set-builder notation; the

solution is $\left[-\dfrac{8}{3}, \ \dfrac{5}{2} \right]$ in interval notation.

Chapter 8 Review

1. $m^2 = 169$

$m = \pm\sqrt{169}$

$m = \pm 13$

The solution set is $\{-13, \ 13\}$.

2. $n^2 = 75$

$n = \pm\sqrt{75}$

$n = \pm 5\sqrt{3}$

The solution set is $\{-5\sqrt{3}, \ 5\sqrt{3}\}$.

3. $a^2 = -16$

$a = \pm\sqrt{-16}$

$a = \pm 4i$

The solution set is $\{-4i, \ 4i\}$.

4. $b^2 = \dfrac{8}{9}$

$b = \pm\sqrt{\dfrac{8}{9}}$

$b = \pm\dfrac{\sqrt{8}}{\sqrt{9}}$

$b = \pm\dfrac{2\sqrt{2}}{3}$

The solution set is $\left\{ -\dfrac{2\sqrt{2}}{3}, \ \dfrac{2\sqrt{2}}{3} \right\}$.

5. $(x-8)^2 = 81$

$x - 8 = \pm\sqrt{81}$

$x - 8 = \pm 9$

$x = 8 \pm 9$

$x = 8 - 9 \ $ or $\ x = 8 + 9$

$x = -1 \ $ or $\ x = 17$

The solution set is $\{-1, \ 17\}$.

6. $(y-2)^2 - 62 = 88$

$(y-2)^2 = 150$

$y - 2 = \pm\sqrt{150}$

$y - 2 = \pm 5\sqrt{6}$

$y = 2 \pm 5\sqrt{6}$

The solution set is $\{2 - 5\sqrt{6}, \ 2 + 5\sqrt{6}\}$.

7. $(3z+5)^2 = 100$

$3z + 5 = \pm\sqrt{100}$

$3z + 5 = \pm 10$

$3z = -5 \pm 10$

$3z = -5 - 10 \ $ or $\ 3z = -5 + 10$

$3z = -15 \quad$ or $\quad 3z = 5$

$z = -5 \qquad$ or $\quad z = \dfrac{5}{3}$

The solution set is $\left\{ -5, \ \dfrac{5}{3} \right\}$.

8. $7p^2 = 18$

$$p^2 = \frac{18}{7}$$

$$p = \pm\sqrt{\frac{18}{7}}$$

$$p = \pm\frac{\sqrt{18}}{\sqrt{7}}\cdot\frac{\sqrt{7}}{\sqrt{7}}$$

$$p = \pm\frac{\sqrt{126}}{\sqrt{49}}$$

$$p = \pm\frac{3\sqrt{14}}{7}$$

The solution set is $\left\{-\dfrac{3\sqrt{14}}{7},\ \dfrac{3\sqrt{14}}{7}\right\}$.

9. $3q^2 + 251 = 11$

$$3q^2 = -240$$

$$q^2 = -80$$

$$q = \pm\sqrt{-80}$$

$$q = \pm 4\sqrt{5}\ i$$

The solution set is $\left\{-4\sqrt{5}\ i,\ 4\sqrt{5}\ i\right\}$.

10. $\left(x+\dfrac{3}{4}\right)^2 = \dfrac{13}{16}$

$$x + \frac{3}{4} = \pm\sqrt{\frac{13}{16}}$$

$$x + \frac{3}{4} = \pm\frac{\sqrt{13}}{4}$$

$$x = -\frac{3}{4} \pm \frac{\sqrt{13}}{4}$$

The solution set is $\left\{-\dfrac{3}{4}-\dfrac{\sqrt{13}}{4},\ -\dfrac{3}{4}+\dfrac{\sqrt{13}}{4}\right\}$.

11. Start: $a^2 + 30a$

Add: $\left(\dfrac{1}{2}\cdot 30\right)^2 = 225$

Result: $a^2 + 30a + 225$

Factored Form: $(a+15)^2$

12. Start: $b^2 - 14b$

Add: $\left[\dfrac{1}{2}\cdot(-14)\right]^2 = 49$

Result: $b^2 - 14b + 49$

Factored Form: $(b-7)^2$

13. Start: $c^2 - 11c$

Add: $\left[\dfrac{1}{2}\cdot(-11)\right]^2 = \dfrac{121}{4}$

Result: $c^2 - 11c + \dfrac{121}{4}$

Factored Form: $\left(c - \dfrac{11}{2}\right)^2$

14. Start: $d^2 + 9d$

Add: $\left(\dfrac{1}{2}\cdot 9\right)^2 = \dfrac{81}{4}$

Result: $d^2 + 9d + \dfrac{81}{4}$

Factored Form: $\left(d + \dfrac{9}{2}\right)^2$

15. Start: $m^2 - \dfrac{1}{4}m$

Add: $\left[\dfrac{1}{2}\cdot\left(-\dfrac{1}{4}\right)\right]^2 = \dfrac{1}{64}$

Result: $m^2 - \dfrac{1}{4}m + \dfrac{1}{64}$

Factored Form: $\left(m - \dfrac{1}{8}\right)^2$

16. Start: $n^2 + \dfrac{6}{7}n$

Add: $\left(\dfrac{1}{2}\cdot\dfrac{6}{7}\right)^2 = \dfrac{9}{49}$

Result: $n^2 + \dfrac{6}{7}n + \dfrac{9}{49}$

Factored Form: $\left(n + \dfrac{3}{7}\right)^2$

17.
$$x^2 - 10x + 16 = 0$$
$$x^2 - 10x = -16$$
$$x^2 - 10x + \left(\frac{1}{2} \cdot (-10)\right)^2 = -16 + \left(\frac{1}{2} \cdot (-10)\right)^2$$
$$x^2 - 10x + 25 = -16 + 25$$
$$(x - 5)^2 = 9$$
$$x - 5 = \pm\sqrt{9}$$
$$x - 5 = \pm 3$$
$$x = 5 \pm 3$$
$$x = 2 \text{ or } x = 8$$
The solution set is $\{2, \, 8\}$.

18.
$$y^2 - 3y - 28 = 0$$
$$y^2 - 3y = 28$$
$$y^2 - 3y + \left(\frac{1}{2} \cdot (-3)\right)^2 = 28 + \left(\frac{1}{2} \cdot (-3)\right)^2$$
$$y^2 - 3y + \frac{9}{4} = 28 + \frac{9}{4}$$
$$\left(y - \frac{3}{2}\right)^2 = \frac{121}{4}$$
$$y - \frac{3}{2} = \pm\sqrt{\frac{121}{4}}$$
$$y - \frac{3}{2} = \pm\frac{11}{2}$$
$$y = \frac{3}{2} \pm \frac{11}{2}$$
$$y = -4 \text{ or } y = 7$$
The solution set is $\{-4, \, 7\}$.

19.
$$z^2 - 6z - 3 = 0$$
$$z^2 - 6z = 3$$
$$z^2 - 6z + \left(\frac{1}{2} \cdot (-6)\right)^2 = 3 + \left(\frac{1}{2} \cdot (-6)\right)^2$$
$$z^2 - 6z + 9 = 3 + 9$$
$$(z - 3)^2 = 12$$
$$z - 3 = \pm\sqrt{12}$$
$$z - 3 = \pm 2\sqrt{3}$$
$$z = 3 \pm 2\sqrt{3}$$
The solution set is $\left\{3 - 2\sqrt{3}, \, 3 + 2\sqrt{3}\right\}$.

20.
$$a^2 - 5a - 7 = 0$$
$$a^2 - 5a = 7$$
$$a^2 - 5a + \left(\frac{1}{2} \cdot (-5)\right)^2 = 7 + \left(\frac{1}{2} \cdot (-5)\right)^2$$
$$a^2 - 5a + \frac{25}{4} = 7 + \frac{25}{4}$$
$$\left(a - \frac{5}{2}\right)^2 = \frac{53}{4}$$
$$a - \frac{5}{2} = \pm\sqrt{\frac{53}{4}}$$
$$a - \frac{5}{2} = \pm\frac{\sqrt{53}}{2}$$
$$a = \frac{5}{2} \pm \frac{\sqrt{53}}{2}$$
The solution set is $\left\{\frac{5}{2} - \frac{\sqrt{53}}{2}, \, \frac{5}{2} + \frac{\sqrt{53}}{2}\right\}$.

21.
$$b^2 + b + 7 = 0$$
$$b^2 + b = -7$$
$$b^2 + b + \left(\frac{1}{2} \cdot 1\right)^2 = -7 + \left(\frac{1}{2} \cdot 1\right)^2$$
$$b^2 + b + \frac{1}{4} = -7 + \frac{1}{4}$$
$$\left(b + \frac{1}{2}\right)^2 = -\frac{27}{4}$$
$$b + \frac{1}{2} = \pm\sqrt{-\frac{27}{4}}$$
$$b + \frac{1}{2} = \pm\frac{3\sqrt{3}}{2}i$$
$$b = -\frac{1}{2} \pm \frac{3\sqrt{3}}{2}i$$
The solution set is $\left\{-\frac{1}{2} - \frac{3\sqrt{3}}{2}i, \, -\frac{1}{2} + \frac{3\sqrt{3}}{2}i\right\}$.

22.
$$c^2 - 6c + 17 = 0$$
$$c^2 - 6c = -17$$
$$c^2 - 6c + \left(\frac{1}{2} \cdot (-6)\right)^2 = -17 + \left(\frac{1}{2} \cdot (-6)\right)^2$$
$$c^2 - 6c + 9 = -17 + 9$$
$$(c - 3)^2 = -8$$
$$c - 3 = \pm\sqrt{-8}$$
$$c - 3 = \pm 2\sqrt{2}\,i$$
$$c = 3 \pm 2\sqrt{2}\,i$$
The solution set is $\left\{3 - 2\sqrt{2}\,i, \, 3 + 2\sqrt{2}\,i\right\}$.

23.

$$2d^2 - 7d + 3 = 0$$

$$\frac{2d^2 - 7d + 3}{2} = \frac{0}{2}$$

$$d^2 - \frac{7}{2}d + \frac{3}{2} = 0$$

$$d^2 - \frac{7}{2}d = -\frac{3}{2}$$

$$d^2 - \frac{7}{2}d + \left[\frac{1}{2}\cdot\left(-\frac{7}{2}\right)\right]^2 = -\frac{3}{2} + \left[\frac{1}{2}\cdot\left(-\frac{7}{2}\right)\right]^2$$

$$d^2 - \frac{7}{2}d + \frac{49}{16} = -\frac{3}{2} + \frac{49}{16}$$

$$\left(d - \frac{7}{4}\right)^2 = \frac{25}{16}$$

$$d - \frac{7}{4} = \pm\sqrt{\frac{25}{16}}$$

$$d - \frac{7}{4} = \pm\frac{5}{4}$$

$$d = \frac{7}{4} \pm \frac{5}{4}$$

$$d = \frac{1}{2} \ \text{ or } \ d = 3$$

The solution set is $\left\{\frac{1}{2}, \ 3\right\}$.

24.

$$2w^2 + 2w + 5 = 0$$

$$\frac{2w^2 + 2w + 5}{2} = \frac{0}{2}$$

$$w^2 + w + \frac{5}{2} = 0$$

$$w^2 + w = -\frac{5}{2}$$

$$w^2 + w + \left(\frac{1}{2}\cdot 1\right)^2 = -\frac{5}{2} + \left(\frac{1}{2}\cdot 1\right)^2$$

$$w^2 + w + \frac{1}{4} = -\frac{5}{2} + \frac{1}{4}$$

$$\left(w + \frac{1}{2}\right)^2 = -\frac{9}{4}$$

$$w + \frac{1}{2} = \pm\sqrt{-\frac{9}{4}}$$

$$w + \frac{1}{2} = \pm\frac{3}{2}i$$

$$w = -\frac{1}{2} \pm \frac{3}{2}i$$

The solution set is $\left\{-\frac{1}{2} - \frac{3}{2}i, \ -\frac{1}{2} + \frac{3}{2}i\right\}$.

25.

$$3x^2 - 9x + 8 = 0$$

$$\frac{3x^2 - 9x + 8}{3} = \frac{0}{3}$$

$$x^2 - 3x + \frac{8}{3} = 0$$

$$x^2 - 3x = -\frac{8}{3}$$

$$x^2 - 3x + \left(\frac{1}{2}\cdot(-3)\right)^2 = -\frac{8}{3} + \left(\frac{1}{2}\cdot(-3)\right)^2$$

$$x^2 - 3x + \frac{9}{4} = -\frac{8}{3} + \frac{9}{4}$$

$$\left(x - \frac{3}{2}\right)^2 = -\frac{5}{12}$$

$$x - \frac{3}{2} = \pm\sqrt{-\frac{5}{12}}$$

$$x - \frac{3}{2} = \pm\frac{\sqrt{5}}{\sqrt{12}}i\cdot\frac{\sqrt{3}}{\sqrt{3}}$$

$$x - \frac{3}{2} = \pm\frac{\sqrt{15}}{\sqrt{36}}i$$

$$x - \frac{3}{2} = \pm\frac{\sqrt{15}}{6}i$$

$$x = \frac{3}{2} \pm \frac{\sqrt{15}}{6}i$$

The solution set is $\left\{\frac{3}{2} - \frac{\sqrt{15}}{6}i, \ \frac{3}{2} + \frac{\sqrt{15}}{6}i\right\}$.

26.

$$3x^2 + 4x - 2 = 0$$

$$x^2 + \frac{4}{3}x - \frac{2}{3} = 0$$

$$x^2 + \frac{4}{3}x = \frac{2}{3}$$

$$x^2 + \frac{4}{3}x + \left(\frac{1}{2}\cdot\frac{4}{3}\right)^2 = \frac{2}{3} + \left(\frac{1}{2}\cdot\frac{4}{3}\right)^2$$

$$x^2 + \frac{4}{3}x + \frac{4}{9} = \frac{2}{3} + \frac{4}{9}$$

$$\left(x + \frac{2}{3}\right)^2 = \frac{10}{9}$$

$$x + \frac{2}{3} = \pm\sqrt{\frac{10}{9}}$$

$$x + \frac{2}{3} = \pm\frac{\sqrt{10}}{3}$$

$$x = -\frac{2}{3} \pm \frac{\sqrt{10}}{3}$$

The solution set is $\left\{-\frac{2}{3} - \frac{\sqrt{10}}{3}, \ -\frac{2}{3} + \frac{\sqrt{10}}{3}\right\}$.

27. $c^2 = 9^2 + 12^2$
$= 81 + 144$
$= 225$
$c = \sqrt{225}$
$= 15$

28. $c^2 = 8^2 + 8^2$
$= 64 + 64$
$= 128$
$c = \sqrt{128}$
$= 8\sqrt{2}$

29. $c^2 = 3^2 + 6^2$
$= 9 + 36$
$= 45$
$c = \sqrt{45}$
$= 3\sqrt{5}$

30. $c^2 = 10^2 + 24^2$
$= 100 + 576$
$= 676$
$c = \sqrt{676}$
$= 26$

31. $c^2 = 5^2 + \left(\sqrt{11}\right)^2$
$= 25 + 11$
$= 36$
$c = \sqrt{36}$
$= 6$

32. $c^2 = 6^2 + \left(\sqrt{13}\right)^2$
$= 36 + 13$
$= 49$
$c = \sqrt{49}$
$= 7$

33. $c^2 = a^2 + b^2$
$12^2 = 9^2 + b^2$
$144 = 81 + b^2$
$63 = b^2$
$b = \sqrt{63}$
$b = 3\sqrt{7}$

34. $c^2 = a^2 + b^2$
$10^2 = a^2 + 5^2$
$100 = a^2 + 25$
$75 = a^2$
$a = \sqrt{75}$
$a = 5\sqrt{3}$

35. $c^2 = a^2 + b^2$
$17^2 = a^2 + 6^2$
$289 = a^2 + 36$
$253 = a^2$
$a = \sqrt{253}$

36. For this problem, we are actually looking for the hypotenuse of a right triangle that has legs 90 feet and 90 feet. We use the Pythagorean Theorem to find the desired distance:
$c^2 = 90^2 + 90^2$
$= 8100 + 8100$
$= 16,200$
$c = \sqrt{16,200}$
$= 90\sqrt{2}$
≈ 127.3
The distance from home plate to 2nd base is exactly $90\sqrt{2}$ feet or approximately 127.3 feet.

37. $x^2 - x - 20 = 0$
For this equation, $a = 1$, $b = -1$, and $c = -20$.
$$x = \frac{-(-1) \pm \sqrt{(-1)^2 - 4(1)(-20)}}{2(1)}$$
$$= \frac{1 \pm \sqrt{1 + 80}}{2}$$
$$= \frac{1 \pm \sqrt{81}}{2}$$
$$= \frac{1 \pm 9}{2}$$
$x = \frac{1-9}{2}$ or $x = \frac{1+9}{2}$
$= \frac{-8}{2}$ or $= \frac{10}{2}$
$= -4$ or $= 5$
The solution set is $\{-4, 5\}$.

38. $4y^2 = 8y + 21$
$4y^2 - 8y - 21 = 0$
For this equation, $a = 4$, $b = -8$, and $c = -21$.
$$y = \frac{-(-8) \pm \sqrt{(-8)^2 - 4(4)(-21)}}{2(4)}$$
$$= \frac{8 \pm \sqrt{64 + 336}}{8}$$
$$= \frac{8 \pm \sqrt{400}}{8}$$
$$= \frac{8 \pm 20}{8}$$

$$y = \frac{8-20}{8} \quad \text{or} \quad y = \frac{8+20}{8}$$

$$= \frac{-12}{8} \quad \text{or} \quad = \frac{28}{8}$$

$$= -\frac{3}{2} \quad \text{or} \quad = \frac{7}{2}$$

The solution set is $\left\{ -\frac{3}{2}, \frac{7}{2} \right\}$.

39. $\quad 3p^2 + 8p = -3$

$3p^2 + 8p + 3 = 0$

For this equation, $a = 3$, $b = 8$, and $c = 3$.

$$p = \frac{-8 \pm \sqrt{8^2 - 4(3)(3)}}{2(3)}$$

$$= \frac{-8 \pm \sqrt{64 - 36}}{6}$$

$$= \frac{-8 \pm \sqrt{28}}{6}$$

$$= \frac{-8 \pm 2\sqrt{7}}{6}$$

$$= \frac{-8}{6} \pm \frac{2\sqrt{7}}{6}$$

$$= -\frac{4}{3} \pm \frac{\sqrt{7}}{3}$$

The solution set is $\left\{ -\frac{4}{3} - \frac{\sqrt{7}}{3}, -\frac{4}{3} + \frac{\sqrt{7}}{3} \right\}$.

40. $\quad 2q^2 - 3 = 4q$

$2q^2 - 4q - 3 = 0$

For this equation, $a = 2$, $b = -4$, and $c = -3$.

$$q = \frac{-(-4) \pm \sqrt{(-4)^2 - 4(2)(-3)}}{2(2)}$$

$$= \frac{4 \pm \sqrt{16 + 24}}{4}$$

$$= \frac{4 \pm \sqrt{40}}{4}$$

$$= \frac{4 \pm 2\sqrt{10}}{4}$$

$$= \frac{4}{4} \pm \frac{2\sqrt{10}}{4}$$

$$= 1 \pm \frac{\sqrt{10}}{2}$$

The solution set is $\left\{ 1 - \frac{\sqrt{10}}{2}, 1 + \frac{\sqrt{10}}{2} \right\}$.

41. $\quad 3w^2 + w = -3$

$3w^2 + w + 3 = 0$

For this equation, $a = 3$, $b = 1$, and $c = 3$.

$$w = \frac{-1 \pm \sqrt{1^2 - 4(3)(3)}}{2(3)}$$

$$= \frac{-1 \pm \sqrt{1 - 36}}{6}$$

$$= \frac{-1 \pm \sqrt{-35}}{6}$$

$$= \frac{-1 \pm \sqrt{35}\, i}{6}$$

$$= -\frac{1}{6} \pm \frac{\sqrt{35}}{6} i$$

The solution set is $\left\{ -\frac{1}{6} - \frac{\sqrt{35}}{6} i, \ -\frac{1}{6} + \frac{\sqrt{35}}{6} i \right\}$.

42. $\quad 9z^2 + 16 = 24z$

$9z^2 - 24z + 16 = 0$

For this equation, $a = 9$, $b = -24$, and $c = 16$.

$$z = \frac{-(-24) \pm \sqrt{(-24)^2 - 4(9)(16)}}{2(9)}$$

$$= \frac{24 \pm \sqrt{576 - 576}}{18}$$

$$= \frac{24 \pm \sqrt{0}}{18}$$

$$= \frac{24}{18}$$

$$= \frac{4}{3}$$

The solution set is $\left\{ \frac{4}{3} \right\}$. It is a double root.

43. $\quad m^2 - 4m + 2 = 0$

For this equation, $a = 1$, $b = -4$, and $c = 2$.

$$m = \frac{-(-4) \pm \sqrt{(-4)^2 - 4(1)(2)}}{2(1)}$$

$$= \frac{4 \pm \sqrt{16 - 8}}{2}$$

$$= \frac{4 \pm \sqrt{8}}{2}$$

$$= \frac{4 \pm 2\sqrt{2}}{2}$$

$$= \frac{4}{2} \pm \frac{2\sqrt{2}}{2}$$

$$= 2 \pm \sqrt{2}$$

The solution set is $\left\{ 2 - \sqrt{2}, \ 2 + \sqrt{2} \right\}$.

44. $5n^2 + 4n + 1 = 0$

    For this equation, $a = 5$, $b = 4$, and $c = 1$.

    $$n = \frac{-4 \pm \sqrt{4^2 - 4(5)(1)}}{2(5)}$$

    $$= \frac{-4 \pm \sqrt{16 - 20}}{10}$$

    $$= \frac{-4 \pm \sqrt{-4}}{10}$$

    $$= \frac{-4 \pm 2i}{10}$$

    $$= -\frac{4}{10} \pm \frac{2i}{10} = -\frac{2}{5} \pm \frac{1}{5}i$$

    The solution set is $\left\{ -\frac{2}{5} - \frac{1}{5}i, \ -\frac{2}{5} + \frac{1}{5}i \right\}$.

45. $5x + 13 = -x^2$

    $x^2 + 5x + 13 = 0$

    For this equation, $a = 1$, $b = 5$, and $c = 13$.

    $$x = \frac{-5 \pm \sqrt{5^2 - 4(1)(13)}}{2(1)}$$

    $$= \frac{-5 \pm \sqrt{25 - 52}}{2}$$

    $$= \frac{-5 \pm \sqrt{-27}}{2}$$

    $$= \frac{-5 \pm 3\sqrt{3}\, i}{2} = -\frac{5}{2} \pm \frac{3\sqrt{3}}{2}i$$

    The solution set is $\left\{ -\frac{5}{2} - \frac{3\sqrt{3}}{2}i, \ -\frac{5}{2} + \frac{3\sqrt{3}}{2}i \right\}$.

46. $-2y^2 = 6y + 7$

    $0 = 2y^2 + 6y + 7$

    For this equation, $a = 2$, $b = 6$, and $c = 7$.

    $$y = \frac{-6 \pm \sqrt{6^2 - 4(2)(7)}}{2(2)}$$

    $$= \frac{-6 \pm \sqrt{36 - 56}}{4}$$

    $$= \frac{-6 \pm \sqrt{-20}}{4}$$

    $$= \frac{-6 \pm 2\sqrt{5}\, i}{4}$$

    $$= -\frac{6}{4} \pm \frac{2\sqrt{5}}{4}i = -\frac{3}{2} \pm \frac{\sqrt{5}}{2}i$$

    The solution set is $\left\{ -\frac{3}{2} - \frac{\sqrt{5}}{2}i, \ -\frac{3}{2} + \frac{\sqrt{5}}{2}i \right\}$.

47. $p^2 - 5p - 8 = 0$

    For this equation, $a = 1$, $b = -5$, and $c = -8$.

    $$b^2 - 4ac = (-5)^2 - 4(1)(-8) = 25 + 32 = 57$$

    Because $b^2 - 4ac = 57$ is positive, but not a perfect square, the quadratic equation will have two irrational solutions.

48. $m^2 + 8m + 16 = 0$

    For this equation, $a = 1$, $b = 8$, and $c = 16$.

    $$b^2 - 4ac = 8^2 - 4(1)(16) = 64 - 64 = 0$$

    Because $b^2 - 4ac = 0$, the quadratic equation will have one repeated real solution.

49. $3n^2 + n = -4$

    $3n^2 + n + 4 = 0$

    For this equation, $a = 3$, $b = 1$, and $c = 4$.

    $$b^2 - 4ac = 1^2 - 4(3)(4) = 1 - 48 = -47$$

    Because $b^2 - 4ac = -47$ is negative, the quadratic equation will have two complex solutions that are not real. The solutions will be complex conjugates of each other.

50. $7w^2 + 3 = 8w$

    $7w^2 - 8w + 3 = 0$

    For this equation, $a = 7$, $b = -8$, and $c = 3$.

    $$b^2 - 4ac = (-8)^2 - 4(7)(3) = 64 - 84 = -20$$

    Because $b^2 - 4ac = -20$ is negative, the quadratic equation will have two complex solutions that are not real. The solutions will be complex conjugates of each other.

51. $4x^2 + 49 = 28x$

    $4x^2 - 28x + 49 = 0$

    For this equation, $a = 4$, $b = -28$, and $c = 49$.

    $$b^2 - 4ac = (-28)^2 - 4(4)(49) = 784 - 784 = 0$$

    Because $b^2 - 4ac = 0$, the quadratic equation will have one repeated real solution.

52. $11z - 12 = 2z^2$

    $0 = 2z^2 - 11z + 12$

    For this equation, $a = 2$, $b = -11$, and $c = 12$.

    $$b^2 - 4ac = (-11)^2 - 4(2)(12) = 121 - 96 = 25$$

    Because $b^2 - 4ac = 25$ is positive and a perfect square, the quadratic equation will have two rational solutions.

53. $x^2 + 8x - 9 = 0$

Because this equation factors easily, solve by factoring.

$(x+9)(x-1) = 0$

$x+9 = 0$ or $x-1 = 0$

$x = -9$ or $x = 1$

The solution set is $\{-9, 1\}$.

54. $6p^2 + 13p = 5$

$6p^2 + 13p - 5 = 0$

Because this equation factors easily, solve by factoring.

$(3p-1)(2p+5) = 0$

$3p-1 = 0$ or $2p+5 = 0$

$3p = 1$ or $2p = -5$

$p = \dfrac{1}{3}$ or $p = -\dfrac{5}{2}$

The solution set is $\left\{-\dfrac{5}{2}, \dfrac{1}{3}\right\}$.

55. $n^2 + 13 = -4n$

$n^2 + 4n + 13 = 0$

Because this equation does not easily factor, solve by using the quadratic formula. For this equation, $a = 1$, $b = 4$, and $c = 13$.

$$n = \frac{-4 \pm \sqrt{4^2 - 4(1)(13)}}{2(1)}$$

$$= \frac{-4 \pm \sqrt{16 - 52}}{2}$$

$$= \frac{-4 \pm \sqrt{-36}}{2}$$

$$= \frac{-4 \pm 6i}{2}$$

$$= -\frac{4}{2} \pm \frac{6i}{2}$$

$$= -2 \pm 3i$$

The solution set is $\{-2-3i, -2+3i\}$.

56. $5y^2 - 60 = 0$

Because this equation has no linear term, solve by using the square root method.

$5y^2 = 60$

$y^2 = 12$

$y = \pm\sqrt{12}$

$y = \pm 2\sqrt{3}$

The solution set is $\left\{-2\sqrt{3},\ 2\sqrt{3}\right\}$.

57. $\dfrac{1}{4}q^2 - \dfrac{1}{2}q - \dfrac{3}{8} = 0$

$8\left(\dfrac{1}{4}q^2 - \dfrac{1}{2}q - \dfrac{3}{8}\right) = 8(0)$

$2q^2 - 4q - 3 = 0$

Because this equation does not easily factor, solve by using the quadratic formula. For this equation, $a = 2$, $b = -4$, and $c = -3$.

$$q = \frac{-(-4) \pm \sqrt{(-4)^2 - 4(2)(-3)}}{2(2)}$$

$$= \frac{4 \pm \sqrt{16 + 24}}{4}$$

$$= \frac{4 \pm \sqrt{40}}{4}$$

$$= \frac{4 \pm 2\sqrt{10}}{4}$$

$$= \frac{4}{4} \pm \frac{2\sqrt{10}}{4}$$

$$= 1 \pm \frac{\sqrt{10}}{2}$$

The solution set is $\left\{1 - \dfrac{\sqrt{10}}{2},\ 1 + \dfrac{\sqrt{10}}{2}\right\}$.

58. $\dfrac{1}{8}m^2 + m + \dfrac{5}{2} = 0$

$8\left(\dfrac{1}{8}m^2 + m + \dfrac{5}{2}\right) = 8(0)$

$m^2 + 8m + 20 = 0$

Because this equation does not easily factor, solve by using the quadratic formula. For this equation, $a = 1$, $b = 8$, and $c = 20$.

$$m = \frac{-8 \pm \sqrt{8^2 - 4(1)(20)}}{2(1)}$$

$$= \frac{-8 \pm \sqrt{64 - 80}}{2}$$

$$= \frac{-8 \pm \sqrt{-16}}{2}$$

$$= \frac{-8 \pm 4i}{2}$$

$$= -\frac{8}{2} \pm \frac{4i}{2}$$

$$= -4 \pm 2i$$

The solution set is $\{-4-2i,\ -4+2i\}$.

59. $(w-8)(w+6)=-33$

$\quad w^2-2w-48=-33$

$\quad w^2-2w-15=0$

Because this equation factors easily, solve by factoring.

$(w-5)(w+3)=0$

$w-5=0 \quad \text{or} \quad w+3=0$

$\quad w=5 \quad \text{or} \qquad w=-3$

The solution set is $\{-3,\ 5\}$.

60. $(x-3)(x+1)=-2$

$\quad x^2-2x-3=-2$

$\quad x^2-2x-1=0$

Because this equation does not easily factor, solve by using the quadratic formula. For this equation, $a=1$, $b=-2$, and $c=-1$.

$x=\dfrac{-(-2)\pm\sqrt{(-2)^2-4(1)(-1)}}{2(1)}$

$\quad=\dfrac{2\pm\sqrt{4+4}}{2}$

$\quad=\dfrac{2\pm\sqrt{8}}{2}$

$\quad=\dfrac{2\pm 2\sqrt{2}}{2}$

$\quad=\dfrac{2}{2}\pm\dfrac{2\sqrt{2}}{2}$

$\quad=1\pm\sqrt{2}$

The solution set is $\{1-\sqrt{2},\ 1+\sqrt{2}\}$.

61. $9z^2=16$

Because this equation has no linear term, solve by using the square root method.

$z^2=\dfrac{16}{9}$

$z=\pm\sqrt{\dfrac{16}{9}}$

$z=\pm\dfrac{4}{3}$

The solution set is $\left\{-\dfrac{4}{3},\ \dfrac{4}{3}\right\}$.

62. $\dfrac{1-2x}{x^2+5}=1$

$(x^2+5)\left(\dfrac{1-2x}{x^2+5}\right)=(x^2+5)(1)$

$\qquad\quad 1-2x=x^2+5$

$\qquad\qquad 0=x^2+2x+4$

Because this equation does not easily factor, solve by using the quadratic formula. For this equation, $a=1$, $b=2$, and $c=4$.

$x=\dfrac{-2\pm\sqrt{2^2-4(1)(4)}}{2(1)}$

$\quad=\dfrac{-2\pm\sqrt{4-16}}{2}$

$\quad=\dfrac{-2\pm\sqrt{-12}}{2}$

$\quad=\dfrac{-2\pm 2\sqrt{3}\ i}{2}$

$\quad=-1\pm\sqrt{3}\ i$

The solution set is $\left\{-1-\sqrt{3}\ i,\ -1+\sqrt{3}\ i\right\}$.

63. $\quad(x+2)^2+(x-5)^2=(x+3)^2$

$x^2+4x+4+x^2-10x+25=x^2+6x+9$

$\qquad\quad 2x^2-6x+29=x^2+6x+9$

$\qquad\qquad\quad x^2-12x+20=0$

$\qquad\qquad\quad (x-2)(x-10)=0$

$\qquad\quad x-2=0 \text{ or } x-10=0$

$\qquad\qquad x=2 \text{ or } \qquad x=10$

Disregard $x=2$ because this value will cause the length of one of the legs to be negative: $x-5=2-5=-3$. Thus, $x=10$ is the only viable answer. Now, $x-5=10-5=5$, $x+2=10+2=12$, and $x+3=10+3=13$. The three measurements are 5, 12, and 13.

64. Let x represent the length of the rectangle. Then $x-3$ will represent the width.

$x(x-3)=108$

$x^2-3x=108$

$x^2-3x-108=0$

$(x-12)(x+9)=0$

$x-12=0 \quad \text{or} \quad x+9=0$

$\quad x=12 \quad \text{or} \qquad x=-9$

Disregard $x=-9$ because x represents the length of the rectangle, which must be positive. Thus, $x=12$ is the only viable answer. Now, $x-3=12-3=9$. Thus, the dimensions of the rectangle are 12 centimeters by 9 centimeters.

65. a.
$$-0.2x^2 + 180x = 36,000$$
$$0 = 0.2x^2 - 180x + 36,000$$

For this equation, $a = 0.2$, $b = -180$, and $c = 36,000$.

$$x = \frac{-(-180) \pm \sqrt{(-180)^2 - 4(0.2)(36,000)}}{2(0.2)}$$
$$= \frac{180 \pm \sqrt{32,400 - 28,800}}{0.4}$$
$$= \frac{180 \pm \sqrt{3600}}{0.4}$$
$$= \frac{180 \pm 60}{0.4}$$

$$x = \frac{180 - 60}{0.4} \quad \text{or} \quad x = \frac{180 + 60}{0.4}$$
$$= 300 \quad \text{or} \quad = 600$$

The revenue will be $36,000 per week if either 300 or 600 cellular phones are sold per week.

b.
$$-0.2x^2 + 180x = 40,500$$
$$0 = 0.2x^2 - 180x + 40,500$$

For this equation, $a = 0.2$, $b = -180$, and $c = 40,500$.

$$x = \frac{-(-180) \pm \sqrt{(-180)^2 - 4(0.2)(40,500)}}{2(0.2)}$$
$$= \frac{180 \pm \sqrt{32,400 - 32,400}}{0.4}$$
$$= \frac{180 \pm \sqrt{0}}{0.4}$$
$$= \frac{180}{0.4}$$
$$= 450$$

The revenue will be $40,500 per week if 450 cellular phones are sold per week.

66. a.
$$200 = -16t^2 + 50t + 180$$
$$16t^2 - 50t + 20 = 0$$

For this equation, $a = 16$, $b = -50$, and $c = 20$.

$$t = \frac{-(-50) \pm \sqrt{(-50)^2 - 4(16)(20)}}{2(16)}$$
$$= \frac{50 \pm \sqrt{2500 - 1280}}{32}$$

$$= \frac{50 \pm \sqrt{1220}}{32}$$
$$= \frac{50 \pm 2\sqrt{305}}{32}$$
$$= \frac{50}{32} \pm \frac{2\sqrt{305}}{32}$$
$$= \frac{25}{16} \pm \frac{\sqrt{305}}{16}$$

$$t = \frac{25}{16} - \frac{\sqrt{305}}{16} \quad \text{or} \quad t = \frac{25}{16} + \frac{\sqrt{305}}{16}$$
$$\approx 0.471 \quad \text{or} \quad \approx 2.654$$

Rounding to the nearest tenth, the height of the ball will be 200 feet after approximately 0.5 seconds and after approximately 2.7 seconds.

b.
$$100 = -16t^2 + 50t + 180$$
$$16t^2 - 50t - 80 = 0$$

For this equation, $a = 16$, $b = -50$, and $c = -80$.

$$t = \frac{-(-50) \pm \sqrt{(-50)^2 - 4(16)(-80)}}{2(16)}$$
$$= \frac{50 \pm \sqrt{2500 + 5120}}{32}$$
$$= \frac{50 \pm \sqrt{7620}}{32}$$
$$= \frac{50 \pm 2\sqrt{1905}}{32}$$
$$= \frac{50}{32} \pm \frac{2\sqrt{1905}}{32}$$
$$= \frac{25}{16} \pm \frac{\sqrt{1905}}{16}$$

$$t = \frac{25}{16} - \frac{\sqrt{1905}}{16} \quad \text{or} \quad t = \frac{25}{16} + \frac{\sqrt{1905}}{16}$$
$$\approx -1.165 \quad \text{or} \quad \approx 4.290$$

Because time cannot be negative, we disregard -1.165. Thus, $t \approx 4.290$ is the only viable answer. Rounding to the nearest tenth, the height of the ball will be 100 feet after approximately 4.3 seconds.

c.
$$300 = -16t^2 + 50t + 180$$
$$16t^2 - 50t + 120 = 0$$

For this equation, $a = 16$, $b = -50$, and $c = 120$.

$$t = \frac{-(-50) \pm \sqrt{(-50)^2 - 4(16)(120)}}{2(16)}$$

$$= \frac{50 \pm \sqrt{2500 - 7680}}{32}$$

$$= \frac{50 \pm \sqrt{-5180}}{32}$$

$$= \frac{50 \pm 2\sqrt{1295}\, i}{32}$$

$$= \frac{50}{32} \pm \frac{2\sqrt{1295}}{32} i$$

$$= \frac{25}{16} \pm \frac{\sqrt{1295}}{16} i$$

$$t = \frac{25}{16} - \frac{\sqrt{1295}}{16} i \text{ or } t = \frac{25}{16} + \frac{\sqrt{1295}}{16} i$$

The ball will never reach a height of 300 feet. This is clear because the solutions to the equation above are complex solutions that are not real.

67. Let x represent the speed the boat would travel in still water.

	Distance	**Rate**	**Time**
Up Stream	10	$x - 3$	$\frac{10}{x-3}$
Down Stream	10	$x + 3$	$\frac{10}{x+3}$

$$\frac{10}{x-3} + \frac{10}{x+3} = 2$$

$$(x-3)(x+3)\left(\frac{10}{x-3} + \frac{10}{x+3}\right) = (x-3)(x+3)(2)$$

$$10(x+3) + 10(x-3) = (x^2 - 9)(2)$$

$$10x + 30 + 10x - 30 = 2x^2 - 18$$

$$20x = 2x^2 - 18$$

$$0 = 2x^2 - 20x - 18$$

For this equation, $a = 2$, $b = -20$, and $c = -18$.

$$x = \frac{-(-20) \pm \sqrt{(-20)^2 - 4(2)(-18)}}{2(2)}$$

$$= \frac{20 \pm \sqrt{400 + 144}}{4}$$

$$= \frac{20 \pm \sqrt{544}}{4}$$

$$= \frac{20 \pm 4\sqrt{34}}{4}$$

$$= 5 \pm \sqrt{34}$$

$$x = 5 - \sqrt{34} \text{ or } x = 5 + \sqrt{34}$$

$$\approx -0.831 \text{ or } \approx 10.831$$

Because the speed should be positive, we disregard $x \approx -0.831$. Thus, the only viable answer is $x \approx 10.831$. Rounding to the nearest tenth, the boat would travel approximately 10.8 miles per hour in still water.

68. Let t represent the time required for Beth to wash the car alone. Then $t - 14$ will represent the time required for Tom to wash the car alone.

$$\begin{pmatrix} \text{Part done} \\ \text{by Beth in} \\ \text{1 minute} \end{pmatrix} + \begin{pmatrix} \text{Part done} \\ \text{by Tom in} \\ \text{1 minute} \end{pmatrix} = \begin{pmatrix} \text{Part done} \\ \text{together in} \\ \text{1 minute} \end{pmatrix}$$

$$\frac{1}{t} + \frac{1}{t-14} = \frac{1}{30}$$

$$30t(t-14)\left(\frac{1}{t} + \frac{1}{t-14}\right) = 30t(t-14)\left(\frac{1}{30}\right)$$

$$30(t-14) + 30t = t(t-14)$$

$$30t - 420 + 30t = t^2 - 14t$$

$$60t - 420 = t^2 - 14t$$

$$0 = t^2 - 74t + 420$$

For this equation, $a = 1$, $b = -74$, and $c = 420$.

$$t = \frac{-(-74) \pm \sqrt{(-74)^2 - 4(1)(420)}}{2(1)}$$

$$= \frac{74 \pm \sqrt{5476 - 1680}}{2}$$

$$= \frac{74 \pm \sqrt{3796}}{2}$$

$$= \frac{74 \pm 2\sqrt{949}}{2}$$

$$= 37 \pm \sqrt{949}$$

$$t = 37 - \sqrt{949} \text{ or } t = 37 + \sqrt{949}$$

$$\approx 6.194 \qquad \text{or} \qquad \approx 67.806$$

Disregard $t \approx 6.194$ because this value makes Tom's time negative: $t - 14 = 6.194 - 14 = -7.806$. The only viable answer is $t \approx 67.806$ minutes. Working alone, it will take Beth approximately 67.8 minutes to wash the car.

69.
$$x^4 + 7x^2 - 144 = 0$$

$$\left(x^2\right)^2 + 7\left(x^2\right) - 144 = 0$$

Let $u = x^2$.

$$u^2 + 7u - 144 = 0$$

$$(u - 9)(u + 16) = 0$$

$$u - 9 = 0 \qquad \text{or} \quad u + 16 = 0$$

$$u = 9 \qquad \text{or} \qquad u = -16$$

$$x^2 = 9 \qquad \text{or} \qquad x^2 = -16$$

$$x = \pm\sqrt{9} \text{ or} \qquad x = \pm\sqrt{-16}$$

$$x = \pm 3 \qquad \text{or} \qquad x = \pm 4i$$

Check:

$$x = -3: \quad (-3)^4 + 7(-3)^2 - 144 \overset{?}{=} 0$$
$$81 + 7 \cdot 9 - 144 \overset{?}{=} 0$$
$$81 + 63 - 144 \overset{?}{=} 0$$
$$0 = 0 \checkmark$$

$$x = 3: \quad 3^4 + 7(3)^2 - 144 \overset{?}{=} 0$$
$$81 + 7 \cdot 9 - 144 \overset{?}{=} 0$$
$$81 + 63 - 144 \overset{?}{=} 0$$
$$0 = 0 \checkmark$$

$$x = -4i: \quad (-4i)^4 + 7(-4i)^2 - 144 \overset{?}{=} 0$$
$$256i^4 + 7 \cdot 16i^2 - 144 \overset{?}{=} 0$$
$$256(1) + 7 \cdot 16(-1) - 144 \overset{?}{=} 0$$
$$256 - 112 - 144 \overset{?}{=} 0$$
$$0 = 0 \checkmark$$

$$x = 4i: \quad (4i)^4 + 7(4i)^2 - 144 \overset{?}{=} 0$$
$$256i^4 + 7 \cdot 16i^2 - 144 \overset{?}{=} 0$$
$$256(1) + 7 \cdot 16(-1) - 144 \overset{?}{=} 0$$
$$256 - 112 - 144 \overset{?}{=} 0$$
$$0 = 0 \checkmark$$

All check; the solution set is $\{-3,\ 3,\ -4i,\ 4i\}$.

70.
$$4w^4 + 5w^2 - 6 = 0$$
$$4(w^2)^2 + 5(w^2) - 6 = 0$$

Let $u = w^2$.
$$4u^2 + 5u - 6 = 0$$
$$(4u - 3)(u + 2) = 0$$
$$4u - 3 = 0 \quad \text{or} \quad u + 2 = 0$$
$$4u = 3 \quad \text{or} \quad u = -2$$
$$u = \frac{3}{4}$$
$$w^2 = \frac{3}{4} \quad \text{or} \quad w^2 = -2$$
$$w = \pm\sqrt{\frac{3}{4}} \quad \text{or} \quad w = \pm\sqrt{-2}$$
$$w = \pm\frac{\sqrt{3}}{2} \quad \text{or} \quad w = \pm\sqrt{2}\,i$$

Check:

$$w = -\frac{\sqrt{3}}{2}: \quad 4\left(-\frac{\sqrt{3}}{2}\right)^4 + 5\left(-\frac{\sqrt{3}}{2}\right)^2 - 6 \overset{?}{=} 0$$
$$4\left(\frac{9}{16}\right) + 5\left(\frac{3}{4}\right) - 6 \overset{?}{=} 0$$
$$\frac{9}{4} + \frac{15}{4} - 6 \overset{?}{=} 0$$
$$0 = 0 \checkmark$$

$$w = \frac{\sqrt{3}}{2}: \quad 4\left(\frac{\sqrt{3}}{2}\right)^4 + 5\left(\frac{\sqrt{3}}{2}\right)^2 - 6 \overset{?}{=} 0$$
$$4\left(\frac{9}{16}\right) + 5\left(\frac{3}{4}\right) - 6 \overset{?}{=} 0$$
$$\frac{9}{4} + \frac{15}{4} - 6 \overset{?}{=} 0$$
$$0 = 0 \checkmark$$

$$w = -\sqrt{2}\,i: \quad 4\left(-\sqrt{2}\,i\right)^4 + 5\left(-\sqrt{2}\,i\right)^2 - 6 \overset{?}{=} 0$$
$$4 \cdot 4i^4 + 5 \cdot 2i^2 - 6 \overset{?}{=} 0$$
$$4 \cdot 4(1) + 5 \cdot 2(-1) - 6 \overset{?}{=} 0$$
$$16 - 10 - 6 \overset{?}{=} 0$$
$$0 = 0 \checkmark$$

$$w = \sqrt{2}\,i: \quad 4\left(\sqrt{2}\,i\right)^4 + 5\left(\sqrt{2}\,i\right)^2 - 6 \overset{?}{=} 0$$
$$4 \cdot 4i^4 + 5 \cdot 2i^2 - 6 \overset{?}{=} 0$$
$$4 \cdot 4(1) + 5 \cdot 2(-1) - 6 \overset{?}{=} 0$$
$$16 - 10 - 6 \overset{?}{=} 0$$
$$0 = 0 \checkmark$$

All check; the solution set is
$$\left\{ -\frac{\sqrt{3}}{2},\ \frac{\sqrt{3}}{2},\ -\sqrt{2}\,i,\ \sqrt{2}\,i \right\}.$$

71. $3(a+4)^2 - 11(a+4) + 6 = 0$

Let $u = a + 4$.
$$3u^2 - 11u + 6 = 0$$
$$(3u - 2)(u - 3) = 0$$
$$3u - 2 = 0 \quad \text{or} \quad u - 3 = 0$$
$$3u = 2 \quad \text{or} \quad u = 3$$
$$u = \frac{2}{3}$$
$$a + 4 = \frac{2}{3} \quad \text{or} \quad a + 4 = 3$$
$$a = -\frac{10}{3} \quad \text{or} \quad a = -1$$

Check:

$$a = -\frac{10}{3}: \quad 3\left(-\frac{10}{3}+4\right)^2 - 11\left(-\frac{10}{3}+4\right)+6 \overset{?}{=} 0$$

$$3\left(\frac{2}{3}\right)^2 - 11\left(\frac{2}{3}\right)+6 \overset{?}{=} 0$$

$$3\left(\frac{4}{9}\right) - \frac{22}{3}+6 \overset{?}{=} 0$$

$$\frac{4}{3} - \frac{22}{3}+6 \overset{?}{=} 0$$

$$0 = 0 \checkmark$$

$$a = -1: \quad 3(-1+4)^2 - 11(-1+4)+6 \overset{?}{=} 0$$

$$3(3)^2 - 11(3)+6 \overset{?}{=} 0$$

$$3(9) - 33 + 6 \overset{?}{=} 0$$

$$27 - 33 + 6 \overset{?}{=} 0$$

$$0 = 0 \checkmark$$

Both check; the solution set is $\left\{-\frac{10}{3}, \, -1\right\}$.

72. $\left(q^2 - 11\right)^2 - 2\left(q^2 - 11\right) - 15 = 0$

Let $u = q^2 - 11$.

$$u^2 - 2u - 15 = 0$$
$$(u+3)(u-5) = 0$$

$$u + 3 = 0 \quad \text{or} \quad u - 5 = 0$$
$$u = -3 \quad \text{or} \quad u = 5$$
$$q^2 - 11 = -3 \quad \text{or} \quad q^2 - 11 = 5$$
$$q^2 = 8 \quad \text{or} \quad q^2 = 16$$
$$q = \pm\sqrt{8} \quad \text{or} \quad q = \pm\sqrt{16}$$
$$q = \pm 2\sqrt{2} \quad \text{or} \quad q = \pm 4$$

Check:

$$q = -2\sqrt{2}:$$

$$\left(\left(-2\sqrt{2}\right)^2 - 11\right)^2 - 2\left(\left(-2\sqrt{2}\right)^2 - 11\right) - 15 \overset{?}{=} 0$$

$$(8-11)^2 - 2(8-11) - 15 \overset{?}{=} 0$$

$$(-3)^2 - 2(-3) - 15 \overset{?}{=} 0$$

$$9 + 6 - 15 \overset{?}{=} 0$$

$$0 = 0 \checkmark$$

$$q = 2\sqrt{2}:$$

$$\left(\left(2\sqrt{2}\right)^2 - 11\right)^2 - 2\left(\left(2\sqrt{2}\right)^2 - 11\right) - 15 \overset{?}{=} 0$$

$$(8-11)^2 - 2(8-11) - 15 \overset{?}{=} 0$$

$$(-3)^2 - 2(-3) - 15 \overset{?}{=} 0$$

$$9 + 6 - 15 \overset{?}{=} 0$$

$$0 = 0 \checkmark$$

$$q = -4: \quad \left((-4)^2 - 11\right)^2 - 2\left((-4)^2 - 11\right) - 15 \overset{?}{=} 0$$

$$(16-11)^2 - 2(16-11) - 15 \overset{?}{=} 0$$

$$(5)^2 - 2(5) - 15 \overset{?}{=} 0$$

$$25 - 10 - 15 \overset{?}{=} 0$$

$$0 = 0 \checkmark$$

$$q = 4: \quad \left(4^2 - 11\right)^2 - 2\left(4^2 - 11\right) - 15 \overset{?}{=} 0$$

$$(16-11)^2 - 2(16-11) - 15 \overset{?}{=} 0$$

$$(5)^2 - 2(5) - 15 \overset{?}{=} 0$$

$$25 - 10 - 15 \overset{?}{=} 0$$

$$0 = 0 \checkmark$$

All check; the solution set is
$\left\{-4, \, -2\sqrt{2}, \, 2\sqrt{2}, \, 4\right\}$.

73. $$y - 13\sqrt{y} + 36 = 0$$

$$\left(\sqrt{y}\right)^2 - 13\left(\sqrt{y}\right) + 36 = 0$$

Let $u = \sqrt{y}$.

$$u^2 - 13u + 36 = 0$$
$$(u-4)(u-9) = 0$$

$$u - 4 = 0 \quad \text{or} \quad u - 9 = 0$$
$$u = 4 \quad \text{or} \quad u = 9$$
$$\sqrt{y} = 4 \quad \text{or} \quad \sqrt{y} = 9$$
$$y = 4^2 \quad \text{or} \quad y = 9^2$$
$$y = 16 \quad \text{or} \quad y = 81$$

Check:

$$y = 16: \quad 16 - 13\sqrt{16} + 36 \overset{?}{=} 0$$

$$16 - 13 \cdot 4 + 36 \overset{?}{=} 0$$

$$16 - 52 + 36 \overset{?}{=} 0$$

$$0 = 0 \checkmark$$

$$y = 16: \quad 81 - 13\sqrt{81} + 36 \overset{?}{=} 0$$

$$81 - 13 \cdot 9 + 36 \overset{?}{=} 0$$

$$81 - 117 + 36 \overset{?}{=} 0$$

$$0 = 0 \ \checkmark$$

Both check, the solution set is $\{16, \ 81\}$.

74.
$$5z + 2\sqrt{z} - 3 = 0$$

$$5\left(\sqrt{z}\right)^2 + 2\left(\sqrt{z}\right) - 3 = 0$$

Let $u = \sqrt{z}$.

$$5u^2 + 2u - 3 = 0$$

$$(5u - 3)(u + 1) = 0$$

$$5u - 3 = 0 \quad \text{or} \quad u + 1 = 0$$

$$5u = 3 \quad \text{or} \quad u = -1$$

$$u = \frac{3}{5}$$

$$\sqrt{z} = \frac{3}{5} \quad \text{or} \quad \sqrt{z} = -1$$

$$z = \left(\frac{3}{5}\right)^2 \quad \text{or} \quad z = (-1)^2$$

$$z = \frac{9}{25} \quad \text{or} \quad z = 1$$

Check:

$$z = \frac{9}{25}: \quad 5 \cdot \frac{9}{25} + 2\sqrt{\frac{9}{25}} - 3 \overset{?}{=} 0$$

$$\frac{9}{5} + 2 \cdot \frac{3}{5} - 3 \overset{?}{=} 0$$

$$\frac{9}{5} + \frac{6}{5} - 3 \overset{?}{=} 0$$

$$0 = 0 \ \checkmark$$

$$z = 1: \quad 5 \cdot 1 + 2\sqrt{1} - 3 \overset{?}{=} 0$$

$$5 + 2 \cdot 1 - 3 \overset{?}{=} 0$$

$$5 + 2 - 3 \overset{?}{=} 0$$

$$4 \neq 0 \ \times$$

$z = 1$ does not check; the solution set is $\left\{\dfrac{9}{25}\right\}$.

75.
$$p^{-2} - 4p^{-1} - 21 = 0$$

$$\left(p^{-1}\right)^2 - 4\left(p^{-1}\right) - 21 = 0$$

Let $u = p^{-1}$.

$$u^2 - 4u - 21 = 0$$

$$(u + 3)(u - 7) = 0$$

$$u + 3 = 0 \quad \text{or} \quad u - 7 = 0$$

$$u = -3 \quad \text{or} \quad u = 7$$

$$p^{-1} = -3 \quad \text{or} \quad p^{-1} = 7$$

$$\frac{1}{p} = -3 \quad \text{or} \quad \frac{1}{p} = 7$$

$$p = -\frac{1}{3} \quad \text{or} \quad p = \frac{1}{7}$$

Check:

$$p = -\frac{1}{3}: \quad \left(-\frac{1}{3}\right)^{-2} - 4\left(-\frac{1}{3}\right)^{-1} - 21 \overset{?}{=} 0$$

$$(-3)^2 - 4(-3) - 21 \overset{?}{=} 0$$

$$9 + 12 - 21 \overset{?}{=} 0$$

$$0 = 0 \ \checkmark$$

$$p = \frac{1}{7}: \quad \left(\frac{1}{7}\right)^{-2} - 4\left(\frac{1}{7}\right)^{-1} - 21 \overset{?}{=} 0$$

$$(7)^2 - 4(7) - 21 \overset{?}{=} 0$$

$$49 - 28 - 21 \overset{?}{=} 0$$

$$0 = 0 \ \checkmark$$

Both check; the solution set is $\left\{-\dfrac{1}{3}, \ \dfrac{1}{7}\right\}$.

76.
$$2b^{2/3} + 13b^{1/3} - 7 = 0$$

$$2\left(b^{1/3}\right)^2 + 13\left(b^{1/3}\right) - 7 = 0$$

Let $u = b^{1/3}$.

$$2u^2 + 13u - 7 = 0$$

$$(2u - 1)(u + 7) = 0$$

$$2u - 1 = 0 \quad \text{or} \quad u + 7 = 0$$

$$2u = 1 \quad \text{or} \quad u = -7$$

$$u = \frac{1}{2}$$

$$b^{1/3} = \frac{1}{2} \quad \text{or} \quad b^{1/3} = -7$$

$$\left(b^{1/3}\right)^3 = \left(\frac{1}{2}\right)^3 \quad \text{or} \quad \left(b^{1/3}\right)^3 = (-7)^3$$

$$b = \frac{1}{8} \quad \text{or} \quad b = -343$$

Check:

$$b = \frac{1}{8}: \quad 2\left(\frac{1}{8}\right)^{2/3} + 13\left(\frac{1}{8}\right)^{1/3} - 7 \overset{?}{=} 0$$

$$2\left(\sqrt[3]{\frac{1}{8}}\right)^2 + 13\left(\sqrt[3]{\frac{1}{8}}\right) - 7 \overset{?}{=} 0$$

$$2\left(\frac{1}{2}\right)^2 + 13\left(\cdot\frac{1}{2}\right) - 7 \overset{?}{=} 0$$

$$2\left(\frac{1}{4}\right) + 13\left(\frac{1}{2}\right) - 7 \overset{?}{=} 0$$

$$\frac{1}{2} + \frac{13}{2} - 7 \overset{?}{=} 0$$

$$0 = 0 \checkmark$$

$$b = -343: \quad 2(-343)^{2/3} + 13(-343)^{1/3} - 7 \overset{?}{=} 0$$

$$2\left(\sqrt[3]{-343}\right)^2 + 13\left(\sqrt[3]{-343}\right) - 7 \overset{?}{=} 0$$

$$2(-7)^2 + 13(-7) - 7 \overset{?}{=} 0$$

$$2(49) - 91 - 7 \overset{?}{=} 0$$

$$98 - 91 - 7 \overset{?}{=} 0$$

$$0 = 0 \checkmark$$

Both check; the solution set is $\left\{-343, \ \frac{1}{8}\right\}$.

77. $\quad m^{1/2} + 2m^{1/4} - 8 = 0$

$$\left(m^{1/4}\right)^2 + 2\left(m^{1/4}\right) - 8 = 0$$

Let $u = m^{1/4}$.

$$u^2 + 2u - 8 = 0$$
$$(u - 2)(u + 4) = 0$$

$$u - 2 = 0 \quad \text{or} \quad u + 4 = 0$$
$$u = 2 \quad \text{or} \quad u = -4$$
$$m^{1/4} = 2 \quad \text{or} \quad m^{1/4} = -4$$
$$\left(m^{1/4}\right)^4 = 2^4 \quad \text{or} \quad \left(m^{1/4}\right)^4 = (-4)^4$$
$$m = 16 \quad \text{or} \quad m = 256$$

Check:

$$m = 16: \quad (16)^{1/2} + 2(16)^{1/4} - 8 \overset{?}{=} 0$$

$$\sqrt{16} + 2\sqrt[4]{16} - 8 \overset{?}{=} 0$$

$$4 + 2\cdot 2 - 8 \overset{?}{=} 0$$

$$4 + 4 - 8 \overset{?}{=} 0$$

$$0 = 0 \checkmark$$

$$m = 256: \quad (256)^{1/2} + 2(256)^{1/4} - 8 \overset{?}{=} 0$$

$$\sqrt{256} + 2\sqrt[4]{256} - 8 \overset{?}{=} 0$$

$$16 + 2\cdot 4 - 8 \overset{?}{=} 0$$

$$16 + 8 - 8 \overset{?}{=} 0$$

$$16 \neq 0 \ \textbf{✗}$$

$m = 256$ does not check; the solution set is $\{16\}$.

78. $\quad \left(\frac{1}{x+5}\right)^2 + \frac{3}{x+5} = 28$

$$\left(\frac{1}{x+5}\right)^2 + 3\left(\frac{1}{x+5}\right) - 28 = 0$$

Let $u = \frac{1}{x+5}$.

$$u^2 + 3u - 28 = 0$$
$$(u - 4)(u + 7) = 0$$

$$u - 4 = 0 \quad \text{or} \quad u + 7 = 0$$
$$u = 4 \quad \text{or} \quad u = -7$$
$$\frac{1}{x+5} = 4 \quad \text{or} \quad \frac{1}{x+5} = -7$$
$$x + 5 = \frac{1}{4} \quad \text{or} \quad x + 5 = -\frac{1}{7}$$
$$x = -\frac{19}{4} \quad \text{or} \quad x = -\frac{36}{7}$$

Check:

$$x = -\frac{19}{4}: \quad \left(\frac{1}{-\frac{19}{4}+5}\right)^2 + \frac{3}{-\frac{19}{4}+5} \overset{?}{=} 28$$

$$\left(\frac{1}{\frac{1}{4}}\right)^2 + \frac{3}{\frac{1}{4}} \overset{?}{=} 28$$

$$(4)^2 + 12 \overset{?}{=} 28$$

$$16 + 12 \overset{?}{=} 28$$

$$28 = 28 \checkmark$$

$$x = -\frac{36}{7}: \quad \left(\frac{1}{-\frac{36}{7}+5}\right)^2 + \frac{3}{-\frac{36}{7}+5} \overset{?}{=} 28$$

$$\left(\frac{1}{-\frac{1}{7}}\right)^2 + \frac{3}{-\frac{1}{7}} \overset{?}{=} 28$$

$$(-7)^2 - 21 \overset{?}{=} 28$$

$$49 - 21 \overset{?}{=} 28$$

$$28 = 28 \checkmark$$

Both check; the solution set is $\left\{-\frac{36}{7}, \ -\frac{19}{4}\right\}$.

79.
$$4x - 20\sqrt{x} + 21 = 0$$
$$4\left(\sqrt{x}\right)^2 - 20\left(\sqrt{x}\right) + 21 = 0$$

Let $u = \sqrt{x}$.
$$4u^2 - 20u + 21 = 0$$
$$(2u - 3)(2u - 7) = 0$$

$2u - 3 = 0$ or $2u - 7 = 0$

$2u = 3$ or $2u = 7$

$u = \dfrac{3}{2}$ or $u = \dfrac{7}{2}$

$\sqrt{x} = \dfrac{3}{2}$ or $\sqrt{x} = \dfrac{7}{2}$

$x = \left(\dfrac{3}{2}\right)^2$ or $x = \left(\dfrac{7}{2}\right)^2$

$x = \dfrac{9}{4}$ or $x = \dfrac{49}{4}$

Check:
$$f\left(\frac{9}{4}\right) = 4 \cdot \frac{9}{4} - 20\sqrt{\frac{9}{4}} + 21$$
$$= 4 \cdot \frac{9}{4} - 20 \cdot \frac{3}{2} + 21$$
$$= 9 - 30 + 21$$
$$= 0 \checkmark$$

$$f\left(\frac{49}{4}\right) = 4 \cdot \frac{49}{4} - 20\sqrt{\frac{49}{4}} + 21$$
$$= 4 \cdot \frac{49}{4} - 20 \cdot \frac{7}{2} + 21$$
$$= 49 - 70 + 21$$
$$= 0 \checkmark$$

Both check; the zeros of f are $\left\{\dfrac{9}{4}, \dfrac{49}{4}\right\}$.

80.
$$x^4 - 17x^2 + 60 = 0$$
$$\left(x^2\right)^2 - 17\left(x^2\right) + 60 = 0$$

Let $u = x^2$.
$$u^2 - 17u + 60 = 0$$
$$(u - 12)(u - 5) = 0$$

$u - 12 = 0$ or $u - 5 = 0$

$u = 12$ or $u = 5$

$x^2 = 12$ or $x^2 = 5$

$x = \pm\sqrt{12}$ or $x = \pm\sqrt{5}$

$x = \pm 2\sqrt{3}$

Check:
$$g\left(-2\sqrt{3}\right) = \left(-2\sqrt{3}\right)^4 - 17\left(-2\sqrt{3}\right)^2 + 60$$
$$= 144 - 17 \cdot 12 + 60$$
$$= 144 - 204 + 60$$
$$= 0 \checkmark$$

$$g\left(2\sqrt{3}\right) = \left(2\sqrt{3}\right)^4 - 17\left(2\sqrt{3}\right)^2 + 60$$
$$= 144 - 17 \cdot 12 + 60$$
$$= 144 - 204 + 60$$
$$= 0 \checkmark$$

$$g\left(-\sqrt{5}\right) = \left(-\sqrt{5}\right)^4 - 17\left(-\sqrt{5}\right)^2 + 60$$
$$= 25 - 17 \cdot 5 + 60$$
$$= 25 - 85 + 60$$
$$= 0 \checkmark$$

$$g\left(\sqrt{5}\right) = \left(\sqrt{5}\right)^4 - 17\left(\sqrt{5}\right)^2 + 60$$
$$= 25 - 17 \cdot 5 + 60$$
$$= 25 - 85 + 60$$
$$= 0 \checkmark$$

All check; the zeros of g are
$\left\{-2\sqrt{3}, -\sqrt{5}, \sqrt{5}, 2\sqrt{3}\right\}$.

81. Begin with the graph of $y = x^2$, then shift the graph up 4 units to obtain the graph of $f(x) = x^2 + 4$.

82. Begin with the graph of $y = x^2$, then shift the graph down 5 units to obtain the graph of $g(x) = x^2 - 5$.

83. Begin with the graph of $y = x^2$, then shift the graph to the left 1 unit to obtain the graph of $h(x) = (x+1)^2$.

84. Begin with the graph of $y = x^2$, then shift the graph to the right 4 units to obtain the graph of $F(x) = (x-4)^2$.

85. Begin with the graph of $y = x^2$, then multiply each y-coordinate by -4 to obtain the graph of $G(x) = -4x^2$.

86. Begin with the graph of $y = x^2$, then vertically compress the graph by a factor of $\frac{1}{5}$ (multiply each y-coordinate by $\frac{1}{5}$) to obtain the graph of $H(x) = \frac{1}{5}x^2$.

87. Begin with the graph of $y = x^2$, then shift the graph 4 units to the right to obtain the graph of $y = (x-4)^2$. Shift this graph down 3 units to obtain the graph of $p(x) = (x-4)^2 - 3$.

88. Begin with the graph of $y = x^2$, then shift the graph 4 units to the left to obtain the graph of $y = (x+4)^2$. Shift this graph up 2 units to obtain the graph of $P(x) = (x+4)^2 + 2$.

89. Begin with the graph of $y = x^2$, then shift the graph 1 unit to the right to obtain the graph of $y = (x-1)^2$. Multiply the y-coordinates by -1 to obtain the graph of $y = -(x-1)^2$. Shift this graph up 4 units to obtain the graph of $f(x) = -(x-1)^2 + 4$.

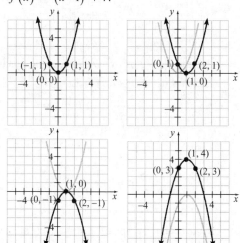

90. Begin with the graph of $y = x^2$, then shift the graph 2 unit to the left to obtain the graph of $y = (x+2)^2$. Multiply the y-coordinates by $\frac{1}{2}$ to obtain the graph of $y = \frac{1}{2}(x+2)^2$. Shift this graph down 1 unit to obtain the graph of $F(x) = \frac{1}{2}(x+2)^2 - 1$

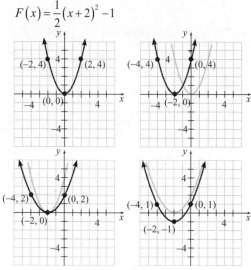

91. Use completing the square to write the function in the form $y = a(x-h)^2 + k$.

$$g(x) = x^2 - 6x + 10$$
$$= \left(x^2 - 6x\right) + 10$$
$$= \left(x^2 - 6x + 9\right) + 10 - 9$$
$$= (x-3)^2 + 1$$

Begin with the graph of $y = x^2$, then shift the graph right 3 units to obtain the graph of $y = (x-3)^2$. Shift this result up 1 unit to obtain the graph of $g(x) = (x-3)^2 + 1$.

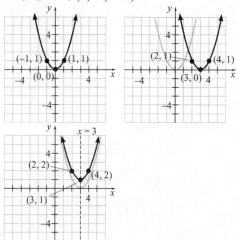

The vertex is $(3, 1)$; The axis of symmetry is $x = 3$.

92. Use completing the square to write the function in the form $y = a(x-h)^2 + k$.

$$G(x) = x^2 + 8x + 11$$
$$= \left(x^2 + 8x\right) + 11$$
$$= \left(x^2 + 8x + 16\right) + 11 - 16$$
$$= (x+4)^2 - 5$$

Begin with the graph of $y = x^2$, then shift the graph left 4 units to obtain the graph of $y = (x+4)^2$. Shift this result down 5 units to obtain the graph of $G(x) = (x+4)^2 - 5$.

The vertex is $(-4, -5)$. The axis of symmetry is $x = -4$.

93. Use completing the square to write the function in the form $y = a(x-h)^2 + k$.

$$h(x) = 2x^2 - 4x - 3$$
$$= (2x^2 - 4x) - 3$$
$$= 2(x^2 - 2x) - 3$$
$$= 2(x^2 - 2x + 1) - 3 - 2$$
$$= 2(x-1)^2 - 5$$

Begin with the graph of $y = x^2$, then shift the graph right 1 unit to obtain the graph of $y = (x-1)^2$. Vertically stretch this graph by a factor of 2 (multiply the y-coordinates by 2) to obtain the graph of $y = 2(x-1)^2$. Lastly, shift the graph down 5 units to obtain the graph of $H(x) = 2(x-1)^2 - 5$.

The vertex is $(1, -5)$. The axis of symmetry is $x = 1$.

94. Use completing the square to write the function in the form $y = a(x-h)^2 + k$.

$$H(x) = -x^2 - 6x - 10$$
$$= (-x^2 - 6x) - 10$$
$$= -(x^2 + 6x) - 10$$
$$= -(x^2 + 6x + 9) - 10 + 9$$
$$= -(x+3)^2 - 1$$

Begin with the graph of $y = x^2$, then shift the graph left 3 units to obtain the graph of $y = (x+3)^2$. Multiply the y-coordinates by -1 to obtain the graph of $y = -(x+3)^2$. Lastly, shift the graph down 1 unit to obtain the graph of $H(x) = -(x+3)^2 - 1$.

The vertex is $(-3, -1)$. The axis of symmetry is $x = -3$.

95. Use completing the square to write the function in the form $y = a(x-h)^2 + k$.

$$p(x) = -3x^2 + 12x - 8$$
$$= \left(-3x^2 + 12x\right) - 8$$
$$= -3\left(x^2 - 4x\right) - 8$$
$$= -3\left(x^2 - 4x + 4\right) - 8 + 12$$
$$= -3(x-2)^2 + 4$$

Begin with the graph of $y = x^2$, then shift the graph right 2 units to obtain the graph of $y = (x-2)^2$. Multiply the y-coordinates by -3 to obtain the graph of $y = -3(x-2)^2$. Lastly, shift the graph up 4 units to obtain the graph of $p(x) = -3(x-2)^2 + 4$.

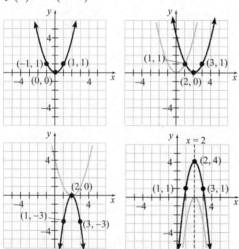

The vertex is $(2,\ 4)$. The axis of symmetry is $x = 2$.

96. Use completing the square to write the function in the form $y = a(x-h)^2 + k$.

$$P(x) = \frac{1}{2}x^2 - 2x + 5$$
$$= \left(\frac{1}{2}x^2 - 2x\right) + 5$$
$$= \frac{1}{2}\left(x^2 - 4x\right) + 5$$
$$= \frac{1}{2}\left(x^2 - 4x + 4\right) + 5 - 2$$
$$= \frac{1}{2}(x-2)^2 + 3$$

Begin with the graph of $y = x^2$, then shift the graph right 2 units to obtain the graph of $y = (x-2)^2$. Vertically compress this graph by a factor of $\frac{1}{2}$ (multiply the y-coordinates by $\frac{1}{2}$) to obtain the graph of $y = \frac{1}{2}(x-2)^2$. Lastly, shift the graph up 3 units to obtain the graph of $P(x) = \frac{1}{2}(x-2)^2 + 3$.

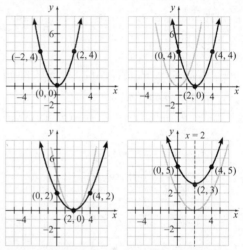

The vertex is $(2,\ 3)$. The axis of symmetry is $x = 2$.

97. Consider the form $y = a(x-h)^2 + k$. From the graph we know that the vertex is $(2,-4)$, so we have $h = 2$ and $k = -4$. The graph also passes through the point $(x, y) = (0,4)$. Substituting values for x, y, h, and k, we can solve for a:

$$4 = a(0-2)^2 - 4$$
$$4 = a(-2)^2 - 4$$
$$8 = 4a$$
$$2 = a$$

The quadratic function is $f(x) = 2(x-2)^2 - 4$ or $f(x) = 2x^2 - 8x + 4$.

98. Consider the form $y = a(x-h)^2 + k$. From the graph we know that the vertex is $(4,3)$, so we have $h = 4$ and $k = 3$. The graph also passes through the point $(x, y) = (3,2)$. Substituting values for $x, y, h,$ and k, we can solve for a:

$$2 = a(3-4)^2 + 3$$
$$2 = a(-1)^2 + 3$$
$$2 = a + 3$$
$$-1 = a$$

The quadratic function is $f(x) = -(x-4)^2 + 3$ or $f(x) = -x^2 + 8x - 13$.

99. Consider the form $y = a(x-h)^2 + k$. From the graph we know that the vertex is $(-2,-1)$, so we have $h = -2$ and $k = -1$. The graph also passes through the point $(x, y) = (0,-3)$. Substituting values for $x, y, h,$ and k, we can solve for a:

$$-3 = a(0-(-2))^2 - 1$$
$$-3 = a(0+2)^2 - 1$$
$$-3 = a(2)^2 - 1$$
$$-2 = 4a$$
$$-\frac{1}{2} = a$$

The quadratic function is $f(x) = -\frac{1}{2}(x+2)^2 - 1$ or $f(x) = -\frac{1}{2}x^2 - 2x - 3$.

100. Consider the form $y = a(x-h)^2 + k$. From the graph we know that the vertex is $(-2,0)$, so we have $h = -2$ and $k = 0$. The graph also passes through the point $(x, y) = (-3,3)$. Substituting values for $x, y, h,$ and k, we can solve for a:

$$3 = a(-3-(-2))^2 - 0$$
$$3 = a(-3+2)^2$$
$$3 = a(-1)^2$$
$$3 = a$$

The quadratic function is $f(x) = 3(x+2)^2$ or $f(x) = 3x^2 + 12x + 12$.

101. $f(x) = x^2 + 2x - 8$

$a = 1, b = 2, c = -8$

The graph opens up because the coefficient on x^2 is positive.

vertex:

$$x = -\frac{b}{2a} = -\frac{2}{2(1)} = -1$$
$$f(-1) = (-1)^2 + 2(-1) - 8 = -9$$

The vertex is $(-1,-9)$ and the axis of symmetry is $x = -1$.

y-intercept:

$$f(0) = (0)^2 + 2(0) - 8 = -8$$

x-intercepts:

$$b^2 - 4ac = 2^2 - 4(1)(-8) = 36 > 0$$

There are two distinct x-intercepts. We find these by solving

$$f(x) = 0$$
$$x^2 + 2x - 8 = 0$$
$$(x-2)(x+4) = 0$$
$$x - 2 = 0 \text{ or } x + 4 = 0$$
$$x = 2 \text{ or } x = -4$$

Graph:

The y-intercept point, $(0,-8)$, is one unit to the right of the axis of symmetry. Therefore, if we move one unit to the left of the axis of symmetry, we obtain the point $(-2,-8)$ which must also be on the graph.

102. $F(x) = 2x^2 - 5x + 3$

$a = 2, b = -5, c = 3$

The graph opens up because the coefficient on x^2 is positive.

vertex:

$$x = -\frac{b}{2a} = -\frac{(-5)}{2(2)} = \frac{5}{4}$$

$$F\left(\frac{5}{4}\right) = 2\left(\frac{5}{4}\right)^2 - 5\left(\frac{5}{4}\right) + 3 = -\frac{1}{8}$$

The vertex is $\left(\frac{5}{4}, -\frac{1}{8}\right)$ and the axis of symmetry is $x = \frac{5}{4}$.

y-intercept:

$$F(0) = 2(0)^2 - 5(0) + 3 = 3$$

x-intercepts:

$$b^2 - 4ac = (-5)^2 - 4(2)(3) = 1 > 0$$

There are two distinct x-intercepts. We find these by solving

$$F(x) = 0$$

$$2x^2 - 5x + 3 = 0$$

$$(2x - 3)(x - 1) = 0$$

$$2x - 3 = 0 \quad \text{or} \quad x - 1 = 0$$

$$2x = 3 \quad \text{or} \quad x = 1$$

$$x = \frac{3}{2}$$

Graph:

The y-intercept point, $(0, 3)$, is five-fourths units to the left of the axis of symmetry. Therefore, if we move five-fourths units to the right of the axis of symmetry, we obtain the point $\left(\frac{5}{2}, 3\right)$ which must also be on the graph.

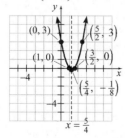

103. $g(x) = -x^2 + 6x - 7$

$a = -1, b = 6, c = -7$

The graph opens down because the coefficient on x^2 is negative.

vertex:

$$x = -\frac{b}{2a} = -\frac{6}{2(-1)} = 3$$

$$g(3) = -(3)^2 + 6(3) - 7 = 2$$

The vertex is $(3, 2)$ and the axis of symmetry is $x = 3$.

y-intercept:

$$g(0) = -(0)^2 + 6(0) - 7 = -7$$

x-intercepts:

$$b^2 - 4ac = 6^2 - 4(-1)(-7) = 8 > 0$$

There are two distinct x-intercepts. We find these by solving

$$g(x) = 0$$

$$-x^2 + 6x - 7 = 0$$

$$x = \frac{-6 \pm \sqrt{8}}{2(-1)}$$

$$= \frac{-6 \pm 2\sqrt{2}}{-2}$$

$$= 3 \pm \sqrt{2}$$

$$x \approx 1.59 \quad \text{or} \quad x \approx 4.41$$

Graph:

The y-intercept point, $(0, -7)$, is three units to the left of the axis of symmetry. Therefore, if we move three units to the right of the axis of symmetry, we obtain the point $(6, -7)$ which must also be on the graph.

104. $G(x) = -2x^2 + 4x + 3$

$a = -2, b = 4, c = 3$

The graph opens down because the coefficient on x^2 is negative.

vertex:

$$x = -\frac{b}{2a} = -\frac{4}{2(-2)} = 1$$

$$G(1) = -2(1)^2 + 4(1) + 3 = 5$$

The vertex is $(1, 5)$ and the axis of symmetry is $x = 1$.

y-intercept:

$$G(0) = -2(0)^2 + 4(0) + 3 = 3$$

x-intercepts:

$$b^2 - 4ac = 4^2 - 4(-2)(3) = 40 > 0$$

There are two distinct x-intercepts. We find these by solving

$$G(x) = 0$$

$$-2x^2 + 4x + 3 = 0$$

$$x = \frac{-4 \pm \sqrt{40}}{2(-2)}$$

$$= \frac{-4 \pm 2\sqrt{10}}{-4}$$

$$= 1 \pm \frac{\sqrt{10}}{2}$$

$$x \approx -0.58 \quad \text{or} \quad x \approx 2.58$$

Graph:

The y-intercept point, $(0, 3)$, is one unit to the left of the axis of symmetry. Therefore, if we move one unit to the right of the axis of symmetry, we obtain the point $(2, 3)$ which must also be on the graph.

105. $h(x) = 4x^2 - 12x + 9$

$a = 4, b = -12, c = 9$

The graph opens up because the coefficient on x^2 is positive.

vertex:

$$x = -\frac{b}{2a} = -\frac{(-12)}{2(4)} = \frac{3}{2}$$

$$h\left(\frac{3}{2}\right) = 4\left(\frac{3}{2}\right)^2 - 12\left(\frac{3}{2}\right) + 9 = 0$$

The vertex is $\left(\frac{3}{2}, 0\right)$ and the axis of symmetry is $x = \frac{3}{2}$.

y-intercept:

$$h(0) = 4(0)^2 - 12(0) + 9 = 9$$

x-intercepts:

$$b^2 - 4ac = (-12)^2 - 4(4)(9) = 0$$

Since the discriminant is 0, the x-coordinate of the vertex is the only x-intercept, $x = \frac{3}{2}$.

Graph:

The y-intercept point, $(0, 9)$, is three-halves units to the left of the axis of symmetry. Therefore, if we move three-halves units to the right of the axis of symmetry, we obtain the point $(3, 9)$ which must also be on the graph.

106. $H(x) = \frac{1}{3}x^2 + 2x + 3$

$a = \frac{1}{3}, b = 2, c = 3$

The graph opens up because the coefficient on x^2 is positive.

vertex:

$$x = -\frac{b}{2a} = -\frac{2}{2\left(\frac{1}{3}\right)} = -3$$

$$H(-3) = \frac{1}{3}(-3)^2 + 2(-3) + 3 = 0$$

The vertex is $(-3, 0)$ and the axis of symmetry is $x = -3$.

y-intercept:

$$H(0) = \frac{1}{3}(0)^2 + 2(0) + 3 = 3$$

x-intercepts:

$$b^2 - 4ac = 2^2 - 4\left(\frac{1}{3}\right)(3) = 0$$

Since the discriminant is 0, the *x*-coordinate of the vertex is the only *x*-intercept, $x = -3$.

Graph:
The *y*-intercept point, $(0, 3)$, is three units to the right of the axis of symmetry. Therefore, if we move three units to the left of the axis of symmetry, we obtain the point $(-6, 3)$ which must also be on the graph.

107. $p(x) = \frac{1}{4}x^2 + 3x + 10$

$a = \frac{1}{4}, b = 3, c = 10$

The graph opens up because the coefficient on x^2 is positive.

vertex:

$$x = -\frac{b}{2a} = -\frac{3}{2\left(\frac{1}{4}\right)} = -6$$

$$p(-6) = \frac{1}{4}(-6)^2 + 3(-6) + 10 = 1$$

The vertex is $(-6, 1)$ and the axis of symmetry is $x = -6$.

y-intercept:

$$p(0) = \frac{1}{4}(0)^2 + 3(0) + 10 = 10$$

x-intercepts:

$$b^2 - 4ac = 3^2 - 4\left(\frac{1}{4}\right)(10) = -1 < 0$$

There are no *x*-intercepts since the discriminant is negative.

Graph:
The *y*-intercept point, $(0, 10)$, is six units to the right of the axis of symmetry. Therefore, if we move six unit to the left of the axis of symmetry, we obtain the point $(-12, 10)$ which must also be on the graph.

108. $P(x) = -x^2 + 4x - 9$

$a = -1, b = 4, c = -9$

The graph opens down because the coefficient on x^2 is negative.

vertex:

$$x = -\frac{b}{2a} = -\frac{4}{2(-1)} = 2$$

$$P(2) = -(2)^2 + 4(2) - 9 = -5$$

The vertex is $(2, -5)$ and the axis of symmetry is $x = 2$.

y-intercept:
$$P(0) = -(0)^2 + 4(0) - 9 = -9$$

x-intercepts:
$$b^2 - 4ac = 4^2 - 4(-1)(-9) = -20 < 0$$
There are no x-intercepts since the discriminant is negative.

Graph:
The y-intercept point, $(0, -9)$, is 2 units to the left of the axis of symmetry. Therefore, if we move 2 units to the right of the axis of symmetry, we obtain the point $(4, -9)$ which must also be on the graph.

109. If we compare $f(x) = -2x^2 + 16x - 10$ to $f(x) = ax^2 + bx + c$, we find that $a = -2$, $b = 16$, and $c = -10$. Because $a < 0$, we know the graph will open down, so the function will have a maximum value.
The maximum value occurs at
$$x = -\frac{b}{2a} = -\frac{16}{2(-2)} = 4.$$
The maximum value is
$$f(4) = -2(4)^2 + 16(4) - 10 = 22.$$
So, the maximum value is 22, and it occurs when $x = 4$.

110. If we compare $g(x) = 6x^2 - 3x - 1$ to $g(x) = ax^2 + bx + c$, we find that $a = 6$, $b = -3$, and $c = -1$. Because $a > 0$, we know the graph will open up, so the function will have a minimum value.
The minimum value occurs at
$$x = -\frac{b}{2a} = -\frac{(-3)}{2(6)} = \frac{1}{4}.$$
The minimum value is

$$g\left(\frac{1}{4}\right) = 6\left(\frac{1}{4}\right)^2 - 3\left(\frac{1}{4}\right) - 1 = -\frac{11}{8}.$$
So, the minimum value is $-\frac{11}{8}$, and it occurs when $x = \frac{1}{4}$.

111. If we compare $h(x) = -4x^2 + 8x + 3$ to $h(x) = ax^2 + bx + c$, we find that $a = -4$, $b = 8$, and $c = 3$. Because $a < 0$, we know the graph will open down, so the function will have a maximum value.
The maximum value occurs at
$$x = -\frac{b}{2a} = -\frac{8}{2(-4)} = 1.$$
The maximum value is
$$h(4) = -4(1)^2 + 8(1) + 3 = 7.$$
So, the maximum value is 7, and it occurs when $x = 1$.

112. If we compare $F(x) = -\frac{1}{3}x^2 + 4x - 7$ to $F(x) = ax^2 + bx + c$, we find that $a = -\frac{1}{3}$, $b = 4$, and $c = -7$. Because $a < 0$, we know the graph will open down, so the function will have a maximum value.
The maximum value occurs at
$$x = -\frac{b}{2a} = -\frac{4}{2\left(-\frac{1}{3}\right)} = 6.$$
The maximum value is
$$F(6) = -\frac{1}{3}(6)^2 + 4(6) - 7 = 5.$$
So, the maximum value is 5, and it occurs when $x = 6$.

113. a. We first recognize that the quadratic function has a negative leading coefficient. This means that the graph will open down and the function indeed has a maximum value. The maximum value occurs when
$$p = -\frac{b}{2a} = -\frac{150}{2\left(-\frac{1}{3}\right)} = 225.$$
The revenue will be maximized when the televisions are sold at a price of $225.

b. The maximum revenue is obtained by evaluating the revenue function at the price found in part (a).

$$R(225) = -\frac{1}{3}(225)^2 + 150(225) = 16,875$$

The maximum revenue is $16,875.

114. a. We first recognize that the quadratic function has a negative leading coefficient. This means that the graph will open down and the function indeed has a maximum value. The maximum value occurs when

$$I = -\frac{b}{2a} = -\frac{120}{2(-16)} = 3.75 .$$

The power will be maximized when the current is 3.75 amperes.

b. The maximum power is obtained by evaluating the power function for the current found in part (a).

$$P(3.75) = -16(3.75)^2 + 120(3.75) = 225$$

The maximum power is 225 watts.

115. Let x represent the first number. Then the second number must be $24 - x$. We can express the product of the two numbers as the function

$$p(x) = x(24-x) = -x^2 + 24x$$

This is a quadratic function with $a = -1$, $b = 24$, and $c = 0$. The function is maximized when

$$x = -\frac{b}{2a} = -\frac{24}{2(-1)} = 12 .$$

The maximum product can be obtained by evaluating $p(x)$ when $x = 12$.

$$p(x) = 12(24-12) = 12(12) = 144$$

Two numbers that sum to 24 have a maximum product of 144 when both numbers are 12.

116. a. Let x represent the width of the rectangular kennel (the side that is not parallel to the garage). Then $15 - 2x$ is the length of the kennel (the side that is parallel to the garage). The area is the product of the length and width:

$$A = (15-2x) \cdot x$$
$$= -2x^2 + 15x$$

The leading coefficient is negative so we know the graph opens down and there will be a maximum area. This value occurs when the width is

$$x = -\frac{b}{2a} = -\frac{15}{2(-2)} = 3.75 .$$

Then the length is $15 - 2(3.75) = 7.5$.

The dimensions that maximize the area of the kennel are 3.75 yards by 7.5 yards.

b. The maximum area can be found by substituting 3.75 for x into the area function.

$$A = 3.75(15 - 2(3.75)) = 28.125$$

The maximum area of the kennel is 28.125 square yards.

117. a. First we recognize that the quadratic function has a negative leading coefficient. This means the graph will open down and the function will indeed have a maximum. The maximum height will occur when

$$x = -\frac{b}{2a} = -\frac{1}{2(-0.005)} = 100 .$$

The ball will reach a maximum height when it is 100 feet from Ted.

b. The maximum height can be found by evaluating $h(x)$ for the value of x found in part (a).

$$h(100) = -0.005(100)^2 + 100 = 50$$

The ball will reach a maximum height of 50 feet.

c. When the ball is on the ground, it will have a height of 0 feet. Thus, we need to solve $h(x) = 0$.

$$-0.005x^2 + x = 0$$
$$200(-0.005x^2 + x) = 200(0)$$
$$-x^2 + 200x = 0$$
$$-x(x - 200) = 0$$
$$-x = 0 \quad \text{or} \quad x - 200 = 0$$
$$x = 0 \quad \text{or} \quad\quad x = 200$$

Zero (0) represents the distance from Ted before he kicks the ball. The ball will strike the ground again when it is 200 feet away from Ted.

118. a. Since $R = x \cdot p$, we have

$$R = x \cdot p$$
$$= (-0.002p + 60) \cdot p$$
$$= -0.002p^2 + 60p$$

b. The revenue function is quadratic with a negative leading coefficient. This means the graph will open down and the function will have a maximum value. This value occurs when

$$p = -\frac{b}{2a} = -\frac{60}{2(-0.002)} = 15,000 .$$

The maximum revenue can be found by substituting this value for p in the revenue equation.

$$R = -0.002(15,000)^2 + 60(15,000) = 450,000$$

The maximum revenue of \$450,000 will occur if the price of each automobile is set at \$15,000.

c. To determine how many automobiles will be sold, we substitute the maximizing price into the demand equation.

$$x = -0.002p + 60$$
$$= -0.002(15,000) + 60$$
$$= 30$$

When the price per automobile is \$15,000, the dealership will sell 30 automobiles per month.

119. a. The graph is greater than 0 for $x < -2$ or $x > 3$. The solution is $\{x | x < -2 \text{ or } x > 3\}$ in set-builder notation. The solution is $(-\infty, -2) \cup (3, \infty)$ using interval notation.

b. The graph is less than 0 for $-2 < x < 3$. The solution is $\{x | -2 < x < 3\}$ using set-builder notation. The solution is $(-2, 3)$ using interval notation.

120. a. The graph is 0 or greater for $-\frac{7}{2} \le x \le 1$.

The solution is $\left\{ x \left| -\frac{7}{2} \le x \le 1 \right. \right\}$ using set-builder notation. The solution is $\left[-\frac{7}{2}, 1 \right]$ using interval notation.

b. The graph is 0 or less for $x \le -\frac{7}{2}$ or $x \ge 1$.

The solution is $\left\{ x \left| x \le -\frac{7}{2} \text{ or } x \ge 1 \right. \right\}$ using set-builder notation. The solution is $\left(-\infty, -\frac{7}{2} \right] \cup [1, \infty)$ using interval notation.

121. $x^2 - 2x - 24 \le 0$

Solve: $x^2 - 2x - 24 = 0$
$$(x - 6)(x + 4) = 0$$
$$x - 6 = 0 \quad \text{or} \quad x + 4 = 0$$
$$x = 6 \quad \text{or} \quad x = -4$$

Determine where each factor is positive and negative and where the product of these factors is positive and negative.

Interval	$(-\infty, -4)$	-4	$(-4, 6)$	6	$(6, \infty)$
$x - 6$	$----$	$-$	$----$	0	$++++$
$x + 4$	$----$	0	$++++$	$+$	$++++$
$(x - 6)(x + 4)$	$++++$	0	$----$	0	$++++$

The inequality is non-strict, so -4 and 6 are part of the solution. Now, $(x - 6)(x + 4)$ is less than zero where the product is negative. The solution is $\{x | -4 \le x \le 6\}$ or, using interval notation, $[-4, 6]$.

122. $y^2 + 7y - 8 \ge 0$

Solve: $y^2 + 7y - 8 = 0$
$$(y - 1)(y + 8) = 0$$
$$y - 1 = 0 \quad \text{or} \quad y + 8 = 0$$
$$y = 1 \quad \text{or} \quad y = -8$$

Determine where each factor is positive and negative and where the product of these factors is positive and negative.

Interval	$(-\infty, -8)$	-8	$(-8, 1)$	1	$(1, \infty)$
$y - 1$	$----$	$-$	$----$	0	$++++$
$y + 8$	$----$	0	$++++$	$+$	$++++$
$(y - 1)(y + 8)$	$++++$	0	$----$	0	$++++$

The inequality is non-strict, so −8 and 1 are part of the solution. Now, $(y-1)(y+8)$ is greater than zero where the product is positive. The solution is $\{y \mid y \le -8 \text{ or } y \ge 1\}$ or, using interval notation; $(-\infty,\ -8]\cup[1,\ \infty)$.

123. $3z^2 -19z+20>0$

Solve: $3z^2 -19z+20=0$
$(3z-4)(z-5)=0$
$3z-4=0 \quad \text{or} \quad z-5=0$
$3z=4 \quad \text{or} \quad z=5$
$z=\dfrac{4}{3}$

Determine where each factor is positive and negative and where the product of these factors is positive and negative.

Interval	$\left(-\infty,\frac{4}{3}\right)$	$\frac{4}{3}$	$\left(\frac{4}{3},5\right)$	5	$(5,\infty)$
$3z-4$	$----$	0	$++++$	$+$	$++++$
$z-5$	$----$	$-$	$----$	0	$++++$
$(3z-4)(z-5)$	$++++$	0	$----$	0	$++++$

The inequality is strict, so $\dfrac{4}{3}$ and 5 are not part of the solution. Now, $(3z-4)(z-5)$ is greater than zero where the product is positive. The solution is $\left\{z \mid z<\dfrac{4}{3} \text{ or } z>5\right\}$ or, using interval notation, $\left(-\infty,\dfrac{4}{3}\right)\cup(5,\infty)$.

124. $p^2 +4p-2<0$

Solve: $p^2 +4p-2=0$
$p=\dfrac{-4\pm\sqrt{4^2-4(1)(-2)}}{2(1)}$
$=\dfrac{-4\pm\sqrt{24}}{2}$

$=\dfrac{-4\pm2\sqrt{6}}{2}$
$=-2\pm\sqrt{6}$
$x=-2-\sqrt{6} \quad \text{or} \quad x=-2+\sqrt{6}$
$\approx-4.45 \quad \text{or} \quad \approx0.45$

Determine where each factor is positive and negative and where the product of these factors is positive and negative.

Interval	$(-\infty,-2-\sqrt6)$	$(-2-\sqrt6,-2+\sqrt6)$	$(-2+\sqrt6,\infty)$
	$-2-\sqrt6$		$-2+\sqrt6$
	≈-4.45		≈0.45
$p-(-2-\sqrt6)$	$----\quad 0$	$++++\quad +$	$++++$
$p-(-2+\sqrt6)$	$----\quad -$	$----\quad 0$	$++++$
$[p-(-2-\sqrt6)][p-(-2+\sqrt6)]$	$++++\quad 0$	$----\quad 0$	$++++$

The inequality is strict, so $-2-\sqrt{6}$ and $-2+\sqrt{6}$ are not part of the solution. Now, $\left[p-\left(-2-\sqrt6\right)\right]\left[p-\left(-2+\sqrt6\right)\right]$ is less than zero where the product is negative. The solution is $\left\{p \mid -2-\sqrt6 < p < -2+\sqrt6\right\}$ or, using interval notation, $\left(-2-\sqrt6,\ -2+\sqrt6\right)$.

125. $4m^2 -20m+25\ge 0$

Solve: $4m^2 -20m+25=0$
$(2m-5)(2m-5)=0$
$2m-5=0 \quad \text{or} \quad 2m-5=0$
$2m=5 \quad \text{or} \quad 2m=5$
$m=\dfrac{5}{2} \quad \text{or} \quad m=\dfrac{5}{2}$

Determine where each factor is positive and negative and where the product of these factors is positive and negative.

Interval	$\left(-\infty,\frac{5}{2}\right)$	$\frac{5}{2}$	$\left(\frac{5}{2},\infty\right)$
$2m-5$	$----$	0	$++++$
$2m-5$	$----$	0	$++++$
$(2m-5)(2m-5)$	$++++$	0	$++++$

The inequality is non-strict, so $\frac{5}{2}$ is part of the solution. Now, $(2m-5)(2m-5)$ is greater than zero where the product is positive. Thus, $4m^2 - 20m + 25$ is always greater than or equal to zero. The solution is $\{m \mid m$ is any real number$\}$ or, using interval notation $(-\infty, \infty)$.

126. $6w^2 - 19w - 7 \le 0$

Solve: $6w^2 - 19w - 7 = 0$

$(3w+1)(2w-7) = 0$

$3w+1 = 0$ or $2w-7 = 0$

$3w = -1$ or $2w = 7$

$w = -\frac{1}{3}$ or $w = \frac{7}{2}$

Determine where each factor is positive and negative and where the product of these factors is positive and negative.

Interval	$\left(-\infty, -\frac{1}{3}\right)$	$-\frac{1}{3}$	$\left(-\frac{1}{3}, \frac{7}{2}\right)$	$\frac{7}{2}$	$\left(\frac{7}{2}, \infty\right)$
$3w+1$	$----$	0	$++++$	$+$	$++++$
$2w-7$	$----$	$-$	$----$	0	$++++$
$(3w+1)(2w-7)$	$++++$	0	$----$	0	$++++$

The inequality is non-strict, so $-\frac{1}{3}$ and $\frac{7}{2}$ are part of the solution. Now, $(3w+1)(2w-7)$ is less than zero where the product is negative. The solution is $\left\{w \mid -\frac{1}{3} \le w \le \frac{7}{2}\right\}$ or, using interval notation, $\left[-\frac{1}{3}, \frac{7}{2}\right]$.

Chapter 8 Test

1. Start: $x^2 - 3x$

   Add: $\left[\frac{1}{2} \cdot (-3)\right]^2 = \frac{9}{4}$

   Result: $x^2 - 3x + \frac{9}{4}$

   Factored Form: $\left(x - \frac{3}{2}\right)^2$

2. Start: $m^2 + \frac{2}{5}m$

   Add: $\left[\frac{1}{2} \cdot \left(\frac{2}{5}\right)\right]^2 = \frac{1}{25}$

   Result: $m^2 + \frac{2}{5}m + \frac{1}{25}$

   Factored Form: $\left(m + \frac{1}{5}\right)^2$

3. $9\left(x + \frac{4}{3}\right)^2 = 1$

   $\left(x + \frac{4}{3}\right)^2 = \frac{1}{9}$

   $x + \frac{4}{3} = \pm\sqrt{\frac{1}{9}}$

   $x + \frac{4}{3} = \pm\frac{1}{3}$

   $x = -\frac{4}{3} \pm \frac{1}{3}$

   $x = -\frac{4}{3} - \frac{1}{3}$ or $x = -\frac{4}{3} + \frac{1}{3}$

   $x = -\frac{5}{3}$ or $x = -1$

   The solution set is $\left\{-\frac{5}{3}, -1\right\}$.

4. $m^2 - 6m + 4 = 0$

Because this equation does not easily factor, solve by using the quadratic formula. For this equation, $a = 1$, $b = -6$, and $c = 4$.

$$m = \frac{-(-6) \pm \sqrt{(-6)^2 - 4(1)(4)}}{2(1)}$$

$$= \frac{6 \pm \sqrt{36 - 16}}{2}$$

$$= \frac{6 \pm \sqrt{20}}{2}$$

$$= \frac{6 \pm 2\sqrt{5}}{2}$$

$$= \frac{6}{2} \pm \frac{2\sqrt{5}}{2}$$

$$= 3 \pm \sqrt{5}$$

The solution set is. $\left\{ 3 - \sqrt{5},\ 3 + \sqrt{5} \right\}$.

5. $2w^2 - 4w + 3 = 0$

Because this equation does not easily factor, solve by using the quadratic formula. For this equation, $a = 2$, $b = -4$, and $c = 3$.

$$w = \frac{-(-4) \pm \sqrt{(-4)^2 - 4(2)(3)}}{2(2)}$$

$$= \frac{4 \pm \sqrt{16 - 24}}{4}$$

$$= \frac{4 \pm \sqrt{-8}}{4}$$

$$= \frac{4 \pm 2\sqrt{2}\,i}{4}$$

$$= \frac{4}{4} \pm \frac{2\sqrt{2}}{4}\,i$$

$$= 1 \pm \frac{\sqrt{2}}{2}\,i$$

The solution set is $\left\{ 1 - \frac{\sqrt{2}}{2}i,\ 1 + \frac{\sqrt{2}}{2}i \right\}$.

6. $\frac{1}{2}z^2 - \frac{3}{2}z = -\frac{7}{6}$

$$6\left(\frac{1}{2}z^2 - \frac{3}{2}z \right) = 6\left(-\frac{7}{6} \right)$$

$$3z^2 - 9z = -7$$

$$3z^2 - 9z + 7 = 0$$

Because this equation does not easily factor, solve by using the quadratic formula. For this equation, $a = 3$, $b = -9$, and $c = 7$.

$$z = \frac{-(-9) \pm \sqrt{(-9)^2 - 4(3)(7)}}{2(3)}$$

$$= \frac{9 \pm \sqrt{81 - 84}}{6}$$

$$= \frac{9 \pm \sqrt{-3}}{6}$$

$$= \frac{9 \pm \sqrt{3}\,i}{6}$$

$$= \frac{9}{6} \pm \frac{\sqrt{3}}{6}\,i$$

$$= \frac{3}{2} \pm \frac{\sqrt{3}}{6}\,i$$

The solution set is $\left\{ \frac{3}{2} - \frac{\sqrt{3}}{6}i,\ \frac{3}{2} + \frac{\sqrt{3}}{6}i \right\}$.

7. $2x^2 + 5x = 4$

$2x^2 + 5x - 4 = 0$

For this equation, $a = 2$, $b = 5$, and $c = -4$.

$b^2 - 4ac = 5^2 - 4(2)(-4) = 25 + 32 = 57$

Because $b^2 - 4ac = 57$, but not a perfect square, the quadratic equation will have two irrational solutions.

8. $c^2 = a^2 + b^2$

$11^2 = a^2 + 7^2$

$121 = a^2 + 49$

$72 = a^2$

$a = \sqrt{72}$

$a = 6\sqrt{2}$

9. $x^4 - 5x^2 - 36 = 0$

$\left(x^2 \right)^2 - 5\left(x^2 \right) - 36 = 0$

Let $u = x^2$.

$u^2 - 5u - 36 = 0$

$(u - 9)(u + 4) = 0$

$u - 9 = 0 \quad$ or $\quad u + 4 = 0$

$u = 9 \quad$ or $\quad u = -4$

$x^2 = 9 \quad$ or $\quad x^2 = -4$

$x = \pm\sqrt{9} \quad$ or $\quad x = \pm\sqrt{-4}$

$x = \pm 3 \quad$ or $\quad x = \pm 2i$

Check:

$x = -3:$ $(-3)^4 - 5(-3)^2 - 36 \overset{?}{=} 0$

$$81 - 5 \cdot 9 - 36 \overset{?}{=} 0$$

$$81 - 45 - 36 \overset{?}{=} 0$$

$$0 = 0 \checkmark$$

$x = 3:$ $3^4 - 5(3)^2 - 36 \overset{?}{=} 0$

$$81 - 5 \cdot 9 - 36 \overset{?}{=} 0$$

$$81 - 45 - 36 \overset{?}{=} 0$$

$$0 = 0 \checkmark$$

$x = -2i:$ $(-2i)^4 - 5(-2i)^2 - 36 \overset{?}{=} 0$

$$16i^4 - 5 \cdot 4i^2 - 36 \overset{?}{=} 0$$

$$16(1) - 5 \cdot 4(-1) - 36 \overset{?}{=} 0$$

$$16 + 20 - 36 \overset{?}{=} 0$$

$$0 = 0 \checkmark$$

$x = 2i:$ $(2i)^4 - 5(2i)^2 - 36 \overset{?}{=} 0$

$$16i^4 - 5 \cdot 4i^2 - 36 \overset{?}{=} 0$$

$$16(1) - 5 \cdot 4(-1) - 36 \overset{?}{=} 0$$

$$16 + 20 - 36 \overset{?}{=} 0$$

$$0 = 0 \checkmark$$

All check; the solution set is $\{-3, \ 3, \ -2i, \ 2i\}$.

10. $6y^{1/2} + 13y^{1/4} - 5 = 0$

$$6\left(y^{1/4}\right)^2 + 13\left(y^{1/4}\right) - 5 = 0$$

Let $u = y^{1/4}$.

$$6u^2 + 13u - 5 = 0$$

$$(3u - 1)(2u + 5) = 0$$

$3u - 1 = 0$ or $2u + 5 = 0$

$3u = 1$ or $2u = -5$

$u = \dfrac{1}{3}$ or $u = -\dfrac{5}{2}$

$y^{1/4} = \dfrac{1}{3}$ or $y^{1/4} = -\dfrac{5}{2}$

$\left(y^{1/4}\right)^4 = \left(\dfrac{1}{3}\right)^4$ or $\left(y^{1/4}\right)^4 = \left(-\dfrac{5}{2}\right)^4$

$y = \dfrac{1}{81}$ or $y = \dfrac{625}{16}$

Check:

$y = \dfrac{1}{81}:$ $6\left(\dfrac{1}{81}\right)^{1/2} + 13\left(\dfrac{1}{81}\right)^{1/4} - 5 \overset{?}{=} 0$

$$6\sqrt{\dfrac{1}{81}} + 13\sqrt[4]{\dfrac{1}{81}} - 5 \overset{?}{=} 0$$

$$6\left(\dfrac{1}{9}\right) + 13\left(\dfrac{1}{3}\right) - 5 \overset{?}{=} 0$$

$$\dfrac{2}{3} + \dfrac{13}{3} - 5 \overset{?}{=} 0$$

$$0 = 0 \checkmark$$

$y = \dfrac{625}{16}:$ $6\left(\dfrac{625}{16}\right)^{1/2} + 13\left(\dfrac{625}{16}\right)^{1/4} - 5 \overset{?}{=} 0$

$$6\sqrt{\dfrac{625}{16}} + 13\sqrt[4]{\dfrac{625}{16}} - 5 \overset{?}{=} 0$$

$$6\left(\dfrac{25}{4}\right) + 13\left(\dfrac{5}{2}\right) - 5 \overset{?}{=} 0$$

$$\dfrac{75}{2} + \dfrac{65}{2} - 5 \overset{?}{=} 0$$

$$65 \neq 0 \; ✗$$

$y = \dfrac{625}{16}$ does not check; the solution set is $\left\{\dfrac{1}{81}\right\}$.

11. Begin with the graph of $y = x^2$, then shift the graph 2 units to the left to obtain the graph of $y = (x + 2)^2$. Shift this graph down 5 units to obtain the graph of $f(x) = (x + 2)^2 - 5$.

The vertex is $(-2, -5)$. The axis of symmetry is $x = -2$.

12. $g(x) = -2x^2 - 8x - 3$

$a = -2, b = -8, c = -3$

The graph opens down because the coefficient on x^2 is negative.

vertex:

$x = -\dfrac{b}{2a} = -\dfrac{(-8)}{2(-2)} = -2$

$g(-2) = -2(-2)^2 - 8(-2) - 3 = 5$

The vertex is $(-2, 5)$. The axis of symmetry is $x = -2$.

y-intercept:

$g(0) = -2(0)^2 - 8(0) - 3 = -3$

x-intercepts:

$b^2 - 4ac = (-8)^2 - 4(-2)(-3) = 40 > 0$

There are two distinct x-intercepts. We find these by solving

$$g(x) = 0$$

$-2x^2 - 8x - 3 = 0$

$x = \dfrac{-(-8) \pm \sqrt{40}}{2(-2)}$

$= \dfrac{8 \pm 2\sqrt{10}}{-4}$

$= -2 \pm \dfrac{\sqrt{10}}{2}$

$x \approx -3.58$ or $x \approx -0.42$

Graph:

The y-intercept point, $(0, -3)$, is two units to the right of the axis of symmetry. Therefore, if we move two units to the left of the axis of symmetry, we obtain the point $(-4, -3)$ which must also be on the graph.

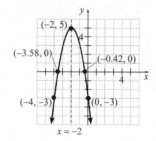

13. Consider the form $y = a(x - h)^2 + k$. From the graph we know that the vertex is $(-3, -5)$, so we have $h = -3$ and $k = -5$. The graph also passes through the point $(x, y) = (0, -2)$. Substituting values for x, y, h, and k, we can solve for a:

$-2 = a(0 - (-3))^2 - 5$

$-2 = a(0 + 3)^2 - 5$

$-2 = a(3)^2 - 5$

$-2 = 9a - 5$

$3 = 9a$

$\dfrac{3}{9} = a$

$\dfrac{1}{3} = a$

The quadratic function is $f(x) = \dfrac{1}{3}(x + 3)^2 - 5$

or $f(x) = \dfrac{1}{3}x^2 + 2x - 2$.

14. If we compare $h(x) = -\dfrac{1}{4}x^2 + x + 5$ to

$f(x) = ax^2 + bx + c$, we find that $a = -\dfrac{1}{4}$, $b = 1$, and $c = 5$. Because $a < 0$, we know the graph will open down, so the function will have a maximum value.

The maximum value occurs at

$x = -\dfrac{b}{2a} = -\dfrac{1}{2\left(-\frac{1}{4}\right)} = -\dfrac{1}{-\frac{1}{2}} = 2$.

The maximum value is

$h(2) = -\dfrac{1}{4}(2)^2 + 2 + 5 = 6$.

So, the maximum value is 6, and it occurs when $x = 2$.

15. $2m^2 + m - 15 > 0$

Solve: $2m^2 + m - 15 = 0$

           $(2m - 5)(m + 3) = 0$

           $2m - 5 = 0$ or $m + 3 = 0$

           $2m = 5$ or $m = -3$

              $m = \dfrac{5}{2}$

Determine where each factor is positive and negative and where the product of these factors is positive and negative.

The inequality is strict, so -3 and $\dfrac{5}{2}$ are not part of the solution. Now, $(2m-5)(m+3)$ is greater than zero where the product is positive. The solution is $\left\{ m \middle| m < -3 \text{ or } m > \dfrac{5}{2} \right\}$ or, using interval notation, $(-\infty, -3) \cup \left(\dfrac{5}{2}, \infty \right)$.

16. $z^2 + 6z - 1 \le 0$

Solve: $z^2 + 6z - 1 = 0$

$z = \dfrac{-6 \pm \sqrt{6^2 - 4(1)(-1)}}{2(1)}$

$= \dfrac{-6 \pm \sqrt{40}}{2}$

$= \dfrac{-6 \pm 2\sqrt{10}}{2}$

$= -3 \pm \sqrt{10}$

$z = -3 - \sqrt{10}$ or $z = -3 + \sqrt{10}$

≈ -6.16 or ≈ 0.16

Determine where each factor is positive and negative and where the product of these factors is positive and negative.

The inequality is non-strict, so $-3 - \sqrt{10}$ and $-3 + \sqrt{10}$ are part of the solution. Now, $\left[z - \left(-3 - \sqrt{10} \right) \right]\left[z - \left(-3 + \sqrt{10} \right) \right]$ is less than zero where the product is negative. The solution is

$\left\{ z \mid -3 - \sqrt{10} \le z \le -3 + \sqrt{10} \right\}$ or, using interval notation, $\left[-3 - \sqrt{10}, \ -3 + \sqrt{10} \right]$.

17. $50 = -16t^2 + 80t + 20$

$16t^2 - 80t + 30 = 0$

For this equation, $a = 16$, $b = -80$, and $c = 30$.

$t = \dfrac{-(-80) \pm \sqrt{(-80)^2 - 4(16)(30)}}{2(16)}$

$= \dfrac{80 \pm \sqrt{6400 - 1920}}{32}$

$= \dfrac{80 \pm \sqrt{4480}}{32}$

$= \dfrac{80 \pm 8\sqrt{70}}{32}$

$= \dfrac{80}{32} \pm \dfrac{8\sqrt{70}}{32}$

$= \dfrac{5}{2} \pm \dfrac{\sqrt{70}}{4}$

$t = \dfrac{5}{2} - \dfrac{\sqrt{70}}{4}$ or $t = \dfrac{5}{2} - \dfrac{\sqrt{70}}{4}$

≈ 0.408 or ≈ 4.592

Rounding to the nearest tenth, the height of the rock will be 50 feet at both 0.4 seconds and 4.6 seconds.

18. Let t represent the time required for Rupert to roof the house alone. Then $t - 4$ will represent the time required for Lex to roof the house alone.

$$\begin{pmatrix} \text{Part done} \\ \text{by Rupert} \\ \text{in 1 hour} \end{pmatrix} + \begin{pmatrix} \text{Part done} \\ \text{by Lex} \\ \text{in 1 hour} \end{pmatrix} = \begin{pmatrix} \text{Part done} \\ \text{together} \\ \text{in 1 hour} \end{pmatrix}$$

$\dfrac{1}{t} + \dfrac{1}{t-4} = \dfrac{1}{16}$

$16t(t-4)\left(\dfrac{1}{t} + \dfrac{1}{t-4} \right) = 16t(t-4)\left(\dfrac{1}{16} \right)$

$16(t-4) + 16t = t(t-4)$

$16t - 64 + 16t = t^2 - 4t$

$32t - 64 = t^2 - 4t$

$0 = t^2 - 36t + 64$

For this equation, $a = 1$, $b = -36$, and $c = 64$.

$$t = \frac{-(-36) \pm \sqrt{(-36)^2 - 4(1)(64)}}{2(1)}$$

$$= \frac{36 \pm \sqrt{1296 - 256}}{2}$$

$$= \frac{36 \pm \sqrt{1040}}{2}$$

$$= \frac{36 \pm 4\sqrt{65}}{2}$$

$$= 18 \pm 2\sqrt{65}$$

$t = 18 - 2\sqrt{65}$ or $t = 18 + 2\sqrt{65}$
≈ 1.875 or ≈ 34.125

Disregard $t \approx 1.875$ because this value makes Lex's time negative: $t - 4 = 1.875 - 4 = -2.125$. The only viable answer is $t \approx 34.125$ hours. Rounding to the nearest tenth, Rupert can roof the house in 34.1 hours when working alone.

19. a. We first recognize that the quadratic function has a negative leading coefficient. This means that the graph will open down and the function indeed has a maximum value. The maximum value occurs when

$$p = -\frac{b}{2a} = -\frac{170}{2(-0.25)} = 340.$$

The revenue will be maximized when the product is sold at a price of $340.

b. The maximum revenue is obtained by evaluating the revenue function at the price found in part (a).

$$R(340) = -0.25(340)^2 + 170(340) = 28,900$$

The maximum weekly revenue is $28,900.

20. a. Let x represent the width of the base of the box. Then $\frac{50 - 2x}{2} = 25 - x$ is the length of the base. The volume is the product of the length, width, and height:

$$V = (25 - x) \cdot x \cdot 12$$

$$= -12x^2 + 300x$$

The leading coefficient is negative so we know the graph opens down and there will be a maximum volume. This value occurs when the width is

$$x = -\frac{b}{2a} = -\frac{300}{2(-12)} = 12.5.$$

Then the length is $25 - 12.5 = 12.5$.
The dimensions that maximize the volume of the box are 12.5 in. by 12.5 in. by 12 in.

b. The maximum volume can be found by substituting 12.5 for x into the volume function.

$$V = (25 - 12.5) \cdot 12.5 \cdot 12 = 1875$$

The maximum volume of the box is 1875 cubic inches.

Chapter 9

9.1 Preparing for Composite Functions and Inverse Functions

1. We need to find all values of x that cause the denominator $x^2 + 3x - 28$ to equal 0.

$$x^2 + 3x - 28 = 0$$
$$(x+7)(x-4) = 0$$
$$x + 7 = 0 \quad \text{or} \quad x - 4 = 0$$
$$x = -7 \quad \text{or} \quad x = 4$$

Thus, the domain of $R(x) = \dfrac{x^2 - 9}{x^2 + 3x - 28}$ is

$\{x \mid x \neq -7, x \neq 4\}$.

2. a. $\begin{aligned} f(-2) &= 2(-2)^2 - (-2) + 1 \\ &= 8 + 2 + 1 \\ &= 11 \end{aligned}$

   b. $\begin{aligned} f(a+1) &= 2(a+1)^2 - (a+1) + 1 \\ &= 2(a^2 + 2a + 1) - (a+1) + 1 \\ &= 2a^2 + 4a + 2 - a - 1 + 1 \\ &= 2a^2 + 3a + 2 \end{aligned}$

3. The graph shown is not a function because it fails the vertical line test.

9.1 Exercises

1. composite function

3. inverse

5. FALSE. The notation $f^{-1}(x)$ represents the inverse function for the function $f(x)$.

7. Answers may vary. One possibility follows: A function is one-to-one if each element of the range corresponds to no more than one element in the domain. If a function is not one-to-one, then there is at least one element in the range that corresponds to more than one element in the domain. For the inverse, we would switch the domain and range. Therefore, if a function is not one-to-one, the domain of its inverse will have at least one element that corresponds to more than one element in its range. Hence, the inverse would not be a function.

9. Horizontal Line Test: If every horizontal line intersects the graph of a function f in at most one point, then f is one-to-one.

Answers may vary. One possibility follows: The horizontal line test works because we are essentially fixing a value in the range and checking to see how many values in the domain correspond to the selected value from the range. If a horizontal line crosses the graph more than once, then there are at least two values in the domain that correspond to the same value in the range. This is not one-to-one.

11. $f(x) = 2x + 5$; $g(x) = x - 4$

    a. $g(3) = 3 - 4 = -1$
    $f(-1) = 2(-1) + 5 = 3$
    $(f \circ g)(3) = f(g(3)) = f(-1) = 3$

    b. $f(-2) = 2(-2) + 5 = 1$
    $g(1) = 1 - 4 = -3$
    $(g \circ f)(-2) = g(f(-2)) = g(1) = -3$

    c. $f(1) = 2(1) + 5 = 7$
    $f(7) = 2(7) + 5 = 19$
    $(f \circ f)(1) = f(f(1)) = f(7) = 19$

    d. $g(-4) = -4 - 4 = -8$
    $g(-8) = -8 - 4 = -12$
    $(g \circ g)(-4) = g(g(-4)) = g(-8) = -12$

13. $f(x) = x^2 + 4$; $g(x) = 2x + 3$

    a. $g(3) = 2(3) + 3 = 9$
    $f(9) = (9)^2 + 4 = 85$
    $(f \circ g)(3) = f(g(3)) = f(9) = 85$

    b. $f(-2) = (-2)^2 + 4 = 8$
    $g(8) = 2(8) + 3 = 19$
    $(g \circ f)(-2) = g(f(-2)) = g(8) = 19$

    c. $f(1) = (1)^2 + 4 = 5$
    $f(5) = (5)^2 + 4 = 29$
    $(f \circ f)(1) = f(f(1)) = f(5) = 29$

d. $g(-4) = 2(-4) + 3 = -5$

$g(-5) = 2(-5) + 3 = -7$

$(g \circ g)(-4) = g(g(-4)) = g(-5) = -7$

15. $f(x) = 2x^3$; $g(x) = -2x^2 + 5$

a. $g(3) = -2(3)^2 + 5 = -2(9) + 5 = -13$

$f(-13) = 2(-13)^3 = -4394$

$(f \circ g)(3) = f(g(3)) = f(-13) = -4394$

b. $f(-2) = 2(-2)^3 = 2(-8) = -16$

$g(-16) = -2(-16)^2 + 5 = -2(256) + 5 = -507$

$(g \circ f)(-2) = g(f(-2)) = g(-16) = -507$

c. $f(1) = 2(1)^3 = 2$

$f(2) = 2(2)^3 = 16$

$(f \circ f)(1) = f(f(1)) = f(2) = 16$

d. $g(-4) = -2(-4)^2 + 5 = -2(16) + 5 = -27$

$g(-27) = -2(-27)^2 + 5 = -2(729) + 5 = -1453$

$(g \circ g)(-4) = g(g(-4)) = g(-27) = -1453$

17. $f(x) = |x - 10|$; $g(x) = \dfrac{12}{x + 3}$

a. $g(3) = \dfrac{12}{3 + 3} = \dfrac{12}{6} = 2$

$f(2) = |2 - 10| = |-8| = 8$

$(f \circ g)(3) = f(g(3)) = f(2) = 8$

b. $f(-2) = |-2 - 10| = |-12| = 12$

$g(12) = \dfrac{12}{12 + 3} = \dfrac{12}{15} = \dfrac{4}{5}$

$(g \circ f)(-2) = g(f(-2)) = g(12) = \dfrac{4}{5}$

c. $f(1) = |1 - 10| = |-9| = 9$

$f(9) = |9 - 10| = |-1| = 1$

$(f \circ f)(1) = f(f(1)) = f(9) = 1$

d. $g(-4) = \dfrac{12}{-4 + 3} = \dfrac{12}{-1} = -12$

$g(-12) = \dfrac{12}{-12 + 3} = \dfrac{12}{-9} = -\dfrac{4}{3}$

$(g \circ g)(-4) = g(g(-4)) = g(-12) = -\dfrac{4}{3}$

19. $f(x) = x + 1$; $g(x) = 2x$

a. $(f \circ g)(x) = f(g(x)) = (2x) + 1 = 2x + 1$

b. $(g \circ f)(x) = g(f(x)) = 2(x + 1) = 2x + 2$

c. $(f \circ f)(x) = f(f(x)) = (x + 1) + 1 = x + 2$

d. $(g \circ g)(x) = g(g(x)) = 2(2x) = 4x$

21. $f(x) = 2x + 7$; $g(x) = -4x + 5$

a. $(f \circ g)(x) = f(g(x))$

$= 2(-4x + 5) + 7$

$= -8x + 10 + 7$

$= -8x + 17$

b. $(g \circ f)(x) = g(f(x))$

$= -4(2x + 7) + 5$

$= -8x - 28 + 5$

$= -8x - 23$

c. $(f \circ f)(x) = f(f(x))$

$= 2(2x + 7) + 7$

$= 4x + 14 + 7$

$= 4x + 21$

d. $(g \circ g)(x) = g(g(x))$

$= -4(-4x + 5) + 5$

$= 16x - 20 + 5$

$= 16x - 15$

23. $f(x) = x^2$; $g(x) = x - 3$

a. $(f \circ g)(x) = f(g(x))$

$= (x - 3)^2 = x^2 - 6x + 9$

b. $(g \circ f)(x) = g(f(x)) = (x^2) - 3 = x^2 - 3$

c. $(f \circ f)(x) = f(f(x)) = (x^2)^2 = x^4$

d. $(g \circ g)(x) = g(g(x)) = (x - 3) - 3 = x - 6$

25. $f(x) = \sqrt{x}$; $g(x) = x + 4$

   a. $(f \circ g)(x) = f(g(x)) = \sqrt{x+4}$

   b. $(g \circ f)(x) = g(f(x)) = \sqrt{x} + 4$

   c. $(f \circ f)(x) = f(f(x)) = \sqrt{\sqrt{x}} = \sqrt[4]{x}$

   d. $(g \circ g)(x) = g(g(x)) = (x+4) + 4 = x + 8$

27. $f(x) = |x+4|$; $g(x) = x^2 - 4$

   a. $(f \circ g)(x) = f(g(x))$

       $= \left| (x^2 - 4) + 4 \right| = \left| x^2 \right| = x^2$

   b. $(g \circ f)(x) = g(f(x))$

       $= (|x+4|)^2 - 4 = (x+4)^2 - 4$

       $= x^2 + 8x + 16 - 4$

       $= x^2 + 8x + 12$

   c. $(f \circ f)(x) = f(f(x)) = \left| |x+4| + 4 \right|$

   d. $(g \circ g)(x) = g(g(x))$

       $= (x^2 - 4)^2 - 4$

       $= x^4 - 8x^2 + 16 - 4$

       $= x^4 - 8x^2 + 12$

29. $f(x) = \dfrac{2}{x+1}$; $g(x) = \dfrac{1}{x}$

   a. $(f \circ g)(x) = f(g(x))$

       $= \dfrac{2}{\dfrac{1}{x} + 1} = \dfrac{2}{\dfrac{1+x}{x}} = \dfrac{2x}{x+1}$

       where $x \neq -1, 0$.

   b. $(g \circ f)(x) = g(f(x))$

       $= \dfrac{1}{\dfrac{2}{x+1}} = 1 \cdot \dfrac{x+1}{2} = \dfrac{x+1}{2}$

       where $x \neq -1$.

   c. $(f \circ f)(x) = f(f(x))$

       $= \dfrac{2}{\dfrac{2}{x+1} + 1} = \dfrac{2}{\dfrac{2 + x + 1}{x+1}}$

       $= 2 \cdot \dfrac{x+1}{x+3} = \dfrac{2(x+1)}{x+3}$

       where $x \neq -1, -3$.

   d. $(g \circ g)(x) = g(g(x)) = \dfrac{1}{\dfrac{1}{x}} = 1 \cdot \dfrac{x}{1} = x$

       where $x \neq 0$.

31. The function is one-to-one. Each element in the range corresponds to exactly one element in the domain.

33. The function is not one-to-one. There is an element in the range ($7.09) that corresponds to more than one element in the domain (30 and 35).

35. The function is one-to-one. Each element in the range corresponds to exactly one element in the domain.

37. The function is not one-to-one. There are elements in the range (2 and 4) that correspond to more than one element in the domain.

39. The function is one-to-one. Each element in the range corresponds to exactly one element in the domain.

41. The graph passes the horizontal line test, so the graph is that of a one-to-one function.

43. The graph fails the horizontal line test. Therefore, the function is not one-to-one.

45. The graph passes the horizontal line test, so the graph is that of a one-to-one function.

47. Inverse:

Weight (g)	U. S. Coin
2.500 ⟶	Cent
5.000 ⟶	Nickel
2.268 ⟶	Dime
5.670 ⟶	Quarter
11.340 ⟶	Half Dollar
8.100 ⟶	Dollar

49. To obtain the inverse, we switch the x- and y-coordinates.

   Inverse: $\{(3,0),(4,1),(5,2),(6,3)\}$

51. To obtain the inverse, we switch the x- and y-coordinates.

    Inverse: $\{(3,-2),(1,-2),(-3,-2),(9,-2)\}$

53. To plot the inverse, switch the x- and y-coordinates in each point and connect the corresponding points. The graph of the function (shaded) and the line $y = x$ (dashed) are included for reference.

55. To plot the inverse, switch the x- and y-coordinates in each point and connect the corresponding points. The graph of the function (shaded) and the line $y = x$ (dashed) are included for reference.

57. To plot the inverse, switch the x- and y-coordinates in each point and connect the corresponding points. The graph of the function (shaded) and the line $y = x$ (dashed) are included for reference.

59. $f(g(x)) = (x-5)+5 = x$

    $g(f(x)) = (x+5)-5 = x$

    Since $f(g(x)) = g(f(x)) = x$, the two functions are inverses of each other.

61. $f(g(x)) = 5\left(\dfrac{x-7}{5}\right)+7 = x-7+7 = x$

    $g(f(x)) = \dfrac{(5x+7)-7}{5} = \dfrac{5x}{5} = x$

    Since $f(g(x)) = g(f(x)) = x$, the two functions are inverses of each other.

63. $f(g(x)) = 10\left(\dfrac{x+1}{10}\right)-1 = x+1-1 = x$

    $g(f(x)) = \dfrac{(10x-1)+1}{10} = \dfrac{10x}{10} = x$

    Since $f(g(x)) = g(f(x)) = x$, the two functions are inverses of each other.

65. $f(g(x)) = \dfrac{3}{\left(\dfrac{3}{x}+1\right)-1} = \dfrac{3}{\dfrac{3}{x}} = 3 \cdot \dfrac{x}{3} = x$

    $g(f(x)) = \dfrac{3}{\dfrac{3}{x-1}}+1 = 3 \cdot \dfrac{x-1}{3}+1 = x-1+1 = x$

    Since $f(g(x)) = g(f(x)) = x$, the two functions are inverses of each other.

67. $f(g(x)) = \sqrt[3]{\left(x^3-4\right)+4} = \sqrt[3]{x^3} = x$

    $g(f(x)) = \left(\sqrt[3]{x+4}\right)^3 - 4 = x+4-4 = x$

    Since $f(g(x)) = g(f(x)) = x$, the two functions are inverses of each other.

69. $f(x) = 6x$

    $y = 6x$

    $x = 6y$

    $\dfrac{x}{6} = y$

    $f^{-1}(x) = \dfrac{x}{6}$

    Check:

    $f\left(f^{-1}(x)\right) = 6\left(\dfrac{x}{6}\right) = x$

    $f^{-1}\left(f(x)\right) = \dfrac{6x}{6} = x$

71. $f(x) = x + 4$

$\quad\quad y = x + 4$

$\quad\quad x = y + 4$

$\quad\quad x - 4 = y$

$\quad\quad f^{-1}(x) = x - 4$

Check:

$\quad f\left(f^{-1}(x)\right) = (x - 4) + 4 = x$

$\quad f^{-1}\left(f(x)\right) = (x + 4) - 4 = x$

73. $h(x) = 2x - 7$

$\quad\quad y = 2x - 7$

$\quad\quad x = 2y - 7$

$\quad\quad x + 7 = 2y$

$\quad\quad \dfrac{x + 7}{2} = y$

$\quad\quad h^{-1}(x) = \dfrac{x + 7}{2}$

Check:

$\quad h\left(h^{-1}(x)\right) = 2\left(\dfrac{x + 7}{2}\right) - 7 = x + 7 - 7 = x$

$\quad h^{-1}\left(h(x)\right) = \dfrac{(2x - 7) + 7}{2} = \dfrac{2x}{2} = x$

75. $G(x) = 2 - 5x$

$\quad\quad y = 2 - 5x$

$\quad\quad x = 2 - 5y$

$\quad\quad x - 2 = -5y$

$\quad\quad \dfrac{x - 2}{-5} = y$

$\quad\quad \dfrac{2 - x}{5} = y$

$\quad\quad G^{-1}(x) = \dfrac{2 - x}{5}$

Check:

$\quad G\left(G^{-1}(x)\right) = 2 - 5\left(\dfrac{2 - x}{5}\right) = 2 - (2 - x) = x$

$\quad G^{-1}\left(G(x)\right) = \dfrac{2 - (2 - 5x)}{5} = \dfrac{5x}{5} = x$

77. $g(x) = x^3 + 3$

$\quad\quad y = x^3 + 3$

$\quad\quad x = y^3 + 3$

$\quad\quad x - 3 = y^3$

$\quad\quad \sqrt[3]{x - 3} = y$

$\quad\quad g^{-1}(x) = \sqrt[3]{x - 3}$

Check:

$\quad g\left(g^{-1}(x)\right) = \left(\sqrt[3]{x - 3}\right)^3 + 3 = x - 3 + 3 = x$

$\quad g^{-1}\left(g(x)\right) = \sqrt[3]{x^3 + 3 - 3} = \sqrt[3]{x^3} = x$

79. $p(x) = \dfrac{1}{x + 3}$

$\quad\quad y = \dfrac{1}{x + 3}$

$\quad\quad x = \dfrac{1}{y + 3}$

$\quad\quad y + 3 = \dfrac{1}{x}$

$\quad\quad y = \dfrac{1}{x} - 3$

$\quad\quad p^{-1}(x) = \dfrac{1}{x} - 3$

Check:

$\quad p\left(p^{-1}(x)\right) = \dfrac{1}{\left(\dfrac{1}{x} - 3\right) + 3} = \dfrac{1}{\dfrac{1}{x}} = 1 \cdot \dfrac{x}{1} = x$

$\quad p^{-1}\left(p(x)\right) = \dfrac{1}{\dfrac{1}{x + 3}} - 3 = x + 3 - 3 = x$

81. $F(x) = \dfrac{5}{2 - x}$

$\quad\quad y = \dfrac{5}{2 - x}$

$\quad\quad x = \dfrac{5}{2 - y}$

$\quad\quad 2 - y = \dfrac{5}{x}$

$\quad\quad -y = -2 + \dfrac{5}{x}$

$\quad\quad y = 2 - \dfrac{5}{x}$

$\quad\quad F^{-1}(x) = 2 - \dfrac{5}{x}$

Check:

$$F\left(F^{-1}(x)\right) = \frac{5}{2 - \left(2 - \frac{5}{x}\right)} = \frac{5}{\frac{5}{x}} = 5 \cdot \frac{x}{5} = x$$

$$F^{-1}\left(F(x)\right) = 2 - \frac{5}{\frac{5}{2-x}} = 2 - (2 - x) = x$$

83. $f(x) = \sqrt[3]{x - 2}$

$y = \sqrt[3]{x - 2}$

$x = \sqrt[3]{y - 2}$

$x^3 = y - 2$

$x^3 + 2 = y$

$f^{-1}(x) = x^3 + 2$

Check: $f\left(f^{-1}(x)\right) = \sqrt[3]{x^3 + 2 - 2} = \sqrt[3]{x^3} = x$

$f^{-1}\left(f(x)\right) = \left(\sqrt[3]{x-2}\right)^3 + 2 = x - 2 + 2 = x$

85. $R(x) = \dfrac{x}{x + 2}$

$y = \dfrac{x}{x + 2}$

$x = \dfrac{y}{y + 2}$

$x(y + 2) = y$

$xy + 2x = y$

$2x = y - xy$

$2x = y(1 - x)$

$\dfrac{2x}{1 - x} = y$

$R^{-1}(x) = \dfrac{2x}{1 - x}$

Check: $R\left(R^{-1}(x)\right) = \dfrac{\dfrac{2x}{1-x}}{\dfrac{2x}{1-x} + 2} = \dfrac{\dfrac{2x}{1-x}}{\dfrac{2x + 2 - 2x}{1-x}}$

$= \dfrac{2x}{1-x} \cdot \dfrac{1-x}{2} = x$

$R^{-1}\left(R(x)\right) = \dfrac{2\left(\dfrac{x}{x+2}\right)}{1 - \dfrac{x}{x+2}} = \dfrac{\dfrac{2x}{x+2}}{\dfrac{x+2-x}{x+2}}$

$= \dfrac{2x}{x+2} \cdot \dfrac{x+2}{2} = x$

87. $f(x) = \sqrt[3]{x - 1} + 4$

$y = \sqrt[3]{x - 1} + 4$

$x = \sqrt[3]{y - 1} + 4$

$x - 4 = \sqrt[3]{y - 1}$

$(x - 4)^3 = y - 1$

$(x - 4)^3 + 1 = y$

$f^{-1}(x) = (x - 4)^3 + 1$

Check:

$f\left(f^{-1}(x)\right) = \sqrt[3]{(x-4)^3 + 1 - 1} + 4$

$\qquad = \sqrt[3]{(x-4)^3} + 4$

$\qquad = x - 4 + 4$

$\qquad = x$

$f^{-1}\left(f(x)\right) = \left[\left(\sqrt[3]{x-1} + 4\right) - 4\right]^3 + 1$

$\qquad = \left(\sqrt[3]{x-1}\right)^3 + 1$

$\qquad = x - 1 + 1$

$\qquad = x$

89. $A(r) = \pi r^2$; $r(t) = 20t$

$A(t) = A(r(t)) = \pi(20t)^2 = 400\pi t^2$

$A(3) = 400\pi(3)^2 = 3600\pi \approx 11,309.73$ sq ft

91. $A(x) = \dfrac{x}{9}$; $C(A) = 18A$

a. $C(x) = C(A(x)) = 18\left(\dfrac{x}{9}\right) = 2x$

b. The area of the room is $15 \cdot 21 = 315$ sq ft.

$C(315) = 2(315) = 630$

It will cost \$630 to install the carpet.

93. $f^{-1}(12) = f^{-1}(f(4)) = 4$

95. To find the domain and range of the inverse, we simply switch the values for the domain and range of the function.

Domain of f^{-1} : $[-5, \infty)$

Range of f^{-1} : $[0, \infty)$

97. To find the domain and range of the inverse, we simply switch the values for the domain and range of the function.

Domain of g^{-1}: $(-6,12)$

Range of g^{-1}: $[-4,10]$

99. $T(x) = 0.15(x-6000)+600$

$$T = 0.15(x-6000)+600$$
$$T = 0.15x - 900 + 600$$
$$T = 0.15x - 300$$
$$T + 300 = 0.15x$$
$$\frac{T+300}{0.15} = x$$
$$x(T) = \frac{T+300}{0.15}$$

To determine the restrictions, we find

$T(6000) = 0.15(6000-6000)+600 = 600$ and

$T(28,400) = 0.15(28,400-6000)+600 = 3960$.

Thus, $x(T) = \dfrac{T+300}{0.15}$ for $600 \le T \le 3960$.

101. $f(x) = 2x^2 - x + 5$; $g(x) = x+a$

$$(f \circ g)(x) = f(g(x))$$
$$= 2(x+a)^2 - (x+a)+5$$
$$= 2(x^2 + 2ax + a^2) - x - a + 5$$
$$= 2x^2 + 4ax + 2a^2 - x - a + 5$$

The *y*-intercept is found by letting $x = 0$ and solving for *y*. We know the *y*-intercept of $(f \circ g)(x)$ is 20. Therefore, we get

$$(f \circ g)(0) = 2(0)^2 + 4a(0) + 2a^2 - 0 - a + 5$$
$$20 = 2a^2 - a + 5$$
$$0 = 2a^2 - a - 15$$
$$0 = (2a+5)(a-3)$$
$$2a+5 = 0 \quad \text{or} \quad a-3 = 0$$
$$2a = -5 \qquad\qquad a = 3$$
$$a = -\frac{5}{2}$$

The solution set for *a* is $\left\{-\dfrac{5}{2}, 3\right\}$.

103. $f(x) = 2x+5$; $g(x) = x-4$

a. $(f \circ g)(3) = 3$

b. $(g \circ f)(-2) = -3$

c. $(f \circ f)(1) = 19$

d. $(g \circ g)(-4) = -12$

105. $f(x) = x^2 + 4$; $g(x) = 2x+3$

a. $(f \circ g)(3) = 85$

b. $(g \circ f)(-2) = 19$

c. $(f \circ f)(1) = 29$

d. $(g \circ g)(-4) = -7$

107. $f(x) = 2x^3$; $g(x) = -2x^2 + 5$

a. $(f \circ g)(3) = -4394$

b. $(g \circ f)(-2) = -507$

c. $(f \circ f)(1) = 16$

d. $(g \circ g)(-4) = -1453$

109. $f(x) = |x - 10|$; $g(x) = \dfrac{12}{x+3}$

a. $(f \circ g)(3) = 8$

b. $(g \circ f)(-2) = \dfrac{4}{5}$

c. $(f \circ f)(1) = 1$

d. $(g \circ g)(-4) = -\dfrac{4}{3}$

111. $f(x) = x + 5$; $g(x) = x - 5$

113. $f(x) = 5x + 7$; $g(x) = \dfrac{x-7}{5}$

115. $f(x) = 10x - 1$; $g(x) = \dfrac{x+1}{10}$

9.2 Preparing for Exponential Functions

1. a. $2^3 = 2 \cdot 2 \cdot 2 = 8$

b. $2^{-1} = \dfrac{1}{2^1} = \dfrac{1}{2}$

c. $3^4 = 3 \cdot 3 \cdot 3 \cdot 3 = 81$

2. Locate some points on the graph of $f(x) = x^2$.

x	$f(x) = x^2$	$(x, f(x))$
-3	$f(-3) = (-3)^2 = 9$	$(-3, 9)$
-2	$f(-2) = (-2)^2 = 4$	$(-2, 4)$
-1	$f(-1) = (-1)^2 = 1$	$(-1, 1)$
0	$f(0) = 0^2 = 0$	$(0, 0)$
1	$f(1) = 1^2 = 1$	$(1, 1)$
2	$f(2) = 2^2 = 4$	$(2, 4)$
3	$f(3) = 3^2 = 9$	$(3, 9)$

Plot the points and connect them with a smooth curve.

3. A **rational number** is a number that can be expressed as a quotient $\dfrac{p}{q}$ of two integers. The integer p is called the *numerator*, and the integer q, which cannot be 0, is called the **denominator**. The set of rational numbers is the numbers

$$\mathbb{Q} = \left\{ x \mid x = \dfrac{p}{q}, \text{ where } p, q \text{ are integers and } q \neq 0 \right\}.$$

4. An irrational number has a decimal representation that neither repeats nor terminates.

5. a. Rounding to 4 decimal places, we obtain $3.20349193 \approx 3.2035$.

b. Truncating to 4 decimal places, we obtain $3.20349193 \approx 3.2034$.

6. a. $m^3 \cdot m^5 = m^{3+5} = m^8$

b. $\dfrac{a^7}{a^2} = a^{7-2} = a^5$

c. $\left(z^3 \right)^4 = z^{3 \cdot 4} = z^{12}$

7.
$$x^2 - 5x = 14$$
$$x^2 - 5x - 14 = 0$$
$$(x - 7)(x + 2) = 0$$
$$x - 7 = 0 \quad \text{or} \quad x + 2 = 0$$
$$x = 7 \quad \text{or} \quad x = -2$$
The solution set is $\{-2, \ 7\}$.

9.2 Exercises

1. $>$; $\neq$

3. $u = v$

5. FALSE. The range of the exponential function $f(x) = a^x$, $a > 0$, $a \neq 1$ is $(0, \infty)$.

7. As the base a increases, the steeper the graph of $f(x) = a^x$ $(a > 1)$ is for $x > 0$ and the closer the graph is to the x-axis for $x < 0$.

9. Answers may vary. One possibility follows: For exponential functions, the base is a constant and the exponent is the independent variable. For polynomial functions, the base is the independent variable and the exponents are constants (more specifically, whole numbers).

11. a. $3^{2.2} \approx 11.212$

b. $3^{2.23} \approx 11.587$

c. $3^{2.236} \approx 11.664$

d. $3^{2.2361} \approx 11.665$

e. $3^{\sqrt{5}} \approx 11.665$

13. **a.** $4^{3.1} \approx 73.517$

    b. $4^{3.14} \approx 77.708$

    c. $4^{3.142} \approx 77.924$

    d. $4^{3.1416} \approx 77.881$

    e. $4^{\pi} \approx 77.880$

15. **a.** $3.1^{2.7} \approx 21.217$

    b. $3.14^{2.72} \approx 22.472$

    c. $3.142^{2.718} \approx 22.460$

    d. $3.1416^{2.7183} \approx 22.460$

    e. $\pi^{e} \approx 22.459$

17. $e^{2} \approx 7.389$

19. $e^{-2} \approx 0.135$

21. $e^{2.3} \approx 9.974$

23. **g.** $f(x) = 2^{x} - 1$ because the following points are on the graph:

x	$f(x) = 2^{x} - 1$	$(x, f(x))$
-1	$f(-1) = 2^{-1} - 1 = \dfrac{1}{2} - 1 = -\dfrac{1}{2}$	$\left(-1, -\dfrac{1}{2}\right)$
0	$f(0) = 2^{0} - 1 = 1 - 1 = 0$	$(0, 0)$
1	$f(1) = 2^{1} - 1 = 2 - 1 = 1$	$(1, 1)$

25. **e.** $f(x) = -2^{x}$ because the following points are on the graph:

x	$f(x) = -2^{x}$	$(x, f(x))$
-1	$f(-1) = -2^{-1} = -\dfrac{1}{2}$	$\left(-1, -\dfrac{1}{2}\right)$
0	$f(0) = -2^{0} = -1$	$(0, -1)$
1	$f(1) = -2^{1} = -2$	$(1, -2)$

27. **f.** $f(x) = 2^{x} + 1$ because the following points are on the graph:

x	$f(x) = 2^{x} + 1$	$(x, f(x))$
-1	$f(-1) = 2^{-1} + 1 = \dfrac{1}{2} + 1 = \dfrac{3}{2}$	$\left(-1, \dfrac{3}{2}\right)$
0	$f(0) = 2^{0} + 1 = 1 + 1 = 2$	$(0, 2)$
1	$f(1) = 2^{1} + 1 = 2 + 1 = 3$	$(1, 3)$

29. **h.** $f(x) = -2^{-x}$ because the following points are on the graph:

x	$f(x) = -2^{-x}$	$(x, f(x))$
-1	$f(-1) = -2^{-(-1)} = -2^{1} = -2$	$(-1, -2)$
0	$f(0) = -2^{-0} = -2^{0} = -1$	$(0, -1)$
1	$f(1) = -2^{-1} = -\dfrac{1}{2}$	$\left(1, -\dfrac{1}{2}\right)$

31. Locate some points on the graph of $f(x) = 5^{x}$.

x	$f(x) = 5^{x}$	$(x, f(x))$
-2	$f(-2) = 5^{-2} = \dfrac{1}{5^{2}} = \dfrac{1}{25}$	$\left(-2, \dfrac{1}{25}\right)$
-1	$f(-1) = 5^{-1} = \dfrac{1}{5^{1}} = \dfrac{1}{5}$	$\left(-1, \dfrac{1}{5}\right)$
0	$f(0) = 5^{0} = 1$	$(0, 1)$
1	$f(1) = 5^{1} = 5$	$(1, 5)$

Plot the points and connect them with a smooth curve.

The domain of f is all real numbers or, using interval notation, $(-\infty, \infty)$. The range of f is $\{y \mid y > 0\}$ or, using interval notation, $(0, \infty)$.

33. Locate some points on the graph of $g(x) = 10^{x}$.

x	$g(x) = 10^{x}$	$(x, g(x))$
-2	$g(-2) = 10^{-2} = \dfrac{1}{10^{2}} = \dfrac{1}{100}$	$\left(-2, \dfrac{1}{100}\right)$
-1	$g(-1) = 10^{-1} = \dfrac{1}{10^{1}} = \dfrac{1}{10}$	$\left(-1, \dfrac{1}{10}\right)$
0	$g(0) = 10^{0} = 1$	$(0, 1)$
1	$g(1) = 10^{1} = 10$	$(1, 10)$

Plot the points and connect them with a smooth curve.

The domain of g is all real numbers or, using interval notation, $(-\infty, \infty)$. The range of g is $\{y \mid y > 0\}$ or, using interval notation, $(0, \infty)$.

35. Locate some points on the graph of $F(x) = \left(\dfrac{1}{5}\right)^x$.

x	$F(x) = \left(\dfrac{1}{5}\right)^x$	$(x,\ F(x))$
-1	$F(-1) = \left(\dfrac{1}{5}\right)^{-1} = 5^1 = 5$	$(-1,\ 5)$
0	$F(0) = \left(\dfrac{1}{5}\right)^0 = 1$	$(0,\ 1)$
1	$F(1) = \left(\dfrac{1}{5}\right)^1 = \dfrac{1}{5}$	$\left(1,\ \dfrac{1}{5}\right)$
2	$F(2) = \left(\dfrac{1}{5}\right)^2 = \dfrac{1}{25}$	$\left(2,\ \dfrac{1}{25}\right)$

Plot the points and connect them with a smooth curve.

The domain of F is all real numbers or, using interval notation, $(-\infty, \infty)$. The range of F is $\{y \mid y > 0\}$ or, using interval notation, $(0, \infty)$.

37. Locate some points on the graph of $G(x) = \left(\dfrac{1}{10}\right)^x$.

x	$G(x) = \left(\dfrac{1}{10}\right)^x$	$(x,\ G(x))$
-1	$G(-1) = \left(\dfrac{1}{10}\right)^{-1} = 10^1 = 10$	$(-1,\ 10)$
0	$G(0) = \left(\dfrac{1}{10}\right)^0 = 1$	$(0,\ 1)$
1	$G(1) = \left(\dfrac{1}{10}\right)^1 = \dfrac{1}{10}$	$\left(1,\ \dfrac{1}{10}\right)$
2	$G(2) = \left(\dfrac{1}{10}\right)^2 = \dfrac{1}{100}$	$\left(2,\ \dfrac{1}{100}\right)$

Plot the points and connect them with a smooth curve.

The domain of G is all real numbers or, using interval notation, $(-\infty, \infty)$. The range of G is $\{y \mid y > 0\}$ or, using interval notation, $(0, \infty)$.

39. Locate some points on the graph of $h(x) = 2^{x+2}$.

x	$h(x) = 2^{x+2}$	$(x,\ h(x))$
-5	$h(-5) = 2^{-5+2} = 2^{-3} = \dfrac{1}{2^3} = \dfrac{1}{8}$	$\left(-5,\ \dfrac{1}{8}\right)$
-4	$h(-4) = 2^{-4+2} = 2^{-2} = \dfrac{1}{2^2} = \dfrac{1}{4}$	$\left(-4,\ \dfrac{1}{4}\right)$
-3	$h(-3) = 2^{-3+2} = 2^{-1} = \dfrac{1}{2^1} = \dfrac{1}{2}$	$\left(-3,\ \dfrac{1}{2}\right)$
-2	$h(-2) = 2^{-2+2} = 2^0 = 1$	$(-2,\ 1)$
-1	$h(-1) = 2^{-1+2} = 2^1 = 2$	$(-1,\ 2)$
0	$h(0) = 2^{0+2} = 2^2 = 4$	$(0,\ 4)$
1	$h(1) = 2^{1+2} = 2^3 = 8$	$(1,\ 8)$

Plot the points and connect them with a smooth curve.

The domain of h is all real numbers or, using interval notation, $(-\infty, \infty)$. The range of h is $\{y \mid y > 0\}$ or, using interval notation, $(0, \infty)$.

41. Locate some points on the graph of $f(x) = 2^x + 3$.

x	$f(x) = 2^x + 3$	$(x, f(x))$
-2	$f(-2) = 2^{-2} + 3 = \dfrac{1}{4} + 3 = \dfrac{13}{4}$	$\left(-2, \dfrac{13}{4}\right)$
-1	$f(-1) = 2^{-1} + 3 = \dfrac{1}{2} + 3 = \dfrac{7}{2}$	$\left(-1, \dfrac{7}{2}\right)$
0	$f(0) = 2^0 + 3 = 1 + 3 = 4$	$(0, 4)$
1	$f(1) = 2^1 + 3 = 2 + 3 = 5$	$(1, 5)$
2	$f(2) = 2^2 + 3 = 4 + 3 = 7$	$(2, 7)$

Plot the points and connect them with a smooth curve.

The domain of f is all real numbers or, using interval notation, $(-\infty, \infty)$. The range of f is $\{y \mid y > 3\}$ or, using interval notation, $(3, \infty)$.

43. Locate some points on the graph of $F(x) = \left(\dfrac{1}{2}\right)^x - 1$.

x	$F(x) = \left(\dfrac{1}{2}\right)^x - 1$	$(x, F(x))$
-3	$F(-3) = \left(\dfrac{1}{2}\right)^{-3} - 1 = 8 - 1 = 7$	$(-3, 7)$
-2	$F(-2) = \left(\dfrac{1}{2}\right)^{-2} - 1 = 4 - 1 = 3$	$(-2, 3)$
-1	$F(-1) = \left(\dfrac{1}{2}\right)^{-1} - 1 = 2 - 1 = 1$	$(-1, 1)$
0	$F(0) = \left(\dfrac{1}{2}\right)^0 - 1 = 1 - 1 = 0$	$(0, 0)$
1	$F(1) = \left(\dfrac{1}{2}\right)^1 - 1 = \dfrac{1}{2} - 1 = -\dfrac{1}{2}$	$\left(1, -\dfrac{1}{2}\right)$
2	$F(2) = \left(\dfrac{1}{2}\right)^2 - 1 = \dfrac{1}{4} - 1 = -\dfrac{3}{4}$	$\left(2, -\dfrac{3}{4}\right)$
3	$F(3) = \left(\dfrac{1}{2}\right)^3 - 1 = \dfrac{1}{8} - 1 = -\dfrac{7}{8}$	$\left(3, -\dfrac{7}{8}\right)$

Plot the points and connect them with a smooth curve.

The domain of F is all real numbers or, using interval notation, $(-\infty, \infty)$. The range of F is $\{y \mid y > -1\}$ or, using interval notation, $(-1, \infty)$.

45. Locate some points on the graph of $P(x) = \left(\dfrac{1}{3}\right)^{x-2}$.

x	$P(x) = \left(\dfrac{1}{3}\right)^{x-2}$	$(x,\ P(x))$
0	$P(0) = \left(\dfrac{1}{3}\right)^{0-2} = \left(\dfrac{1}{3}\right)^{-2} = 3^2 = 9$	$(0,\ 9)$
1	$P(1) = \left(\dfrac{1}{3}\right)^{1-2} = \left(\dfrac{1}{3}\right)^{-1} = 3^1 = 3$	$(1,\ 3)$
2	$P(2) = \left(\dfrac{1}{3}\right)^{2-2} = \left(\dfrac{1}{3}\right)^{0} = 1$	$(2,\ 1)$
3	$P(3) = \left(\dfrac{1}{3}\right)^{3-2} = \left(\dfrac{1}{3}\right)^{1} = \dfrac{1}{3}$	$\left(3,\ \dfrac{1}{3}\right)$
4	$P(4) = \left(\dfrac{1}{3}\right)^{4-2} = \left(\dfrac{1}{3}\right)^{2} = \dfrac{1}{9}$	$\left(4,\ \dfrac{1}{9}\right)$

Plot the points and connect them with a smooth curve.

The domain of P is all real numbers or, using interval notation, $(-\infty, \infty)$. The range of P is $\{y \mid y > 0\}$ or , using interval notation, $(0, \infty)$.

47. Locate some points on the graph of $g(x) = e^{x-1}$.

x	$g(x) = e^{x-1}$	$(x,\ g(x))$
-1	$g(-1) = e^{-1-1} = e^{-2} = \dfrac{1}{e^2} \approx 0.135$	$\left(-1,\ \dfrac{1}{e^2}\right)$
0	$g(0) = e^{0-1} = e^{-1} = \dfrac{1}{e} \approx 0.368$	$\left(0,\ \dfrac{1}{e}\right)$
1	$g(1) = e^{1-1} = e^{0} = 1$	$(1,\ 1)$
2	$g(2) = e^{2-1} = e^{1} = e \approx 2.718$	$(2,\ e)$
3	$g(3) = e^{3-1} = e^{2} \approx 7.389$	$\left(3,\ e^2\right)$

Plot the points and connect them with a smooth curve.

The domain of g is all real numbers or, using interval notation, $(-\infty, \infty)$. The range of g is $\{y \mid y > 0\}$ or , using interval notation, $(0, \infty)$.

49. $2^x = 2^5$
$x = 5$
The solution set is $\{5\}$.

51. $3^{-x} = 81$
$3^{-x} = 3^4$
$-x = 4$
$x = -4$
The solution set is $\{-4\}$.

53. $\left(\dfrac{1}{2}\right)^x = \dfrac{1}{32}$
$\left(\dfrac{1}{2}\right)^x = \left(\dfrac{1}{2}\right)^5$
$x = 5$
The solution set is $\{5\}$.

55. $5^{x-2} = 125$
$5^{x-2} = 5^3$
$x - 2 = 3$
$x = 5$
The solution set is $\{5\}$.

57. $4^x = 8$
$\left(2^2\right)^x = 2^3$
$2^{2x} = 2^3$
$2x = 3$
$x = \dfrac{3}{2}$
The solution set is $\left\{\dfrac{3}{2}\right\}$.

59. $2^{-x+5} = 16^x$

$2^{-x+5} = \left(2^4\right)^x$

$2^{-x+5} = 2^{4x}$

$-x + 5 = 4x$

$5 = 5x$

$1 = x$

The solution set is $\{1\}$.

61. $3^{x^2-4} = 27^x$

$3^{x^2-4} = \left(3^3\right)^x$

$3^{x^2-4} = 3^{3x}$

$x^2 - 4 = 3x$

$x^2 - 3x - 4 = 0$

$(x-4)(x+1) = 0$

$x - 4 = 0$ or $x + 1 = 0$

$x = 4$ or $x = -1$

The solution set is $\{-1, \ 4\}$.

63. $4^x \cdot 2^{x^2} = 16^2$

$\left(2^2\right)^x \cdot 2^{x^2} = \left(2^4\right)^2$

$2^{2x} \cdot 2^{x^2} = 2^8$

$2^{x^2+2x} = 2^8$

$x^2 + 2x = 8$

$x^2 + 2x - 8 = 0$

$(x+4)(x-2) = 0$

$x + 4 = 0$ or $x - 2 = 0$

$x = -4$ or $x = 2$

The solution set is $\{-4, \ 2\}$.

65. $2^x \cdot 8 = 4^{x-3}$

$2^x \cdot 2^3 = \left(2^2\right)^{x-3}$

$2^{x+3} = 2^{2x-6}$

$x + 3 = 2x - 6$

$-x = -9$

$x = 9$

The solution set is $\{9\}$.

67. $\left(\dfrac{1}{5}\right)^x - 25 = 0$

$\left(\dfrac{1}{5}\right)^x = 25$

$\left(5^{-1}\right)^x = 5^2$

$5^{-x} = 5^2$

$-x = 2$

$x = -2$

The solution set is $\{-2\}$.

69. $\left(2^x\right)^x = 16$

$2^{x^2} = 2^4$

$x^2 = 4$

$x = \pm\sqrt{4}$

$x = \pm 2$

The solution set is $\{-2, \ 2\}$.

71. $e^x = e^{3x+4}$

$x = 3x + 4$

$-2x = 4$

$x = -2$

The solution set is $\{-2\}$.

73. $\left(e^x\right)^2 = e^{3x-2}$

$e^{2x} = e^{3x-2}$

$2x = 3x - 2$

$-x = -2$

$x = 2$

The solution set is $\{2\}$.

75. a. $f(3) = 2^3 = 8$.

The point $(3, 8)$ is on the graph of f.

b. $f(x) = \dfrac{1}{8}$

$2^x = \dfrac{1}{8}$

$2^x = \dfrac{1}{2^3} = 2^{-3}$

$x = -3$

The point $\left(-3, \dfrac{1}{8}\right)$ is on the graph of f.

77. a. $g(-1) = 4^{-1} - 1 = \frac{1}{4} - 1 = -\frac{3}{4}$.

The point $\left(-1, -\frac{3}{4}\right)$ is on the graph of g.

b. $g(x) = 15$

$4^x - 1 = 15$

$\quad\quad 4^x = 16$

$\quad\quad 4^x = 4^2$

$\quad\quad\quad x = 2$

The point $(2, 15)$ is on the graph of g.

79. a. $H(-3) = 3 \cdot \left(\frac{1}{2}\right)^{-3} = 3 \cdot 2^3 = 3 \cdot 8 = 24$.

The point $(-3,\ 24)$ is on the graph of H.

b. $H(x) = \frac{3}{4}$

$3 \cdot \left(\frac{1}{2}\right)^x = \frac{3}{4}$

$\quad \left(\frac{1}{2}\right)^x = \frac{1}{4}$

$\quad \left(\frac{1}{2}\right)^x = \left(\frac{1}{2}\right)^2$

$\quad\quad\quad x = 2$

The point $\left(2, \frac{3}{4}\right)$ is on the graph of H.

81. a. $P(2008) = 296(1.011)^{2008-2005} \approx 305.876$.

According to the model, the population of the U.S. in 2008 will be approximately 306 million people.

b. $P(2042) = 296(1.011)^{2042-2005} \approx 443.695$.

According to the model, the population of the U.S. in 2042 will be approximately 444 million people.

c. $444 - 400 = 44$. The U.S. Census Bureau's prediction for the population in 2042 is 44 million people fewer than that of the model.

Reasons given for the differences may vary. One possibility is that perhaps the U.S. Census Bureau expects the rate of population growth to decline below 1.1% per year over time.

83. We use the compound interest formula with $P = \$5000$, $r = 0.06$, and $n = 12$, so that

$$A = 5000\left(1 + \frac{0.06}{12}\right)^{12t} = 5000(1.005)^{12t}$$

a. The value of the account after $t = 1$ years is

$A = 5000(1.005)^{12(1)} \approx \$5,308.39$.

b. The value of the account after $t = 3$ years is

$A = 5000(1.005)^{12(3)} \approx \$5,983.40$.

c. The value of the account after $t = 5$ years is

$A = 5000(1.005)^{12(5)} \approx \$6,744.25$.

85. a. We use the compound interest formula with $P = \$2000$, $r = 0.03$, $t = 5$, and $n = 1$, so

that $A = 2000\left(1 + \frac{0.03}{1}\right)^{1(5)} \approx \$2,318.55$.

b. We use the compound interest formula with $P = \$2000$, $r = 0.03$, $t = 5$, and $n = 4$, so

that $A = 2000\left(1 + \frac{0.03}{4}\right)^{4(5)} \approx \$2,322.37$.

c. We use the compound interest formula with $P = \$2000$, $r = 0.03$, $t = 5$, and $n = 12$, so

that $A = 2000\left(1 + \frac{0.03}{12}\right)^{12(5)} \approx \$2,323.23$.

d. We use the compound interest formula with $P = \$2000$, $r = 0.03$, $t = 5$, and $n = 365$, so

that $A = 2000\left(1 + \frac{0.03}{365}\right)^{365(5)} \approx \$2,323.65$.

e. Answers may vary. One possibility follows: All other things equal, the number of compounding periods does not have a very significant impact on the future value. In this case, for example, the difference between compounding annually $(n = 1)$ and daily $(n = 365)$ is only $5.10 over 5 years.

87. a. $V(0) = 14,512(0.82)^0 = 14,512$.

According to the model, the value of a brand-new Dodge Neon is $14,512.

b. $V(2) = 14,512(0.82)^2 \approx 9,757.87$.

According to the model, the value of a 2-year-old Dodge Neon is $9,757.87.

c. $V(5) = 14,512(0.82)^5 \approx 5,380.18$.

According to the model, the value of a 5-year-old Dodge Neon is $5,380.18.

89. a. $A(1) = 100\left(\dfrac{1}{2}\right)^{1/13.81} \approx 95.105$.

After 1 second, approximately 95.105 grams of beryllium-11 will be left in the sample.

b. $A(13.81) = 100\left(\dfrac{1}{2}\right)^{13.81/13.81} = 50$.

After 13.81 seconds, 50 grams of beryllium-11 will be left in the sample.

c. $A(27.62) = 100\left(\dfrac{1}{2}\right)^{27.62/13.81} = 25$.

After 27.62 seconds, 25 grams of beryllium-11 will be left in the sample.

d. $A(100) = 100\left(\dfrac{1}{2}\right)^{100/13.81} \approx 0.661$.

After 100 seconds, approximately 0.661 gram of beryllium-11 will be left in the sample.

91. a. $u(5) = 70 + 330e^{-0.072(5)} \approx 300.233$.

According to the model, the temperature of the pizza after 5 minutes will be approximately $300.233°F$.

b. $u(10) = 70 + 330e^{-0.072(10)} \approx 230.628$.

According to the model, the temperature of the pizza after 10 minutes will be approximately $230.628°F$.

c. $u(13) = 70 + 330e^{-0.072(13)} \approx 199.424$.

According to the model, the temperature of the pizza after 13 minutes will be approximately $199.424°F$. Since this is below $200°F$, the pizza will be ready to eat after cooling for 13 minutes.

93. a. $L(45) = 200\left(1 - e^{-0.0035(45)}\right) \approx 29.14$.

According to the model, the student will learn approximately 29 words after 45 minutes.

b. $L(60) = 200\left(1 - e^{-0.0035(60)}\right) \approx 37.88$.

According to the model, the student will learn approximately 38 words after 60 minutes.

95. a. We use the equation with $E = 120$, $R = 10$, $L = 25$, and $t = 0.05$, so that

$$I = \frac{120}{10}\left[1 - e^{-(10/25)0.05}\right] \approx 0.238 \text{ ampere.}$$

b. We use the equation with $E = 240$, $R = 10$, $L = 25$, and $t = 0.05$, so that

$$I = \frac{240}{10}\left[1 - e^{-(10/25)0.05}\right] \approx 0.475 \text{ ampere.}$$

97. The exponential function will be of the form $y = a^x$. Now the function contains the points $\left(-1, \dfrac{1}{3}\right)$, $(0,1)$, and $(1,3)$, so $a = 3$. Thus, the equation of the function is $y = 3^x$.

99. a. $x = -2:$ $x^2 - 5x + 1 = (-2)^2 - 5(-2) + 1$
$$= 4 + 10 + 1$$
$$= 15$$

b. $x = 3:$ $x^2 - 5x + 1 = 3^2 - 5(3) + 1$
$$= 9 - 15 + 1$$
$$= -5$$

101. a. $x = -2:$ $\dfrac{4}{x+2} = \dfrac{4}{-2+2} = \dfrac{4}{0} =$ undefined

b. $x = 3:$ $\dfrac{4}{x+2} = \dfrac{4}{3+2} = \dfrac{4}{5}$

103. a. $x = 2:$ $\sqrt{2x+5} = \sqrt{2(2)+5}$
$$= \sqrt{4+5} = \sqrt{9} = 3$$

b. $x = 11:$ $\sqrt{2x+5} = \sqrt{2(11)+5}$
$$= \sqrt{22+5}$$
$$= \sqrt{27} = \sqrt{9 \cdot 3} = 3\sqrt{3}$$

105. Let $Y_1 = 1.5^x$.

The domain of $f(x) = 1.5^x$ is all real numbers, or using interval notation $(-\infty, \infty)$. The range is $\{y \mid y > 0\}$, or using interval notation $(0, \infty)$.

107. Let $Y_1 = 0.9^x$.

The domain of $H(x) = 0.9^x$ is all real numbers, or using interval notation $(-\infty, \infty)$. The range is $\{y \mid y > 0\}$, or using interval notation $(0, \infty)$.

109. Let $Y_1 = 2.5^x + 3$.

The domain of $g(x) = 2.5^x + 3$ is all real numbers, or using interval notation $(-\infty, \infty)$. The range is $\{y \mid y > 3\}$, or using interval notation $(3, \infty)$.

111. Let $Y_1 = 1.6^{x-3}$.

The domain of $F(x) = 1.6^{x-3}$ is all real numbers, or using interval notation $(-\infty, \infty)$. The range is $\{y \mid y > 0\}$, or using interval notation $(0, \infty)$.

9.3 Preparing for Logarithmic Functions

1.
$$3x + 2 > 0$$
$$3x + 2 - 2 > 0 - 2$$
$$3x > -2$$
$$\frac{3x}{3} > \frac{-2}{3}$$
$$x > -\frac{2}{3}$$

The solution set is $\left\{ x \mid x > -\frac{2}{3} \right\}$ or, using interval notation, $\left(-\frac{2}{3}, \infty \right)$.

2.
$$\sqrt{x+2} = x$$
$$\left(\sqrt{x+2} \right)^2 = (x)^2$$
$$x + 2 = x^2$$
$$0 = x^2 - x - 2$$
$$0 = (x-2)(x+1)$$
$$x - 2 = 0 \quad \text{or} \quad x + 1 = 0$$
$$x = 2 \quad \text{or} \quad x = -1$$

Check:
$$x = 2: \quad \sqrt{2+2} \overset{?}{=} 2$$
$$\sqrt{4} \overset{?}{=} 2$$
$$2 = 2 \checkmark$$

$$x = -1: \quad \sqrt{-1+2} \overset{?}{=} -1$$
$$\sqrt{1} \overset{?}{=} -1$$
$$1 \neq -1 \; \textbf{✗}$$

The potential solution $x = -1$ does not check; the solution set is $\{2\}$.

3.
$$x^2 = 6x + 7$$
$$x^2 - 6x - 7 = 0$$
$$(x-7)(x+1) = 0$$
$$x - 7 = 0 \quad \text{or} \quad x + 1 = 0$$
$$x = 7 \quad \text{or} \quad x = -1$$
The solution set is $\{-1, 7\}$.

9.3 Exercises

1. $x = a^y$; $>$; $\neq$

3. $\left(\dfrac{1}{a}, -1 \right)$, $(1, 0)$, $(a, 1)$

5. FALSE. If $y = \log_2 x$, then $x = 2^y$.

7. Answers may vary. One possibility follows: Recall that if $y = \log_a x$, then $x = a^y$. We exclude the base $a = 1$ because the result would simplify to the vertical line $x = 1^y = 1$.

9. If $25 = 5^2$, then $2 = \log_5 25$.

11. If $64 = 4^3$, then $3 = \log_4 64$.

13. If $\dfrac{1}{8} = 2^{-3}$, then $-3 = \log_2\left(\dfrac{1}{8}\right)$.

15. If $e^x = 12$, then $\ln 12 = x$.

17. If $a^3 = 19$, then $\log_a 19 = 3$.

19. If $5^{-6} = c$, then $\log_5 c = -6$.

21. If $\log_2 16 = 4$, then $2^4 = 16$.

23. If $\log_3 \dfrac{1}{9} = -2$, then $3^{-2} = \dfrac{1}{9}$.

25. If $\ln x = 4$, then $e^4 = x$.

27. If $\log_5 a = -3$, then $5^{-3} = a$.

29. If $\log_a 4 = 2$, then $a^2 = 4$.

31. If $\log_{1/2} 12 = y$, then $\left(\dfrac{1}{2}\right)^y = 12$.

33. Let $y = \log_3 1$. Then,
$$3^y = 1$$
$$3^y = 3^0$$
$$y = 0$$
Thus, $\log_3 1 = 0$.

35. Let $y = \log_2 8$. Then,
$$2^y = 8$$
$$2^y = 2^3$$
$$y = 3$$
Thus, $\log_2 8 = 3$.

37. Let $y = \log_4\left(\dfrac{1}{16}\right)$. Then,
$$4^y = \dfrac{1}{16}$$
$$4^y = \dfrac{1}{4^2} = 4^{-2}$$
$$y = -2$$
Thus, $\log_4 \dfrac{1}{16} = -2$.

39. Let $y = \log_{\sqrt{2}} 4$. Then,
$$\left(\sqrt{2}\right)^y = 4$$
$$\left(2^{\frac{1}{2}}\right)^y = 2^2$$
$$2^{\frac{1}{2}y} = 2^2$$
$$\dfrac{1}{2}y = 2$$
$$y = 4$$
Thus, $\log_{\sqrt{2}} 4 = 4$.

41. $f(81) = \log_3 81$. To determine the value, let
$y = \log_3 81$. Then,
$$3^y = 81$$
$$3^y = 3^4$$
$$y = 4$$
Therefore, $f(81) = 4$.

43. $g\left(\sqrt{5}\right) = \log_5 \sqrt{5}$. To determine the value, let
$y = \log_5 \sqrt{5}$. Then,
$$5^y = \sqrt{5}$$
$$5^y = 5^{\frac{1}{2}}$$
$$y = \dfrac{1}{2}$$
Therefore, $g\left(\sqrt{5}\right) = \dfrac{1}{2}$.

45. $H(0.1) = \log 0.1$. To determine the value, let
$y = \log 0.1$. Then,
$$10^y = 0.1$$
$$10^y = \dfrac{1}{10}$$
$$10^y = 10^{-1}$$
$$y = -1$$
Therefore, $H(0.1) = -1$.

47. $P\left(e^3\right) = \ln e^3$. To determine the value, let
$y = \ln e^3$. Then,
$$e^y = e^3$$
$$y = 3$$
Therefore, $P\left(e^3\right) = 3$.

49. The domain of $f(x) = \log_2(x-4)$ is the set of all real numbers x such that
$$x - 4 > 0$$
$$x > 4$$
Thus, the domain of $f(x) = \log_2(x-4)$ is $\{x \mid x > 4\}$, or using interval notation, $(4, \infty)$.

51. The domain of $G(x) = \log_5(x+6)$ is the set of all real numbers x such that
$$x + 6 > 0$$
$$x > -6$$
Thus, the domain of $G(x) = \log_5(x+6)$ is $\{x \mid x > -6\}$, or using interval notation, $(-6, \infty)$.

53. The domain of $F(x) = \log_3(2x)$ is the set of all real numbers x such that
$$2x > 0$$
$$x > 0$$
Thus, the domain of $F(x) = \log_3(2x)$ is $\{x \mid x > 0\}$, or using interval notation, $(0, \infty)$.

55. The domain of $f(x) = \log_8(3x-2)$ is the set of all real numbers x such that
$$3x - 2 > 0$$
$$3x > 2$$
$$x > \frac{2}{3}$$
Thus, the domain of $f(x) = \log_8(3x-2)$ is $\left\{x \mid x > \frac{2}{3}\right\}$, or using interval notation, $\left(\frac{2}{3}, \infty\right)$.

57. The domain of $H(x) = \log_7(2x+1)$ is the set of all real numbers x such that

$$2x + 1 > 0$$
$$2x > -1$$
$$x > -\frac{1}{2}$$
Thus, the domain of $H(x) = \log_7(2x+1)$ is $\left\{x \mid x > -\frac{1}{2}\right\}$, or using interval notation, $\left(-\frac{1}{2}, \infty\right)$.

59. The domain of $H(x) = \log_2(1-4x)$ is the set of all real numbers x such that
$$1 - 4x > 0$$
$$-4x > -1$$
$$x < \frac{-1}{-4}$$
$$x < \frac{1}{4}$$

Thus, the domain of $H(x) = \log_2(1-4x)$ is $\left\{x \mid x < \frac{1}{4}\right\}$, or using interval notation, $\left(-\infty, \frac{1}{4}\right)$.

61. Rewrite $y = f(x) = \log_5 x$ as $x = 5^y$. Locate some points on the graph of $x = 5^y$.

y	$x = 5^y$	(x, y)
-2	$x = 5^{-2} = \dfrac{1}{5^2} = \dfrac{1}{25}$	$\left(\dfrac{1}{25}, -2\right)$
-1	$x = 5^{-1} = \dfrac{1}{5^1} = \dfrac{1}{5}$	$\left(\dfrac{1}{5}, -1\right)$
0	$x = 5^0 = 1$	$(1, 0)$
1	$x = 5^1 = 5$	$(5, 1)$

Plot the points and connect them with a smooth curve.

The domain of f is $\{x \mid x > 0\}$ or, using interval notation, $(0, \infty)$. The range of f is all real numbers or, using interval notation, $(-\infty, \infty)$.

63. Rewrite $y = g(x) = \log_6 x$ as $x = 6^y$. Locate some points on the graph of $x = 6^y$.

y	$x = 6^y$	(x, y)
-2	$x = 6^{-2} = \dfrac{1}{6^2} = \dfrac{1}{36}$	$\left(\dfrac{1}{36}, -2\right)$
-1	$x = 6^{-1} = \dfrac{1}{6^1} = \dfrac{1}{6}$	$\left(\dfrac{1}{6}, -1\right)$
0	$x = 6^0 = 1$	$(1, 0)$
1	$x = 6^1 = 6$	$(6, 1)$

Plot the points and connect them with a smooth curve.

The domain of g is $\{x \mid x > 0\}$ or, using interval notation, $(0, \infty)$. The range of g is all real numbers or, using interval notation, $(-\infty, \infty)$.

65. Rewrite $y = F(x) = \log_{1/5} x$ as $x = \left(\dfrac{1}{5}\right)^y$. Locate some points on the graph of $x = \left(\dfrac{1}{5}\right)^y$.

y	$x = \left(\dfrac{1}{5}\right)^y$	(x, y)
-1	$x = \left(\dfrac{1}{5}\right)^{-1} = 5^1 = 5$	$(5, -1)$
0	$x = \left(\dfrac{1}{5}\right)^0 = 1$	$(1, 0)$
1	$x = \left(\dfrac{1}{5}\right)^1 = \dfrac{1}{5}$	$\left(\dfrac{1}{5}, 1\right)$
2	$x = \left(\dfrac{1}{5}\right)^2 = \dfrac{1}{25}$	$\left(\dfrac{1}{25}, 2\right)$

Plot the points and connect them with a smooth curve.

The domain of F is $\{x \mid x > 0\}$ or, using interval notation, $(0, \infty)$. The range of F is all real numbers or, using interval notation, $(-\infty, \infty)$.

67. Rewrite $y = G(x) = \log_{1/6} x$ as $x = \left(\dfrac{1}{6}\right)^y$. Locate some points on the graph of $x = \left(\dfrac{1}{6}\right)^y$.

y	$x = \left(\dfrac{1}{6}\right)^y$	(x, y)
-1	$x = \left(\dfrac{1}{6}\right)^{-1} = 6^1 = 6$	$(6, -1)$
0	$x = \left(\dfrac{1}{6}\right)^0 = 1$	$(1, 0)$
1	$x = \left(\dfrac{1}{6}\right)^1 = \dfrac{1}{6}$	$\left(\dfrac{1}{6}, 1\right)$
2	$x = \left(\dfrac{1}{6}\right)^2 = \dfrac{1}{36}$	$\left(\dfrac{1}{36}, 2\right)$

Plot the points and connect them with a smooth curve.

The domain of G is $\{x \mid x > 0\}$ or, using interval notation, $(0, \infty)$. The range of G is all real numbers or, using interval notation, $(-\infty, \infty)$.

69. Rewrite $y = f(x) = \ln x$ as $x = e^y$. Locate some points on the graph of $x = e^y$.

y	$x = e^y$	(x, y)
-2	$x = e^{-2} = \dfrac{1}{e^2} \approx 0.135$	$\left(\dfrac{1}{e^2}, -2\right)$
-1	$x = e^{-1} = \dfrac{1}{e} \approx 0.368$	$\left(\dfrac{1}{e}, -1\right)$
0	$x = e^0 = 1$	$(1, 0)$
1	$x = e^1 = e \approx 2.718$	$(e, 1)$
2	$x = e^2 \approx 7.389$	$\left(e^2, 2\right)$

Plot the points and connect them with a smooth curve.

The domain of f is $\{x \mid x > 0\}$ or, using interval notation, $(0, \infty)$. The range of f is all real numbers or, using interval notation, $(-\infty, \infty)$.

71. $\log 67 \approx 1.826$

73. $\ln 5.4 \approx 1.686$

75. $\log 0.35 \approx -0.456$

77. $\ln 0.2 \approx -1.609$

79. $\log \dfrac{5}{4} \approx 0.097$

81. $\ln \dfrac{3}{8} \approx -0.981$

83. $\log_3 (2x + 1) = 2$
$$2x + 1 = 3^2$$
$$2x + 1 = 9$$
$$2x = 8$$
$$x = 4$$
The solution set is $\{4\}$.

85. $\log_5 (20x - 5) = 3$
$$20x - 5 = 5^3$$
$$20x - 5 = 125$$
$$20x = 130$$
$$x = \frac{130}{20} = \frac{13}{2}$$
The solution set is $\left\{\dfrac{13}{2}\right\}$.

87. $\log_a 36 = 2$
$$a^2 = 36$$
$$a = \pm\sqrt{36}$$
$$a = \pm 6$$
Since the base of a logarithm must always be positive, we know that $a = -6$ is extraneous. The solution set is $\{6\}$.

89. $\log_a 18 = 2$
$$a^2 = 18$$
$$a = \pm\sqrt{18}$$
$$a = \pm 3\sqrt{2}$$
Since the base of a logarithm must always be positive, we know that $a = -3\sqrt{2}$ is extraneous. The solution set is $\{3\sqrt{2}\}$.

91. $\log_a 1000 = 3$
$$a^3 = 1000$$
$$a = \sqrt[3]{1000}$$
$$a = 10$$
The solution set is $\{10\}$.

93. $\ln x = 5$
$$x = e^5 \approx 148.413$$
The solution set is $\{e^5\}$.

95. $\log(2x - 1) = -1$
$$2x - 1 = 10^{-1}$$
$$2x - 1 = \frac{1}{10}$$
$$2x = \frac{11}{10}$$
$$x = \frac{1}{2} \cdot \frac{11}{10} = \frac{11}{20}$$
The solution set is $\left\{\dfrac{11}{20}\right\}$.

97. $\ln e^x = -3$

$\quad e^x = e^{-3}$

$\quad\quad x = -3$

The solution set is $\{-3\}$.

99. $\log_3 (81) = x$

$\quad\quad 3^x = 81$

$\quad\quad 3^x = 3^4$

$\quad\quad\; x = 4$

The solution set is $\{4\}$.

101. $\log_2 (x^2 - 1) = 3$

$\quad\quad x^2 - 1 = 2^3$

$\quad\quad x^2 - 1 = 8$

$\quad\quad\quad x^2 = 9$

$\quad\quad\quad\; x = \pm\sqrt{9}$

$\quad\quad\quad\; x = \pm 3$

The solution set is $\{-3,\; 3\}$.

103. a. $f(16) = \log_2 16$. To determine the value,

let $y = \log_2 16$. Then,

$\quad 2^y = 16$

$\quad 2^y = 2^4$

$\quad\;\; y = 4$

Therefore, $f(16) = 4$, and the point $(16, 4)$ is on the graph of f.

b. $f(x) = -3$

$\log_2 x = -3$

$\quad\quad x = 2^{-3}$

$\quad\quad x = \dfrac{1}{2^3} = \dfrac{1}{8}$

The point $\left(\dfrac{1}{8}, -3\right)$ is on the graph of f.

105. a. $G(7) = \log_4 (7+1) = \log_4 8$. To determine

the value, let $y = \log_4 8$. Then,

$\quad\quad 4^y = 8$

$\quad \left(2^2\right)^y = 2^3$

$\quad\quad 2^{2y} = 2^3$

$\quad\quad 2y = 3$

$\quad\quad\; y = \dfrac{3}{2}$

Therefore, $G(7) = \dfrac{3}{2}$, and the point $\left(7, \dfrac{3}{2}\right)$

is on the graph of G.

b. $\quad\quad G(x) = 2$

$\log_4 (x+1) = 2$

$\quad\quad x + 1 = 4^2$

$\quad\quad x + 1 = 16$

$\quad\quad\quad x = 15$

The point $(15, 2)$ is on the graph of G.

107. We evaluate $L(x) = 10\log\dfrac{x}{10^{-12}}$ at $x = 10^{-10}$.

$L(10^{-10}) = 10\log\dfrac{10^{-10}}{10^{-12}}$

$\quad\quad\quad = 10\log 10^{-10-(-12)}$

$\quad\quad\quad = 10\log 10^2 = 10(2) = 20$

The loudness of a whisper is 20 decibels.

109. We evaluate $L(x) = 10\log\dfrac{x}{10^{-12}}$ at $x = 10^1$.

$L(10^1) = 10\log\dfrac{10^1}{10^{-12}}$

$\quad\quad\quad = 10\log 10^{1-(-12)}$

$\quad\quad\quad = 10\log 10^{13} = 10(13) = 130$

The threshold of pain is 130 decibels.

111. We evaluate $M(x) = \log\left(\dfrac{x}{10^{-3}}\right)$ at $x = 63,096$.

$M(63,096) = \log\left(\dfrac{63,096}{10^{-3}}\right)$

$\quad\quad\quad = \log(63,096,000) \approx 7.8$

The magnitude of the 1906 San Francisco earthquake was approximately 7.8 on the Richter scale.

113. We solve $M(x) = \log\left(\dfrac{x}{10^{-3}}\right)$ for $M(x) = 8.8$.

$\quad\quad M(x) = 8.8$

$\log\left(\dfrac{x}{10^{-3}}\right) = 8.8$

$\quad\quad \dfrac{x}{10^{-3}} = 10^{8.8}$

$\quad\quad\quad x = 10^{8.8} \cdot 10^{-3}$

$\quad\quad\quad\; = 10^{8.8+(-3)}$

$\quad\quad\quad\; = 10^{5.8}$

$\quad\quad\quad\; \approx 630,957$

The seismographic reading of the 1906 Ecuador earthquake 100 kilometers from the epicenter was approximately 630,957 millimeters.

115. a. We evaluate $pH = -\log\left[H^+\right]$ for

$\left[H^+\right] = 10^{-12}$.

$pH = -\log 10^{-12} = -(-12) = 12$

The pH of household ammonia is 12, so household ammonia is basic.

b. We evaluate $pH = -\log\left[H^+\right]$ for

$\left[H^+\right] = 10^{-5}$.

$pH = -\log 10^{-5} = -(-5) = 5$

The pH of black coffee is 5, so black coffee is acidic.

c. We evaluate $pH = -\log\left[H^+\right]$ for

$\left[H^+\right] = 10^{-2}$.

$pH = -\log 10^{-2} = -(-2) = 2$

The pH of lemon juice is 2, so lemon juice is acidic.

d. We solve $pH = -\log\left[H^+\right]$ for $pH = 7.4$.

$$7.4 = -\log\left[H^+\right]$$
$$-7.4 = \log\left[H^+\right]$$
$$\left[H^+\right] = 10^{-7.4}$$

The concentration of hydrogen ions in human blood is $10^{-7.4}$ moles per liter.

117. The domain of $f(x) = \log_2\left(x^2 - 3x - 10\right)$ is the set of all real numbers x such that $x^2 - 3x - 10 > 0$.

Solve: $\quad x^2 - 3x - 10 = 0$
$$(x+2)(x-5) = 0$$
$$x+2 = 0 \quad \text{or} \quad x-5 = 0$$
$$x = -2 \quad \text{or} \quad x = 5$$

Determine where each factor is positive and negative and where the product of these factors is positive and negative.

Interval	$(-\infty, -2)$	-2	$(-2, 5)$	5	$(5, \infty)$
$x + 2$	$----$	0	$++++$	$+$	$++++$
$x - 5$	$----$	$-$	$----$	0	$++++$
$(x+2)(x-5)$	$++++$	0	$----$	0	$++++$

The inequality is strict, so –2 and 5 are not part of the solution. Now, $(x+2)(x-5)$ is greater than zero where the product is positive. Thus, the solution of the inequality and the domain of f is $\{x \mid x < -2 \text{ or } x > 5\}$, or using interval notation, $(-\infty, -2) \cup (5, \infty)$.

119. The domain of $f(x) = \ln\left(\dfrac{x-3}{x+1}\right)$ is the set of all real numbers x such that $\dfrac{x-3}{x+1} > 0$.

The rational expression will equal 0 when $x = 3$. It is undefined when $x = -1$. Determine where the numerator and the denominator are positive and negative and where the quotient is positive and negative:

Interval	$(-\infty, -1)$	-1	$(-1, 3)$	3	$(3, \infty)$
$x - 3$	$----$	$-$	$----$	0	$++++$
$x + 1$	$----$	0	$++++$	$+$	$++++$
$\frac{x-3}{x+1}$	$++++$	$\varnothing$	$----$	0	$++++$

The rational function is undefined at $x = -1$, so -1 is not part of the solution. The inequality is strict, so 3 is not part of the solution. Now, $\dfrac{x-3}{x+1}$ is greater than zero where the quotient is positive. Thus, the solution of the inequality and the domain of f is $\{x \mid x < -1 \text{ or } x > 3\}$, or using interval notation, $(-\infty, -1) \cup (3, \infty)$.

121. If the graph of $f(x) = \log_a x$ contains the point $(16, \ 2)$, then

$$\log_a 16 = 2$$
$$a^2 = 16$$
$$a = \pm\sqrt{16} = \pm 4$$

Since the base of a logarithm must always be positive, we know that $a = -4$ is extraneous. Thus, $a = 4$.

123. $\left(2x^2 - 6x + 1\right) - \left(5x^2 + x - 9\right)$
$$= 2x^2 - 6x + 1 - 5x^2 - x + 9$$
$$= -3x^2 - 7x + 10$$

125. $x^2 - 1 = (x+1)(x-1)$

$x^2 + 3x + 2 = (x+1)(x+2)$

$LCD = (x+1)(x-1)(x+2)$

$$\frac{3x}{x^2-1} + \frac{x-3}{x^2+3x+2}$$

$$= \frac{3x}{(x+1)(x-1)} \cdot \frac{x+2}{x+2} + \frac{x-3}{(x+1)(x+2)} \cdot \frac{x-1}{x-1}$$

$$= \frac{3x^2+6x}{(x+1)(x-1)(x+2)} + \frac{x^2-x-3x+3}{(x+1)(x-1)(x+2)}$$

$$= \frac{3x^2+6x+x^2-x-3x+3}{(x+1)(x-1)(x+2)}$$

$$= \frac{4x^2+2x+3}{(x+1)(x-1)(x+2)}$$

127. $\sqrt{8x^3} + x\sqrt{18x} = \sqrt{4x^2 \cdot 2x} + x\sqrt{9 \cdot 2x}$

$$= 2x\sqrt{2x} + 3x\sqrt{2x} = 5x\sqrt{2x}$$

129. Let $Y_1 = \log(x+1)$.

The domain of $f(x) = \log(x+1)$ is $\{x \mid x > -1\}$ or, using interval notation, $(-1, \infty)$. The range is all real numbers or, using interval notation, $(-\infty, \infty)$.

Note: The graph shown above is a bit misleading. The curve does not terminate at $x = -1$. Instead, the curve has an asymptote at $x = -1$. More specifically, as x approaches -1 (but stays larger than -1), f goes to $-\infty$.

131. Let $Y_1 = \ln(x) + 1$.

 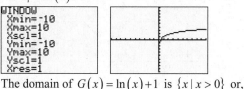

The domain of $G(x) = \ln(x) + 1$ is $\{x \mid x > 0\}$ or, using interval notation, $(0, \infty)$. The range is all real numbers or, using interval notation, $(-\infty, \infty)$.

Note: The graph shown above is a bit misleading. The curve does not terminate at $x = 0$. Instead, the curve has an asymptote at $x = 0$. More specifically, as x approaches 0 (but stays larger than 0), G goes to $-\infty$.

133. Let $Y_1 = 2\log(x-3) + 1$.

The domain of $f(x) = 2\log(x-3) + 1$ is $\{x \mid x > 3\}$ or, using interval notation, $(3, \infty)$. The range is all real numbers or, using interval notation, $(-\infty, \infty)$.

Note: The graph shown above is a bit misleading. The curve does not terminate at $x = 3$. Instead, the curve has an asymptote at $x = 3$. More specifically, as x approaches 3 (but stays larger than 3), f goes to $-\infty$.

Putting the Concepts Together (Sections 9.1 – 9.3)

1. $f(x) = 2x + 3$; $g(x) = 2x^2 - 4x$

a. $(f \circ g)(x) = f(g(x))$

$$= 2(2x^2 - 4x) + 3$$

$$= 4x^2 - 8x + 3$$

b. $(g \circ f)(x) = g(f(x))$

$$= 2(2x+3)^2 - 4(2x+3)$$

$$= 2(4x^2 + 12x + 9) - 4(2x+3)$$

$$= 8x^2 + 24x + 18 - 8x - 12$$

$$= 8x^2 + 16x + 6$$

c. Using the result from part (a):

$(f \circ g)(3) = 4(3)^2 - 8(3) + 3$

$$= 4(9) - 8(3) + 3$$

$$= 36 - 24 + 3$$

$$= 15$$

d. Using the result from part (b):

$(g \circ f)(-2) = 8(-2)^2 + 16(-2) + 6$

$$= 8(4) + 16(-2) + 6$$

$$= 32 - 32 + 6$$

$$= 6$$

e. $f(1) = 2(1) + 3 = 2 + 3 = 5$

$f(5) = 2(5) + 3 = 10 + 3 = 13$

$(f \circ f)(1) = f(f(1)) = f(5) = 13$

2. a.
$$f(x) = 3x + 4$$
$$y = 3x + 4$$
$$x = 3y + 4$$
$$x - 4 = 3y$$
$$\frac{x-4}{3} = y$$
$$f^{-1}(x) = \frac{x-4}{3}$$

Check:
$$f\left(f^{-1}(x)\right) = 3\left(\frac{x-4}{3}\right) + 4 = x - 4 + 4 = x$$

$$f^{-1}\left(f(x)\right) = \frac{(3x+4)-4}{3} = \frac{3x}{3} = x$$

b.
$$g(x) = x^3 - 4$$
$$y = x^3 - 4$$
$$x = y^3 - 4$$
$$x + 4 = y^3$$
$$\sqrt[3]{x+4} = y$$
$$g^{-1}(x) = \sqrt[3]{x+4}$$

Check:
$$g\left(g^{-1}(x)\right) = \left(\sqrt[3]{x+4}\right)^3 - 4 = x + 4 - 4 = x$$

$$g^{-1}\left(g(x)\right) = \sqrt[3]{(x^3-4)+4} = \sqrt[3]{x^3} = x$$

3. To plot the inverse, switch the x- and y-coordinates in each point and connect the corresponding points. The graphs of the function (shaded) and the line $y = x$ (dashed) are included for reference.

4. a. $2.7^{2.7} \approx 14.611$
b. $2.72^{2.72} \approx 15.206$
c. $2.718^{2.718} \approx 15.146$
d. $2.7183^{2.7183} \approx 15.155$
e. $e^e \approx 15.154$

5. a. If $a^4 = 6.4$, then $\log_a 6.4 = 4$.
b. If $10^x = 278$, then $\log 278 = x$.

6. a. If $\log_2 x = 7$, then $2^7 = x$.
b. If $\ln 16 = M$, then $e^M = 16$.

7. a. Let $y = \log_5 625$. Then,
$$5^y = 625$$
$$5^y = 5^4$$
$$y = 4$$
Thus, $\log_5 625 = 4$.

b. Let $y = \log_{\frac{2}{3}}\left(\frac{9}{4}\right)$. Then,
$$\left(\frac{2}{3}\right)^y = \frac{9}{4}$$
$$\left(\frac{2}{3}\right)^y = \left(\frac{3}{2}\right)^2$$
$$\left(\frac{2}{3}\right)^y = \left(\frac{2}{3}\right)^{-2}$$
$$y = -2$$
Thus, $\log_{\frac{2}{3}}\left(\frac{9}{4}\right) = -2$.

8. The domain of $f(x) = \log_{13}(2x + 12)$ is the set of all real numbers x such that
$$2x + 12 > 0$$
$$2x > -12$$
$$x > -6$$
Thus, the domain of $f(x) = \log_{13}(2x + 12)$ is $\{x \mid x > -6\}$, or using interval notation, $(-6, \infty)$.

9. Locate some points on the graph of
$$f(x) = \left(\frac{1}{6}\right)^x.$$

x	$f(x) = \left(\frac{1}{6}\right)^x$	$(x, f(x))$
-1	$f(-1) = \left(\frac{1}{6}\right)^{-1} = \left(\frac{6}{1}\right)^1 = 6$	$(-1, 6)$
0	$f(0) = \left(\frac{1}{6}\right)^0 = 1$	$(0, 1)$
1	$f(1) = \left(\frac{1}{6}\right)^1 = \frac{1}{6}$	$\left(1, \frac{1}{6}\right)$
2	$f(2) = \left(\frac{1}{6}\right)^2 = \frac{1}{36}$	$\left(2, \frac{1}{36}\right)$

Plot the points and connect them with a smooth curve.

The domain of f is all real numbers or, using interval notation, $(-\infty, \infty)$. The range of f is $\{y \mid y > 0\}$ or , using interval notation, $(0, \infty)$.

10. Rewrite $y = g(x) = \log_{\frac{3}{2}} x$ as $x = \left(\frac{3}{2}\right)^y$. Locate some points on the graph of $x = \left(\frac{3}{2}\right)^y$.

y	$x = \left(\frac{3}{2}\right)^y$	(x, y)
-2	$x = \left(\frac{3}{2}\right)^{-2} = \left(\frac{2}{3}\right)^2 = \frac{4}{9}$	$\left(\frac{4}{9}, -2\right)$
-1	$x = \left(\frac{3}{2}\right)^{-1} = \left(\frac{2}{3}\right)^1 = \frac{2}{3}$	$\left(\frac{2}{3}, -1\right)$
0	$x = \left(\frac{3}{2}\right)^0 = 1$	$(1, 0)$
1	$x = \left(\frac{3}{2}\right)^1 = \frac{3}{2}$	$\left(\frac{3}{2}, 1\right)$
2	$x = \left(\frac{3}{2}\right)^2 = \frac{9}{4}$	$\left(\frac{9}{4}, 2\right)$

Plot the points and connect them with a smooth curve.

The domain of g is $\{x \mid x > 0\}$ or, using interval notation, $(0, \infty)$. The range of g is all real numbers or , using interval notation, $(-\infty, \infty)$.

11. $3^{-x+2} = 27$
$$3^{-x+2} = 3^3$$
$$-x + 2 = 3$$
$$-x = 1$$
$$x = -1$$
The solution set is $\{-1\}$.

12. $e^x = e^{2x+5}$
$$x = 2x + 5$$
$$-x = 5$$
$$x = -5$$
The solution set is $\{-5\}$.

13. $\log_2(2x + 5) = 4$
$$2x + 5 = 2^4$$
$$2x + 5 = 16$$
$$2x = 11$$
$$x = \frac{11}{2}$$
The solution set is $\left\{\frac{11}{2}\right\}$.

14. $\ln x = 7$
$$x = e^7 \approx 1096.633$$
The solution set is $\{e^7\}$.

15. $L(90) = 150\left(1 - e^{-0.0052(90)}\right) \approx 56.06$.

According to the model, the student will learn approximately 56 terms after 90 minutes.

9.4 Preparing for Properties of Logarithms

1. $3.03468 \approx 3.035$

2. If $a \neq 0$, then $a^0 = 1$.

9.4 Exercises

1. $0; 1$

3. $\dfrac{\log 10}{\log 3} = \dfrac{\ln 10}{\ln 3}$

5. FALSE. In order to use the product rule in this manner, the bases would have to be the same.

7. Answers may vary. One possibility follows: The log of a product is equal to the sum of the logs.

9. Answers may vary. One example follows: Let $x = 2$ and $y = 1$. Then

$\log_2 (x + y) = \log_2 (2 + 1) = \log_2 3$, and

$\log_2 x + \log_2 y = \log_2 2 + \log_2 1 = 1 + 0 = 1$.

However, $\log_2 3 \neq 1$ because $2^1 \neq 3$. Thus,

$\log_2 (x + y) \neq \log_2 x + \log_2 y$.

11. $\log_2 2^3 = 3$

13. $\ln e^{-7} = -7$

15. $3^{\log_3 5} = 5$

17. $e^{\ln 2} = 2$

19. $\log 2 + \log 5 = \log (2 \cdot 5) = \log 10 = 1$

21. $\log_3 12 - \log_3 4 = \log_3 \left(\dfrac{12}{4} \right) = \log_3 3 = 1$

23. $10^{\log 8 - \log 2} = 10^{\log(8/2)} = 10^{\log 4} = 4$

25. $\ln 6 = \ln (2 \cdot 3) = \ln 2 + \ln 3 = a + b$

27. $\ln 9 = \ln 3^2 = 2 \ln 3 = 2b$

29. $\ln 12 = \ln (2^2 \cdot 3)$

$= \ln 2^2 + \ln 3$

$= 2 \ln 2 + \ln 3$

$= 2a + b$

31. $\ln \sqrt{2} = \ln 2^{1/2} = \dfrac{1}{2} \ln 2 = \dfrac{1}{2} a$

33. $\log (ab) = \log a + \log b$

35. $\log_5 x^4 = 4 \log_5 x$

37. $\log_2 (xy^2) = \log_2 x + \log_2 y^2 = \log_2 x + 2 \log_2 y$

39. $\log_5 (25x) = \log_5 25 + \log_5 x$

$= \log_5 5^2 + \log_5 x$

$= 2 + \log_5 x$

41. $\log_7 \left(\dfrac{49}{y} \right) = \log_7 49 - \log_7 y$

$= \log_7 7^2 - \log_7 y$

$= 2 - \log_7 y$

43. $\ln (e^2 x) = \ln e^2 + \ln x = 2 + \ln x$

45. $\log_3 (27 \sqrt{x}) = \log_3 27 + \log_3 \sqrt{x}$

$= \log_3 3^3 + \log_3 x^{1/2}$

$= 3 + \dfrac{1}{2} \log_3 x$

47. $\log_5 \left(x^2 \sqrt{x^2 + 1} \right) = \log_5 x^2 + \log_5 \sqrt{x^2 + 1}$

$= \log_5 x^2 + \log_5 (x^2 + 1)^{1/2}$

$= 2 \log_5 x + \dfrac{1}{2} \log_5 (x^2 + 1)$

49. $\log \left(\dfrac{x^4}{\sqrt[3]{x - 1}} \right) = \log x^4 - \log \sqrt[3]{x - 1}$

$= \log x^4 - \log (x - 1)^{1/3}$

$= 4 \log x - \dfrac{1}{3} \log (x - 1)$

51. $\log_7 \sqrt{\dfrac{x + 1}{x}} = \log_7 \left(\dfrac{x + 1}{x} \right)^{\frac{1}{2}}$

$= \dfrac{1}{2} \log_7 \left(\dfrac{x + 1}{x} \right)$

$= \dfrac{1}{2} \left[\log_7 (x + 1) - \log_7 x \right]$

$= \dfrac{1}{2} \log_7 (x + 1) - \dfrac{1}{2} \log_7 x$

53. $\log_2 \left[\dfrac{x(x - 1)^2}{\sqrt{x + 1}} \right]$

$= \log_2 \left[x(x - 1)^2 \right] - \log_2 \sqrt{x + 1}$

$= \log_2 x + \log_2 (x - 1)^2 - \log_2 \sqrt{x + 1}$

$= \log_2 x + \log_2 (x - 1)^2 - \log_2 (x + 1)^{1/2}$

$= \log_2 x + 2 \log_2 (x - 1) - \dfrac{1}{2} \log_2 (x + 1)$

55. $\log 25 + \log 4 = \log(25 \cdot 4)$
$$= \log 100$$
$$= \log 10^2$$
$$= 2$$

57. $\log x + \log 3 = \log(3x)$

59. $\log_3 36 - \log_3 4 = \log_3\left(\dfrac{36}{4}\right)$
$$= \log_3 9$$
$$= \log_3 3^2$$
$$= 2$$

61. $3\log_3 x = \log_3 x^3$

63. $\log_4(x+1) - \log_4 x = \log_4\left(\dfrac{x+1}{x}\right)$

65. $2\ln x + 3\ln y = \ln x^2 + \ln y^3 = \ln\left(x^2 y^3\right)$

67. $\dfrac{1}{2}\log_3 x + 3\log_3(x-1) = \log_3 x^{\frac{1}{2}} + \log_3(x-1)^3$
$$= \log_3 \sqrt{x} + \log_3(x-1)^3$$
$$= \log_3\left[\sqrt{x}(x-1)^3\right]$$

69. $\log x^5 - 3\log x = \log x^5 - \log x^3$
$$= \log\left(\dfrac{x^5}{x^3}\right)$$
$$= \log\left(x^2\right)$$

71. $\dfrac{1}{2}\left[3\log x + \log y\right] = \dfrac{1}{2}\left[\log x^3 + \log y\right]$
$$= \dfrac{1}{2}\log\left(x^3 y\right)$$
$$= \log\left(x^3 y\right)^{\frac{1}{2}}$$
$$= \log \sqrt{x^3 y}$$
$$= \log\left(x\sqrt{xy}\right)$$

73. $\log_8\left(x^2-1\right) - \log_8(x+1) = \log_8\left(\dfrac{x^2-1}{x+1}\right)$
$$= \log_8\left[\dfrac{(x-1)(x+1)}{x+1}\right]$$
$$= \log_8(x-1)$$

75. $18\log \sqrt{x} + 9\log \sqrt[3]{x} - \log 10$
$$= 18\log x^{\frac{1}{2}} + 9\log x^{\frac{1}{3}} - \log 10$$
$$= \log\left(x^{\frac{1}{2}}\right)^{18} + \log\left(x^{\frac{1}{3}}\right)^9 - \log 10$$
$$= \log x^9 + \log x^3 - \log 10$$
$$= \log\left(\dfrac{x^9 \cdot x^3}{10}\right)$$
$$= \log\left(\dfrac{x^{12}}{10}\right)$$

77. Using common logarithms:
$$\log_2 10 = \dfrac{\log 10}{\log 2} \approx 3.322$$

79. Using common logarithms:
$$\log_8 3 = \dfrac{\log 3}{\log 8} \approx 0.528$$

81. Using natural logarithms:
$$\log_{\frac{1}{3}} 19 = \dfrac{\ln 19}{\ln\left(\dfrac{1}{3}\right)} \approx -2.680$$

83. Using natural logarithms:
$$\log_{\sqrt{2}} 5 = \dfrac{\ln 5}{\ln \sqrt{2}} \approx 4.644$$

85. $\log_2 3 \cdot \log_3 4 \cdot \log_4 5 \cdot \log_5 6 \cdot \log_6 7 \cdot \log_7 8$
$$= \dfrac{\log 3}{\log 2} \cdot \dfrac{\log 4}{\log 3} \cdot \dfrac{\log 5}{\log 4} \cdot \dfrac{\log 6}{\log 5} \cdot \dfrac{\log 7}{\log 6} \cdot \dfrac{\log 8}{\log 7}$$
$$= \dfrac{\log 3}{\log 2} \cdot \dfrac{\log 4}{\log 3} \cdot \dfrac{\log 5}{\log 4} \cdot \dfrac{\log 6}{\log 5} \cdot \dfrac{\log 7}{\log 6} \cdot \dfrac{\log 8}{\log 7}$$
$$= \dfrac{\log 8}{\log 2}$$
$$= \log_2 8$$
$$= \log_2 2^3$$
$$= 3$$

87. $\log_2 3 \cdot \log_3 4 \cdot \ldots \cdot \log_n (n+1) \cdot \log_{n+1} 2$

$= \dfrac{\log 3}{\log 2} \cdot \dfrac{\log 4}{\log 3} \cdot \ldots \cdot \dfrac{\log(n+1)}{\log n} \cdot \dfrac{\log 2}{\log(n+1)}$

$= \dfrac{\cancel{\log 3}}{\cancel{\log 2}} \cdot \dfrac{\log 4}{\cancel{\log 3}} \cdot \ldots \cdot \dfrac{\cancel{\log(n+1)}}{\log n} \cdot \dfrac{\cancel{\log 2}}{\cancel{\log(n+1)}}$

$= 1$

Note: The expression "log 4" in the numerator of the second fraction will cancel with the expression "log 4" in the denominator of the third fraction (if the third fraction were written out). Similarly, the expression "log n" in the denominator of the next-to-the-last fraction will cancel with the expression "log n" in the numerator of the third-from-the-last fraction (if it were written out). Likewise, everything in between will cancel leaving an overall value of 1.

89. $\log_a \left(x + \sqrt{x^2 - 1} \right) + \log_a \left(x - \sqrt{x^2 - 1} \right)$

$= \log_a \left[\left(x + \sqrt{x^2 - 1} \right)\left(x - \sqrt{x^2 - 1} \right) \right]$

$= \log_a \left[x^2 - x\sqrt{x^2 - 1} + x\sqrt{x^2 - 1} - \left(x^2 - 1 \right) \right]$

$= \log_a \left(x^2 - x^2 + 1 \right)$

$= \log_a 1$

$= 0$

91. If $f(x) = \log_a x$, then

$f(AB) = \log_a (AB)$

$= \log_a A + \log_a B$

$= f(A) + f(B)$

93. $4x + 3 = 13$

$4x = 10$

$x = \dfrac{10}{4} = \dfrac{5}{2}$

The solution set is $\left\{ \dfrac{5}{2} \right\}$.

95. $x^2 + 4x + 2 = 0$

Because this equation does not easily factor, solve by using the quadratic formula. For this equation, $a = 1$, $b = 4$, and $c = 2$.

$x = \dfrac{-4 \pm \sqrt{4^2 - 4(1)(2)}}{2(1)}$

$= \dfrac{-4 \pm \sqrt{16 - 8}}{2}$

$= \dfrac{-4 \pm \sqrt{8}}{2}$

$= \dfrac{-4 \pm 2\sqrt{2}}{2}$

$= -2 \pm \sqrt{2}$

The solution set is $\left\{ -2 - \sqrt{2}, \ -2 + \sqrt{2} \right\}$.

97.

$\sqrt{x + 2} - 3 = 4$

$\sqrt{x + 2} = 7$

$\left(\sqrt{x + 2} \right)^2 = 7^2$

$x + 2 = 49$

$x = 47$

Check:

$\sqrt{47 + 2} - 3 \overset{?}{=} 4$

$\sqrt{49} - 3 \overset{?}{=} 4$

$7 - 3 \overset{?}{=} 4$

$4 = 4 \ \checkmark$

The solution set is $\{47\}$.

99. Since $\log_3 x = \dfrac{\log x}{\log 3}$, let $Y_1 = \dfrac{\log x}{\log 3}$.

The domain of $f(x) = \log_3 x$ is $\{x \mid x > 0\}$, or using interval notation, $(0, \infty)$; the range is all real numbers or, using interval notation, $(-\infty, \infty)$.

Note: The graph shown above is a bit misleading. The curve does not terminate at $x = 0$. Instead, the curve has an asymptote at $x = 0$. More specifically, as x approaches 0 (but stays larger than 0), f goes to $-\infty$.

101. Since $\log_{1/2} x = \dfrac{\log x}{\log\left(\frac{1}{2}\right)}$, let $Y_1 = \dfrac{\log x}{\log\left(\frac{1}{2}\right)}$.

```
WINDOW
Xmin=-10
Xmax=10
Xscl=1
Ymin=-10
Ymax=10
Yscl=1
Xres=1
```

The domain of $F(x) = \log_{1/2} x$ is $\{x \mid x > 0\}$, or

using interval notation, $(0, \infty)$; the range is all

real numbers or, using interval notation, $(-\infty, \infty)$.

Note: The graph shown above is a bit misleading. The curve does not terminate at $x = 0$. Instead, the curve has an asymptote at $x = 0$. More specifically, as x approaches 0 (but stays larger than 0), F goes to ∞.

9.5 Preparing for Exponential and Logarithmic Equations

1.
$$2x + 5 = 13$$
$$2x + 5 - 5 = 13 - 5$$
$$2x = 8$$
$$\frac{2x}{2} = \frac{8}{2}$$
$$x = 4$$

The solution set is $\{4\}$.

2.
$$x^2 - 4x = -3$$
$$x^2 - 4x + 3 = 0$$
$$(x-1)(x-3) = 0$$
$$x - 1 = 0 \quad \text{or} \quad x - 3 = 0$$
$$x = 1 \quad \text{or} \quad x = 3$$

The solution set is $\{1, 3\}$.

3.
$$3a^2 = a + 5$$
$$3a^2 - a - 5 = 0$$
For this equation, $a = 3$, $b = -1$, and $c = -5$.
$$a = \frac{-(-1) \pm \sqrt{(-1)^2 - 4(3)(-5)}}{2(3)}$$
$$= \frac{1 \pm \sqrt{1 + 60}}{6}$$
$$= \frac{1 \pm \sqrt{61}}{6}$$

The solution set is $\left\{\dfrac{1 - \sqrt{61}}{6}, \dfrac{1 + \sqrt{61}}{6}\right\}$.

4. $(x+3)^2 + 2(x+3) - 8 = 0$

Let $u = x + 3$.
$$u^2 + 2u - 8 = 0$$
$$(u+4)(u-2) = 0$$
$$u + 4 = 0 \quad \text{or} \quad u - 2 = 0$$
$$u = -4 \quad \text{or} \quad u = 2$$
$$x + 3 = -4 \quad \text{or} \quad x + 3 = 2$$
$$x = -7 \quad \text{or} \quad x = -1$$

Check:
$$x = -7: \ (-7+3)^2 + 2(-7+3) - 8 \overset{?}{=} 0$$
$$(-4)^2 + 2(-4) - 8 \overset{?}{=} 0$$
$$16 - 8 - 8 \overset{?}{=} 0$$
$$0 = 0 \ \checkmark$$

$$x = -1: \ (-1+3)^2 + 2(-1+3) - 8 \overset{?}{=} 0$$
$$(2)^2 + 2(2) - 8 \overset{?}{=} 0$$
$$4 + 4 - 8 \overset{?}{=} 0$$
$$0 = 0 \ \checkmark$$

Both check; the solution set is $\{-7, \ -1\}$.

9.5 Exercises

1. $M = N$

3. TRUE (so long as the logarithms have the same base)

5. Answers may vary. One possibility follows: Because we cannot write 7 so that it is 2 raised to an integer power, it is difficult to solve the equation $2^x = 7$ by using the fact that if $a^u = a^v$, then $u = v$.

Note: Technically, we <u>can</u> use the property $a^{\log_a x} = x$ along with the fact that if $a^u = a^v$, then $u = v$, to solve the equation:
$$2^x = 7$$
$$2^x = 2^{\log_2 7}$$
$$x = \log_2 7$$

7.
$$\log_2 x = \log_2 7$$
$$x = 7$$

The solution set is $\{7\}$.

9. $2\log_3 x = \log_3 81$

$\log_3 x^2 = \log_3 81$

$x^2 = 81$

$x = \pm\sqrt{81} = \pm 9$

The apparent solution $x = -9$ is extraneous because the argument of a logarithm must be positive. The solution set is $\{9\}$.

11. $\log_6(3x+1) = \log_6 10$

$3x+1 = 10$

$3x = 9$

$x = 3$

The solution set is $\{3\}$.

13. $\dfrac{1}{2}\ln x = 2\ln 3$

$\ln x = 4\ln 3$

$\ln x = \ln 3^4$

$\ln x = \ln 81$

$x = 81$

The solution set is $\{81\}$.

15. $\log_2(x+3) + \log_2 x = 2$

$\log_2[x(x+3)] = 2$

$\log_2(x^2 + 3x) = 2$

$x^2 + 3x = 2^2$

$x^2 + 3x = 4$

$x^2 + 3x - 4 = 0$

$(x+4)(x-1) = 0$

$x+4 = 0$ or $x-1 = 0$

$x = -4$ or $x = 1$

The apparent solution $x = -4$ is extraneous because it causes the argument of a logarithm to be negative. The solution set is $\{1\}$.

17. $\log_2(x-1) + \log_2(x+5) = 4$

$\log_2[(x-1)(x+5)] = 4$

$\log_2(x^2 + 4x - 5) = 4$

$x^2 + 4x - 5 = 2^4$

$x^2 + 4x - 5 = 16$

$x^2 + 4x - 21 = 0$

$(x+7)(x-3) = 0$

$x+7 = 0$ or $x-3 = 0$

$x = -7$ or $x = 3$

The apparent solution $x = -7$ is extraneous because it causes the argument of a logarithm to be negative. The solution set is $\{3\}$.

19. $\log(x+3) - \log x = 1$

$\log\left(\dfrac{x+3}{x}\right) = 1$

$\dfrac{x+3}{x} = 10^1$

$x\left(\dfrac{x+3}{x}\right) = x(10)$

$x+3 = 10x$

$3 = 9x$

$x = \dfrac{3}{9} = \dfrac{1}{3}$

The solution set is $\left\{\dfrac{1}{3}\right\}$.

21. $\log_4(x+5) - \log_4(x-1) = 2$

$\log_4\left(\dfrac{x+5}{x-1}\right) = 2$

$\dfrac{x+5}{x-1} = 4^2$

$(x-1)\left(\dfrac{x+5}{x-1}\right) = (x-1)16$

$x+5 = 16x - 16$

$-15x = -21$

$x = \dfrac{-21}{-15} = \dfrac{7}{5}$

The solution set is $\left\{\dfrac{7}{5}\right\}$.

23. $\log_4(x+3) + \log_4(x-6) = \log_4 3$

$\log_4[(x+3)(x-6)] = \log_4 3$

$\log_4(x^2 - 3x - 18) = \log_4 3$

$x^2 - 3x - 18 = 3$

$x^2 - 3x - 21 = 0$

This equation does not factor, so we solve by using the quadratic formula: $a = 1$, $b = -3$, and $c = -21$.

$x = \dfrac{-(-3)\pm\sqrt{(-3)^2 - 4(1)(-21)}}{2(1)} = \dfrac{3\pm\sqrt{9+84}}{2}$

$= \dfrac{3\pm\sqrt{93}}{2}$

$x \approx -3.322$ or $x \approx 6.322$

The apparent solution $x = \dfrac{3-\sqrt{93}}{2} \approx -3.322$ is extraneous because it causes the argument of a logarithm to be negative. The solution set is

$\left\{\dfrac{3+\sqrt{93}}{2}\right\} \approx \{6.322\}$.

25. $2^x = 10$

$\log 2^x = \log 10$

$x \log 2 = 1$

$x = \dfrac{1}{\log 2} \approx 3.322$

The solution set is $\left\{ \dfrac{1}{\log 2} \right\} \approx \{3.322\}$. If we had

taken the natural logarithm of both sides, the

solution set would be $\left\{ \dfrac{\ln 10}{\ln 2} \right\} \approx \{3.322\}$.

27. $5^x = 20$

$\log 5^x = \log 20$

$x \log 5 = \log 20$

$x = \dfrac{\log 20}{\log 5} \approx 1.861$

The solution set is $\left\{ \dfrac{\log 20}{\log 5} \right\} \approx \{1.861\}$. If we had

taken the natural logarithm of both sides, the

solution set would be $\left\{ \dfrac{\ln 20}{\ln 5} \right\} \approx \{1.861\}$.

29. $\left(\dfrac{1}{2} \right)^x = 7$

$\log \left(\dfrac{1}{2} \right)^x = \log 7$

$x \log \left(\dfrac{1}{2} \right) = \log 7$

$x = \dfrac{\log 7}{\log \left(\dfrac{1}{2} \right)} \approx -2.807$

The solution set is $\left\{ \dfrac{\log 7}{\log \left(\frac{1}{2} \right)} \right\} \approx \{-2.807\}$. If we

had taken the natural logarithm of both sides, the

solution set would be $\left\{ \dfrac{\ln 7}{\ln \left(\frac{1}{2} \right)} \right\} \approx \{-2.807\}$.

31. $e^x = 5$

$\ln e^x = \ln 5$

$x = \ln 5 \approx 1.609$

The solution set is $\{\ln 5\} \approx \{1.609\}$.

33. $10^x = 5$

$\log 10^x = \log 5$

$x = \log 5 \approx 0.699$

The solution set is $\{\log 5\} \approx \{0.699\}$.

35. $3^{2x} = 13$

$\log 3^{2x} = \log 13$

$2x \log 3 = \log 13$

$x = \dfrac{\log 13}{2 \log 3} \approx 1.167$

The solution set is $\left\{ \dfrac{\log 13}{2 \log 3} \right\} \approx \{1.167\}$. If we

had taken the natural logarithm of both sides, the

solution set would be $\left\{ \dfrac{\ln 13}{2 \ln 3} \right\} \approx \{1.167\}$.

37. $\left(\dfrac{1}{2} \right)^{4x} = 3$

$\log \left(\dfrac{1}{2} \right)^{4x} = \log 3$

$4x \log \left(\dfrac{1}{2} \right) = \log 3$

$x = \dfrac{\log 3}{4 \log \left(\dfrac{1}{2} \right)} \approx -0.396$

The solution set is $\left\{ \dfrac{\log 3}{4 \log \left(\frac{1}{2} \right)} \right\} \approx \{-0.396\}$. If

we had taken the natural logarithm of both sides,

the solution set would be $\left\{ \dfrac{\ln 3}{4 \ln \left(\frac{1}{2} \right)} \right\} \approx \{-0.396\}$.

39. $4 \cdot 2^x + 3 = 8$

$4 \cdot 2^x = 5$

$2^x = \dfrac{5}{4}$

$\log 2^x = \log \left(\dfrac{5}{4} \right)$

$x \log 2 = \log \left(\dfrac{5}{4} \right)$

$x = \dfrac{\log \left(\frac{5}{4} \right)}{\log 2} \approx 0.322$

The solution set is $\left\{ \dfrac{\log \left(\frac{5}{4} \right)}{\log 2} \right\} \approx \{0.322\}$. If we

had taken the natural logarithm of both sides, the

solution set would be $\left\{ \dfrac{\ln \left(\frac{5}{4} \right)}{\ln 2} \right\} \approx \{0.322\}$.

41. $-3e^x = -18$
$e^x = 6$
$\ln e^x = \ln 6$
$x = \ln 6 \approx 1.792$
The solution set is $\{\ln 6\} \approx \{1.792\}$.

43.
$$0.2^{x+1} = 3^x$$
$$\log 0.2^{x+1} = \log 3^x$$
$$(x+1)\log 0.2 = x\log 3$$
$$x\log 0.2 + \log 0.2 = x\log 3$$
$$\log 0.2 = x\log 3 - x\log 0.2$$
$$\log 0.2 = x(\log 3 - \log 0.2)$$
$$\frac{\log 0.2}{\log 3 - \log 0.2} = x$$
$$-0.594 \approx x$$
The solution set is $\left\{\dfrac{\log 0.2}{\log 3 - \log 0.2}\right\} \approx \{-0.594\}$.
If we had taken the natural logarithm of both sides, the solution set would be $\left\{\dfrac{\ln 0.2}{\ln 3 - \ln 0.2}\right\} \approx \{-0.594\}$.

45. $\log_4 x + \log_4 (x-6) = 2$
$$\log_4 [x(x-6)] = 2$$
$$\log_4 (x^2 - 6x) = 2$$
$$x^2 - 6x = 4^2$$
$$x^2 - 6x = 16$$
$$x^2 - 6x - 16 = 0$$
$$(x-8)(x+2) = 0$$
$$x - 8 = 0 \quad \text{or} \quad x + 2 = 0$$
$$x = 8 \quad \text{or} \quad x = -2$$
The apparent solution $x = -2$ is extraneous because it causes the argument of a logarithm to be negative. The solution set is $\{8\}$.

47. $5^{3x} = 7$
$$\log 5^{3x} = \log 7$$
$$3x\log 5 = \log 7$$
$$x = \frac{\log 7}{3\log 5} \approx 0.403$$
The solution set is $\left\{\dfrac{\log 7}{3\log 5}\right\} \approx \{0.403\}$. If we had taken the natural logarithm of both sides, the solution set would be $\left\{\dfrac{\ln 7}{3\ln 5}\right\} \approx \{0.403\}$.

49. $3\log_2 x = \log_2 8$
$$\log_2 x^3 = \log_2 8$$
$$x^3 = 8$$
$$x = \sqrt[3]{8}$$
$$x = 2$$
The solution set is $\{2\}$.

51. $\dfrac{1}{3}e^x = 5$
$$e^x = 15$$
$$\ln e^x = \ln 15$$
$$x = \ln 15 \approx 2.708$$
The solution set is $\{\ln 15\} \approx \{2.708\}$.

53.
$$\left(\frac{1}{4}\right)^{x+1} = 8^x$$
$$\left(\frac{1}{2^2}\right)^{x+1} = \left(2^3\right)^x$$
$$\left(2^{-2}\right)^{x+1} = \left(2^3\right)^x$$
$$2^{-2(x+1)} = 2^{3x}$$
$$-2(x+1) = 3x$$
$$-2x - 2 = 3x$$
$$-2 = 5x$$
$$-\frac{2}{5} = x$$
The solution set is $\left\{-\dfrac{2}{5}\right\}$.

55. $\log_3 x = \log_3 16$
$$x = 16$$
The solution set is $\{16\}$.

57. $\log_2 (x+4) + \log_2 (x-1) = \log_2 6$
$$\log_2 [(x+4)(x-1)] = \log_2 6$$
$$\log_2 (x^2 + 3x - 4) = \log_2 6$$
$$x^2 + 3x - 4 = 6$$
$$x^2 + 3x - 10 = 0$$
$$(x+5)(x-2) = 0$$
$$x + 5 = 0 \quad \text{or} \quad x - 2 = 0$$
$$x = -5 \quad \text{or} \quad x = 2$$
The apparent solution $x = -5$ is extraneous because it causes the argument of a logarithm to be negative. The solution set is $\{2\}$.

59. a. We need to determine the year when $P = 351$ million. So we solve the equation

$$351 = 296(1.011)^{t-2005}$$

$$\frac{351}{296} = (1.011)^{t-2005}$$

$$\log\frac{351}{296} = \log(1.011)^{t-2005}$$

$$\log\frac{351}{296} = (t-2005)\log(1.011)$$

$$\frac{\log\frac{351}{296}}{\log 1.011} = t - 2005$$

$$\frac{\log\frac{351}{296}}{\log 1.011} + 2005 = t$$

$$2020.578 \approx t$$

Thus, according to the model, the population of the United States will reach 351 million in about the year 2021.

b. We need to determine the year when $P = 482$ million. So we solve the equation

$$482 = 296(1.011)^{t-2005}$$

$$\frac{482}{296} = (1.011)^{t-2005}$$

$$\log\frac{482}{296} = \log(1.011)^{t-2005}$$

$$\log\frac{482}{296} = (t-2005)\log(1.011)$$

$$\frac{\log\frac{482}{296}}{\log 1.011} = t - 2005$$

$$\frac{\log\frac{482}{296}}{\log 1.011} + 2005 = t$$

$$2049.569 \approx t$$

Thus, according to the model, the population of the United States will reach 482 million in about the year 2050.

61. We first write the model with the parameters $P = 5000$, $r = 0.06$, and $n = 12$ to obtain

$$A = 5000\left(1 + \frac{0.06}{12}\right)^{12t} \text{ or } A = 5000(1.005)^{12t}.$$

a. We need to determine the time until $A = \$7000$, so we solve the equation

$$7000 = 5000(1.005)^{12t}$$

$$1.4 = (1.005)^{12t}$$

$$\log 1.4 = \log(1.005)^{12t}$$

$$\log 1.4 = 12t\log 1.005$$

$$\frac{\log 1.4}{12\log 1.005} = t$$

$$5.622 \approx t$$

Thus, after approximately 5.6 years (5 years, 7 months), the account will be worth $7000.

b. We need to determine the time until $A = \$10,000$, so we solve the equation

$$10,000 = 5000(1.005)^{12t}$$

$$2 = (1.005)^{12t}$$

$$\log 2 = \log(1.005)^{12t}$$

$$\log 2 = 12t\log 1.005$$

$$\frac{\log 2}{12\log 1.005} = t$$

So, $t = \dfrac{\log 2}{12\log 1.005} \approx 11.581$. After about 11.6 years (11 years, 7 months), the account will be worth $7000.

63. a. We need to determine the time until $V = \$10,000$. So we solve the equation

$$10,000 = 14,512(0.82)^t$$

$$\frac{10,000}{14,512} = (0.82)^t$$

$$\log\frac{10,000}{14,512} = \log(0.82)^t$$

$$\log\frac{10,000}{14,512} = t\log 0.82$$

$$\frac{\log\frac{10,000}{14,512}}{\log 0.82} = t$$

$$1.876 \approx t$$

According to the model, the car will be worth $10,000 after about 1.876 years.

b. We need to determine the time until $V = \$5000$. So we solve the equation

$$5000 = 14{,}512(0.82)^t$$

$$\frac{5000}{14{,}512} = (0.82)^t$$

$$\log\frac{5000}{14{,}512} = \log(0.82)^t$$

$$\log\frac{5000}{14{,}512} = t\log 0.82$$

$$\frac{\log\dfrac{5000}{14{,}512}}{\log 0.82} = t$$

$$5.369 \approx t$$

According to the model, the car will be worth $5000 in about 5.369 years.

c. We need to determine the time until $V = \$1000$. So we solve the equation

$$1000 = 14{,}512(0.82)^t$$

$$\frac{1000}{14{,}512} = (0.82)^t$$

$$\log\frac{1000}{14{,}512} = \log(0.82)^t$$

$$\log\frac{1000}{14{,}512} = t\log 0.82$$

$$\frac{\log\dfrac{1000}{14{,}512}}{\log 0.82} = t$$

$$13.479 \approx t$$

According to the model, the car will be worth $1000 in about 13.479 years.

65. a. We need to determine the time until $A = 90$ grams. So we solve the equation

$$90 = 100\left(\frac{1}{2}\right)^{t/13.81}$$

$$0.9 = \left(\frac{1}{2}\right)^{t/13.81}$$

$$\log 0.9 = \log\left(\frac{1}{2}\right)^{t/13.81}$$

$$\log 0.9 = \frac{t}{13.81}\log\left(\frac{1}{2}\right)$$

$$\frac{13.81 \cdot \log 0.9}{\log(1/2)} = t$$

$$2.099 \approx t$$

Thus, 90 grams of beryllium-11 will be left after approximately 2.099 seconds.

b. We need to determine the time until $A = 25$ grams. So we solve the equation

$$25 = 100\left(\frac{1}{2}\right)^{t/13.81}$$

$$0.25 = \left(\frac{1}{2}\right)^{t/13.81}$$

$$\log 0.25 = \log\left(\frac{1}{2}\right)^{t/13.81}$$

$$\log 0.25 = \frac{t}{13.81}\log\left(\frac{1}{2}\right)$$

$$\frac{13.81 \cdot \log 0.25}{\log(1/2)} = t$$

$$27.62 = t$$

Thus, 25 grams of beryllium-11 will be left after 27.62 seconds.

c. We need to determine the time until $A = 10$ grams. So we solve the equation

$$10 = 100\left(\frac{1}{2}\right)^{t/13.81}$$

$$0.1 = \left(\frac{1}{2}\right)^{t/13.81}$$

$$\log 0.1 = \log\left(\frac{1}{2}\right)^{t/13.81}$$

$$\log 0.1 = \frac{t}{13.81}\log\left(\frac{1}{2}\right)$$

$$\frac{13.81 \cdot \log 0.1}{\log(1/2)} = t$$

$$45.876 \approx t$$

Thus, 10 grams of beryllium-11 will be left after approximately 45.876 seconds.

67. a. We need to determine the time until $u = 300°F$. So we solve the equation

$$300 = 70 + 330e^{-0.072t}$$

$$230 = 330e^{-0.072t}$$

$$\frac{230}{330} = e^{-0.072t}$$

$$\ln\left(\frac{230}{330}\right) = \ln e^{-0.072t}$$

$$\ln\left(\frac{230}{330}\right) = -0.072t$$

$$\frac{\ln\left(\dfrac{230}{330}\right)}{-0.072} = t$$

$$5.014 \approx t$$

According to the model, the temperature of the pizza will be $300°F$ after about 5 minutes.

b. We need to determine the time until $u = 220°F$. So we solve the equation

$$220 = 70 + 330e^{-0.072t}$$

$$150 = 330e^{-0.072t}$$

$$\frac{150}{330} = e^{-0.072t}$$

$$\ln\left(\frac{150}{330}\right) = \ln e^{-0.072t}$$

$$\ln\left(\frac{150}{330}\right) = -0.072t$$

$$\frac{\ln\left(\frac{150}{330}\right)}{-0.072} = t$$

$$10.951 \approx t$$

According to the model, the temperature of the pizza will be $220°F$ after about 11 minutes.

69. a. We need to determine the time at which $L = 50$ words. So we solve the equation

$$50 = 200\left(1 - e^{-0.0035t}\right)$$

$$0.25 = 1 - e^{-0.0035t}$$

$$e^{-0.0035t} = 0.75$$

$$\ln e^{-0.0035t} = \ln 0.75$$

$$-0.0035t = \ln 0.75$$

$$t = \frac{\ln 0.75}{-0.0035}$$

$$t \approx 82.195$$

According to the model, the student must study about 82 minutes in order to learn 50 words.

b. We need to determine the time at which $L = 150$ words. So we solve the equation

$$150 = 200\left(1 - e^{-0.0035t}\right)$$

$$0.75 = 1 - e^{-0.0035t}$$

$$e^{-0.0035t} = 0.25$$

$$\ln e^{-0.0035t} = \ln 0.25$$

$$-0.0035t = \ln 0.25$$

$$t = \frac{\ln 0.25}{-0.0035}$$

$$t \approx 396.084$$

According to the model, the student must study about 396 minutes (or 6.6 hours) in order to learn 150 words.

71. a. $t = \dfrac{72}{8} = 9$

According to the Rule of 72, an investment earning 8% annual interest will take about 9 years to double.

b. Let $A = 2P$ in the formula $A = P\left(1 + \dfrac{r}{n}\right)^{nt}$:

$$2P = P\left(1 + \frac{r}{n}\right)^{nt}$$

$$2 = \left(1 + \frac{r}{n}\right)^{nt}$$

$$\log 2 = \log\left(1 + \frac{r}{n}\right)^{nt}$$

$$\log 2 = nt \log\left(1 + \frac{r}{n}\right)$$

$$\frac{\log 2}{n \log\left(1 + \frac{r}{n}\right)} = t$$

c. Letting $r = 0.08$ and $n = 12$, we obtain

$$t = \frac{\log 2}{12 \cdot \log\left(1 + \frac{0.08}{12}\right)} \approx 8.693.$$

According to our formula from part (b), an investment earning 8% annual interest will take about 8.693 years to double, which is about the same as the result from the Rule of 72.

73. Since the bacteria doubled every minute, the container would have been half full one minute before it was completely full. Now since it was full after 30 minutes, it would have been half full after $30 - 1 = 29$ minutes.

75. $f(x) = -2x + 7$

a. $f(3) = -2(3) + 7 = -6 + 7 = 1$

b. $f(-2) = -2(-2) + 7 = 4 + 7 = 11$

c. $f(0) = -2(0) + 7 = 0 + 7 = 7$

77. $f(x) = \dfrac{x}{x - 5}$

a. $f(3) = \dfrac{3}{3 - 5} = \dfrac{3}{-2} = -\dfrac{3}{2}$

b. $f(-2) = \dfrac{-2}{-2 - 5} = \dfrac{-2}{-7} = \dfrac{2}{7}$

c. $f(0) = \dfrac{0}{0 - 5} = \dfrac{0}{-5} = 0$

79. $f(x) = 2^x$

   a. $f(3) = 2^3 = 8$

   b. $f(-2) = 2^{-2} = \dfrac{1}{2^2} = \dfrac{1}{4}$

   c. $f(0) = 2^0 = 1$

81. Let $Y_1 = e^x$ and $Y_2 = -2x + 5$.

The solution set is approximately $\{1.06\}$.

83. Let $Y_1 = e^x$ and $Y_2 = x^2$.

The solution set is approximately $\{-0.70\}$.

85. Let $Y_1 = e^x - \ln x$ and $Y_2 = 4$.

The solution set is approximately $\{0.05, 1.48\}$.

87. Let $Y_1 = \ln x$ and $Y_2 = x^2 - 1$.

The solution set is approximately $\{0.45, 1\}$.

Chapter 9 Review

1. $f(x) = 3x + 5$; $g(x) = 2x - 1$

   a. $g(5) = 2(5) - 1 = 9$
      $f(9) = 3(9) + 5 = 32$
      $(f \circ g)(5) = f(g(5)) = f(9) = 32$

   b. $f(-3) = 3(-3) + 5 = -4$
      $g(-4) = 2(-4) - 1 = -9$
      $(g \circ f)(-3) = g(f(-3)) = g(-4) = -9$

   c. $f(-2) = 3(-2) + 5 = -1$
      $f(-1) = 3(-1) + 5 = 2$
      $(f \circ f)(-2) = f(f(-2)) = f(-1) = 2$

   d. $g(4) = 2(4) - 1 = 7$
      $g(7) = 2(7) - 1 = 13$
      $(g \circ g)(4) = g(g(4)) = g(7) = 13$

2. $f(x) = x - 3$; $g(x) = 5x + 2$

   a. $g(5) = 5(5) + 2 = 27$
      $f(27) = 27 - 3 = 24$
      $(f \circ g)(5) = f(g(5)) = f(27) = 24$

   b. $f(-3) = -3 - 3 = -6$
      $g(-6) = 5(-6) + 2 = -28$
      $(g \circ f)(-3) = g(f(-3)) = g(-6) = -28$

   c. $f(-2) = -2 - 3 = -5$
      $f(-5) = -5 - 3 = -8$
      $(f \circ f)(-2) = f(f(-2)) = f(-5) = -8$

   d. $g(4) = 5(4) + 2 = 22$
      $g(22) = 5(22) + 2 = 112$
      $(g \circ g)(4) = g(g(4)) = g(22) = 112$

3. $f(x) = 2x^2 + 1$; $g(x) = x + 5$

   a. $g(5) = 5 + 5 = 10$
      $f(10) = 2(10)^2 + 1 = 201$
      $(f \circ g)(5) = f(g(5)) = f(10) = 201$

b. $f(-3) = 2(-3)^2 + 1 = 19$

$g(19) = 19 + 5 = 24$

$(g \circ f)(-3) = g(f(-3)) = g(19) = 24$

c. $f(-2) = 2(-2)^2 + 1 = 9$

$f(9) = 2(9)^2 + 1 = 163$

$(f \circ f)(-2) = f(f(-2)) = f(9) = 163$

d. $g(4) = 4 + 5 = 9$

$g(9) = 9 + 5 = 14$

$(g \circ g)(4) = g(g(4)) = g(9) = 14$

4. $f(x) = x - 3$; $g(x) = x^2 + 1$

a. $g(5) = (5)^2 + 1 = 26$

$f(26) = 26 - 3 = 23$

$(f \circ g)(5) = f(g(5)) = f(26) = 23$

b. $f(-3) = -3 - 3 = -6$

$g(-6) = (-6)^2 + 1 = 37$

$(g \circ f)(-3) = g(f(-3)) = g(-6) = 37$

c. $f(-2) = -2 - 3 = -5$

$f(-5) = -5 - 3 = -8$

$(f \circ f)(-2) = f(f(-2)) = f(-5) = -8$

d. $g(4) = (4)^2 + 1 = 17$

$g(17) = (17)^2 + 1 = 290$

$(g \circ g)(4) = g(g(4)) = g(17) = 290$

5. $f(x) = x + 1$; $g(x) = 5x$

a. $(f \circ g)(x) = f(g(x)) = f(5x) = 5x + 1$

b. $(g \circ f)(x) = g(f(x))$

$= g(x + 1)$

$= 5(x + 1)$

$= 5x + 5$

c. $(f \circ f)(x) = f(f(x))$

$= f(x + 1)$

$= (x + 1) + 1$

$= x + 2$

d. $(g \circ g)(x) = g(g(x)) = g(5x) = 5(5x) = 25x$

6. $f(x) = 2x - 3$; $g(x) = x + 6$

a. $(f \circ g)(x) = f(g(x))$

$= f(x + 6)$

$= 2(x + 6) - 3$

$= 2x + 12 - 3$

$= 2x + 9$

b. $(g \circ f)(x) = g(f(x))$

$= g(2x - 3)$

$= (2x - 3) + 6$

$= 2x + 3$

c. $(f \circ f)(x) = f(f(x))$

$= f(2x - 3)$

$= 2(2x - 3) - 3$

$= 4x - 6 - 3$

$= 4x - 9$

d. $(g \circ g)(x) = g(g(x))$

$= g(x + 6)$

$= (x + 6) + 6$

$= x + 12$

7. $f(x) = x^2 + 1$; $g(x) = 2x + 1$

a. $(f \circ g)(x) = f(g(x))$

$= f(2x + 1)$

$= (2x + 1)^2 + 1$

$= 4x^2 + 4x + 1 + 1$

$= 4x^2 + 4x + 2$

b. $(g \circ f)(x) = g(f(x))$

$= g(x^2 + 1)$

$= 2(x^2 + 1) + 1$

$= 2x^2 + 2 + 1$

$= 2x^2 + 3$

c. $(f \circ f)(x) = f(f(x))$

$= f(x^2 + 1)$

$= (x^2 + 1)^2 + 1$

$= x^4 + 2x^2 + 1 + 1$

$= x^4 + 2x^2 + 2$

d. $(g \circ g)(x) = g(g(x))$

$$= g(2x+1)$$
$$= 2(2x+1)+1$$
$$= 4x+2+1$$
$$= 4x+3$$

8. $f(x) = \dfrac{2}{x+1}; \ g(x) = \dfrac{1}{x}$

a. $(f \circ g)(x) = f(g(x))$

$$= f\left(\dfrac{1}{x}\right)$$
$$= \dfrac{2}{\dfrac{1}{x}+1}$$
$$= \dfrac{2}{\dfrac{1+x}{x}}$$
$$= \dfrac{2x}{x+1} \quad \text{where } x \neq -1, 0 \, .$$

b. $(g \circ f)(x) = g(f(x))$

$$= g\left(\dfrac{2}{x+1}\right)$$
$$= \dfrac{1}{\dfrac{2}{x+1}}$$
$$= 1 \cdot \dfrac{x+1}{2}$$
$$= \dfrac{x+1}{2} \quad \text{where } x \neq -1 \, .$$

c. $(f \circ f)(x) = f(f(x))$

$$= f\left(\dfrac{2}{x+1}\right)$$
$$= \dfrac{2}{\dfrac{2}{x+1}+1}$$
$$= \dfrac{2}{\dfrac{2+x+1}{x+1}}$$
$$= 2 \cdot \dfrac{x+1}{x+3}$$
$$= \dfrac{2(x+1)}{x+3} \quad \text{where } x \neq -1, -3 \, .$$

d. $(g \circ g)(x) = g(g(x))$

$$= g\left(\dfrac{1}{x}\right)$$
$$= \dfrac{1}{\dfrac{1}{x}}$$
$$= 1 \cdot \dfrac{x}{1}$$
$$= x \quad \text{where } x \neq 0 \, .$$

9. The function is not one-to-one. There is an element in the range (8) that corresponds to more than one element in the domain (-5 and -1).

10. The function is one-to-one. Each element in the range corresponds to exactly one element in the domain.

11. The graph passes the horizontal line test, so the graph is that of a one-to-one function.

12. The graph fails the horizontal line test. Therefore, the function is not one-to-one.

13. Inverse:

Height (inches)	Age
69 ⟶	24
71 ⟶	59
72 ⟶	29
73 ⟶	81
74 ⟶	37

14. Inverse:

Quantity Demanded	Price ($)
112 ⟶	300
129 ⟶	200
144 ⟶	170
161 ⟶	150
176 ⟶	130

15. To obtain the inverse, we switch the x- and y-coordinates.

Inverse: $\{(3,-5),(1,-3),(-3,1),(9,2)\}$

16. To obtain the inverse, we switch the x- and y-coordinates.

Inverse: $\{(1,-20),(4,-15),(3,5),(2,25)\}$

17. To plot the inverse, switch the x- and y-coordinates in each point and connect the corresponding points. The graphs of the function (shaded) and the line $y = x$ (dashed) are included for reference.

18. To plot the inverse, switch the *x*- and *y*-coordinates in each point and connect the corresponding points. The graphs of the function (shaded) and the line $y = x$ (dashed) are included for reference.

19. $f(x) = 5x$

$$y = 5x$$

$$x = 5y$$

$$\frac{x}{5} = y$$

$$f^{-1}(x) = \frac{x}{5}$$

Check: $f\left(f^{-1}(x)\right) = 5\left(\dfrac{x}{5}\right) = x$

$$f^{-1}\left(f(x)\right) = \frac{5x}{5} = x$$

20. $H(x) = 2x + 7$

$$y = 2x + 7$$

$$x = 2y + 7$$

$$x - 7 = 2y$$

$$\frac{x - 7}{2} = y$$

$$H^{-1}(x) = \frac{x - 7}{2}$$

Check:

$$H\left(H^{-1}(x)\right) = 2\left(\frac{x - 7}{2}\right) + 7 = x - 7 + 7 = x$$

$$H^{-1}\left(H(x)\right) = \frac{(2x + 7) - 7}{2} = \frac{2x}{2} = x$$

21. $P(x) = \dfrac{4}{x + 2}$

$$y = \frac{4}{x + 2}$$

$$x = \frac{4}{y + 2}$$

$$x(y + 2) = 4$$

$$y + 2 = \frac{4}{x}$$

$$y = \frac{4}{x} - 2$$

$$P^{-1}(x) = \frac{4}{x} - 2$$

Check:

$$P\left(P^{-1}(x)\right) = \frac{4}{\left(\dfrac{4}{x} - 2\right) + 2} = \frac{4}{\dfrac{4}{x}} = 4 \cdot \frac{x}{4} = x$$

$$P^{-1}\left(P(x)\right) = \frac{4}{\dfrac{4}{x + 2}} - 2$$

$$= 4 \cdot \frac{x + 2}{4} - 2 = (x + 2) - 2 = x$$

22. $g(x) = 2x^3 - 1$

$$y = 2x^3 - 1$$

$$x = 2y^3 - 1$$

$$x + 1 = 2y^3$$

$$\frac{x + 1}{2} = y^3$$

$$\sqrt[3]{\frac{x + 1}{2}} = y$$

$$g^{-1}(x) = \sqrt[3]{\frac{x + 1}{2}}$$

Check:

$$g\left(g^{-1}(x)\right) = 2\left(\sqrt[3]{\frac{x + 1}{2}}\right)^3 - 1$$

$$= 2\left(\frac{x + 1}{2}\right) - 1 = (x + 1) - 1 = x$$

$$g^{-1}\left(g(x)\right) = \sqrt[3]{\frac{(2x^3 - 1) + 1}{2}} = \sqrt[3]{\frac{2x^3}{2}} = \sqrt[3]{x^3} = x$$

23. **a.** $7^{1.7} \approx 27.332$

   b. $7^{1.73} \approx 28.975$

   c. $7^{1.732} \approx 29.088$

   d. $7^{1.7321} \approx 29.093$

   e. $7^{\sqrt{3}} \approx 29.091$

24. **a.** $10^{3.1} \approx 1258.925$

   b. $10^{3.14} \approx 1380.384$

   c. $10^{3.142} \approx 1386.756$

   d. $10^{3.1416} \approx 1385.479$

   e. $10^{\pi} \approx 1385.456$

25. **a.** $e^{0.5} \approx 1.649$

   b. $e^{-1} \approx 0.368$

   c. $e^{1.5} \approx 4.482$

   d. $e^{-0.8} \approx 0.449$

   e. $e^{\sqrt{\pi}} \approx 5.885$

26. Locate some points on the graph of $f(x) = 9^x$.

x	$f(x) = 9^x$	$(x, f(x))$
-2	$f(-2) = 9^{-2} = \dfrac{1}{9^2} = \dfrac{1}{81}$	$\left(-2, \dfrac{1}{81}\right)$
-1	$f(-1) = 9^{-1} = \dfrac{1}{9^1} = \dfrac{1}{9}$	$\left(-1, \dfrac{1}{9}\right)$
0	$f(0) = 9^0 = 1$	$(0, 1)$
1	$f(1) = 9^1 = 9$	$(1, 9)$

Plot the points and connect them with a smooth curve.

The domain of f is all real numbers or, using interval notation, $(-\infty, \infty)$. The range of f is $\{y \mid y > 0\}$ or , using interval notation, $(0, \infty)$.

27. Locate some points on the graph of $g(x) = \left(\dfrac{1}{9}\right)^x$.

x	$g(x) = \left(\dfrac{1}{9}\right)^x$	$(x, g(x))$
-1	$g(-1) = \left(\dfrac{1}{9}\right)^{-1} = 9^1 = 9$	$(-1, 9)$
0	$g(0) = \left(\dfrac{1}{9}\right)^0 = 1$	$(0, 1)$
1	$g(1) = \left(\dfrac{1}{9}\right)^1 = \dfrac{1}{9}$	$\left(1, \dfrac{1}{9}\right)$
2	$g(1) = \left(\dfrac{1}{9}\right)^2 = \dfrac{1}{81}$	$\left(2, \dfrac{1}{81}\right)$

Plot the points and connect them with a smooth curve.

The domain of g is all real numbers or, using interval notation, $(-\infty, \infty)$. The range of g is $\{y \mid y > 0\}$ or , using interval notation, $(0, \infty)$.

28. Locate some points on the graph of $H(x) = 4^{x-2}$.

x	$H(x) = 4^{x-2}$	$(x, H(x))$
0	$H(0) = 4^{0-2} = 4^{-2} = \dfrac{1}{4^2} = \dfrac{1}{16}$	$\left(0, \dfrac{1}{16}\right)$
1	$H(1) = 4^{1-2} = 4^{-1} = \dfrac{1}{4^1} = \dfrac{1}{4}$	$\left(1, \dfrac{1}{4}\right)$
2	$H(2) = 4^{2-2} = 4^0 = 1$	$(2, 1)$
3	$H(3) = 4^{3-2} = 4^1 = 4$	$(3, 4)$

Plot the points and connect them with a smooth curve.

The domain of H is all real numbers or, using interval notation, $(-\infty, \infty)$. The range of H is $\{y \mid y > 0\}$ or , using interval notation, $(0, \infty)$.

29. Locate some points on the graph of $h(x) = 4^x - 2$.

x	$h(x) = 4^x - 2$	$(x, h(x))$
-2	$h(-2) = 4^{-2} - 2 = \dfrac{1}{16} - 2 = -\dfrac{31}{16}$	$\left(-2, -\dfrac{31}{16}\right)$
-1	$h(-1) = 4^{-1} - 2 = \dfrac{1}{4} - 2 = -\dfrac{7}{4}$	$\left(-1, -\dfrac{7}{4}\right)$
0	$h(0) = 4^0 - 2 = 1 - 2 = -1$	$(0, -1)$
1	$h(1) = 4^1 - 2 = 4 - 2 = 2$	$(1, 2)$

Plot the points and connect them with a smooth curve.

The domain of h is all real numbers or, using interval notation, $(-\infty, \infty)$. The range of h is $\{y \mid y > -2\}$ or , using interval notation, $(-2, \infty)$.

30. The number e is defined as the number that the expression $\left(1 + \dfrac{1}{n}\right)^n$ approaches as n becomes unbounded in the positive direction.

31. $2^x = 64$
$2^x = 2^6$
$x = 6$
The solution set is $\{6\}$.

32. $25^{x-2} = 125$
$\left(5^2\right)^{x-2} = 5^3$
$5^{2(x-2)} = 5^3$
$5^{2x-4} = 5^3$
$2x - 4 = 3$
$2x = 7$
$x = \dfrac{7}{2}$
The solution set is $\left\{\dfrac{7}{2}\right\}$.

33. $27^x \cdot 3^{x^2} = 9^2$
$\left(3^3\right)^x \cdot 3^{x^2} = \left(3^2\right)^2$
$3^{3x} \cdot 3^{x^2} = 3^4$
$3^{x^2 + 3x} = 3^4$
$x^2 + 3x = 4$
$x^2 + 3x - 4 = 0$
$(x + 4)(x - 1) = 0$
$x + 4 = 0 \quad$ or $\quad x - 1 = 0$
$x = -4 \quad$ or $\qquad x = 1$
The solution set is $\{-4, 1\}$.

34. $\left(\dfrac{1}{4}\right)^x = 16$
$\left(4^{-1}\right)^x = 4^2$
$4^{-x} = 4^2$
$-x = 2$
$x = -2$
The solution set is $\{-2\}$.

35. $\left(e^2\right)^{x-1} = e^x \cdot e^7$
$e^{2(x-1)} = e^{x+7}$
$e^{2x-2} = e^{x+7}$
$2x - 2 = x + 7$
$x - 2 = 7$
$x = 9$
The solution set is $\{9\}$.

36. $\left(2^x\right)^x = 512$
$2^{x^2} = 2^9$
$x^2 = 9$
$x = \pm\sqrt{9}$
$x = \pm 3$
The solution set is $\{-3, 3\}$.

37. **a.** We use the compound interest formula with $P = \$2500$, $r = 0.045$, $t = 25$, and $n = 1$, so that $A = 2500\left(1 + \dfrac{0.045}{1}\right)^{1(25)} \approx \$7513.59$.

b. We use the compound interest formula with $P = \$2500$, $r = 0.045$, $t = 25$, and $n = 4$, so that $A = 2500\left(1 + \dfrac{0.045}{4}\right)^{4(25)} \approx \$7652.33$.

c. We use the compound interest formula with $P = \$2500$, $r = 0.045$, $t = 25$, and $n = 12$, so that $A = 2500\left(1 + \dfrac{0.045}{12}\right)^{12(25)} \approx \$7684.36$.

d. We use the compound interest formula with $P = \$2500$, $r = 0.045$, $t = 25$, and $n = 365$, so that $A = 2500\left(1 + \dfrac{0.045}{365}\right)^{365(25)} \approx \$7700.01$.

38. a. $A(1) = 100\left(\dfrac{1}{2}\right)^{1/3.5} \approx 82.034$.

After 1 day, approximately 82.034 grams of radon gas will be left in the sample.

b. $A(3.5) = 100\left(\dfrac{1}{2}\right)^{3.5/3.5} = 50$.

After 3.5 days, 50 grams of radon gas will be left in the sample.

c. $A(7) = 100\left(\dfrac{1}{2}\right)^{7/3.5} = 25$.

After 7 days, 25 grams of radon gas will be left in the sample.

d. $A(30) = 100\left(\dfrac{1}{2}\right)^{30/3.5} \approx 0.263$.

After 30 days, approximately 0.263 gram of radon gas will be left in the sample.

39. a. $P(2006) = 1.998(1.052)^{2006-2000} \approx 2.708$.

According to the model, the population of Nevada in 2006 will be approximately 2.708 million people.

b. $P(2010) = 1.998(1.052)^{2010-2000} \approx 3.317$.

According to the model, the population of Nevada in 2010 will be approximately 3.317 million people.

40. a. $u(15) = 72 + 278e^{-0.0835(15)} \approx 151.449$.

According to the model, the temperature of the cake after 15 minutes will be approximately $151.449°F$.

b. $u(30) = 72 + 278e^{-0.0835(30)} \approx 94.706$.

According to the model, the temperature of the cake after 30 minutes will be approximately $94.706°F$.

41. If $3^4 = 81$, then $\log_3 81 = 4$.

42. If $4^{-3} = \dfrac{1}{64}$, then $\log_4\left(\dfrac{1}{64}\right) = -3$.

43. If $b^3 = 5$, then $\log_b 5 = 3$.

44. If $10^{3.74} = x$, then $\log x = 3.74$.

45. If $\log_8 2 = \dfrac{1}{3}$, then $8^{1/3} = 2$.

46. If $\log_5 18 = r$, then $5^r = 18$.

47. If $\ln(x+3) = 2$, then $e^2 = x+3$.

48. If $\log x = -4$, then $10^{-4} = x$.

49. Let $y = \log_8 128$. Then,
$$8^y = 128$$
$$\left(2^3\right)^y = 2^7$$
$$2^{3y} = 2^7$$
$$3y = 7$$
$$y = \dfrac{7}{3}$$

Thus, $\log_8 128 = \dfrac{7}{3}$.

50. Let $y = \log_6 1$. Then,
$$6^y = 1$$
$$6^y = 6^0$$
$$y = 0$$
Thus, $\log_6 1 = 0$.

51. Let $y = \log \dfrac{1}{100}$. Then,
$$10^y = \dfrac{1}{100}$$
$$10^y = \dfrac{1}{10^2}$$
$$10^y = 10^{-2}$$
$$y = -2$$

Thus, $\log \dfrac{1}{100} = -2$.

52. Let $y = \log_9 27$. Then
$$9^y = 27$$
$$\left(3^2\right)^y = 3^3$$
$$3^{2y} = 3^3$$
$$2y = 3$$
$$y = \frac{3}{2}$$
Thus, $\log_9 27 = \frac{3}{2}$.

53. The domain of $f(x) = \log_2(x+5)$ is the set of all real numbers x such that
$$x + 5 > 0$$
$$x > -5$$
Thus, the domain of $f(x) = \log_2(x+5)$ is $\{x \mid x > -5\}$, or using interval notation, $(-5, \infty)$.

54. The domain of $g(x) = \log_8(7-3x)$ is the set of all real numbers x such that
$$7 - 3x > 0$$
$$-3x > -7$$
$$x < \frac{-7}{-3}$$
$$x < \frac{7}{3}$$
Thus, the domain of $g(x) = \log_8(7-3x)$ is $\left\{x \mid x < \frac{7}{3}\right\}$, or using interval notation, $\left(-\infty, \frac{7}{3}\right)$.

55. The domain of $h(x) = \ln(3x)$ is the set of all real numbers x such that
$$3x > 0$$
$$x > 0$$
Thus, the domain of $h(x) = \ln(3x)$ is $\{x \mid x > 0\}$, or using interval notation, $(0, \infty)$.

56. The domain of $F(x) = \log_{1/2}(4x+10)$ is the set of all real numbers x such that
$$4x + 10 > 0$$
$$4x > -10$$
$$x > \frac{-10}{4}$$
$$x > -\frac{5}{2}$$
Thus, the domain of $F(x) = \log_{1/2}(4x+10)$ is $\left\{x \mid x > -\frac{5}{2}\right\}$, or using interval notation, $\left(-\frac{5}{2}, \infty\right)$.

57. Rewrite $y = f(x) = \log_{5/2} x$ as $x = \left(\frac{5}{2}\right)^y$. Locate some points on the graph of $x = \left(\frac{5}{2}\right)^y$.

y	$x = \left(\dfrac{5}{2}\right)^y$	(x, y)
-2	$x = \left(\dfrac{5}{2}\right)^{-2} = \left(\dfrac{2}{5}\right)^2 = \dfrac{4}{25}$	$\left(\dfrac{4}{25}, -2\right)$
-1	$x = \left(\dfrac{5}{2}\right)^{-1} = \left(\dfrac{2}{5}\right)^1 = \dfrac{2}{5}$	$\left(\dfrac{2}{5}, -1\right)$
0	$x = \left(\dfrac{5}{2}\right)^0 = 1$	$(1, 0)$
1	$x = \left(\dfrac{5}{2}\right)^1 = \dfrac{5}{2}$	$\left(\dfrac{5}{2}, 1\right)$
2	$x = \left(\dfrac{5}{2}\right)^2 = \dfrac{25}{4}$	$\left(\dfrac{25}{4}, 2\right)$

Plot the points and connect them with a smooth curve.

$f(x) = \log_{5/2} x$

58. Rewrite $y = g(x) = \log_{2/5} x$ as $x = \left(\frac{2}{5}\right)^y$. Locate some points on the graph of $x = \left(\frac{2}{5}\right)^y$.

y	$x = \left(\dfrac{2}{5}\right)^y$	(x, y)
-2	$x = \left(\dfrac{2}{5}\right)^{-2} = \left(\dfrac{5}{2}\right)^2 = \dfrac{25}{4}$	$\left(\dfrac{25}{4}, -2\right)$
-1	$x = \left(\dfrac{2}{5}\right)^{-1} = \left(\dfrac{5}{2}\right)^1 = \dfrac{5}{2}$	$\left(\dfrac{5}{2}, -1\right)$
0	$x = \left(\dfrac{2}{5}\right)^0 = 1$	$(1, 0)$
1	$x = \left(\dfrac{2}{5}\right)^1 = \dfrac{2}{5}$	$\left(\dfrac{2}{5}, 1\right)$
2	$x = \left(\dfrac{2}{5}\right)^2 = \dfrac{4}{25}$	$\left(\dfrac{4}{25}, 2\right)$

Plot the points and connect them with a smooth curve.

$g(x) = \log_{\frac{1}{3}} x$

59. $\ln 24 \approx 3.178$

60. $\ln \dfrac{5}{6} \approx -0.182$

61. $\log 257 \approx 2.410$

62. $\log 0.124 \approx -0.907$

63. $\log_7(4x-19) = 2$
$$4x-19 = 7^2$$
$$4x-19 = 49$$
$$4x = 68$$
$$x = 17$$
The solution set is $\{17\}$.

64. $\log_{\frac{1}{3}}(x^2 + 8x) = -2$
$$x^2 + 8x = \left(\dfrac{1}{3}\right)^{-2}$$
$$x^2 + 8x = 3^2$$
$$x^2 + 8x = 9$$
$$x^2 + 8x - 9 = 0$$
$$(x+9)(x-1) = 0$$
$$x+9 = 0 \quad \text{or} \quad x-1 = 0$$
$$x = -9 \quad \text{or} \qquad x = 1$$
The solution set is $\{-9, 1\}$.

65. $\log_a \dfrac{4}{9} = -2$
$$a^{-2} = \dfrac{4}{9}$$
$$a^2 = \dfrac{9}{4}$$
$$a = \pm\sqrt{\dfrac{9}{4}} = \pm\dfrac{3}{2}$$
Since the base of a logarithm must always be positive, we know that $a = -\dfrac{3}{2}$ is extraneous.

The solution set is $\left\{\dfrac{3}{2}\right\}$.

66. $\ln e^{5x} = 30$
$$5x = 30$$
$$x = 6$$
The solution set is $\{6\}$.

67. $\log(6-7x) = 3$
$$6-7x = 10^3$$
$$6-7x = 1000$$
$$-7x = 994$$
$$x = -142$$
The solution set is $\{-142\}$.

68. $\log_b 75 = 2$
$$b^2 = 75$$
$$b = \pm\sqrt{75}$$
$$b = \pm 5\sqrt{3}$$
Since the base of a logarithm must always be positive, we know that $b = -5\sqrt{3}$ is extraneous.
The solution set is $\left\{5\sqrt{3}\right\}$.

69. We evaluate $L(x) = 10\log\dfrac{x}{10^{-12}}$ at $x = 10^{-4}$.
$$L(10^{-4}) = 10\log\dfrac{10^{-4}}{10^{-12}}$$
$$= 10\log 10^{-4-(-12)}$$
$$= 10\log 10^{8}$$
$$= 10(8)$$
$$= 80$$
The loudness of the vacuum cleaner is 80 decibels.

70. We solve $M(x) = \log\left(\dfrac{x}{10^{-3}}\right)$ for $M(x) = 8$.
$$M(x) = 8$$
$$\log\left(\dfrac{x}{10^{-3}}\right) = 8$$
$$\dfrac{x}{10^{-3}} = 10^8$$
$$x = 10^8 \cdot 10^{-3}$$
$$= 10^{8+(-3)}$$
$$= 10^5$$
$$= 100,000$$
The seismographic reading of the Great New Madrid Earthquake 100 kilometers from the epicenter would have been 100,000 millimeters.

71. $\log_4 4^{21} = 21$

72. $7^{\log_7 9.34} = 9.34$

73. $\log_5 5 = 1$

74. $\log_9 1 = 0$

75. $\log_4 12 - \log_4 3 = \log_4 \dfrac{12}{3} = \log_4 4 = 1$

76. $12^{\log_{12} 2 + \log_{12} 8} = 12^{\log_{12}(2\cdot 8)} = 12^{\log_{12} 16} = 16$

77. $\log_7\left(\dfrac{xy}{z}\right) = \log_7(xy) - \log_7 z$
$$= \log_7 x + \log_7 y - \log_7 z$$

78. $\log_3\left(\dfrac{81}{x^2}\right) = \log_3 81 - \log_3 x^2$
$$= \log_3 3^4 - \log_3 x^2$$
$$= 4 - 2\log_3 x$$

79. $\log 1000 r^4 = \log 1000 + \log r^4$
$$= \log 10^3 + \log r^4$$
$$= 3 + 4\log r$$

80. $\ln\sqrt{\dfrac{x-1}{x}} = \ln\left(\dfrac{x-1}{x}\right)^{\frac{1}{2}}$
$$= \frac{1}{2}\ln\left(\frac{x-1}{x}\right)$$
$$= \frac{1}{2}\left[\ln(x-1) - \ln x\right]$$
$$= \frac{1}{2}\ln(x-1) - \frac{1}{2}\ln x$$

81. $4\log_3 x + 2\log_3 y = \log_3 x^4 + \log_3 y^2$
$$= \log_3\left(x^4 y^2\right)$$

82. $\dfrac{1}{4}\ln x + \ln 7 - 2\ln 3 = \ln x^{\frac{1}{4}} + \ln 7 - \ln 3^2$
$$= \ln\sqrt[4]{x} + \ln 7 - \ln 9$$
$$= \ln\left(7\sqrt[4]{x}\right) - \ln 9$$
$$= \ln\left(\frac{7\sqrt[4]{x}}{9}\right)$$

83. $\log_2 3 - \log_2 6 = \log_2 \dfrac{3}{6} = \log_2 \dfrac{1}{2} = \log_2 2^{-1} = -1$

84. $\log_6\left(x^2 - 7x + 12\right) - \log_6(x-3)$
$$= \log_6\left[(x-4)(x-3)\right] - \log_6(x-3)$$
$$= \log_6(x-4) + \log_6(x-3) - \log_6(x-3)$$
$$= \log_6(x-4)$$

85. Using common logarithms:
$$\log_6 50 = \frac{\log 50}{\log 6} \approx 2.183$$

86. Using common logarithms:
$$\log_\pi 2 = \frac{\log 2}{\log \pi} \approx 0.606$$

87. Using natural logarithms:
$$\log_{2/3} 6 = \frac{\ln 6}{\ln\left(\dfrac{2}{3}\right)} \approx -4.419$$

88. Using natural logarithms:
$$\log_{\sqrt{5}} 20 = \frac{\ln 20}{\ln \sqrt{5}} \approx 3.723$$

89. $3\log_4 x = \log_4 1000$
$$\log_4 x^3 = \log_4 1000$$
$$x^3 = 1000$$
$$x = \sqrt[3]{1000}$$
$$x = 10$$
The solution set is $\{10\}$.

90. $\log_3 x + \log_3(x+6) = 3$
$$\log_3\left[x(x+6)\right] = 3$$
$$\log_3\left(x^2 + 6x\right) = 3$$
$$x^2 + 6x = 3^3$$
$$x^2 + 6x = 27$$
$$x^2 + 6x - 27 = 0$$
$$(x+9)(x-3) = 0$$
$$x+9=0 \quad \text{or} \quad x-3=0$$
$$x=-9 \quad \text{or} \quad x=3$$
The apparent solution $x=-9$ is extraneous because it causes the argument of a logarithm to be negative. The solution set is $\{3\}$.

91. $\ln(x+2) - \ln x = \ln(x+1)$

$$\ln\left(\frac{x+2}{x}\right) = \ln(x+1)$$

$$\frac{x+2}{x} = x+1$$

$$x(x+1) = x+2$$

$$x^2 + x = x+2$$

$$x^2 = 2$$

$$x = \pm\sqrt{2} \approx \pm 1.414$$

The apparent solution $x = -\sqrt{2} \approx -1.414$ is extraneous because it causes the argument of a logarithm to be negative. The solution set is $\left\{\sqrt{2}\right\} \approx \{1.414\}$.

92. $\dfrac{1}{3}\log_{12} x = 2\log_{12} 2$

$$\log_{12} x^{\frac{1}{3}} = \log_{12} 2^2$$

$$\log_{12} \sqrt[3]{x} = \log_{12} 4$$

$$\sqrt[3]{x} = 4$$

$$x = 4^3 = 64$$

The solution set is $\{64\}$.

93. $2^x = 15$

$$\log 2^x = \log 15$$

$$x \log 2 = \log 15$$

$$x = \frac{\log 15}{\log 2} \approx 3.907$$

The solution set is $\left\{\dfrac{\log 15}{\log 2}\right\} \approx \{3.907\}$. If we had taken the natural logarithm of both sides, the solution set would be $\left\{\dfrac{\ln 15}{\ln 2}\right\} \approx \{3.907\}$.

94. $10^{3x} = 27$

$$\log 10^{3x} = \log 27$$

$$3x = \log 27$$

$$x = \frac{\log 27}{3} \approx 0.477$$

The solution set is $\left\{\dfrac{\log 27}{3}\right\} \approx \{0.477\}$.

95. $\dfrac{1}{3}e^{7x} = 13$

$$e^{7x} = 39$$

$$\ln e^{7x} = \ln 39$$

$$7x = \ln 39$$

$$x = \frac{\ln 39}{7} \approx 0.523$$

The solution set is $\left\{\dfrac{\ln 39}{7}\right\} \approx \{0.523\}$.

96. $\qquad 3^x = 2^{x+1}$

$$\log 3^x = \log 2^{x+1}$$

$$x \log 3 = (x+1)\log 2$$

$$x \log 3 = x \log 2 + \log 2$$

$$x \log 3 - x \log 2 = \log 2$$

$$x(\log 3 - \log 2) = \log 2$$

$$x = \frac{\log 2}{\log 3 - \log 2} \approx 1.710$$

The solution set is $\left\{\dfrac{\log 2}{\log 3 - \log 2}\right\} \approx \{1.710\}$. If we had taken the natural logarithm of both sides, the solution set would be $\left\{\dfrac{\ln 2}{\ln 3 - \ln 2}\right\} \approx \{1.710\}$.

97. a. We need to determine the time until $A = 75$ grams. So we solve the equation

$$75 = 100\left(\frac{1}{2}\right)^{t/3.5}$$

$$0.75 = \left(\frac{1}{2}\right)^{t/3.5}$$

$$\log 0.75 = \log\left(\frac{1}{2}\right)^{t/3.5}$$

$$\log 0.75 = \frac{t}{3.5}\log\left(\frac{1}{2}\right)$$

$$\frac{3.5\log 0.75}{\log\left(\frac{1}{2}\right)} = t$$

So, $t = \dfrac{3.5\log 0.75}{\log\left(\dfrac{1}{2}\right)} \approx 1.453$ days.

Thus, 75 grams of radon gas will be left after approximately 1.453 days.

b. We need to determine the time until $A = 1$ gram. So we solve the equation

$$1 = 100\left(\frac{1}{2}\right)^{t/3.5}$$

$$0.01 = \left(\frac{1}{2}\right)^{t/3.5}$$

$$\log 0.01 = \log\left(\frac{1}{2}\right)^{t/3.5}$$

$$\log 0.01 = \frac{t}{3.5}\log\left(\frac{1}{2}\right)$$

$$\frac{3.5\log 0.01}{\log\left(\frac{1}{2}\right)} = t$$

So, $t = \dfrac{3.5\log 0.01}{\log\left(\frac{1}{2}\right)} \approx 23.253$ days.

Thus, 1 gram of radon gas will be left after approximately 23.253 days.

98. a. We need to determine the year when $P = 3.0$ million people. So we solve the equation

$$3.0 = 1.998(1.052)^{t-2000}$$

$$\frac{3.0}{1.998} = (1.052)^{t-2000}$$

$$\log\frac{3.0}{1.998} = \log(1.052)^{t-2000}$$

$$\log\frac{3.0}{1.998} = (t-2000)\log 1.052$$

$$\frac{\log\dfrac{3.0}{1.998}}{\log 1.052} = t - 2000$$

$$\frac{\log\dfrac{3.0}{1.998}}{\log 1.052} + 2000 = t$$

$$2008.018 \approx t$$

According to the model, the population of Nevada will be 3.0 million people in about 2008.

b. We need to determine the year when $P = 4.5$ million people. So we solve the equation

$$4.5 = 1.998(1.052)^{t-2000}$$

$$\frac{4.5}{1.998} = (1.052)^{t-2000}$$

$$\log\frac{4.5}{1.998} = \log(1.052)^{t-2000}$$

$$\log\frac{4.5}{1.998} = (t-2000)\log 1.052$$

$$\frac{\log\dfrac{4.5}{1.998}}{\log 1.052} = t - 2000$$

$$\frac{\log\dfrac{4.5}{1.998}}{\log 1.052} + 2000 = t$$

$$2016.017 \approx t$$

According to the model, the population of Nevada will be 4.5 million people in about 2016.

Chapter 9 Test

1. The function is not one-to-one. There is an element in the range (4) that corresponds to more than one element in the domain (1 and -1).

2.
$$f(x) = 4x - 3$$
$$y = 4x - 3$$
$$x = 4y - 3$$
$$x + 3 = 4y$$
$$\frac{x+3}{4} = y$$
$$f^{-1}(x) = \frac{x+3}{4}$$

Check:

$$f\left(f^{-1}(x)\right) = 4\left(\frac{x+3}{4}\right) - 3 = x + 3 - 3 = x$$

$$f^{-1}\left(f(x)\right) = \frac{(4x-3)+3}{4} = \frac{4x}{4} = x$$

3. **a.** $3.1^{3.1} \approx 33.360$

    b. $3.14^{3.14} \approx 36.338$

    c. $3.142^{3.142} \approx 36.494$

    d. $3.1416^{3.1416} \approx 36.463$

    e. $\pi^{\pi} \approx 36.462$

4. If $4^x = 19$, then $\log_4 19 = x$.

5. If $\log_b x = y$, then $b^y = x$.

6. a. Let $y = \log_3\left(\dfrac{1}{27}\right)$. Then,

$$3^y = \frac{1}{27}$$
$$3^y = \frac{1}{3^3}$$
$$3^y = 3^{-3}$$
$$y = -3$$

Thus, $\log_3\left(\dfrac{1}{27}\right) = -3$.

b. Let $y = \log 10{,}000$. Then,
$$10^y = 10{,}000$$
$$10^y = 10^4$$
$$y = 4$$
Thus, $\log 10{,}000 = 4$.

7. The domain of $f(x) = \log_5(7 - 4x)$ is the set of all real numbers x such that
$$7 - 4x > 0$$
$$-4x > -7$$
$$x < \frac{-7}{-4}$$
$$x < \frac{7}{4}$$
Thus, the domain of $f(x) = \log_5(7 - 4x)$ is
$\left\{x \,\middle|\, x < \dfrac{7}{4}\right\}$ or, using interval notation, $\left(-\infty, \dfrac{7}{4}\right)$.

8. Locate some points on the graph of $f(x) = 6^x$.

x	$f(x) = 6^x$	$(x, f(x))$
-2	$f(-2) = 6^{-2} = \dfrac{1}{6^2} = \dfrac{1}{36}$	$\left(-2, \dfrac{1}{36}\right)$
-1	$f(-1) = 6^{-1} = \dfrac{1}{6^1} = \dfrac{1}{6}$	$\left(-1, \dfrac{1}{6}\right)$
0	$f(0) = 6^0 = 1$	$(0, 1)$
1	$f(1) = 6^1 = 6$	$(1, 6)$

Plot the points and connect them with a smooth curve.

The domain of f is all real numbers or, using interval notation, $(-\infty, \infty)$. The range of f is $\{y \mid y > 0\}$ or, using interval notation, $(0, \infty)$.

9. Rewrite $y = g(x) = \log_{1/9} x$ as $x = \left(\dfrac{1}{9}\right)^y$. Locate some points on the graph of $x = \left(\dfrac{1}{9}\right)^y$.

y	$x = \left(\dfrac{1}{9}\right)^y$	(x, y)
-1	$x = \left(\dfrac{1}{9}\right)^{-1} = \left(\dfrac{9}{1}\right)^1 = 9$	$(9, -1)$
0	$x = \left(\dfrac{1}{9}\right)^0 = 1$	$(1, 0)$
1	$x = \left(\dfrac{1}{9}\right)^1 = \dfrac{1}{9}$	$\left(\dfrac{1}{9}, 1\right)$
2	$x = \left(\dfrac{1}{9}\right)^2 = \dfrac{1}{81}$	$\left(\dfrac{1}{81}, 2\right)$

Plot the points and connect them with a smooth curve.

The domain of g is $\{x \mid x > 0\}$ or, using interval notation, $(0, \infty)$. The range of g is all real numbers or, using interval notation, $(-\infty, \infty)$.

10. a. $\log_7 7^{10} = 10$

b. $3^{\log_3 15} = 15$

11. $\log_4 \dfrac{\sqrt{x}}{y^3} = \log_4 \sqrt{x} - \log_4 y^3$

$\qquad\qquad = \log_4 x^{\frac{1}{2}} - \log_4 y^3$

$\qquad\qquad = \dfrac{1}{2}\log_4 x - 3\log_4 y$

12. $4\log M + 3\log N = \log M^4 + \log N^3$

$\qquad\qquad\qquad\quad = \log\left(M^4 N^3\right)$

13. Using common logarithms:

$\log_{3/4} 10 = \dfrac{\log 10}{\log \dfrac{3}{4}} \approx -8.004$

14. $\quad 4^{x+1} = 2^{3x+1}$

$\left(2^2\right)^{x+1} = 2^{3x+1}$

$\quad 2^{2x+2} = 2^{3x+1}$

$\quad 2x+2 = 3x+1$

$\quad -x+2 = 1$

$\qquad -x = -1$

$\qquad\; x = 1$

The solution set is $\{1\}$.

15. $\quad 5^{x^2}\cdot 125 = 25^{2x}$

$\quad 5^{x^2}\cdot 5^3 = \left(5^2\right)^{2x}$

$\qquad 5^{x^2+3} = 5^{4x}$

$\qquad x^2 + 3 = 4x$

$\quad x^2 - 4x + 3 = 0$

$\quad (x-1)(x-3) = 0$

$x-1 = 0 \quad\text{or}\quad x-3 = 0$

$\quad x = 1 \quad\text{or}\qquad x = 3$

The solution set is $\{1,\ 3\}$.

16. $\log_a 64 = 3$

$\qquad a^3 = 64$

$\qquad a = \sqrt[3]{64} = 4$

The solution set is $\{4\}$.

17. $\log_2\left(x^2 - 33\right) = 8$

$\qquad 2^8 = x^2 - 33$

$\qquad 256 = x^2 - 33$

$\qquad 289 = x^2$

$\qquad x = \pm\sqrt{289} = \pm 17$

The solution set is $\{-17,\ 17\}$.

18. $2\log_7(x-3) = \log_7 3 + \log_7 12$

$\log_7(x-3)^2 = \log_7(3\cdot 12)$

$\log_7(x-3)^2 = \log_7 36$

$\quad (x-3)^2 = 36$

$\qquad x-3 = \pm 6$

$\qquad x = 3 \pm 6$

$\qquad x = 9 \quad\text{or}\quad x = -3$

The apparent solution $x = -3$ is extraneous because it causes the argument of a logarithm to be negative. The solution set is $\{9\}$.

19. $\qquad\qquad 3^{x-1} = 17$

$\qquad\qquad \log 3^{x-1} = \log 17$

$\qquad (x-1)\log 3 = \log 17$

$\quad x\log 3 - \log 3 = \log 17$

$\qquad\quad x\log 3 = \log 17 + \log 3$

$\qquad\qquad x = \dfrac{\log 17 + \log 3}{\log 3} \approx 3.579$

The solution set is $\left\{\dfrac{\log 17 + \log 3}{\log 3}\right\} \approx \{3.579\}$. If we had taken the natural logarithm of both sides, the solution set would be $\left\{\dfrac{\ln 17 + \ln 3}{\ln 3}\right\} \approx \{3.579\}$.

20. $\log(x-2) + \log(x+2) = 2$

$\log\left[(x-2)(x+2)\right] = 2$

$\qquad \log\left(x^2 - 4\right) = 2$

$\qquad\qquad 10^2 = x^2 - 4$

$\qquad\qquad x^2 - 4 = 100$

$\qquad\qquad x^2 = 104$

$\qquad\qquad x = \pm\sqrt{104}$

$\qquad\qquad x = \pm 2\sqrt{26} \approx \pm 10.198$

The apparent solution $x = -2\sqrt{26} \approx -10.198$ is extraneous because it causes the argument of a logarithm to be negative. The solution set is $\left\{2\sqrt{26}\right\} \approx \{10.198\}$.

21. a. Evaluate $P(t) = 31.9(1.008)^{t-2002}$ at $t = 2010$.

$P(2010) = 31.9(1.008)^{2010-2002} \approx 34.000$.

According to the model, the population of Canada in 2010 will be about 34 million people.

b. We need to determine the year when $P = 50$ million people. So we solve the equation

$$50 = 31.9(1.008)^{t-2002}$$

$$\frac{50}{31.9} = (1.008)^{t-2002}$$

$$\log\frac{50}{31.9} = \log(1.008)^{t-2002}$$

$$\log\frac{50}{31.9} = (t-2002)\log 1.008$$

$$\frac{\log\frac{50}{31.9}}{\log 1.008} = t - 2002$$

$$\frac{\log\frac{50}{31.9}}{\log 1.008} + 2002 = t$$

$$2058.402 \approx t$$

According to the model, the population of Canada will be 50 million people in about 2058.

22. We evaluate $L(x) = 10\log\frac{x}{10^{-12}}$ at $x = 10^{-11}$.

$$L(10^{-11}) = 10\log\frac{10^{-11}}{10^{-12}}$$

$$= 10\log 10^{-11-(-12)}$$

$$= 10\log 10^{1}$$

$$= 10(1)$$

$$= 10$$

The loudness of rustling leaves is 10 decibels.

Cumulative Review Chapters R-9

1. $3(5-2x)+8 = 4(x-7)+1$

$15 - 6x + 8 = 4x - 28 + 1$

$-6x + 23 = 4x - 27$

$-10x = -50$

$x = 5$

The solution set is {5}.

2. $5 - 3|x-2| \geq -7$

$-3|x-2| \geq -12$

$|x-2| \leq 4$

$-4 \leq x - 2 \leq 4$

$-2 \leq x \leq 6$

The solution set is $\{x \mid -2 \leq x \leq 6\}$ or, using interval notation, $[-2, 6]$.

3. We need to find all values of x that cause the denominator $2x^2 - x - 21$ to equal 0.

$2x^2 - x - 21 = 0$

$(2x-7)(x+3) = 0$

$2x - 7 = 0$ or $x + 3 = 0$

$x = \frac{7}{2}$ $x = -3$

Thus, the domain of $f(x) = \dfrac{9-x^2}{2x^2-x-21}$ is

$$\left\{ x \,\middle|\, x \neq -3 \text{ and } x \neq \frac{7}{2} \right\}.$$

4. $4x + 3y = 6$

$3y = -4x + 6$

$y = \dfrac{-4x+6}{3}$

$y = -\dfrac{4}{3}x + 2$

The slope is $-\dfrac{4}{3}$ and the y-intercept is 2. Begin at the point $(0, 2)$ and move to the right 3 units and down 4 units to find the point $(3, -2)$.

5. The slope of the line we seek is

$$m = \frac{y_2 - y_1}{x_2 - x_1} = \frac{-4 - 17}{5 - (-10)} = \frac{-21}{15} = -\frac{7}{5}.$$

Thus, the equation of the line we seek is:

$$y - y_1 = m(x - x_1)$$

$$y - (-4) = -\frac{7}{5}(x - 5)$$

$$y + 4 = -\frac{7}{5}x + 7$$

$$y = -\frac{7}{5}x + 3 \quad \text{or} \quad 7x + 5y = 15$$

6. $\begin{cases} x - 2y + z = 4 & (1) \\ y - z = -2 & (2) \\ 2z = -6 & (3) \end{cases}$

Solve equation (3) for z:

$$2z = -6$$

$$z = -3$$

Substituting -3 for z into equation (2), we obtain

$$y - (-3) = -2$$

$$y + 3 = -2$$

$$y = -5$$

Substituting -3 for z and -5 for y into equation (1), we obtain

$$x - 2(-5) + (-3) = 4$$

$$x + 10 - 3 = 4$$

$$x + 7 = 4$$

$$x = -3$$

The solution is the ordered triple $(-3, -5, -3)$.

7. $\begin{vmatrix} 4 & 0 & -2 \\ 2 & -1 & 1 \\ 1 & 3 & 1 \end{vmatrix} = 4\begin{vmatrix} -1 & 1 \\ 3 & 1 \end{vmatrix} - 0\begin{vmatrix} 2 & 1 \\ 1 & 1 \end{vmatrix} + (-2)\begin{vmatrix} 2 & -1 \\ 1 & 3 \end{vmatrix}$

$$= 4\left[-1(1) - 3(1)\right] - 0\left[2(1) - 1(1)\right]$$
$$+ (-2)\left[2(3) - 1(-1)\right]$$

$$= 4(-1 - 3) - 0(2 - 1) - 2(6 + 1)$$

$$= 4(-4) - 0(1) - 2(7)$$

$$= -16 - 0 - 14$$

$$= -30$$

8. $\begin{cases} x + 2y \geq 8 \\ 2x - y < 1 \end{cases}$

First, graph the inequality $x + 2y \geq 8$. To do so, replace the inequality symbol with an equal sign to obtain $x + 2y = 8$. Because the inequality is

not strict, graph $x + 2y = 8$ $\left(y = -\frac{1}{2}x + 4\right)$

using a solid line.

Test Point: $(0,0)$: $(0) + 2(0) \not\geq 8$

Therefore, the half-plane not containing $(0,0)$ is the solution set of $x + 2y \geq 8$.

Second, graph the inequality $2x - y < 1$. To do so, replace the inequality symbol with an equal sign to obtain $2x - y = 1$. Because the inequality is strict, graph $2x - y = 1$ $(y = 2x - 1)$ using a dashed line.

Test Point: $(0,0)$: $2(0) - (0) < 1$

Therefore, the half-plane containing $(0,0)$ is the solution set of $2x - y < 1$.

The overlapping shaded region (that is, the shaded region in the graph below) is the solution to the system of linear inequalities.

9. $\left(m^2 - 5m + 13\right) - \left(6 - 2m - 3m^2\right)$

$$= m^2 - 5m + 13 - 6 + 2m + 3m^2$$

$$= 4m^2 - 3m + 7$$

10. $(2n + 3)\left(n^2 - 4n + 6\right)$

$$= 2n\left(n^2\right) + 2n(-4n) + 2n(6) + 3\left(n^2\right)$$
$$+ 3(-4n) + 3(6)$$

$$= 2n^3 - 8n^2 + 12n + 3n^2 - 12n + 18$$

$$= 2n^3 - 5n^2 + 18$$

11. $16a^2 + 8ab + b^2 = \left(4a\right)^2 + 2(4a)(b) + b^2$

$$= \left(4a + b\right)^2$$

12. $a \cdot c = 6(7) = 42$.

The factors of 42 that add to -17 (the linear coefficient) are -3 and -14. Thus,

$$6y^2 - 17y + 7 = 6y^2 - 3y - 14y + 7$$
$$= 3y(2y-1) - 7(2y-1)$$
$$= (3y-7)(2y-1)$$

13.
$$\frac{2x^2 - 9x - 5}{x^2 - 3x - 10} \cdot \frac{3x^2 + 2x - 8}{2x^2 - 13x - 7}$$
$$= \frac{(2x+1)(x-5)}{(x+2)(x-5)} \cdot \frac{(3x-4)(x+2)}{(2x+1)(x-7)}$$
$$= \frac{(2x+1)\,(x-5)}{(x+2)\,(x-5)} \cdot \frac{(3x-4)(x+2)}{(2x+1)(x-7)}$$
$$= \frac{3x-4}{x-7}$$

14.
$$\frac{4}{p^2 - 6p + 5} + \frac{2}{p^2 - 3p - 10}$$
$$= \frac{4}{(p-5)(p-1)} + \frac{2}{(p-5)(p+2)}$$
$$= \frac{4(p+2)}{(p-5)(p-1)(p+2)} + \frac{2(p-1)}{(p-5)(p-1)(p+2)}$$
$$= \frac{4(p+2) + 2(p-1)}{(p-5)(p-1)(p+2)}$$
$$= \frac{4p + 8 + 2p - 2}{(p-5)(p-1)(p+2)}$$
$$= \frac{6p+6}{(p-5)(p-1)(p+2)} = \frac{6(p+1)}{(p-5)(p-1)(p+2)}$$

15.
$$\frac{2}{x-5} = \frac{x-2}{x+1} + \frac{6x-12}{x^2 - 4x - 5}$$
$$\frac{2}{x-5} = \frac{x-2}{x+1} + \frac{6x-12}{(x-5)(x+1)}$$
$$(x-5)(x+1)\left(\frac{2}{x-5}\right)$$
$$= (x-5)(x+1)\left(\frac{x-2}{x+1} + \frac{6x-12}{(x-5)(x+1)}\right)$$
$$2(x+1) = (x-5)(x-2) + (6x-12)$$
$$2x+2 = x^2 - 2x - 5x + 10 + 6x - 12$$
$$2x+2 = x^2 - x - 2$$
$$0 = x^2 - 3x - 4$$
$$0 = (x+1)(x-4)$$
$$x+1 = 0 \quad \text{or} \quad x-4 = 0$$
$$x = -1 \quad \text{or} \quad x = 4$$

Since $x = -1$ is not in the domain of the variable, it is an extraneous solution. Thus, the solution set is $\{4\}$.

16.
$$\sqrt{150} + 4\sqrt{6} - \sqrt{24} = \sqrt{25 \cdot 6} + 4\sqrt{6} - \sqrt{4 \cdot 6}$$
$$= 5\sqrt{6} + 4\sqrt{6} - 2\sqrt{6}$$
$$= 7\sqrt{6}$$

17.
$$\frac{1+\sqrt{5}}{3-\sqrt{5}} = \frac{1+\sqrt{5}}{3-\sqrt{5}} \cdot \frac{3+\sqrt{5}}{3+\sqrt{5}}$$
$$= \frac{3+\sqrt{5}+3\sqrt{5}+5}{9+3\sqrt{5}-3\sqrt{5}-5} = \frac{8+4\sqrt{5}}{4} = 2+\sqrt{5}$$

18.
$$\sqrt{x-8} + \sqrt{x} = 4$$
$$\sqrt{x-8} = 4 - \sqrt{x}$$
$$\left(\sqrt{x-8}\right)^2 = \left(4 - \sqrt{x}\right)^2$$
$$x - 8 = 16 - 8\sqrt{x} + x$$
$$8\sqrt{x} = 24$$
$$\sqrt{x} = 3$$
$$\left(\sqrt{x}\right)^2 = (3)^2$$
$$x = 9$$

Check:
$$\sqrt{9-8} + \sqrt{9} \overset{?}{=} 4$$
$$\sqrt{1} + \sqrt{9} \overset{?}{=} 4$$
$$1 + 3 \overset{?}{=} 4$$
$$4 = 4 \checkmark$$

The solution set is $\{9\}$.

19.
$$3x^2 = 4x + 6$$
$$3x^2 - 4x - 6 = 0$$

Because this equation does not easily factor, solve by using the quadratic formula. For this equation, $a = 3$, $b = -4$, and $c = -6$.

$$x = \frac{-(-4) \pm \sqrt{(-4)^2 - 4(3)(-6)}}{2(3)}$$
$$= \frac{4 \pm \sqrt{88}}{6} = \frac{4 \pm 2\sqrt{22}}{6} = \frac{2 \pm \sqrt{22}}{3}$$

The solution set is $\left\{\dfrac{2-\sqrt{22}}{3}, \dfrac{2+\sqrt{22}}{3}\right\}$.

20.
$$2a - 7\sqrt{a} + 6 = 0$$
$$2\left(\sqrt{a}\right)^2 - 7\left(\sqrt{a}\right) + 6 = 0$$

Let $u = \sqrt{a}$.
$$2u^2 - 7u + 6 = 0$$
$$(2u-3)(u-2) = 0$$

$$2u - 3 = 0 \quad \text{or} \quad u - 2 = 0$$

$$u = \frac{3}{2} \quad \text{or} \quad u = 2$$

$$\sqrt{a} = \frac{3}{2} \quad \text{or} \quad \sqrt{a} = 2$$

$$a = \left(\frac{3}{2}\right)^2 \quad \text{or} \quad a = 2^2$$

$$a = \frac{9}{4} \quad \text{or} \quad a = 4$$

Check:

$$a = \frac{9}{4}: \quad 2 \cdot \frac{9}{4} - 7\sqrt{\frac{9}{4}} + 6 \overset{?}{=} 0$$

$$\frac{9}{2} - 7 \cdot \frac{3}{2} + 6 \overset{?}{=} 0$$

$$\frac{9}{2} - \frac{21}{2} + 6 \overset{?}{=} 0$$

$$0 = 0 \checkmark$$

$$a = 4: \quad 2 \cdot 4 - 7\sqrt{4} + 6 \overset{?}{=} 0$$

$$8 - 7 \cdot 2 + 6 \overset{?}{=} 0$$

$$8 - 14 + 6 \overset{?}{=} 0$$

$$0 = 0 \checkmark$$

Both check; the solution set is $\left\{\frac{9}{4}, 4\right\}$.

21. $f(x) = -x^2 + 6x - 4$

$a = -1, b = 6, c = -4$

The graph opens down because the coefficient on x^2 is negative.

vertex:

$$x = -\frac{b}{2a} = -\frac{6}{2(-1)} = 3$$

$$y = f(3) = -(3)^2 + 6(3) - 4 = 5$$

The vertex is $(3, 5)$. The axis of symmetry is $x = 3$.

y-intercept:

$$f(0) = -(0)^2 + 6(0) - 4 = -4$$

x-intercepts:

$$b^2 - 4ac = 6^2 - 4(-1)(-4) = 20$$

There are two distinct x-intercepts. We find these by solving

$$f(x) = 0$$

$$-x^2 + 6x - 4 = 0$$

$$x = \frac{-6 \pm \sqrt{20}}{2(-1)} = \frac{-6 \pm 2\sqrt{5}}{-2} = 3 \pm \sqrt{5}$$

$$x \approx 0.76 \quad \text{or} \quad x \approx 5.24$$

Graph:

The y-intercept point, $(0, -4)$, is three units to the left of the axis of symmetry. Therefore, if we move three units to the right of the axis of symmetry, we obtain the point $(6, -4)$ which must also be on the graph.

22. $3x^2 + 2x - 8 < 0$

Solve: $\quad 3x^2 + 2x - 8 = 0$

$$(3x - 4)(x + 2) = 0$$

$$3x - 4 = 0 \quad \text{or} \quad x + 2 = 0$$

$$x = \frac{4}{3} \quad \text{or} \quad x = -2$$

Determine where each factor is positive and negative and where the product of these factors is positive and negative.

Interval	$(-\infty, -2)$	-2	$\left(-2, \frac{4}{3}\right)$	$\frac{4}{3}$	$\left(\frac{4}{3}, \infty\right)$
$3x - 4$	$- - - -$	$-$	$- - - -$	0	$+ + + +$
$x + 2$	$- - - -$	0	$+ + + +$	$+$	$+ + + +$
$(3x - 4)(x + 2)$	$+ + + +$	0	$- - - -$	0	$+ + + +$

The inequality is strict, so -2 and $\frac{4}{3}$ are not part of the solution. Now, $(3x - 4)(x + 2)$ is less than zero where the product is negative. The solution is $\left\{x \mid -2 < x < \frac{4}{3}\right\}$ or, using interval notation, $\left(-2, \frac{4}{3}\right)$.

23. Locate some points on the graph of $g(x) = 3^x - 4$.

x	$g(x) = 3^x - 4$	$(x, g(x))$
-2	$g(-2) = 3^{-2} - 4 = \dfrac{1}{9} - 4 = -\dfrac{35}{9}$	$\left(-2, -\dfrac{35}{9}\right)$
-1	$g(-1) = 3^{-1} - 4 = \dfrac{1}{3} - 4 = -\dfrac{11}{3}$	$\left(-1, -\dfrac{11}{3}\right)$
0	$g(0) = 3^0 - 4 = 1 - 4 = -3$	$(0, -3)$
1	$g(1) = 3^1 - 4 = 3 - 4 = -1$	$(1, -1)$
2	$g(2) = 3^2 - 4 = 9 - 4 = 5$	$(2, 5)$

Plot the points and connect them with a smooth curve.

24. Let $y = \log_9\left(\dfrac{1}{27}\right)$. Then,

$$9^y = \frac{1}{27}$$
$$\left(3^2\right)^y = \frac{1}{3^3}$$
$$3^{2y} = 3^{-3}$$
$$2y = -3$$
$$y = -\frac{3}{2}$$

Thus, $\log_9\left(\dfrac{1}{27}\right) = -\dfrac{3}{2}$.

Chapter 10

10.1 Preparing for Distance and Midpoint Formulas

1. **a.** $\sqrt{64} = 8$

   b. $\sqrt{24} = \sqrt{4 \cdot 6} = 2\sqrt{6}$

2. $c^2 = a^2 + b^2$
   $c^2 = 6^2 + 8^2$
   $c^2 = 36 + 64$
   $c^2 = 100$
   $c = \sqrt{100} = 10$
   The length of the hypotenuse is 10.

10.1 Exercises

1. $\sqrt{(x_2 - x_1)^2 + (y_2 - y_1)^2}$

3. FALSE. Distance must always be positive.

5. Answers may vary. One possibility follows:
   The distance formula is derived from the Pythagorean Theorem. The absolute value of the difference between the x-coordinates, $|x_2 - x_1|$, is the length of one leg of a right triangle. The absolute value of the difference between the y-coordinates, $|y_2 - y_1|$, is the length of the other leg of the right triangle. The length of the hypotenuse is $d(P_1, P_2)$. By the Pythagorean Theorem,
   $$[d(P_1, P_2)]^2 = |x_2 - x_1|^2 + |y_2 - y_1|^2$$
   $$= (x_2 - x_1)^2 + (y_2 - y_1)^2$$
   $$d(P_1, P_2) = \sqrt{(x_2 - x_1)^2 + (y_2 - y_1)^2}$$

7. $d(P_1, P_2) = \sqrt{(x_2 - x_1)^2 + (y_2 - y_1)^2}$
   $= \sqrt{(3 - 0)^2 + (4 - 0)^2}$
   $= \sqrt{3^2 + 4^2}$
   $= \sqrt{9 + 16}$
   $= \sqrt{25}$
   $= 5$

9. $d(P_1, P_2) = \sqrt{(x_2 - x_1)^2 + (y_2 - y_1)^2}$
   $= \sqrt{(4 - (-4))^2 + (1 - 5)^2}$
   $= \sqrt{8^2 + (-4)^2}$
   $= \sqrt{64 + 16}$
   $= \sqrt{80}$
   $= 4\sqrt{5} \approx 8.94$

11. $d(P_1, P_2) = \sqrt{(x_2 - x_1)^2 + (y_2 - y_1)^2}$
    $= \sqrt{(6 - 2)^2 + (4 - 1)^2}$
    $= \sqrt{4^2 + 3^2}$
    $= \sqrt{16 + 9}$
    $= \sqrt{25}$
    $= 5$

13. $d(P_1, P_2) = \sqrt{(x_2 - x_1)^2 + (y_2 - y_1)^2}$
    $= \sqrt{(9 - (-3))^2 + (-3 - 2)^2}$
    $= \sqrt{12^2 + (-5)^2}$
    $= \sqrt{144 + 25}$
    $= \sqrt{169}$
    $= 13$

15. $d(P_1, P_2) = \sqrt{(x_2 - x_1)^2 + (y_2 - y_1)^2}$
    $= \sqrt{(2 - (-4))^2 + (2 - 2)^2}$
    $= \sqrt{6^2 + 0^2}$
    $= \sqrt{36 + 0}$
    $= \sqrt{36}$
    $= 6$

17. $d(P_1, P_2) = \sqrt{(x_2 - x_1)^2 + (y_2 - y_1)^2}$
    $= \sqrt{(-3 - 0)^2 + (3 - (-3))^2}$
    $= \sqrt{(-3)^2 + 6^2}$
    $= \sqrt{9 + 36}$
    $= \sqrt{45}$
    $= 3\sqrt{5} \approx 6.71$

19. $d(P_1, P_2) = \sqrt{(x_2 - x_1)^2 + (y_2 - y_1)^2}$

$= \sqrt{(5\sqrt{2} - 2\sqrt{2})^2 + (4\sqrt{5} - \sqrt{5})^2}$

$= \sqrt{(3\sqrt{2})^2 + (3\sqrt{5})^2}$

$= \sqrt{9(2) + 9(5)}$

$= \sqrt{18 + 45}$

$= \sqrt{63}$

$= 3\sqrt{7} \approx 7.94$

21. $d(P_1, P_2) = \sqrt{(x_2 - x_1)^2 + (y_2 - y_1)^2}$

$= \sqrt{(1.3 - 0.3)^2 + (0.1 - (-3.3))^2}$

$= \sqrt{1^2 + 3.4^2}$

$= \sqrt{1 + 11.56}$

$= \sqrt{12.56} \approx 3.54$

23. $M = \left(\dfrac{x_1 + x_2}{2}, \dfrac{y_1 + y_2}{2} \right)$

$= \left(\dfrac{2+6}{2}, \dfrac{2+4}{2} \right) = \left(\dfrac{8}{2}, \dfrac{6}{2} \right) = (4, 3)$

25. $M = \left(\dfrac{x_1 + x_2}{2}, \dfrac{y_1 + y_2}{2} \right)$

$= \left(\dfrac{-3+9}{2}, \dfrac{2+(-4)}{2} \right) = \left(\dfrac{6}{2}, \dfrac{-2}{2} \right) = (3, -1)$

27. $M = \left(\dfrac{x_1 + x_2}{2}, \dfrac{y_1 + y_2}{2} \right)$

$= \left(\dfrac{-4+2}{2}, \dfrac{3+4}{2} \right) = \left(\dfrac{-2}{2}, \dfrac{7}{2} \right) = \left(-1, \dfrac{7}{2} \right)$

29. $M = \left(\dfrac{x_1 + x_2}{2}, \dfrac{y_1 + y_2}{2} \right)$

$= \left(\dfrac{0+(-3)}{2}, \dfrac{-3+3}{2} \right) = \left(\dfrac{-3}{2}, \dfrac{0}{2} \right) = \left(-\dfrac{3}{2}, 0 \right)$

31. $M = \left(\dfrac{x_1 + x_2}{2}, \dfrac{y_1 + y_2}{2} \right)$

$= \left(\dfrac{2\sqrt{2} + 5\sqrt{2}}{2}, \dfrac{\sqrt{5} + 4\sqrt{5}}{2} \right) = \left(\dfrac{7\sqrt{2}}{2}, \dfrac{5\sqrt{5}}{2} \right)$

33. $M = \left(\dfrac{x_1 + x_2}{2}, \dfrac{y_1 + y_2}{2} \right)$

$= \left(\dfrac{0.3 + 1.3}{2}, \dfrac{-3.3 + 0.1}{2} \right)$

$= \left(\dfrac{1.6}{2}, \dfrac{-3.2}{2} \right)$

$= (0.8, -1.6)$

35. a.

b. $d(A, B) = \sqrt{(2-0)^2 + (1-3)^2}$

$= \sqrt{2^2 + (-2)^2}$

$= \sqrt{4+4}$

$= \sqrt{8} = 2\sqrt{2} \approx 2.83$

$d(B, C) = \sqrt{(6-2)^2 + (5-1)^2}$

$= \sqrt{4^2 + 4^2}$

$= \sqrt{16 + 16}$

$= \sqrt{32} = 4\sqrt{2} \approx 5.66$

$d(A, C) = \sqrt{(6-0)^2 + (5-3)^2}$

$= \sqrt{6^2 + 2^2}$

$= \sqrt{36 + 4}$

$= \sqrt{40} = 2\sqrt{10} \approx 6.32$

c. To verify that triangle ABC is a right triangle, we show that

$$[d(A,B)]^2 + [d(B,C)]^2 \overset{?}{=} [d(A,C)]^2$$

$$(2\sqrt{2})^2 + (4\sqrt{2})^2 \overset{?}{=} (2\sqrt{10})^2$$

$$4 \cdot 2 + 16 \cdot 2 \overset{?}{=} 4 \cdot 10$$

$$8 + 32 \overset{?}{=} 40$$

$$40 = 40 \leftarrow \text{True}$$

Therefore, triangle ABC is a right triangle.

d. The length of the "base" of the triangle is $d(B,C) = 4\sqrt{2}$ and the length of the "height" of the triangle is $d(A,B) = 2\sqrt{2}$. Thus, the area of triangle ABC is

$$\text{Area} = \frac{1}{2} \cdot \text{base} \cdot \text{height} = \frac{1}{2} \cdot 4\sqrt{2} \cdot 2\sqrt{2} = 8$$

square units.

37. a.

b.
$$d(A,B) = \sqrt{(3-(-2))^2 + (1-(-4))^2}$$
$$= \sqrt{5^2 + 5^2}$$
$$= \sqrt{25 + 25}$$
$$= \sqrt{50}$$
$$= 5\sqrt{2} \approx 7.07$$

$$d(B,C) = \sqrt{(15-3)^2 + (-11-1)^2}$$
$$= \sqrt{12^2 + (-12)^2}$$
$$= \sqrt{144 + 144}$$
$$= \sqrt{288}$$
$$= 12\sqrt{2} \approx 16.97$$

$$d(A,C) = \sqrt{(15-(-2))^2 + (-11-(-4))^2}$$
$$= \sqrt{17^2 + (-7)^2}$$
$$= \sqrt{289 + 49}$$
$$= \sqrt{338}$$
$$= 13\sqrt{2} \approx 18.38$$

c. To verify that triangle ABC is a right triangle, we show that
$$[d(A,B)]^2 + [d(B,C)]^2 \overset{?}{=} [d(A,C)]^2$$
$$\left(5\sqrt{2}\right)^2 + \left(12\sqrt{2}\right)^2 \overset{?}{=} \left(13\sqrt{2}\right)^2$$
$$25 \cdot 2 + 144 \cdot 2 \overset{?}{=} 169 \cdot 2$$
$$50 + 288 \overset{?}{=} 338$$
$$338 = 338 \leftarrow \text{True}$$
Therefore, triangle ABC is a right triangle.

d. The length of the "base" of the triangle is $d(B,C) = 12\sqrt{2}$ and the length of the "height" of the triangle is $d(A,B) = 5\sqrt{2}$. Thus, the area of triangle ABC is

$$\text{Area} = \frac{1}{2} \cdot \text{base} \cdot \text{height} = \frac{1}{2} \cdot 12\sqrt{2} \cdot 5\sqrt{2} = 60$$

square units.

39. We want to find y such that the distance between $P_1 = (5,1)$ and $P_2 = (2,y)$ is 5.
$$d(P_1,P_2) = \sqrt{(x_2 - x_1)^2 + (y_2 - y_1)^2}$$
$$5 = \sqrt{(2-5)^2 + (y-1)^2}$$
$$5 = \sqrt{(-3)^2 + (y-1)^2}$$
$$5 = \sqrt{9 + (y-1)^2}$$
$$25 = 9 + (y-1)^2$$
$$16 = (y-1)^2$$
$$y - 1 = \pm\sqrt{16}$$
$$y - 1 = \pm 4$$
$$y = 1 \pm 4$$
$$y = -3 \text{ or } y = 5$$

Thus, the distance between the points $(5,1)$ and $(2,-3)$ is 5, and the distance between $(5,1)$ and $(2,5)$ is 5.

41. We want to find x such that the distance between $P_1 = (2,3)$ and $P_2 = (x,-3)$ is 10.
$$d(P_1,P_2) = \sqrt{(x_2 - x_1)^2 + (y_2 - y_1)^2}$$
$$10 = \sqrt{(x-2)^2 + (-3-3)^2}$$
$$10 = \sqrt{(x-2)^2 + (-6)^2}$$
$$10 = \sqrt{(x-2)^2 + 36}$$
$$100 = (x-2)^2 + 36$$
$$64 = (x-2)^2$$
$$x - 2 = \pm\sqrt{64}$$
$$x - 2 = \pm 8$$
$$x = 2 \pm 8$$
$$x = -6 \text{ or } x = 10$$

Thus, the distance between the points $(2,3)$ and $(-6,-3)$ is 10, and the distance between $(2,3)$ and $(10,-3)$ is 10.

43. a. Treating the intersection of Madison and State Streets as the origin, $(0,0)$, of a Cartesian plane, Wrigley Field is located at the coordinates $(-10,36)$.

$$d = \sqrt{(-10-0)^2 + (36-0)^2}$$
$$= \sqrt{(-10)^2 + 36^2}$$
$$= \sqrt{100+1296}$$
$$= \sqrt{1396}$$
$$= 2\sqrt{349} \approx 37.36$$

The distance "as the crow flies" from Madison and State Street to Wrigley Field is approximately 37.36 blocks.

b. U.S. Cellular Field is located at the coordinates $(-3,-35)$.

$$d = \sqrt{(-3-0)^2 + (-35-0)^2}$$
$$= \sqrt{(-3)^2 + (-35)^2}$$
$$= \sqrt{9+1225}$$
$$= \sqrt{1234} \approx 35.13$$

The distance "as the crow flies" from Madison and State Street to U.S. Cellular Field is approximately 35.13 blocks.

c. $d = \sqrt{(-10-(-3))^2 + (36-(-35))^2}$
$$= \sqrt{(-7)^2 + 71^2}$$
$$= \sqrt{49+5041}$$
$$= \sqrt{5090} \approx 71.34$$

The distance "as the crow flies" from Wrigley Field to U.S. Cellular Field is approximately 71.34 blocks.

45. a. The distance from the right fielder to second base is

$$d = \sqrt{(320-90)^2 + (20-90)^2}$$
$$= \sqrt{230^2 + (-70)^2}$$
$$= \sqrt{52,900+4900}$$
$$= \sqrt{57,800}$$
$$= 170\sqrt{2} \approx 240.42 \text{ feet}$$

Now, $\text{time} = \dfrac{\text{distance}}{\text{speed}} \approx \dfrac{240.42}{130} \approx 1.85$.

It will take about 1.85 seconds for the ball to reach the second baseman from the right fielder.

b. The time for the runner to reach second base will be

$$\text{time} = \frac{\text{distance}}{\text{speed}} = \frac{90}{27} \approx 3.33 \text{ seconds.}$$

The total time for the ball to reach second base from the time the right fielder catches it will be $1.85+0.8 = 2.65$ seconds.

Since the ball will reach second base before the runner, the first base coach should not send the runner.

47. $3^2 = 3 \cdot 3 = 9$; $\sqrt{9} = 3$

49. $(-3)^4 = (-3)(-3)(-3)(-3) = 81$; $\sqrt[4]{81} = |-3| = 3$

51. If n is a positive integer and $a^n = b$, then

$$\sqrt[n]{b} = \begin{cases} |a|, & \text{if } n \text{ is even} \\ a, & \text{if } n \text{ is odd} \end{cases}$$

10.2 Preparing for Circles

1. Start: $x^2 - 8x$

Add: $\left(\dfrac{1}{2} \cdot (-8)\right)^2 = 16$

Result: $x^2 - 8x + 16$

Factored Form: $(x-4)^2$

10.2 Exercises

1. circle

3. FALSE. The center is $(-1, 3)$.

5. Answers may vary. One possibility follows: If a circle has center (h,k) and radius r, then the distance from the center to any point (x, y) on that circle must always be r. By the distance formula, we have $r = \sqrt{(x-h)^2 + (y-k)^2}$.

Now, if we square both sides of this formula, we obtain the standard equation of the circle:

$(x-h)^2 + (y-k)^2 = r^2$.

7. Yes, $x^2 = 36 - y^2$ is the equation of a circle. In standard form, the equation is

$$x^2 + y^2 = 36$$
$$(x-0)^2 + (y-0)^2 = 6^2$$

The center is $(0,0)$, and the radius is 6.

9. The center of the circle is $(1,2)$. The radius of the circle is the distance from the center point to the point $(-1,2)$ on the circle. Thus,

$$r = \sqrt{(1-(-1))^2 + (2-2)^2} = 2 .$$

The equation of the circle is

$$(x-h)^2 + (y-k)^2 = r^2$$
$$(x-1)^2 + (y-2)^2 = 2^2$$
$$(x-1)^2 + (y-2)^2 = 4$$

11. The center of the circle will be the midpoint of the line segment with endpoints $(-2,-1)$ and $(6,-1)$.

Thus, $(h,k) = \left(\dfrac{-2+6}{2}, \dfrac{-1+(-1)}{2}\right) = (2,-1)$. The

radius of the circle will be the distance from the center point $(2,-1)$ to a point on the circle, say

$(6,-1)$. Thus, $r = \sqrt{(6-2)^2 + (-1-(-1))^2} = 4$.

The equation of the circle is

$$(x-h)^2 + (y-k)^2 = r^2$$
$$(x-2)^2 + (y-(-1))^2 = 4^2$$
$$(x-2)^2 + (y+1)^2 = 16$$

13. $(x-h)^2 + (y-k)^2 = r^2$
$(x-0)^2 + (y-0)^2 = 3^2$
$x^2 + y^2 = 9$

15. $(x-h)^2 + (y-k)^2 = r^2$
$(x-1)^2 + (y-4)^2 = 2^2$
$(x-1)^2 + (y-4)^2 = 4$

17. $(x-h)^2 + (y-k)^2 = r^2$
$(x-(-2))^2 + (y-4)^2 = 6^2$
$(x+2)^2 + (y-4)^2 = 36$

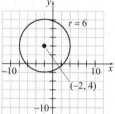

19. $(x-h)^2 + (y-k)^2 = r^2$
$(x-0)^2 + (y-3)^2 = 4^2$
$x^2 + (y-3)^2 = 16$

21. $(x-h)^2 + (y-k)^2 = r^2$
$(x-5)^2 + (y-(-5))^2 = 5^2$
$(x-5)^2 + (y+5)^2 = 25$

23. $(x-h)^2 + (y-k)^2 = r^2$

$(x-1)^2 + (y-2)^2 = \left(\sqrt{5}\right)^2$

$(x-1)^2 + (y-2)^2 = 5$

25. $\qquad x^2 + y^2 = 36$

$(x-0)^2 + (y-0)^2 = 6^2$

The center is $(h,k) = (0,0)$, and the radius is $r = 6$.

27. $(x-4)^2 + (y-1)^2 = 25$

$(x-4)^2 + (y-1)^2 = 5^2$

The center is $(h,k) = (4,1)$, and the radius is $r = 5$.

29. $\qquad (x+3)^2 + (y-2)^2 = 81$

$(x-(-3))^2 + (y-2)^2 = 9^2$

The center is $(h,k) = (-3,2)$, and the radius is $r = 9$.

31. $\qquad x^2 + (y-3)^2 = 64$

$(x-0)^2 + (y-3)^2 = 8^2$

The center is $(h,k) = (0,3)$, and the radius is $r = 8$.

33. $\quad (x-1)^2 + (y+1)^2 = \dfrac{1}{4}$

$(x-1)^2 + (y-(-1))^2 = \left(\dfrac{1}{2}\right)^2$

The center is $(h,k) = (1,-1)$, and the radius is

$r = \dfrac{1}{2}$.

35. $\qquad x^2 + y^2 - 6x + 2y + 1 = 0$

$(x^2 - 6x) + (y^2 + 2y) = -1$

$(x^2 - 6x + 9) + (y^2 + 2y + 1) = -1 + 9 + 1$

$(x-3)^2 + (y+1)^2 = 9$

$(x-3)^2 + (y-(-1))^2 = 3^2$

The center is $(h,k) = (3,-1)$, and the radius is $r = 3$.

37.
$$x^2 + y^2 + 10x + 4y + 4 = 0$$
$$\left(x^2 + 10x\right) + \left(y^2 + 4y\right) = -4$$
$$\left(x^2 + 10x + 25\right) + \left(y^2 + 4y + 4\right) = -4 + 25 + 4$$
$$\left(x + 5\right)^2 + \left(y + 2\right)^2 = 25$$
$$\left(x - (-5)\right)^2 + \left(y - (-2)\right)^2 = 5^2$$

The center is $(h, k) = (-5, -2)$, and the radius is $r = 5$.

39.
$$2x^2 + 2y^2 - 12x + 24y - 72 = 0$$
$$\frac{2x^2 + 2y^2 - 12x + 24y - 72}{2} = \frac{0}{2}$$
$$x^2 + y^2 - 6x + 12y - 36 = 0$$
$$\left(x^2 - 6x\right) + \left(y^2 + 12y\right) = 36$$
$$\left(x^2 - 6x + 9\right) + \left(y^2 + 12y + 36\right) = 36 + 9 + 36$$
$$\left(x - 3\right)^2 + \left(y + 6\right)^2 = 81$$
$$\left(x - 3\right)^2 + \left(y - (-6)\right)^2 = 9^2$$

The center is $(h, k) = (3, -6)$, and the radius is $r = 9$.

41. The radius of the circle will be the distance from the center point $(0, 0)$ to the point on the circle $(4, -2)$. Thus,
$$r = \sqrt{(4-0)^2 + (-2-0)^2} = \sqrt{20} = 2\sqrt{5}.$$
The equation of the circle is
$$\left(x - h\right)^2 + \left(y - k\right)^2 = r^2$$
$$\left(x - 0\right)^2 + \left(y - 0\right)^2 = \left(2\sqrt{5}\right)^2$$
$$x^2 + y^2 = 20$$

43. Since the center of the circle is $(-3, 2)$ and since the circle is tangent to the y-axis, the circle must contain the point $(0, 2)$. The radius of the circle will be the distance from the center point $(-3, 2)$ to the point on the circle $(0, 2)$. Thus,
$$r = \sqrt{(-3-0)^2 + (2-2)^2} = 3.$$
The equation of the circle is
$$\left(x - h\right)^2 + \left(y - k\right)^2 = r^2$$
$$\left(x - (-3)\right)^2 + \left(y - 2\right)^2 = 3^2$$
$$\left(x + 3\right)^2 + \left(y - 2\right)^2 = 9$$

45. The center of the circle will be the midpoint of the diameter with endpoints $(2, 3)$ and $(-4, -5)$.
Thus, $(h, k) = \left(\dfrac{2 + (-4)}{2}, \dfrac{3 + (-5)}{2}\right) = (-1, -1)$.

The radius of the circle will be the distance from the center point $(-1, -1)$ to one of the endpoints of the diameter, say $(2, 3)$. Thus,
$$r = \sqrt{(2 - (-1))^2 + (3 - (-1))^2} = 5.$$
The equation of the circle is
$$\left(x - h\right)^2 + \left(y - k\right)^2 = r^2$$
$$\left(x - (-1)\right)^2 + \left(y - (-1)\right)^2 = 5^2$$
$$\left(x + 1\right)^2 + \left(y + 1\right)^2 = 25$$

47. The radius of the circle $\left(x - 3\right)^2 + \left(y - 8\right)^2 = 64$ is $r = \sqrt{64} = 8$. Thus, the area of the circle is
$$A = \pi r^2 = \pi(8)^2 = 64\pi \text{ square units.}$$
The circumference of the circle is
$$C = 2\pi r = 2\pi(8) = 16\pi \text{ units.}$$

49. To find the area of the square, we must first find the length of the square's sides. To do so, we recognize that the x- and y-coordinates of the corner point in the first quadrant where the square touches the circle must be equal. That is, $x = y$.

Thus, $x^2 + y^2 = 16$

$$x^2 + x^2 = 16$$
$$2x^2 = 16$$
$$x^2 = 8$$
$$x = \sqrt{8} = 2\sqrt{2}$$

This means the length of each side of the square is $s = 2x = 2\left(2\sqrt{2}\right) = 4\sqrt{2}$, and the area of the square is $A = s^2 = \left(4\sqrt{2}\right)^2 = 32$ square units.

51. The circle shown has its center point on the positive x-axis. Thus, the center point will be of the form $(h, 0)$ with $h > 0$. Also, the entire circle stays to the right of the y-axis, so $h > r$.

   a. $(x-2)^2 + y^2 = 1$ has center $(2,0)$ and radius $r = 1$, which meets the proper conditions. Thus, this equation <u>could</u> have the graph shown.

   b. $x^2 + (y-2)^2 = 1$ has center $(0,2)$, which is not on the x-axis. Thus, this equation could <u>not</u> have the graph shown.

   c. $(x+4)^2 + y^2 = 9$ has center $(-4,0)$, which is on the negative x-axis, not on the positive x-axis. Thus, this equation could <u>not</u> have the graph shown.

   d. $(x-5)^2 + y^2 = 25$ has center $(5,0)$ and radius $r = 5$. This means the graph of this circle would pass through the origin. Thus, this equation could <u>not</u> have the graph shown.

   e. $x^2 + y^2 - 8x + 7 = 0$

   $$\left(x^2 - 8x + 16\right) + y^2 = -7 + 16$$
   $$(x-4)^2 + y^2 = 9$$

   This circle has center $(4,0)$ and radius $r = 3$, which meets the proper conditions. Thus, this equation <u>could</u> have the graph shown.

   f. $x^2 + y^2 + 10x + 18 = 0$

   $$\left(x^2 + 10x + 25\right) + y^2 = -18 + 25$$
   $$(x+5)^2 + y^2 = 7$$

   This circle has center $(-5,0)$, which is on the negative x-axis, not on the positive x-axis. Thus, this equation could <u>not</u> have the graph shown.

53. $f(x) = 4x - 3$

To use point plotting, let $x = -1$, 0, and 1.

$$f(-1) = 4(-1) - 3 = -4 - 3 = -7$$
$$f(0) = 4(0) - 3 = 0 - 3 = -3$$
$$f(1) = 4(1) - 3 = 4 - 3 = 1$$

Thus, the points $(-1, -7)$, $(0, -3)$, and $(1, 1)$ are on the graph.

Using properties of linear functions, for $f(x) = 4x - 3$, the slope is 4 and the y-intercept is -3. Begin at $(0, -3)$ and move to the right 1 unit and up 4 units to find point $(1, 1)$.

55. $g(x) = x^2 - 4x - 5$

To use point plotting, let $x = 0$, 1, 2, 3, and 4.

$$g(0) = 0^2 - 4(0) - 5 = 0 - 0 - 5 = -5$$
$$g(1) = 1^2 - 4(1) - 5 = 1 - 4 - 5 = -8$$
$$g(2) = 2^2 - 4(2) - 5 = 4 - 8 - 5 = -9$$
$$g(3) = 3^2 - 4(3) - 5 = 9 - 12 - 5 = -8$$
$$g(4) = 4^2 - 4(4) - 5 = 16 - 16 - 5 = -5$$

Thus, the points $(0, -5)$, $(1, -8)$, $(2, -9)$, $(3, -8)$, and $(4, -5)$ are on the graph.

Using properties of quadratic functions, for
$g(x) = x^2 - 4x - 5$, $a = 1$, $b = -4$, and $c = -5$.
The graph opens up because the coefficient on
x^2 is positive.

vertex:
$$x = -\frac{b}{2a} = -\frac{(-4)}{2(1)} = 2$$
$$g(2) = (2)^2 - 4(2) - 5 = -9$$
The vertex is $(2, -9)$ and the axis of symmetry
is $x = 2$.

y-intercept:
$$g(0) = (0)^2 - 4(0) - 5 = -5$$

x-intercepts:
$$b^2 - 4ac = (-4)^2 - 4(1)(-5) = 36 > 0$$
There are two distinct x-intercepts. We find these
by solving
$$g(x) = 0$$
$$x^2 - 4x - 5 = 0$$
$$(x-5)(x+1) = 0$$
$$x - 5 = 0 \text{ or } x + 1 = 0$$
$$x = 5 \text{ or } x = -1$$

Graph:
The y-intercept point, $(0, -5)$, is two units to the
left of the axis of symmetry. Therefore, if we
move two units to the right of the axis of
symmetry, we obtain the point $(4, -5)$ which
must also be on the graph.

57. $G(x) = -2(x+3)^2 - 5$

To use point plotting, let $x = -4, -3$, and -2.
$$G(-4) = -2(-4+3)^2 - 5$$
$$= -2(-1)^2 - 5$$
$$= -2(1) - 5$$
$$= -2 - 5$$
$$= -7$$

$$G(-3) = -2(-3+3)^2 - 5$$
$$= -2(0)^2 - 5$$
$$= -2(0) - 5$$
$$= 0 - 5$$
$$= -5$$

$$G(-2) = -2(-2+3)^2 - 5$$
$$= -2(1)^2 - 5$$
$$= -2(1) - 5$$
$$= -2 - 5$$
$$= -7$$

Thus, the points $(-4, -7)$, $(-3, -5)$, and $(-2, -7)$
are on the graph.

Using properties of quadratic functions, begin
with the graph of $y = x^2$, then shift the graph 3
units to the left to obtain the graph of
$y = (x+3)^2$. Multiply the y-coordinates by -2
to obtain the graph of $y = -2(x+3)^2$. Lastly,
shift the graph down 5 units to obtain the graph
of $G(x) = -2(x+3)^2 - 5$.

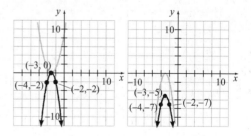

59. $x^2 + y^2 = 36$

$$y^2 = 36 - x^2$$

$$y = \pm\sqrt{36 - x^2}$$

Let $Y_1 = \sqrt{36 - x^2}$ and $Y_2 = -\sqrt{36 - x^2}$.

The graph here agrees with that in Problem 25.

61. $(x-4)^2 + (y-1)^2 = 25$

$$(y-1)^2 = 25 - (x-4)^2$$

$$y - 1 = \pm\sqrt{25 - (x-4)^2}$$

$$y = 1 \pm \sqrt{25 - (x-4)^2}$$

Let $Y_1 = 1 + \sqrt{25 - (x-4)^2}$ and

$Y_2 = 1 - \sqrt{25 - (x-4)^2}$.

The graph here agrees with that in Problem 27.

63. $(x+3)^2 + (y-2)^2 = 81$

$$(y-2)^2 = 81 - (x+3)^2$$

$$y - 2 = \pm\sqrt{81 - (x+3)^2}$$

$$y = 2 \pm \sqrt{81 - (x+3)^2}$$

Let $Y_1 = 2 + \sqrt{81 - (x+3)^2}$ and $Y_2 = 2 - \sqrt{81 - (x+3)^2}$.

The graph here agrees with that in Problem 29.

65. $x^2 + (y-3)^2 = 64$

$$(y-3)^2 = 64 - x^2$$

$$y - 3 = \pm\sqrt{64 - x^2}$$

$$y = 3 \pm \sqrt{64 - x^2}$$

Let $Y_1 = 3 + \sqrt{64 - x^2}$ and $Y_2 = 3 - \sqrt{64 - x^2}$.

The graph here agrees with that in Problem 31.

67. $(x-1)^2 + (y+1)^2 = \dfrac{1}{4}$

$$(y+1)^2 = \frac{1}{4} - (x-1)^2$$

$$y + 1 = \pm\sqrt{\frac{1}{4} - (x-1)^2}$$

$$y = -1 \pm \sqrt{\frac{1}{4} - (x-1)^2}$$

Let $Y_1 = -1 + \sqrt{\dfrac{1}{4} - (x-1)^2}$ and

$Y_2 = -1 - \sqrt{\dfrac{1}{4} - (x-1)^2}$.

The graph here agrees with that in Problem 33.

10.3 Preparing for Parabolas

1. For the function $f(x) = -3(x+4)^2 - 5$, we see that $a = -3$, $h = -4$, and $k = -5$. Thus, the vertex is $(h,\ k) = (-4, -5)$, and the axis of symmetry is $x = -4$. The parabola opens down since $a = -3 < 0$.

2. For the function $f(x) = 2x^2 - 8x + 1$, we see that $a = 2$, $b = -8$, and $c = 1$. The x-coordinate of the vertex is $x = -\dfrac{b}{2a} = -\dfrac{(-8)}{2(2)} = 2$. The y-coordinate of the vertex is

$$f\left(-\frac{b}{2a}\right) = f(2)$$
$$= 2(2)^2 - 8(2) + 1$$
$$= 8 - 16 + 1$$
$$= -7$$

Thus, the vertex is $(2, -7)$ and the axis of symmetry is the line $x = 2$. The parabola opens up because $a = 2 > 0$.

3. Start: $x^2 - 12x$

Add: $\left(\dfrac{1}{2} \cdot (-12)\right)^2 = 36$

Result: $x^2 - 12x + 36$

Factored Form: $(x - 6)^2$

4. $(x - 3)^2 = 25$
$$x - 3 = \pm\sqrt{25}$$
$$x - 3 = \pm 5$$
$$x = 3 \pm 5$$
$$x = 3 - 5 \quad \text{or} \quad x = 3 + 5$$
$$x = -2 \quad \text{or} \quad x = 8$$

The solution set is $\{-2, 8\}$.

10.3 Exercises

1. Conics

3. vertex

5. FALSE. The parabola opens downward.

7. If the distance from the point on the parabola to the focus is 8 units, then by the definition of a parabola, the distance from the same point on the parabola to the directrix must also be 8 units.

9. Answers may vary. One possibility follows:

11. c. The parabola opens upward and has vertex $(0,0)$ and focus $(0,2)$, so the equation is of the form $x^2 = 4ay$ with $a = 2$:
$$x^2 = 4(2)y$$
$$x^2 = 8y$$

13. a. The parabola opens to the right and has vertex $(0,0)$ and focus $(2,0)$, so the equation is of the form $y^2 = 4ax$ with $a = 2$:
$$y^2 = 4(2)x$$
$$y^2 = 8x$$

15. b. The parabola opens to the left and has vertex $(0,0)$ and focus $(-2,0)$, so the equation is of the form $y^2 = -4ax$ with $a = 2$:
$$y^2 = -4(2)x$$
$$y^2 = -8x$$

17. e. The parabola opens to the right and has vertex $(-1, 2)$ and focus $(1, 2)$, so the equation is of the form $(y-k)^2 = 4a(x-h)$, with $a = 1 - (-1) = 2$, $h = -1$, and $k = 2$:
$$(y-2)^2 = 4 \cdot 2(x - (-1))$$
$$(y-2)^2 = 8(x+1)$$

19. The distance from the vertex $(0,0)$ to the focus $(5,0)$ is $a = 5$. Because the focus lies on the positive x-axis, we know that the parabola will open to the right and the axis of symmetry is the x-axis. This means the equation of the parabola is of the form $y^2 = 4ax$ with $a = 5$:
$$y^2 = 4(5)x$$
$$y^2 = 20x$$

The directrix is the line $x = -5$. To help graph the parabola, we plot the two points on the graph

above and below the focus. Let $x = 5$:
$$y^2 = 20(5) = 100$$
$$y = \pm 10$$
The points $(5, -10)$ and $(5, 10)$ are on the graph.

21. The distance from the vertex $(0,0)$ to the focus $(0, -6)$ is $a = 6$. Because the focus lies on the negative y-axis, we know that the parabola will open downward and the axis of symmetry is the y-axis. This means the equation of the parabola is of the form $x^2 = -4ay$ with $a = 6$:
$$x^2 = -4(6)y$$
$$x^2 = -24y$$
The directrix is the line $y = 6$. To help graph the parabola, we plot the two points on the graph to the left and right of the focus. Let $y = -6$:
$$x^2 = -24(-6) = 144$$
$$x = \pm 12$$
The points $(-12, -6)$ and $(12, -6)$ are on the graph.

23. The vertex is at the origin and the axis of symmetry is the y-axis, so the parabola either opens upward or downward. Because the graph contains the point $(6, 6)$, which is in quadrant I, the parabola must open upward. Therefore, the equation of the parabola is of the form $x^2 = 4ay$.
Now $y = 6$ when $x = 6$, so
$$x^2 = 4ay$$
$$6^2 = 4a(6)$$
$$36 = 24a$$
$$a = \frac{36}{24} = \frac{3}{2}$$

The equation of the parabola is
$$x^2 = 4\left(\frac{3}{2}\right)y$$
$$x^2 = 6y$$
With $a = \frac{3}{2}$, we know that the focus is $\left(0, \frac{3}{2}\right)$ and the directrix is the line $y = -\frac{3}{2}$. To help graph the parabola, we plot the two points on the graph to the left and right of the focus. Let $y = \frac{3}{2}$:
$$x^2 = 6\left(\frac{3}{2}\right)$$
$$x^2 = 9$$
$$x = \pm 3$$
The points $\left(-3, \frac{3}{2}\right)$ and $\left(3, \frac{3}{2}\right)$ are on the graph.

25. The vertex is at the origin and the directrix is the line $y = 3$, so the focus must be $(0, -3)$. Accordingly, the parabola opens downward with $a = 3$. This means the equation of the parabola is of the form $x^2 = -4ay$ with $a = 3$:
$$x^2 = -4(3)y$$
$$x^2 = -12y$$
To help graph the parabola, we plot the two points on the graph to the left and right of the focus. Let $y = -3$:
$$x^2 = -12(-3) = 36$$
$$x = \pm 6$$
The points $(-6, -3)$ and $(6, -3)$ are on the graph.

27. Notice that the directrix is the vertical line $x = 3$ and that the focus $(-3, 0)$ is on the x-axis. Thus, the axis of symmetry is the x-axis, the vertex is at the origin, and the parabola opens to the left. Now, the distance from the vertex $(0, 0)$ to the focus $(-3, 0)$ is $a = 3$, so the equation of the parabola is of the form $y^2 = -4ax$ with $a = 3$:

$$y^2 = -4(3)x$$
$$y^2 = -12x$$

To help graph the parabola, we plot the two points on the graph above and below the focus. Let $x = -3$:

$$y^2 = -12(-3) = 36$$
$$y = \pm 6$$

The points $(-3, -6)$ and $(-3, 6)$ are on the graph.

29. Notice that $x^2 = 24y$ is of the form $x^2 = 4ay$, where $4a = 24$, so that $a = 6$. Now, the graph of an equation of the form $x^2 = 4ay$ will be a parabola that opens upward with the vertex at the origin, focus at $(0, a)$, and directrix of $y = -a$. Thus, the graph of $x^2 = 24y$ is a parabola that opens upward with vertex $(0, 0)$, focus $(0, 6)$, and directrix $y = -6$. To help graph the parabola, we plot the two points on the graph to the left and to the right of the focus. Let $y = 6$:

$$x^2 = 24(6)$$
$$x^2 = 144$$
$$x = \pm 12$$

The points $(-12, 6)$ and $(12, 6)$ are on the graph.

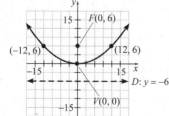

31. Notice that $y^2 = -6x$ is of the form $y^2 = -4ax$, where $-4a = -6$, so that $a = \dfrac{-6}{-4} = \dfrac{3}{2}$. Now, the graph of an equation of the form $y^2 = -4ax$ will be a parabola that opens to the left with the vertex at the origin, focus at $(-a, 0)$, and directrix of $x = a$. Thus, the graph of $y^2 = -6x$ is a parabola that opens to the left with vertex $(0, 0)$, focus $\left(-\dfrac{3}{2}, 0\right)$, and directrix $x = \dfrac{3}{2}$. To help graph the parabola, we plot the two points on the graph above and below the focus. Let $x = -\dfrac{3}{2}$:

$$y^2 = -6\left(-\dfrac{3}{2}\right)$$
$$y^2 = 9$$
$$y = \pm 3$$

The points $\left(-\dfrac{3}{2}, -3\right)$ and $\left(-\dfrac{3}{2}, 3\right)$ are on the graph.

33. Notice that $x^2 = -8y$ is of the form $x^2 = -4ay$, where $-4a = -8$, so that $a = 2$. Now, the graph of an equation of the form $x^2 = -4ay$ will be a parabola that opens downward with the vertex at the origin, focus at $(0, -a)$, and directrix of $y = a$. Thus, the graph of $x^2 = -8y$ is a parabola that opens downward with vertex $(0, 0)$, focus $(0, -2)$, and directrix $y = 2$. To help graph the parabola, we plot the two points on the graph to the left and to the right of the focus. Let $y = -2$:

$$x^2 = -8(-2)$$
$$x^2 = 16$$
$$x = \pm 4$$

The points $(-4, -2)$ and $(4, -2)$ are on the graph.

35. Notice that $(x-2)^2 = 4(y-4)$ is of the form $(x-h)^2 = 4a(y-k)$, where $4a = 4$, so that $a = 1$ and $(h,k) = (2,\ 4)$. Now, the graph of an equation of the form $(x-h)^2 = 4a(y-k)$ will be a parabola that opens upward with vertex at (h,k), focus at $(h,k+a)$, and directrix of $y = k-a$. Note that $k+a = 4+1 = 5$ and $k-a = 4-1 = 3$. Thus, the graph of $(x-2)^2 = 4(y-4)$ is a parabola that opens upward with vertex $(2,\ 4)$, focus $(2,\ 5)$, and directrix $y = 3$. To help graph the parabola, we plot the two points to the left and to the right of the focus. Let $y = 5$:

$$(x-2)^2 = 4(5-4)$$
$$(x-2)^2 = 4(1)$$
$$(x-2)^2 = 4$$
$$x-2 = \pm 2$$
$$x = 2 \pm 2$$
$$x = 0 \ \text{ or } \ x = 4$$

The points $(0,\ 5)$ and $(4,\ 5)$ are on the graph.

37. Notice that $(y+3)^2 = -8(x+2)$ is of the form $(y-k)^2 = -4a(x-h)$, where $(h,k) = (-2,-3)$ and $-4a = -8$, so that $a = 2$. Now, the graph of an equation of the form $(y-k)^2 = -4a(x-h)$ will be a parabola that opens to the left with the vertex at (h,k), focus at $(h-a,k)$, and directrix of $x = h+a$. Note that $h-a = -2-2 = -4$ and $h+a = -2+2 = 0$. Thus, the graph of $(y+3)^2 = -8(x+2)$ is a parabola that opens to

the left with vertex $(-2,-3)$, focus $(-4,-3)$, and directrix $x = 0$. To help graph the parabola, we plot the two points on the graph above and below the focus. Let $x = -4$:

$$(y+3)^2 = -8(-4+2)$$
$$(y+3)^2 = -8(-2)$$
$$(y+3)^2 = 16$$
$$y+3 = \pm 4$$
$$y = -3 \pm 4$$
$$y = -7 \ \text{ or } \ y = 1$$

The points $(-4,-7)$ and $(-4,\ 1)$ are on the graph.

39. Notice that $(x+5)^2 = -20(y-1)$ is of the form $(x-h)^2 = -4a(y-k)$, where $(h,k) = (-5,1)$ and $-4a = -20$, so that $a = 5$. Now, the graph of an equation of the form $(x-h)^2 = -4a(y-k)$ will be a parabola that opens downward with the vertex at (h,k), focus at $(h,k-a)$, and directrix of $y = k+a$. Note that $k-a = 1-5 = -4$ and $k+a = 1+5 = 6$. Thus, the graph of $(x+5)^2 = -20(y-1)$ is a parabola that opens downward with vertex $(-5,\ 1)$, focus $(-5,-4)$, and directrix $y = 6$. To help graph the parabola, we plot the two points on the graph to the left and right of the focus. Let $y = -4$:

$$(x+5)^2 = -20(-4-1)$$
$$(x+5)^2 = -20(-5)$$
$$(x+5)^2 = 100$$
$$x+5 = \pm 10$$
$$x = -5 \pm 10$$
$$x = -15 \ \text{ or } \ x = 5$$

The points $(-15,-4)$ and $(5,-4)$ are on the graph.

41. We complete the square in x to write the equation in standard form:

$$x^2 + 4x + 12y + 16 = 0$$
$$x^2 + 4x = -12y - 16$$
$$x^2 + 4x + 4 = -12y - 16 + 4$$
$$x^2 + 4x + 4 = -12y - 12$$
$$(x+2)^2 = -12(y+1)$$

Notice that $(x+2)^2 = -12(y+1)$ is of the form $(x-h)^2 = -4a(y-k)$, where $(h,k) = (-2,-1)$ and $-4a = -12$, so that $a = 3$. Now, the graph of an equation of the form $(x-h)^2 = -4a(y-k)$ will be a parabola that opens downward with the vertex at (h,k), focus at $(h, k-a)$, and directrix of $y = k+a$. Note that $k - a = -1 - 3 = -4$ and $k + a = -1 + 3 = 2$. Thus, the graph of $(x+2)^2 = -12(y+1)$ is a parabola that opens downward with vertex $(-2,-1)$, focus $(-2,-4)$, and directrix $y = 2$. To help graph the parabola, we plot the two points on the graph to the left and right of the focus. Let $y = -4$:

$$(x+2)^2 = -12(-4+1)$$
$$(x+2)^2 = -12(-3)$$
$$(x+2)^2 = 36$$
$$x + 2 = \pm 6$$
$$x = -2 \pm 6$$
$$x = -8 \text{ or } x = 4$$

The points $(-8,-4)$ and $(4,-4)$ are on the graph.

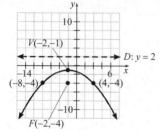

43. We complete the square in y to write the equation in standard form:

$$y^2 - 8y - 4x + 20 = 0$$
$$y^2 - 8y = 4x - 20$$
$$y^2 - 8y + 16 = 4x - 20 + 16$$
$$y^2 - 8y + 16 = 4x - 4$$
$$(y-4)^2 = 4(x-1)$$

Notice that $(y-4)^2 = 4(x-1)$ is of the form $(y-k)^2 = 4a(x-h)$, where $(h,k) = (1,4)$ and $4a = 4$, so that $a = 1$. Now, the graph of an equation of the form $(y-k)^2 = 4a(x-h)$ will be a parabola that opens to the right with the vertex at (h,k), focus at $(h+a,k)$, and directrix of $x = h-a$. Note that $h + a = 1 + 1 = 2$ and $h - a = 1 - 1 = 0$. Thus, the graph of $(y-4)^2 = 4(x-1)$ is a parabola that opens to the right with vertex $(1, 4)$, focus $(2, 4)$, and directrix $x = 0$. To help graph the parabola, we plot the two points on the graph above and below the focus. Let $x = 2$:

$$(y-4)^2 = 4(2-1)$$
$$(y-4)^2 = 4$$
$$y - 4 = \pm 2$$
$$y = 4 \pm 2$$
$$y = 2 \text{ or } y = 6$$

The points $(2, 2)$ and $(2, 6)$ are on the graph.

45. We complete the square in x to write the equation in standard form:

$$x^2 + 10x + 6y + 13 = 0$$
$$x^2 + 10x = -6y - 13$$
$$x^2 + 10x + 25 = -6y - 13 + 25$$
$$x^2 + 10x + 25 = -6y + 12$$
$$(x+5)^2 = -6(y-2)$$

Notice that $(x+5)^2 = -6(y-2)$ is of the form $(x-h)^2 = -4a(y-k)$, where $(h,k) = (-5,2)$ and $-4a = -6$, so that $a = \dfrac{-6}{-4} = \dfrac{3}{2}$. Now, the graph of an equation of the form $(x-h)^2 = -4a(y-k)$ will be a parabola that opens downward with the vertex at (h,k), focus at $(h,k-a)$, and directrix of $y=k+a$. Note that $k-a = 2-\dfrac{3}{2} = \dfrac{1}{2}$ and $k+a = 2+\dfrac{3}{2} = \dfrac{7}{2}$.

Thus, the graph of $(x+5)^2 = -6(y-2)$ is a parabola that opens downward with vertex $\left(-5,2\right)$, focus $\left(-5,\dfrac{1}{2}\right)$, and directrix $y=\dfrac{7}{2}$.

To help graph the parabola, we plot the two points on the graph to the left and right of the

focus. Let $y=\dfrac{1}{2}$:

$$(x+5)^2 = -6\left(\dfrac{1}{2}-2\right)$$
$$(x+5)^2 = -6\left(-\dfrac{3}{2}\right)$$
$$(x+5)^2 = 9$$
$$x+5 = \pm 3$$
$$x = -5 \pm 3$$
$$x = -8 \text{ or } x = -2$$

The points $\left(-8,\dfrac{1}{2}\right)$ and $\left(-2,\dfrac{1}{2}\right)$ are on the graph.

47. The parabola opens to the right and has vertex $(0, 0)$, so the equation must have the form $y^2 = 4ax$. Because the point $(4, 2)$ is on the parabola, we let $x=4$ and $y=2$ to determine a:

$$2^2 = 4a(4)$$
$$4 = 16a$$
$$a = \dfrac{4}{16} = \dfrac{1}{4}$$

Thus, the equation of the parabola is

$$y^2 = 4\left(\dfrac{1}{4}\right)x$$
$$y^2 = x$$

49. The light bulb should be located at the focus of the headlight, so we need to find where the focus of the headlight is. To solve this problem, we draw a parabola on a Cartesian plane so that the vertex is the origin and the focus is on the positive y-axis. The width of the parabola is 4 inches, and the depth is 1 inch. Therefore, we know two points on the graph of the parabola: $(-2, 1)$ and $(2, 1)$.

The equation of the parabola has the form $x^2 = 4ay$. Since $(2, 1)$ is a point on the graph, we have

$$2^2 = 4a(1)$$
$$4 = 4a$$
$$1 = a$$

The light bulb should be located 1 inch above the vertex, along its axis of symmetry.

51. To solve this problem, we draw a parabola on a Cartesian plane so that the vertex is the origin and the focus is on the positive y-axis. The distance between the towers is 500 feet, and the height of the towers is 60 feet. Therefore, we know two points on the graph of the parabola: $(-250, 60)$ and $(250, 60)$.

The equation of the parabola has the form $x^2 = 4ay$. Since $(250, 60)$ is a point on the graph, we have

$$250^2 = 4a(60)$$
$$62{,}500 = 240a$$
$$a = \dfrac{62{,}500}{240} = \dfrac{3125}{12}$$

Then the equation of the parabola is

$$x^2 = 4\left(\dfrac{3125}{12}\right)y$$
$$x^2 = \dfrac{3125}{3}y$$

To find the height of the cable at a point 150 feet from the center of the bridge, let $x=150$:

$$150^2 = \frac{3125}{3}y$$

$$22{,}500 = \frac{3125}{3}y$$

$$y = \frac{3}{3125} \cdot 22{,}500 = 21.6$$

At a point 150 feet from the center of the bridge, the height of the cable is 21.6 feet.

53. To solve this problem, we draw a parabola on a Cartesian plane so that the vertex is on the positive y-axis and the base of the bridge is along the x-axis. The maximum height of the bridge is 30 feet, so we know the vertex of the parabola is $(0, 30)$. The span of the bridge is 100 feet, so we know two other points on the graph of the parabola: $(-50, 0)$ and $(50, 0)$.

Because the parabola opens downward, its equation has the form $(x-h)^2 = -4a(y-k)$. Substituting the vertex $(h,k) = (0, 30)$ into this equation, we obtain

$$(x-0)^2 = -4a(y-30)$$
$$x^2 = -4a(y-30)$$

Because the point $(50, 0)$ is on the parabola, we let $x = 50$ and $y = 0$ to determine a:

$$50^2 = -4a(0-30)$$
$$2500 = 120a$$
$$a = \frac{2500}{120} = \frac{125}{6}$$

Thus, the equation of the parabola is

$$x^2 = -4 \cdot \frac{125}{6}(y-30)$$
$$x^2 = -\frac{250}{3}(y-30)$$

To find the height of the bridge at points 10, 30, and 50 feet from the center of the bridge, let $x = 10$, 30, and 50 respectively:

$$x=10: \quad 10^2 = -\frac{250}{3}(y-30)$$
$$100 = -\frac{250}{3}(y-30)$$
$$300 = -250(y-30)$$
$$-1.2 = y-30$$
$$28.8 = y$$

$$x=30: \quad 30^2 = -\frac{250}{3}(y-30)$$
$$900 = -\frac{250}{3}(y-30)$$
$$2700 = -250(y-30)$$
$$-10.8 = y-30$$
$$19.2 = y$$

$$x=50: \quad 50^2 = -\frac{250}{3}(y-30)$$
$$2500 = -\frac{250}{3}(y-30)$$
$$7500 = -250(y-30)$$
$$-30 = y-30$$
$$0 = y$$

The height of the bridge is 28.8 feet at a distance of 10 feet from the center, 19.2 feet at a distance of 30 feet from the center, and 0 feet (i.e. ground level) at a distance of 50 feet from the center.

55. The parabola opens upward, so the equation must have the form $(x-h)^2 = 4a(y-k)$. Substituting the vertex $(h,k) = (3,-2)$ into this equation, we obtain $(x-3)^2 = 4a(y+2)$. Because the point $(5,-1)$ is on the parabola, we let $x = 5$ and $y = -1$ to determine a:

$$(5-3)^2 = 4a(-1+2)$$
$$2^2 = 4a(1)$$
$$4 = 4a$$
$$1 = a$$

Thus, the equation of the parabola is

$$(x-3)^2 = 4 \cdot 1(y+2)$$
$$(x-3)^2 = 4(y+2)$$

57. The parabola opens to the left, so the equation must have the form $(y-k)^2 = -4a(x-h)$. Substituting the vertex $(h,k) = (2, 3)$ into this equation, we obtain $(y-3)^2 = -4a(x-2)$. Because the point $(-2,-1)$ is on the parabola, we let $x = -2$ and $y = -1$ to determine a:

$$(-1-3)^2 = -4a(-2-2)$$
$$(-4)^2 = -4a(-4)$$
$$16 = 16a$$
$$1 = a$$

Thus, the equation of the parabola is

$$(y-3)^2 = -4 \cdot 1(x-2)$$
$$(y-3)^2 = -4(x-2)$$

59. $x^2 = 8y$

   a. Let $x = 4$ and $y = 2$:

      $4^2 \overset{?}{=} 8 \cdot 2$

      $16 = 16 \leftarrow$ True

      Thus, the point $(4,\ 2)$ in on the parabola.

   b. Notice that $x^2 = 8y$ is of the form

      $x^2 = 4ay$, where $4a = 8$, so that $a = 2$.

      Thus, the focus of the parabola is $F(0,\ 2)$,

      and the directrix is $D: y = -2$. Now, the

      distance from the point $P(4,\ 2)$ to the focus

      is $d(F,P) = \sqrt{(0-4)^2 + (2-2)^2} = \sqrt{16} = 4$,

      and the distance from the point $P(4,\ 2)$ to

      the directrix $D: y = -2$ is

      $d(P,D) = 2 - (-2) = 4$.

      Thus, $d(F,P) = d(P,D) = 4$.

61. Begin with the graph of $y = x^2$, then shift the graph 3 units to the left to obtain the graph of $y = (x+3)^2$.

63. Notice that $y = (x+3)^2$ is of the form

$(x-h)^2 = 4a(y-k)$, where $4a = 1$, so that

$a = \dfrac{1}{4}$ and $(h,k) = (-3,\ 0)$. Now, the graph of

an equation of the form $(x-h)^2 = 4a(y-k)$ will

be a parabola that opens upward with vertex at

(h,k), focus at $(h, k+a)$, and directrix of

$y = k - a$. Note that $k + a = 0 + \dfrac{1}{4} = \dfrac{1}{4}$ and

$k - a = 0 - \dfrac{1}{4} = -\dfrac{1}{4}$. Thus, the graph of

$y = (x+3)^2$ is a parabola that opens upward

with vertex $(-3,\ 0)$, focus $\left(-3,\ \dfrac{1}{4}\right)$, and

directrix $y = -\dfrac{1}{4}$. To help graph the parabola,

we plot the two points to the left and to the right

of the focus. Let $y = \dfrac{1}{4}$:

$$\frac{1}{4} = (x+3)^2$$

$$\pm\frac{1}{2} = x + 3$$

$$-3 \pm \frac{1}{2} = x$$

$$x = -\frac{7}{2} \text{ or } x = -\frac{5}{2}$$

The points $\left(-\dfrac{7}{2}, \dfrac{1}{4}\right)$ and $\left(-\dfrac{5}{2}, \dfrac{1}{4}\right)$ are on the

graph.

65. Note that $4(y+2) = (x-2)^2$ is of the form

$(x-h)^2 = 4a(y-k)$, where $4a = 4$, so that

$a = 1$ and $(h,k) = (2,-2)$. Now, the graph of an

equation of the form $(x-h)^2 = 4a(y-k)$ will be

a parabola that opens upward with vertex at

(h,k), focus at $(h, k+a)$, and directrix of

$y = k - a$. Note that $k + a = -2 + 1 = -1$ and

$k - a = -2 - 1 = -3$. Thus, the graph of

$4(y+2) = (x-2)^2$ is a parabola that opens

upward with vertex $(2,-2)$, focus $(2,-1)$, and

directrix $y = -3$. To help graph the parabola,

we plot the two points to the left and to the right

of the focus. Let $y = -1$:

$$4(-1+2) = (x-2)^2$$

$$4 = (x-2)^2$$

$$\pm 2 = x - 2$$

$$2 \pm 2 = x$$

$$x = 0 \text{ or } x = 4$$

The points $(0,-1)$ and $(4,-1)$ are on the graph.

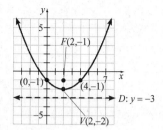

$F(2,-1)$
$(0,-1)$ $(4,-1)$
$D: y = -3$
$V(2,-2)$

67. $x^2 = 24y$

$\dfrac{1}{24}x^2 = y$

Let $Y_1 = \dfrac{1}{24}x^2$.

69. $y^2 = -6x$

$y = \pm\sqrt{-6x}$

Let $Y_1 = -\sqrt{-6x}$ and $Y_2 = \sqrt{-6x}$.

71. $(x-2)^2 = 4(y-4)$

$\dfrac{1}{4}(x-2)^2 = y-4$

$\dfrac{1}{4}(x-2)^2 + 4 = y$

Let $Y_1 = \dfrac{1}{4}(x-2)^2 + 4$.

73. $(y+3)^2 = -8(x+2)$

$y+3 = \pm\sqrt{-8(x+2)}$

$y = -3 \pm \sqrt{-8(x+2)}$

Let $Y_1 = -3 - \sqrt{-8(x+2)}$ and

$Y_2 = -3 + \sqrt{-8(x+2)}$.

75. $x^2 + 4x + 12y + 16 = 0$

$x^2 + 4x + 16 = -12y$

$-\dfrac{1}{12}(x^2 + 4x + 16) = y$

Let $Y_1 = -\dfrac{1}{12}(x^2 + 4x + 16)$.

77. $y^2 - 8y - 4x + 20 = 0$

$y^2 - 8y = 4x - 20$

$y^2 - 8y + 16 = 4x - 20 + 16$

$(y-4)^2 = 4x - 4$

$y - 4 = \pm\sqrt{4x-4}$

$y = 4 \pm \sqrt{4x-4}$

Let $Y_1 = 4 - \sqrt{4x-4}$ and $Y_2 = 4 + \sqrt{4x-4}$.

10.4 Preparing for Ellipses

1. Start: $x^2 + 10x$

Add: $\left(\dfrac{1}{2} \cdot 10\right)^2 = 25$

Result: $x^2 + 10x + 25$

Factored Form: $(x+5)^2$

2. Begin with the graph of $y = x^2$, then shift the graph 2 units to the left to obtain the graph of $y = (x+2)^2$. Shift this graph down 1 unit to obtain the graph of $f(x) = (x+2)^2 - 1$.

10.4 Exercises

1. ellipse, foci

3. vertices

5. TRUE.

7. Since the center of the ellipse is the origin O, the major axis is along the x-axis, and point B is the y-intercept, then by definition, $F = (c, 0)$ and $B = (0, b)$. Thus, $d(O, F) = c$ $d(O, B) = b$. Now, the sum of the distances from the two foci to a point on the ellipse is defined to be $2a$. Since B is a point on the ellipse that is midway between the two foci, then the distance from F to B must be half this total distance: $d(F, B) = \dfrac{1}{2}(2a) = a$.

9. **c.** The center of the ellipse is the origin, the major axis is the x-axis, and the vertices are $(\pm 4, 0)$, and the y-intercepts are $(0, \pm 3)$. Thus, the equation is of the form $\dfrac{x^2}{a^2} + \dfrac{y^2}{b^2} = 1$, with $a = 4$ and $b = 3$.

Thus, the equation is: $\dfrac{x^2}{4^2} + \dfrac{y^2}{3^2} = 1$

$$\dfrac{x^2}{16} + \dfrac{y^2}{9} = 1$$

11. **d.** The center of the ellipse is the origin, the major axis is the y-axis, and the vertices are $(0, \pm 4)$, and the x-intercepts are $(\pm 3, 0)$. Thus, the equation is of the form $\dfrac{x^2}{b^2} + \dfrac{y^2}{a^2} = 1$, with $a = 3$ and $b = 4$.

Thus, the equation is: $\dfrac{x^2}{3^2} + \dfrac{y^2}{4^2} = 1$

$$\dfrac{x^2}{9} + \dfrac{y^2}{16} = 1$$

13. $\dfrac{x^2}{25} + \dfrac{y^2}{16} = 1$

The larger number, 25, is in the denominator of the x^2-term. This means that the major axis is the x-axis and that the equation of the ellipse is of the form $\dfrac{x^2}{a^2} + \dfrac{y^2}{b^2} = 1$, so that $a^2 = 25$ and $b^2 = 16$.

The center of the ellipse is $(0, 0)$. Because $b^2 = a^2 - c^2$, or $c^2 = a^2 - b^2$, we have that $c^2 = 25 - 16 = 9$, so that $c = \pm\sqrt{9} = \pm 3$. Since the major axis is the x-axis, the foci are $(-3, 0)$ and $(3, 0)$. To find the x-intercepts (vertices), let $y = 0$; to find the y-intercepts, let $x = 0$:

x-intercepts:

$\dfrac{x^2}{25} + \dfrac{0^2}{16} = 1$

$\dfrac{x^2}{25} = 1$

$x^2 = 25$

$x = \pm 5$

y-intercepts:

$\dfrac{0^2}{25} + \dfrac{y^2}{16} = 1$

$\dfrac{y^2}{16} = 1$

$y^2 = 16$

$y = \pm 4$

The intercepts are $(-5,0)$, $(5,0)$, $(0,-4)$, and $(0,4)$.

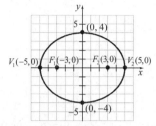

15. $\dfrac{x^2}{36}+\dfrac{y^2}{100}=1$

The larger number, 100, is in the denominator of the y^2-term. This means that the major axis is the y-axis and that the equation of the ellipse is of the form $\dfrac{x^2}{b^2}+\dfrac{y^2}{a^2}=1$, so that $a^2=100$ and $b^2=36$.

The center of the ellipse is $(0,0)$. Because $b^2=a^2-c^2$, or $c^2=a^2-b^2$, we have that $c^2=100-36=64$, so that $c=\pm\sqrt{64}=\pm8$. Since the major axis is the y-axis, the foci are $(0,-8)$ and $(0,8)$. To find the x-intercepts, let $y=0$; to find the y-intercepts (vertices), let $x=0$:

x-intercepts:	y-intercepts:
$\dfrac{x^2}{36}+\dfrac{0^2}{100}=1$	$\dfrac{0^2}{36}+\dfrac{y^2}{100}=1$
$\dfrac{x^2}{36}=1$	$\dfrac{y^2}{100}=1$
$x^2=36$	$y^2=100$
$x=\pm6$	$y=\pm10$

The intercepts are $(-6,0)$, $(6,0)$, $(0,-10)$, and $(0,10)$.

17. $\dfrac{x^2}{49}+\dfrac{y^2}{4}=1$

The larger number, 49, is in the denominator of the x^2-term. This means that the major axis is the x-axis and that the equation of the ellipse is of the form $\dfrac{x^2}{a^2}+\dfrac{y^2}{b^2}=1$, so that $a^2=49$ and $b^2=4$.

The center of the ellipse is $(0,0)$. Because $b^2=a^2-c^2$, or $c^2=a^2-b^2$, we have that $c^2=49-4=45$, so that $c=\pm\sqrt{45}=\pm3\sqrt{5}$. Since the major axis is the x-axis, the foci are $\left(-3\sqrt{5},0\right)$ and $\left(3\sqrt{5},0\right)$. To find the x-intercepts (vertices), let $y=0$; to find the y-intercepts, let $x=0$:

x-intercepts:	y-intercepts:
$\dfrac{x^2}{49}+\dfrac{0^2}{4}=1$	$\dfrac{0^2}{49}+\dfrac{y^2}{4}=1$
$\dfrac{x^2}{49}=1$	$\dfrac{y^2}{4}=1$
$x^2=49$	$y^2=4$
$x=\pm7$	$y=\pm2$

The intercepts are $(-7,0)$, $(7,0)$, $(0,-2)$, and $(0,2)$.

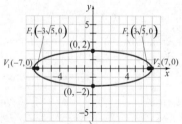

19. $x^2+\dfrac{y^2}{49}=1$

$\dfrac{x^2}{1}+\dfrac{y^2}{49}=1$

The larger number, 49, is in the denominator of the y^2-term. This means that the major axis is the y-axis and that the equation of the ellipse is of the form $\dfrac{x^2}{b^2}+\dfrac{y^2}{a^2}=1$, so that $a^2=49$ and $b^2=1$. The center of the ellipse is $(0,0)$. Because $b^2=a^2-c^2$, or $c^2=a^2-b^2$, we have that $c^2=49-1=48$, so that $c=\pm\sqrt{48}=\pm4\sqrt{3}$. Since the major axis is the y-axis, the foci are

$\left(0,-4\sqrt{3}\right)$ and $\left(0,4\sqrt{3}\right)$. To find the x-intercepts, let $y=0$; to find the y-intercepts (vertices), let $x=0$:

x-intercepts:

$$x^2 + \frac{0^2}{49} = 1$$
$$x^2 = 1$$
$$x = \pm 1$$

y-intercepts:

$$0^2 + \frac{y^2}{49} = 1$$
$$y^2 = 49$$
$$y = \pm 7$$

The intercepts are $(-1,0)$, $(1,0)$, $(0,-7)$, and $(0,7)$.

21. $4x^2 + y^2 = 16$

$$\frac{4x^2 + y^2}{16} = \frac{16}{16}$$

$$\frac{x^2}{4} + \frac{y^2}{16} = 1$$

The larger number, 16, is in the denominator of the y^2-term. This means that the major axis is the y-axis and that the equation of the ellipse is of the form $\frac{x^2}{b^2} + \frac{y^2}{a^2} = 1$, so that $a^2 = 16$ and $b^2 = 4$. The center of the ellipse is $(0,0)$. Because $b^2 = a^2 - c^2$, or $c^2 = a^2 - b^2$, we have that $c^2 = 16 - 4 = 12$, so that $c = \pm\sqrt{12} = \pm 2\sqrt{3}$. Since the major axis is the y-axis, the foci are $\left(0,-2\sqrt{3}\right)$ and $\left(0,2\sqrt{3}\right)$. To find the x-intercepts, let $y=0$; to find the y-intercepts (vertices), let $x=0$:

x-intercepts:

$$4x^2 + 0^2 = 16$$
$$4x^2 = 16$$
$$x^2 = 4$$
$$x = \pm 2$$

y-intercepts:

$$4(0)^2 + y^2 = 16$$
$$y^2 = 16$$
$$y = \pm 4$$

The intercepts are $(-2,0)$, $(2,0)$, $(0,-4)$, and $(0,4)$.

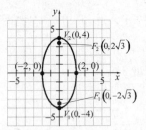

23. The given focus $(4,0)$ and the given vertex $(6,0)$ lie on the x-axis. Thus, the equation of the ellipse is of the form $\frac{x^2}{a^2} + \frac{y^2}{b^2} = 1$. The distance from the center of the ellipse to the vertex is $a = 6$ units. The distance from the center of the ellipse to the focus is $c = 4$ units. Because $b^2 = a^2 - c^2$, we have that $b^2 = 6^2 - 4^2 = 36 - 16 = 20$. Thus, the equation of the ellipse is $\frac{x^2}{36} + \frac{y^2}{20} = 1$.

To help graph the ellipse, find the y-intercepts:

Let $x = 0$:
$$\frac{0^2}{36} + \frac{y^2}{20} = 1$$
$$\frac{y^2}{20} = 1$$
$$y^2 = 20$$
$$y = \pm\sqrt{20} = \pm 2\sqrt{5}$$

The y-intercepts are $\left(0,-2\sqrt{5}\right)$ and $\left(0,2\sqrt{5}\right)$.

25. The given focus $(0,-4)$ and the given vertex $(0,7)$ lie on the y-axis. Thus, the equation of the ellipse is of the form $\frac{x^2}{b^2} + \frac{y^2}{a^2} = 1$. The distance from the center of the ellipse to the vertex is $a = 7$ units. The distance from the center of the ellipse to the focus is $c = 4$ units. Because $b^2 = a^2 - c^2$, we have that $b^2 = 7^2 - 4^2 = 49 - 16 = 33$. Thus, the equation of the ellipse is $\frac{x^2}{33} + \frac{y^2}{49} = 1$.

To help graph the ellipse, find the x-intercepts:

Let $y = 0$: $\dfrac{x^2}{33} + \dfrac{0^2}{49} = 1$

$$\dfrac{x^2}{33} = 1$$

$$x^2 = 33$$

$$x = \pm\sqrt{33}$$

The x-intercepts are $\left(-\sqrt{33}, 0\right)$ and $\left(\sqrt{33}, 0\right)$.

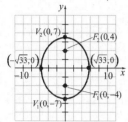

27. The given foci $(\pm 6, 0)$ and the given vertices $(\pm 10, 0)$ lie on the x-axis. The center of the ellipse is the midpoint between the two vertices (or foci). Thus, the center of the ellipse is $(0, 0)$, and its equation is of the form $\dfrac{x^2}{a^2} + \dfrac{y^2}{b^2} = 1$. The distance from the center of the ellipse to the vertex is $a = 10$ units. The distance from the center of the ellipse to the focus is $c = 6$ units. Because $b^2 = a^2 - c^2$, we have that $b^2 = 10^2 - 6^2 = 100 - 36 = 64$. Thus, the equation of the ellipse is $\dfrac{x^2}{100} + \dfrac{y^2}{64} = 1$.

To help graph the ellipse, find the y-intercepts:

Let $x = 0$: $\dfrac{0^2}{100} + \dfrac{y^2}{64} = 1$

$$\dfrac{y^2}{64} = 1$$

$$y^2 = 64$$

$$y = \pm 8$$

The y-intercepts are $(0, -8)$ and $(0, 8)$.

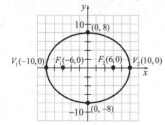

29. The given foci $(0, \pm 5)$ lie on the y-axis. The center of the ellipse is the midpoint between the two foci. Thus, center of the ellipse is $(0, 0)$ and its equation is of the form $\dfrac{x^2}{b^2} + \dfrac{y^2}{a^2} = 1$. Now, the length of the major axis is 16, so the vertices must be $(0, \pm 8)$, and the distance from the center of the ellipse to each vertex is $a = 8$ units. The distance from the center of the ellipse to each focus is $c = 5$ units. Because $b^2 = a^2 - c^2$, we have that $b^2 = 8^2 - 5^2 = 64 - 25 = 39$. Thus, the equation of the ellipse is $\dfrac{x^2}{39} + \dfrac{y^2}{64} = 1$.

To help graph the ellipse, we find the x-intercepts:

Let $y = 0$: $\dfrac{x^2}{39} + \dfrac{0^2}{64} = 1$

$$\dfrac{x^2}{39} = 1$$

$$x^2 = 39$$

$$x = \pm\sqrt{39}$$

The x-intercepts are $\left(-\sqrt{39}, 0\right)$ and $\left(\sqrt{39}, 0\right)$.

31. $\dfrac{(x-3)^2}{9} + \dfrac{(y+2)^2}{25} = 1$

The center of the ellipse is $(h, k) = (3, -2)$. Because the larger number, 25, is in the denominator of the y^2-term, the major axis is parallel to the y-axis. Because $a^2 = 25$ and $b^2 = 9$, we have that $c^2 = a^2 - b^2 = 25 - 9 = 16$. The vertices are $a = 5$ units below and above the center at $V_1(3, -7)$ and $V_2(3, 3)$. The foci are $c = \sqrt{16} = 4$ units below and above the center at $F_1(3, -6)$ and $F_2(3, 2)$. We plot the points $b = 3$ units to the left and right of the center point at $(0, -2)$ and $(6, -2)$.

We plot the points $b = 1$ unit to the left and right of the center point at $(4, -1)$ and $(6, -1)$.

33. $\dfrac{(x+2)^2}{16} + \dfrac{(y-5)^2}{4} = 1$

The center of the ellipse is $(h, k) = (-2, 5)$. Because the larger number, 16, is in the denominator of the x^2-term, the major axis is parallel to the x-axis. Because $a^2 = 16$ and $b^2 = 4$, we have that $c^2 = a^2 - b^2 = 16 - 4 = 12$. The vertices are $a = 4$ units to the left and right of the center at $V_1(-6, 5)$ and $V_2(2, 5)$. The foci are $c = \sqrt{12} = 2\sqrt{3}$ units to the left and right of the center at $F_1\left(-2 - 2\sqrt{3},\ 5\right)$ and $F_2\left(-2 + 2\sqrt{3},\ 5\right)$. We plot the points $b = 2$ units above and below the center point at $(-2, 7)$ and $(-2, 3)$.

35. $(x-5)^2 + \dfrac{(y+1)^2}{49} = 1$

$\dfrac{(x-5)^2}{1} + \dfrac{(y+1)^2}{49} = 1$

The center of the ellipse is $(h, k) = (5, -1)$. Because the larger number, 49, is in the denominator of the y^2-term, the major axis is parallel to the y-axis. Because $a^2 = 49$ and $b^2 = 1$, we have that $c^2 = a^2 - b^2 = 49 - 1 = 48$. The vertices are $a = 7$ units below and above the center at $V_1(5, -8)$ and $V_2(5, 6)$. The foci are $c = \sqrt{48} = 4\sqrt{3}$ units below and above the center at $F_1\left(5, -1 - 4\sqrt{3}\right)$ and $F_2\left(5, -1 + 4\sqrt{3}\right)$.

37. $4(x+2)^2 + 16(y-1)^2 = 64$

$\dfrac{4(x+2)^2 + 16(y-1)^2}{64} = \dfrac{64}{64}$

$\dfrac{(x+2)^2}{16} + \dfrac{(y-1)^2}{4} = 1$

The center of the ellipse is $(h, k) = (-2, 1)$. Because the larger number, 16, is in the denominator of the x^2-term, the major axis is parallel to the x-axis. Because $a^2 = 16$ and $b^2 = 4$, we have that $c^2 = a^2 - b^2 = 16 - 4 = 12$. The vertices are $a = 4$ units to the left and right of the center at $V_1(-6, 1)$ and $V_2(2, 1)$. The foci are $c = \sqrt{12} = 2\sqrt{3}$ units to the left and right of the center at $F_1\left(-2 - 2\sqrt{3},\ 1\right)$ and $F_2\left(-2 + 2\sqrt{3},\ 1\right)$. We plot the points $b = 2$ units above and below the center point at $(-2, 3)$ and $(-2, -1)$.

39.
$$4x^2 + y^2 - 24x + 2y - 63 = 0$$
$$4x^2 - 24x + y^2 + 2y = 63$$
$$4\left(x^2 - 6x\right) + \left(y^2 + 2y\right) = 63$$
$$4\left(x^2 - 6x + 9\right) + \left(y^2 + 2y + 1\right) = 63 + 4(9) + 1$$
$$4(x-3)^2 + (y+1)^2 = 100$$
$$\frac{4(x-3)^2 + (y+1)^2}{100} = \frac{100}{100}$$
$$\frac{(x-3)^2}{25} + \frac{(y+1)^2}{100} = 1$$

The center of the ellipse is $(h,k) = (3,-1)$.
Because the larger number, 100, is in the denominator of the y^2-term, the major axis is parallel to the y-axis. Because $a^2 = 100$ and $b^2 = 25$, we have that
$c^2 = a^2 - b^2 = 100 - 25 = 75$. The vertices are $a = 10$ units below and above the center at $V_1(3,-11)$ and $V_2(3,9)$. The foci are
$c = \sqrt{75} = 5\sqrt{3}$ units below and above the center at $F_1\left(3,-1-5\sqrt{3}\right)$ and $F_2\left(3,-1+5\sqrt{3}\right)$. We plot the points $b = 5$ units to the left and right of the center point at $(-2,-1)$ and $(8,-1)$.

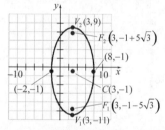

41. a. To solve this problem, we draw the ellipse on a Cartesian plane so that the x-axis coincides with the water and the y-axis passes through the center of the arch. Thus, the origin is the center of the ellipse. Now, the "center" of the arch is 10 meters above the water, so the point $(0,10)$ is on the ellipse. The river is 30 meters wide, so the two points $(-15,0)$ and $(15,0)$ are the two vertices of the ellipse and the major axis is along the x-axis.

The equation of the ellipse must have the form $\dfrac{x^2}{a^2} + \dfrac{y^2}{b^2} = 1$. The distance from the center of the ellipse to each vertex is $a = 15$. Also, the height of the semi-ellipse is 10 feet, so $b = 10$. Thus, the equation of the ellipse is
$$\frac{x^2}{15^2} + \frac{y^2}{10^2} = 1$$
$$\frac{x^2}{225} + \frac{y^2}{100} = 1$$

b. To determine if the barge can fit through the opening of the bridge, we center it beneath the arch so that the points $(-9,7)$ and $(9,7)$ represent the top corners of the barge. Now, we determine the height of the arch above the water at points 9 meters to the left and right of the center by substituting $x = 9$ into the equation of the ellipse and solving for y:
$$\frac{9^2}{225} + \frac{y^2}{100} = 1$$
$$\frac{9}{25} + \frac{y^2}{100} = 1$$
$$\frac{y^2}{100} = \frac{16}{25}$$
$$y^2 = 64$$
$$y = 8$$

At points 9 meters from the center of the river, the arch is 8 meters above the surface of the water. Thus, the barge can fit through the opening with about 1 meter of clearance above the top corners.

c. No. From part (b), the barge only has 1 meter of clearance when the water level is at it normal stage. Thus, if the water level increases by 1.1 meters, then the barge will not be able to pass under the bridge.

43. To find the perihelion of Earth, we recognize that Perihilion = 2(Mean distance) − Aphelion .
Thus, the perihelion of Earth is
$$2 \cdot 93 - 94.5 = 91.5 \text{ million miles.}$$

To find the equation of the elliptical orbit of Earth, we draw the ellipse on a Cartesian plane so that the center of the ellipse is at the origin and the major axis is along the x-axis. The equation of the ellipse is of the form
$$\frac{x^2}{a^2} + \frac{y^2}{b^2} = 1. \text{ Now, the mean distance of Earth}$$

from the Sun is 93 million miles, so the distance from the center of the orbit to each vertex is $a = 93$ million miles. Since the aphelion of Earth is 94.5 million miles, the distance from the center of the orbit to each focus is $c = 94.5 - 93 = 1.5$ million miles.

Now, because $b^2 = a^2 - c^2$, we have that $b^2 = 93^2 - 1.5^2 = 8649 - 2.25 = 8646.75$. Thus, the equation that describes the orbit of Earth is:

$$\frac{x^2}{8649} + \frac{y^2}{8646.75} = 1.$$

45. The mean distance of Jupiter from the Sun is $507 - 23.2 = 483.8$ million miles.

To find the perihelion of Jupiter, we recognize that $\text{Perihilion} = 2(\text{Mean distance}) - \text{Aphelion}$. Thus, the perihelion of Jupiter is
$$2 \cdot 483.8 - 507 = 460.6 \text{ million miles.}$$

To find the equation of the elliptical orbit of Jupiter, we draw the ellipse on a Cartesian plane so that the center of the ellipse is at the origin and the major axis is along the x-axis. The equation of the ellipse is of the form $\frac{x^2}{a^2} + \frac{y^2}{b^2} = 1$. Now, we found above that the mean distance of Jupiter from the Sun is 483.8 million miles, so the distance from the center of the orbit to each vertex is $a = 483.8$ million miles. We are given the distance from the center of the orbit to the Sun (that is, to each focus) is $c = 23.2$ million miles.

Now, because $b^2 = a^2 - c^2$, we have that
$$\begin{aligned} b^2 &= 483.8^2 - 23.2^2 \\ &= 234{,}062.44 - 538.24 \\ &= 233{,}524.2 \end{aligned}$$

Thus, the equation that describes the orbit of Jupiter is: $\dfrac{x^2}{234{,}062.44} + \dfrac{y^2}{233{,}524.2} = 1$.

47. The major axis of the ellipse is the line $y = 2$, which is parallel to the x-axis, so the equation of the ellipse is of the form $\frac{(x-h)^2}{a^2} + \frac{(y-k)^2}{b^2} = 1$. The center is $(h,k) = (1,2)$. The vertices are $(-3,\ 2)$ and $(5,\ 2)$, so $a = 5 - 1 = 4$. The points $(1,-1)$ and $(1,\ 5)$ are the points on the ellipse that are below and above the center, so $b = 5 - 2 = 3$. Thus, the equation is
$$\frac{(x-1)^2}{4^2} + \frac{(y-2)^2}{3^2} = 1$$
$$\frac{(x-1)^2}{16} + \frac{(y-2)^2}{9} = 1$$

49. The major axis of the ellipse is the line $x = 2$, which is parallel to the y-axis, so the equation of the ellipse is of the form $\frac{(x-h)^2}{b^2} + \frac{(y-k)^2}{a^2} = 1$. The center is $(h,k) = (2,0)$. The vertices are $(2,-4)$ and $(2,\ 4)$, so $a = 4 - 0 = 4$. The points $(0,\ 0)$ and $(4,\ 0)$ are the points on the ellipse that are left and right of the center, so $b = 4 - 2 = 2$. Thus, the equation is
$$\frac{(x-2)^2}{2^2} + \frac{(y-0)^2}{4^2} = 1$$
$$\frac{(x-2)^2}{4} + \frac{y^2}{16} = 1$$

51. Let $a = b$, then
$$\frac{x^2}{a^2} + \frac{y^2}{b^2} = 1$$
$$\frac{x^2}{a^2} + \frac{y^2}{a^2} = 1$$
$$a^2\left(\frac{x^2}{a^2} + \frac{y^2}{a^2}\right) = a^2(1)$$
$$x^2 + y^2 = a^2$$
which is the equation of a circle with center $(0,0)$ and radius a.

Because $c^2 = a^2 - b^2$, we have that $c^2 = a^2 - a^2 = 0$, so that $c = 0$. This means that the foci are a distance of 0 units from the center point. In other words, the foci are located at the center point.

53. $f(x) = \dfrac{5}{x+2}$

$$f(5) = \dfrac{5}{5+2} = \dfrac{5}{7} \approx 0.71429$$

$$f(10) = \dfrac{5}{10+2} = \dfrac{5}{12} \approx 0.41667$$

$$f(100) = \dfrac{5}{100+2} = \dfrac{5}{102} \approx 0.04902$$

$$f(1000) = \dfrac{5}{1000+2} = \dfrac{5}{1002} \approx 0.00499$$

x	5	10	100	100
$f(x)$	0.71429	0.41667	0.04902	0.00499

55. $f(x) = \dfrac{2x+1}{x-3}$

$$f(5) = \dfrac{2(5)+1}{5-3} = \dfrac{10+1}{5-3} = \dfrac{11}{2} = 5.5$$

$$f(10) = \dfrac{2(10)+1}{10-3} = \dfrac{20+1}{10-3} = \dfrac{21}{7} = 3$$

$$f(100) = \dfrac{2(100)+1}{100-3} = \dfrac{200+1}{100-3} = \dfrac{201}{97} \approx 2.07216$$

$$f(1000) = \dfrac{2(1000)+1}{1000-3} = \dfrac{2000+1}{1000-3} = \dfrac{2001}{997} \approx 2.00702$$

x	5	10	100	100
$f(x)$	5.5	3	2.07216	2.00702

57. $f(x) = \dfrac{x^2+3x+1}{x+1}$; $g(x) = x+2$

$$f(5) = \dfrac{5^2+3(5)+1}{5+1} = \dfrac{41}{6} \approx 6.83333$$

$$f(10) = \dfrac{10^2+3(10)+1}{10+1} = \dfrac{131}{11} \approx 11.90909$$

$$f(100) = \dfrac{100^2+3(100)+1}{100+1} = \dfrac{10{,}301}{101} \approx 101.99010$$

$$f(1000) = \dfrac{1000^2+3(1000)+1}{1000+1}$$
$$= \dfrac{1{,}003{,}001}{1001} \approx 1001.99900$$

$g(5) = 5+2 = 7$

$g(10) = 10+2 = 12$

$g(100) = 100+2 = 102$

$g(1000) = 1000+2 = 1002$

x	5	10	100	100
$f(x)$	6.83333	11.90909	101.99010	1001.99900
$g(x)$	7	12	102	1002

59. In Problems 53 and 54, the degrees of the numerators are less than the degrees of the denominators. In Problems 55 and 56, the degrees of the numerators and denominators are the same.

<u>Conjecture 1</u>: If the degree of the numerator of a rational function is less than the degree of the denominator, then as x increases, the value of the function will approach zero (0).

<u>Conjecture 2</u>: If the degree of the numerator of a rational function equals the degree of the denominator, then as x increases, the value of the function will approach the ratio of the leading coefficients of the numerator and denominator.

61. $\dfrac{x^2}{25} + \dfrac{y^2}{16} = 1$

$$\dfrac{y^2}{16} = 1 - \dfrac{x^2}{25}$$

$$y^2 = 16\left(1 - \dfrac{x^2}{25}\right)$$

$$y = \pm\sqrt{16\left(1 - \dfrac{x^2}{25}\right)} = \pm 4\sqrt{1 - \dfrac{x^2}{25}}$$

Let $Y_1 = 4\sqrt{1 - \dfrac{x^2}{25}}$ and $Y_2 = -4\sqrt{1 - \dfrac{x^2}{25}}$.

63. $4x^2 + y^2 = 16$

$$y^2 = 16 - 4x^2$$

$$y = \pm\sqrt{16 - 4x^2}$$

Let $Y_1 = \sqrt{16 - 4x^2}$ and $Y_2 = -\sqrt{16 - 4x^2}$.

65. $\dfrac{(x-3)^2}{9} + \dfrac{(y+2)^2}{25} = 1$

$\dfrac{(y+2)^2}{25} = 1 - \dfrac{(x-3)^2}{9}$

$(y+2)^2 = 25\left(1 - \dfrac{(x-3)^2}{9}\right)$

$y+2 = \pm\sqrt{25\left(1 - \dfrac{(x-3)^2}{9}\right)}$

$y+2 = \pm 5\sqrt{1 - \dfrac{(x-3)^2}{9}}$

$y = -2 \pm 5\sqrt{1 - \dfrac{(x-3)^2}{9}}$

Let $Y_1 = -2 + 5\sqrt{1 - \dfrac{(x-3)^2}{9}}$ and

$Y_2 = -2 - 5\sqrt{1 - \dfrac{(x-3)^2}{9}}$.

```
WINDOW
Xmin=-9.4
Xmax=9.4
Xscl=1
Ymin=-8.2
Ymax=4.2
Yscl=1
Xres=1
```

67. $\dfrac{(x+2)^2}{16} + \dfrac{(y-5)^2}{4} = 1$

$\dfrac{(y-5)^2}{4} = 1 - \dfrac{(x+2)^2}{16}$

$(y-5)^2 = 4\left(1 - \dfrac{(x+2)^2}{16}\right)$

$y-5 = \pm\sqrt{4\left(1 - \dfrac{(x+2)^2}{16}\right)}$

$y-5 = \pm 2\sqrt{1 - \dfrac{(x+2)^2}{16}}$

$y = 5 \pm 2\sqrt{1 - \dfrac{(x+2)^2}{16}}$

Let $Y_1 = 5 + 2\sqrt{1 - \dfrac{(x+2)^2}{16}}$ and

$Y_2 = 5 - 2\sqrt{1 - \dfrac{(x+2)^2}{16}}$.

```
WINDOW
Xmin=-9.4
Xmax=9.4
Xscl=1
Ymin=-4.2
Ymax=8.2
Yscl=1
Xres=1
```

10.5 Preparing for Hyperbolas

1. Start: $x^2 - 5x$

Add: $\left(\dfrac{1}{2} \cdot (-5)\right)^2 = \dfrac{25}{4}$

Result: $x^2 - 5x + \dfrac{25}{4}$

Factored Form: $\left(x - \dfrac{5}{2}\right)^2$

2. $y^2 = 64$

$y = \pm\sqrt{64}$

$y = \pm 8$

The solution set is $\{-8,\ 8\}$.

Section 10.5

1. hyperbola

3. $y = -\dfrac{b}{a}x$; $y = \dfrac{b}{a}x$

5. TRUE

7. Answers may vary. One possibility follows: The asymptotes provide a means for determining the opening of each branch of the hyperbola without having to find and plot additional points.

9. b The transverse axis is the x-axis and the hyperbola opens left and right. Also, the distance between the vertices $(\pm 1, 0)$ and the center $(0,0)$ is $a = 1$ unit. This means that the equation of the hyperbola is of the form

$\dfrac{x^2}{a^2} - \dfrac{y^2}{b^2} = 1$

$\dfrac{x^2}{1^2} - \dfrac{y^2}{b^2} = 1$

$x^2 - \dfrac{y^2}{b^2} = 1$

Of the list of provided equations, only equation

(b): $x^2 - \dfrac{y^2}{4} = 1$ is of this form.

11. a The transverse axis is the x-axis and the hyperbola opens left and right. Also, the distance between the vertices $(\pm 2, 0)$ and the center $(0,0)$ is $a = 2$ units. This means that the equation of the hyperbola is of the form

$$\frac{x^2}{a^2} - \frac{y^2}{b^2} = 1$$
$$\frac{x^2}{2^2} - \frac{y^2}{b^2} = 1$$
$$\frac{x^2}{4} - \frac{y^2}{b^2} = 1$$

Of the list of provided equations, only equation

(a): $\dfrac{x^2}{4} - y^2 = 1$ is of this form.

13. $\dfrac{x^2}{4} - \dfrac{y^2}{16} = 1$

Notice the equation is of the form $\dfrac{x^2}{a^2} - \dfrac{y^2}{b^2} = 1$.

Because the x^2-term is first, the transverse axis is the x-axis and the hyperbola opens left and right. The center of the hyperbola is the origin. We have that $a^2 = 4$ and $b^2 = 16$. Because $c^2 = a^2 + b^2$, we have that $c^2 = 4 + 16 = 20$, so that $c = \sqrt{20} = 2\sqrt{5}$. The vertices are $(\pm a, 0) = (\pm 2, 0)$, and the foci are $(\pm c, 0) = (\pm 2\sqrt{5}, 0)$. Since $a = 2$ and $b = 4$, the equations of the asymptotes are

$y = \dfrac{4}{2}x = 2x$ and $y = -\dfrac{4}{2}x = -2x$. To help

graph the hyperbola, we form the rectangle using the points $(\pm a, 0) = (\pm 2, 0)$ and $(0, \pm b) = (0, \pm 4)$. The diagonals are the asymptotes.

15. $\dfrac{y^2}{25} - \dfrac{x^2}{36} = 1$

Notice the equation is of the form $\dfrac{y^2}{a^2} - \dfrac{x^2}{b^2} = 1$.

Because the y^2-term is first, the transverse axis is the y-axis and the hyperbola opens up and down. The center of the hyperbola is the origin. We have that $a^2 = 25$ and $b^2 = 36$. Because $c^2 = a^2 + b^2$, we have that $c^2 = 25 + 36 = 61$, so that $c = \sqrt{61}$. The vertices are $(0, \pm a) = (0, \pm 5)$, and the foci are $(0, \pm c) = (0, \pm\sqrt{61})$. To help graph the hyperbola, we plot the points on the graph to the left and right of the foci. Let $y = \pm\sqrt{61}$:

$$\frac{\left(\pm\sqrt{61}\right)^2}{25} - \frac{x^2}{36} = 1$$
$$\frac{61}{25} - \frac{x^2}{36} = 1$$
$$-\frac{x^2}{36} = -\frac{36}{25}$$
$$x^2 = \frac{1296}{25}$$
$$x = \pm\frac{36}{5}$$

The points to the left and right of the foci are

$\left(\dfrac{36}{5}, \sqrt{61}\right)$, $\left(-\dfrac{36}{5}, \sqrt{61}\right)$, $\left(\dfrac{36}{5}, -\sqrt{61}\right)$, and

$\left(-\dfrac{36}{5}, -\sqrt{61}\right)$.

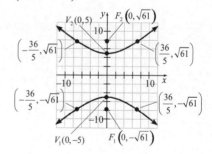

17. $4x^2 - y^2 = 36$

$$\frac{4x^2 - y^2}{36} = \frac{36}{36}$$

$$\frac{x^2}{9} - \frac{y^2}{36} = 1$$

Notice the equation is of the form $\frac{x^2}{a^2} - \frac{y^2}{b^2} = 1$.

Because the x^2-term is first, the transverse axis is the x-axis and the hyperbola opens left and right. The center of the hyperbola is the origin. We have that $a^2 = 9$ and $b^2 = 36$. Because $c^2 = a^2 + b^2$, we have that $c^2 = 9 + 36 = 45$, so that $c = \sqrt{45} = 3\sqrt{5}$. The vertices are $(\pm a, 0) = (\pm 3, 0)$, and the foci are $(\pm c, 0) = (\pm 3\sqrt{5}, 0)$. To help graph the hyperbola, we plot the points on the graph above and below the foci. Let $x = \pm 3\sqrt{5}$:

$$\frac{\left(\pm 3\sqrt{5}\right)^2}{9} - \frac{y^2}{36} = 1$$

$$\frac{45}{9} - \frac{y^2}{36} = 1$$

$$5 - \frac{y^2}{36} = 1$$

$$-\frac{y^2}{36} = -4$$

$$y^2 = 144$$

$$y = \pm 12$$

The points above and below the foci are $\left(3\sqrt{5}, 12\right)$, $\left(3\sqrt{5}, -12\right)$, $\left(-3\sqrt{5}, 12\right)$, and $\left(-3\sqrt{5}, -12\right)$.

19. $25y^2 - x^2 = 100$

$$\frac{25y^2 - x^2}{100} = \frac{100}{100}$$

$$\frac{y^2}{4} - \frac{x^2}{100} = 1$$

Notice the equation is of the form $\frac{y^2}{a^2} - \frac{x^2}{b^2} = 1$.

Because the y^2-term is first, the transverse is along the y-axis and the hyperbola opens up and down. The center of the hyperbola is $(0,0)$. We have that $a^2 = 4$ and $b^2 = 100$. Because $c^2 = a^2 + b^2$, we have that $c^2 = 100 + 4 = 104$, so that $c = \sqrt{104} = 2\sqrt{26}$. The vertices are $(0, \pm a) = (0, \pm 2)$, and the foci are $\left(0, \pm c\right) = \left(0, \pm 2\sqrt{26}\right)$. Since $a = 2$ and $b = 10$, the equations of the asymptotes are

$$y = \frac{2}{10}x = \frac{1}{5}x \text{ and } y = -\frac{2}{10}x = -\frac{1}{5}x. \text{ To help}$$

graph the hyperbola, we form the rectangle using the points $(0, \pm a) = (0, \pm 2)$ and $(\pm b, 0) = (\pm 10, 0)$. The diagonals are the asymptotes.

21. The given center $(0,0)$, focus $(3,0)$, and vertex $(2,0)$ all lie on the x-axis. Thus, the transverse axis is the x-axis and the hyperbola opens left and right. This means that the equation of the hyperbola is of the form $\frac{x^2}{a^2} - \frac{y^2}{b^2} = 1$. Now, the distance between the given vertex $(2,0)$ and the center $(0,0)$ is $a = 2$ units. Likewise, the distance between the given focus $(3,0)$ and the center is $c = 3$ units. Because $b^2 = c^2 - a^2$, we have that $b^2 = 3^2 - 2^2 = 9 - 4 = 5$. Thus, the equation of the hyperbola is $\frac{x^2}{4} - \frac{y^2}{5} = 1$.

To help graph the hyperbola, we first find the vertex and focus that were not given. Since the center is at $(0,0)$ and since one vertex is at $(2,0)$, the other vertex must be at $(-2,0)$. Similarly, one focus is at $(3,0)$, so the other focus is at $(-3,0)$. Next, plot the points on the graph above and below the foci. Let $x = \pm 3$:

$$\frac{(\pm 3)^2}{4} - \frac{y^2}{5} = 1$$

$$\frac{9}{4} - \frac{y^2}{5} = 1$$

$$-\frac{y^2}{5} = -\frac{5}{4}$$

$$y^2 = \frac{25}{4}$$

$$y = \pm \frac{5}{2}$$

The points above and below the foci are $\left(3, \frac{5}{2}\right)$,

$\left(3, -\frac{5}{2}\right)$, $\left(-3, \frac{5}{2}\right)$, and $\left(-3, -\frac{5}{2}\right)$.

23. The given vertices $(0, \pm 5)$ and focus $(0,7)$ all lie on the y-axis. Thus, the transverse axis is the y-axis and the hyperbola opens up and down. The center of the hyperbola is the midpoint between the two vertices. Therefore, the center is $(0,0)$ and the equation of the hyperbola is of

the form $\frac{y^2}{a^2} - \frac{x^2}{b^2} = 1$. Now, the distance from

the center $(0,0)$ to each vertex is $a = 5$ units. Likewise, the distance from the center to the given focus $(0,7)$ is $c = 7$ units. Also,

$b^2 = c^2 - a^2$, so $b^2 = 7^2 - 5^2 = 49 - 25 = 24$. Thus, the equation of the hyperbola is

$\frac{y^2}{25} - \frac{x^2}{24} = 1$.

To help graph the hyperbola, we first find the focus that was not given. Since the center is at $(0,0)$ and since one focus is at $(0,7)$, the other

focus must be at $(0,-7)$. Next, plot the points on the graph to the left and right of the foci. Let $y = \pm 7$:

$$\frac{(\pm 7)^2}{25} - \frac{x^2}{24} = 1$$

$$\frac{49}{25} - \frac{x^2}{24} = 1$$

$$-\frac{x^2}{24} = -\frac{24}{25}$$

$$x^2 = \frac{576}{25}$$

$$x = \pm \frac{24}{5}$$

The points to the left and right of the foci are

$\left(\frac{24}{5}, 7\right)$, $\left(-\frac{24}{5}, 7\right)$, $\left(\frac{24}{5}, -7\right)$, and $\left(-\frac{24}{5}, -7\right)$.

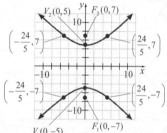

25. The given foci $(\pm 10, 0)$ and vertex $(-7, 0)$ all lie on the x-axis. Thus, the transverse axis is the x-axis and the hyperbola opens left and right. The center of the hyperbola is the midpoint between the two vertices. Therefore, the center is $(0,0)$ and the equation of the hyperbola is of

the form $\frac{x^2}{a^2} - \frac{y^2}{b^2} = 1$. Now, the distance

between the given vertex $(-7, 0)$ and the center $(0,0)$ is $a = 7$ units. Likewise, the distance between the given foci and the center is $c = 10$ units. Also, $b^2 = c^2 - a^2$, so

$b^2 = 10^2 - 7^2 = 100 - 49 = 51$. Thus, the

equation of the hyperbola is $\frac{x^2}{49} - \frac{y^2}{51} = 1$.

To help graph the hyperbola, we first find the vertex that was not given. Since the center is at $(0,0)$ and since one vertex is at $(-7, 0)$, the other vertex must be at $(7, 0)$. Next, plot the points on the graph above and below the foci. Let $x = \pm 10$:

$$\frac{(\pm 10)^2}{49} - \frac{y^2}{51} = 1$$

$$\frac{100}{49} - \frac{y^2}{51} = 1$$

$$-\frac{y^2}{51} = -\frac{51}{49}$$

$$y^2 = \frac{2601}{49}$$

$$y = \pm \frac{51}{7}$$

The points above and below the foci are

$\left(10, \frac{51}{7}\right)$, $\left(10, -\frac{51}{7}\right)$, $\left(-10, \frac{51}{7}\right)$, and

$\left(-10, -\frac{51}{7}\right)$.

27. The given vertices $(0, \pm 8)$ both lie on the y-axis. Thus, the transverse axis is the y-axis and the hyperbola opens up and down. The center of the hyperbola is the midpoint between the two vertices. Therefore, the center is $(0,0)$ and the equation of the hyperbola is of the form

    $\frac{y^2}{a^2} - \frac{x^2}{b^2} = 1$. Now, the distance from the center

    $(0,0)$ to each vertex is $a = 8$ units. We are given that an asymptote of the hyperbola is $y = 2x$. Now the equation of the asymptote is

    of the form is $y = \frac{a}{b}x$ and $a = 8$. So,

    $$\frac{a}{b} = 2$$

    $$\frac{8}{b} = 2$$

    $$8 = 2b$$

    $$4 = b$$

    Thus, the equation of the hyperbola is

    $$\frac{y^2}{8^2} - \frac{x^2}{4^2} = 1$$

    $$\frac{y^2}{64} - \frac{x^2}{16} = 1$$

To help graph the hyperbola, we first find the foci. Since $c^2 = a^2 + b^2$, we have that $c^2 = 64 + 16 = 80$, so $c = 4\sqrt{5}$. Since the center is $(0,0)$, the foci are $\left(0, \pm 4\sqrt{5}\right)$. We form the rectangle using the points $(0, \pm a) = (0, \pm 8)$ and $(\pm b, 0) = (\pm 4, 0)$. The diagonals are the two asymptotes $y = 2x$ and $y = -2x$.

29. The given foci $(\pm 3, 0)$ both lie on the x-axis. Thus, the transverse axis is the x-axis and the hyperbola opens left and right. The center of the hyperbola is the midpoint between the two vertices. Therefore, the center is $(0,0)$ and the equation of the hyperbola is of the form

    $\frac{x^2}{a^2} - \frac{y^2}{b^2} = 1$. We are given that an asymptote of

    the hyperbola is $y = x$. Now the equation of the

    asymptote is of the form $y = \frac{b}{a}x$. So, $\frac{b}{a} = 1$

    which means $a = b$. Because each focus is 3 units from the center, we have $c = 3$ and $c^2 = 9$. So,

    $$a^2 + b^2 = c^2$$

    $$a^2 + a^2 = 9$$

    $$2a^2 = 9$$

    $$a^2 = \frac{9}{2}$$

    $$a = \sqrt{\frac{9}{2}} = \frac{3}{\sqrt{2}} = \frac{3\sqrt{2}}{2}$$

    Since $a = b$, we have that $a^2 = b^2 = \frac{9}{2} = 4.5$.

    Thus, the equation of the hyperbola is

    $$\frac{x^2}{4.5} - \frac{y^2}{4.5} = 1.$$

To help graph the hyperbola, we find the vertices. Since $a = \dfrac{3\sqrt{2}}{2}$ and the center is $(0,0)$, the vertices are $\left(\pm\dfrac{3\sqrt{2}}{2}, 0\right)$. We form the rectangle using the points $(\pm a, 0) = \left(\pm\dfrac{3\sqrt{2}}{2}, 0\right)$ and $(0, \pm b) = \left(0, \pm\dfrac{3\sqrt{2}}{2}\right)$.

The diagonals are the two asymptotes $y = x$ and $y = -x$.

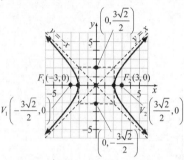

31. The graph of the hyperbola opens left and right and the center is $(0,0)$, so the equation is of the form $\dfrac{x^2}{a^2} - \dfrac{y^2}{b^2} = 1$. From the graph, we observe that the asymptotes are $y = -x$ and $y = x$. Now the equations of the asymptotes are of the form $y = -\dfrac{b}{a}x$ and $y = \dfrac{b}{a}x$. So, $\dfrac{b}{a} = 1$ which means $b = a$. We also observe that the vertices are $(\pm 1, 0)$, so the distance from the center to each vertex is $a = 1$. Thus, $a = b = 1$ and $a^2 = b^2 = 1$. Thus, the equation of the hyperbola is $\dfrac{x^2}{1} - \dfrac{y^2}{1} = 1$ or $x^2 - y^2 = 1$.

33. The graph of the hyperbola opens up and down and the center is $(0,0)$, so the equation is of the form $\dfrac{y^2}{a^2} - \dfrac{x^2}{b^2} = 1$. From the graph, we observe that the asymptotes are $y = -2x$ and $y = 2x$. Now the equations of the asymptotes are of the form $y = -\dfrac{a}{b}x$ and $y = \dfrac{a}{b}x$. So, $\dfrac{a}{b} = 2$ which means $a = 2b$ or $b = \dfrac{1}{2}a$. We also observe that

the vertices are $(0, \pm 6)$, so the distance from the center to each vertex is $a = 6$ and $b = \dfrac{1}{2}(6) = 3$. Thus, $a^2 = 36$ and $b^2 = 9$, and the equation of the hyperbola is $\dfrac{y^2}{36} - \dfrac{x^2}{9} = 1$.

35. We observe that the equation $\dfrac{x^2}{4} - y^2 = 1$ is of the form $\dfrac{x^2}{a^2} - \dfrac{y^2}{b^2} = 1$ with $a = 2$ and $b = 1$. The asymptotes of such a hyperbola are $y = -\dfrac{b}{a}x$ and $y = \dfrac{b}{a}x$. Thus, the asymptotes are $y = -\dfrac{1}{2}x$ and $y = \dfrac{1}{2}x$.

Similarly, we observe that the equation $y^2 - \dfrac{x^2}{4} = 1$ is of the form $\dfrac{y^2}{a^2} - \dfrac{x^2}{b^2} = 1$ with $a = 1$ and $b = 2$. The asymptotes of such a hyperbola are $y = -\dfrac{a}{b}x$ and $y = \dfrac{a}{b}x$. Thus, the asymptotes are $y = -\dfrac{1}{2}x$ and $y = \dfrac{1}{2}x$.

Since the two hyperbolas have the same asymptotes, they are conjugate.

Now, the vertices of $y^2 - \dfrac{x^2}{4} = 1$ are $(0, \pm 1)$, each of which is $a = 1$ unit above and below the center. Utilizing the vertices and the asymptotes, we draw the graph of $y^2 - \dfrac{x^2}{4} = 1$. Similarly, the vertices of $\dfrac{x^2}{4} - y^2 = 1$ are $(\pm 2, 0)$, each of which is $a = 2$ units to the left and right of the center. We draw the graph of $\dfrac{x^2}{4} - y^2 = 1$ by utilizing the vertices and the asymptotes.

37. $\begin{cases} 2x - 3y = -9 & (1) \\ -x + 5y = 8 & (2) \end{cases}$

Because equation (2) is easily solved for x, we use substitution to solve the system.

Equation (2) solved for x is $x = 5y - 8$.

Substituting $5y - 8$ for x in equation (1), we obtain

$2(5y - 8) - 3y = -9$

$10y - 16 - 3y = -9$

$7y - 16 = -9$

$7y = 7$

$y = 1$

Substituting 1 for y into equation (2), we obtain

$-x + 5(1) = 8$

$-x + 5 = 8$

$-x = 3$

$x = -3$

The solution is the ordered pair $(-3, 1)$.

39. $\begin{cases} 2x - 3y = 6 & (1) \\ -6x + 9y = -18 & (2) \end{cases}$

Because none of the variables have a coefficient of 1, we use elimination to solve the system. Multiply both sides of equation (1) by 3, and add the result to equation (2).

$6x - 9y = 18$

$\underline{-6x + 9y = -18}$

$0 = 0$

The system is dependent. The solution is

$\{(x, y) \mid 2x - 3y = 6\}$.

41. $\begin{cases} 6x + 3y = 4 & (1) \\ -2x - y = -\dfrac{4}{3} & (2) \end{cases}$

We use elimination to solve the system. Multiply both sides of equation (2) by 3, and add the result to equation (1).

$-6x - 3y = -4$

$\underline{6x + 3y = 4}$

$0 = 0$

The system is dependent. The solution is

$\{(x, y) \mid 6x + 3y = 4\}$.

43. $\dfrac{x^2}{4} - \dfrac{y^2}{16} = 1$

$-\dfrac{y^2}{16} = 1 - \dfrac{x^2}{4}$

$-16\left(-\dfrac{y^2}{16}\right) = -16\left(1 - \dfrac{x^2}{4}\right)$

$y^2 = 16\left(\dfrac{x^2}{4} - 1\right)$

$y = \pm\sqrt{16\left(\dfrac{x^2}{4} - 1\right)}$

$y = \pm 4\sqrt{\dfrac{x^2}{4} - 1}$

Let $Y_1 = 4\sqrt{\dfrac{x^2}{4} - 1}$ and $Y_2 = -4\sqrt{\dfrac{x^2}{4} - 1}$.

45. $\dfrac{y^2}{25} - \dfrac{x^2}{36} = 1$

$\dfrac{y^2}{25} = \dfrac{x^2}{36} + 1$

$y^2 = 25\left(\dfrac{x^2}{36} + 1\right)$

$y = \pm\sqrt{25\left(\dfrac{x^2}{36} + 1\right)}$

$y = \pm 5\sqrt{\dfrac{x^2}{36} + 1}$

Let $Y_1 = 5\sqrt{\dfrac{x^2}{36} + 1}$ and $Y_2 = -5\sqrt{\dfrac{x^2}{36} + 1}$.

47. $4x^2 - y^2 = 36$

$-y^2 = -4x^2 + 36$

$y^2 = 4x^2 - 36$

$y = \pm\sqrt{4x^2 - 36}$

Let $Y_1 = \sqrt{4x^2 - 36}$ and $Y_2 = -\sqrt{4x^2 - 36}$.

```
WINDOW
Xmin=-9.4
Xmax=9.4
Xscl=1
Ymin=-6.2
Ymax=6.2
Yscl=1
Xres=1
```

49. $25y^2 - x^2 = 100$

$25y^2 = x^2 + 100$

$y^2 = \dfrac{x^2 + 100}{25}$

$y = \pm\sqrt{\dfrac{x^2 + 100}{25}}$

$y = \pm\dfrac{\sqrt{x^2 + 100}}{5}$

Let $Y_1 = \dfrac{\sqrt{x^2 + 100}}{5}$ and $Y_2 = -\dfrac{\sqrt{x^2 + 100}}{5}$.

```
WINDOW
Xmin=-23.5
Xmax=23.5
Xscl=5
Ymin=-15.5
Ymax=15.5
Yscl=5
Xres=1
```

Putting the Concepts Together (Sections 10.1 – 10.5)

1. $d(P_1, P_2) = \sqrt{(x_2 - x_1)^2 + (y_2 - y_1)^2}$

$= \sqrt{(3 - (-6))^2 + (-2 - 4)^2}$

$= \sqrt{(9)^2 + (-6)^2}$

$= \sqrt{81 + 36}$

$= \sqrt{117}$

$= 3\sqrt{13}$

2. $M = \left(\dfrac{x_1 + x_2}{2}, \dfrac{y_1 + y_2}{2}\right)$

$= \left(\dfrac{-3 + 5}{2}, \dfrac{1 + (-7)}{2}\right) = \left(\dfrac{2}{2}, \dfrac{-6}{2}\right) = (1, -3)$

3. $(x + 2)^2 + (y - 8)^2 = 36$

$(x - (-2))^2 + (y - 8)^2 = 6^2$

The center is $(h, k) = (-2, 8)$, and the radius is $r = 6$.

4. $x^2 + y^2 + 6x - 4y - 3 = 0$

$(x^2 + 6x) + (y^2 - 4y) = 3$

$(x^2 + 6x + 9) + (y^2 - 4y + 4) = 3 + 9 + 4$

$(x + 3)^2 + (y - 2)^2 = 16$

$(x - (-3))^2 + (y - 2)^2 = 4^2$

The center is $(h, k) = (-3, 2)$, and the radius is $r = 4$.

5. The radius of the circle will be the distance from the center point $(0, 0)$ to the point on the circle $(-5, 12)$. Thus, $r = \sqrt{(-5 - 0)^2 + (12 - 0)^2} = 13$.

The equation of the circle is

$(x - h)^2 + (y - k)^2 = r^2$

$(x - 0)^2 + (y - 0)^2 = 13^2$

$x^2 + y^2 = 169$

6. The center of the circle will be the midpoint of the diameter with endpoints $(-1,5)$ and $(5,-3)$.

Thus, $(h,k) = \left(\dfrac{-1+5}{2}, \dfrac{5+(-3)}{2}\right) = (2,1)$. The radius of the circle will be the distance from the center point $(2,1)$ to one of the endpoints of the diameter, say $(-1,5)$. Thus,

$r = \sqrt{(-1-2)^2 + (5-1)^2} = \sqrt{25} = 5$.

The equation of the circle is

$(x-h)^2 + (y-k)^2 = r^2$

$(x-2)^2 + (y-1)^2 = 5^2$

$(x-2)^2 + (y-1)^2 = 25$

7. Notice that $(x+2)^2 = -4(y-4)$ is of the form $(x-h)^2 = -4a(y-k)$, where $(h,k) = (-2,4)$ and $-4a = -4$, so that $a = 1$. Now, the graph of an equation of the form $(x-h)^2 = -4a(y-k)$ will be a parabola that opens downward with the vertex at (h,k), focus at $(h,k-a)$, and directrix of $y = k+a$. Note that $k-a = 4-1 = 3$ and $k+a = 4+1 = 5$. Thus, the graph of $(x+2)^2 = -4(y-4)$ is a parabola that opens downward with vertex $(-2,4)$, focus $(-2,3)$, and directrix $y = 5$. To help graph the parabola, we plot the two points on the graph to the left and right of the focus. Let $y = 3$:

$(x+2)^2 = -4(3-4)$

$(x+2)^2 = 4$

$x+2 = \pm 2$

$x = -2 \pm 2$

$x = -4$ or $x = 0$

The points $(-4,3)$ and $(0,3)$ are on the graph.

8. We complete the square in y to write the equation in standard form:

$y^2 + 2y - 8x + 25 = 0$

$y^2 + 2y = 8x - 25$

$y^2 + 2y + 1 = 8x - 25 + 1$

$y^2 + 2y + 1 = 8x - 24$

$(y+1)^2 = 8(x-3)$

Notice that $(y+1)^2 = 8(x-3)$ is of the form $(y-k)^2 = 4a(x-h)$, where $(h,k) = (3,-1)$ and $4a = 8$, so that $a = 2$. Now, the graph of an equation of the form $(y-k)^2 = 4a(x-h)$ will be a parabola that opens to the right with the vertex at (h,k), focus at $(h+a,k)$, and directrix of $x = h-a$. Note that $h+a = 3+2 = 5$ and $h-a = 3-2 = 1$. Thus, the graph of $(y+1)^2 = 8(x-3)$ is a parabola that opens to the right with vertex $(3,-1)$, focus $(5,-1)$, and directrix $x = 1$. To help graph the parabola, we plot the two points on the graph below and above the focus. Let $x = 5$:

$(y+1)^2 = 8(5-3)$

$(y+1)^2 = 16$

$y+1 = \pm 4$

$y = -1 \pm 4$

$y = -5$ or $y = 3$

The points $(5,-5)$ and $(5,3)$ are on the graph.

9. The distance from the vertex $(h,k) = (-1,-2)$ to the focus $(-1,-5)$ is $a = 3$. The vertex and focus both lie on the vertical line $x = -1$, which is the axis of symmetry (parallel to the y-axis). Because the focus is below the vertex, we know that the parabola will open downward. This means the equation of the parabola is of the form $(x-h)^2 = -4a(y-k)$ with $a = 3$, $h = -1$, and $k = -2$:

$(x-(-1))^2 = -4 \cdot 3(y-(-2))$

$(x+1)^2 = -12(y+2)$

10. The vertex is $(-3,3)$ and the axis of symmetry is parallel to the x-axis, so the axis of symmetry is the line $y = 3$ and the parabola either opens to the left or right. Because the graph contains the point $(-1,7)$, which is to the right of the vertex, the parabola must open to the right. Therefore, the equation of the parabola is of the form $(y-k)^2 = 4a(x-h)$, with $h = -3$ and $k = 3$.

Now $y = 7$ when $x = -1$, so

$$(7-3)^2 = 4a(-1-(-3))$$
$$(4)^2 = 4a(2)$$
$$16 = 8a$$
$$a = 2$$

The equation of the parabola is

$$(y-3)^2 = 4 \cdot 2(x-(-3))$$
$$(y-3)^2 = 8(x+3)$$

11. $x^2 + 9y^2 = 81$

$$\frac{x^2 + 9y^2}{81} = \frac{81}{81}$$

$$\frac{x^2}{81} + \frac{y^2}{9} = 1$$

The larger number, 81, is in the denominator of the x^2-term. This means that the major axis is the x-axis and that the equation of the ellipse is of the form $\frac{x^2}{a^2} + \frac{y^2}{b^2} = 1$, so that $a^2 = 81$ and $b^2 = 9$. The center of the ellipse is $(0,0)$.

Because $c^2 = a^2 - b^2$, we have that $c^2 = 81 - 9 = 72$, so that $c = \pm\sqrt{72} = \pm 6\sqrt{2}$. Since the major axis is the x-axis, the foci are $\left(-6\sqrt{2},0\right)$ and $\left(6\sqrt{2},0\right)$. To find the x-intercepts (vertices), let $y = 0$; to find the y-intercepts, let $x = 0$:

x-intercepts:
$$x^2 + 9(0)^2 = 81$$
$$x^2 = 81$$
$$x = \pm 9$$

y-intercepts:
$$0^2 + 9y^2 = 81$$
$$9y^2 = 81$$
$$y^2 = 9$$
$$y = \pm 3$$

The intercepts are $(-9,0)$, $(9,0)$, $(0,-3)$, and $(0,3)$.

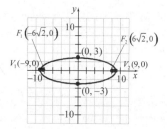

12. $\dfrac{(x+1)^2}{36} + \dfrac{(y-2)^2}{49} = 1$

The center of the ellipse is $(h,k) = (-1,2)$. Because the larger number, 49, is the denominator of the y^2-term, the major axis is parallel to the y-axis. Because $a^2 = 49$ and $b^2 = 36$, we have that $c^2 = a^2 - b^2 = 49 - 36 = 13$. The vertices are $a = 7$ units below and above the center at $V_1(-1,-5)$ and $V_2(-1,9)$. The foci are $c = \sqrt{13}$ units below and above the center at $F_1\left(-1, 2-\sqrt{13}\right)$ and $F_2\left(-1, 2+\sqrt{13}\right)$. We plot the points $b = 6$ units to the left and right of the center point at $(-7,2)$ and $(5,2)$.

13. The given foci $(0, \pm 6)$ and the given vertices $(0, \pm 9)$ lie on the y-axis. The center of the ellipse is the midpoint between the two vertices (or foci). Thus, the center of the ellipse is $(0,0)$ and its equation is of the form $\frac{x^2}{b^2} + \frac{y^2}{a^2} = 1$. The distance from the center of the ellipse to the vertex is $a = 9$ units. The distance from the center of the ellipse to the focus is $c = 6$ units. Because $b^2 = a^2 - c^2$, we have that $b^2 = 9^2 - 6^2 = 81 - 36 = 45$. Thus, the equation of the ellipse is $\frac{x^2}{45} + \frac{y^2}{81} = 1$.

14. The center is $(h,k) = (3,-4)$. The center, focus, and vertex given all lie on the horizontal line $y = -4$. Therefore, the major axis is parallel to the x-axis, and the equation of the ellipse is of the form $\frac{(x-h)^2}{a^2} + \frac{(y-k)^2}{b^2} = 1$. Now, $a = 4$ is the distance from the center $(3,-4)$ to a vertex $(7,-4)$, and $c = 3$ is the distance from the center to a focus $(6,-4)$. Also, $b^2 = a^2 - c^2$, so $b^2 = 4^2 - 3^2 = 16 - 9 = 7$. Thus, the equation of the ellipse is

$$\frac{(x-3)^2}{16} + \frac{(y-(-4))^2}{7} = 1$$

$$\frac{(x-3)^2}{16} + \frac{(y+4)^2}{7} = 1$$

15. $\frac{y^2}{81} - \frac{x^2}{9} = 1$

Notice the equation is of the form $\frac{y^2}{a^2} - \frac{x^2}{b^2} = 1$.

Because the y^2-term is first, the transverse is along the y-axis and the hyperbola opens up and down. The center of the hyperbola is $(0,0)$. We have that $a^2 = 81$ and $b^2 = 9$. Because $c^2 = a^2 + b^2$, we have that $c^2 = 81 + 9 = 90$, so that $c = \sqrt{90} = 3\sqrt{10}$. The vertices are $(0, \pm a) = (0, \pm 9)$, and the foci are $(0, \pm c) = (0, \pm 3\sqrt{10})$. Since $a = 9$ and $b = 3$, the equations of the asymptotes are $y = \frac{9}{3}x = 3x$ and $y = -\frac{9}{3}x = -3x$. To help graph the hyperbola, we form the rectangle using the points $(0, \pm a) = (0, \pm 9)$ and $(\pm b, 0) = (\pm 3, 0)$. The diagonals are the asymptotes.

16. $25x^2 - y^2 = 25$

$$\frac{25x^2 - y^2}{25} = \frac{25}{25}$$

$$\frac{x^2}{1} - \frac{y^2}{25} = 1$$

Notice the equation is of the form $\frac{x^2}{a^2} - \frac{y^2}{b^2} = 1$.

Because the x^2-term is first, the transverse is along the x-axis and the hyperbola opens left and right. The center of the hyperbola is $(0,0)$. We have that $a^2 = 1$ and $b^2 = 25$. Because $c^2 = a^2 + b^2$, we have that $c^2 = 1 + 25 = 26$, so that $c = \sqrt{26}$. The vertices are $(\pm a, 0) = (\pm 1, 0)$, and the foci are $(\pm c, 0) = (\pm \sqrt{26}, 0)$. Since $a = 1$ and $b = 5$, the equations of the asymptotes are $y = \frac{5}{1}x = 5x$ and $y = -\frac{5}{1}x = -5x$. To help graph the hyperbola, we form the rectangle using the points $(\pm a, 0) = (\pm 1, 0)$ and $(0, \pm b) = (0, \pm 5)$. The diagonals are the asymptotes.

17. The given center $(0,0)$, focus $(0,-5)$, and vertex $(0,-2)$ all lie on the y-axis. Thus, the transverse axis is the y-axis and the hyperbola opens up and down. This means that the equation of the hyperbola is $\frac{y^2}{a^2} - \frac{x^2}{b^2} = 1$. Now, the distance between the given vertex $(0,-2)$ and the center $(0,0)$ is $a = 2$ units. Likewise, the distance between the given focus $(0,-5)$ and the center is $c = 5$ units. Because $b^2 = c^2 - a^2$, we have that $b^2 = 5^2 - 2^2 = 25 - 4 = 21$. Thus, the equation of the hyperbola is $\frac{y^2}{4} - \frac{x^2}{21} = 1$.

18. The light bulb should be located at the focus of the flood light, so we need to find where the focus of the flood light is. To solve this problem, we draw a parabola on a Cartesian plane so that the vertex is the origin and the focus is on the positive y-axis. The width of the parabola is 36 inches, and the depth is 12 inches. Therefore, we know two points on the graph of the parabola: $(-18, 12)$ and $(18, 12)$.

The equation of the parabola has the form $x^2 = 4ay$. Since $(18, 12)$ is a point on the graph, we have: $18^2 = 4a(12)$

$$324 = 48a$$

$$a = \frac{324}{48} = 6.75$$

The light bulb should be located 6.75 inches above the vertex, along its axis of symmetry.

10.6 Preparing for Nonlinear Systems of Equations

1. $\begin{cases} y = 2x - 5 & (1) \\ 2x - 3y = 7 & (2) \end{cases}$

Substituting $2x - 5$ for y in equation (2), we obtain

$$2x - 3(2x - 5) = 7$$

$$2x - 6x + 15 = 7$$

$$-4x + 15 = 7$$

$$-4x = -8$$

$$x = 2$$

Substituting 2 for x in equation (1), we obtain

$y = 2(2) - 5 = 4 - 5 = -1$.

The solution is the ordered pair $(2, -1)$.

2. $\begin{cases} 2x - 4y = -11 & (1) \\ -x + 5y = 13 & (2) \end{cases}$

Multiply both sides of equation (2) by 2, and add the result to equation (1).

$$2x - 4y = -11$$

$$-2x + 10y = 26$$

$$\overline{6y = 15}$$

$$y = \frac{15}{6} = \frac{5}{2}$$

Substituting $\frac{5}{2}$ for y in equation (1), we obtain

$$2x - 4\left(\frac{5}{2}\right) = -11$$

$$2x - 10 = -11$$

$$2x = -1$$

$$x = -\frac{1}{2}$$

The solution is the ordered pair $\left(-\frac{1}{2}, \frac{5}{2}\right)$.

3. $\begin{cases} 3x - 5y = 4 & (1) \\ -6x + 10y = -8 & (2) \end{cases}$

Multiply both sides of equation (1) by 2, and add the result to equation (2).

$$6x - 10y = 8$$

$$-6x + 10y = -8$$

$$\overline{0 = 0}$$

The system is dependent. The solution is $\{(x, y) \mid 3x - 5y = 4\}$.

10.6 Exercises

1. substitution, elimination

3. In a system of nonlinear equations, at least one of its equations is not linear.

5. $\begin{cases} y = x^2 + 4 \\ y = x + 4 \end{cases}$

First, graph each equation in the system.

The system apparently has two solutions. Now substitute $x^2 + 4$ for y into the second equation:

$$x^2 + 4 = x + 4$$

$$x^2 - x = 0$$

$$x(x - 1) = 0$$

$$x = 0 \quad \text{or} \quad x = 1$$

Substitute these x-values into the first equation to find the corresponding y-values:

$x = 0$: $y = 0^2 + 4 = 4$

$x = 1$: $y = 1^2 + 4 = 1 + 4 = 5$

Both pairs check, so the solutions are $(0, 4)$ and $(1, 5)$.

7. $\begin{cases} y = \sqrt{25 - x^2} \\ x + y = 7 \end{cases}$

First, graph each equation in the system.

The system apparently has two solutions. Now substitute $\sqrt{25 - x^2}$ for y into the second equation:

$$x + \sqrt{25 - x^2} = 7$$
$$\sqrt{25 - x^2} = 7 - x$$
$$\left(\sqrt{25 - x^2}\right)^2 = (7 - x)^2$$
$$25 - x^2 = 49 - 14x + x^2$$
$$-2x^2 + 14x - 24 = 0$$
$$x^2 - 7x + 12 = 0$$
$$(x - 3)(x - 4) = 0$$
$$x = 3 \quad \text{or} \quad x = 4$$

Substitute these x-values into the first equation to find the corresponding y-values:

$x = 3$: $\quad y = \sqrt{25 - 3^2} = \sqrt{25 - 9} = \sqrt{16} = 4$

$x = 4$: $\quad y = \sqrt{25 - 4^2} = \sqrt{25 - 16} = \sqrt{9} = 3$

Both pairs check, so the solutions are $(3, 4)$ and $(4, 3)$.

9. $\begin{cases} x^2 + y^2 = 4 \\ y = x^2 - 2 \end{cases}$

First, graph each equation in the system.

The system apparently has three solutions. Now solve the first equation for x^2: $x^2 = 4 - y^2$.

Substitute the result for x^2 into the second equation:

$$y = (4 - y^2) - 2$$
$$y = 2 - y^2$$

$$y^2 + y - 2 = 0$$
$$(y + 2)(y - 1) = 0$$
$$y = -2 \quad \text{or} \quad y = 1$$

Substitute these y-values into the first equation to find the corresponding x-values:

$y = -2$: $\quad x^2 + (-2)^2 = 4$
$$x^2 + 4 = 4$$
$$x^2 = 0$$
$$x = 0$$

$y = 1$: $\quad x^2 + 1^2 = 4$
$$x^2 + 1 = 4$$
$$x^2 = 3$$
$$x = \pm\sqrt{3}$$

All three pairs check, so the solutions are $(0, -2)$, $\left(-\sqrt{3}, 1\right)$, and $\left(\sqrt{3}, 1\right)$.

11. $\begin{cases} xy = 4 \\ x^2 + y^2 = 8 \end{cases}$

First, graph each equation in the system.

The system apparently has two solutions. Now solve the first equation for y: $y = \dfrac{4}{x}$.

Substitute the result into the second equation.

$$x^2 + \left(\frac{4}{x}\right)^2 = 8$$
$$x^2 + \frac{16}{x^2} = 8$$
$$x^2\left(x^2 + \frac{16}{x^2}\right) = x^2(8)$$
$$x^4 + 16 = 8x^2$$
$$x^4 - 8x^2 + 16 = 0$$
$$\left(x^2 - 4\right)^2 = 0$$
$$x^2 - 4 = 0$$
$$(x + 2)(x - 2) = 0$$
$$x = -2 \quad \text{or} \quad x = 2$$

Substitute these *x*-values into the equation

$y = \dfrac{4}{x}$ to find the corresponding *y*-values.

$x = -2: \ y = \dfrac{4}{-2} = -2$

$x = 2: \ y = \dfrac{4}{2} = 2$

Both pairs check, so the solutions are $(-2, -2)$ and $(2, 2)$.

13. $\begin{cases} x^2 + y^2 = 4 \\ y^2 - x = 4 \end{cases}$

First, graph each equation in the system.

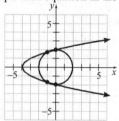

The system apparently has four solutions. Now multiply the second equation by -1 and add the result to the first equation:

$x^2 + \quad y^2 = 4$

$\underline{\qquad x - y^2 = -4}$

$x^2 + x \qquad = 0$

$\quad x(x+1) = 0$

$x = 0 \ $ or $ \ x = -1$

Substitute these *x*-values into the second equation to find the corresponding *y*-values:

$x = 0: \ y^2 - 0 = 4$

$\qquad\qquad y = \pm\sqrt{4} = \pm 2$

$x = -1: \ y^2 - (-1) = 4$

$\qquad\qquad y^2 + 1 = 4$

$\qquad\qquad y^2 = 3$

$\qquad\qquad y = \pm\sqrt{3}$

All four pairs check, so the solutions are $(0, -2)$, $(0, 2)$, $\left(-1, -\sqrt{3}\right)$ and $\left(-1, \sqrt{3}\right)$.

15. $\begin{cases} x^2 + y^2 = 7 \\ x^2 - y^2 = 25 \end{cases}$

First, graph each equation in the system.

The system apparently has no solution. Now add the two equations:

$x^2 + y^2 = 7$

$\underline{x^2 - y^2 = 25}$

$2x^2 \qquad = 32$

$\quad x^2 = 16$

$\quad x = \pm 4$

Substitute 16 for x^2 into the first equation to find the *y* values.

$16 + y^2 = 7$

$\qquad y^2 = -9$

$\qquad y = \pm\sqrt{-9}$

which yields no real solutions. The system is inconsistent. The solution set is $\varnothing$.

17. $\begin{cases} x^2 + y^2 = 6y \\ x^2 = 3y \end{cases}$

First, graph each equation in the system.

The system apparently has three solutions. Now multiply the second equation by -1 and add the result to the first equation:

$x^2 + y^2 = 6y$

$\underline{-x^2 \qquad = -3y}$

$\qquad y^2 = 3y$

$y^2 - 3y = 0$

$y(y - 3) = 0$

$y = 0 \ $ or $ \ y = 3$

Substitute these y-values into the second equation to find the corresponding x-values:

$y = 0:\ x^2 = 3(0)$
$\qquad\ \ x^2 = 0$
$\qquad\ \ \ x = 0$

$y = 3:\ x^2 = 3(3)$
$\qquad\ \ x^2 = 9$
$\qquad\ \ \ x = \pm 3$

All three pairs check, so the solutions are $(0,\ 0)$, $(-3,\ 3)$, and $(3,\ 3)$.

19. $\begin{cases} x^2 - 2x - y = 8 \\ 6x + 2y = -4 \end{cases}$

First, graph each equation in the system.

The system apparently has two solutions. Now divide the second equation by 2 and add the result to the first equation:

$\quad x^2 - 2x - y = 8$
$\quad \underline{\ \ \ \ 3x + y = -2\ }$
$\quad x^2 + x \quad\ \ = 6$
$\quad x^2 + x - 6 = 0$
$\ (x + 3)(x - 2) = 0$
$\quad x = -3 \text{ or } x = 2$

Substitute these results into the second equation to find the corresponding y-values.

$x = -3:\ 6(-3) + 2y = -4$
$\qquad\qquad\ -18 + 2y = -4$
$\qquad\qquad\qquad\ \ 2y = 14$
$\qquad\qquad\qquad\qquad y = 7$

$x = 2:\ 6(2) + 2y = -4$
$\qquad\qquad\ 12 + 2y = -4$
$\qquad\qquad\qquad\ 2y = -16$
$\qquad\qquad\qquad\quad y = -8$

Both pairs check, so the solutions are $(-3,\ 7)$ and $(2, -8)$.

21. $\begin{cases} y = x^2 - 6x + 4 \\ 5x + y = 6 \end{cases}$

First, graph each equation in the system.

The system apparently has two solutions. Now solve the second equation for y: $y = -5x + 6$.

Substitute the result into the first equation:

$-5x + 6 = x^2 - 6x + 4$
$\qquad\ 0 = x^2 - x - 2$
$\qquad\ 0 = (x + 1)(x - 2)$
$\qquad\ x = -1 \text{ or } x = 2$

Substitute these x-values into the equation $y = -5x + 6$ to find the corresponding y-values:

$x = -1:\ y = -5(-1) + 6 = 5 + 6 = 11$

$x = 2:\ y = -5(2) + 6 = -10 + 6 = -4$

Both pairs check, so the solutions are $(-1,\ 11)$ and $(2, -4)$.

23. $\begin{cases} x^2 + y^2 = 16 \\ x^2 - y^2 = 16 \end{cases}$

First, graph each equation in the system.

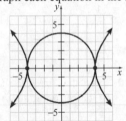

The system apparently has two solutions. Now add the two equations:

$\quad x^2 + y^2 = 16$
$\quad \underline{x^2 - y^2 = 16\ }$
$\quad 2x^2 \qquad\ = 32$
$\qquad\ x^2 = 16$
$\qquad\ \ x = \pm 4$

Substitute 16 for x^2 into the first equation to find the y-values.

$16 + y^2 = 16$
$\qquad\ y^2 = 0$
$\qquad\ \ y = 0$

Both pairs check, so the solutions are $(-4,\ 0)$ and $(4,\ 0)$.

25. $\begin{cases} (x-4)^2 + y^2 = 25 \\ x - y = -3 \end{cases}$

First, graph each equation in the system.

The system apparently has two solutions. Now solve the second equation for y: $y = x + 3$.

Substitute the result into the first equation:
$$(x-4)^2 + (x+3)^2 = 25$$
$$x^2 - 8x + 16 + x^2 + 6x + 9 = 25$$
$$2x^2 - 2x = 0$$
$$2x(x-1) = 0$$
$$x = 0 \ \text{ or } \ x = 1$$

Substitute these x-values into the equation $y = x + 3$ to find the corresponding y-values:

$x = 0$: $y = 0 + 3 = 3$

$x = 1$: $y = 1 + 3 = 4$

Both pairs check, so the solutions are $(0, 3)$ and $(1, 4)$.

27. $\begin{cases} (x-1)^2 + (y+2)^2 = 4 \\ y^2 + 4y - x = -1 \end{cases}$

First, graph each equation in the system.

The system apparently has four solutions. Now expand the first equation and simplify:
$$(x-1)^2 + (y+2)^2 = 4$$
$$x^2 - 2x + 1 + y^2 + 4y + 4 = 4$$
$$x^2 - 2x + y^2 + 4y = -1$$

Multiply the second equation by -1 and add the result to the expanded form of the first equation:
$$x^2 - 2x + y^2 + 4y = -1$$
$$\underline{ x - y^2 - 4y = 1}$$
$$x^2 - x = 0$$
$$x(x-1) = 0$$

$x = 0 \ \text{ or } \ x = 1$

Substitute these x-values into the first equation to find the corresponding y-values.

$x = 0$: $(0-1)^2 + (y+2)^2 = 4$
$$1 + (y+2)^2 = 4$$
$$(y+2)^2 = 3$$
$$y + 2 = \pm\sqrt{3}$$
$$y = -2 \pm \sqrt{3}$$

$x = 1$: $(1-1)^2 + (y+2)^2 = 4$
$$(y+2)^2 = 4$$
$$y + 2 = \pm 2$$
$$y = -2 \pm 2$$
$$y = -4 \ \text{ or } \ y = 0$$

All four pairs check, so the solutions are $\left(0, -2-\sqrt{3}\right)$, $\left(0, -2+\sqrt{3}\right)$, $(1, -4)$, and $(1, 0)$.

29. $\begin{cases} (x+3)^2 + 4y^2 = 4 \\ x^2 + 6x - y = 13 \end{cases}$

First, graph each equation in the system.

The system apparently has no solution. Now expand the first equation and simplify:
$$(x+3)^2 + 4y^2 = 4$$
$$x^2 + 6x + 9 + 4y^2 = 4$$
$$x^2 + 6x + 4y^2 = -5$$

Multiply the second equation by -1 and add the result to the expanded form of the first equation:
$$x^2 + 6x + 4y^2 = -5$$
$$\underline{-x^2 - 6x + y = -13}$$
$$4y^2 + y = -18$$
$$4y^2 + y + 18 = 0$$
$$y = \frac{-1 \pm \sqrt{1^2 - 4(4)(18)}}{2(4)} = \frac{-1 \pm \sqrt{-287}}{8}$$

which yields no real solutions. The system is inconsistent. The solution set is $\varnothing$.

31. $\begin{cases} x^2 - y^2 = 21 \\ x + y = 7 \end{cases}$

First, graph each equation in the system.

The system apparently has one solution. Now solve the second equation for y: $y = 7 - x$.

Substitute the result into the first equation:

$$x^2 - (7-x)^2 = 21$$
$$x^2 - \left(49 - 14x + x^2\right) = 21$$
$$x^2 - 49 + 14x - x^2 = 21$$
$$14x - 49 = 21$$
$$14x = 70$$
$$x = 5$$

Substitute 5 for x into the equation $y = 7 - x$ to find the corresponding y value: $y = 7 - 5 = 2$.

The pair checks, so the solution is $(5,\ 2)$.

33. $\begin{cases} x^2 + 2y^2 = 16 \\ 4x^2 - y^2 = 24 \end{cases}$

First, graph each equation in the system.

The system apparently has four solutions. Now multiply the second equation by 2 and add the result to the first equation:

$$x^2 + 2y^2 = 16$$
$$\underline{8x^2 - 2y^2 = 48}$$
$$9x^2 \qquad = 64$$
$$x^2 = \frac{64}{9}$$
$$x = \pm\frac{8}{3}$$

Substitute $\frac{64}{9}$ for x^2 into the first equation to find the y-values:

$$\frac{64}{9} + 2y^2 = 16$$
$$9\left(\frac{64}{9} + 2y^2\right) = 9(16)$$
$$64 + 18y^2 = 144$$
$$18y^2 = 80$$
$$y^2 = \frac{80}{18} = \frac{40}{9}$$
$$y = \pm\sqrt{\frac{40}{9}} = \pm\frac{\sqrt{40}}{\sqrt{9}} = \pm\frac{2\sqrt{10}}{3}$$

All four pairs check, so the solutions are

$\left(-\frac{8}{3}, -\frac{2\sqrt{10}}{3}\right)$, $\left(-\frac{8}{3}, \frac{2\sqrt{10}}{3}\right)$, $\left(\frac{8}{3}, -\frac{2\sqrt{10}}{3}\right)$, and

$\left(\frac{8}{3}, \frac{2\sqrt{10}}{3}\right)$.

35. $\begin{cases} x^2 + y^2 = 25 \\ y = -x^2 + 6x - 5 \end{cases}$

First, graph each equation in the system.

The system apparently has four solutions. Now substitute $-x^2 + 6x - 5$ for y into the first equation:

$$x^2 + \left(-x^2 + 6x - 5\right)^2 = 25$$
$$\left(x^2 - 25\right) + \left(-x^2 + 6x - 5\right)^2 = 0$$
$$(x-5)(x+5) + \left[-1(x-5)(x-1)\right]^2 = 0$$
$$(x-5)(x+5) + (x-5)^2(x-1)^2 = 0$$
$$(x-5)\left[(x+5) + (x-5)(x-1)^2\right] = 0$$
$$(x-5)\left[(x+5) + \left(x^3 - 7x^2 + 11x - 5\right)\right] = 0$$
$$(x-5)\left(x^3 - 7x^2 + 12x\right) = 0$$
$$x(x-5)\left(x^2 - 7x + 12\right) = 0$$
$$x(x-5)(x-3)(x-4) = 0$$
$$x = 0,\ x = 5,\ x = 3,\ \text{or}\ x = 4$$

Substitute these x-values into the second equation to find the corresponding y-values:

$x = 0$: $y = -(0)^2 + 6(0) - 5 = 0 + 0 - 5 = -5$

$x = 3$: $y = -(3)^2 + 6(3) - 5 = -9 + 18 - 5 = 4$

$x = 4$: $y = -(4)^2 + 6(4) - 5 = -16 + 24 - 5 = 3$

$x = 5$: $y = -(5)^2 + 6(5) - 5 = -25 + 30 - 5 = 0$

All four pairs check, so the solutions are $(0, -5)$, $(3, 4)$, $(4, 3)$, and $(5, 0)$.

37. Let x represent the larger of the two numbers and y represent the smaller of the two numbers.

$$\begin{cases} x - y = 2 \\ x^2 + y^2 = 34 \end{cases}$$

Solve the first equation for x: $x = y + 2$.

Substitute the result into the second equation:

$$(y + 2)^2 + y^2 = 34$$
$$(y^2 + 4y + 4) + y^2 = 34$$
$$2y^2 + 4y - 30 = 0$$
$$y^2 + 2y - 15 = 0$$
$$(y + 5)(y - 3) = 0$$
$$y = -5 \text{ or } y = 3$$

Substitute these y-values into the equation $x = y + 2$ to find the corresponding x-values.

$y = -5$: $x = -5 + 2 = -3$

$y = 3$: $x = 3 + 2 = 5$

The numbers are either -5 and -3, or 3 and 5.

39. Let x represent the length and y represent the width of the rectangle.

$$\begin{cases} 2x + 2y = 48 \\ xy = 140 \end{cases}$$

Solve the first equation for y: $y = 24 - x$.

Substitute the result into the second equation:

$$x(24 - x) = 140$$
$$24x - x^2 = 140$$
$$x^2 - 24x + 140 = 0$$
$$(x - 14)(x - 10) = 0$$
$$x = 14 \text{ or } x = 10$$

Substitute these x-values into the second equation to find the corresponding y-values:

$x = 14$: $14y = 140$

$y = 10$

$x = 10$: $10y = 140$

$y = 14$

Note that the two outcomes result in the same overall dimensions. Assuming the length is the longer of the two sides, the length is 14 feet and the width is 10 feet.

41. Let x represent the length and y represent the width of the rectangular piece of cardboard.

The area of the cardboard is $A = xy = 190 \text{ cm}^2$.

If 2-cm squares are cut from each corner of the rectangle in order to from the box, then the box will be $x - 4$ cm long, $y - 4$ cm wide, 2 cm high. Thus, the volume of the box will be $V = 2(x - 4)(y - 4) = 180 \text{ cm}^3$.

The system of equations follow:

$$\begin{cases} xy = 190 \\ 2(x - 4)(y - 4) = 180 \end{cases}$$

Solve the first equation for y: $y = \dfrac{190}{x}$.

Substitute the result into the second equation:

$$2(x - 4)(y - 4) = 180$$
$$(x - 4)(y - 4) = 90$$
$$xy - 4x - 4y + 16 = 90$$
$$xy - 4x - 4y = 74$$
$$x\left(\frac{190}{x}\right) - 4x - 4\left(\frac{190}{x}\right) = 74$$
$$190 - 4x - \frac{760}{x} = 74$$
$$-4x + 116 - \frac{760}{x} = 0$$
$$x\left(-4x + 116 - \frac{760}{x}\right) = 0$$
$$-4x^2 + 116x - 760 = 0$$
$$-4\left(x^2 - 29x + 190\right) = 0$$
$$x^2 - 29x + 190 = 0$$
$$(x - 19)(x - 10) = 0$$
$$x = 19 \text{ or } x = 10$$

Substitute these x-values into the equation $y = \dfrac{190}{x}$ to find the corresponding y-values:

$x = 19$: $y = \dfrac{190}{19} = 10$

$x = 10$: $y = \dfrac{190}{10} = 19$

Note that the two outcomes result in the same overall dimensions. The rectangular piece of cardboard must be 19 cm by 10 cm.

43. $\begin{cases} y^2 + y + x^2 - x - 2 = 0 \\ \qquad y + 1 + \dfrac{x-2}{y} = 0 \end{cases}$

Multiply the second equation by $-y$:

$$-y\left(y + 1 + \frac{x-2}{y} \right) = -y(0)$$

$$-y^2 - y - x + 2 = 0$$

Add the result to the first equation:

$$\begin{array}{r} y^2 + y + x^2 - x - 2 = 0 \\ \underline{-y^2 - y \qquad\quad -x + 2 = 0} \\ x^2 - 2x = 0 \\ x(x-2) = 0 \end{array}$$

$$x = 0 \quad \text{or} \quad x = 2$$

Substitute these x-values into the first equation to find the corresponding y-values:

$x = 0$: $y^2 + y + 0^2 - 0 - 2 = 0$

$$y^2 + y - 2 = 0$$
$$(y+2)(y-1) = 0$$
$$y = -2 \quad \text{or} \quad y = 1$$

$x = 2$: $y^2 + y + 2^2 - 2 - 2 = 0$

$$y^2 + y + 4 - 2 - 2 = 0$$
$$y^2 + y = 0$$
$$y(y+1) = 0$$
$$y = 0 \quad \text{or} \quad y = -1$$

The apparent solution $y = 0$ is extraneous because the denominator of a fraction cannot be 0.
The solutions are $(0, -2)$, $(0, 1)$, and $(2, -1)$.

45. $\begin{cases} \ln x = 4 \ln y \\ \log_3 x = 2 + 2 \log_3 y \end{cases}$

Write the first equation in exponential form:

$\ln x = 4 \ln y$

$\ln x = \ln y^4$

$\quad x = y^4$

Write the second equation in exponential form:

$\log_3 x = 2 + 2 \log_3 y$

$\log_3 x = \log_3 9 + \log_3 y^2$

$\log_3 x = \log_3 \left(9 y^2 \right)$

$\quad x = 9 y^2$

Thus, we have that

$$y^4 = 9 y^2$$
$$y^4 - 9 y^2 = 0$$
$$y^2 \left(y^2 - 9 \right) = 0$$
$$y^2 (y+3)(y-3) = 0$$

$$y^2 = 0 \quad \text{or} \quad y + 3 = 0 \quad \text{or} \quad y - 3 = 0$$
$$y = 0 \qquad\qquad y = -3 \qquad\quad y = 3$$

The apparent y-values 0 and -3 are extraneous because the argument of a logarithm must be positive. Thus, the only possible y-value is 3. Substitute 3 for y into the equation $x = y^4$ to find the corresponding x-value: $x = 3^4 = 81$. The solution is $(81, 3)$.

47. $\begin{cases} r_1 + r_2 = -\dfrac{b}{a} \\ r_1 r_2 = \dfrac{c}{a} \end{cases}$

Solve the second equation for r_1: $r_1 = \dfrac{c}{a r_2}$

Substitute the result into the first equation:

$$\frac{c}{a r_2} + r_2 = -\frac{b}{a}$$

$$a r_2 \left(\frac{c}{a r_2} + r_2 \right) = a r_2 \left(-\frac{b}{a} \right)$$

$$c + a \left(r_2 \right)^2 = -b r_2$$

$$a \left(r_2 \right)^2 + b r_2 + c = 0$$

$$r_2 = \frac{-b \pm \sqrt{b^2 - 4ac}}{2a}$$

Substitute this result into the first equation to find the corresponding value of r_1:

$$r_1 + \frac{-b \pm \sqrt{b^2 - 4ac}}{2a} = -\frac{b}{a}$$

$$r_1 - \frac{b}{2a} \pm \frac{\sqrt{b^2 - 4ac}}{2a} = -\frac{b}{a}$$

$$r_1 = -\frac{b}{a} + \frac{b}{2a} \mp \frac{\sqrt{b^2 - 4ac}}{2a}$$

$$r_1 = -\frac{2b}{2a} + \frac{b}{2a} \mp \frac{\sqrt{b^2 - 4ac}}{2a}$$

$$r_1 = -\frac{b}{2a} \pm \frac{\sqrt{b^2 - 4ac}}{2a}$$

$$r_1 = \frac{-b \mp \sqrt{b^2 - 4ac}}{2a}$$

If $r_1 = \dfrac{-b + \sqrt{b^2 - 4ac}}{2a}$, then $r_2 = \dfrac{-b - \sqrt{b^2 - 4ac}}{2a}$;

if $r_1 = \dfrac{-b - \sqrt{b^2 - 4ac}}{2a}$, then $r_2 = \dfrac{-b + \sqrt{b^2 - 4ac}}{2a}$.

49. a. $f(1) = 3(1) + 4 = 3 + 4 = 7$

    b. $g(1) = 2^1 = 2$

51. a. $f(3) = 3(3) + 4 = 9 + 4 = 13$

    b. $g(3) = 2^3 = 8$

53. a. $f(5) = 3(5) + 4 = 15 + 4 = 19$

    b. $g(5) = 2^5 = 32$

55. $\begin{cases} y = x^2 - 6x + 4 \\ 5x + y = 6 \quad (y = -5x + 6) \end{cases}$

Let $Y_1 = x^2 - 6x + 4$ and $Y_2 = -5x + 6$.

The solutions are $(-1, 11)$ and $(2, -4)$.

57. $\begin{cases} x^2 + y^2 = 16 \quad \left(y = \pm\sqrt{16 - x^2} \right) \\ x^2 - y^2 = 16 \quad \left(y = \pm\sqrt{x^2 - 16} \right) \end{cases}$

Let $Y_1 = \sqrt{16 - x^2}$, $Y_2 = -\sqrt{16 - x^2}$,

$Y_3 = \sqrt{x^2 - 16}$, and $Y_4 = -\sqrt{x^2 - 16}$.

The solutions are $(-4, 0)$ and $(4, 0)$.

59. $\begin{cases} (x-4)^2 + y^2 = 25 \quad \left(y = \pm\sqrt{25 - (x-4)^2} \right) \\ x - y = -3 \quad (y = x + 3) \end{cases}$

Let $Y_1 = \sqrt{25 - (x-4)^2}$, $Y_2 = -\sqrt{25 - (x-4)^2}$,

and $Y_3 = x + 3$.

The solutions are $(0, 3)$ and $(1, 4)$.

61. $\begin{cases} (x-1)^2 + (y+2)^2 = 4 \quad \left(y = -2 \pm\sqrt{4 - (x-1)^2} \right) \\ x^2 + 4y - x = -1 \quad \left(y = \dfrac{-x^2 + x - 1}{4} \right) \end{cases}$

Let $Y_1 = -2 + \sqrt{4 - (x-1)^2}$, $Y_2 = -2 + \sqrt{4 - (x-1)^2}$,

and $Y_3 = \dfrac{-x^2 + x - 1}{4}$.

The solutions are approximately $(0.056, -0.237)$

and $(2.981, -1.727)$.

63. $\begin{cases} x^2 + 4y^2 = 4 \\ x^2 + 6x - y = -13 \end{cases}$ $\begin{array}{l}\left(y = \pm\sqrt{1-\dfrac{x^2}{4}}\right) \\ \left(y = x^2 + 6x + 13\right)\end{array}$

Let $Y_1 = \sqrt{1-\dfrac{x^2}{4}}$, $Y_2 = -\sqrt{1-\dfrac{x^2}{4}}$, and

$Y_3 = x^2 + 6x + 13$.

Because the graphs do not intersect, the system has no solution, $\varnothing$.

Chapter 10 Review

1. $d(P_1, P_2) = \sqrt{(x_2 - x_1)^2 + (y_2 - y_1)^2}$

$= \sqrt{(-4-0)^2 + (-3-0)^2}$

$= \sqrt{(-4)^2 + (-3)^2}$

$= \sqrt{16+9} = \sqrt{25} = 5$

2. $d(P_1, P_2) = \sqrt{(x_2 - x_1)^2 + (y_2 - y_1)^2}$

$= \sqrt{(5-(-3))^2 + (-4-2)^2}$

$= \sqrt{8^2 + (-6)^2}$

$= \sqrt{64+36} = \sqrt{100} = 10$

3. $d(P_1, P_2) = \sqrt{(x_2 - x_1)^2 + (y_2 - y_1)^2}$

$= \sqrt{(5-(-1))^2 + (3-1)^2}$

$= \sqrt{6^2 + 2^2}$

$= \sqrt{36+4} = \sqrt{40} = 2\sqrt{10} \approx 6.32$

4. $d(P_1, P_2) = \sqrt{(x_2 - x_1)^2 + (y_2 - y_1)^2}$

$= \sqrt{(6-6)^2 + (-1-(-7))^2}$

$= \sqrt{0^2 + 6^2} = \sqrt{0+36} = \sqrt{36} = 6$

5. $d(P_1, P_2) = \sqrt{(x_2 - x_1)^2 + (y_2 - y_1)^2}$

$= \sqrt{\left(4\sqrt{7} - \sqrt{7}\right)^2 + \left(5\sqrt{3} - \left(-\sqrt{3}\right)\right)^2}$

$= \sqrt{\left(3\sqrt{7}\right)^2 + \left(6\sqrt{3}\right)^2}$

$= \sqrt{9(7) + 36(3)}$

$= \sqrt{63+108} = \sqrt{171} = 3\sqrt{19} \approx 13.08$

6. $d(P_1, P_2) = \sqrt{(x_2 - x_1)^2 + (y_2 - y_1)^2}$

$= \sqrt{(1.3 - (-0.2))^2 + (3.7 - 1.7)^2}$

$= \sqrt{1.5^2 + 2^2}$

$= \sqrt{2.25+4} = \sqrt{6.25} = 2.5$

7. $M = \left(\dfrac{x_1 + x_2}{2}, \dfrac{y_1 + y_2}{2}\right)$

$= \left(\dfrac{-1 + (-3)}{2}, \dfrac{6+4}{2}\right) = \left(\dfrac{-4}{2}, \dfrac{10}{2}\right) = (-2, 5)$

8. $M = \left(\dfrac{x_1 + x_2}{2}, \dfrac{y_1 + y_2}{2}\right)$

$= \left(\dfrac{7+5}{2}, \dfrac{0 + (-4)}{2}\right) = \left(\dfrac{12}{2}, \dfrac{-4}{2}\right) = (6, -2)$

9. $M = \left(\dfrac{x_1 + x_2}{2}, \dfrac{y_1 + y_2}{2}\right)$

$= \left(\dfrac{-\sqrt{3} + \left(-7\sqrt{3}\right)}{2}, \dfrac{2\sqrt{6} + \left(-8\sqrt{6}\right)}{2}\right)$

$= \left(\dfrac{-8\sqrt{3}}{2}, \dfrac{-6\sqrt{6}}{2}\right) = \left(-4\sqrt{3}, -3\sqrt{6}\right)$

10. $M = \left(\dfrac{x_1 + x_2}{2}, \dfrac{y_1 + y_2}{2}\right)$

$= \left(\dfrac{5+0}{2}, \dfrac{-2+3}{2}\right) = \left(\dfrac{5}{2}, \dfrac{1}{2}\right)$

11. $M = \left(\dfrac{x_1 + x_2}{2}, \dfrac{y_1 + y_2}{2}\right)$

$= \left(\dfrac{\frac{1}{4} + \frac{5}{4}}{2}, \dfrac{\frac{2}{3} + \frac{1}{3}}{2}\right) = \left(\dfrac{\frac{3}{2}}{2}, \dfrac{1}{2}\right) = \left(\dfrac{3}{4}, \dfrac{1}{2}\right)$

12. **a.**

b. $d(A,B) = \sqrt{(1-(-2))^2 + (-1-2)^2}$
$= \sqrt{3^2 + (-3)^2}$
$= \sqrt{9+9}$
$= \sqrt{18}$
$= 3\sqrt{2} \approx 4.24$

$d(B,C) = \sqrt{(-1-1)^2 + (-3-(-1))^2}$
$= \sqrt{(-2)^2 + (-2)^2}$
$= \sqrt{4+4}$
$= \sqrt{8}$
$= 2\sqrt{2} \approx 2.83$

$d(A,C) = \sqrt{(-1-(-2))^2 + (-3-2)^2}$
$= \sqrt{1^2 + (-5)^2}$
$= \sqrt{1+25}$
$= \sqrt{26} \approx 5.10$

c. To determine if triangle ABC is a right triangle, we check to see if
$$[d(A,B)]^2 + [d(B,C)]^2 \overset{?}{=} [d(A,C)]^2$$
$$\left(3\sqrt{2}\right)^2 + \left(2\sqrt{2}\right)^2 \overset{?}{=} \left(\sqrt{26}\right)^2$$
$$9 \cdot 2 + 4 \cdot 2 \overset{?}{=} 26$$
$$18 + 8 \overset{?}{=} 26$$
$$26 = 26 \leftarrow \text{True}$$
Therefore, triangle ABC is a right triangle.

d. The length of the "base" of the triangle is $d(B,C) = 2\sqrt{2}$ and the length of the "height" of the triangle is $d(A,B) = 3\sqrt{2}$. Thus, the area of triangle ABC is
$$\text{Area} = \frac{1}{2} \cdot \text{base} \cdot \text{height} = \frac{1}{2} \cdot 2\sqrt{2} \cdot 3\sqrt{2} = 6$$
square units.

13. The center of the circle will be the midpoint of the line segment with endpoints $(-6,1)$ and $(2,1)$. Thus, $(h,k) = \left(\dfrac{-6+2}{2}, \dfrac{1+1}{2}\right) = (-2,1)$.

The radius of the circle will be the distance from the center point $(-2,1)$ to a point on the circle, say $(2,1)$. Thus, $r = \sqrt{(2-(-2))^2 + (1-1)^2} = 4$.
The equation of the circle is
$$(x-h)^2 + (y-k)^2 = r^2$$
$$(x-(-2))^2 + (y-1)^2 = 4^2$$
$$(x+2)^2 + (y-1)^2 = 16$$

14. The center of the circle will be the midpoint of the line segment with endpoints $(2,3)$ and $(8,3)$. Thus, $(h,k) = \left(\dfrac{2+8}{2}, \dfrac{3+3}{2}\right) = (5,3)$.

The radius of the circle will be the distance from the center point $(5,3)$ to a point on the circle, say $(8,3)$. Thus, $r = \sqrt{(8-5)^2 + (3-3)^2} = 3$.
The equation of the circle is
$$(x-h)^2 + (y-k)^2 = r^2$$
$$(x-5)^2 + (y-3)^2 = 3^2$$
$$(x-5)^2 + (y-3)^2 = 9$$

15. $(x-h)^2 + (y-k)^2 = r^2$
$(x-0)^2 + (y-0)^2 = 4^2$
$x^2 + y^2 = 16$

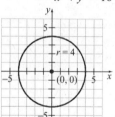

16.
$$\left(x-h\right)^2 + \left(y-k\right)^2 = r^2$$
$$\left(x-(-3)\right)^2 + \left(y-1\right)^2 = 3^2$$
$$\left(x+3\right)^2 + \left(y-1\right)^2 = 9$$

17.
$$\left(x-h\right)^2 + \left(y-k\right)^2 = r^2$$
$$\left(x-5\right)^2 + \left(y-(-2)\right)^2 = 1^2$$
$$\left(x-5\right)^2 + \left(y+2\right)^2 = 1$$

18.
$$\left(x-h\right)^2 + \left(y-k\right)^2 = r^2$$
$$\left(x-4\right)^2 + \left(y-0\right)^2 = \left(\sqrt{7}\right)^2$$
$$\left(x-4\right)^2 + y^2 = 7$$

19. The radius of the circle will be the distance from the center point $(2,-1)$ to the point on the circle

$(5,3)$. Thus, $r = \sqrt{\left(5-2\right)^2 + \left(3-(-1)\right)^2} = 5$.

The equation of the circle is
$$\left(x-h\right)^2 + \left(y-k\right)^2 = r^2$$
$$\left(x-2\right)^2 + \left(y-(-1)\right)^2 = 5^2$$
$$\left(x-2\right)^2 + \left(y+1\right)^2 = 25$$

20. The center of the circle will be the midpoint of the diameter with endpoints $(-3,-1)$ and $(1,7)$.

Thus, $(h,k) = \left(\dfrac{-3+1}{2}, \dfrac{-1+7}{2}\right) = (-1,3)$. The

radius of the circle will be the distance from the center point $(-1,3)$ to one of the endpoints of the diameter, say $(1,7)$. Thus,

$r = \sqrt{\left(1-(-1)\right)^2 + \left(7-3\right)^2} = \sqrt{20} = 2\sqrt{5}$.

The equation of the circle is
$$\left(x-h\right)^2 + \left(y-k\right)^2 = r^2$$
$$\left(x-(-1)\right)^2 + \left(y-3\right)^2 = \left(2\sqrt{5}\right)^2$$
$$\left(x+1\right)^2 + \left(y-3\right)^2 = 20$$

21.
$$x^2 + y^2 = 25$$
$$\left(x-0\right)^2 + \left(y-0\right)^2 = 5^2$$

The center is $(h,k) = (0,0)$, and the radius is $r = 5$.

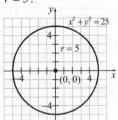

22.
$$\left(x-1\right)^2 + \left(y-2\right)^2 = 4$$
$$\left(x-1\right)^2 + \left(y-2\right)^2 = 2^2$$

The center is $(h,k) = (1,2)$, and the radius is $r = 2$.

23.
$$x^2 + (y-4)^2 = 16$$
$$(x-0)^2 + (y-4)^2 = 4^2$$
The center is $(h,k) = (0,4)$, and the radius is
$r = 4$.

24.
$$(x+1)^2 + (y+6)^2 = 49$$
$$(x-(-1))^2 + (y-(-6))^2 = 7^2$$
The center is $(h,k) = (-1,-6)$, and the radius is
$r = 7$.

25.
$$(x+2)^2 + \left(y - \frac{3}{2}\right)^2 = \frac{1}{4}$$
$$(x-(-2))^2 + \left(y - \frac{3}{2}\right)^2 = \left(\frac{1}{2}\right)^2$$
The center is $(h,k) = \left(-2, \frac{3}{2}\right)$, and the radius is
$r = \frac{1}{2}$.

26.
$$(x+3)^2 + (y+3)^2 = 4$$
$$(x-(-3))^2 + (y-(-3))^2 = 2^2$$
The center is $(h,k) = (-3,-3)$, and the radius is
$r = 2$.

27.
$$x^2 + y^2 + 6x + 10y - 2 = 0$$
$$(x^2 + 6x) + (y^2 + 10y) = 2$$
$$(x^2 + 6x + 9) + (y^2 + 10y + 25) = 2 + 9 + 25$$
$$(x+3)^2 + (y+5)^2 = 36$$
$$(x-(-3))^2 + (y-(-5))^2 = 6^2$$
The center is $(h,k) = (-3,-5)$, and the radius is
$r = 6$.

28.
$$x^2 + y^2 - 8x + 4y + 16 = 0$$
$$(x^2 - 8x) + (y^2 + 4y) = -16$$
$$(x^2 - 8x + 16) + (y^2 + 4y + 4) = -16 + 16 + 4$$
$$(x-4)^2 + (y+2)^2 = 4$$
$$(x-4)^2 + (y-(-2))^2 = 2^2$$
The center is $(h,k) = (4,-2)$, and the radius is
$r = 2$.

29.
$$x^2 + y^2 + 2x - 4y - 4 = 0$$
$$\left(x^2 + 2x\right) + \left(y^2 - 4y\right) = 4$$
$$\left(x^2 + 2x + 1\right) + \left(y^2 - 4y + 4\right) = 4 + 1 + 4$$
$$\left(x+1\right)^2 + \left(y-2\right)^2 = 9$$
$$\left(x-(-1)\right)^2 + \left(y-2\right)^2 = 3^2$$

The center is $(h,k) = (-1,2)$, and the radius is $r = 3$.

30.
$$x^2 + y^2 - 10x - 2y + 17 = 0$$
$$\left(x^2 - 10x\right) + \left(y^2 - 2y\right) = -17$$
$$\left(x^2 - 10x + 25\right) + \left(y^2 - 2y + 1\right) = -17 + 25 + 1$$
$$\left(x-5\right)^2 + \left(y-1\right)^2 = 9$$
$$\left(x-5\right)^2 + \left(y-1\right)^2 = 3^2$$

The center is $(h,k) = (5,1)$, and the radius is $r = 3$.

31. The distance from the vertex $(0,0)$ to the focus $(0,-3)$ is $a = 3$. Because the focus lies on the negative y-axis, we know that the parabola will open downward and the axis of symmetry is the y-axis. This means the equation of the parabola is of the form $x^2 = -4ay$ with $a = 3$:
$$x^2 = -4(3)y$$
$$x^2 = -12y$$

The directrix is the line $y = 3$. To help graph the parabola, we plot the two points on the graph to the left and right of the focus. Let $y = -3$:
$$x^2 = -12(-3) = 36$$
$$x = \pm 6$$

The points $(-6,-3)$ and $(6,-3)$ are on the graph.

32. Notice that the directrix is the vertical line $x = 4$ and that the focus $(-4,0)$ is on the x-axis. Thus, the axis of symmetry is the x-axis, the vertex is at the origin, and the parabola opens to the left. Now, the distance from the vertex $(0,0)$ to the focus $(-4,0)$ is $a = 4$, so the equation of the parabola is of the form $y^2 = -4ax$ with $a = 4$:
$$y^2 = -4(4)x$$
$$y^2 = -16x$$

To help graph the parabola, we plot the two points on the graph above and below the focus. Let $x = -4$:
$$y^2 = -16(-4) = 64$$
$$y = \pm 8$$

The points $(-4,-8)$ and $(-4,8)$ are on the graph.

33. The vertex is at the origin and the axis of symmetry is the x-axis, so the parabola either opens to the left or to the right. Because the graph contains the point $(8,-2)$, which is in quadrant IV, the parabola must open to the right. Therefore, the equation of the parabola is of the form $y^2 = 4ax$. Now $y = -2$ when $x = 8$, so
$$y^2 = 4ax$$
$$\left(-2\right)^2 = 4a(8)$$
$$4 = 32a$$
$$a = \frac{4}{32} = \frac{1}{8}$$

The equation of the parabola is

$$y^2 = 4\left(\frac{1}{8}\right)x$$

$$y^2 = \frac{1}{2}x$$

With $a = \frac{1}{8}$, we know that the focus is $\left(\frac{1}{8}, 0\right)$ and the directrix is the line $x = -\frac{1}{8}$. To help graph the parabola, we plot the two points on the graph above and below the focus. Let $x = \frac{1}{8}$:

$$y^2 = \frac{1}{2}\left(\frac{1}{8}\right) = \frac{1}{16}$$

$$y = \pm\frac{1}{4}$$

The points $\left(\frac{1}{8}, -\frac{1}{4}\right)$ and $\left(\frac{1}{8}, \frac{1}{4}\right)$ are on the graph.

34. The vertex is at the origin and the directrix is the line $y = -2$, so the focus must be $(0, 2)$.

Accordingly, the parabola opens upward with $a = 2$. This means the equation of the parabola is of the form $x^2 = 4ay$ with $a = 2$:

$$x^2 = 4(2)y$$

$$x^2 = 8y$$

To help graph the parabola, we plot the two points on the graph to the left and right of the focus. Let $y = 2$:

$$x^2 = 8(2) = 16$$

$$x = \pm 4$$

The points $(-4, 2)$ and $(4, 2)$ are on the graph.

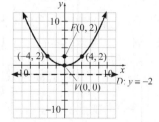

35. Notice that $x^2 = 2y$ is of the form $x^2 = 4ay$, where $4a = 2$, so that $a = \frac{2}{4} = \frac{1}{2}$. Now, the graph of an equation of the form $x^2 = 4ay$ will be a parabola that opens upward with the vertex at the origin, focus at $(0, a)$, and directrix of $y = -a$. Thus, the graph of $x^2 = 2y$ is a parabola that opens upward with vertex $(0, 0)$, focus $\left(0, \frac{1}{2}\right)$, and directrix $y = -\frac{1}{2}$. To help graph the parabola, we plot the two points on the graph to the left and to the right of the focus. Let $y = \frac{1}{2}$:

$$x^2 = 2\left(\frac{1}{2}\right)$$

$$x^2 = 1$$

$$x = \pm 1$$

The points $\left(-1, \frac{1}{2}\right)$ and $\left(1, \frac{1}{2}\right)$ are on the graph.

36. Notice that $y^2 = 16x$ is of the form $y^2 = 4ax$, where $4a = 16$, so that $a = 4$. Now, the graph of an equation of the form $y^2 = 4ax$ will be a parabola that opens to the right with the vertex at the origin, focus at $(a, 0)$, and directrix of $x = -a$. Thus, the graph of $y^2 = 16x$ is a parabola that opens to the right with vertex $(0, 0)$, focus $(4, 0)$, and directrix $x = -4$. To help graph the parabola, we plot the two points on the graph above and below the focus. Let $x = 4$:

$$y^2 = 16(4)$$

$$y^2 = 64$$

$$y = \pm 8$$

The points $(4, -8)$ and $(4, 8)$ are on the graph.

37. Notice that $(x+1)^2 = 8(y-3)$ is of the form $(x-h)^2 = 4a(y-k)$, where $4a = 8$, so that $a = 2$ and $(h,k) = (-1,3)$. Now, the graph of an equation of the form $(x-h)^2 = 4a(y-k)$ will be a parabola that opens upward with vertex at (h,k), focus at $(h,k+a)$, and directrix of $y = k-a$. Note that $k+a = 3+2 = 5$ and $k-a = 3-2 = 1$. Thus, the graph of $(x+1)^2 = 8(y-3)$ is a parabola that opens upward with vertex $(-1,3)$, focus $(-1,5)$, and directrix $y = 1$. To help graph the parabola, we plot the two points on the left and on the right of the focus. Let $y = 5$:

$$(x+1)^2 = 8(5-3)$$
$$(x+1)^2 = 16$$
$$x+1 = \pm 4$$
$$x = -1 \pm 4$$
$$x = -5 \text{ or } x = 3$$

The points $(-5,5)$ and $(3,5)$ are on the graph.

38. Notice that $(y-4)^2 = -2(x+3)$ is of the form $(y-k)^2 = -4a(x-h)$, where $(h,k) = (-3,4)$ and $-4a = -2$, so that $a = \dfrac{-2}{-4} = \dfrac{1}{2}$. Now, the graph of an equation of the form $(y-k)^2 = -4a(x-h)$ will be a parabola that opens to the left with the vertex at (h,k), focus at $(h-a,k)$, and directrix of $x = h+a$. Note that $h-a = -3-\dfrac{1}{2} = -\dfrac{7}{2}$ and

$h+a = -3+\dfrac{1}{2} = -\dfrac{5}{2}$. Thus, the graph of $(y-4)^2 = -2(x+3)$ is a parabola that opens to the left with vertex $(-3,4)$, focus $\left(-\dfrac{7}{2},4\right)$, and directrix $x = -\dfrac{5}{2}$. To help graph the parabola, we plot the two points on the graph above and below the focus. Let $x = -\dfrac{7}{2}$:

$$(y-4)^2 = -2\left(-\dfrac{7}{2}+3\right)$$
$$(y-4)^2 = -2\left(-\dfrac{1}{2}\right)$$
$$(y-4)^2 = 1$$
$$y-4 = \pm 1$$
$$y = 4 \pm 1$$
$$y = 3 \text{ or } y = 5$$

The points $\left(-\dfrac{7}{2},3\right)$ and $\left(-\dfrac{7}{2},5\right)$ are on the graph.

39. We complete the square in x to write the equation in standard form:
$$x^2 - 10x + 3y + 19 = 0$$
$$x^2 - 10x = -3y - 19$$
$$x^2 - 10x + 25 = -3y - 19 + 25$$
$$x^2 - 10x + 25 = -3y + 6$$
$$(x-5)^2 = -3(y-2)$$

Notice that $(x-5)^2 = -3(y-2)$ is of the form $(x-h)^2 = -4a(y-k)$, where $(h,k) = (5,2)$ and $-4a = -3$, so that $a = \dfrac{3}{4}$. Now, the graph of an equation of the form $(x-h)^2 = -4a(y-k)$ will be a parabola that opens downward with the vertex at (h,k), focus at $(h,k-a)$, and directrix of $y = k+a$. Note that $k-a = 2-\dfrac{3}{4} = \dfrac{5}{4}$ and

$k + a = 2 + \dfrac{3}{4} = \dfrac{11}{4}$. Thus, the graph of

$(x-5)^2 = -3(y-2)$ is a parabola that opens

downward with vertex $(5,2)$, focus $\left(5, \dfrac{5}{4}\right)$, and

directrix $y = \dfrac{11}{4}$. To help graph the parabola,

we plot the two points on the graph to the left

and right of the focus. Let $y = \dfrac{5}{4}$:

$$\left(x-5\right)^2 = -3\left(\dfrac{5}{4}-2\right)$$

$$\left(x-5\right)^2 = -3\left(-\dfrac{3}{4}\right)$$

$$\left(x-5\right)^2 = \dfrac{9}{4}$$

$$x - 5 = \pm\dfrac{3}{2}$$

$$x = 5 \pm \dfrac{3}{2}$$

$$x = \dfrac{7}{2} \text{ or } x = \dfrac{13}{2}$$

The points $\left(\dfrac{7}{2}, \dfrac{5}{4}\right)$ and $\left(\dfrac{13}{2}, \dfrac{5}{4}\right)$ are on the graph.

40. The receiver should be located at the focus of the dish, so we need to find where the focus of the dish is. To solve this problem, we draw a parabola on a Cartesian plane so that the vertex is the origin and the focus is on the positive y-axis. The width of the dish is 300 feet, and the depth is 44 feet. Therefore, we know two points on the graph of the parabola: $(-150, 44)$ and $(150, 44)$.

The equation of the parabola has the form $x^2 = 4ay$. Since $(150, 44)$ is a point on the graph, we have

$$150^2 = 4a(44)$$
$$22{,}500 = 176a$$
$$a = \dfrac{22{,}500}{176} \approx 127.84$$

The receiver should be located approximately 127.84 feet above the center of the dish, along its axis of symmetry.

41. $\dfrac{x^2}{9} + y^2 = 1$

$$\dfrac{x^2}{9} + \dfrac{y^2}{1} = 1$$

The larger number, 9, is in the denominator of the x^2-term. This means that the major axis is the x-axis and that the equation of the ellipse is

of the form $\dfrac{x^2}{a^2} + \dfrac{y^2}{b^2} = 1$, so that $a^2 = 9$ and

$b^2 = 1$. The center of the ellipse is $(0,0)$.

Because $b^2 = a^2 - c^2$, or $c^2 = a^2 - b^2$, we have

that $c^2 = 9 - 1 = 8$, so that $c = \pm\sqrt{8} = \pm 2\sqrt{2}$.

Since the major axis is the x-axis, the foci are

$\left(-2\sqrt{2}, 0\right)$ and $\left(2\sqrt{2}, 0\right)$. To find the x-

intercepts (vertices), let $y = 0$; to find the y-

intercepts, let $x = 0$:

x-intercepts:	y-intercepts:
$\dfrac{x^2}{9} + 0^2 = 1$	$\dfrac{0^2}{9} + y^2 = 1$
$\dfrac{x^2}{9} = 1$	$y^2 = 1$
$x^2 = 9$	$y = \pm 1$
$x = \pm 3$	

The intercepts are $(-3, 0)$, $(3, 0)$, $(0, -1)$, and $(0, 1)$.

42. $9x^2 + 4y^2 = 36$

$$\frac{9x^2 + 4y^2}{36} = \frac{36}{36}$$

$$\frac{x^2}{4} + \frac{y^2}{9} = 1$$

The larger number, 9, is in the denominator of the y^2-term. This means that the major axis is the y-axis and that the equation of the ellipse is of the form $\frac{x^2}{b^2} + \frac{y^2}{a^2} = 1$, so that $a^2 = 9$ and $b^2 = 4$. The center of the ellipse is $(0,0)$. Because $b^2 = a^2 - c^2$, or $c^2 = a^2 - b^2$, we have that $c^2 = 9 - 4 = 5$, so that $c = \pm\sqrt{5}$. Since the major axis is the y-axis, the foci are $\left(0, -\sqrt{5}\right)$ and $\left(0, \sqrt{5}\right)$. To find the x-intercepts, let $y = 0$; to find the y-intercepts (vertices), let $x = 0$:

x-intercepts:

$9x^2 + 4(0)^2 = 36$

$9x^2 = 36$

$x^2 = 4$

$x = \pm 2$

y-intercepts:

$9(0)^2 + 4y^2 = 36$

$4y^2 = 36$

$y^2 = 9$

$y = \pm 3$

The intercepts are $(-2, 0)$, $(2, 0)$, $(0, -3)$, and $(0, 3)$.

43. The given focus $(0, 3)$ and the given vertex $(0, 5)$ lie on the y-axis. Thus, the equation of the ellipse is of the form $\frac{x^2}{b^2} + \frac{y^2}{a^2} = 1$. The distance from the center of the ellipse to the vertex is $a = 5$ units. The distance from the center of the ellipse to the focus is $c = 3$ units. Because $b^2 = a^2 - c^2$, we have that $b^2 = 5^2 - 3^2 = 25 - 9 = 16$. Thus, the equation of the ellipse is $\frac{x^2}{16} + \frac{y^2}{25} = 1$.

To help graph the ellipse, find the x-intercepts:

Let $y = 0$: $\frac{x^2}{16} + \frac{0^2}{25} = 1$

$$\frac{x^2}{16} = 1$$

$$x^2 = 16$$

$$x = \pm 4$$

The x-intercepts are $(-4, 0)$ and $(4, 0)$.

44. The given focus $(-2, 0)$ and the given vertex $(-6, 0)$ lie on the x-axis. Thus, the equation of the ellipse is of the form $\frac{x^2}{a^2} + \frac{y^2}{b^2} = 1$. The distance from the center of the ellipse to the vertex is $a = 6$ units. The distance from the center of the ellipse to the focus is $c = 2$ units. Because $b^2 = a^2 - c^2$, we have that $b^2 = 6^2 - 2^2 = 36 - 4 = 32$. Thus, the equation of the ellipse is $\frac{x^2}{36} + \frac{y^2}{32} = 1$.

To help graph the ellipse, find the y-intercepts:

Let $x = 0$: $\frac{0^2}{36} + \frac{y^2}{32} = 1$

$$\frac{y^2}{32} = 1$$

$$y^2 = 32$$

$$y = \pm\sqrt{32} = \pm 4\sqrt{2}$$

The y-intercepts are $\left(0, -4\sqrt{2}\right)$ and $\left(0, 4\sqrt{2}\right)$.

45. The given foci $(\pm 8,0)$ and the given vertices $(\pm 10,0)$ lie on the x-axis. The center of the ellipse is the midpoint between the two vertices (or foci). Thus, the center of the ellipse is $(0,0)$ and its equation is of the form $\dfrac{x^2}{a^2}+\dfrac{y^2}{b^2}=1$. The distance from the center of the ellipse to the vertex is $a=10$ units. The distance from the center of the ellipse to the focus is $c=8$ units. Because $b^2=a^2-c^2$, we have that $b^2=10^2-8^2=100-64=36$. Thus, the equation of the ellipse is $\dfrac{x^2}{100}+\dfrac{y^2}{36}=1$.

To help graph the ellipse, find the y-intercepts:

Let $x=0$: $\dfrac{0^2}{100}+\dfrac{y^2}{36}=1$
$$\dfrac{y^2}{36}=1$$
$$y^2=36$$
$$y=\pm 6$$

The y-intercepts are $(0,-6)$ and $(0,6)$.

46. $\dfrac{(x-1)^2}{49}+\dfrac{(y+2)^2}{25}=1$

The center of the ellipse is $(h,k)=(1,-2)$. Because the larger number, 49, is the denominator of the x^2-term, the major axis is parallel to the x-axis. Because $a^2=49$ and $b^2=25$, we have that $c^2=a^2-b^2=49-25=24$. The vertices are $a=7$ units to the left and right of the center at $V_1(-6,-2)$ and $V_2(8,-2)$. The foci are $c=\sqrt{24}=2\sqrt{6}$ units to the left and right of the center at $F_1\left(1-2\sqrt{6},-2\right)$ and $F_2\left(1+2\sqrt{6},-2\right)$.

We plot the points $b=5$ units above and below the center point at $(1,3)$ and $(1,-7)$.

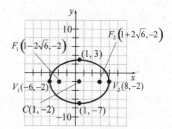

47. $25(x+3)^2+9(y-4)^2=225$
$$\dfrac{25(x+3)^2+9(y-4)^2}{225}=\dfrac{225}{225}$$
$$\dfrac{(x+3)^2}{9}+\dfrac{(y-4)^2}{25}=1$$

The center of the ellipse is $(h,k)=(-3,4)$. Because the larger number, 25, is the denominator of the y^2-term, the major axis is parallel to the y-axis. Because $a^2=25$ and $b^2=9$, we have that $c^2=a^2-b^2=25-9=16$. The vertices are $a=5$ units below and above the center at $V_1(-3,-1)$ and $V_2(-3,9)$. The foci are $c=\sqrt{16}=4$ units below and above the center at $F_1(-3,0)$ and $F_2(-3,8)$.

We plot the points $b=3$ units to the left and right of the center point at $(-6,4)$ and $(0,4)$.

48. a. To solve this problem, we draw the ellipse on a Cartesian plane so that the x-axis coincides with the water and the y-axis passes through the center of the arch. Thus, the origin is the center of the ellipse. Now, the "center" of the arch is 16 feet above the water, so the point $(0,16)$ is on the ellipse. The river is 60 feet wide, so the two points $(-30,0)$ and $(30,0)$ are the two vertices of the ellipse and the major axis is along the x-axis.

The equation of the ellipse must have the form $\dfrac{x^2}{a^2}+\dfrac{y^2}{b^2}=1$. The distance from the center of the ellipse to each vertex is $a=30$. Also, the height of the semi-ellipse is 16 feet, so $b=16$. Thus, the equation of the ellipse is

$$\frac{x^2}{30^2}+\frac{y^2}{16^2}=1$$
$$\frac{x^2}{900}+\frac{y^2}{256}=1$$

b. To determine if the barge can fit through the opening of the bridge, we center it beneath the arch so that the points $(-12.5,12)$ and $(12.5,12)$ represent the top corners of the barge. Now, we determine the height of the arch above the water at points 12.5 feet to the left and right of the center by substituting $x=12.5$ into the equation of the ellipse and solving for y:

$$\frac{12.5^2}{900}+\frac{y^2}{256}=1$$
$$\frac{156.25}{900}+\frac{y^2}{256}=1$$
$$\frac{y^2}{256}=\frac{119}{144}$$
$$y^2=\frac{1904}{9}$$
$$y=\sqrt{\frac{1904}{9}}\approx 14.54$$

At points 12.5 feet from the center of the river, the arch is approximately 14.54 feet above the surface of the water. Thus, the barge can fit through the opening with about 2.54 feet of clearance above the top corners.

49. $\dfrac{x^2}{4}-\dfrac{y^2}{9}=1$

Notice the equation is of the form $\dfrac{x^2}{a^2}-\dfrac{y^2}{b^2}=1$.

Because the x^2-term is first, the transverse axis is the x-axis and the hyperbola opens left and right. The center of the hyperbola is the origin. We have that $a^2=4$ and $b^2=9$. Because $c^2=a^2+b^2$, we have that $c^2=4+9=13$, so that $c=\sqrt{13}$. The vertices are $(\pm a,0)=(\pm 2,0)$, and the foci are $(\pm c,0)=(\pm\sqrt{13},0)$. To help graph the hyperbola,

we plot the points on the graph above and below the foci. Let $x=\pm\sqrt{13}$:

$$\frac{\left(\pm\sqrt{13}\right)^2}{4}-\frac{y^2}{9}=1$$
$$\frac{13}{4}-\frac{y^2}{9}=1$$
$$-\frac{y^2}{9}=-\frac{9}{4}$$
$$y^2=\frac{81}{4}$$
$$y=\pm\frac{9}{2}$$

The points above and below the foci are $\left(\sqrt{13},\dfrac{9}{2}\right)$, $\left(\sqrt{13},-\dfrac{9}{2}\right)$, $\left(-\sqrt{13},\dfrac{9}{2}\right)$, and $\left(-\sqrt{13},-\dfrac{9}{2}\right)$.

50. $\dfrac{y^2}{25}-\dfrac{x^2}{49}=1$

Notice the equation is of the form $\dfrac{y^2}{a^2}-\dfrac{x^2}{b^2}=1$.

Because the y^2-term is first, the transverse axis is the y-axis and the hyperbola opens up and down. The center of the hyperbola is the origin. We have that $a^2=25$ and $b^2=49$. Because $c^2=a^2+b^2$, we have that $c^2=25+49=74$, so that $c=\sqrt{74}$. The vertices are $(0,\pm a)=(0,\pm 5)$, and the foci are $(0,\pm c)=\left(0,\pm\sqrt{74}\right)$. To help graph the hyperbola, we plot the points on the graph to the left and right of the foci. Let $y=\pm\sqrt{74}$:

$$\frac{\left(\pm\sqrt{74}\right)^2}{25}-\frac{x^2}{49}=1$$
$$\frac{74}{25}-\frac{x^2}{49}=1$$
$$-\frac{x^2}{49}=-\frac{49}{25}$$

$$x^2 = \frac{2401}{25}$$

$$x = \pm\frac{49}{5}$$

The points to the left and right of the foci are

$$\left(\frac{49}{5}, \sqrt{74}\right), \left(-\frac{49}{5}, \sqrt{74}\right), \left(\frac{49}{5}, -\sqrt{74}\right), \text{ and}$$

$$\left(-\frac{49}{5}, -\sqrt{74}\right).$$

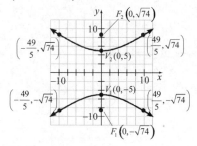

51. $16y^2 - 25x^2 = 400$

$$\frac{16y^2 - 25x^2}{400} = \frac{400}{400}$$

$$\frac{y^2}{25} - \frac{x^2}{16} = 1$$

Notice the equation is of the form $\dfrac{y^2}{a^2} - \dfrac{x^2}{b^2} = 1$.

Because the y^2-term is first, the transverse axis is the y-axis and the hyperbola opens up and down. The center of the hyperbola is the origin. We have that $a^2 = 25$ and $b^2 = 16$. Because $c^2 = a^2 + b^2$, we have that $c^2 = 25 + 16 = 41$, so that $c = \sqrt{41}$. The vertices are $(0, \pm a) = (0, \pm 5)$, and the foci are $(0, \pm c) = \left(0, \pm\sqrt{41}\right)$. To help graph the hyperbola, we plot the points on the graph to the left and right of the foci. Let $y = \pm\sqrt{41}$:

$$\frac{\left(\pm\sqrt{41}\right)^2}{25} - \frac{x^2}{16} = 1$$

$$\frac{41}{25} - \frac{x^2}{16} = 1$$

$$-\frac{x^2}{16} = -\frac{16}{25}$$

$$x^2 = \frac{256}{25}$$

$$x = \pm\frac{16}{5}$$

The points to the left and right of the foci are

$$\left(\frac{16}{5}, \sqrt{41}\right), \left(\frac{16}{5}, -\sqrt{41}\right), \left(-\frac{16}{5}, \sqrt{41}\right), \text{ and}$$

$$\left(-\frac{16}{5}, -\sqrt{41}\right).$$

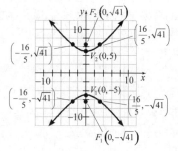

52. $\dfrac{x^2}{36} - \dfrac{y^2}{36} = 1$

Notice the equation is of the form $\dfrac{x^2}{a^2} - \dfrac{y^2}{b^2} = 1$.

Because the x^2-term is first, the transverse is along the x-axis and the hyperbola opens left and right. The center of the hyperbola is $(0,0)$. We have that $a^2 = 36$ and $b^2 = 36$. Because $c^2 = a^2 + b^2$, we have that $c^2 = 36 + 36 = 72$, so that $c = \sqrt{72} = 6\sqrt{2}$. The vertices are $(\pm a, 0) = (\pm 6, 0)$, and the foci are $(\pm c, 0) = \left(\pm 6\sqrt{2}, 0\right)$. Since $a = 6$ and $b = 6$, the equations of the asymptotes are $y = \dfrac{6}{6}x = x$ and $y = -\dfrac{6}{6}x = -x$. To help graph the hyperbola, we form the rectangle using the points $(\pm a, 0) = (\pm 6, 0)$ and $(0, \pm b) = (0, \pm 6)$. The diagonals are the asymptotes.

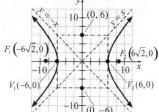

53. $\dfrac{y^2}{25} - \dfrac{x^2}{4} = 1$

Notice the equation is of the form $\dfrac{y^2}{a^2} - \dfrac{x^2}{b^2} = 1$.

Because the y^2-term is first, the transverse is along the y-axis and the hyperbola opens up and down. The center of the hyperbola is $(0,0)$. We have that $a^2 = 25$ and $b^2 = 4$. Because $c^2 = a^2 + b^2$, we have that $c^2 = 25 + 4 = 29$, so that $c = \sqrt{29}$. The vertices are $(0, \pm a) = (0, \pm 5)$, and the foci are $(0, \pm c) = \left(0, \pm\sqrt{29}\right)$. Since $a = 5$ and $b = 2$, the equations of the asymptotes are $y = \dfrac{5}{2}x$ and $y = -\dfrac{5}{2}x$. To help graph the hyperbola, we form the rectangle using the points $(0, \pm a) = (0, \pm 5)$ and $(\pm b, 0) = (\pm 2, 0)$. The diagonals are the asymptotes.

54. The given center $(0,0)$, focus $(-4,0)$, and vertex $(-3,0)$ all lie on the x-axis. Thus, the transverse axis is the x-axis and the hyperbola opens left and right. This means that the equation of the hyperbola is of the form $\dfrac{x^2}{a^2} - \dfrac{y^2}{b^2} = 1$. Now, the distance between the given vertex $(-3,0)$ and the center $(0,0)$ is $a = 3$ units. Likewise, the distance between the given focus $(-4,0)$ and the center is $c = 4$ units. Because $b^2 = c^2 - a^2$, we have that $b^2 = 4^2 - 3^2 = 16 - 9 = 7$. Thus, the equation of the hyperbola is $\dfrac{x^2}{9} - \dfrac{y^2}{7} = 1$.

To help graph the hyperbola, we first find the vertex and focus that were not given. Since the center is at $(0,0)$ and since one vertex is at $(-3,0)$, the other vertex must be at $(3,0)$.

Similarly, one the focus is at $(-4,0)$, so the other focus is at $(4,0)$. Next, plot the points on the graph above and below the foci. Let $x = \pm 4$:

$$\dfrac{(\pm 4)^2}{9} - \dfrac{y^2}{7} = 1$$

$$\dfrac{16}{9} - \dfrac{y^2}{7} = 1$$

$$-\dfrac{y^2}{7} = -\dfrac{7}{9}$$

$$y^2 = \dfrac{49}{9}$$

$$y = \pm\dfrac{7}{3}$$

The points above and below the foci are $\left(4, \dfrac{7}{3}\right)$, $\left(4, -\dfrac{7}{3}\right)$, $\left(-4, \dfrac{7}{3}\right)$, and $\left(-4, -\dfrac{7}{3}\right)$.

55. The given vertices $(0, \pm 3)$ and focus $(0,5)$ all lie on the y-axis. Thus, the transverse axis is the y-axis and the hyperbola opens up and down. The center of the hyperbola is the midpoint between the two vertices. Therefore, the center is $(0,0)$ and the equation of the hyperbola is of the form $\dfrac{y^2}{a^2} - \dfrac{x^2}{b^2} = 1$. Now, the distance from the center $(0,0)$ to each vertex is $a = 3$ units. Likewise, the distance from the center to the given focus $(0,5)$ is $c = 5$ units. Also, $b^2 = c^2 - a^2$, so $b^2 = 5^2 - 3^2 = 25 - 9 = 16$. Thus, the equation of the hyperbola is $\dfrac{y^2}{9} - \dfrac{x^2}{16} = 1$.

To help graph the hyperbola, we first find the focus that was not given. Since the center is at $(0,0)$ and since one focus is at $(0,5)$, the other focus must be at $(0,-5)$. Next, plot the points on the graph to the left and right of the foci. Let $y = \pm 5$:

$$\frac{(\pm 5)^2}{9} - \frac{x^2}{16} = 1$$

$$\frac{25}{9} - \frac{x^2}{16} = 1$$

$$-\frac{x^2}{16} = -\frac{16}{9}$$

$$x^2 = \frac{256}{9}$$

$$x = \pm\frac{16}{3}$$

The points to the left and right of the foci are

$$\left(\frac{16}{3}, 5\right), \left(-\frac{16}{3}, 5\right), \left(\frac{16}{3}, -5\right), \text{ and } \left(-\frac{16}{3}, -5\right).$$

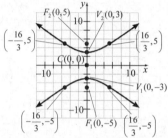

56. The given vertices $(0, \pm 4)$ both lie on the y-axis. Thus, the transverse axis is the y-axis and the hyperbola opens up and down. The center of the hyperbola is the midpoint between the two vertices. Therefore, the center is $(0,0)$ and the equation of the hyperbola is of the form $\frac{y^2}{a^2} - \frac{x^2}{b^2} = 1$. Now, the distance from the center $(0,0)$ to each vertex is $a = 4$ units. We are given that an asymptote of the hyperbola is $y = \frac{4}{3}x$. Now the equation of the asymptote is of the form is $y = \frac{a}{b}x$ and $a = 4$. So,

$$\frac{a}{b} = \frac{4}{3}$$

$$\frac{4}{b} = \frac{4}{3}$$

$$4b = 12$$

$$b = 3$$

Thus, the equation of the hyperbola is

$$\frac{y^2}{4^2} - \frac{x^2}{3^2} = 1.$$

$$\frac{y^2}{16} - \frac{x^2}{9} = 1$$

To help graph the hyperbola, we first find the foci. Since $c^2 = a^2 + b^2$, we have that $c^2 = 16 + 9 = 25$, so $c = 5$. Since the center is $(0,0)$, the foci are $(0, \pm 5)$. We form the rectangle using the points $(0, \pm a) = (0, \pm 4)$ and $(\pm b, 0) = (\pm 3, 0)$. The diagonals are the two asymptotes $y = \frac{4}{3}x$ and $y = -\frac{4}{3}x$.

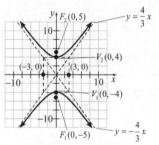

57. $\begin{cases} 4x^2 + y^2 = 10 \\ y = x \end{cases}$

First, graph each equation in the system.

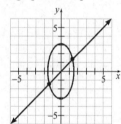

The system apparently has two solutions. Now substitute x for y into the first equation:

$$4x^2 + x^2 = 10$$

$$5x^2 = 10$$

$$x^2 = 2$$

$$x = \pm\sqrt{2}$$

Substitute these x-values into the second equation to find the corresponding y-values:

$$x = \sqrt{2}: \quad y = x = \sqrt{2}$$

$$x = -\sqrt{2}: \quad y = x = -\sqrt{2}$$

Both pairs check, so the solutions are $\left(\sqrt{2}, \sqrt{2}\right)$ and $\left(-\sqrt{2}, -\sqrt{2}\right)$.

58. $\begin{cases} y = 2x^2 + 1 \\ y = x + 2 \end{cases}$

First, graph each equation in the system.

The system apparently has two solutions. Now substitute $2x^2 + 1$ for y into the second equation:

$$2x^2 + 1 = x + 2$$
$$2x^2 - x - 1 = 0$$
$$(2x + 1)(x - 1) = 0$$

$$x = -\frac{1}{2} \quad \text{or} \quad x = 1$$

Substitute these x-values into the first equation to find the corresponding y-values:

$$x = -\frac{1}{2}: \ y = 2\left(-\frac{1}{2}\right)^2 + 1 = 2\left(\frac{1}{4}\right) + 1 = \frac{1}{2} + 1 = \frac{3}{2}$$

$$x = 1: \ y = 2(1)^2 + 1 = 2(1) + 1 = 2 + 1 = 3$$

Both pairs check, so the solutions are $\left(-\frac{1}{2}, \frac{3}{2}\right)$ and $(1, 3)$.

59. $\begin{cases} 6x - y = 5 \\ xy = 1 \end{cases}$

First, graph each equation in the system.

The system apparently has two solutions. Now solve the first equation for y: $y = 6x - 5$.

Substitute the result into the second equation.

$$x(6x - 5) = 1$$
$$6x^2 - 5x - 1 = 0$$
$$(6x + 1)(x - 1) = 0$$

$$x = -\frac{1}{6} \quad \text{or} \quad x = 1$$

Substitute these x-values into the equation $y = 6x - 5$ to find the corresponding y-values.

$$x = -\frac{1}{6}: \ y = 6\left(-\frac{1}{6}\right) - 5 = -1 - 5 = -6$$

$$x = 1: \ y = 6(1) - 5 = 6 - 5 = 1$$

Both pairs check, so the solutions are $\left(-\frac{1}{6}, -6\right)$ and $(1, 1)$.

60. $\begin{cases} x^2 + y^2 = 26 \\ x^2 - 2y^2 = 23 \end{cases}$

First, graph each equation in the system.

The system apparently has four solutions. Now solve the first equation for x^2: $x^2 = 26 - y^2$.

Substitute the result into the second equation.

$$\left(26 - y^2\right) - 2y^2 = 23$$
$$-3y^2 = -3$$
$$y^2 = 1$$
$$y = \pm 1$$

Substitute 1 for y^2 into the first equation.

$$x^2 + 1 = 26$$
$$x^2 = 25$$
$$x = \pm 5$$

All four pairs check, so the solutions are $(-5, -1)$, $(-5, 1)$, $(5, -1)$, and $(5, 1)$.

61. $\begin{cases} 4x - y^2 = 0 \\ 2x^2 + y^2 = 16 \end{cases}$

First, graph each equation in the system.

The system apparently has two solutions. Now add the two equations:

$$4x - y^2 = 0$$
$$\underline{2x^2 \quad + y^2 = 16}$$
$$2x^2 \quad + 4x = 16$$
$$2x^2 + 4x - 16 = 0$$
$$x^2 + 2x - 8 = 0$$
$$(x+4)(x-2) = 0$$
$$x = -4 \text{ or } x = 2$$

Substitute these x-values into the first equation to find the corresponding y-values:

$$x = -4: \quad 4(-4) - y^2 = 0$$
$$-16 - y^2 = 0$$
$$-16 = y^2$$
$$y = \pm\sqrt{-16} \quad (\text{not real})$$

$$x = 2: \quad 4(2) - y^2 = 0$$
$$8 - y^2 = 0$$
$$8 = y^2$$
$$y = \pm\sqrt{8} = \pm 2\sqrt{2}$$

Both real-number pairs check, so the solutions are $\left(2, -2\sqrt{2}\right)$ and $\left(2, 2\sqrt{2}\right)$.

62. $\begin{cases} x^2 - y = -2 \\ x^2 + y = 4 \end{cases}$

First, graph each equation in the system.

The system apparently has two solutions. Now multiply the first equation by -1 and add the result to the second equation:

$$-x^2 + y = 2$$
$$\underline{x^2 + y = 4}$$
$$2y = 6$$
$$y = 3$$

Substitute this y-value into the second equation to find the corresponding x-values.

$$x^2 + 3 = 4$$
$$x^2 = 1$$
$$x = \pm 1$$

Both pairs check, so the solutions are $(-1, 3)$ and $(1, 3)$.

63. $\begin{cases} 4x^2 - 2y^2 = 2 \\ -x^2 + y^2 = 2 \end{cases}$

First, graph each equation in the system.

The system apparently has four solutions. Now multiply the second equation by 2 and add the result to the first equation:

$$4x^2 - 2y^2 = 2$$
$$\underline{-2x^2 + 2y^2 = 4}$$
$$2x^2 \quad = 6$$
$$x^2 = 3$$
$$x = \pm\sqrt{3}$$

Substitute 3 for x^2 into the second equation:

$$-3 + y^2 = 2$$
$$y^2 = 5$$
$$y = \pm\sqrt{5}$$

All four check, so the solutions are $\left(-\sqrt{3}, \ -\sqrt{5}\right)$, $\left(-\sqrt{3}, \sqrt{5}\right)$, $\left(\sqrt{3}, \ -\sqrt{5}\right)$, and $\left(\sqrt{3}, \sqrt{5}\right)$.

64. $\begin{cases} x^2 + y^2 = 8x \\ y^2 = 3x \end{cases}$

First, graph each equation in the system.

The system apparently has three solutions. Now multiply the second equation by -1 and add the result to the first equation:

$$x^2 + y^2 = 8x$$
$$\underline{-y^2 = -3x}$$
$$x^2 \quad = 5x$$
$$x^2 - 5x = 0$$
$$x(x-5) = 0$$
$$x = 0 \text{ or } x = 5$$

Substitute these *x*-values into the second equation to find the corresponding *y*-values:

$$x = 0: \quad y^2 = 3(0)$$
$$y^2 = 0$$
$$y = 0$$
$$x = 5: \quad y^2 = 3(5)$$
$$y^2 = 15$$
$$y = \pm\sqrt{15}$$

All three pairs check, so the solutions are $(0,0)$, $\left(5, -\sqrt{15}\right)$, and $\left(5, \sqrt{15}\right)$.

65. $\begin{cases} y = x + 2 \\ y = x^2 \end{cases}$

First, graph each equation in the system.

The system apparently has two solutions. Now Substitute x^2 for *y* into the first equation:

$$x^2 = x + 2$$
$$x^2 - x - 2 = 0$$
$$(x - 2)(x + 1) = 0$$
$$x = 2 \text{ or } x = -1$$

Substitute these results into the first equation to find the corresponding *y* values.

$$x = 2: \quad y = 2 + 2 = 4$$
$$x = -1: \quad y = -1 + 2 = 1$$

Both pairs check, so the solutions are $(2, 4)$ and $(-1, 1)$.

66. $\begin{cases} x^2 + 2y = 9 \\ 5x - 2y = 5 \end{cases}$

First, graph each equation in the system.

The system apparently has two solutions. Now add the two equations:

$$\begin{aligned} x^2 \quad + 2y &= 9 \\ 5x - 2y &= 5 \end{aligned}$$
$$\overline{ \quad }$$
$$x^2 \quad + 5x = 14$$
$$x^2 + 5x - 14 = 0$$
$$(x + 7)(x - 2) = 0$$
$$x = -7 \text{ or } x = 2$$

Substitute these results into the first equation to find the corresponding *y* values.

$$x = -7: \quad (-7)^2 + 2y = 9$$
$$49 + 2y = 9$$
$$2y = -40$$
$$y = -20$$
$$x = 2: \quad (2)^2 + 2y = 9$$
$$4 + 2y = 9$$
$$2y = 5$$
$$y = \frac{5}{2}$$

Both pairs check, so the solutions are $(-7, -20)$ and $\left(2, \dfrac{5}{2}\right)$.

67. $\begin{cases} x^2 + y^2 = 36 \\ x - y = -6 \end{cases}$

First, graph each equation in the system.

The system apparently has two solutions. Now solve the second equation for *y*: $y = x + 6$.

Substitute the result into the first equation:

$$x^2 + (x + 6)^2 = 36$$
$$x^2 + (x^2 + 12x + 36) = 36$$
$$2x^2 + 12x = 0$$
$$2x(x + 6) = 0$$
$$2x = 0 \text{ or } x + 6 = 0$$
$$x = 0 \text{ or } \quad x = -6$$

Substitute these *x* values into the equation $y = x + 6$ to find the corresponding *y* values:

$$x = 0: \quad y = 0 + 6 = 6$$
$$x = -6: \quad y = -6 + 6 = 0$$

Both pairs check, so the solutions are $(0, 6)$ and $(-6, 0)$.

68. $\begin{cases} y = 2x - 4 \\ y^2 = 4x \end{cases}$

First, graph each equation in the system.

The system apparently has two solutions. Now substitute $2x - 4$ for y into the second equation:

$$(2x - 4)^2 = 4x$$
$$4x^2 - 16x + 16 = 4x$$
$$4x^2 - 20x + 16 = 0$$
$$x^2 - 5x + 4 = 0$$
$$(x - 4)(x - 1) = 0$$
$$x = 4 \text{ or } x = 1$$

Substitute these results into the first equation to find the corresponding y values.

$x = 4 : y = 2(4) - 4 = 4$
$x = 1 : y = 2(1) - 4 = -2$

Both pairs check, so the solutions are $(4, 4)$ and $(1, -2)$.

69. $\begin{cases} x^2 + y^2 = 9 \\ x + y = 7 \end{cases}$

First, graph each equation in the system.

The system apparently has no solution. Now solve the second equation for y: $y = 7 - x$.

Substitute the result into the first equation:

$$x^2 + (7 - x)^2 = 9$$
$$x^2 + (49 - 14x + x^2) = 9$$
$$2x^2 - 14x + 49 = 9$$
$$2x^2 - 14x + 40 = 0$$

$$x = \frac{-(-14) \pm \sqrt{(-14)^2 - 4(2)(40)}}{2(2)}$$
$$= \frac{14 \pm \sqrt{-124}}{4}$$
$$= \frac{14 \pm 2\sqrt{31}\, i}{4}$$
$$= \frac{7}{2} \pm \frac{\sqrt{31}}{2}\, i$$

Since the solutions are not real, the system is inconsistent. The solution set is $\varnothing$.

70. $\begin{cases} 2x^2 + 3y^2 = 14 \\ x^2 - y^2 = -3 \end{cases}$

First, graph each equation in the system.

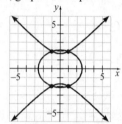

The system apparently has four solutions. Now multiply the second equation by 3 and add the result to the first equation.

$$3x^2 - 3y^2 = -9$$
$$\underline{2x^2 + 3y^2 = 14}$$
$$5x^2 \quad\quad = 5$$
$$x^2 = 1$$
$$x = \pm 1$$

Substitute 1 for x^2 into the second equation to find the y values.

$$1 - y^2 = -3$$
$$-y^2 = -4$$
$$y^2 = 4$$
$$y = \pm 2$$

All four pairs check, so the solutions are $(-1, -2)$, $(-1, 2)$, $(1, -2)$, and $(1, 2)$.

71. $\begin{cases} x^2 + y^2 = 16 \\ x^2 + 4y = 16 \end{cases}$

First, graph each equation in the system.

The system apparently has three solutions. Now multiply the second equation by -1 and add the result to the first equation:

$$\begin{aligned} x^2 + y^2 \quad &= 16 \\ -x^2 \quad -4y &= -16 \\ \hline y^2 - 4y &= 0 \\ y(y - 4) &= 0 \end{aligned}$$

$y = 0 \ \text{ or } \ y = 4$

Substitute these y-values into the first equation to find the corresponding x-values:

$y = 0: \ x^2 + 0^2 = 16$
$\qquad\qquad x^2 = 16$
$\qquad\qquad x = \pm 4$

$y = 4: \ x^2 + 4^2 = 16$
$\qquad\qquad x^2 + 16 = 16$
$\qquad\qquad x^2 = 0$
$\qquad\qquad x = 0$

All three pairs check, so the solutions are $(-4, 0)$, $(4, 0)$, and $(0, 4)$.

72. $\begin{cases} x = 4 - y^2 \\ x = 2y + 4 \end{cases}$

First, graph each equation in the system.

The system apparently has two solutions. Now substitute $2y + 4$ for x into the first equation:

$2y + 4 = 4 - y^2$
$y^2 + 2y = 0$
$y(y + 2) = 0$

$y = 0 \ \text{ or } \ y = -2$

Substitute these y-values into the second equation to find the corresponding x-values:

$y = 0: \ x = 2(0) + 4 = 4$

$y = -2: \ x = 2(-2) + 4 = 0$

Both pairs check, so the solutions are $(4, 0)$ and $(0, -2)$.

73. Let x represent the larger of the two numbers and y represent the smaller of the two numbers.

$\begin{cases} x + y = 12 \\ x^2 - y^2 = 24 \end{cases}$

Solve the first equation for y: $y = 12 - x$.

Substitute the result into the second equation:

$$x^2 - (12 - x)^2 = 24$$
$$x^2 - \left(144 - 24x + x^2\right) = 24$$
$$x^2 - 144 + 24x - x^2 = 24$$
$$24x = 168$$
$$x = 7$$

Substitute 7 for x into the first equation to find the corresponding y-value:

$7 + y = 12$
$\quad\ \ y = 5$

The two numbers are 7 and 5.

74. Let x represent the length and y represent the width of the rectangle.

$\begin{cases} 2x + 2y = 34 \\ xy = 60 \end{cases}$

Solve the first equation for y: $y = 17 - x$.

Substitute the result into the second equation:

$$x(17 - x) = 60$$
$$17x - x^2 = 60$$
$$x^2 - 17x + 60 = 0$$
$$(x - 12)(x - 5) = 0$$
$$x = 12 \ \text{ or } \ x = 5$$

Substitute these x-values into the second equation to find the corresponding y-values:

$x = 12: \ 12y = 60$
$\qquad\qquad\ \ y = 5$

$x = 5: \ 5y = 60$
$\qquad\qquad\ y = 12$

Note that the two outcomes result in the same overall dimensions. Assuming the length is the longer of the two sides, the length is 12 centimeters and the width is 5 centimeters.

75. Let x represent the length and y represent the width of the rectangle.

$$\begin{cases} xy = 2160 \\ x^2 + y^2 = 78^2 \end{cases}$$

Solve the first equation for y: $y = \dfrac{2160}{x}$.

Substitute the result into the second equation:

$$x^2 + \left(\frac{2160}{x}\right)^2 = 78^2$$

$$x^2 + \frac{4,665,600}{x^2} = 6084$$

$$x^4 + 4,665,600 = 6084x^2$$

$$x^4 - 6084x^2 + 4,665,600 = 0$$

$$\left(x^2 - 5184\right)\left(x^2 - 900\right) = 0$$

$$(x-72)(x+72)(x-30)(x+30) = 0$$

$$x = 72 \text{ or } x = -72 \text{ or } x = 30 \text{ or } x = -30$$

Since the length cannot be negative, we discard $x = -72$ and $x = -30$, so we are left with the possible answers $x = 72$ and $x = 30$. Substitute these x-values into the first equation to find the corresponding y-values:

$$x = 72: \quad 72y = 2160$$
$$y = 30$$
$$x = 30: \quad 30y = 2160$$
$$y = 72$$

Note that the two outcomes result in the same overall dimensions. Assuming the length is the longer of the two sides, the length is 72 inches and the width is 30 inches.

76. Let x and y represent the lengths of the two legs of the right triangle.

$$\begin{cases} x + y + 15 = 36 \\ x^2 + y^2 = 15^2 \end{cases}$$

Solve the first equation for y: $y = 21 - x$.

Substitute the result into the second equation:

$$x^2 + (21 - x)^2 = 15^2$$
$$x^2 + 441 - 42x + x^2 = 225$$
$$2x^2 - 42x + 216 = 0$$
$$x^2 - 21x + 108 = 0$$
$$(x-12)(x-9) = 0$$
$$x = 12 \text{ or } x = 9$$

Substitute these x-values into the first equation to find the corresponding y-values:

$$x = 12: \quad 12 + y + 15 = 36$$
$$y + 27 = 36$$
$$y = 9$$
$$x = 9: \quad 9 + y + 15 = 36$$
$$y + 24 = 36$$
$$y = 12$$

Note that the two outcomes result in the same overall dimensions. The lengths of the two legs are 12 inches and 9 inches.

Chapter 10 Test

1. $d(P_1, P_2) = \sqrt{(x_2 - x_1)^2 + (y_2 - y_1)^2}$
$$= \sqrt{(3-(-1))^2 + (-5-3)^2}$$
$$= \sqrt{4^2 + (-8)^2}$$
$$= \sqrt{16 + 64}$$
$$= \sqrt{80}$$
$$= 4\sqrt{5}$$

2. $M = \left(\dfrac{x_1 + x_2}{2}, \dfrac{y_1 + y_2}{2}\right)$
$$= \left(\frac{-7+5}{2}, \frac{6+(-2)}{2}\right) = \left(\frac{-2}{2}, \frac{4}{2}\right) = (-1, 2)$$

3. $(x-4)^2 + (y+1)^2 = 9$
$$(x-4)^2 + (y-(-1))^2 = 3^2$$

The center is $(h, k) = (4, -1)$, and the radius is $r = 3$.

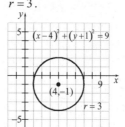

4.
$$x^2 + y^2 + 10x - 4y + 13 = 0$$
$$\left(x^2 + 10x + 25\right) + \left(y^2 - 4y + 4\right) = -13 + 25 + 4$$
$$(x+5)^2 + (y-2)^2 = 16$$
$$(x-(-5))^2 + (y-2)^2 = 4^2$$

The center is $(h,k) = (-5, 2)$, and the radius is $r = 4$.

5.
$$(x-h)^2 + (y-k)^2 = r^2$$
$$(x-(-3))^2 + (y-7)^2 = 6^2$$
$$(x+3)^2 + (y-7)^2 = 36$$

6. The radius of the circle will be the distance from the center point $(-5, 8)$ to the point on the circle $(3, 2)$. Thus, $r = \sqrt{\left(3-(-5)\right)^2 + \left(2-8\right)^2} = 10$. The equation of the circle is
$$(x-h)^2 + (y-k)^2 = r^2$$
$$(x-(-5))^2 + (y-8)^2 = 10^2$$
$$(x+5)^2 + (y-8)^2 = 100$$

7. Notice that $(y+2)^2 = 4(x-1)$ is of the form $(y-k)^2 = 4a(x-h)$, where $(h,k) = (1,-2)$ and $4a = 4$, so that $a = 1$. Now, the graph of an equation of the form $(y-k)^2 = 4a(x-h)$ will be a parabola that opens to the right with the vertex at (h,k), focus at $(h+a, k)$, and directrix of $x = h - a$. Note that $h + a = 1 + 1 = 2$ and $h - a = 1 - 1 = 0$. Thus, the graph of $(y+2)^2 = 4(x-1)$ is a parabola that opens to the right with vertex $(1,-2)$, focus $(2,-2)$, and directrix $x = 0$. To help graph the parabola, we plot the two points on the graph above and below the focus. Let $x = 2$:
$$(y+2)^2 = 4(2-1)$$
$$(y+2)^2 = 4$$
$$y + 2 = \pm 2$$
$$y = -2 \pm 2$$
$$y = -4 \text{ or } y = 0$$

The points $(2, -4)$ and $(2, 0)$ are on the graph.

8. We complete the square in x to write the equation in standard form:
$$x^2 - 4x + 3y - 8 = 0$$
$$x^2 - 4x = -3y + 8$$
$$x^2 - 4x + 4 = -3y + 8 + 4$$
$$x^2 - 4x + 4 = -3y + 12$$
$$(x-2)^2 = -3(y-4)$$

Notice that $(x-2)^2 = -3(y-4)$ is of the form $(x-h)^2 = -4a(y-k)$, where $(h,k) = (2,4)$ and $-4a = -3$, so that $a = \dfrac{3}{4}$. Now, the graph of an equation of the form $(x-h)^2 = -4a(y-k)$ will be a parabola that opens downward with the vertex at (h,k), focus at $(h, k-a)$, and directrix of $y = k + a$. Note that $k - a = 4 - \dfrac{3}{4} = \dfrac{13}{4}$ and $k + a = 4 + \dfrac{3}{4} = \dfrac{19}{4}$. Thus, the graph of $(x-2)^2 = -3(y-4)$ is a parabola that opens downward with vertex $(2,4)$, focus $\left(2, \dfrac{13}{4}\right)$, and directrix $y = \dfrac{19}{4}$. To help graph the parabola, we plot the two points on the graph to the left and right of the focus. Let $y = \dfrac{13}{4}$:
$$(x-2)^2 = -3\left(\frac{13}{4} - 4\right)$$
$$(x-2)^2 = -3\left(-\frac{3}{4}\right)$$
$$(x-2)^2 = \frac{9}{4}$$
$$x - 2 = \pm\frac{3}{2}$$
$$x = 2 \pm \frac{3}{2}$$
$$x = \frac{1}{2} \text{ or } x = \frac{7}{2}$$

The points $\left(\dfrac{1}{2},\dfrac{13}{4}\right)$ and $\left(\dfrac{7}{2},\dfrac{13}{4}\right)$ are on the graph.

9. The distance from the vertex $(0,0)$ to the focus $(0,-4)$ is $a=4$. Because the focus lies on the negative y-axis, we know that the parabola will open downward and the axis of symmetry is the y-axis. This means the equation of the parabola is of the form $x^2=-4ay$ with $a=4$:

$$x^2=-4(4)y$$
$$x^2=-16y$$

10. Notice that the directrix $x=-1$ is a vertical line and that the focus is $(3,4)$. Therefore, the axis of symmetry must be the line $y=4$. Because the focus is to the right of the directrix, the parabola must open to the right. Since the vertex must be the point on the axis of symmetry that is midway between the focus and the directrix, the vertex is $(1,4)$. Now, the distance from the vertex $(1,4)$ to the focus $(3,4)$ is $a=2$, so the equation of the parabola is of the form $(y-k)^2=4a(x-h)$ with $a=2$, $h=1$, and $k=4$:

$$(y-4)^2=4\cdot2(x-1)$$
$$(y-4)^2=8(x-1)$$

11. $9x^2+25y^2=225$

$$\dfrac{9x^2+25y^2}{225}=\dfrac{225}{225}$$

$$\dfrac{x^2}{25}+\dfrac{y^2}{9}=1$$

The larger number, 25, is in the denominator of the x^2-term. This means that the major axis is the x-axis and that the equation of the ellipse is of the form $\dfrac{x^2}{a^2}+\dfrac{y^2}{b^2}=1$, so that $a^2=25$ and $b^2=9$. The center of the ellipse is $(0,0)$.

Because $c^2=a^2-b^2$, we have that $c^2=25-9=16$, so that $c=\pm\sqrt{16}=\pm4$. Since

the major axis is the x-axis, the foci are $(-4,0)$ and $(4,0)$. To find the x-intercepts (vertices), let $y=0$; to find the y-intercepts, let $x=0$:

x-intercepts:
$$9x^2+25(0)^2=225$$
$$9x^2=225$$
$$x^2=25$$
$$x=\pm5$$

y-intercepts:
$$9(0)^2+25y^2=225$$
$$25y^2=225$$
$$y^2=9$$
$$y=\pm3$$

The intercepts are $(-5,0)$, $(5,0)$, $(0,-3)$, and $(0,3)$.

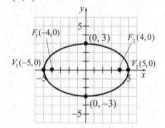

12. $\dfrac{(x-2)^2}{9}+\dfrac{(y+4)^2}{16}=1$

The center of the ellipse is $(h,k)=(2,-4)$. Because the larger number, 16, is the denominator of the y^2-term, the major axis is parallel to the y-axis. Because $a^2=16$ and $b^2=9$, we have that $c^2=a^2-b^2=16-9=7$. The vertices are $a=4$ units below and above the center at $V_1(2,-8)$ and $V_2(2,0)$. The foci are $c=\sqrt{7}$ units below and above the center at $F_1\left(2,-4-\sqrt{7}\right)$ and $F_2\left(2,-4+\sqrt{7}\right)$. We plot the points $b=3$ units to the left and right of the center point at $(-1,-4)$ and $(5,-4)$.

13. The given focus $(0,-4)$ and the given vertex $(0,-5)$ lie on the y-axis. Thus, the equation of the ellipse is of the form $\frac{x^2}{b^2}+\frac{y^2}{a^2}=1$. The distance from the center of the ellipse to the vertex is $a=5$ units. The distance from the center of the ellipse to the focus is $c=4$ units. Because $b^2=a^2-c^2$, we have that $b^2=5^2-4^2=25-16=9$. Thus, the equation of the ellipse is $\frac{x^2}{9}+\frac{y^2}{25}=1$.

14. The given vertices and focus all lie on the vertical line $x=-1$. Therefore, the major axis is parallel to the y-axis, and the equation of the ellipse is of the form $\frac{(x-h)^2}{b^2}+\frac{(y-k)^2}{a^2}=1$.

Now, the center will be the midpoint between the two vertices $(-1,7)$ and $(-1,-3)$, which is $(h,k)=(-1,2)$. Now, $a=5$ is the distance from the center $(-1,2)$ to a vertex $(-1,7)$, and $c=3$ is the distance from the center to a focus $(-1,-1)$. Also, $b^2=a^2-c^2=5^2-3^2=25-9=16$. Thus, the equation of the ellipse is

$$\frac{\left(x-(-1)\right)^2}{16}+\frac{(y-2)^2}{25}=1$$
$$\frac{(x+1)^2}{16}+\frac{(y-2)^2}{25}=1$$

15. $x^2-\frac{y^2}{4}=1$

$$\frac{x^2}{1}-\frac{y^2}{4}=1$$

Notice the equation is of the form $\frac{x^2}{a^2}-\frac{y^2}{b^2}=1$.

Because the x^2-term is first, the transverse is along the x-axis and the hyperbola opens left and right. The center of the hyperbola is $(0,0)$. We have that $a^2=1$ and $b^2=4$. Because $c^2=a^2+b^2$, we have that $c^2=1+4=5$, so that $c=\sqrt{5}$. The vertices are $(\pm a,0)=(\pm1,0)$, and the foci are $(\pm c,0)=\left(\pm\sqrt{5},0\right)$. Since $a=1$ and $b=2$, the equations of the asymptotes are

$y=\frac{2}{1}x=2x$ and $y=-\frac{2}{1}x=-2x$. To help

graph the hyperbola, we form the rectangle using the points $(\pm a,0)=(\pm1,0)$ and $(0,\pm b)=(0,\pm2)$. The diagonals are the asymptotes.

16. $16y^2-25x^2=1600$

$$\frac{16y^2-25x^2}{1600}=\frac{1600}{1600}$$
$$\frac{y^2}{100}-\frac{x^2}{64}=1$$

Notice the equation is of the form $\frac{y^2}{a^2}-\frac{x^2}{b^2}=1$.

Because the y^2-term is first, the transverse is along the y-axis and the hyperbola opens up and down. The center of the hyperbola is $(0,0)$. We have that $a^2=100$ and $b^2=64$. Because $c^2=a^2+b^2$, we have that $c^2=100+64=164$, so that $c=\sqrt{164}=2\sqrt{41}$. The vertices are $(0,\pm a)=(0,\pm10)$, and the foci are $(0,\pm c)=\left(0,\pm2\sqrt{41}\right)$. Since $a=10$ and $b=8$, the equations of the asymptotes are

$y=\frac{10}{8}x=\frac{5}{4}x$ and $y=-\frac{10}{8}x=-\frac{5}{4}x$. To help

graph the hyperbola, we form the rectangle using the points $(0,\pm a)=(0,\pm10)$ and $(\pm b,0)=(\pm8,0)$. The diagonals are the asymptotes.

17. The given foci $(\pm 8, 0)$ and vertex $(-3, 0)$ all lie on the x-axis. Thus, the transverse axis is the x-axis and the hyperbola opens left and right. The center of the hyperbola is the midpoint between the two foci. Therefore, the center is $(0, 0)$ and the equation of the hyperbola is of the form $\dfrac{x^2}{a^2} - \dfrac{y^2}{b^2} = 1$. Now, the distance between the given vertex $(-3, 0)$ and the center $(0, 0)$ is $a = 3$ units. Likewise, the distance between the given foci and the center is $c = 8$ units. Also, $b^2 = c^2 - a^2$, so $b^2 = 8^2 - 3^2 = 64 - 9 = 55$. Thus, the equation of the hyperbola is
$$\frac{x^2}{9} - \frac{y^2}{55} = 1.$$

18. $\begin{cases} x^2 + y^2 = 17 \\ x + y = -3 \end{cases}$

First, graph each equation in the system.

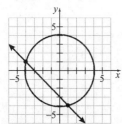

The system apparently has two solutions. Now solve the second equation for y: $y = -x - 3$.

Substitute the result into the first equation:
$$x^2 + (-x - 3)^2 = 17$$
$$x^2 + (x^2 + 6x + 9) = 17$$
$$2x^2 + 6x - 8 = 0$$
$$x^2 + 3x - 4 = 0$$
$$(x + 4)(x - 1) = 0$$
$$x = -4 \quad \text{or} \quad x = 1$$

Substitute these results into the first equation to find the corresponding y-values.
$$x = -4: \quad -4 + y = -3$$
$$y = 1$$
$$x = 1: \quad 1 + y = -3$$
$$y = -4$$

Both pairs check, so the solutions are $(-4, 1)$ and $(1, -4)$.

19. $\begin{cases} x^2 + y^2 = 9 \\ 4x^2 - y^2 = 16 \end{cases}$

First, graph each equation in the system.

The system apparently has four solutions. Now add the two equations:
$$\begin{array}{r} x^2 + y^2 = 9 \\ 4x^2 - y^2 = 16 \\ \hline 5x^2 \quad\quad = 25 \\ x^2 = 5 \\ x = \pm\sqrt{5} \end{array}$$

Substitute 5 for x^2 into the first equation:
$$5 + y^2 = 9$$
$$y^2 = 4$$
$$y = \pm\sqrt{4} = \pm 2$$

All four pairs check, so the solutions are
$$\left(-\sqrt{5}, -2\right), \left(-\sqrt{5}, 2\right), \left(\sqrt{5}, -2\right), \text{ and } \left(\sqrt{5}, 2\right).$$

20. a. To solve this problem, we draw the ellipse on a Cartesian plane so that the x-axis coincides with the water and the y-axis passes through the center of the arch. Thus, the origin is the center of the ellipse. Now, the "center" of the arch is 10 feet above the water, so the point $(0, 10)$ is on the ellipse. The creek is 30 feet wide, so the two points $(-15, 0)$ and $(15, 0)$ are the two vertices of the ellipse and the major axis is along the x-axis.

The equation of the ellipse must have the form $\dfrac{x^2}{a^2} + \dfrac{y^2}{b^2} = 1$. The distance from the center of the ellipse to each vertex is $a = 15$. Also, the height of the semi-ellipse is 10

feet, so $b = 10$. Thus, the equation of the ellipse is

$$\frac{x^2}{15^2} + \frac{y^2}{10^2} = 1$$

$$\frac{x^2}{225} + \frac{y^2}{100} = 1$$

b. Substitute $x = 12$ into the equation, and solve for y:

$$\frac{12^2}{225} + \frac{y^2}{100} = 1$$

$$\frac{144}{225} + \frac{y^2}{100} = 1$$

$$\frac{y^2}{100} = \frac{9}{25}$$

$$y^2 = 36$$

$$y = 6$$

Thus, the height of the arch at a distance 12 feet from the center of the creek is 6 feet.

Chapter 11

11.1 Preparing for Sequences

1. $f(x) = x^2 - 4$

   a. $f(3) = (3)^2 - 4 = 9 - 4 = 5$

   b. $f(-7) = (-7)^2 - 4 = 49 - 4 = 45$

2. $g(x) = 2x - 3$

$g(1) = 2(1) - 3 = 2 - 3 = -1$

$g(2) = 2(2) - 3 = 4 - 3 = 1$

$g(3) = 2(3) - 3 = 6 - 3 = 3$

Therefore,

$g(1) + g(2) + g(3) = -1 + 1 + 3 = 3$

3. In the function $f(n) = n^2 - 4$, the independent variable is n (the input variable).

11.1 Exercises

1. sequence

3. partial sum

5. False; the index of the summation (in this case) is the integer k; $5k$ is the kth term.

7. Answers may vary. A sequence is a function whose domain is the set of positive integers.

9. Answers may vary. The symbol Σ represents summation and indicates that we will need to add up the values of several terms.

11. $\{3n + 5\}$

$a_1 = 3 \cdot 1 + 5 = 3 + 5 = 8$

$a_2 = 3 \cdot 2 + 5 = 6 + 5 = 11$

$a_3 = 3 \cdot 3 + 5 = 9 + 5 = 14$

$a_4 = 3 \cdot 4 + 5 = 12 + 5 = 17$

$a_5 = 3 \cdot 5 + 5 = 15 + 5 = 20$

The first five terms of the sequence are 8, 11, 14, 17, and 20.

13. $\left\{ \dfrac{n}{n+2} \right\}$

$a_1 = \dfrac{1}{1+2} = \dfrac{1}{3}$

$a_2 = \dfrac{2}{2+2} = \dfrac{2}{4} = \dfrac{1}{2}$

$a_3 = \dfrac{3}{3+2} = \dfrac{3}{5}$

$a_4 = \dfrac{4}{4+2} = \dfrac{4}{6} = \dfrac{2}{3}$

$a_5 = \dfrac{5}{5+2} = \dfrac{5}{7}$

The first five terms of the sequence are $\dfrac{1}{3}$, $\dfrac{1}{2}$, $\dfrac{3}{5}$, $\dfrac{2}{3}$, and $\dfrac{5}{7}$.

15. $\{(-1)^n n\}$

$a_1 = (-1)^1 \cdot 1 = -1$

$a_2 = (-1)^2 \cdot 2 = 2$

$a_3 = (-1)^3 \cdot 3 = -3$

$a_4 = (-1)^4 \cdot 4 = 4$

$a_5 = (-1)^5 \cdot 5 = -5$

The first five terms of the sequence are -1, 2, -3, 4, and -5.

17. $\{2^n + 1\}$

$a_1 = 2^1 + 1 = 2 + 1 = 3$

$a_2 = 2^2 + 1 = 4 + 1 = 5$

$a_3 = 2^3 + 1 = 8 + 1 = 9$

$a_4 = 2^4 + 1 = 16 + 1 = 17$

$a_5 = 2^5 + 1 = 32 + 1 = 33$

The first five terms of the sequence are 3, 5, 9, 17, and 33.

19. $\left\{ \dfrac{2n}{2^n} \right\}$

$a_1 = \dfrac{2 \cdot 1}{2^1} = \dfrac{2}{2} = 1$

$a_2 = \dfrac{2 \cdot 2}{2^2} = \dfrac{4}{4} = 1$

$a_3 = \dfrac{2 \cdot 3}{2^3} = \dfrac{6}{8} = \dfrac{3}{4}$

$a_4 = \dfrac{2 \cdot 4}{2^4} = \dfrac{8}{16} = \dfrac{1}{2}$

$a_5 = \dfrac{2 \cdot 5}{2^5} = \dfrac{10}{32} = \dfrac{5}{16}$

The first five terms of the sequence are 1, 1, $\dfrac{3}{4}$,

$\dfrac{1}{2}$, and $\dfrac{5}{16}$.

21. $\left\{ \dfrac{n}{e^n} \right\}$

$a_1 = \dfrac{1}{e^1} = \dfrac{1}{e}, \quad a_2 = \dfrac{2}{e^2}, \quad a_3 = \dfrac{3}{e^3}$

$a_4 = \dfrac{4}{e^4}, \quad a_5 = \dfrac{5}{e^5}$

The first five terms of the sequence are $\dfrac{1}{e}$, $\dfrac{2}{e^2}$,

$\dfrac{3}{e^3}$, $\dfrac{4}{e^4}$, and $\dfrac{5}{e^5}$.

23. The terms are all multiples of 2 with the first term equaling $2 \cdot 1$, the second term equaling $2 \cdot 2$, and so on. A formula for the nth term is given by $a_n = 2n$.

25. Each term is a fraction with the denominator equaling 1 more than the numerator. When $n = 1$, the numerator equals 1. Each subsequent numerator is one more than previous. A formula for the nth term is given by $a_n = \dfrac{n}{n+1}$.

27. When $n = 1$, we have that $a_1 = 3 = 1^2 + 2$; when $n = 2$, we have that $a_2 = 6 = 2^2 + 2$; when $n = 3$, we have that $a_3 = 11 = 3^2 + 2$. Notice that each term is equal to 2 more than the square of the term number. Therefore, a formula for the nth term is given by $a_n = n^2 + 2$.

29. Notice that the terms alternate signs with the first term being negative. Ignoring the signs, also notice that the terms are all perfect squares. Therefore, a formula for the nth term is given by $a_n = (-1)^n n^2$.

31. $\displaystyle\sum_{i=1}^{4} (5i + 1)$

$= (5 \cdot 1 + 1) + (5 \cdot 2 + 1) + (5 \cdot 3 + 1) + (5 \cdot 4 + 1)$

$= 6 + 11 + 16 + 21$

$= 54$

33. $\displaystyle\sum_{i=1}^{5} \dfrac{i^2}{2} = \dfrac{1^2}{2} + \dfrac{2^2}{2} + \dfrac{3^2}{2} + \dfrac{4^2}{2} + \dfrac{5^2}{2}$

$= \dfrac{1}{2} + \dfrac{4}{2} + \dfrac{9}{2} + \dfrac{16}{2} + \dfrac{25}{2}$

$= \dfrac{55}{2}$

35. $\displaystyle\sum_{k=1}^{3} 2^k = 2^1 + 2^2 + 2^3 = 2 + 4 + 8 = 14$

37. $\displaystyle\sum_{k=1}^{5} \left[(-1)^{k+1} \cdot 2k \right]$

$= (-1)^{1+1} \cdot 2(1) + (-1)^{2+1} \cdot 2(2) + (-1)^{3+1} \cdot 2(3)$

$\quad + (-1)^{4+1} \cdot 2(4) + (-1)^{5+1} \cdot 2(5)$

$= (-1)^2 \cdot 2 + (-1)^3 \cdot 4 + (-1)^4 \cdot 6$

$\quad + (-1)^5 \cdot 8 + (-1)^6 \cdot 10$

$= 2 - 4 + 6 - 8 + 10$

$= 6$

39. $\displaystyle\sum_{j=1}^{10} 5 = 5 + 5 + 5 + 5 + 5 + 5 + 5 + 5 + 5 + 5 = 50$

41. $\displaystyle\sum_{k=3}^{7} (2k - 1) = (2 \cdot 3 - 1) + (2 \cdot 4 - 1) + (2 \cdot 5 - 1)$

$\quad + (2 \cdot 6 - 1) + (2 \cdot 7 - 1)$

$= 5 + 7 + 9 + 11 + 13$

$= 45$

43. The sum $1 + 2 + 3 + \ldots + 15$ has 15 terms, each terms has the form k, starts at $k = 1$, and ends at $k = 15$.

$1 + 2 + 3 + \ldots + 15 = \displaystyle\sum_{k=1}^{15} k$

45. The sum $1+\dfrac{1}{2}+\dfrac{1}{3}+\ldots+\dfrac{1}{12}$ has 12 terms, each

term has the form $\dfrac{1}{i}$, starts at $i=1$, and ends at

$i=12$.

$$1+\frac{1}{2}+\frac{1}{3}+\ldots+\frac{1}{12}=\sum_{i=1}^{12}\frac{1}{i}$$

47. To see the pattern, note that the first term can be

written as $1=\dfrac{1}{1}$. We see that the denominators

are all powers of 3 and that the terms alternate
signs with the first term being positive. When
$n=1$, we have the denominator $1=3^0$; when
$n=2$, we have the denominator $3=3^1$; when
$n=3$, we have the denominator $9=3^2$; and so
on. Thus, the power on 3 in the denominator is
always one less than the term number. Looking
at the form of the last term, we see that there will
be 9 terms and that the power on -1 will be one
more than the term number.

$$1-\frac{1}{3}+\frac{1}{9}-\frac{1}{27}+\ldots+(-1)^{9+1}\left(\frac{1}{3^{9-1}}\right)$$

$$=\sum_{i=1}^{9}(-1)^{i+1}\left(\frac{1}{3^{i-1}}\right)$$

49. To see the pattern, note that the first term can be
written as $5=(5+2\cdot0)$. Each term is 5 more
than a multiple of two. The multiple is one less
than the term number. Therefore, there are 11
terms being added together.

$$5+(5+2\cdot1)+(5+2\cdot2)+(5+2\cdot3)+\ldots+(5+2\cdot10)$$

$$=\sum_{k=1}^{11}\left[5+2(k-1)\right] \quad \text{or} \quad \sum_{k=1}^{11}(2k+3)$$

51. $a_n=12,000\left(1+\dfrac{0.06}{4}\right)^n$

a. $n=1$

$$a_1=12,000\left(1+\frac{0.06}{4}\right)^1$$

$$=12,000(1.015)$$

$$=12,180$$

After 1 quarter, the account will have a
balance of $12,180.

b. $n=4$ (4 quarters in each year)

$$a_4=12,000\left(1+\frac{0.06}{4}\right)^4$$

$$=12,000(1.015)^4$$

$$=12,000(1.06136)$$

$$=\$12,736.36$$

After 1 year (i.e. 4 quarters), the account
will have a balance of $12,736.36.

c. $n=40$

$$a_{40}=12,000\left(1+\frac{0.06}{4}\right)^{40}$$

$$=12,000(1.015)^{40}$$

$$\approx12,000(1.8140184)$$

$$\approx21,768.22$$

After 10 years (40 quarters), the account will
have a balance of $21,768.22.

53. $p_n=296(1.011)^n$

a. In 2010 we have $n=5$.

$$p_{10}=296(1.011)^5\approx312.64$$

In 2010, the population of the United States
will be an estimated 313 million.

b. In 2050 we have $n=45$.

$$p_{50}=296(1.011)^{45}\approx484.28$$

In 2050, the population of the United States
will be an estimated 484 million.

55. $u_n=\dfrac{\left(1+\sqrt{5}\right)^n-\left(1-\sqrt{5}\right)^n}{2^n\cdot\sqrt{5}}$

$$u_1=\frac{\left(1+\sqrt{5}\right)-\left(1-\sqrt{5}\right)}{2\cdot\sqrt{5}}=\frac{2\sqrt{5}}{2\cdot\sqrt{5}}=1$$

$$u_2=\frac{\left(1+\sqrt{5}\right)^2-\left(1-\sqrt{5}\right)^2}{2^2\cdot\sqrt{5}}=\frac{4\sqrt{5}}{4\cdot\sqrt{5}}=1$$

$$u_3=\frac{\left(1+\sqrt{5}\right)^3-\left(1-\sqrt{5}\right)^3}{2^3\cdot\sqrt{5}}$$

$$=\frac{\left(16+8\sqrt{5}\right)-\left(16-8\sqrt{5}\right)}{8\cdot\sqrt{5}}=\frac{16\sqrt{5}}{8\sqrt{5}}=2$$

$$u_4=\frac{\left(1+\sqrt{5}\right)^4-\left(1-\sqrt{5}\right)^4}{2^4\cdot\sqrt{5}}$$

$$=\frac{\left(56+24\sqrt{5}\right)-\left(56-24\sqrt{5}\right)}{16\cdot\sqrt{5}}=\frac{48\sqrt{5}}{16\sqrt{5}}=3$$

$$u_5 = \frac{\left(1+\sqrt{5}\right)^5 - \left(1-\sqrt{5}\right)^5}{2^5 \cdot \sqrt{5}}$$

$$= \frac{\left(176+80\sqrt{5}\right) - \left(176-80\sqrt{5}\right)}{32 \cdot \sqrt{5}} = \frac{160\sqrt{5}}{32\sqrt{5}} = 5$$

$$u_6 = \frac{\left(1+\sqrt{5}\right)^6 - \left(1-\sqrt{5}\right)^6}{2^6 \cdot \sqrt{5}}$$

$$= \frac{\left(576+256\sqrt{5}\right) - \left(576-256\sqrt{5}\right)}{64 \cdot \sqrt{5}} = \frac{512\sqrt{5}}{64\sqrt{5}}$$

$$= 8$$

$$u_7 = \frac{\left(1+\sqrt{5}\right)^7 - \left(1-\sqrt{5}\right)^7}{2^7 \cdot \sqrt{5}}$$

$$= \frac{\left(1856+832\sqrt{5}\right) - \left(1856-832\sqrt{5}\right)}{128 \cdot \sqrt{5}}$$

$$= \frac{1664\sqrt{5}}{128\sqrt{5}} = 13$$

$$u_8 = \frac{\left(1+\sqrt{5}\right)^8 - \left(1-\sqrt{5}\right)^8}{2^8 \cdot \sqrt{5}}$$

$$= \frac{\left(6016+2688\sqrt{5}\right) - \left(6016-2688\sqrt{5}\right)}{256 \cdot \sqrt{5}}$$

$$= \frac{5376\sqrt{5}}{256\sqrt{5}} = 21$$

$$u_9 = \frac{\left(1+\sqrt{5}\right)^9 - \left(1-\sqrt{5}\right)^9}{2^9 \cdot \sqrt{5}}$$

$$= \frac{\left(19456+8704\sqrt{5}\right) - \left(19456-8704\sqrt{5}\right)}{512 \cdot \sqrt{5}}$$

$$= \frac{17408\sqrt{5}}{512\sqrt{5}} = 34$$

$$u_{10} = \frac{\left(1+\sqrt{5}\right)^{10} - \left(1-\sqrt{5}\right)^{10}}{2^{10} \cdot \sqrt{5}}$$

$$= \frac{\left(62976+28160\sqrt{5}\right) - \left(62976-28160\sqrt{5}\right)}{1024 \cdot \sqrt{5}}$$

$$= \frac{56320\sqrt{5}}{1024\sqrt{5}} = 55$$

The first 10 terms of the sequence are 1, 1, 2, 3, 5, 8, 13, 21, 34, and 55.
Notice that, beginning with the third term, each term in the sequence can be obtained by adding the two previous terms together. For example, $2 = 1+1$, $3 = 1+2$, $5 = 2+3$, etc.

57. $a_1 = 10$
$a_2 = 1.05a_1 = 1.05(10) = 10.5$
$a_3 = 1.05a_2 = 1.05(10.5) = 11.025$
$a_4 = 1.05a_3 = 1.05(11.025) = 11.57625$
$a_5 = 1.05a_4 = 1.05(11.57625) = 12.1550625$
The first five terms of the sequence are 10, 10.5, 11.025, 11.57625, and 12.1550625.

59. $b_1 = 8$
$b_2 = 2+b_1 = 2+8 = 10$
$b_3 = 3+b_2 = 3+10 = 13$
$b_4 = 4+b_3 = 4+13 = 17$
$b_5 = 5+b_4 = 5+17 = 22$
The first five terms of the sequence are 8, 10, 13, 17, and 22.

61. a. $\dfrac{u_2}{u_1} = \dfrac{1}{1} = 1$; $\dfrac{u_3}{u_2} = \dfrac{2}{1} = 2$; $\dfrac{u_4}{u_3} = \dfrac{3}{2} = 1.5$;

$\dfrac{u_5}{u_4} = \dfrac{5}{3} = 1.\overline{6}$; $\dfrac{u_6}{u_5} = \dfrac{8}{5} = 1.6$;

$\dfrac{u_7}{u_6} = \dfrac{13}{8} = 1.625$; $\dfrac{u_8}{u_7} = \dfrac{21}{13} \approx 1.615385$;

$\dfrac{u_9}{u_8} = \dfrac{34}{21} \approx 1.619048$; $\dfrac{u_{10}}{u_9} = \dfrac{55}{34} \approx 1.617647$;

$\dfrac{u_{11}}{u_{10}} = \dfrac{89}{55} \approx 1.618182$

b. The ratio approaches a value around 1.618. Note: As n goes off to infinity, the ratio approaches the exact value $\dfrac{1+\sqrt{5}}{2}$.

c. $\dfrac{u_1}{u_2} = \dfrac{1}{1} = 1$; $\dfrac{u_2}{u_3} = \dfrac{1}{2} = 0.5$; $\dfrac{u_3}{u_4} = \dfrac{2}{3} = 0.\overline{6}$;

$\dfrac{u_4}{u_5} = \dfrac{3}{5} = 0.6$; $\dfrac{u_5}{u_6} = \dfrac{5}{8} = 0.625$;

$\dfrac{u_6}{u_7} = \dfrac{8}{13} \approx 0.615385$; $\dfrac{u_7}{u_8} = \dfrac{13}{21} \approx 0.619048$;

$\dfrac{u_8}{u_9} = \dfrac{21}{34} \approx 0.617647$; $\dfrac{u_9}{u_{10}} = \dfrac{34}{55} \approx 0.618182$;

$\dfrac{u_{10}}{u_{11}} = \dfrac{55}{89} \approx 0.617978$

d. The ratio approaches a value around 0.618. Note: As n goes to infinity, the ratio approaches the exact value $\dfrac{\sqrt{5}-1}{2}$.

63. a. The function is in slope-intercept form so the slope is $m = 4$.

b. $f(x) = 4x - 6$
$f(1) = 4(1) - 6 = -2$
$f(2) = 4(2) - 6 = 2$
$f(3) = 4(3) - 6 = 6$
$f(4) = 4(4) - 6 = 10$

65. a. The function is in slope-intercept form so the slope is $m = -5$.

b. $f(x) = -5x + 8$
$f(1) = -5(1) + 8 = 3$
$f(2) = -5(2) + 8 = -2$
$f(3) = -5(3) + 8 = -7$
$f(4) = -5(4) + 8 = -12$

67. $\{3n + 5\}$

```
seq(3X+5,X,1,5,1
)
  {8 11 14 17 20}
```

The first five terms of the sequence are 8, 11, 14, 17, and 20.

69. $\left\{\dfrac{n}{n+2}\right\}$

The first five terms of the sequence are $\dfrac{1}{3}$, $\dfrac{1}{2}$, $\dfrac{3}{5}$, $\dfrac{2}{3}$, and $\dfrac{5}{7}$.

71. $\{(-1)^n \, n\}$

```
seq((-1)^X*X,X,1
,5,1)
  {-1 2 -3 4 -5}
```

The first five terms of the sequence are -1, 2, -3, 4, and -5.

73. $\{2^n + 1\}$

```
seq(2^X+1,X,1,5,
1)
  {3 5 9 17 33}
```

The first five terms of the sequence are 3, 5, 9, 17, and 33.

75. $\displaystyle\sum_{i=1}^{4}(5i + 1)$

```
sum(seq(5X+1,X,1
,4,1)
             54
```

The sum is 54.

77. $\displaystyle\sum_{i=1}^{5}\dfrac{i^2}{2}$

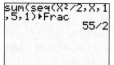
```
sum(seq(X²/2,X,1
,5,1)▶Frac
           55/2
```

The sum is $\dfrac{55}{2}$.

79. $\displaystyle\sum_{k=1}^{3} 2^k$

```
sum(seq(2^X,X,1,
3,1)
             14
```

The sum is 14.

81. $\displaystyle\sum_{k=1}^{5}\left[(-1)^{k+1} \cdot 2k\right]$

```
sum(seq((-1)^(X+
1)*2X,X,1,5,1)
              6
```

The sum is 6.

11.2 Preparing for Arithmetic Sequences

1. $y = -3x + 1$ is in the (slope-intercept) form $y = mx + b$. Therefore, the slope is $m = -3$.

2. $g(x) = 5x + 2$
$$g(3) = 5(3) + 2$$
$$= 15 + 2$$
$$= 17$$

3. $\begin{cases} x - 3y = -17 & (1) \\ 2x + y = 1 & (2) \end{cases}$

   Multiply both sides of equation (1) by -2.
   $$\begin{cases} -2x + 6y = 34 & (1) \\ 2x + y = 1 & (2) \end{cases}$$
   Add equation (1) and equation (2).
   $$\begin{array}{r} \begin{cases} -2x + 6y = 34 \ (1) \\ 2x + y = 1 \ (2) \end{cases} \\ \hline 7y = 35 \\ y = 5 \end{array}$$
   Substitute this result into the original equation (1) and solve for x.
   $$x - 3y = -17$$
   $$x - 3(5) = -17$$
   $$x - 15 = -17$$
   $$x = -2$$
   The solution is the ordered pair $(-2, 5)$.

11.2 Exercises

1. arithmetic

3. False; the sum of the first and last terms is equal to twice the average of all the terms. That is, twice the sum of all the terms *divided by* the total number of terms.

5. Answers may vary. A sequence is arithmetic only if the difference between consecutive terms is constant. That is, $a_n - a_{n-1} = d$ where d is a constant.

7. $\{n + 5\}$
$$a_n - a_{n-1} = [n + 5] - [(n-1) + 5]$$
$$= n + 5 - (n + 4) = n + 5 - n - 4 = 1$$
$$a_1 = 1 + 5 = 6$$
This is an arithmetic sequence whose first term is $a = 6$ and whose common difference is $d = 1$. The first four terms are 6, 7, 8, and 9.

9. $\{7n + 2\}$
$$a_n - a_{n-1} = [7n + 2] - [7(n-1) + 2]$$
$$= [7n + 2] - [7n - 7 + 2]$$
$$= 7n + 2 - 7n + 5$$
$$= 7$$
$$a_1 = 7(1) + 2 = 9$$
This is an arithmetic sequence whose first term is $a = 9$ and whose common difference is $d = 7$. The first four terms are 9, 16, 23, and 30.

11. $\{7 - 3n\}$
$$a_n - a_{n-1} = [7 - 3n] - [7 - 3(n-1)]$$
$$= [7 - 3n] - [7 - 3n + 3]$$
$$= 7 - 3n - 10 + 3n$$
$$= -3$$
$$a_1 = 7 - 3(1) = 4$$
This is an arithmetic sequence whose first term is $a = 4$ and whose common difference is $d = -3$. The first four terms are 4, 1, -2, and -5.

13. $\left\{\dfrac{1}{2}n + 5\right\}$
$$a_n - a_{n-1} = \left[\frac{1}{2}n + 5\right] - \left[\frac{1}{2}(n-1) + 5\right]$$
$$= \left[\frac{1}{2}n + 5\right] - \left[\frac{1}{2}n - \frac{1}{2} + 5\right]$$
$$= \frac{1}{2}n + 5 - \frac{1}{2}n - \frac{9}{2}$$
$$= \frac{1}{2}$$
$$a_1 = \frac{1}{2}(1) + 5 = \frac{11}{2}$$
This is an arithmetic sequence whose first term is $a = \dfrac{11}{2}$ and whose common difference is $d = \dfrac{1}{2}$.

The first four terms are $\dfrac{11}{2}$, 6, $\dfrac{13}{2}$, and 7.

15. $a = 4$, $d = 3$

$$a_n = a + (n-1)d$$
$$= 4 + (n-1)3$$
$$= 4 + 3n - 3$$
$$= 3n + 1$$

To find the fifth term we let $n = 5$.

$$a_5 = 3(5) + 1 = 15 + 1 = 16$$

The fifth term of the sequence is 16.

17. $a = 10$, $d = -5$

$$a_n = a + (n-1)d$$
$$= 10 + (n-1)(-5)$$
$$= 10 - 5n + 5$$
$$= -5n + 15$$

To find the fifth term we let $n = 5$.

$$a_5 = -5(5) + 15 = -25 + 15 = -10$$

The fifth term of the sequence is -10.

19. $a = 2$, $d = \dfrac{1}{3}$

$$a_n = a + (n-1)d = 2 + (n-1)\left(\frac{1}{3}\right)$$
$$= 2 + \frac{1}{3}n - \frac{1}{3}$$
$$= \frac{1}{3}n + \frac{5}{3}$$

To find the fifth term we let $n = 5$.

$$a_5 = \frac{1}{3}(5) + \frac{5}{3} = \frac{5}{3} + \frac{5}{3} = \frac{10}{3}$$

The fifth term of the sequence is $\dfrac{10}{3}$.

21. $a = 5$, $d = -\dfrac{1}{5}$

$$a_n = a + (n-1)d = 5 + (n-1)\left(-\frac{1}{5}\right)$$
$$= 5 - \frac{1}{5}n + \frac{1}{5}$$
$$= -\frac{1}{5}n + \frac{26}{5}$$

To find the fifth term we let $n = 5$.

$$a_5 = -\frac{1}{5}(5) + \frac{26}{5} = -1 + \frac{26}{5} = \frac{21}{5}$$

The fifth term of the sequence is $\dfrac{21}{5}$.

23. $2, 7, 12, 17, \ldots$

Notice that the difference between consecutive terms is $d = 5$. Since the first term is $a = 2$, the nth term can be written as

$$a_n = a + (n-1)d$$
$$= 2 + (n-1)(5)$$
$$= 2 + 5n - 5$$
$$= 5n - 3$$

To find the twentieth term, we let $n = 20$.

$$a_{20} = 5(20) - 3 = 100 - 3 = 97$$

The twentieth term of the sequence is 97.

25. $12, 9, 6, 3, \ldots$

Notice that the difference between consecutive terms is $d = -3$. Since the first term is $a = 12$, the nth term can be written as

$$a_n = a + (n-1)d$$
$$= 12 + (n-1)(-3)$$
$$= 12 - 3n + 3$$
$$= -3n + 15$$

To find the twentieth term, we let $n = 20$.

$$a_{20} = -3(20) + 15 = -60 + 15 = -45$$

The twentieth term of the sequence is -45.

27. $1, \dfrac{5}{4}, \dfrac{3}{2}, \dfrac{7}{4}, \ldots$

Notice that the difference between consecutive terms is $d = \dfrac{1}{4}$. Since the first term is $a = 1$, the nth term can be written as

$$a_n = a + (n-1)d$$
$$= 1 + (n-1)\left(\frac{1}{4}\right)$$
$$= 1 + \frac{1}{4}n - \frac{1}{4}$$
$$= \frac{1}{4}n + \frac{3}{4}$$

To find the twentieth term, we let $n = 20$.

$$a_{20} = \frac{1}{4}(20) + \frac{3}{4} = \frac{20}{4} + \frac{3}{4} = \frac{23}{4}$$

The twentieth term of the sequence is $\dfrac{23}{4}$.

29. We know that the nth term of an arithmetic sequence is given by $a_n = a + (n-1)d$ where a is the first term and d is the common difference. Since $a_3 = 17$ and $a_7 = 37$, we have

$$\begin{cases} a_3 = a + (3-1)d \\ a_7 = a + (7-1)d \end{cases} \text{ or } \begin{cases} 17 = a + 2d & (1) \\ 37 = a + 6d & (2) \end{cases}$$

This is a system of linear equations in two variables, a and d. We can solve the system by elimination. If we subtract equation (2) from equation (1), we obtain

$-20 = -4d$
$5 = d$

Let $d = 5$ in equation (1) to find a.

$17 = a + 2(5)$
$17 = a + 10$
$7 = a$

The first term is $a = 7$ and the common difference is $d = 5$. Thus, a formula for the nth term is

$a_n = 7 + (n-1)(5)$
$= 7 + 5n - 5$
$= 5n + 2$

31. We know that the nth term of an arithmetic sequence is given by $a_n = a + (n-1)d$ where a is the first term and d is the common difference. Since $a_4 = -2$ and $a_8 = 26$, we have

$$\begin{cases} a_4 = a + (4-1)d \\ a_8 = a + (8-1)d \end{cases} \text{ or } \begin{cases} -2 = a + 3d & (1) \\ 26 = a + 7d & (2) \end{cases}$$

This is a system of linear equations in two variables, a and d. We can solve the system by elimination. If we subtract equation (2) from equation (1), we obtain

$-28 = -4d$
$7 = d$

Let $d = 7$ in equation (1) to find a.

$-2 = a + 3(7)$
$-2 = a + 21$
$-23 = a$

The first term is $a = -23$ and the common difference is $d = 7$. Thus, a formula for the nth term is

$a_n = -23 + (n-1)(7)$
$= -23 + 7n - 7$
$= 7n - 30$

33. We know that the nth term of an arithmetic sequence is given by $a_n = a + (n-1)d$ where a is the first term and d is the common difference. Since $a_5 = -1$ and $a_{12} = -22$, we have

$$\begin{cases} a_5 = a + (5-1)d \\ a_{12} = a + (12-1)d \end{cases} \text{ or } \begin{cases} -1 = a + 4d & (1) \\ -22 = a + 11d & (2) \end{cases}$$

This is a system of linear equations in two variables, a and d. We can solve the system by elimination. If we subtract equation (2) from equation (1), we obtain

$21 = -7d$
$-3 = d$

Let $d = -3$ in equation (1) to find a.

$-1 = a + 4(-3)$
$-1 = a - 12$
$11 = a$

The first term is $a = 11$ and the common difference is $d = -3$. Thus, a formula for the nth term is

$a_n = 11 + (n-1)(-3)$
$= 11 - 3n + 3$
$= -3n + 14$

35. We know that the nth term of an arithmetic sequence is given by $a_n = a + (n-1)d$ where a is the first term and d is the common difference. Since $a_3 = 3$ and $a_9 = 0$, we have

$$\begin{cases} a_3 = a + (3-1)d \\ a_9 = a + (9-1)d \end{cases} \text{ or } \begin{cases} 3 = a + 2d & (1) \\ 0 = a + 8d & (2) \end{cases}$$

This is a system of linear equations in two variables, a and d. We can solve the system by elimination. If we subtract equation (2) from equation (1), we obtain

$3 = -6d$
$-\dfrac{1}{2} = d$

Let $d = -\dfrac{1}{2}$ in equation (1) to find a.

$3 = a + 2\left(-\dfrac{1}{2}\right)$
$3 = a - 1$
$4 = a$

The first term is $a = 4$ and the common difference is $d = -\dfrac{1}{2}$. Thus, a formula for the nth term is

$a_n = 4 + (n-1)\left(-\dfrac{1}{2}\right)$
$= 4 - \dfrac{1}{2}n + \dfrac{1}{2} = -\dfrac{1}{2}n + \dfrac{9}{2}$

37. We know that the first term is $a = 2$ and the common difference is $d = 8 - 2 = 6$. The sum of the first $n = 30$ terms of this arithmetic sequence is given by

$$S_{30} = \frac{30}{2}\left[2a + (30-1)d\right]$$
$$= 15\left[2(2) + 29(6)\right]$$
$$= 15(178)$$
$$= 2670$$

39. We know that the first term is $a = -8$ and the common difference is $d = -5 - (-8) = 3$. The sum of the first $n = 25$ terms of this arithmetic sequence is given by

$$S_{25} = \frac{25}{2}\left[2a + (25-1)d\right]$$
$$= \frac{25}{2}\left[2(-8) + 24(3)\right]$$
$$= \frac{25}{2}(56)$$
$$= 700$$

41. We know that the first term is $a = 10$ and the common difference is $d = 3 - 10 = -7$. The sum of the first $n = 40$ terms of this arithmetic sequence is given by

$$S_{40} = \frac{40}{2}\left[2a + (40-1)d\right]$$
$$= 20\left[2(10) + 39(-7)\right]$$
$$= 20(20 - 273)$$
$$= 20(-253)$$
$$= -5060$$

43. The first term of the sequence is given by $a_1 = a = 4(1) - 3 = 1$ and the 40th term is given by $a_{40} = 4(40) - 3 = 157$. We can now use the formula $S_n = \frac{n}{2}\left[a + a_n\right]$ to find the sum.

$$S_{40} = \frac{40}{2}\left[1 + 157\right]$$
$$= 20(158)$$
$$= 3160$$

The sum of the first 40 terms is 3160.

45. The first term of the sequence is given by $a_1 = a = -5(1) + 70 = 65$ and the 75th term is given by $a_{75} = -5(75) + 70 = -305$. We can now use the formula $S_n = \frac{n}{2}\left[a + a_n\right]$ to find the sum.

$$S_{75} = \frac{75}{2}\left[65 + (-305)\right]$$
$$= \frac{75}{2}(-240)$$
$$= -9000$$

The sum of the first 75 terms is -9000.

47. The first term of the sequence is given by $a_1 = a = 5 + \frac{2}{3}(1) = \frac{17}{3}$ and the 30th term is given by $a_{30} = 5 + \frac{2}{3}(30) = 25$. We can now use the formula $S_n = \frac{n}{2}\left[a + a_n\right]$ to find the sum.

$$S_{30} = \frac{30}{2}\left[\frac{17}{3} + 25\right]$$
$$= 15\left(\frac{92}{3}\right)$$
$$= 460$$

The sum of the first 30 terms is 460.

49. To be an arithmetic sequence, the difference between successive terms must be constant. Therefore, we start by finding the differences between the terms.

$$d_1 = (2x + 1) - (x + 3)$$
$$= 2x + 1 - x - 3$$
$$= x - 2$$
$$d_2 = (5x + 2) - (2x + 1)$$
$$= 5x + 2 - 2x - 1$$
$$= 3x + 1$$

Now we set the two differences equal to each other and solve the resulting equation for x.

$$d_1 = d_2$$
$$x - 2 = 3x + 1$$
$$-2x = 3$$
$$x = -\frac{3}{2}$$

51. To determine the total number of cans, we first need to determine how many rows are in the stack. Letting the bottom row be the first row, we have $a = 35$. Since each row decreases by 1 can, we have $d = -1$.

$$a_n = a + (n-1)d$$
$$1 = 35 + (n-1)(-1)$$
$$1 = 35 - n + 1$$
$$-35 = -n$$
$$35 = n$$

The total number of cans in the 35 rows is

$$S_{35} = \frac{35}{2}(35+1) = \frac{35}{2}(36) = 630$$

There are 630 cans in the stack.

53. Since the first row has 40 seats, we know that $a = 40$. Each of the $n = 25$ successive rows has 2 more seats, so we also know that $d = 2$. To determine the total number of seats, we first need to know how many seats are in the last row.

$$a_{25} = a + (25-1)d$$
$$= 40 + 24(2)$$
$$= 40 + 48$$
$$= 88$$

The last row has 88 seats so the total number of seats is given by

$$S_{25} = \frac{25}{2}[40+88] = \frac{25}{2}(128) = 1600$$

There are 1600 seats in the auditorium.

55. From the terms listed, we see that the first term is $a = -5$, the last term is $a_n = 244$, and the common difference is $d = -2 - (-5) = 3$. We can determine the number of terms in the sequence by using the formula for the nth term.

$$a_n = a + (n-1)d$$
$$244 = -5 + (n-1)(3)$$
$$244 = -5 + 3n - 3$$
$$252 = 3n$$
$$84 = n$$

There are 84 terms in the sequence.

57. From the terms listed, we see that the first term is $a = 108$, the last term is $a_n = -326$, and the common difference is $d = 101 - 108 = -7$. We can determine the number of terms in the sequence by using the formula for the nth term.

$$a_n = a + (n-1)d$$
$$-326 = 108 + (n-1)(-7)$$
$$-326 = 108 - 7n + 7$$
$$-441 = -7n$$
$$63 = n$$

There are 63 terms in the sequence.

59. Since your starting salary is $32,000 and you get a $2500 raise each year, your salary each year will form an arithmetic sequence with $a = 32,000$ and $d = 2500$. Your aggregate salary at any point is the sum of what you have earned up to that point. To find how long it would take to have an aggregate of $757,500 we can use the formula

$$S_n = \frac{n}{2}[a + a_n] = \frac{n}{2}[2a + (n-1)d]$$
$$757,500 = \frac{n}{2}[2(32,000) + (n-1)2500]$$
$$757,500 = \frac{n}{2}[64,000 + 2500n - 2500]$$
$$1,515,000 = n(61,500 + 2500n)$$
$$0 = 2500n^2 + 61,500n - 1,515,000$$
$$0 = n^2 + 24.6n - 606$$

We can solve this quadratic equation by using the quadratic formula.

$$n = \frac{-24.6 \pm \sqrt{(24.6)^2 - 4(1)(-606)}}{2(1)}$$
$$= \frac{-24.6 \pm \sqrt{3029.16}}{2}$$

Since n must be positive, we only need to consider the positive solution.

$$n = \frac{-24.6 + \sqrt{3029.16}}{2} \approx 15.22$$

It will take about 15.22 years for you to have an aggregate salary of $757,500.

61. a. $f(x) = 3^x$ is in the form $y = a^x$ so the base is 3.

b. $f(1) = 3^1 = 3$
$f(2) = 3^2 = 9$
$f(3) = 3^3 = 27$
$f(4) = 3^4 = 81$

63. a. $f(x) = 10\left(\frac{1}{2}\right)^x$ is in the form $y = k \cdot a^x$ so

the base is $\frac{1}{2}$.

b. $f(1) = 10\left(\frac{1}{2}\right)^1 = 5$

$f(2) = 10\left(\frac{1}{2}\right)^2 = \frac{5}{2}$

$f(3) = 10\left(\frac{1}{2}\right)^3 = \frac{5}{4}$

$f(4) = 10\left(\frac{1}{2}\right)^4 = \frac{5}{8}$

65. $\{3.45n + 4.12\}$; $n = 20$

```
sum(seq(3.45n+4.
12,n,1,20))
            806.9
```

The sum of the first 20 terms of this arithmetic sequence is 806.9.

67. $a = 85.9$; $d = 83.5 - 85.9 = -2.4$

$a_n = 85.9 + (n-1)(-2.4)$

$\quad = 85.9 - 2.4n + 2.4$

$\quad = 88.3 - 2.4n$

$\{88.3 - 2.4n\}$; $n = 25$

```
sum(seq(88.3-2.4
n,n,1,25))
            1427.5
```

The sum of the first 25 terms of this arithmetic sequence is 1427.5.

11.3 Preparing for Geometric Sequences and Series

1. $g(x) = 4^x$

$g(1) = 4^1 = 4$

$g(2) = 4^2 = 16$

$g(3) = 4^3 = 64$

2. $\dfrac{x^4}{x^3} = x^{4-3} = x$

11.3 Exercises

1. geometric

3. False; to be a geometric sequence, the common ratio need only be constant. It is possible for the ratio to be negative.

5. Answers may vary. We can determine if a sequence is geometric by looking at the ratio $\dfrac{a_n}{a_{n-1}}$. If the ratio is constant, then the sequence is geometric.

7. $\{4^n\}$;

$\dfrac{a_n}{a_{n-1}} = \dfrac{4^n}{4^{n-1}} = 4^{n-(n-1)} = 4$

$a_1 = 4^1 = 4$

$a_2 = 4^2 = 16$

$a_3 = 4^3 = 64$

$a_4 = 4^4 = 256$

The common ratio is $r = 4$ and the first four terms of the sequence are 4, 16, 64, and 256.

9. $\left\{\left(\dfrac{2}{3}\right)^n\right\}$

$\dfrac{a_n}{a_{n-1}} = \dfrac{\left(\frac{2}{3}\right)^n}{\left(\frac{2}{3}\right)^{n-1}} = \left(\dfrac{2}{3}\right)^{n-(n-1)} = \dfrac{2}{3}$

$a_1 = \left(\dfrac{2}{3}\right)^1 = \dfrac{2}{3}$; $\qquad a_2 = \left(\dfrac{2}{3}\right)^2 = \dfrac{4}{9}$;

$a_3 = \left(\dfrac{2}{3}\right)^3 = \dfrac{8}{27}$; $\qquad a_4 = \left(\dfrac{2}{3}\right)^4 = \dfrac{16}{81}$

The common ratio is $r = \dfrac{2}{3}$ and the first four terms of the sequence are $\dfrac{2}{3}, \dfrac{4}{9}, \dfrac{8}{27}$, and $\dfrac{16}{81}$.

11. $\{3 \cdot 2^{-n}\}$

$\dfrac{a_n}{a_{n-1}} = \dfrac{3 \cdot 2^{-n}}{3 \cdot 2^{-(n-1)}} = \dfrac{2^{-n}}{2^{-n+1}} = 2^{-n-(-n+1)} = 2^{-1} = \dfrac{1}{2}$

$a_1 = 3 \cdot 2^{-1} = \dfrac{3}{2}$; $\quad a_2 = 3 \cdot 2^{-2} = \dfrac{3}{4}$;

$a_3 = 3 \cdot 2^{-3} = \dfrac{3}{8}$; $\quad a_4 = 3 \cdot 2^{-4} = \dfrac{3}{16}$

The common ratio is $r = \dfrac{1}{2}$ and the first four terms of the sequence are $\dfrac{3}{2}, \dfrac{3}{4}, \dfrac{3}{8}$, and $\dfrac{3}{16}$.

SSM – 677

13. $\left\{\dfrac{5^{n-1}}{2^n}\right\}$

$$\frac{a_n}{a_{n-1}} = \frac{\left(\dfrac{5^{n-1}}{2^n}\right)}{\left(\dfrac{5^{(n-1)-1}}{2^{n-1}}\right)}$$

$$= \frac{5^{n-1}}{2^n} \cdot \frac{2^{n-1}}{5^{n-2}}$$

$$= 5^{(n-1)-(n-2)} \cdot 2^{(n-1)-n}$$

$$= 5 \cdot 2^{-1}$$

$$= \frac{5}{2}$$

$$a_1 = \frac{5^{1-1}}{2^1} = \frac{5^0}{2} = \frac{1}{2}$$

$$a_2 = \frac{5^{2-1}}{2^2} = \frac{5}{4}$$

$$a_3 = \frac{5^{3-1}}{2^3} = \frac{5^2}{2^3} = \frac{25}{8}$$

$$a_4 = \frac{5^{4-1}}{2^4} = \frac{5^3}{2^4} = \frac{125}{16}$$

The common ratio is $r = \frac{5}{2}$ and the first four terms of the sequence are $\frac{1}{2}$, $\frac{5}{4}$, $\frac{25}{8}$, and $\frac{125}{16}$.

15. $\{5n+1\}$

$$a_n - a_{n-1} = [5n+1] - [5(n-1)+1]$$

$$= [5n+1] - [5n-5+1]$$

$$= 5n+1-5n+4$$

$$= 5$$

Since the difference between successive terms is constant, this is an arithmetic sequence. The common difference is $d = 5$.

17. $\{2n^2\}$

$$a_n - a_{n-1} = \left[2n^2\right] - \left[2(n-1)^2\right]$$

$$= \left[2n^2\right] - \left[2n^2 - 4n + 2\right]$$

$$= 2n^2 - 2n^2 + 4n - 2$$

$$= 4n - 2$$

Since the difference between consecutive terms is not constant, the sequence is not arithmetic.

$$\frac{a_n}{a_{n-1}} = \frac{2n^2}{2(n-1)^2} = \frac{n^2}{n^2 - 2n + 1}$$

Since the ratio of consecutive terms is not constant, the sequence is not geometric.

19. $\left\{\dfrac{2^{-n}}{5}\right\}$

$$a_n - a_{n-1} = \frac{2^{-n}}{5} - \frac{2^{-(n-1)}}{5}$$

$$= \frac{2^{-n}}{5} - \frac{2^{-n+1}}{5}$$

$$= \frac{2^{-n}}{5} - \frac{2 \cdot 2^{-n}}{5}$$

$$= -\frac{2^{-n}}{5}$$

Since the difference between consecutive terms is not constant, the sequence is not arithmetic.

$$\frac{a_n}{a_{n-1}} = \frac{\left(\dfrac{2^{-n}}{5}\right)}{\left(\dfrac{2^{-(n-1)}}{5}\right)} = \frac{2^{-n}}{5} \cdot \frac{5}{2^{-n+1}}$$

$$= 2^{-n-(-n+1)}$$

$$= 2^{-1}$$

$$= \frac{1}{2}$$

Since the ratio of consecutive terms is constant, the sequence is geometric. The common ratio is $r = \frac{1}{2}$.

21. $a_2 - a_1 = 36 - 54 = -18$
$a_3 - a_2 = 24 - 36 = -12$

Consecutive differences are not the same so the sequence is not arithmetic.

$$\frac{a_2}{a_1} = \frac{36}{54} = \frac{2}{3}; \quad \frac{a_3}{a_2} = \frac{24}{36} = \frac{2}{3}; \quad \frac{a_4}{a_3} = \frac{16}{24} = \frac{2}{3}$$

The ratio of consecutive terms is constant so the sequence is geometric. The common ratio is $r = \frac{2}{3}$.

23. $a_2 - a_1 = 6 - 2 = 4$
$a_3 - a_2 = 10 - 6 = 4$
$a_4 - a_3 = 14 - 10 = 4$

The difference between consecutive terms is constant so the sequence is arithmetic. The common difference is $d = 4$.

25. $a_2 - a_1 = 2 - 1 = 1$
$a_3 - a_2 = 3 - 2 = 1$
$a_4 - a_3 = 5 - 3 = 2$
$a_5 - a_4 = 8 - 5 = 3$

The difference between consecutive terms is not constant so the sequence is not arithmetic.

$$\frac{a_2}{a_1} = \frac{2}{1} = 2$$

$$\frac{a_3}{a_2} = \frac{3}{2} = 1.5$$

$$\frac{a_4}{a_3} = \frac{5}{3} \approx 1.67$$

$$\frac{a_5}{a_4} = \frac{8}{5} = 1.6$$

The ratio of consecutive terms is not constant so the sequence is not geometric.

27. a. $a_n = a \cdot r^{n-1} = 10 \cdot 2^{n-1}$

b. $a_8 = 10 \cdot 2^{8-1} = 10 \cdot 2^7 = 10 \cdot 128 = 1280$

29. a. $a_n = a \cdot r^{n-1} = 100 \cdot \left(\frac{1}{2}\right)^{n-1}$

b. $a_8 = 100 \cdot \left(\frac{1}{2}\right)^{8-1} = 100 \cdot \left(\frac{1}{2}\right)^7 = \frac{100}{128} = \frac{25}{32}$

31. a. $a_n = a \cdot r^{n-1} = 1 \cdot (-3)^{n-1} = (-3)^{n-1}$

b. $a_8 = (-3)^{8-1} = (-3)^7 = -2187$

33. a. $a_n = a \cdot r^{n-1} = 100 \cdot (1.05)^{n-1}$

b. $a_8 = 100 \cdot (1.05)^{8-1} = 100 \cdot (1.05)^7 \approx 140.71$

35. $r = \frac{6}{3} = 2$; $a = 3$

$a_n = a \cdot r^{n-1}$

$a_{10} = 3 \cdot 2^{10-1} = 3 \cdot 2^9 = 3 \cdot 512 = 1536$

37. $r = \frac{-2}{4} = -\frac{1}{2}$; $a = 4$

$a_n = a \cdot r^{n-1}$

$a_{15} = 4 \cdot \left(-\frac{1}{2}\right)^{15-1} = 4 \cdot \left(-\frac{1}{2}\right)^{14} = \frac{4}{16,384} = \frac{1}{4096}$

39. $r = \frac{0.05}{0.5} = \frac{1}{10}$; $a = 0.5$

$a_n = a \cdot r^{n-1}$

$a_9 = 0.5 \cdot (0.1)^{9-1} = 0.5 \cdot (0.1)^8 = 0.000000005$

41. $2 + 4 + 8 + \ldots + 2^{12}$

This is a geometric sequence with $a = 2$ and common ratio $r = 2$. We wish to find the sum of the first 12 terms, S_{12}.

$$S_n = a \cdot \frac{1-r^n}{1-r}$$

$$S_{12} = 2 \cdot \frac{1-2^{12}}{1-2} = 2 \cdot \frac{-4095}{-1} = 8190$$

$$2 + 4 + 8 + \ldots + 2^{12} = 8190$$

43. $50 + 20 + 8 + \frac{16}{5} + \ldots + 50\left(\frac{2}{5}\right)^{10-1}$

This is a geometric sequence with $a = 50$ and common ratio $r = \frac{2}{5}$. We wish to find the sum of the first 10 terms, S_{10}.

$$S_n = a \cdot \frac{1-r^n}{1-r}$$

$$S_{10} = 50 \cdot \frac{1-\left(\frac{2}{5}\right)^{10}}{1-\frac{2}{5}} = 50 \cdot \frac{\frac{9764601}{9765625}}{\frac{3}{5}} \approx 83.3245952$$

$$50 + 20 + 8 + \frac{16}{5} + \ldots + 50\left(\frac{2}{5}\right)^{10-1} \approx 83.3245952$$

45. $\sum_{n=1}^{10}\left[3 \cdot 2^n\right] = \sum_{n=1}^{10}\left[3 \cdot 2 \cdot 2^{n-1}\right] = \sum_{n=1}^{10}\left[6 \cdot 2^{n-1}\right]$

Here we want to find the sum of the first 10 terms of a geometric sequence with $a = 6$ and common ratio $r = 2$.

$$S_n = a \cdot \frac{1-r^n}{1-r}$$

$$S_{10} = 6 \cdot \frac{1-2^{10}}{1-2} = 6 \cdot \frac{-1023}{-1} = 6138$$

$$\sum_{n=1}^{10}\left[3 \cdot 2^n\right] = 6138$$

47. $\displaystyle\sum_{n=1}^{8}\left[\frac{4}{2^{n-1}}\right]=\sum_{n=1}^{8}\left[4\cdot\left(\frac{1}{2}\right)^{n-1}\right]$

Here we want the sum of the first eight terms of a geometric sequence with $a=4$ and common ratio $r=\dfrac{1}{2}$.

$$S_n = a\cdot\frac{1-r^n}{1-r}$$

$$S_8 = 4\cdot\frac{1-\left(\frac{1}{2}\right)^8}{1-\frac{1}{2}}=4\cdot\frac{\frac{255}{256}}{\frac{1}{2}}=8\cdot\frac{255}{256}=7.96875$$

$$\sum_{n=1}^{8}\left[\frac{4}{2^{n-1}}\right]=7.96875\,.$$

49. This is an infinite geometric series with $a=1$ and common ratio $r=\dfrac{\frac{1}{2}}{1}=\dfrac{1}{2}$. Since the common ratio, r, is between -1 and 1, we can use the formula for the sum of an infinite geometric series.

$$1+\frac{1}{2}+\frac{1}{4}+\ldots=\frac{a}{1-r}=\frac{1}{1-\frac{1}{2}}=\frac{1}{\frac{1}{2}}=2$$

51. This is an infinite geometric series with $a=10$ and common ratio $r=\dfrac{\frac{10}{3}}{10}=\dfrac{1}{3}$. Since the common ratio, r, is between -1 and 1, we can use the formula for the sum of an infinite geometric series.

$$10+\frac{10}{3}+\frac{10}{9}+\ldots=\frac{10}{1-\frac{1}{3}}=\frac{10}{\frac{2}{3}}=15$$

53. This is an infinite geometric series with $a=6$ and common ratio $r=\dfrac{-2}{6}=-\dfrac{1}{3}$. Since the common ratio, r, is between -1 and 1, we can use the formula for the sum of an infinite geometric series.

$$6-2+\frac{2}{3}-\frac{2}{9}+\ldots=\frac{6}{1-\left(-\frac{1}{3}\right)}=\frac{6}{\frac{4}{3}}=6\cdot\frac{3}{4}=\frac{9}{2}$$

55. This is an infinite geometric series with $a=5\cdot\left(\dfrac{1}{5}\right)^{1}=1$ and common ratio $r=\dfrac{1}{5}$. Since the common ratio, r, is between -1 and 1, we can use the formula for the sum of an infinite geometric series.

$$\sum_{n=1}^{\infty}\left(5\cdot\left(\frac{1}{5}\right)^{n}\right)=\frac{1}{1-\frac{1}{5}}=\frac{1}{\frac{4}{5}}=\frac{5}{4}$$

57. This is an infinite geometric series with $a=12\cdot\left(-\dfrac{1}{3}\right)^{1-1}=12$ and common ratio $r=-\dfrac{1}{3}$.

Since the common ratio, r, is between -1 and 1, we can use the formula for the sum of an infinite geometric series.

$$\sum_{n=1}^{\infty}\left(12\cdot\left(-\frac{1}{3}\right)^{n-1}\right)=\frac{12}{1-\left(-\frac{1}{3}\right)}=\frac{12}{\frac{4}{3}}$$

$$=12\cdot\frac{3}{4}$$

$$=9$$

59. $0.\overline{5}=0.5+0.05+0.005+0.0005+\ldots$

$$=\sum_{n=1}^{\infty}\left[0.5\cdot\left(\frac{1}{10}\right)^{n-1}\right]$$

This is an infinite geometric series with $a=0.5$ and common ratio $r=\dfrac{1}{10}$. Since the common ratio, r, is between -1 and 1, we can use the formula for the sum of an infinite geometric series.

$$0.\overline{5}=\frac{0.5}{1-\frac{1}{10}}=\frac{\frac{1}{2}}{\frac{9}{10}}=\frac{1}{2}\cdot\frac{10}{9}=\frac{5}{9}$$

61. $0.\overline{89}=0.89+0.0089+0.000089+\ldots$

$$=\sum_{n=1}^{\infty}\left[0.89\cdot\left(\frac{1}{100}\right)^{n-1}\right]$$

This is an infinite geometric series with $a=0.89$ and common ratio $r=\dfrac{1}{100}$. Since the common ratio, r, is between -1 and 1, we can use the formula for the sum of an infinite geometric series.

$$0.\overline{89}=\frac{0.89}{1-\frac{1}{100}}=\frac{0.89}{0.99}=\frac{89}{99}$$

63. To be a geometric sequence, the ratio of consecutive terms must be the same. Therefore, we need to solve the equation

$$\frac{x+2}{x} = \frac{x+3}{x+2}$$

$$x(x+2) \cdot \frac{x+2}{x} = x(x+2) \cdot \frac{x+3}{x+2}$$

$$(x+2)^2 = x(x+3)$$

$$x^2 + 4x + 4 = x^2 + 3x$$

$$4x + 4 = 3x$$

$$x + 4 = 0$$

$$x = -4$$

65. Your annual salaries will form a geometric sequence with $a = 40,000$ and common ratio $r = 1.05$.

a. Your salary at the beginning of the second year is the value of the second term in the sequence.

$$a_2 = a \cdot r^{2-1} = 40,000 \cdot (1.05)^1 = 42,000$$

Your salary at the beginning of the second year will be $42,000.

b. Your salary at the beginning of the tenth year is the value of the tenth term in the sequence.

$$a_{10} = a \cdot r^{10-1} = 40,000 \cdot (1.05)^9 \approx 62,053$$

Your salary at the beginning of the tenth year will be about $62,053.

c. Your cumulative earnings after completing your tenth year is the sum of the first ten terms of the sequence.

$$S_{10} = a \cdot \frac{1 - r^{10}}{1 - r}$$

$$= 40,000 \cdot \frac{1 - (1.05)^{10}}{1 - 1.05}$$

$$\approx 40,000 \cdot (12.577893)$$

$$\approx 503,116$$

Your cumulative earnings after finishing your tenth year will be about $503,116.

67. The value of the car at the beginning of the year forms a geometric sequence with $a = 20,000$ and common ratio $r = 0.92$. The value of the car after you have owned it for five years will be the sixth term of the sequence (the beginning of the sixth year of ownership).

$$a_6 = 20,000 \cdot (0.92)^{6-1}$$

$$= 20,000 \cdot (0.92)^5 \approx 13,182$$

After five years of ownership, the car will be worth about $13,182.

69. The lengths of the arc of the pendulum swings form a geometric sequence with $a = 3$ and common ratio $r = 0.95$.

a. $a_{10} = a \cdot r^{10-1}$

$$= 3 \cdot (0.95)^9$$

$$\approx 1.891$$

The length of the arc in the 10th swing is about 1.891 feet.

b. Here we need to determine the term number. We start with the following equation:

$$a_n = 1$$

$$a \cdot r^{n-1} = 1$$

$$3 \cdot (0.95)^{n-1} = 1$$

$$(0.95)^{n-1} = \frac{1}{3}$$

$$\ln\left[(0.95)^{n-1}\right] = \ln\left(\tfrac{1}{3}\right)$$

$$(n-1) \cdot \ln(0.95) = \ln\left(\tfrac{1}{3}\right)$$

$$n - 1 = \frac{\ln\left(\tfrac{1}{3}\right)}{\ln(0.95)}$$

$$n = 1 + \frac{\ln\left(\tfrac{1}{3}\right)}{\ln(0.95)}$$

$$n \approx 22.42$$

Since the terms in the sequence are decreasing, the length of the arc will be less than 1 foot on the 23rd swing.

c. $S_{10} = a \cdot \dfrac{1 - r^{10}}{1 - r}$

$$= 3 \cdot \frac{1 - (0.95)^{10}}{1 - 0.95} \approx 24.08$$

After 10 swings, the pendulum will have swung a total of about 24.08 feet.

d. To find the total length the pendulum will swing requires an infinite geometric series.

$$S_\infty = \frac{a}{1 - r}$$

$$= \frac{3}{1 - 0.95}$$

$$= \frac{3}{0.05}$$

$$= 60$$

The pendulum will swing a total of 60 feet.

71. The annual salaries under option A form a geometric sequence with $a = 30,000$ and common ratio $r = 1.05$. The annual salaries under option B form a geometric sequence with $a = 31,000$ and common ratio $r = 1.04$.

To determine which option gives the larger annual salary in the final year of the contract, we need to find the 5th term of each sequence.

Option A: $a_5 = 30,000 \cdot (1.05)^{5-1} \approx 36,465.19$

Option B: $a_5 = 31,000 \cdot (1.04)^{5-1} \approx 36,265.62$

To determine which option gives the largest cumulative salary for five years, we need the sum of the first five terms of each sequence.

Option A: $S_5 = 30,000 \cdot \dfrac{1 - (1.05)^5}{1 - 1.05} \approx 165,768.94$

Option B: $S_5 = 31,000 \cdot \dfrac{1 - (1.04)^5}{1 - 1.04} \approx 167,906.00$

Therefore, option A will yield the larger annual salary in the final year of the contract and option B will yield the larger cumulative salary over the life of the contract.

73. The multiplier in this case is the geometric series with first term $a = 1$ and common ratio $r = 0.98$.

$$1 + 0.98 + (0.98)^2 + \ldots = \dfrac{1}{1 - 0.98} = 50$$

The multiplier is 50.

75. $\dfrac{1+i}{1+r} = \dfrac{1+.02}{1+.09} = \dfrac{1.02}{1.09} \approx 0.93578$

The price is an infinite geometric series with $a = 2$ and a common ratio of $\dfrac{1.02}{1.09}$. The maximum price is given by

$$\text{Price} = \dfrac{2}{1 - \dfrac{1.02}{1.09}} \approx 31.14$$

The maximum price you should pay for the stock is $31.14 per share.

77. $A = P \cdot \dfrac{(1+i)^n - 1}{i}$

In this case we have $P = 100$, $n = 30 \cdot 12 = 360$, and $i = \dfrac{0.08}{12}$.

$$A = 100 \cdot \left[\dfrac{\left(1 + \dfrac{0.08}{12}\right)^{360} - 1}{\dfrac{0.08}{12}} \right]$$

$$= 100 \cdot [1490.359449]$$

$$= \$149,035.94$$

After 30 years, Christina's 401(k) will be worth $149,035.94.

79. $A = P \cdot \dfrac{(1+i)^n - 1}{i}$

In this case we have $P = 500$, $n = 25 \cdot 4 = 100$, and $i = \dfrac{0.06}{4} = 0.015$.

$$A = 500 \cdot \left[\dfrac{(1 + 0.015)^{100} - 1}{0.015} \right]$$

$$= 500 \cdot [228.8030433]$$

$$= \$114,401.52$$

After 25 years, Jackson's IRA will be worth $114,401.52.

81. $A = P \cdot \dfrac{(1+i)^n - 1}{i}$

In this case we have $A = 1,500,000$, $n = 35 \cdot 12 = 420$, and $i = \dfrac{0.10}{12}$.

$$1,500,000 = P \cdot \left[\dfrac{\left(1 + \dfrac{0.10}{12}\right)^{420} - 1}{\dfrac{0.10}{12}} \right]$$

$$1,500,000 = P \cdot [3796.638052]$$

$$P = \$395.09$$

Aaliyah will need to contribute $395.09, or about $395, each month in order to achieve her goal.

83. $0.4\overline{9} = 0.4 + 0.09 + 0.009 + 0.0009 + \ldots$

After the 0.4, the rest of the sum forms an infinite geometric series with $a = 0.09$ and common ratio $r = 0.1$. We can find the sum of this part as $S_\infty = \dfrac{a}{1-r} = \dfrac{0.09}{1 - 0.1} = \dfrac{0.09}{0.9} = 0.1$

Thus, $0.4\overline{9} = 0.4 + 0.1 = 0.5 = \dfrac{1}{2}$

85. The sum is a geometric series with $a = 2$ and common ratio $r = 2$. We can find the sum by using the summation formula, after we determine how many terms are in the sum.

$$a_n = a \cdot r^{n-1}$$
$$1{,}073{,}741{,}824 = 2 \cdot 2^{n-1}$$
$$1{,}073{,}741{,}824 = 2^n$$
$$\ln 1{,}073{,}741{,}824 = \ln 2^n$$
$$\ln 1{,}073{,}741{,}824 = n \cdot \ln 2$$
$$\frac{\ln 1{,}073{,}741{,}824}{\ln 2} = n$$
$$30 = n$$
$$S_{30} = a \cdot \frac{1 - r^{30}}{1 - r} = 2 \cdot \frac{1 - 2^{30}}{1 - 2} = 2{,}147{,}483{,}646$$

87. Answers may vary. The comparison of growth rates really depends on the common difference and the common ratio. It is possible for an arithmetic sequence to grow at a faster rate initially. However, the geometric sequence will always end up growing at a faster rate if given enough time. For example, consider the following sequences:

arithmetic: $\{20 + (n-1) \cdot 2\}$

geometric: $\{20 \cdot 1.05^{n-1}\}$

These two sequences begin at the same value, but then the arithmetic sequence begins growing at a faster rate. After about 27 years, the geometric sequence will take over.

If Malthus' conjecture is correct, it would mean that we would eventually be unable to produce enough food to feed everyone on the planet, even if current supply exceeds demand.

89. $\dfrac{1}{3} = 0.333333\ldots$

$\dfrac{2}{3} = 0.666666\ldots$

$\dfrac{1}{3} + \dfrac{2}{3} = (0.333333\ldots) + (0.666666\ldots)$
$\qquad\qquad = 0.999999\ldots$

Since $\dfrac{1}{3} + \dfrac{2}{3} = \dfrac{3}{3} = 1$, we would conjecture that $0.999999\ldots = 1$.

91. This is a geometric series with $a = 4$ and common ratio $r = 1.2$. Based on the form of the last term, it appears that there are $n = 15$ terms in the series.

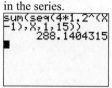

The sum is approximately 288.1404315.

93. $\displaystyle\sum_{n=1}^{20} \left[1.2(1.05)^n \right]$

This is a geometric series with $a = 1.26$ (that is, $1.2(1.05)^1$), common ratio $r = 1.05$, and $n = 20$ terms.

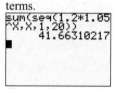

The sum is approximately 41.66310217.

Putting the Concepts Together (Sections 11.1 – 11.3)

1. $\dfrac{3/16}{3/4} = \dfrac{3}{16} \cdot \dfrac{4}{3} = \dfrac{1}{4}$

$\dfrac{3/64}{3/16} = \dfrac{3}{64} \cdot \dfrac{16}{3} = \dfrac{1}{4}$

$\dfrac{3/256}{3/64} = \dfrac{3}{256} \cdot \dfrac{64}{3} = \dfrac{1}{4}$

The ratio of consecutive terms is a constant so the sequence is geometric with $a = \dfrac{3}{4}$ and common ratio $r = \dfrac{1}{4}$.

2. $a_n - a_{n-1} = \left[2(n+3) \right] - \left[2(n-1+3) \right]$
$\qquad\qquad = 2(n+3) - 2(n+2)$
$\qquad\qquad = 2n + 6 - 2n - 4$
$\qquad\qquad = 2$

The difference between consecutive terms is a constant so the sequence is arithmetic with $a = 2(1+3) = 8$ and common difference $d = 2$.

3. $a_n - a_{n-1} = \left[\dfrac{7n+2}{9}\right] - \left[\dfrac{7(n-1)+2}{9}\right]$

$\qquad = \left(\dfrac{7n+2}{9}\right) - \left(\dfrac{7n-7+2}{9}\right)$

$\qquad = \dfrac{7n+2-7n+5}{9}$

$\qquad = \dfrac{7}{9}$

The difference between consecutive terms is a constant so the sequence is arithmetic with

$a = \dfrac{7(1)+2}{9} = 1$ and common difference $d = \dfrac{7}{9}$.

4. $-4 - 1 = -5$

$9 - (-4) = 13$

$\dfrac{-4}{1} = -4$

$\dfrac{9}{-4} = -\dfrac{9}{4}$

The sequence is neither arithmetic nor geometric. The difference between consecutive terms is not constant so the sequence is not arithmetic. Likewise, the ratio of consecutive terms is not constant so the sequence is not geometric.

5. $\dfrac{a_n}{a_{n-1}} = \dfrac{3 \cdot 2^{n+1}}{3 \cdot 2^{(n-1)+1}} = \dfrac{3 \cdot 2^n \cdot 2}{3 \cdot 2^n} = 2$

The ratio of consecutive terms is a constant so the sequence is geometric with $a = 3 \cdot 2^{1+1} = 12$ and common ratio $r = 2$.

6. $a_n - a_{n-1} = \left[n^2 - 5\right] - \left[(n-1)^2 - 5\right]$

$\qquad = n^2 - 5 - \left(n^2 - 2n + 1 - 5\right)$

$\qquad = n^2 - 5 - n^2 + 2n + 4$

$\qquad = 2n - 1$

$\dfrac{a_n}{a_{n-1}} = \dfrac{n^2 - 5}{(n-1)^2 - 5} = \dfrac{n^2 - 5}{n^2 - 2n - 4}$

The sequence is neither arithmetic nor geometric. The difference between consecutive terms is not constant so the sequence is not arithmetic. Likewise, the ratio of consecutive terms is not constant so the sequence is not geometric.

7. $\displaystyle\sum_{k=1}^{6} [3k + 4]$

$= (3 \cdot 1 + 4) + (3 \cdot 2 + 4) + (3 \cdot 3 + 4)$
$+ (3 \cdot 4 + 4) + (3 \cdot 5 + 4) + (3 \cdot 6 + 4)$
$= 3 + 4 + 6 + 4 + 9 + 4 + 12 + 4 + 15 + 4 + 18 + 4$
$= 87$

8. Each term is written in the form $\dfrac{1}{2(6+i)}$, where i is the term number, and there are $n = 12$ terms.

$\dfrac{1}{2(6+1)} + \dfrac{1}{2(6+2)} + \ldots + \dfrac{1}{2(6+12)} = \displaystyle\sum_{i=1}^{12} \dfrac{1}{2(6+i)}$

9. $a_n = a + (n-1)d$

$\qquad = 25 + (n-1)(-2)$

$\qquad = 25 - 2n + 2$

$\qquad = 27 - 2n$

$a_1 = 27 - 2(1) = 25$

$a_2 = 27 - 2(2) = 23$

$a_3 = 27 - 2(3) = 21$

$a_4 = 27 - 2(4) = 19$

$a_5 = 27 - 2(5) = 17$

The first five terms of the sequence are 25, 23, 21, 19, and 17.

10. $a_n = a + (n-1)d$

$\qquad a_4 = a + (4-1)(11) = 9$

$a + 33 = 9$

$\qquad a = -24$

$a_n = -24 + (n-1)(11)$

$\qquad = -24 + 11n - 11$

$\qquad = 11n - 35$

$a_1 = 11(1) - 35 = -24$

$a_2 = 11(2) - 35 = -13$

$a_3 = 11(3) - 35 = -2$

$a_4 = 11(4) - 35 = 9$

$a_5 = 11(5) - 35 = 20$

The first five terms of the sequence are -24, -13, -2, 9, and 20.

11. $a_n = a \cdot r^{n-1}$

$$a_4 = a \cdot \left(\frac{1}{5}\right)^{4-1} = \frac{9}{25}$$

$$a \cdot \frac{1}{125} = \frac{9}{25} \qquad \rightarrow \qquad a = 125 \cdot \frac{9}{25} = 45$$

$$a_n = 45 \cdot \left(\frac{1}{5}\right)^{n-1}$$

$$a_1 = 45 \cdot \left(\frac{1}{5}\right)^{1-1} = 45$$

$$a_2 = 45 \cdot \left(\frac{1}{5}\right)^{2-1} = 9$$

$$a_3 = 45 \cdot \left(\frac{1}{5}\right)^{3-1} = \frac{9}{5}$$

$$a_4 = 45 \cdot \left(\frac{1}{5}\right)^{4-1} = \frac{9}{25}$$

$$a_5 = 45 \cdot \left(\frac{1}{5}\right)^{5-1} = \frac{9}{125}$$

The first five terms of the sequence are $45, 9, \dfrac{9}{5}$, $\dfrac{9}{25}$, and $\dfrac{9}{125}$.

12. $a_n = a \cdot r^{n-1}$

$$= 150 \cdot (1.04)^{n-1}$$

$$a_1 = 150 \cdot (1.04)^{1-1} = 150$$
$$a_2 = 150 \cdot (1.04)^{2-1} = 156$$
$$a_3 = 150 \cdot (1.04)^{3-1} = 162.24$$
$$a_4 = 150 \cdot (1.04)^{4-1} = 168.7296$$
$$a_5 = 150 \cdot (1.04)^{5-1} = 175.478784$$

The first five terms of the sequence are 150, 156, 162.24, 168.7296, and 175.478784.

13. The terms form a geometric sequence with first term $a = 2$, common ratio $r = 3$, and $n = 11$ terms.

$$S_{11} = 2 \cdot \frac{1 - 3^{11}}{1 - 3} = 177,146$$

14. The terms form an arithmetic sequence with first term $a = 2$, common difference $d = 5$, and $n = 20$ terms.

$$a_{20} = 2 + (20 - 1) \cdot 5 = 97$$

$$S_{20} = \frac{20}{2}[2 + 97] = 990$$

15. This is an infinite geometric series with $a = 1000$ and $r = \dfrac{1}{10}$.

$$S_\infty = \frac{a}{1-r} = \frac{1000}{1 - \frac{1}{10}} = \frac{1000}{\frac{9}{10}} = \frac{10,000}{9} \text{ or } 1111\frac{1}{9}$$

16. The number of people who can be seated forms an arithmetic sequence with first term $a = 4$ and common difference $d = 2$. The number of tables required is the same as the term number, n.
To find the number of tables required to seat a party of 24 people, we solve the following for n:

$$a_n = a + (n-1)d$$
$$24 = 4 + (n-1)(2)$$
$$24 = 4 + 2n - 2$$
$$24 = 2n + 2$$
$$22 = 2n$$
$$11 = n$$

A party of 24 people would require 11 tables.

11.4 Preparing for the Binomial Theorem

1. $(x - 5)^2 = x^2 - 2 \cdot x \cdot 5 + 5^2$

$$= x^2 - 10x + 25$$

2. $(2x + 3)^2 = (2x + 3)(2x + 3)$

$$= \left((2x)^2 + 2 \cdot 2x \cdot 3 + 3^2\right)$$

$$= 4x^2 + 12x + 9$$

11.4 Exercises

1. $n! = n(n-1)(n-2) \cdot \ldots \cdot 3 \cdot 2 \cdot 1$

3. Pascal's triangle

5. False; $\dbinom{n}{0} = \dfrac{n!}{0!(n-0)!} = \dfrac{n!}{n!} = 1$

7. Beginning with n, the exponents of x decrease by 1 in subsequent terms until the exponent is 0.

9. The degree of each monomial (sum of the exponents) in the expansion of $(x + a)^n$ is equal to n.

11. $(x+1)^5 = \binom{5}{0}x^5 + \binom{5}{1}1^1 \cdot x^{5-1} + \binom{5}{2}1^2 \cdot x^{5-2} + \binom{5}{3}1^3 \cdot x^{5-3} + \binom{5}{4}1^4 \cdot x^{5-4} + \binom{5}{5}1^5$

$\qquad = x^5 + 5x^4 + 10x^3 + 10x^2 + 5x + 1$

13. $(x-4)^4 = \left(x+(-4)\right)^4$

$\qquad = \binom{4}{0}x^4 + \binom{4}{1}(-4)^1 \cdot x^{4-1} + \binom{4}{2}(-4)^2 \cdot x^{4-2} + \binom{4}{3}(-4)^3 \cdot x^{4-3} + \binom{4}{4}(-4)^4$

$\qquad = x^4 + 4(-4)x^3 + 6(16)x^2 + 4(-64)x + 256$

$\qquad = x^4 - 16x^3 + 96x^2 - 256x + 256$

15. $(3p+2)^4 = \left((3p)+2\right)^4$

$\qquad = \binom{4}{0}(3p)^4 + \binom{4}{1}2^1 \cdot (3p)^{4-1} + \binom{4}{2}2^2 \cdot (3p)^{4-2} + \binom{4}{3}2^3 \cdot (3p)^{4-3} + \binom{4}{4}2^4$

$\qquad = 81p^4 + 4 \cdot 2 \cdot 27p^3 + 6 \cdot 4 \cdot 9p^2 + 4 \cdot 8 \cdot 3p + 16$

$\qquad = 81p^4 + 216p^3 + 216p^2 + 96p + 16$

17. $(2z-3)^5$

$\qquad = \left((2z)+(-3)\right)^5$

$\qquad = \binom{5}{0}(2z)^5 + \binom{5}{1}(-3)^1 \cdot (2z)^{5-1} + \binom{5}{2}(-3)^2 \cdot (2z)^{5-2} + \binom{5}{3}(-3)^3 \cdot (2z)^{5-3} + \binom{5}{4}(-3)^4 \cdot (2z)^{5-4} + \binom{5}{5}(-3)^5$

$\qquad = 32z^5 + 5(-3) \cdot 16z^4 + 10(9) \cdot 8z^3 + 10(-27) \cdot 4z^2 + 5(81) \cdot 2z + (-243)$

$\qquad = 32z^5 - 240z^4 + 720z^3 - 1080z^2 + 810z - 243$

19. $(x^2+2)^4 = \binom{4}{0}(x^2)^4 + \binom{4}{1}2^1 \cdot (x^2)^{4-1} + \binom{4}{2}2^2 \cdot (x^2)^{4-2} + \binom{4}{3}2^3 \cdot (x^2)^{4-3} + \binom{4}{4}2^4$

$\qquad = x^8 + 4 \cdot 2x^6 + 6 \cdot 4x^4 + 4 \cdot 8x^2 + 16$

$\qquad = x^8 + 8x^6 + 24x^4 + 32x^2 + 16$

21. $(2p^3+1)^5 = \left((2p^3)+1\right)^5$

$\qquad = \binom{5}{0}(2p^3)^5 + \binom{5}{1}1^1 \cdot (2p^3)^{5-1} + \binom{5}{2}1^2 \cdot (2p^3)^{5-2} + \binom{5}{3}1^3 \cdot (2p^3)^{5-3} + \binom{5}{4}1^4 \cdot (2p^3)^{5-4} + \binom{5}{5}1^5$

$\qquad = 32p^{15} + 5 \cdot 16p^{12} + 10 \cdot 8p^9 + 10 \cdot 4p^6 + 5 \cdot 2p^3 + 1$

$\qquad = 32p^{15} + 80p^{12} + 80p^9 + 40p^6 + 10p^3 + 1$

23. $(x+2)^6 = \binom{6}{0}x^6 + \binom{6}{1}2^1 \cdot x^{6-1} + \binom{6}{2}2^2 \cdot x^{6-2} + \binom{6}{3}2^3 \cdot x^{6-3} + \binom{6}{4}2^4 \cdot x^{6-4} + \binom{6}{5}2^5 \cdot x^{6-5} + \binom{6}{6}2^6$

$\qquad = x^6 + 6 \cdot 2x^5 + 15 \cdot 4x^4 + 20 \cdot 8x^3 + 15 \cdot 16x^2 + 6 \cdot 32x + 64$

$\qquad = x^6 + 12x^5 + 60x^4 + 160x^3 + 240x^2 + 192x + 64$

25. $(2p^2-q^2)^4 = \left((2p^2)+(-q^2)\right)^4$

$\qquad = \binom{4}{0}(2p^2)^4 + \binom{4}{1}(2p^2)^{4-1} \cdot (-q^2)^1 + \binom{4}{2}(2p^2)^{4-2} \cdot (-q^2)^2 + \binom{4}{3}(2p^2)^{4-3} \cdot (-q^2)^3 + \binom{4}{4}(-q^2)^4$

$\qquad = 16p^8 + 4 \cdot 8p^6 \cdot (-q^2) + 6 \cdot 4p^4 \cdot (q^4) + 4 \cdot 2p^2 \cdot (-q^6) + (q^8)$

$\qquad = 16p^8 - 32p^6q^2 + 24p^4q^4 - 8p^2q^6 + q^8$

27. $(1.001)^4 = (1+0.001)^4$

$$= \binom{4}{0}1^4 + \binom{4}{1}1^{4-1} \cdot (0.001)^1 + \binom{4}{2}1^{4-2} \cdot (0.001)^2 + \binom{4}{3}1^{4-3} \cdot (0.001)^3 + \binom{4}{4}(0.001)^4$$

$$= 1 + 4(0.001) + 6(0.000001) + 4(0.000000001) + (0.000000000001)$$

$$= 1 + 0.004 + 0.000006 + 0.000000004 + 0.000000000001$$

$$= 1.004006004001$$

$$\approx 1.00401$$

29. $(0.998)^5 = (1-0.002)^5$

$$= \left(1 + (-0.002)\right)^5$$

$$= \binom{5}{0}1^5 + \binom{5}{1}1^{5-1}(-0.002)^1 + \binom{5}{2}1^{5-2}(-0.002)^2 + \binom{5}{3}1^{5-3}(-0.002)^3 + \binom{5}{4}1^{5-4}(-0.002)^4 + \binom{5}{5}(-0.002)^5$$

$$= 1 + 5(-0.002) + 10(0.000004) + 10(-0.000000008) + 5(0.000000000016) + (-0.000000000000032)$$

$$= 1 - 0.01 + 0.00004 - 0.00000008 + 0.00000000008 - 0.000000000000032$$

$$= 1.000040000080000 - 0.010000080000032$$

$$= 0.990039920079968$$

$$\approx 0.99004$$

31. The third term of the expansion of $(x+2)^7$ is

$$\binom{7}{2}2^2 \cdot x^{7-2} = 21 \cdot 4x^5 = 84x^5$$

33. The sixth term of the expansion of $(2p-3)^8 = \left((2p)+(-3)\right)^8$ is

$$\binom{8}{5}(-3)^5 \cdot (2p)^{8-5} = 56(-243) \cdot 8p^3$$

$$= -108,864p^3$$

35. $\binom{n}{n-1} = \frac{n!}{(n-1)!(n-(n-1))!} = \frac{n!}{(n-1)!1!} = \frac{n \cdot (n-1)!}{(n-1)!} = n$

$\binom{n}{n} = \frac{n!}{n!(n-n)!} = \frac{n!}{n!0!} = \frac{n!}{n!} = 1$

37. $f(x) = x^4$

$f(a-2) = (a-2)^4$

$$= \binom{4}{0}a^4 + \binom{4}{1}(-2)^1 \cdot a^{4-1} + \binom{4}{2}(-2)^2 \cdot a^{4-2} + \binom{4}{3}(-2)^3 \cdot a^{4-3} + \binom{4}{4}(-2)^4$$

$$= a^4 + 4(-2)a^3 + 6(4)a^2 + 4(-8)a + (16)$$

$$= a^4 - 8a^3 + 24a^2 - 32a + 16$$

39. $H(x) = x^5 - 4x^4$

$H(p+1) = (p+1)^5 - 4(p+1)^4$

$$= \left[\binom{5}{0}p^5 + \binom{5}{1}1^1 \cdot p^{5-1} + \binom{5}{2}1^2 \cdot p^{5-2} + \binom{5}{3}1^3 \cdot p^{5-3} + \binom{5}{4}1^4 \cdot p^{5-4} + \binom{5}{5}1^5 \right]$$

$$-4\left[\binom{4}{0}p^4 + \binom{4}{1}1^1 \cdot p^{4-1} + \binom{4}{2}1^2 \cdot p^{4-2} + \binom{4}{3}1^3 \cdot p^{4-3} + \binom{4}{4}1^4 \right]$$

$$= \left[p^5 + 5p^4 + 10p^3 + 10p^2 + 5p + 1 \right]$$

$$-4\left[p^4 + 4p^3 + 6p^2 + 4p + 1 \right]$$

$$= p^5 + 5p^4 + 10p^3 + 10p^2 + 5p + 1 - 4p^4 - 16p^3 - 24p^2 - 16p - 4$$

$$= p^5 + p^4 - 6p^3 - 14p^2 - 11p - 3$$

Chapter 11 Review

1. $a_n = -3n + 2$

$a_1 = -3(1) + 2 = -1$

$a_2 = -3(2) + 2 = -4$

$a_3 = -3(3) + 2 = -7$

$a_4 = -3(4) + 2 = -10$

$a_5 = -3(5) + 2 = -13$

The first five terms of the sequence are -1, -4, -7, -10, and -13.

2. $a_n = \dfrac{n-2}{n+4}$

$a_1 = \dfrac{1-2}{1+4} = \dfrac{-1}{5} = -\dfrac{1}{5}$; $\quad a_2 = \dfrac{2-2}{2+4} = \dfrac{0}{6} = 0$;

$a_3 = \dfrac{3-2}{3+4} = \dfrac{1}{7}$; $\quad a_4 = \dfrac{4-2}{4+4} = \dfrac{2}{8} = \dfrac{1}{4}$;

$a_5 = \dfrac{5-2}{5+4} = \dfrac{3}{9} = \dfrac{1}{3}$

The first five terms of the sequence are $-\dfrac{1}{5}$, 0, $\dfrac{1}{7}$, $\dfrac{1}{4}$, and $\dfrac{1}{3}$.

3. $a_n = 5^n + 1$

$a_1 = 5^1 + 1 = 5 + 1 = 6$

$a_2 = 5^2 + 1 = 25 + 1 = 26$

$a_3 = 5^3 + 1 = 125 + 1 = 126$

$a_4 = 5^4 + 1 = 625 + 1 = 626$

$a_5 = 5^5 + 1 = 3125 + 1 = 3126$

The first five terms of the sequence are 6, 26, 126, 626, and 3126.

4. $a_n = (-1)^{n-1} \cdot 3n$

$a_1 = (-1)^{1-1} \cdot 3(1) = (-1)^0 \cdot 3 = 3$

$a_2 = (-1)^{2-1} \cdot 3(2) = (-1)^1 \cdot 6 = -6$

$a_3 = (-1)^{3-1} \cdot 3(3) = (-1)^2 \cdot 9 = 9$

$a_4 = (-1)^{4-1} \cdot 3(4) = (-1)^3 \cdot 12 = -12$

$a_5 = (-1)^{5-1} \cdot 3(5) = (-1)^4 \cdot 15 = 15$

The first five terms of the sequence are 3, -6, 9, -12, and 15.

5. $a_n = \dfrac{n^2}{n+1}$

$a_1 = \dfrac{1^2}{1+1} = \dfrac{1}{2}$, $\qquad a_2 = \dfrac{2^2}{2+1} = \dfrac{4}{3}$,

$a_3 = \dfrac{3^2}{3+1} = \dfrac{9}{4}$, $\qquad a_4 = \dfrac{4^2}{4+1} = \dfrac{16}{5}$,

$a_5 = \dfrac{5^2}{5+1} = \dfrac{25}{6}$

The first five terms of the sequence are $\dfrac{1}{2}$, $\dfrac{4}{3}$, $\dfrac{9}{4}$, $\dfrac{16}{5}$, and $\dfrac{25}{6}$.

6. $a_n = \dfrac{\pi^n}{n}$

$a_1 = \dfrac{\pi^1}{1} = \pi; \quad a_2 = \dfrac{\pi^2}{2};$

$a_3 = \dfrac{\pi^3}{3}; \quad a_4 = \dfrac{\pi^4}{4};$

$a_5 = \dfrac{\pi^5}{5}$

The first five terms of the sequence are π, $\dfrac{\pi^2}{2}$,

$\dfrac{\pi^3}{3}$, $\dfrac{\pi^4}{4}$, and $\dfrac{\pi^5}{5}$.

7. The terms can be expressed as multiples of -3.
$-3 = -3 \cdot 1$
$-6 = -3 \cdot 2$
$-9 = -3 \cdot 3$
$-12 = -3 \cdot 4$
$-15 = -3 \cdot 5$
The nth term of the sequence is given by
$a_n = -3n$.

8. The terms are rational numbers with a denominator of 3. The numerators are consecutive integers beginning with 1. The nth term of the sequence is given by $a_n = \dfrac{n}{3}$.

9. The terms can be expressed as the product of 5 and a power of 2.
$5 = 5 \cdot 2^0$
$10 = 5 \cdot 2^1$
$20 = 5 \cdot 2^2$
$40 = 5 \cdot 2^3$
$80 = 5 \cdot 2^4$
The exponent is one less than the term number. Therefore, the nth term of the sequence is given by $a_n = 5 \cdot 2^{n-1}$.

10. Rewrite as $-\dfrac{1}{2}, \dfrac{2}{2}, -\dfrac{3}{2}, \dfrac{4}{2}, \ldots$

The terms are rational numbers with alternating signs. The denominator is always 2, and the numerators are consecutive integers beginning with 1. The nth term of the sequence is given by
$a_n = (-1)^n \cdot \dfrac{n}{2}$.

11. The terms can be expressed as 5 more than the square of the term number.
$6 = 1^2 + 5$
$9 = 2^2 + 5$
$14 = 3^2 + 5$
$21 = 4^2 + 5$
$30 = 5^2 + 5$
The nth term of the sequence is given by
$a_n = n^2 + 5$.

12. Rewrite the terms as $\dfrac{0}{2}, \dfrac{1}{3}, \dfrac{2}{4}, \dfrac{3}{5}, \ldots$

The terms are rational numbers whose numerators are consecutive integers beginning with 0 and whose denominators are consecutive integers beginning with 2. The nth term of the sequence is given by $a_n = \dfrac{n-1}{n+1}$.

13. $\displaystyle\sum_{k=1}^{5} (5k - 2)$
$= \left(5(1) - 2\right) + \left(5(2) - 2\right) + \left(5(3) - 2\right)$
$\quad + \left(5(4) - 2\right) + \left(5(5) - 2\right)$
$= 3 + 8 + 13 + 18 + 23$
$= 65$

14. $\displaystyle\sum_{k=1}^{6} \left(\dfrac{k+2}{2}\right)$
$= \dfrac{1+2}{2} + \dfrac{2+2}{2} + \dfrac{3+2}{2} + \dfrac{4+2}{2} + \dfrac{5+2}{2} + \dfrac{6+2}{2}$
$= \dfrac{3}{2} + \dfrac{4}{2} + \dfrac{5}{2} + \dfrac{6}{2} + \dfrac{7}{2} + \dfrac{8}{2}$
$= \dfrac{33}{2}$

15. $\displaystyle\sum_{i=1}^{5} (-2i)$
$= (-2 \cdot 1) + (-2 \cdot 2) + (-2 \cdot 3) + (-2 \cdot 4) + (-2 \cdot 5)$
$= -2 - 4 - 6 - 8 - 10$
$= -30$

16. $\displaystyle\sum_{i=1}^{4} \dfrac{i^2 - 1}{3} = \dfrac{1^2 - 1}{3} + \dfrac{2^2 - 1}{3} + \dfrac{3^2 - 1}{3} + \dfrac{4^2 - 1}{3}$
$= \dfrac{0}{3} + \dfrac{3}{3} + \dfrac{8}{3} + \dfrac{15}{3}$
$= \dfrac{26}{3}$

17. Each term takes on the form $4 + 3i$ and there are $n = 15$ terms.

$$(4 + 3 \cdot 1) + (4 + 3 \cdot 2) + \ldots + (4 + 3 \cdot 15) = \sum_{i=1}^{15} (4 + 3i)$$

18. Each term takes on the form $\dfrac{1}{3^i}$ and there are $n = 8$ terms.

$$\frac{1}{3^1} + \frac{1}{3^2} + \ldots + \frac{1}{3^8} = \sum_{i=1}^{8} \frac{1}{3^i}$$

19. Each term takes on the form $\dfrac{i^3 + 1}{i + 1}$ and there are $n = 10$ terms.

$$\frac{1^3 + 1}{1 + 1} + \frac{2^3 + 1}{2 + 1} + \ldots + \frac{10^3 + 1}{10 + 1} = \sum_{i=1}^{10} \frac{i^3 + 1}{i + 1}$$

20. This is an alternating series. Each term takes on the form $(-1)^{i-1} \cdot i^2$ and there are $n = 7$ terms.

$$(-1)^{1-1} \cdot 1^2 + (-1)^{2-1} \cdot 2^2 + \ldots + (-1)^{7-1} \cdot 7^2$$
$$= \sum_{i=1}^{7} \left[(-1)^{i-1} \cdot i^2 \right]$$

21. $10 - 4 = 6$
$16 - 10 = 6$
$22 - 16 = 6$
The sequence is arithmetic with a common difference of $d = 6$.

22. $\dfrac{1}{2} - (-1) = \dfrac{3}{2}$
$2 - \dfrac{1}{2} = \dfrac{3}{2}$
$\dfrac{7}{2} - 2 = \dfrac{3}{2}$
The sequence is arithmetic with a common difference of $d = \dfrac{3}{2}$.

23. $-5 - (-2) = -3$
$-9 - (-5) = -4$
$-14 - (-9) = -5$
The differences between consecutive terms is not constant. Therefore, the sequence is not arithmetic.

24. $3 - (-1) = 4$
$-5 - 3 = -8$
$7 - (-5) = 12$
The difference between consecutive terms is not constant. Therefore, the sequence is not arithmetic.

25. $a_n - a_{n-1} = [4n + 7] - [4(n - 1) + 7]$
$= 4n + 7 - (4n - 4 + 7)$
$= 4n + 7 - 4n + 4 - 7$
$= 4$
The sequence is arithmetic with a common difference of $d = 4$.

26. $a_n - a_{n-1} = \left[\dfrac{n+1}{2n} \right] - \left[\dfrac{(n-1)+1}{2(n-1)} \right]$
$= \dfrac{n+1}{2n} - \dfrac{n}{2(n-1)}$
$= \dfrac{(n+1)(n-1)}{2n(n-1)} - \dfrac{n(n)}{2n(n-1)}$
$= \dfrac{n^2 - 1 - n^2}{2n(n-1)}$
$= \dfrac{-1}{2n(n-1)}$

The difference between consecutive terms is not constant. Therefore, the sequence is not arithmetic.

27. $a_n = a + (n - 1)d$
$= 3 + (n - 1)(8)$
$= 3 + 8n - 8$
$= 8n - 5$

$a_{25} = 8(25) - 5 = 200 - 5 = 195$

28. $a_n = a + (n - 1)d$
$= -4 + (n - 1)(-3)$
$= -4 - 3n + 3$
$= -3n - 1$

$a_{25} = -3(25) - 1 = -75 - 1 = -76$

29. $d = \dfrac{20}{3} - 7 = -\dfrac{1}{3}$; $a = 7$

$a_n = a + (n-1)d$

$\quad = 7 + (n-1)\left(-\dfrac{1}{3}\right)$

$\quad = 7 - \dfrac{1}{3}n + \dfrac{1}{3}$

$\quad = -\dfrac{1}{3}n + \dfrac{22}{3}$

$a_{25} = -\dfrac{1}{3}(25) + \dfrac{22}{3} = -\dfrac{3}{3} = -1$

30. $d = 17 - 11 = 6$; $a = 11$

$a_n = a + (n-1)d$

$\quad = 11 + (n-1)(6)$

$\quad = 11 + 6n - 6$

$\quad = 6n + 5$

$a_{25} = 6(25) + 5 = 150 + 5 = 155$

31. Since $a_3 = 7$ and $a_8 = 25$, we have

$\begin{cases} 7 = a + (3-1)d \\ 25 = a + (8-1)d \end{cases}$ or $\begin{cases} 7 = a + 2d \\ 25 = a + 7d \end{cases}$

Subtract the second equation from the first equation to obtain

$-18 = -5d$

$\dfrac{18}{5} = d$

Let $d = \dfrac{18}{5}$ in the first equation to find a.

$7 = a + 2\left(\dfrac{18}{5}\right)$

$7 = a + \dfrac{36}{5}$

$-\dfrac{1}{5} = a$

The nth term of the sequence is given by

$a_n = a + (n-1)d$

$\quad = -\dfrac{1}{5} + (n-1)\left(\dfrac{18}{5}\right)$

$\quad = -\dfrac{1}{5} + \dfrac{18}{5}n - \dfrac{18}{5}$

$\quad = \dfrac{18}{5}n - \dfrac{19}{5}$

$a_{25} = \dfrac{18}{5}(25) - \dfrac{19}{5} = \dfrac{450}{5} - \dfrac{19}{5} = \dfrac{431}{5}$

32. Since $a_4 = -20$ and $a_7 = -32$, we have

$\begin{cases} -20 = a + (4-1)d \\ -32 = a + (7-1)d \end{cases}$ or $\begin{cases} -20 = a + 3d \\ -32 = a + 6d \end{cases}$

Subtract the second equation from the first equation to obtain

$12 = -3d$

$-4 = d$

Let $d = -4$ in the first equation to find a.

$-20 = a + 3(-4)$

$-20 = a - 12$

$-8 = a$

The nth term of the sequence is given by

$a_n = a + (n-1)d$

$\quad = -8 + (n-1)(-4)$

$\quad = -8 - 4n + 4$

$\quad = -4n - 4$

$a_{25} = -4(25) - 4 = -100 - 4 = -104$

33. We know the first term is $a = -1$ and the common difference is $d = 9 - (-1) = 10$.

$S_n = \dfrac{n}{2}\left[2a + (n-1)d\right]$

$S_{30} = \dfrac{30}{2}\left[2(-1) + (30-1)(10)\right]$

$\quad = 15\left[-2 + 29(10)\right]$

$\quad = 15(-2 + 290)$

$\quad = 15(288)$

$\quad = 4320$

34. We know the first term is $a = 5$ and the common difference is $d = 2 - 5 = -3$.

$S_n = \dfrac{n}{2}\left[2a + (n-1)d\right]$

$S_{40} = \dfrac{40}{2}\left[2(5) + (40-1)(-3)\right]$

$\quad = 20\left[10 + 39(-3)\right]$

$\quad = 20(10 - 117)$

$\quad = 20(-107)$

$\quad = -2140$

35. $a_n = -2n - 7$

$$a = a_1 = -2(1) - 7 = -9$$

$$a_{60} = -2(60) - 7 = -127$$

$$S_n = \frac{n}{2}[a + a_n]$$

$$S_{60} = \frac{60}{2}\left[-9 + (-127)\right]$$

$$= 30(-136)$$

$$= -4080$$

36. $a_n = \frac{1}{4}n + 3$

$$a = a_1 = \frac{1}{4}(1) + 3 = \frac{13}{4}$$

$$a_{50} = \frac{1}{4}(50) + 3 = \frac{62}{4}$$

$$S_n = \frac{n}{2}[a + a_n]$$

$$S_{50} = \frac{50}{2}\left[\frac{13}{4} + \frac{62}{4}\right]$$

$$= 25\left(\frac{75}{4}\right)$$

$$= \frac{1875}{4} \quad \text{or} \quad 468.75$$

37. We could list terms of the sequence formed by the years when the Brood X cicada returns, or we could use the general formula for the *n*th term. We have $a = 2004$ and $d = 17$. We wish to know the first time when $a_n \geq 2101$.

$$a_n \geq 2101$$

$$a + (n - 1)d \geq 2101$$

$$2004 + (n - 1)(17) \geq 2101$$

$$2004 + 17n - 17 \geq 2101$$

$$17n + 1987 \geq 2101$$

$$17n \geq 114$$

$$n \geq \frac{114}{17} \approx 6.71$$

The Brood X cicada will first appear in the 22nd century when $n = 7$.

$$a_7 = 2004 + (7 - 1)(17) = 2106$$

The Brood X cicada will first appear in the 22nd century in the year 2106.

38. Since the distance to each line is the same as the distance back to the goal line, we can consider the sequence of distances run away from the goal line and double our result. The sequence of distances is 10, 20, 30, 40, and 50. This is an arithmetic sequence with first term $a = 10$ and fifth term $a_5 = 50$.

$$S_5 = \frac{5}{2}[10 + 50] = \frac{5}{2}(60) = 150$$

Doubling this result gives a total distance of 300 yards run by each player during wind sprints.

39. $\dfrac{2}{\frac{1}{3}} = 2 \cdot \dfrac{3}{1} = 6$

$$\frac{12}{2} = 6$$

$$\frac{72}{12} = 6$$

The ratio of consecutive terms is constant so the sequence is geometric with common ratio $r = 6$.

40. $\dfrac{3}{-1} = -3$

$$\frac{-9}{3} = -3$$

$$\frac{27}{-9} = -3$$

The ratio of consecutive terms is constant so the sequence is geometric with common ratio $r = -3$.

41. $\dfrac{1}{1} = 1$

$$\frac{2}{1} = 2$$

$$\frac{6}{2} = 3$$

The ratio of consecutive terms is not constant so the sequence is not geometric.

42. $\dfrac{4}{6} = \dfrac{2}{3}$

$$\frac{\frac{8}{3}}{4} = \frac{8}{3} \cdot \frac{1}{4} = \frac{2}{3}$$

$$\frac{\frac{16}{9}}{\frac{8}{3}} = \frac{16}{9} \cdot \frac{3}{8} = \frac{2}{3}$$

The ratio of consecutive terms is constant so the sequence is geometric with common ratio $r = \dfrac{2}{3}$.

43. $\dfrac{a_n}{a_{n-1}} = \dfrac{5 \cdot (-2)^n}{5 \cdot (-2)^{n-1}} = \dfrac{(-2)^{n-1} \cdot (-2)}{(-2)^{n-1}} = -2$

The ratio of consecutive terms is constant so the sequence is geometric with common ratio $r = -2$.

44. $\dfrac{a_n}{a_{n-1}} = \dfrac{3n - 14}{3(n-1) - 14} = \dfrac{3n - 14}{3n - 17}$

The ratio of consecutive terms is not constant so the sequence is not geometric.

45. $a_n = a \cdot r^{n-1}$

$a_n = 4 \cdot 3^{n-1}$

$a_{10} = 4 \cdot 3^{10-1} = 4 \cdot 3^9 = 4(19,683) = 78,732$

46. $a_n = a \cdot r^{n-1}$

$a_n = 8 \cdot \left(\dfrac{1}{4}\right)^{n-1}$

$a_{10} = 8 \cdot \left(\dfrac{1}{4}\right)^{10-1}$

$= 8 \cdot \left(\dfrac{1}{4}\right)^9$

$= 8 \cdot \left(\dfrac{1}{262,144}\right)$

$= \dfrac{1}{32,768}$

47. $a_n = a \cdot r^{n-1}$

$a_n = 5 \cdot (-2)^{n-1}$

$a_{10} = 5 \cdot (-2)^{10-1} = 5 \cdot (-2)^9 = 5(-512) = -2560$

48. $a_n = a \cdot r^{n-1}$

$a_n = 1000 \cdot (1.08)^{n-1}$

$a_{10} = 1000 \cdot (1.08)^{10-1}$

$= 1000 \cdot (1.08)^9$

$\approx 1000 (1.999005)$

$= 1999.005$

49. This is a geometric series with first term $a = 2$, common ratio $r = \dfrac{4}{2} = 2$, and $n = 15$ terms.

$S_n = a \cdot \dfrac{1 - r^n}{1 - r}$

$S_{15} = 2 \cdot \dfrac{1 - 2^{15}}{1 - 2}$

$= 2 \cdot \dfrac{-32,767}{-1}$

$= 65,534$

50. This is a geometric series with first term $a = 40$, common ratio $r = \dfrac{1}{8}$, and $n = 13$ terms.

$S_n = a \cdot \dfrac{1 - r^n}{1 - r}$

$S_{13} = 40 \cdot \dfrac{1 - \left(\dfrac{1}{8}\right)^{13}}{1 - \dfrac{1}{8}}$

≈ 45.71428571

51. This is a geometric series with $n = 12$ terms. The first term is $a = \dfrac{3}{4} \cdot 2^{1-1} = \dfrac{3}{4}$ and the common ratio is $r = 2$.

$S_n = a \cdot \dfrac{1 - r^n}{1 - r}$

$S_{12} = \dfrac{3}{4} \cdot \dfrac{1 - 2^{12}}{1 - 2}$

$= \dfrac{3}{4} \cdot \dfrac{-4095}{-1}$

$= \dfrac{12,285}{4}$ or 3071.25

52. This is a geometric series with $n = 16$ terms. The first term is $a = -4\left(3^1\right) = -12$ and the common ratio is $r = 3$.

$S_n = a \cdot \dfrac{1 - r^n}{1 - r}$

$S_{16} = -12 \cdot \dfrac{1 - 3^{16}}{1 - 3}$

$= -12(21,523,360)$

$= -258,280,320$

53. This is an infinite geometric series with first term

$a = 20 \cdot \left(\frac{1}{4}\right)^1 = 5$ and common ratio $r = \frac{1}{4}$.

Since the ratio is between -1 and 1, we can use the formula for the sum of an infinite geometric series.

$$S_{\infty} = \frac{a}{1-r} = \frac{5}{1 - \frac{1}{4}} = \frac{5}{\frac{3}{4}} = 5 \cdot \frac{4}{3} = \frac{20}{3}$$

54. This is an infinite geometric series with first term

$a = 50 \cdot \left(-\frac{1}{2}\right)^{1-1} = 50$ and common ratio

$r = -\frac{1}{2}$. Since the ratio is between -1 and 1, we can use the formula for the sum of an infinite geometric series.

$$S_{\infty} = \frac{a}{1-r} = \frac{50}{1 - \left(-\frac{1}{2}\right)} = \frac{50}{\frac{3}{2}} = 50 \cdot \frac{2}{3} = \frac{100}{3}$$

55. This is an infinite geometric series with first term

$a = 1$ and common ratio $r = \frac{\frac{1}{5}}{1} = \frac{1}{5}$. The ratio

is between -1 and 1, so we can use the formula for the sum of an infinite geometric series.

$$S_{\infty} = \frac{a}{1-r} = \frac{1}{1 - \frac{1}{5}} = \frac{1}{\frac{4}{5}} = \frac{5}{4}$$

56. This is an infinite geometric series with first term

$a = 0.8$ and common ratio $r = \frac{0.08}{0.8} = 0.1$. Since

the ratio is between -1 and 1, we can use the formula for the sum of an infinite geometric series.

$$S_{\infty} = \frac{a}{1-r} = \frac{0.8}{1 - 0.1} = \frac{0.8}{0.9} = \frac{8}{9}$$

57. Here we consider a geometric sequence with first

term $a = 200$ and common ratio $r = \frac{1}{2}$. Each

term in the sequence represents the amount after each half-life, or the amount remaining after

every 12 years. Since $\frac{72}{12} = 6$, we are interested

in the 7th term of the sequence (that is, after 6 common ratios).

$a_n = a \cdot r^{n-1}$

$a_7 = 200 \cdot \left(\frac{1}{2}\right)^{7-1}$

$\quad = 200 \cdot \left(\frac{1}{2}\right)^6$

$\quad = \frac{200}{64}$

$\quad = 3.125$

After 72 years, there will be 3.125 grams of the Tritium remaining.

58. The number of emails in each cycle forms a geometric sequence with first term $a = 5$ and common ratio $r = 5$. To find the total e-mails sent after 15 minutes, we need to find the sum of the first 15 terms of this sequence.

$S_n = a \cdot \frac{1 - r^n}{1 - r}$

$S_{15} = 5 \cdot \frac{1 - 5^{15}}{1 - 5}$

$\quad \approx 3.815 \times 10^{10}$

After 15 minutes a total of about 38.15 billion e-mails will have been sent.

59. $A = P \cdot \left[\frac{(1+i)^n - 1}{i} \right]$

Note that the total contribution each quarter is the sum of Scott's contribution and the matching contribution from his employer.
In this case we have $P = 900 + 450 = 1350$,

$n = 25 \cdot 4 = 100$, and $i = \frac{0.07}{4} = 0.0175$.

$A = 1350 \cdot \left[\frac{(1 + 0.0175)^{100} - 1}{0.0175} \right]$

$\quad = 1350 \cdot [266.7517679]$

$\quad = \$360,114.89$

After 25 years, Scott's 403(b) will be worth $\$360,114.89$.

60. <u>Lump sum option:</u>

For this option, we use the compound interest formula.

$A = P(1+i)^n$

In this case we have $P = \$28,000,000$,

$n = 26 \cdot 1 = 26$, and $i = \dfrac{0.065}{1} = 0.065$.

$A = 28,000,000 \cdot (1+0.065)^{26} = \$143,961,987.40$

<u>Annuity option:</u>

For this option, we use the annuity formula.

$A = P \cdot \left[\dfrac{(1+i)^n - 1}{i} \right]$

In this case we have $P = 2,000,000$,

$n = 26 \cdot 1 = 26$, and $i = \dfrac{0.065}{1} = 0.065$.

$A = 2,000,000 \cdot \left[\dfrac{(1+0.065)^{26} - 1}{0.065} \right]$

$= 2,000,000 \cdot [63.71537769]$

$= \$127,430,755.40$

The lump sum option would yield more money after 26 years.

61. $A = P \cdot \left[\dfrac{(1+i)^n - 1}{i} \right]$

In this case we have $A = 2,500,000$,

$n = 40 \cdot 12 = 480$, and $i = \dfrac{0.09}{12} = 0.0075$.

$2,500,000 = P \cdot \left[\dfrac{(1+0.0075)^{480} - 1}{0.0075} \right]$

$2,500,000 = P \cdot [4681.320273]$

$\qquad P = \$534.04$

Sheri would need to contribute \$534.04, or about \$534, each month to reach her goal.

62. $A = P \cdot \left[\dfrac{(1+i)^n - 1}{i} \right]$

In this case we have $P = 400$, $n = 10 \cdot 12 = 120$,

and $i = \dfrac{0.0525}{12} = 0.004375$.

$A = 400 \cdot \left[\dfrac{(1+0.004375)^{120} - 1}{0.004375} \right]$

$= 400 \cdot [157.3769632]$

$= \$62,950.79$

$\dfrac{62,950.79}{340} \approx 185.15$

When Samantha turns 18, the plan will be worth \$62,950.79 and will cover about 185 credit hours.

63. $5! = 5 \cdot 4 \cdot 3 \cdot 2 \cdot 1 = 120$

64. $\dfrac{11!}{7!} = \dfrac{11 \cdot 10 \cdot 9 \cdot 8 \cdot 7!}{7!} = 11 \cdot 10 \cdot 9 \cdot 8 = 7920$

65. $\dfrac{10!}{6!} = \dfrac{10 \cdot 9 \cdot 8 \cdot 7 \cdot 6!}{6!} = 10 \cdot 9 \cdot 8 \cdot 7 = 5040$

66. $\dfrac{13!}{6!7!} = \dfrac{13 \cdot 12 \cdot 11 \cdot 10 \cdot 9 \cdot 8 \cdot 7!}{6 \cdot 5 \cdot 4 \cdot 3 \cdot 2 \cdot 1 \cdot 7!}$

$= \dfrac{13 \cdot 12 \cdot 11 \cdot 10 \cdot 9 \cdot 8}{6 \cdot 5 \cdot 4 \cdot 3 \cdot 2 \cdot 1}$

$= \dfrac{13 \cdot \cancel{12}^{2} \cdot 11 \cdot \cancel{10} \cdot \cancel{9}^{3} \cdot \cancel{8}^{4}}{\cancel{2} \cancel{6} \cdot \cancel{5} \cdot \cancel{4} \cancel{3} \cdot \cancel{2} \cdot 1}$

$= 13 \cdot 11 \cdot 3 \cdot 4$

$= 1716$

67. $\dbinom{7}{3} = \dfrac{7!}{3!4!}$

$= \dfrac{7 \cdot 6 \cdot 5 \cdot 4!}{3 \cdot 2 \cdot 1 \cdot 4!}$

$= \dfrac{7 \cdot 6 \cdot 5}{3 \cdot 2 \cdot 1}$

$= 35$

68. $\dbinom{10}{5} = \dfrac{10!}{5!5!}$

$= \dfrac{10 \cdot 9 \cdot 8 \cdot 7 \cdot 6 \cdot 5!}{5! \cdot 5 \cdot 4 \cdot 3 \cdot 2 \cdot 1}$

$= \dfrac{10 \cdot 9 \cdot 8 \cdot 7 \cdot 6}{5 \cdot 4 \cdot 3 \cdot 2 \cdot 1}$

$= 252$

69. $\dbinom{8}{8} = \dfrac{8!}{8!0!} = 1$

70. $\dbinom{6}{0} = \dfrac{6!}{0!6!} = 1$

71. $(z+1)^4 = \dbinom{4}{0}z^4 + \dbinom{4}{1}z^3 + \dbinom{4}{2}z^2 + \dbinom{4}{3}z + \dbinom{4}{4}$

$\qquad = 1 \cdot z^4 + 4 \cdot z^3 + 6 \cdot z^2 + 4 \cdot z + 1$

$\qquad = z^4 + 4z^3 + 6z^2 + 4z + 1$

72. $(y-3)^5 = \dbinom{5}{0}y^5 + \dbinom{5}{1}y^4 \cdot (-3) + \dbinom{5}{2}y^3 \cdot (-3)^2 + \dbinom{5}{3}y^2 \cdot (-3)^3 + \dbinom{5}{4}y \cdot (-3)^4 + \dbinom{5}{5} \cdot (-3)^5$

$\qquad = 1 \cdot y^5 + 5 \cdot y^4 \cdot (-3) + 10 \cdot y^3 \cdot 9 + 10 \cdot y^2 \cdot (-27) + 5 \cdot y \cdot 81 + (-243)$

$\qquad = y^5 - 15y^4 + 90y^3 - 270y^2 + 405y - 243$

73. $(3y+4)^6$

$\qquad = \dbinom{6}{0}(3y)^6 + \dbinom{6}{1}(3y)^5(4) + \dbinom{6}{2}(3y)^4(4)^2 + \dbinom{6}{3}(3y)^3(4)^3 + \dbinom{6}{4}(3y)^2(4)^4 + \dbinom{6}{5}(3y)(4)^5 + \dbinom{6}{6}(4)^6$

$\qquad = 1 \cdot 729y^6 + 6 \cdot 243y^5 \cdot 4 + 15 \cdot 81y^4 \cdot 16 + 20 \cdot 27y^3 \cdot 64 + 15 \cdot 9y^2 \cdot 256 + 6 \cdot 3y \cdot 1024 + 4096$

$\qquad = 729y^6 + 5832y^5 + 19,440y^4 + 34,560y^3 + 34,560y^2 + 18,432y + 4096$

74. $(2x^2 - 3)^4 = \dbinom{4}{0}(2x^2)^4 + \dbinom{4}{1}(2x^2)^3(-3) + \dbinom{4}{2}(2x^2)^2(-3)^2 + \dbinom{4}{3}(2x^2)(-3)^3 + \dbinom{4}{4}(-3)^4$

$\qquad = 16x^8 + 4 \cdot 8x^6 \cdot (-3) + 6 \cdot 4x^4 \cdot 9 + 4 \cdot 2x^2 \cdot (-27) + 81$

$\qquad = 16x^8 - 96x^6 + 216x^4 - 216x^2 + 81$

75. $(3p-2q)^4 = \dbinom{4}{0}(3p)^4 + \dbinom{4}{1}(3p)^3(-2q) + \dbinom{4}{2}(3p)^2(-2q)^2 + \dbinom{4}{3}(3p)(-2q)^3 + \dbinom{4}{4}(-2q)^4$

$\qquad = 81p^4 + 4 \cdot 27p^3 \cdot (-2q) + 6 \cdot 9p^2 \cdot (4q^2) + 4 \cdot 3p \cdot (-8q^3) + 16q^4$

$\qquad = 81p^4 - 216p^3q + 216p^2q^2 - 96pq^3 + 16q^4$

76. $(a^3+3b)^5 = \dbinom{5}{0}(a^3)^5 + \dbinom{5}{1}(a^3)^4(3b) + \dbinom{5}{2}(a^3)^3(3b)^2 + \dbinom{5}{3}(a^3)^2(3b)^3 + \dbinom{5}{4}(a^3)(3b)^4 + \dbinom{5}{5}(3b)^5$

$\qquad = a^{15} + 5a^{12} \cdot 3b + 10a^9 \cdot 9b^2 + 10a^6 \cdot 27b^3 + 5a^3 \cdot 81b^4 + 243b^5$

$\qquad = a^{15} + 15a^{12}b + 90a^9b^2 + 270a^6b^3 + 405a^3b^4 + 243b^5$

77. The fourth term of the expansion of $(x-2)^8 = (x+(-2))^8$ is

$\qquad \dbinom{8}{3}(-2)^3 x^5 = 56x^5 \cdot (-8) = -448x^5$

78. The seventh term of the expansion of $(2x+1)^{11} = ((2x)+1)^{11}$ is

$\qquad \dbinom{11}{6}1^6 (2x)^5 = 462 \cdot 32x^5 = 14,784x^5$

Chapter 11 Test

1. $-7-(-15)=8$
$1-(-7)=8$
$9-1=8$

The difference between consecutive terms is a constant so the sequence is arithmetic with $a=-15$ and common difference $d=8$.

2. $\dfrac{a_n}{a_{n-1}}=\dfrac{(-4)^n}{(-4)^{n-1}}=\dfrac{-4\cdot(-4)^{n-1}}{(-4)^{n-1}}=-4$

The ratio of consecutive terms is a constant so the sequence is geometric with $a=(-4)^1=-4$ and common ratio $r=-4$.

3. $a_n=\dfrac{4}{n!}; \; a_{n-1}=\dfrac{4}{(n-1)!}$

$a_n-a_{n-1}=\dfrac{4}{n!}-\dfrac{4}{(n-1)!}=\dfrac{4}{n!}-\dfrac{4n}{n(n-1)!}$

$=\dfrac{4-4n}{n!}$

$\dfrac{a_n}{a_{n-1}}=\dfrac{\frac{4}{n!}}{\frac{4}{(n-1)!}}=\dfrac{4}{n!}\cdot\dfrac{(n-1)!}{4}=\dfrac{1}{n}$

The sequence is neither arithmetic nor geometric. The difference between consecutive terms is not constant so the sequence is not arithmetic. Likewise, the ratio of consecutive terms is not constant so the sequence is not geometric.

4. $a_n-a_{n-1}=\left[\dfrac{2n-3}{5}\right]-\left[\dfrac{2(n-1)-3}{5}\right]$

$=\dfrac{2n-3-(2n-2-3)}{5}$

$=\dfrac{2n-3-2n+5}{5}=\dfrac{2}{5}$

The difference between consecutive terms is constant so the sequence is arithmetic with $a=\dfrac{2(1)-3}{5}=-\dfrac{1}{5}$ and common difference $d=\dfrac{2}{5}$.

5. $2-(-3)=5$
$0-2=2$
$\dfrac{2}{-3}=-\dfrac{2}{3}$
$\dfrac{0}{2}=0$

The sequence is neither arithmetic nor geometric. The difference between consecutive terms is not constant so the sequence is not arithmetic. Likewise, the ratio of consecutive terms is not constant so the sequence is not geometric.

6. $\dfrac{a_n}{a_{n-1}}=\dfrac{7\cdot3^n}{7\cdot3^{n-1}}=\dfrac{7\cdot3\cdot3^{n-1}}{7\cdot3^{n-1}}=3$

The ratio of consecutive terms is a constant so the sequence is geometric with $a=7\cdot3^1=21$ and common ratio $r=3$.

7. $\displaystyle\sum_{i=1}^{5}\left[\dfrac{3}{i^2}+2\right]$

$=\left(\dfrac{3}{1^2}+2\right)+\left(\dfrac{3}{2^2}+2\right)+\left(\dfrac{3}{3^2}+2\right)+\left(\dfrac{3}{4^2}+2\right)+\left(\dfrac{3}{5^2}+2\right)$

$=3+2+\dfrac{3}{4}+2+\dfrac{1}{3}+2+\dfrac{3}{16}+2+\dfrac{3}{25}+2$

$=13+\dfrac{900+400+225+144}{1200}=13+\dfrac{1669}{1200}$

$=14\dfrac{469}{1200}$ or $\dfrac{17269}{1200}$

8. Note that $\dfrac{2}{3}=\dfrac{4}{6}$, $\dfrac{3}{4}=\dfrac{6}{8}$, and $\dfrac{5}{6}=\dfrac{10}{12}$.

Each term can be written as $\dfrac{i+2}{i+4}$, where i is the term number, and there are $n=8$ terms.

$\dfrac{3}{5}+\dfrac{2}{3}+\dfrac{5}{7}+\dfrac{3}{4}+...+\dfrac{5}{6}=\displaystyle\sum_{i=1}^{8}\dfrac{i+2}{i+4}$

9. $a_n=a+(n-1)d$
$=6+(n-1)(10)$
$=6+10n-10$
$=10n-4$
$a_1=10\cdot1-4=6$
$a_2=10\cdot2-4=16$
$a_3=10\cdot3-4=26$
$a_4=10\cdot4-4=36$
$a_5=10\cdot5-4=46$

The first five terms of the sequence are 6, 16, 26, 36, and 46.

10. $a_n = a + (n-1)d$
$\qquad = 0 + (n-1)(-4)$
$\qquad = -4n + 4$
$\qquad = 4 - 4n$
$a_1 = 4 - 4 \cdot 1 = 0$
$a_2 = 4 - 4 \cdot 2 = -4$
$a_3 = 4 - 4 \cdot 3 = -8$
$a_4 = 4 - 4 \cdot 4 = -12$
$a_5 = 4 - 4 \cdot 5 = -16$
The first five terms of the sequence are 0, -4, -8, -12, and -16.

11. $a_n = a \cdot r^{n-1}$
$\qquad = 10 \cdot 2^{n-1}$
$a_1 = 10 \cdot 2^{1-1} = 10$
$a_2 = 10 \cdot 2^{2-1} = 20$
$a_3 = 10 \cdot 2^{3-1} = 40$
$a_4 = 10 \cdot 2^{4-1} = 80$
$a_5 = 10 \cdot 2^{5-1} = 160$
The first five terms of the sequence are 10, 20, 40, 80, and 160.

12. $\qquad a_n = a \cdot r^{n-1}$
$\qquad a_3 = a \cdot (-3)^{3-1} = 9$
$a(-3)^2 = 9$
$\qquad 9a = 9$
$\qquad\quad a = 1$
$a_n = 1 \cdot (-3)^{n-1}$
$\quad = (-3)^{n-1}$
$a_1 = (-3)^{1-1} = 1$
$a_2 = (-3)^{2-1} = -3$
$a_3 = (-3)^{3-1} = 9$
$a_4 = (-3)^{4-1} = -27$
$a_5 = (-3)^{5-1} = 81$
The first five terms of the sequence are 1, -3, 9, -27, and 81.

13. The terms form an arithmetic sequence with $n = 20$ terms, common difference $d = 4$, and first term $a = -2$.

$S_n = \dfrac{n}{2}\left[2a + (n-1)d\right]$
$S_{20} = \dfrac{20}{2}\left[2(-2) + (20-1)(4)\right]$
$\qquad = 10(72)$
$\qquad = 720$

14. The terms form a geometric sequence with $n = 12$ terms, common ratio $r = -3$, and first term $a = \dfrac{1}{9}$.

$S_n = a \cdot \dfrac{1 - r^n}{1 - r}$

$S_{12} = \dfrac{1}{9} \cdot \dfrac{1 - (-3)^{12}}{1 - (-3)}$

$\qquad = \dfrac{1}{9} \cdot \dfrac{1 - 3^{12}}{1 + 3}$

$\qquad = -\dfrac{132,860}{9}$

15. The terms form an infinite geometric series with first term $a = 216$ and common ratio $r = \dfrac{1}{3}$.

$S_\infty = \dfrac{a}{1 - r} = \dfrac{216}{1 - \left(\dfrac{1}{3}\right)} = \dfrac{216}{2/3} = 216 \cdot \dfrac{3}{2} = 324$

16. $\dfrac{15!}{8!7!} = \dfrac{15 \cdot 14 \cdot 13 \cdot 12 \cdot 11 \cdot 10 \cdot 9 \cdot 8!}{8! \cdot 7 \cdot 6 \cdot 5 \cdot 4 \cdot 3 \cdot 2 \cdot 1}$
$\qquad = \dfrac{15 \cdot 14 \cdot 13 \cdot 12 \cdot 11 \cdot 10 \cdot 9}{7 \cdot 6 \cdot 5 \cdot 4 \cdot 3 \cdot 2 \cdot 1}$
$\qquad = 6435$

17. $\dbinom{12}{5} = \dfrac{12!}{5!7!} = \dfrac{12 \cdot 11 \cdot 10 \cdot 9 \cdot 8 \cdot 7!}{5 \cdot 4 \cdot 3 \cdot 2 \cdot 1 \cdot 7!}$
$\qquad = \dfrac{12 \cdot 11 \cdot 10 \cdot 9 \cdot 8}{5 \cdot 4 \cdot 3 \cdot 2 \cdot 1}$
$\qquad = 792$

18. $(5m-2)^4 = \binom{4}{0}(5m)^4 + \binom{4}{1}(5m)^3(-2) + \binom{4}{2}(5m)^2(-2)^2 + \binom{4}{3}(5m)(-2)^3 + \binom{4}{4}(-2)^4$

$= 625m^4 + 4 \cdot 125m^3 \cdot (-2) + 6 \cdot 25m^2 \cdot 4 + 4 \cdot 5m \cdot (-8) + 16$

$= 625m^4 - 1000m^3 + 600m^2 - 160m + 16$

19. The average tuition values form a geometric sequence with first term $a = 4694$ and common ratio $r = 1.14$. To determine the average tuition and fees for the 2023-2024 school year, we need the 21st term of the sequence.

$a_{21} = a \cdot r^{21-1}$

$\quad\;\; = 4694 \cdot 1.14^{20}$

$\quad\;\; \approx 64,512$

If the percent increase continues, the average tuition and fees for in-state students would be about \$64,512 during the 2023-2024 academic year.

20. $1639 - 1631 = 8$

$1761 - 1639 = 122$

$1769 - 1761 = 8$

$1874 - 1769 = 105$

$1882 - 1874 = 8$

$2004 - 1882 = 122$

Following this pattern, the next three Venus transits should occur after intervals of 8, 105, and 8 years.

$2004 + 8 = 2012$

$2012 + 105 = 2117$

$2117 + 8 = 2125$

The next three Venus transits should occur in 2012, 2117, and 2125.

Cumulative Review Chapters R-11

1. $\frac{1}{2}(x+2) = \frac{5}{4}(x-3y)$

$4 \cdot \frac{1}{2}(x+2) = 4 \cdot \frac{5}{4}(x-3y)$

$2(x+2) = 5(x-3y)$

$2x + 4 = 5x - 15y$

$15y = 3x - 4$

$y = \frac{3x-4}{15}$ or $y = \frac{1}{5}x - \frac{4}{15}$

2. $f(x) = x^2 - x + 7$

$f(2) = (2)^2 - (2) + 7 = 4 - 2 + 7 = 9$

$f(-3) = (-3)^2 - (-3) + 7 = 9 + 3 + 7 = 19$

3. $\frac{1}{2}x - 2 = \frac{1}{3}(x+1) + 3$

$6\left(\frac{1}{2}x - 2\right) = 6\left(\frac{1}{3}(x+1) + 3\right)$

$3x - 12 = 2(x+1) + 18$

$3x - 12 = 2x + 2 + 18$

$3x - 2x = 20 + 12$

$x = 32$

The solution set is $\{32\}$.

4. $5x^2 - 3x = 2$

$5x^2 - 3x - 2 = 0$

$(5x+2)(x-1) = 0$

$5x + 2 = 0 \quad$ or $\quad x - 1 = 0$

$5x = -2 \qquad\qquad\quad x = 1$

$x = -\frac{2}{5}$

The solution set is $\left\{-\frac{2}{5}, 1\right\}$.

5. $3x^2 + 7x - 2 = 0$

$a = 3, b = 7, c = -2$

$x = \frac{-b \pm \sqrt{b^2 - 4ac}}{2a}$

$\;\; = \frac{-7 \pm \sqrt{7^2 - 4(3)(-2)}}{2(3)}$

$\;\; = \frac{-7 \pm \sqrt{49 + 24}}{6}$

$\;\; = \frac{-7 \pm \sqrt{73}}{6}$

The solution set is $\left\{\frac{-7-\sqrt{73}}{6}, \frac{-7+\sqrt{73}}{6}\right\}$.

6. $\sqrt{2x+1} - 3 = 8$

$\sqrt{2x+1} = 11$

$\left(\sqrt{2x+1}\right)^2 = 11^2$

$2x + 1 = 121$

$2x = 120$

$x = 60$

The solution set is $\{60\}$.

7. $4^{x+1} = 8^{2x-3}$

$\left(2^2\right)^{x+1} = \left(2^3\right)^{2x-3}$

$2^{2x+2} = 2^{6x-9}$

Therefore, we get

$2x + 2 = 6x - 9$

$-4x = -11$

$x = \dfrac{11}{4}$

The solution set is $\left\{\dfrac{11}{4}\right\}$.

8. $x^2(2x+1) + 40 = (x^2 - 8)(x - 5)$

$2x^3 + x^2 + 40 = x^3 - 8x - 5x^2 + 40$

$x^3 + 6x^2 + 8x = 0$

$x(x^2 + 6x + 8) = 0$

$x(x+4)(x+2) = 0$

$x = 0$ or $x + 4 = 0$ or $x + 2 = 0$

$\qquad\qquad x = -4 \qquad\quad x = -2$

The solution set is $\{-4, -2, 0\}$.

9. $\dfrac{2}{3}x + 1 > \dfrac{1}{4}x - \dfrac{3}{2}$

$12\left(\dfrac{2}{3}x + 1\right) > 12\left(\dfrac{1}{4}x - \dfrac{3}{2}\right)$

$8x + 12 > 3x - 18$

$5x > -30$

$\dfrac{5x}{5} > \dfrac{-30}{5}$

$x > -6$

Interval: $(-6, \infty)$

10. $3x^2 - 2x \le 3 - 10x$

$3x^2 + 8x - 3 \le 0$

$(3x - 1)(x + 3) \le 0$

$3x - 1 = 0 \qquad x + 3 = 0$

$3x = 1 \qquad\qquad x = -3$

$x = \dfrac{1}{3}$

Interval	$(-\infty, -3)$	-3	$\left(-3, \frac{1}{3}\right)$	$\frac{1}{3}$	$\left(\frac{1}{3}, \infty\right)$
$(3x - 1)$	$---$	$-$	$---$	0	$+++$
$(x + 3)$	$---$	0	$+++$	$+$	$+++$
$(3x-1)(x+3)$	$+++$	0	$---$	0	$+++$

The inequality is non-strict, so $\dfrac{1}{3}$ and -3 are part of the solution. Now, $(3x - 1)(x + 3)$ is less than zero where the product is negative. The solution is $\left\{x \,\middle|\, -3 \le x \le \dfrac{1}{3}\right\}$ or, using interval notation, $\left[-3, \dfrac{1}{3}\right]$.

11. $2x^2 - 5x - 18$

$ac = 2(-18) = -36$

We are looking for two factors of -36 whose sum is -5 . Since the product is negative, the factors will have opposite signs. The sum is negative so the factor with the largest absolute value will be negative.

factor 1	factor 2	sum
1	-36	-35
2	-18	-16
3	-12	-9
4	-9	$-5 \leftarrow$ okay

$2x^2 - 5x - 18 = 2x^2 + 4x - 9x - 18$

$\qquad\qquad\qquad = 2x(x + 2) - 9(x + 2)$

$\qquad\qquad\qquad = (x + 2)(2x - 9)$

12. $6x^3 - 3x^2 + 4x - 2 = 3x^2(2x - 1) + 2(2x - 1)$

$\qquad\qquad\qquad\qquad\qquad = (2x - 1)(3x^2 + 2)$

13. $(5x-3)(4x^2-2x+1)$

$$= 20x^3 - 10x^2 + 5x - 12x^2 + 6x - 3$$
$$= 20x^3 - 22x^2 + 11x - 3$$

14. $\dfrac{x}{x+4} - \dfrac{3}{x-1} = \dfrac{x(x-1)}{(x+4)(x-1)} - \dfrac{3(x+4)}{(x+4)(x-1)}$

$$= \dfrac{x(x-1)-3(x+4)}{(x+4)(x-1)} = \dfrac{x^2-x-3x-12}{(x+4)(x-1)}$$

$$= \dfrac{x^2-4x-12}{(x+4)(x-1)} = \dfrac{(x-6)(x+2)}{(x+4)(x-1)}$$

15. $\dfrac{3-i}{2+i} = \dfrac{(3-i)(2-i)}{(2+i)(2-i)}$

$$= \dfrac{6-2i-3i+i^2}{4-i^2}$$

$$= \dfrac{6-5i-1}{4-(-1)}$$

$$= \dfrac{5-5i}{5}$$

$$= 1-i$$

16. Because of the two radicals, we need

$$x - 15 \geq 0 \quad \text{and} \quad 2x - 5 \geq 0$$
$$x \geq 15 \qquad\qquad 2x \geq 5$$
$$\qquad\qquad\qquad x \geq \dfrac{5}{2}$$

Therefore, the domain is $\{x \mid x \geq 15\}$ or $[15, \infty)$.

17. Begin by finding the slope of the line connecting the two points.

$$m = \dfrac{y_2 - y_1}{x_2 - x_1} = \dfrac{4-(-3)}{1-2} = \dfrac{7}{-1} = -7$$

$$y - y_1 = m(x - x_1)$$
$$y - (-3) = -7(x-2)$$
$$y + 3 = -7x + 14$$
$$y = -7x + 11$$

18. $2x + 3y = 5$
$x - 2y = 6$

We can solve this system by using elimination. Multiply the second equation by -2 and add the two equations.

$$2x + 3y = 5$$
$$\underline{-2x + 4y = -12}$$
$$7y = -7$$
$$y = -1$$

Let $y = -1$ in the second equation to find x.

$$x - 2(-1) = 6$$
$$x + 2 = 6$$
$$x = 4$$

The ordered pair $(4, -1)$ is the solution to the system.

19. $f(x) = 2x^2 - 8x - 3$

The graph of f will be a parabola. The parabola will open up because $a = 2 > 0$.

The x-coordinate of the vertex is

$$x = -\dfrac{b}{2a} = -\dfrac{(-8)}{2(2)} = 2$$

The y-coordinate of the vertex is

$$f(2) = 2(2)^2 - 8(2) - 3 = -11$$

The vertex is $(2, -11)$ and the axis of symmetry is $x = 2$.

$$f(0) = 2(0)^2 - 8(0) - 3 = -3$$

The y-intercept is -3.

To find the x-intercepts we solve the equation $2x^2 - 8x - 3 = 0$.

$$x = \dfrac{-(-8) \pm \sqrt{(-8)^2 - 4(2)(-3)}}{2(2)}$$

$$= \dfrac{8 \pm \sqrt{88}}{4}$$

$$= \dfrac{8 \pm 2\sqrt{22}}{4}$$

$$\dfrac{4 \pm \sqrt{22}}{2}$$

The graph will have x-intercepts of $x \approx -0.35$ and $x \approx 4.35$.

20. $(x-h)^2 + (y-k)^2 = r^2$

$(x-4)^2 + (y-(-3))^2 = 6^2$

$(x-4)^2 + (y+3)^2 = 36$

To sketch the graph of the circle, we can plot four additional points that are $r = 6$ units above, below, left, and right of the center. These points are $(4,3), (4,-9), (-2,-3),$ and $(10,-3)$.

21. Begin by writing the equation in standard form.

$$\frac{4x^2}{64} + \frac{y^2}{64} = \frac{64}{64}$$

$$\frac{x^2}{16} + \frac{y^2}{64} = 1$$

The larger number, 64, is in the denominator of the y^2-term. This means that the major axis is the y-axis and the equation of the ellipse is of the form $\frac{x^2}{b^2} + \frac{y^2}{a^2} = 1$ so that $a^2 = 64$ and $b^2 = 16$.

The center of the ellipse is the origin, $(0,0)$.

$c^2 = a^2 - b^2 = 64 - 16 = 48$, so that $c = \pm 4\sqrt{3}$.

The foci are $\left(0, -4\sqrt{3}\right)$ and $\left(0, 4\sqrt{3}\right)$.

$$\frac{x^2}{16} + \frac{0^2}{64} = 1 \qquad \frac{0^2}{16} + \frac{y^2}{64} = 1$$

$$\frac{x^2}{16} = 1 \qquad \frac{y^2}{64} = 1$$

$$x^2 = 16 \qquad y^2 = 64$$

$$x = \pm 4 \qquad y = \pm 8$$

The intercepts are $(-4,0), (4,0), (0,-8),$ and $(0,8)$.

22. $S_n = \dfrac{n}{2}\left[2a + (n-1)d\right]$

$S_{20} = \dfrac{20}{2}\left[2(-47) + (20-1)(12)\right]$

$= 10(134)$

$= 1340$

23. For this infinite geometric series we have $a = 2$ and $r = \dfrac{3/2}{2} = \dfrac{3}{4}$.

$$S_\infty = \frac{a}{1-r} = \frac{2}{1-\frac{3}{4}} = \frac{2}{\frac{1}{4}} = 8$$

24.

Machine	# of lots	time (hrs)	rate
Robomower	1	5	$\frac{1}{5}$
Mowbot	1	6	$\frac{1}{6}$
Together	1	t	$\frac{1}{t}$

We can't add the times, but we can add the rates.

$$\frac{1}{5} + \frac{1}{6} = \frac{1}{t}$$

$$\frac{11}{30} = \frac{1}{t}$$

$$t = \frac{30}{11} \approx 2.73$$

It would take about 2.73 hours to cut the lot if both machines worked together.

25. Let x = metric tons of pure aluminum.

We can solve the problem by writing an equation for the total amount of manganese.

$$\text{Mn}_{tot} = \text{Mn}_{init} + \text{Mn}_{added}$$

$$(\%)(\text{wt.})_{tot} = (\%)(\text{wt.})_{init} + (\%)(\text{wt.})_{added}$$

$$(1.2)(100 + x) = (2.5)(100) + (0)(x)$$

$$120 + 1.2x = 250$$

$$1.2x = 130$$

$$x = \frac{130}{1.2}$$

$$x = \frac{325}{3} \quad \text{or} \quad 108\frac{1}{3}$$

$108\frac{1}{3}$ metric tons of pure aluminum must be added.

Appendix A

Preparing for the Library of Functions

1. $y = x^2$

x	$y = x^2$	(x, y)
-3	$y = (-3)^2 = 9$	$(-3, 9)$
-2	$y = (-2)^2 = 4$	$(-2, 4)$
0	$y = (0)^2 = 0$	$(0, 0)$
2	$y = (2)^2 = 4$	$(2, 4)$
3	$y = (3)^2 = 9$	$(3, 9)$

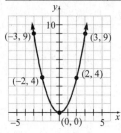

2. $y = x^3$

x	$y = x^3$	(x, y)
-2	$y = (-2)^3 = -8$	$(-2, -8)$
-1	$y = (-1)^3 = -1$	$(-1, -1)$
0	$y = (0)^3 = 0$	$(0, 0)$
1	$y = (1)^3 = 1$	$(1, 1)$
2	$y = (2)^3 = 8$	$(2, 8)$

3. $x = y^2$

y	$x = y^2$	(x, y)
-2	$x = (-2)^2 = 4$	$(4, -2)$
-1	$x = (-1)^2 = 1$	$(1, -1)$
0	$x = (0)^2 = 0$	$(0, 0)$
1	$x = (1)^2 = 1$	$(1, 1)$
2	$x = (2)^2 = 4$	$(4, 2)$

Appendix A Exercises

1. constant function

3. False; the domain of the square function is all real numbers, but the range is the set of nonnegative real numbers.

5. Square function, (c).

7. Square root function, (e)

9. Linear function, (b)

11. Reciprocal function, (f)

13. $f(x) = x^2$

x	$y = f(x) = x^2$	(x, y)
-3	$y = (-3)^2 = 9$	$(-3, 9)$
-2	$y = (-2)^2 = 4$	$(-2, 4)$
0	$y = (0)^2 = 0$	$(0, 0)$
2	$y = (2)^2 = 4$	$(2, 4)$
3	$y = (3)^2 = 9$	$(3, 9)$

15. $f(x) = \sqrt{x}$

x	$y = f(x) = \sqrt{x}$	(x, y)
0	$y = \sqrt{0} = 0$	$(0, 0)$
1	$y = \sqrt{1} = 1$	$(1, 1)$
4	$y = \sqrt{4} = 2$	$(4, 2)$
9	$y = \sqrt{9} = 3$	$(9, 3)$

17. $f(x) = \dfrac{1}{x}$

x	$y = f(x) = \dfrac{1}{x}$	(x, y)
-5	$y = \dfrac{1}{-5} = -\dfrac{1}{5}$	$\left(-5, -\dfrac{1}{5}\right)$
-1	$y = \dfrac{1}{-1} = -1$	$(-1, -1)$
$-\dfrac{1}{2}$	$y = \dfrac{1}{-1/2} = -2$	$\left(-\dfrac{1}{2}, -2\right)$
$\dfrac{1}{2}$	$y = \dfrac{1}{1/2} = 2$	$\left(\dfrac{1}{2}, 2\right)$
1	$y = \dfrac{1}{1} = 1$	$(1, 1)$
5	$y = \dfrac{1}{5}$	$\left(5, \dfrac{1}{5}\right)$